BLOOD AND OTHER BODY FLUIDS

Biological Handbooks

. . . .

Blood and Other Body Fluids

ANALYSIS AND COMPILATION BY Philip L. Altman

EDITED BY Dorothy S. Dittmer

PREPARED UNDER THE AUSPICES OF THE Committee on Biological Handbooks

Federation of American Societies for Experimental Biology

WASHINGTON, D. C.

Foreword

Blood and Other Body Fluids is the first of the biological handbooks to appear under the general direction of the Committee on Biological Handbooks, Federation of American Societies for Experimental Biology. This volume, however, does not inaugurate a new series, but is in fact a continuation of the handbooks prepared under the auspices of the National Academy of Sciences - National Research Council.*

The contents and contributors for this compilation were determined with the approval of the Advisory Committee on Blood and Other Body Fluids. After the data were analyzed, compiled, and edited by the Handbook Office staff, they were submitted for review to the contributors and other authorities in the areas covered in this volume.

On behalf of the Committee on Biological Handbooks, acknowledgement is made to the numerous scientists who have been so liberal with their time and advice, and to the National Institutes of Health, the National Science Foundation, and Wright Air Development Division of the United States Air Force for the generous support and co-operation which have made possible the production of this book. Participation in this undertaking was fulfilled under National Institutes of Health Grant No. RG-6553, National Science Foundation Grant No. NSF-G11180, and Air Force Contract No. AF 33(616)-6773.

COMMITTEE ON BIOLOGICAL HANDBOOKS

Raymund L. Zwemer, Chairman

Philip L. Altman, Executive Secretary

George B. Brown	Dwight E. Gray	Milton O. Lee
Theodore C. Byerly	J. W. Heim	Frank B. Rogers
Cyrus C. Erickson**	Chauncey D. Leake**	J. Franklin Yeager

** ex officio

ADVISORY COMMITTEE ON BLOOD AND OTHER BODY FLUIDS

Raymund L. Zwemer, Chairman

Ray G. Daggs	W. H. Larrimer
J. W. Heim	Milton O. Lee

HANDBOOK STAFF

Philip L. Altman, Director

Dorothy S. Dittmer, Editor

Judith P. Bloomer	Betty R. Connors	Gilbert R. Magee
Marlene Cherry	Mary J. Grant	Olga G. Stanczak
	Saki Himel	

* Previous publications in the Biological Handbooks Series

Standard Values in Blood	1952		Handbook of Toxicology:	
Standard Values in Nutrition			Volume I, Acute Toxicities	1955
and Metabolism	1954		Volume II, Antibodies	1957
Handbook of Biological Data	1956		Volume III, Insecticides	1959
Handbook of Respiration	1958		Volume IV, Tranquilizers	1959
Handbook of Circulation	1959		Volume V, Fungicides	1959

Contributors and Reviewers

Aballi, Arturo J.
Abood, L. G.
Adler, Harry F.
Adolph, E. F.
Alexander, James K.
Allen, Fred H., Jr.
Allison, James B.
Alt, Howard L.
Altland, Paul D.
Altschule, Mark D.
Asdell, S. A.
Assali, N. S.

Babers, Frank H.
Bacchus, Habeeb
Baez, Silvio
Ballintine, Elmer J.
Barker, J. N.
Barnett, Henry L.
Barron, Donald H.
Bartels, Heinz
Bass, David E.
Battaglia, Frederick C.
Bauer, Walter
Beatty, Clarissa H.
Beerstecher, Ernest, Jr.
Behnke, Albert R.
Bergeim, Olaf
Berliner, Robert W.
Berman, Lawrence
Best, Charles H.
*Bethell, Frank H.
Bing, Richard J.
Bischoff, Fritz E.
Bishop, David W.
Bitman, Joel
Block, Matthew
Block, Richard J.
Bonnycastle, Desmond D.
Booker, Walter M.
Boolootian, Richard A.
Bowman, Russel O.
Brecher, George
Brinkhous, K. M.
Britton, C. J. C.
Brodsky, William A.
Broun, Goronwy O.
Brown, Ellen
Brown, Royal L.
Brun, Robert
Buck, John B.

Calcagno, Philip L.
Carlsen, Elizabeth
Cartwright, G. E.
Catchpole, H. R.
Caton, William L.
Chaikoff, I. L.
Chance, Britton
Chanutin, Alfred
Chaplin, Hugh, Jr.
Chesley, Leon C.
Cohagen, D. L.
Cole, Warren H.
Collier, H. B.

Conklin, Ruth E.
Coon, William W.
Cotlove, Ernest
Cournand, Andre
Courtice, F. C.
*Craige, A. H., Jr.
Cronkite, Eugene P.
Cumings, J. N.
Cummins, Alvin J.

Darling, Robert C.
Das, Jogananda
Davidsohn, Israel
Davis, Hallowell
*De Beer, Edwin J.
DeLalla, Oliver F.
DeMarsh, Q. B.
Denstedt, Orville F.
Dessauer, Herbert C.
Deutsch, Harold F.
Diggs, L. W.
Dill, D. B.
Dische, Zacharias
Doan, Charles A.
Dole, Vincent P.
Doran, David J.
Dugdale, Marion
Duke-Elder, W. Stewart
Duncan, C. W.
Dunlap, J. S.

Eastham, M. D.
Ebaugh, Franklin G., Jr.
Ebert, Richard V.
Edsall, John T.
Eichelberger, Lillian
Elliott, K. A. C.
Endicott, Kenneth M.
Engel, Frank L.
Erdoes, Ervin
Escoffier-Lambiotte, C.
Everett, Newton B.
Eversole, W. J.

Feldman, Joseph D.
Ferguson, John H.
Finch, Clement A.
Fine, Jacob
Fingerman, Milton
Fisk, Albert A.
Fitts, William T., Jr.
Flock, Eunice V.
Foord, Alvin G.
Forbes, Thomas R.
Forbes, William H.
Forrest, Andrew P. M.
Frank, Howard A.
Frazer, A. C.
Freeman, Smith
Fregly, Melvin J.
Friedman, J. J.

Gabrio, Beverly W.
Gamble, Clarence J.
Gaudino, Mario

Giere, Frederic A.
Glaser, Kurt
Gofman, John W.
Goldstein, Leon
Goodyer, Allan V. N.
Grad, Bernard
Gram, H. C.
Granick, S.
Guest, George M.
Guest, M. Mason
Gutman, Alexander B.

Hallpike, C. S.
Hamilton, Paul B.
Hamre, Christopher J.
Handler, Philip
Handley, Charles O., Jr.
Hansard, Sam L.
Hansel, William
Hardenbergh, Esther
Harrell, George T.
Harris, John E.
Hart, J. Sanford
Hastings, A. Baird
Heath, Clark Wright
Hegnauer, A. H.
Hellman, Louis M.
Hendry, E. B.
Henschel, Austin
Hernandez, Thomas
Hetzer, Herbert O.
Hiatt, Edwin P.
Hickam, John B.
Hier, Stanley W.
Hill, Robert M.
Hilpert, Peter
Himwich, Williamina A.
Hinman, Frank, Jr.
Hirschboeck, John S.
Hoch, Hans
Holaday, Duncan A.
Hollander, Franklin
Holman, H. H.
Hubbard, Ruth
Huckabee, William E.
Huffman, C. F.
Hunt, J. N.
Hunter, F. R.
Hunter, George
Hunter, John
Hurtado, Alberto
Hutton, Kenneth E.

Ingram, Marylou
Irvin, J. Logan
Israëls, M. C. G.

Jaques, L. B.
Jones, Jack Colvard
Jones, Oliver P.

Kabat, Elvin A.
Kaiser, Irwin H.
Kanter, Gerald S.
Kelly, Harriet J.

---

*Deceased

v

Kerr, Stanley E.
Keys, Ancel
Kirk, John E.
Kisch, Bruno
Klein, J. Raymond
Klingman, Walter O.
Koelle, George B.
Koenig, Virgil L.
Korman, Henry
Krause, Arlington C.
Krupp, Marcus A.
Kvorning, Sven Ancher

Langham, Maurice E.
Largent, Edward J.
Larson, Daniel L.
Lasker, Reuben
Lauber, Frances U.
Lauson, Henry D.
LeBrie, Stephen J.
Lehninger, Albert L.
Leopold, Irving H.
Levenstein, Irving
Levey, Stanley
Levine, Philip
Levine, Victor E.
*Lewis, Howard B.
Lewis, Jessica H.
Liebowitz, Daniel
Limarzi, Louis R.
Livermore, George R., Jr.
Logan, J. E.
Looney, Joseph M.
Lorincz, Allan L.
Lotspeich, W. D.
Love, R. Malcolm
Lucas, Miriam Scott
Lucia, Salvatore P.
Luckey, T. D.
Ludwig, Daniel
Luft, Ulrich C.
Lundquist, Frank

Macy, Icie G.
Manery, J. F.
Mann, George V.
Mann, T.
Manwell, Clyde
Marbarger, John P.
Martin, Arthur W.
Mayerson, H. S.
McCartney, M. G.
McCutcheon, F. Harold
McKenzie, Fred F.
Meister, Alton
Mendlowitz, Milton
Miller, John H.
Mirsky, I. Arthur
Monkhouse, Frank C.
Moore, Dan H.
Morales, Daniel R.
Mulligan, Richard M.
Musacchia, X. J.
Muus, Jytte

Naumann, Hans N.
Neiland, Kenneth A.
Nesbitt, Robert E. L., Jr.
Niedermeier, William

Notkin, Louis J.

Oberholzer, R.
Okunzua, G.
*Opitz, E.
Osgood, Edwin E.
Overman, R. R.
Owen, Charles A.
Owren, Paul A.

Page, Irvine H.
Paschkis, Karl E.
Patton, Robert L.
Pearson, William N.
Penrod, Kenneth E.
Perlman, H. B.
Peschel, Ernst
Petermann, Mary L.
Platner, W. S.
Platt, David
Ponder, Eric
Prosser, C. Ladd
Prystowsky, Harry

Quick, Armand J.

Radford, Edward P., Jr.
Randall, Walter C.
Rebuck, John W.
Redmond, James R.
Reinhardt, William O.
Rekers, Paul E.
Reynolds, Monica
Ridley, Frederick
Riegel, Klaus
Rigdon, R. H.
Riser, William H., Jr.
Roberts, Sidney
Robertson, James D.
Rodbard, Simon
Rogers, W. P.
Root, Raymond W.
Rooth, Gösta
Ropes, Marian W.
Rossiter, Roger J.
Roth, James L. A.
Rothman, Stephen
Rubin, Mitchell I.

Sabine, Jean C.
Sammons, H. G.
Samuels, Leo T.
Savel, Jean
Sayers, George
Schaefer, Karl E.
Schafer, David E.
Schechtman, A. M.
Scheer, Bradley T.
Scheinberg, Peritz
Schmid, Karl
Schmidt-Nielsen, Knut
Schwartz, Irving L.
Schweigert, B. S.
Seegers, Walter H.
Selkurt, Ewald E.
Senior, John
Severinghaus, John W.
Shaffner, C. S.
Share, Leonard

Singer, Richard B.
Sizer, Irwin W.
Skaug, Odvar
Skoryna, Stanley C.
Smith, Catherine A.
Smith, Clement A.
Smith, Ralph I.
Smyth, J. D.
Sokoloff, Leon
Spangler, S.
Spicer, Samuel S.
Stasney, Joseph
Stearner, S. Phyllis
Stearns, Genevieve
Steele, Betty F.
Stefanini, Mario
Stickney, J. Clifford
Stone, Alan
Stowe, Clarence M., Jr.
Sundberg, R. Dorothy
Surgenor, Douglas M.

Tcherdakoff, Philippe
Thomas, J. Earl
Thorson, Thomas B.
Tietz, Norbert W.
Tocantins, Leandro M.
Tompkins, Edna H.
Travis, Dorothy F.
Tromba, Francis G.
Truter, E. V.

Van Drimmelen, G. C.
Van Pilsum, John F.
Van Slyke, Donald D.
Vaughan, Stuart L.
Venning, Eleanor H.
Visscher, Maurice B.
Von Euler, U. S.

Ware, Arnold G.
Warner, E. D.
Wasserman, Karl
Webster, Donald R.
Wedgwood, Ralph J.
Weil, William B., Jr.
Wesson, Laurence G., Jr.
West, Clark D.
Wheatley, Victor R.
White, I. G.
Whitehorn, W. V.
Wiener, Alexander S.
Wiggers, Carl J.
Wilber, Charles G.
Wilson, D. Wright
Windle, William F.
Wintrobe, M. M.
Winzler, Richard J.
Wirtschafter, Z. T.
Wise, John P.
Wroblewski, Felix
Wu, S. H.
Wyatt, Gerard R.

Yoffey, J. M.
Young, I. Maureen

Zarrow, M. X.
Zwemer, Raymund L.

*Deceased

vi

Contents

XI. BLOOD COAGULATION

XII. BLOOD GROUPS

XIII. HEMOLYMPH

XX. DIGESTIVE SECRETIONS

XXI. REPRODUCTIVE SECRETIONS

Introduction

This handbook, which includes a revision of Standard Values in Blood published in 1952, presents comprehensive data on blood and other body fluids specifically compiled for reference purposes. The material is conveniently organized in the form of tables, graphs, diagrams, nomograms, and line charts. Most of the tables have been prepared especially for the Biological Handbooks Series from various authoritative collections of data and from the current literature. Contents of the volume have been authenticated by 380 leading investigators in the fields of biology and medicine. The review process to which the tables have been subjected was designed to eliminate, insofar as possible, errors of transcription and material of questionable validity.

For the convenience of the user, the tables have been arranged in 25 sections. An explanatory headnote, designed to serve as an introduction to the subject matter, occasionally precedes the tables in a section. Individual tables may be prefaced by a short headnote containing such important information as units of measurement, abbreviations, definitions, and estimate of the range of variation. To interpret the data, reading of the related headnote is essential.

On occasion, differences in values for the same specifications, certain inconsistencies in nomenclature, and some overlapping of coverage may occur among tables. These result not from oversights or failure to choose between alternatives, but from the deliberate intention of the handbook staff to respect the judgment and preferences of the contributor. Although units of measurement may vary within a table, values can be converted by using the information given in APPENDIX I: CONVERSION FACTORS AND FORMULAS.

Appended to the tables are the names of the contributors, and a list of the literature citations arranged in alphabetical order. The reference abbreviations conform to the LIST OF ABBREVIATIONS FOR SERIAL PUBLICATIONS, Fourth Series, Volume X, Army Medical Library, Washington, D. C. (U. S. Government Printing Office, 1948), and the 1955 SUPPLEMENT thereto. Abbreviations for new or unlisted publications were constructed from the "Dictionary of Abbreviated and Contracted Words" in the SYNOPSIS OF STYLE, Fourth Series, Volume II, Army Medical Library, Washington, D. C. (U. S. Government Printing Office, 1937).

It is suggested that the table of contents be used in conjunction with the index: the table of contents to determine the scope of the data for a particular fluid, and the index to locate a specific constituent, property, or animal. Because of the animal nomenclature used in the tables, the index lists vertebrates by common name and invertebrates according to genus.

Values are generally presented as a mean and the lower and upper limit of the range of individual values about the mean. This range may be estimated in several ways, the method depending on the information available. Letter designations (a, b, c, d) identify types of ranges in descending order of accuracy.

(a) When the group of values is relatively large, a 95% range is derived by curve fitting. A recognized type of normal frequency curve is fitted to a group of measured values, and the extreme 2.5% of the area under the curve at each end is excluded (see illustration).

(b) When the group of values is too small for curve fitting, as is usually the case, a 95% range is estimated by a simple statistical calculation. Assuming a normal symmetrical distribution, the standard deviation is multiplied by a factor of 2, then subtracted from and added to the mean to give the lower and upper range limits.

(c) A less dependable, but commonly applied, procedure takes as range limits the lowest value and the highest value of the reported sample group of measurements. It underestimates the 95% range for small samples and overestimates for larger sample sizes, but may be used in preference to the preceding method where there is marked asymmetry in the position of the mean within the sample range.

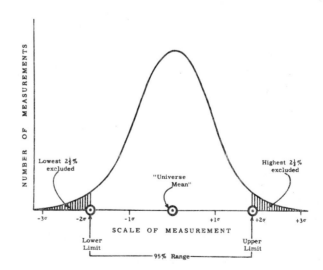

(d) Another estimate of the lower and upper limits of the range of variation is based on the judgment of an individual experienced in measuring the quantity in question. The trustworthiness of such limits should not be underestimated.

Abbreviations and Symbols

MEASUREMENT

yr = year
mo = month
wk = week
da = day
hr = hour
min = minute
sec = second

wt = weight
lb = pound
g = gram
kg = kilogram
mg = milligram
μg = microgram
μμg = micromicrogram
mEq = milliequivalent
μEq = microequivalent
M = mole
gM = gram-mole
mM = millimole
μM = micromole
mOsm = milliosmole

ht = height
mi = mile
ft = foot
in. = inch
m = meter
cm = centimeter
mm = millimeter
μ = micron
mμ = millimicron

sq in. = square inch
sq m = square meter
sq cm = square centimeter
sq mm = square millimeter
sq μ = square micron

L = liter
ml = milliliter
μL = microliter
cu cm = cubic centimeter
cu mm = cubic millimeter
cu μ = cubic micron

v = volt
kv = kilovolt
mv = millivolt
mho = conductance unit
(reciprocal of re-
sistance in ohms)

IU = international unit
ppm = parts per million
rpm = revolutions per minute
av = average

sat % = saturation per cent
vol % = volumes per cent
g % = grams per cent
mg % = milligrams per cent

g-cal = gram-calorie
kg-cal = kilogram-calorie

$^{\circ}$C = degree Centigrade
$^{\circ}$F = degree Fahrenheit
> = greater than
< = less than
σ = standard deviation

BIOLOGICAL SPECIFICATION

Hb = hemoglobin
RBC = red blood cell (erythrocyte)
WBC = white blood cell (leukocyte)
CSF = cerebrospinal fluid

STP = standard temperature and pressure
sp = species
♂ = male
♀ = female

BLOOD AND OTHER BODY FLUIDS

I. Blood Physical Properties and General Chemical Components

1. BLOOD VOLUMES

For a summary of blood methods and interpretations, consult reference 10, Part I.

Part I: MAN

Subjects were unanesthetized, predominantly white adults (normal individuals or hospital controls), under average environmental temperature (22-28°C) and sea-level barometric pressure conditions. Number of determinations is the same as the number of subjects, unless otherwise indicated. Plasma and erythrocyte volumes were obtained by various dilution methods, the diluent or tagging substance being given in the pertinent method column. A tagging substance listed under erythrocyte volume (column E) indicates that cell volume was determined after in vivo dilution of the tagged cells, either by counting radioactivity of washed or dried cells, or by multiplying radioactivity of whole blood by venous or arterial hematocrit uncorrected for trapped plasma. Venous hematocrit values were obtained by centrifuging the blood sample (3000 rpm, 30 minutes, 18 cm radius) and were not corrected for trapped plasma, unless otherwise specified. In most instances, whole blood volume was calculated from other values in the same study; where a tagging substance is given in column H, blood volume was determined directly by dilution of the tagged erythrocytes in whole blood, on the assumption that the erythrocyte concentration in the sampled blood represented the total body erythrocyte concentration. Method (columns C and H): PV = plasma volume, EV = erythrocyte volume, VH = venous hematocrit, BV = whole blood volume. Values in parentheses are ranges, estimate "c" (cf. Introduction).

	Subjects		Plasma Volume		Erythrocyte Volume		Venous Hematocrit % cells	Whole Blood Volume		Refer-ence
	Sex	No.	Method	ml/kg body wt	Method	ml/kg body wt		Method	ml/kg body wt	
	(A)	(B)	(C)	(D)	(E)	(F)	(G)	(H)	(I)	(J)
1	Male	30	T-1824	41.1	P^{32}	28.0^1		PV + EV	69.1	23
2		40	T-1824	47.9 (39.2-62.5)	Fe^{55} or Fe^{59}	29.8 (21.5-36.3)		PV + EV	77.7 (63.8-97.0)	7
3		20	T-1824	45.7 (35.8-56.5)			44.1 (39.3-49.4)	$\frac{PV}{100-VH} \times 100$	81.6 (65.4-95.2)	29
4		49	T-1824	43.1 (32.0-58.2)			$44.7 (36.0-51.8)^2$	$\frac{PV}{100-VH} \times 100$	77.7 (62.7-97.7)	6
5		11	T-1824	40.5 (28.5-48.2)			$47.2 (42.0-53.0)^3$	$\frac{PV}{100-VH} \times 100$	76.7 (60.5-92.6)	4
6		31	I^{131}, human serum albumin	41.4 (33.6-61.8)			$44.1 (34.9-49.0)^4$	$\frac{PV}{100-VH} \times 100$	74.2 (60.0-96.0)	28
7		53	T-1824	45.6 (31.7-56.5)			44.7^1	$\frac{PV}{100-VH} \times 100$	82.3 (59.8-101.7)	9
8		51	T-1824	44.7 (34-58)			45.0^1	$\frac{PV}{100-VH} \times 100$	85.1	20
9		32	T-1824	47.4 (36.5-59.7)			$42.6 (37.9-49.2)^1$	$\frac{PV}{100-VH} \times 100$	82.6 (62.2-102.2)	24
10		11	T-1824	47.4 (43.7-61.4)				$\frac{PV}{100-VH}^5 \times 100$	82.8 (72.7-99.4)	12
11		34	T-1824	45.3 (32.4-56.9)			43.5 (39-51)	$\frac{PV}{100-VH} \times 100$	80.1 (57.5-106.0)	19
12		42			Cr^{51} as sodium chromate	28.2 (20.0-39.8)	45.8 (39.0-54.6)	Cr^{51} as sodium chromate	61.5 (45.9-81.0)	16
13		32^6	T-1824	45.2 (35.3-55.9)			46.5			14
14		21	Cr^{51} as chromic chloride	39.3 (28.7-48.5)						5
15		59	T-1824	36.7			48.2			11
16		25			Cr^{51} as sodium chromate	31.8 (25.4-38.7)				26

/1/ Hematocrit corrected for trapped plasma by factor of 0.96. /2/ Venous hematocrit calculated from formula: $\frac{\text{reading of packed cells}}{\text{reading of fluid level} - 2.0}$. /3/ Centrifuged until cells completely packed. /4/ Measured by specific gravity (dropping blood into copper sulfate solutions of known density). /5/ Centrifuged at 8000 rpm, and 7.2 cm radius, for 1 hour. /6/ 62 determinations.

1. BLOOD VOLUMES (Continued)

Part I: MAN (Continued)

Subjects		Plasma Volume		Erythrocyte Volume		Venous Hematocrit % cells	Whole Blood Volume		Reference
Sex	No.	Method	ml/kg body wt	Method	ml/kg body wt		Method	ml/kg body wt	
(A)	(B)	(C)	(D)	(E)	(F)	(G)	(H)	(I)	(J)
17 Male (con-cluded)	201			Cr^{51} as sodium chromate	28.3 (21.6-35.5)				31
18	35			P^{32}	29.6				13
19	89						Cr^{51} as sodium chromate	65.5 (45.8-77.6)	22
20 Female	8	T-1824	43.1	P^{32}	23.4[7]		PV + EV	66.5	30
21	30	T-1824	40.5	P^{32}	21.6[1]		PV + EV	63.1	23
22	20	T-1824	44.7 (37.2-58.5)			39.8 (37.1-41.9)	$\frac{PV}{100-VH} \times 100$	74.3 (63.0-97.5)	29
23	41	T-1824	41.5 (26.9-52.3)			40.0 (33.7-44.4)[2]	$\frac{PV}{100-VH} \times 100$	66.1 (46.3-85.4)	6
24	35	T-1824	48.2 (37.7-57.2)			39.2 (34.5-43.8)[1]	$\frac{PV}{100-VH} \times 100$	79.5 (65.0-99.8)	25
25	16			P^{32}	27.0 (21.1-32.7)	42 (37-46)	$\frac{EV}{VH} \times 100$	64.4 (49.6-77.5)	1
26	20			Cr^{51} as sodium chromate	24.2 (19.3-29.5)	41.1 (36.3-44.7)	Cr^{51} as sodium chromate	59.0 (47.6-66.5)	16
27	7			P^{32}	24.0				13
28 Unspec-ified	13	T-1824	47.1 (39.7-52.2)	P^{32}	30.1 (25.6-33.7)[1]		PV + EV	77.1 (67.6-83.7)	21
29	10	Cr^{51} as chromic chloride	41.1 (31.6-48.5)	Cr^{51} as sodium chromate	30.3 (23.7-42.1)		PV + EV	71.4 (62.4-84.3)	8
30	49	T-1824	40.7 (28.3-47.8)			43.6 (34-50)	$\frac{PV}{100-VH} \times 100$	71.3 (44.4-90.1)	17
31	33	T-1824	44.8 (36.9-54.7)			43.8 (34.5-50.0)	$\frac{PV}{100-VH} \times 100$	81.3 (59.2-103.7)	27
32	45	I^{131}, human serum albumin	39.6				$\frac{PV}{100-VH8} \times 100$	75.1	18
33	25	I^{131}, human serum albumin	43.6 (32.6-53.7)			44.1 (40.3-48.5)[1]	$\frac{PV}{100-VH} \times 100$	78.1 (58.4-97.1)	2
34		T-1824	45.4 (32.3-54.2)			44.1 (40.3-48.5)[1]	$\frac{PV}{100-VH} \times 100$	81.3 (56.9-100.0)	
35		BV-EV	38.2 (27.5-49.3)	P^{32}	30.1 (21.1-44.1)	44.1 (40.3-48.5)[1]	$\frac{EV}{VH} \times 100$	68.3 (49.3-91.8)	
36	22			P^{32}	36.0 (30.2-42.2)[9]	44.9 (37.0-63.0)			15

/1/ Hematocrit corrected for trapped plasma by factor of 0.96. /2/ Venous hematocrit calculated from formula: $\frac{\text{reading of packed cells}}{\text{reading of fluid level} - 2.0}$. /7/ Hematocrit corrected for trapped plasma by factors from Chaplin and Mollison [3]. /8/ Corrected for trapped plasma by factor of 0.915. /9/ g/kg body weight.

Contributors: (a) Reynolds, Monica, (b) Brown, Ellen

References: [1] Berlin, N. I., G. M. Hyde, R. J. Parsons, J. H. Lawrence, and S. Port. 1951. Proc. Soc. Exp. Biol., N. Y. 76:831. [2] Brady, L. W., D. Y. Cooper, M. Colodzin, J. E. McClenathan, E. R. King, and R. Williams. 1953. Surg. Gyn. Obst. 97:25. [3] Chaplin, H., Jr., and P. L. Mollison. 1952. Blood, N. Y. 7:1227. [4] Davis, L. J. 1942. Edinburgh M. J. 49:465. [5] Frank, H., and S. J. Gray. 1953. J. Clin. Invest. 32:991. [6] Gibson, J. G., II, and W. A. Evans, Jr. 1937. Ibid. 16:317. [7] Gibson, J. G., II, W. C. Peacock, A. M. Seligman, and T. Sack. 1946. Ibid. 25:838. [8] Gray, S. J., and H. Frank. 1953. Ibid. 32:1000. [9] Gregersen,

1. BLOOD VOLUMES (Continued)

Part I: MAN (Concluded)

M. I., and J. L. Nickerson. 1950-51. J. Appl. Physiol. 3:329. [10] Gregersen, M. I., and R. Rawson. 1959. Physiol. Rev. 39:307. [11] Griffin, G. E., W. E. Abbott, M. P. Pride, E. Muntwyler, F. R. Mautz, and L. Griffith. 1945. Ann. Surg. 121:352. [12] Harington, C. R., E. E. Pochin, and J. R. Squire. 1940. Clin. Sc., Lond. 4:311. [13] Hedlund, S. 1953. Acta med. scand., Suppl. 146. [14] Henschel, A., O. Mickelsen, H. L. Taylor, and A. Keys. 1947. Am. J. Physiol. 150:170. [15] Hevesy, G., K. H. Köster, G. Sørensen, E. Warburg, and K. Zerahn. 1944. Acta med. scand. 116:561. [16] Huff, R. L., and D. D. Feller. 1955. J. Clin. Invest. 35:1. [17] Inkley, S. R., L. Brooks, and H. Krieger. 1955. J. Laborat. Clin. M. 45:841. [18] Likoff, W., D. B. Berkowitz, S. Geyer, H. Strauss, and A. Reale. 1955. Am. Heart J. 49:1. [19] Ling, W. S. M., and H. Sprinz. 1948. Am. J. M. Sc. 215:555. [20] Noble, R. P., and M. I. Gregersen. 1946. J. Clin. Invest. 25:172. [21] Reeve, E. B., and N. Veall. 1949. J. Physiol., Lond. 108:12. [22] Reilly, W. A., R. M. French, F. Y. K. Lau, K. G. Scott, and W. E. White. 1954. Circulation, N. Y. 9:571. [23] Samet, P., H. W. Fritts, Jr., A. P. Fishman, and A. Cournand. 1957. Medicine, Balt. 36:211. [24] Steinbeck, A. W. 1950. Austral. J. Exp. Biol. 28:477. [25] Steinbeck, A. W. 1954. Ibid. 32:95. [26] Sterling, K., and S. J. Gray. 1950. J. Clin. Invest. 29:1614. [27] Stewart, J. D., and G. M. Rourke. 1940-41. J. Laborat. Clin. M. 26:1383. [28] Storaasli, J. P., H. Krieger, H. L. Friedell, and W. R. Holden. 1950. Surg. Gyn. Obst. 91:458. [29] von Porat, B. 1951. Acta med. scand., Suppl. 256. [30] Wadsworth, G. R. 1954. Blood, N. Y. 9:1205. [31] Wennesland, R., et al. 1959. J. Clin. Invest. 38:1065.

Part II: MAMMALS OTHER THAN MAN

Subjects were normal, adult animals; females were neither pregnant nor lactating, unless otherwise specified. Number of determinations is the same as the number of subjects, unless otherwise indicated. Plasma and erythrocyte volumes were obtained by various dilution methods, the diluent or tagging substance being given in the pertinent method column. Venous hematocrit values were obtained by centrifuging the blood sample (3000 rpm, 30 minutes, 18 cm radius) and were not corrected for trapped plasma, unless otherwise specified. In most instances, whole blood volume was calculated from other values in the same study; where a tagging substance is given in column H, blood volume was determined directly by dilution of the tag in whole blood, on the assumption that the ratio of plasma to erythrocytes in the sampled blood was the same as in the entire vascular bed. Method (columns C, E, and H): PV = plasma volume, EV = erythrocyte volume, VH = venous hematocrit, BV = whole blood volume. Values in parentheses are ranges, estimate "c" (cf. Introduction),

	Animal	No. of Sub- jects	Plasma Volume		Erythrocyte Volume		Venous Hematocrit % cells	Whole Blood Volume		Ref- er- ence
			Method	ml/kg body wt	Method	ml/kg body wt		Method	ml/kg body wt	
	(A)	(B)	(C)	(D)	(E)	(F)	(G)	(H)	(I)	(J)
1	Burro	16					37	I^{131} plasma	65	18
2		17					35	P^{32} erythro- cytes	63	
3	Cat	52[1]	T-1824	47.7 (34-56)						17
4		13	T-1824	46.5 (34.3-65.8)						9
5	Cattle Beef	4[2]					41[3]	P^{32} erythro- cytes	57	18
6	Dairy cow	10	T-1824	38.8 (36.3-40.6)			32.4 (30.3-34.9)[4]	$\frac{PV}{100-VH} \times 100$	57.4 (52.4-60.6)	34
7		3[5]	T-1824	36.6			40.9	$\frac{PV}{100-VH} \times 100$	62.0	12
8	Dog	39[6]	T-1824	53.8 (31.7-83.9)	Fe^{55} or Fe^{59}	38.8 (22.5-64.4)		PV + EV	92.6 (63.9-134.8)	14

/1/ 73 determinations. /2/ During late lactation. /3/ Corrected for trapped plasma by factor of 0.95. /4/ Corrected for trapped plasma by factor of 0.94. /5/ Many determinations. /6/ Anesthetized.

Animal	No. of Subjects	Plasma Volume Method	Plasma Volume ml/kg body wt	Erythrocyte Volume Method	Erythrocyte Volume ml/kg body wt	Venous Hematocrit % cells	Whole Blood Volume Method	Whole Blood Volume ml/kg body wt	Reference
(A)	(B)	(C)	(D)	(E)	(F)	(G)	(H)	(I)	(J)
9 Dog (concluded)	10[6]	T-1824	58.0 (51.9-66.0)	P[32]	42.9 (35.8-64.8)		PV + EV	100.9 (91.2-123.4)	24
10		I[131] human plasma albumin	51.8 (47.2-56.8)	P[32]	42.9 (35.8-64.8)		PV + EV	94.7 (86.3-114.8)	
11	11[7]	T-1824	55.2 (43.7-73.0)	P[32]	39.0 (28.0-55.0)	44 (35-54)[8]	PV + EV	94.1 (76.5-107.3)	38
12	10[6,9]	T-1824	46.9 (40.4-59.2)	Cr[51] as sodium chromate	27.1 (20.4-38.7)		PV + EV	73.6 (66.6-79.8)	32
13	14	T-1824	46.3 (36.7-67.4)	Methemoglobin	37.2 (18.8-66.3)		PV + EV	83.8 (58.9-115.7)	11
14	10[10]						Heintz granule erythrocytes	66.1 (47-83)	30
15	21[11]						P[32] erythrocytes	95.0 (71.0-127.0)	29
16	16[6]	$EV \times \frac{100 - VH^3}{VH^3}$	42.0 (22.7-58.4)	Cr[51] as sodium chromate	39.4 (28.6-57.3)		PV + EV	81.4 (55.5-98.8)	21
17	50	T-1824	48.9 (37.0-62.2)			47.6 (37.6-60.0)[12]	$\frac{PV}{100-VH} \times 100$	92.7 (84.0-97.3)	13
18	15[13]	T-1824	54.7 (40.0-66.0)						16
19	106	T-1824	48.3 (31.8-64.6)			42.0 (28-52)	$\frac{PV}{100-VH} \times 100$	82.9 (58.3-107.7)	6
20	23	T-1824	57.0 (43.0-83.2)			42.9 (31.1-52.7)[8]	$\frac{PV}{100-VH} \times 100$	100.0 (79.6-121.0)	40
21	23	T-1824	52.3 (44-59)			43.2[8]	$\frac{PV}{100-VH} \times 100$	94.2 (76-111)	33
22	10[6,10]	T-1824	47				$\frac{PV}{100-VH}[14] \times 100$	89	27
23	18[15]	T-1824	53.6 (38.5-74.1)			46.9 (32.0-59.4)[8]	$\frac{PV}{100-VH} \times 100$	97.5 (78.2-123.0)	41
24	12	T-1824	54.7 (45.2-71.2)			45.7 (38.6-55.1)[8]	$\frac{PV}{100-VH} \times 100$	101.3 (79.0-127.5)	15
25	16[6]	T-1824	51.6 (37.1-70.8)						37
26		Rose Bengal	52.7 (39.6-70.6)						
27 Goat	20	T-1824	55.9 (42.6-75.1)	Cr[51] as sodium chromate	14.7 (9.7-19.3)	24.3 (18.5-30.8)[16]	PV + EV	70.5 (56.8-89.4)	23
28							$\frac{EV}{VH} \times 100$	61.0 (48.2-76.1)	
29							$\frac{PV}{100-VH} \times 100$	73.5 (59.8-92.1)	
30	30[17]	T-1824	53			17	$\frac{PV}{100-VH} \times 100$	70 (57-82)	10

/3/ Corrected for trapped plasma by factor of 0.95. /6/ Anesthetized. /7/ 22 determinations. /8/ Corrected for trapped plasma by factor of 0.96. /9/ 13 determinations. /10/ Number of determinations. /11/ Blood from femoral vein. /12/ Calculated from formula: $\frac{\text{reading of packed cells}}{\text{reading of fluid level} - 2.02}$. /13/ 72 determinations. /14/ Arterial hematocrit. /15/ 36 determinations. /16/ Corrected for trapped plasma by factor of 0.81. /17/ 32 determinations.

1. BLOOD VOLUMES (Continued)

Part II: MAMMALS OTHER THAN MAN (Continued)

Animal	No. of Subjects	Plasma Volume — Method	Plasma Volume — ml/kg body wt	Erythrocyte Volume — Method	Erythrocyte Volume — ml/kg body wt	Venous Hematocrit % cells	Whole Blood Volume — Method	Whole Blood Volume — ml/kg body wt	Reference
(A)	(B)	(C)	(D)	(E)	(F)	(G)	(H)	(I)	(J)
31 Guinea pig	18[11]	$BV \times \frac{100-VH}{100}$[18]	38.6				T-1824[19]	72.0	2
32	13	I[131] rabbit globulin	39.4 (35.1-48.4)[20]				$\frac{PV}{100-VH} \times 100$	75.3 (67.0-92.4)	26
33 Horse	2	T-1824	51			21	$\frac{PV}{100-VH} \times 100$	72	10
34 Light wt	6	BV - EV	61.9 (45.5-79.1)	P[32]	47.1 (39.6-57.5)	43.3 (37-56)	$\frac{EV}{VH} \times 100$	109.6 (94.3-136.0)	22
35 Heavy wt	4	BV - EV	43.2 (30.6-64.1)	P[32]	28.5 (23.1-37.6)	40.3 (37-46)	$\frac{EV}{VH} \times 100$	71.7 (56.7-101.7)	
36 Monkey	23[21]	T-1824	44.7 (31-63)			40.4 (29-49)	$\frac{PV}{100-VH} \times 100$	75.1 (52-109)	31
37	20[22]						I[131] human serum albumin	60.9 (49-71)	4
38 Mouse	11	T-1824	48.8	P[32]	29.0		PV + EV	77.8	42
39	5	I[131] mouse plasma	49.2 (41-54)						
40	5	T-1824	57.4 (55-63)						
41 Opossum	10[6]	T-1824	37.8 (29.6-52.2)	P[32]	19.2 (14.2-29.2)		PV + EV	57.0 (44.5-69.8)	7
42 Rabbit	29	T-1824	38.8 (27.8-51.4)	P[32]	16.8 (13.7-25.5)		PV + EV	55.6 (44.0-70.0)	3
43	71			P[32]	17.5 (13.4-22.8)	35.2 (28.6-41.0)[8]	$\frac{EV \times 100}{0.858(VH) - 0.2}$	57.3 (47.8-69.5)	
44	60	T-1824	50			28.6	$\frac{PV}{100-VH} \times 100$	70.0	10
45	39[23]	T-1824	42.3 (29-58)			38.8 (27-48)	$\frac{PV}{100-VH} \times 100$	69.8 (50-93)	1
46	20	T-1824	43.5 (35.1-49.8)			37.2 (25.8-43.2)	$\frac{PV}{100-VH} \times 100$	69.4 (57.6-78.3)	39
47	15[6,10]	T-1824	45				$\frac{PV}{100-VH}$[14]$\times 100$	72	27
48 Rat	35[6]	T-1824	31.3	P[32]	26.3		PV + EV	57.5	10
49	29[6,24]						P[32] erythrocytes[25]	63 (46-74)	28
50	22[6]			Fe[59] and Fe[55]	23.2 (18.9-25.5)	48.1 (45-52)	$\frac{EV}{VH} \times 100$	49.5 (41.9-54.0)	36
51	42[6,26]			P[32]	21.6 (17.2-25.8)	45.5 (43-54)[25]	$\frac{EV}{VH} \times 100$	45.9 (34.6-59.5)	5
52 Sheep	6					41[3]	PV + EV	58 (50-73)	35
53 Ewe	8						P[32] erythrocytes	57	18
54	11	T-1824	61.9			31.5			25
55 Swine 45 kg[27]	4			P[32]	25.9 (20.2-29.0)	39.1 (30.3-43.1)[3]	$\frac{EV}{VH} \times 100$	65 (61-68)	19
56 50 kg[27]	6[6]	BV - EV	41.9	$BV \times \frac{VH}{100}$	27.5		P[32] erythrocytes	69.4	8

/3/ Corrected for trapped plasma by factor of 0.95. /6/ Anesthetized. /8/ Corrected for trapped plasma by factor of 0.96. /10/ Number of determinations. /11/ Blood from femoral vein. /14/ Arterial hematocrit. /18/ 10 animals, cardiac blood. /19/ In hemolyzed cardiac blood. /20/ Calculated from an average hematocrit of 47.6 obtained from 10 other guinea pigs. /21/ 10 summer and 13 winter monkeys. /22/ 10 males and 10 females, all prepubescent. /23/ 65-67 determinations. /24/ 34 determinations. /25/ Cardiac blood. /26/ 3 lactating rats. /27/ Average weight.

1. BLOOD VOLUMES (Continued)

Part II: MAMMALS OTHER THAN MAN (Concluded)

Contributors: (a) Reynolds, Monica, (b) Brown, Ellen

References: [1] Aikawa, J. K. 1950. Am. J. Physiol. 162:695. [2] Ancill, R. J. 1956. J. Physiol., Lond. 132:469. [3] Armin, J., R. T. Grant, H. Pels, and E. B. Reeve. 1952. Ibid. 116:59. [4] Bender, M. A. 1955. Science 122:156. [5] Berlin, N. I., R. L. Huff, D. C. Van Dyke, and T. G. Hennessey. 1949. Proc. Soc. Exp. Biol., N. Y. 71:176. [6] Bonnycastle, D. D., and R. A. Cleghorn. 1942. Am. J. Physiol. 137:380. [7] Burke, J. D. 1954. Physiol. Zool. 27:1. [8] Bush, J. A., W. N. Jensen, G. E. Cartwright, and M. M. Wintrobe. 1955. Am. J. Physiol. 181:9. [9] Conley, C. L. 1941. Ibid. 132:796. [10] Courtice, F. C. 1943. J. Physiol., Lond. 102:290. [11] Cruz, W. O., and H. P. Oliveira. 1952. Acta physiol. lat. amer. 2:74. [12] Dale, H. E., S. Brady, and G. J. Burge. 1957. Am. J. Vet. Res. 18:97. [13] Gibson, J. G., II, J. L. Keeley, and M. Pijoan. 1938. Am. J. Physiol. 121:800. [14] Gibson, J. G., II, W. C. Peacock, A. M. Seligman, and T. Sack. 1946. J. Clin. Invest. 25:838. [15] Gregersen, M. I., A. A. Boyden, and J. B. Allison. 1950. Am. J. Physiol. 163:517. [16] Gregersen, M. I., and J. D. Stewart. 1939. Ibid. 125:142. [17] Hamlin, E., and M. I. Gregersen. 1939. Ibid. 125:713. [18] Hansard, S. L., W. O. Butler, C. L. Comar, and C. S. Hobbs. 1953. J. Anim. Sc. 12:402. [19] Hansard, S. L., H. E. Sauberlich, and C. L. Comar. 1951. Proc. Soc. Exp. Biol., N. Y. 78:544. [20] Huang, K. C., and J. H. Bondurant. 1956. Am. J. Physiol. 185:441. [21] Huggins, R. A., E. L. Smith, S. Deavers, and R. C. Overton. 1957. Ibid. 189:249. [22] Julian, L. M., J. H. Lawrence, N. I. Berlin, and G. M. Hyde. 1956. J. Appl. Physiol. 8:651. [23] Klement, A. W., Jr., D. E. Ayer, and E. B. Rogers. 1955. Am. J. Physiol. 181:15. [24] Krieger, H., J. P. Storaasli, H. L. Friedell, and W. D. Holden. 1948. Proc. Soc. Exp. Biol., N. Y. 68:511. [25] Macfarlane, W. V., R. J. H. Morris, B. Howard, and O. E. Budtz-Olsen. 1959. Austral. J. Agr. Res. 10:269. [26] Masouredis, S. P., and L. R. Melcher. 1951. Proc. Soc. Exp. Biol., N. Y. 78:264. [27] McLain, P. L., C. H. W. Ruhe, and T. K. Kruse. 1951. Am. J. Physiol. 164:611. [28] Montgomery, P. O'B. 1951. Proc. Soc. Exp. Biol., N. Y. 77:445. [29] Mukherjee, S. R., and S. Rowlands. 1951. Lancet, Lond. 2:98. [30] Nizet, A. 1948. Q. J. Exp. Physiol., Lond. 34:123. [31] Overman, R. R., and H. A. Feldman. 1947. Am. J. Physiol. 148:455. [32] Rapaport, E., H. Kuida, F. W. Haynes, and L. Dexter. 1956. Ibid. 185:127. [33] Reynolds, M. 1949. Ibid. 158:418. [34] Reynolds, M. 1953. Ibid. 173:421. [35] Schambye, A. P. 1952. Nord. Vet. Med. 4:929. [36] Sharpe, L. M., G. G. Culberth, and J. R. Klein. 1950. Proc. Soc. Exp. Biol., N. Y. 74:681. [37] Simpson, A. M., L. Ezrow, and L. A. Sapirstein. 1954. Am. J. Physiol. 177:319. [38] Sisson, G., A. Cain, and W. S. Root. 1955. Ibid. 180:485. [39] von Porat, B. 1951. Acta med. scand., Suppl. 256. [40] Walcott, W. W. 1945. Am. J. Physiol. 143:247. [41] Wang, C. I., S. L. Einhorn, H. J. Thompson, Jr., and W. W. Walcott. 1952. Ibid. 170:136. [42] Wish, L., J. Furth, and R. H. Storey. 1950. Proc. Soc. Exp. Biol., N. Y. 74:644.

Part III: BIRDS

Subjects were normal, adult animals. Plasma, erythrocyte, and whole blood volumes were obtained by dilution methods, the diluent being given in the pertinent method column. Venous hematocrit values were obtained by centrifuging the blood sample in Wintrobe tubes (3000 rpm, 30 minutes, 18 cm radius). Method (columns C and I): PV = plasma volume, VH = venous hematocrit, BV = whole blood volume.

Animal	No. of Subjects	Plasma Volume Method	Plasma Volume ml/100 g body wt	Erythrocyte Volume Method	Erythrocyte Volume ml/100 g body wt	Venous Hematocrit Method	Venous Hematocrit % cells	Whole Blood Volume Method	Whole Blood Volume ml/100 g body wt	Reference
(A)	(B)	(C)	(D)	(E)	(F)	(G)	(H)	(I)	(J)	(K)
1 Chicken New Hampshire	3♂			Cr^{51} as sodium chromate	2.1	Capillary tube technique	38.8[1]			6
2	4♀			Cr^{51} as sodium chromate	1.0	Capillary tube technique	27.1[1]			
3	110♂[2]	T-1824						$\frac{PV}{100 - VH} \times 100$		4
4	113♀[2]	T-1824						$\frac{PV}{100 - VH} \times 100$		
5 White Leghorn	32[3,4]	$BV \times 1 - \frac{VH}{100}$	6.56			Van Allen tubes	30.5[5]	T-1824 read directly in diluted blood	9.55[5]	3
6	3♂	T-1824	3.1	Consult ref. 1	2.5	Van Allen tubes	45	Consult ref. 1	5.6	2
7	4♀	T-1824	4.4	Consult ref. 1	1.9	Van Allen tubes	30	Consult ref. 1	6.3	2
8 Coot	2	T-1824	5.1	Consult ref. 1	4.4	Van Allen tubes	46	Consult ref. 1	9.5	2
9 Duck Mallard and black	7	T-1824	6.4	Consult ref. 1	4.8	Van Allen tubes	43	Consult ref. 1	11.3	2
10 Redhead and canvas back	6	T-1824	7.1	Consult ref. 1	4.1	Van Allen tubes	37	Consult ref. 1	11.1	2
11 White Peking	2♂			Cr^{51} as sodium chromate	3.00	Capillary tube technique	38.5			6
12	2♀			Cr^{51} as sodium chromate	2.50	Capillary tube technique	43.5[6]			
13	42	I^{131} human serum albumin	6.55					$\frac{PV}{100 - VH} \times 100$	10.2	5
14 Hawk, red-tailed	3[7]	T-1824	3.5	Consult ref. 1	2.7	Van Allen tubes	43	Consult ref. 1	6.2	2
15 Loon, red-throated	1	T-1824	6.1	Consult ref. 1	7.1	Van Allen tubes	54	Consult ref. 1	13.2	2
16 Owl, great horned	1	T-1824	3.4	Consult ref. 1	2.0	Van Allen tubes	32	Consult ref. 1	6.4	2
17 Pheasant, ringnecked	4♂	T-1824	4.5	Consult ref. 1	2.2	Van Allen tubes	33	Consult ref. 1	6.7	2
18	2♀	T-1824	3.2	Consult ref. 1	1.6	Van Allen tubes	34	Consult ref. 1	4.8	
19 Pigeon, palmetto strain (white Carneaux)	2♂			Cr^{51} as sodium chromate	3.21	Capillary tube technique	49.3[6]			6
20	2♀			Cr^{51} as sodium chromate	3.46	Capillary tube technique	49.7[1]			
21	6	T-1824	4.4	Consult ref. 1	4.9	Van Allen tubes	52	Consult ref. 1	9.2	2

/1/ 5 subjects. /2/ 6 weeks old to maturity. /3/ Chicks, 13-35 days old. /4/ Anesthetized. /5/ Cardiac blood. /6/ 4 subjects. /7/ Immature subjects.

1. BLOOD VOLUMES (Concluded)

Part III: BIRDS (Concluded)

Contributors: (a) Reynolds, Monica, (b) Brown, Ellen

References: [1] Bond, C. F. 1957. Ph. D. Thesis. Cornell University. [2] Bond, C. F., and P. W. Gilbert. 1958. Am. J. Physiol. 194:519. [3] Hegsted, D. M., D. Wilson, J. P. Milner, and P. H. Ginna. 1952. Proc. Soc. Exp. Biol., N. Y. 78:114. [4] Newell, G. W., and C. S. Shaffner. 1950. Poult. Sc. 29:78. [5] Portman, O. W., K. P. McConnell, and R. H. Rigdon. 1952. Proc. Soc. Exp. Biol., N. Y. 81:599. [6] Rodnan, G. P., E. G. Ebaugh, Jr., and M. R. S. Fox. 1957. Blood, N. Y. 12:355.

Part IV: REPTILES, AMPHIBIANS, FISHES

Subjects were normal, adult animals. Plasma volume was obtained by dilution methods, the diluent being given in column C. Venous hematocrit values were obtained by centrifuging the blood sample in Wintrobe tubes (3000 rpm, 30 minutes, 18 cm radius). Values in parentheses are ranges, estimate "c" (cf. Introduction).

	Animal	No. of Subjects	Plasma Volume		Venous Hematocrit % cells	Whole Blood Volume[1] ml/100 g body wt	Reference
			Method	ml/100 g body wt			
	(A)	(B)	(C)	(D)	(E)	(F)	(G)
	Reptiles						
1	Turtle, painted (Pseudomys elegans)	26[2]	T-1824 and high molecular weight Dextran	7.40(5.82-9.08)	18.5(12.0-25.4)	9.08(7.25-11.02)	3
	Amphibians						
2	Frog Rana catesbeiana	2	T-1824	8.0[3]	15.5[3]	9.5	2
3	R. pipiens	7	T-1824	7.0[3]	13.9[3,4]	8.2	
	Fishes						
4	Bullhead, yellow (Ameiurus natalis)	6	T-1824	1.25[3]	30.1[3]	1.77	2
5	Cod, ling (Ophiodon elongatus)	9	T-1824		35[3]	2.5	1
6	Dogfish (Squalus acanthias)	24[5]	T-1824	5.5(2.5-9.0)	18.2(14-24)[6]	6.8(3.1-10.9)	4
7	Ratfish Chimera colliaei	2	T-1824		18[3]	2.6	1
8	Hydrolagus colliaei	8[5]	T-1824	4.2(3.2-5.7)[3]	20.2(15-25)[3,7]	5.2(4.1-7.4)	4
9	Skate Big (Raja binoculata)	4[5]	T-1824	6.5(5.3-7.9)	17.5(15-20)[3]	8.0(6.5-9.9)	4
10	Long-nosed (R. rhina)	8[5]	T-1824	5.9(3.4-7.9)	16.8(12-21.5)[3,8]	7.2(4.0-9.5)	

/1/ Method: $\dfrac{\text{plasma volume}}{100 - \text{venous hematocrit}} \times 100$. /2/ Unfed 3-8 weeks. /3/ Cardiac blood. /4/ 10 determinations. /5/ Anesthetized. /6/ 25 subjects. /7/ 12 subjects. /8/ 11 subjects.

Contributors: (a) Reynolds, Monica, (b) Brown, Ellen

References: [1] Martin, A. W. In M. H. Hatch, ed. 1950. Studies honoring Trevor Kincaid. University of Washington Press, Seattle. [2] Prosser, C. L., and S. J. F. Weinstein. 1950. Physiol. Zool. 23:113. [3] Semple, R. E. 1960. Fed. Proc., Balt. 19:79. [4] Thorson, T. B. 1958. Physiol. Zool. 31:16.

2. BLOOD VOLUME IN TISSUE: VERTEBRATES

Part I: TOTAL

Values were obtained from determination of hemoglobin or labelled erythrocyte, and/or plasma volume. Where only one element was measured, it was assumed that the ratio of erythrocyte to plasma volume is the same in tissue as in peripheral circulating blood.

	Animal	No. and Sex	Measured Element (Labelling Substance)	Tissue	Total Blood Volume $\mu L/g$ tissue	Reference
	(A)	(B)	(C)	(D)	(E)	(F)
1	Cat[1]	2 or more	Erythrocyte mass (Hemoglobin)	Brain	30	7
2				Heart	84	
3				Kidney	93	
4				Liver	52	
5				Lung	147	
6				Skeletal muscle	27	
7				Spleen	195	
8	Dog[1,2]	7	Erythrocyte mass (Iron[59])	Brain	11	5
9				Heart	66	
10			Plasma volume	Intestine	41	
11			(Iodine[131])	Kidney	81	
12				Liver	147	
13				Lung	301	
14				Skeletal muscle	11	
15				Spleen	510	
16	Mouse	9[3]	Plasma volume	Kidney	250	12
17			(Iodine[131])	Liver	350	
18				Lung	400	
19				Spleen	190	
20		9[4]	Plasma volume	Adrenal	30	6
21			(Iodine[131])	Bone	110	
22				Brain	30	
23				Intestine	90	
24				Kidney	340	
25				Liver	360	
26				Lung	490	
27				Skeletal muscle	30	
28				Spleen	170	
29				Submaxillary gland	110	
30				Testis	60	
31		12♂[5]	Erythrocyte mass	Intestine	48	3, 4
32			(Iron[59])	Kidney	117	
33		40♂[5]	Plasma volume	Liver	234	
34			(Iodine[131])	Lung	616	
35				Skeletal muscle	45	
36				Skin	30	
37				Spleen	179	
38	Rat	4-14[4]	Erythrocyte mass (Hemoglobin)	Heart and lungs combined	379	8
39			Plasma volume (T-1824)	Kidney	278	
40				Liver	178	
41				Spleen	481	
42		♂[2]	Plasma volume (T-1824)	Bone	45	1
43				Brain	11	
44				Heart	60	
45				Intestine	20	
46				Large intestine	23.3	
47				Kidney	92	
48				Liver	99	
49				Lung	111	
50				Skeletal muscle	4	
51				Skin	20	
52				Spleen	86	
53				Stomach	41.1	
54				Testis	6	

/1/ Sacrificed with barbiturate. /2/ Blood permitted to ooze from tissue. /3/ Average hematocrit = 42.8%.
/4/ Sacrificed with ether. /5/ Sacrificed by rapid immersion in liquid nitrogen.

Part I: TOTAL (Concluded)

	Animal	No. and Sex	Measured Element (Labelling Substance)	Tissue	Total Blood Volume μL/g tissue	Reference
	(A)	(B)	(C)	(D)	(E)	(F)
55	Rat (con-cluded)	10-17♂[5]	Erythrocyte mass (Iron59)	Adrenal	238	2
56				Bone	41	
57			Plasma volume	Brain	33	
58			(Iodine131)	Heart	262	
59				Intestine	34	
60				Kidney	128	
61				Liver	270	
62				Lung	519	
63				Pituitary	93	
64				Seminal vesicle	23	
65				Skeletal muscle	26	
66				Skin	19	
67				Spinal cord	25	
68				Spleen	170	
69				Submaxillary gland	81	
70				Thyroid	181	
71				Testis	16	
72	Chicken	9-13♂[6]	Erythrocyte mass (Chromium51)	Intestine	78	9-11
73				Kidney	326	
74			Plasma volume	Liver	231	
75			(Iodine131)	Lung	575	
76				Proventriculus	72.5	
77				Skeletal muscle	38	
78				Spleen	198	
79		7-9♂[7]	Erythrocyte mass (Chromium51)	Intestine	103	
80				Kidney	481	
81			Plasma volume	Liver	542	
82			(Iodine131)	Lung	563	
83				Proventriculus	94.3	
84				Skeletal muscle	9	
85				Spleen	386	
86				Testis	20	

/5/ Sacrificed by rapid immersion in liquid nitrogen. /6/ 3-4 days old. /7/ 6-8 months old.

Contributors: (a) Hansard, Sam L., (b) Klein, J. Raymond, (c) Stearner, S. Phyllis, (d) Everett, Newton B., (e) Friedman, J. J.

References: [1] Caster, W. O., A. B. Simon, and W. D. Armstrong. 1955. Am. J. Physiol. 183:317. [2] Everett, N. B., B. Simmons, and E. P. Lasher. 1956. Circul. Res., N. Y. 4:419. [3] Friedman, J. J. 1955. Proc. Soc. Exp. Biol., N. Y. 88:323. [4] Friedman, J. J. 1959. Am. J. Physiol. 196:420. [5] Gibson, J. G., A. M. Seligman, W. C. Peacock, J. C. Aub, J. Fine, and R. D. Evans. 1946. J. Clin. Invest. 25:848. [6] Kaliss, N., and O. Pressman. 1950. Proc. Soc. Exp. Biol., N. Y. 75:16. [7] Klein, J. R. 1945. Arch. Biochem., N. Y. 8:421. [8] Lewis, A. E., R. D. Goodman, and E. A. Shuck. 1952. J. Laborat. Clin. M. 39:704. [9] Stearner, S. P., M. H. Sanderson, and E. J. Christian. 1956. ANL-5597. Q. Rep. Div. Biol. M. Res., Argonne National Laboratory, Chicago. p. 21. [10] Stearner, S. P., M. H. Sanderson, and E. J. Christian. 1957. ANL-5696. Q. Rep. Div. Biol. M. Res., Argonne National Laboratory, Chicago. p. 31. [11] Stearner, S. P., M. H. Sanderson, E. J. Christian, and A. M. Brues. 1958. Am. J. Physiol. 192:620. [12] Wish, L., J. Furth, and R. H. Storey. 1950. Proc. Soc. Exp. Biol., N. Y. 74:644.

2. BLOOD VOLUME IN TISSUE: VERTEBRATES (Concluded)

Part II: RESIDUAL

In quantitative studies of tissue distribution of blood-borne substances, it may be necessary to correct for the amount of the substance present in residual blood that has been trapped in the tissue at the time of sampling; values for organ residual blood volume after maximal free bleeding may be used to estimate such corrections. Values were obtained from determination of labelled erythrocytes. Values in parentheses are ranges, estimate "a" (cf. Introduction).

	Animal	No. of Subjects	Labelling Substance	Tissue	Residual Blood Volume μL/g tissue	Reference
	(A)	(B)	(C)	(D)	(E)	(F)
1	Cattle[1]	7	Phosphorus[32]	Adrenal	35(28-41)	1
2				Heart	32(22-44)	
3				Kidney	53(34-70)	
4				Liver	78(60-104)	
5				Lung	224(182-262)	
6				Pancreas	30(22-46)	
7				Pituitary	41	
8				Skeletal muscle	10(8-11)	
9				Spleen	331(221-394)	
10	Rat[2]	7	Iron[59]	Heart	42	2
11				Kidney	49	
12				Liver	47	
13				Skeletal muscle	4	
14				Spleen	166	
15	Sheep[1]	6	Phosphorus[32]	Adrenal	25(17-42)	1
16				Heart	55(44-63)	
17				Kidney	56(53-64)	
18				Liver	88(66-103)	
19				Lung	224(163-294)	
20				Pancreas	32(21-40)	
21				Pituitary	21	
22				Skeletal muscle	14(7-20)	
23				Spleen	348(330-368)	
24	Swine[1]	10	Phosphorus[32]	Adrenal	50(36-63)	1
25				Heart	35(28-46)	
26				Kidney	74(53-111)	
27				Liver	72(51-84)	
28				Lung	251(229-282)	
29				Pancreas	22(17-25)	
30				Skeletal muscle	9(7-12)	
31				Spleen	124(99-163)	

/1/ Sacrificed by blow on head and bled for 5 minutes. /2/ Anesthetized with ether and bled to death.

Contributors: (a) Hansard, Sam L., (b) Klein, J. Raymond, (c) Stearner, S. Phyllis, (d) Everett, Newton B., (e) Friedman, J. J.

References: [1] Hansard, S. L. 1956. Proc. Soc. Exp. Biol., N. Y. 91:31. [2] Sharpe, L. M., G. G. Culbreth, and J. R. Klein. 1950. Ibid. 74:681.

3. BLOOD PHYSICAL PROPERTIES OTHER THAN VOLUMES: VERTEBRATES

Part I: MAN

Values in parentheses are ranges, estimate "c" unless otherwise indicated (cf. Introduction).

	Property	Subjects Specification	No. of Observations	Value	Remarks	Reference
	(A)	(B)	(C)	(D)	(E)	(F)
	Whole Blood					
1	Dielectric constant			8.25(8.0-8.5)		13
2	Freezing point depression	30 subjects		0.567(0.557-0.577) °C		14
3	pH	2-3 yr		7.35	Arterial blood	6
4		3-18 yr		(7.38-7.40)		
5				7.31	Venous blood	7
6		50 subjects, >70 yr		(7.35-7.40)		10
7	Refractive index	30 subjects		17.4(16.2-18.5)		14
	Relative viscosity					
8	At 20°C	♂	5	4.71(4.09-5.10)	In vitro determination; hirudin anticoagulant	25
9		♀	5	4.46(4.08-4.66)		
10	At 37°C	♀	32	3.00(2.18-3.59)	Oxalated blood; in vitro determination	29
11	Specific gravity	♂	577	1.058(1.052-1.064)	Copper sulfate method; no anticoagulant	26
12		Infant, ♂♀	126	1.0638(1.0557-1.0743)	Falling drop method	16
13		♂♀	32	1.0557(1.0501-1.0619)		
14	At 25/4°C	♂		1.0564(1.0520-1.0608)	Copper sulfate method[1]	30
15	Specific heat			0.92 g-cal		3
16	Surface tension			(55.5-61.2) dynes/cm		5
	Erythrocytes					
17	Electrical charge	♂♀		5.21 electrostatic units x 1000	In M/15 phosphate buffer at pH 7.4	1
18	Electrophoretic mobility			1.31 sq cm/volt sec x 10^{-4}	In M/15 phosphate buffer at pH 7.4	1
19	pH			7.396		17
20	Specific gravity			1.0989(1.0942-1.1069)	Gravimetric method	22
21	At 25/4°C	♂		1.0932(1.0894-1.0970)[b]	Not corrected for an estimated 7% trapped plasma; copper sulfate method[1]	30
22				1.098(1.095-1.101)[b]	Corrected for trapped plasma; copper sulfate method[1]	
23	Specific heat			0.77 g-cal		24
	Plasma or Serum					
24	Colloid osmotic pressure			330(280-480) mm H_2O		19
25		Fasting	25	344(310-376) mm H_2O	Arterial blood	20
26		Fasting	25	337(300-373) mm H_2O	Venous blood	20
	Electrical conductivity					15
27	At 20°C			106(105-111) mho x 10,000		
28	At 25°C			120(117-124) mho x 10,000		
29	Freezing point depression	30♂, 20♀		0.532(0.512-0.552)[b] °C	Vapor pressure method	9
30		21 subjects		0.537(0.515-0.559)[b] °C	Vapor pressure method	4
31		28♂		0.534(0.521-0.547)[b] °C	Vapor pressure method	21
32		44♂, 31♀		0.540(0.512-0.568)[b] °C	Beckmann thermometer method	27
33		22♂, 17♀		0.536(0.524-0.548)[b] °C	Fiske osmometer method	18
34	Isoelectric point pH	♂		5.5		12
35		♀		6.0		
36	pH			(7.30-7.40)		15
37				(7.40-7.52)		11

/1/ Consult reference 28 for details.

Part I: MAN (Concluded)

| | Subjects | | | | |
Property	Specification	No. of Observations	Value	Remarks	Reference
(A)	(B)	(C)	(D)	(E)	(F)
Plasma or Serum (concluded)					
38 Refractive index			17.1(16.0-18.2)		2
39 At 17.5°C			(1.34920-1.35110)	Abbé refractometer method	23
Relative viscosity					
40 At 13-22°C	♂	5	1.86(1.80-1.95)	In vitro determination; hirudin anticoagulant	25
41 At 14-23°C	♀	5	1.89(1.75-2.05)		
42 At 37°C	♀	21	1.32(1.18-1.59)	Plasma from oxalated blood; in vitro determination	29
43		19	1.22(1.11-1.41)	In vitro determination	
44 Specific gravity	♂	574	1.0273(1.024-1.030)	Copper sulfate method; no anticoagulant	26
45	♂♀	194	1.0266(1.0242-1.0299)	Falling drop method	16
46			1.0284(1.0260-1.0308)[b]	Gravimetric method	22
47 At 25/4°C	♂		1.0239(1.0220-1.0258)[b]	Copper sulfate method[1]	30
48 Specific heat			0.94 g-cal		3, 24
49 Surface tension	Child		52(42-62)[b] dynes/cm		8
50	♂		75.1 dynes/cm		31
51			69.9 dynes/cm		
52	♀		75.4 dynes/cm		
53			70.2 dynes/cm		

/1/ Consult reference 28 for details.

Contributors: (a) Luckey, T. D., and Cohagen, D. L., (b) Hendry, E. B., (c) Dole, Vincent P., (d) Mendlowitz, Milton, (e) Keys, Ancel

References: [1] Abramson, H. A., and L. S. Moyer. 1936. J. Gen. Physiol. 19:601. [2] Atchley, D. W., R. F. Loeb, E. M. Benedict, and W. W. Palmer. 1923. Arch. Int. M. 31:606. [3] Atzler, E., and F. Richter. 1919. Biochem. Zschr. 100:193. [4] Benham, G. H., W. S. Duke-Elder, and T. H. Hodgson. 1938. J. Physiol., Lond. 92:355. [5] Brinkman, R. 1922. Arch. néerl. physiol. 7:258. [6] Cassels, D. E., and M. Morse. 1953. J. Clin. Invest. 32:824. [7] Chambers, W. H. 1923. J. Biol. Chem. 55:229. [8] Clark, E. B. 1928. Am. J. Dis. Child. 35:18. [9] Culbert, R. W. 1935. J. Biol. Chem. 109:547. [10] Dogliotti, G. C., and M. Santi. 1933. Minerva med., Tor. 2:378. [11] Earle, I. P., and G. E. Cullen. 1929. J. Biol. Chem. 83:539. [12] Faguet, M. 1936. Bull. Ass. fr. cancer 25:645. [13] Fürth, R. 1923. Ann. Phys., Lpz., Ser. 4, 70:63. [14] Gettler, A. O., and W. Baker. 1916. J. Biol. Chem. 25:211. [15] Gram, H. C. 1924. Am. J. M. Sc. 168:511. [16] Gray, P. A., and A. H. Elliot. 1943. Ibid. 205:356. [17] Hampson, A. C., and M. Maizels. 1927. J. Physiol., Lond. 64:xx. [18] Hendry, E. B. Unpublished. [19] Keys, A., and R. M. Hill. 1934. J. Exp. Biol., Lond. 11:28. [20] Kylin, E. 1931. Naunyn-Schmiedeberg's Arch. exp. Path. 161:91. [21] Lifson, N. 1944. J. Biol. Chem. 152:659. [22] MacLeod, J. 1932. Q. J. Exp. Physiol., Lond. 22:275. [23] Mann, F. D. 1948. Am. J. Clin. Path. 18:79. [24] Mendlowitz, M. 1948. Science 107:97. [25] Moll, K. 1943-44. Pflügers Arch. 247:74. [26] Muirhead, E., M. H. Grow, and A. T. Walker. 1946. Surg. Gyn. Obst. 82:405. [27] Olmstead, E. G., and D. A. Roth. 1957. Am. J. M. Sc. 233:392. [28] Phillips, R. A., D. D. Van Slyke, P. B. Hamilton, V. P. Dole, K. Emerson, Jr., and R. M. Archibald. 1950. J. Biol. Chem. 183:305. [29] Schwalm, H. 1941-42. Arch. Gyn., Berl. 172:288. [30] Van Slyke, D. D., R. A. Phillips, V. P. Dole, P. B. Hamilton, R. M. Archibald, and J. Plazin. 1950. J. Biol. Chem. 183:349. [31] Zunz, E., and J. La Barre. 1924. Bull. Acad. méd. Belgique, Ser. 5, 4:74.

Part II: MAMMALS OTHER THAN MAN

Values in parentheses are ranges, estimate "c" unless otherwise indicated (cf. Introduction).

	Animal	Blood	Property	Subjects Specification	No. of Observations	Value	Remarks	Reference
	(A)	(B)	(C)	(D)	(E)	(F)	(G)	(H)
1	Cat	Whole blood	Specific gravity	♂		1.050(1.046-1.054)[b]	Falling drop method[1]	20
2				♀		1.051(1.045-1.057)[b]		
3		Erythrocytes	Electrical charge			-17.8 mv	In M/15 phosphate buffer at pH 7.4	1
4			Electrophoretic mobility			1.39 sq cm/volt sec x 10^{-4}		
5		Plasma or serum	Colloid osmotic pressure	4 adults	4	336(305-382) mm H_2O	Hepp cellophane membrane method[2]	15
6						300(240-330) mm H_2O		13
7	Cattle	Whole blood	Specific gravity, at 20/4°C	♀, 18-30 mo		1.053(1.046-1.061)[b3]	Mostly Holstein-Friesian strain; gravimetric method	3
8				♀, 2½-18 yr		1.052(1.046-1.058)[b3]		
9		Erythrocytes	Specific gravity	♂		1.084(1.079-1.090)[b]	Gravimetric method	14
10		Serum	Colloid osmotic pressure	Ox		280(260-300) mm H_2O		13
11			Freezing point depression	Beef	14	0.587(0.540-0.630) °C		4
12				Ox		0.585°C		7
13			Relative viscosity, at 25°C	Calf	15	1.39(1.315-1.465)		8
14				Ox	20	1.67(1.489-1.851)		
15			Specific gravity, at 25°C	Calf	15	1.0225(1.0207-1.0243)	Gravimetric method	8
16				Ox	20	1.0269(1.0246-1.0292)		
17	Dog	Whole blood	Relative viscosity, at 20°C	♂	5	5.61(5.12-5.94)	Hirudin anticoagulant	16
18				♀	5	4.59(3.96-5.05)		
19			Specific gravity, at 22-26/4°C	1-3 da old		1.045[3]	Falling drop method[1]	9
20				Mongrel		1.052[3]		
21		Erythrocytes	Electrical charge			-21.1 mv	In M/15 phosphate buffer at pH 7.4	1
22			Electrophoretic mobility			1.65 sq cm/volt sec x 10^{-4}		
23		Plasma or serum	Colloid osmotic pressure	53 adults	53	296(264-357) mm H_2O	Hepp cellophane membrane method[2]	15
24						310(230-470) mm H_2O		13
25			Freezing point depression		21	0.600(0.528-0.727) °C		4
26						0.571°C		7
27			Relative viscosity At 11-17°C	♂	5	1.93(1.85-2.06)	Hirudin anticoagulant	16
28			At 10-22°C	♀	5	1.75(1.65-1.95)		
29	Goat	Whole blood	Specific gravity, at 25/4°C	♂, 1-2 yr		1.042(1.036-1.048)[b3]	Angora and Toggenburg strains; copper sulfate method[4]	5
30				♀, 1-2 yr		1.044(1.036-1.051)[b3]		
31		Plasma or serum	Colloid osmotic pressure			300(300-310) mm H_2O		13
32			Specific gravity, at 25/4°C	♂, 1-2 yr		1.0227(1.0194-1.0260)[b3]	Angora and Toggenburg strains; copper sulfate method[4]	5
33				♀, 1-2 yr		1.0211(1.0178-1.0244)[b3]		
34	Guinea pig	Erythrocytes	Electrical charge			-14.2 mv	In M/15 phosphate buffer at pH 7.4	1
35			Electrophoretic mobility			1.11 sq cm/volt sec x 10^{-4}		
36		Serum	Colloid osmotic pressure			250(230-280) mm H_2O		13
37	Horse	Whole blood	Specific gravity, at 20/4°C	♂, castrated; ♀		1.053(1.046-1.059)[3]	Benzene-chloroform method	18

/1/ Consult reference 2 for details. /2/ Consult reference 10 for details. /3/ Values in literature converted to standard reference temperature of water at 4°C. /4/ Consult reference 19 for details.

Part II: MAMMALS OTHER THAN MAN (Continued)

	Animal	Blood	Property	Subjects Specification	No. of Observations	Value	Remarks	Reference
	(A)	(B)	(C)	(D)	(E)	(F)	(G)	(H)
38	Horse (concluded)	Serum	Colloid osmotic pressure			280(230-350) mm H_2O		13
39			Freezing point depression			0.564°C		7
40			Relative viscosity, at 25°C		10	1.51(1.437-1.583)		8
41			Specific gravity, at 25/4°C		10	1.0267(1.0253-1.0281)	Gravimetric method	8
42	Monkey, rhesus	Erythrocytes	Electrical charge			-17.0 mv	In M/15 phosphate buffer at pH 7.4	1
43			Electrophoretic mobility			1.33 sq cm/volt sec x 10^{-4}		
44	Mouse	Whole blood	Specific gravity, at 25/4°C	60-80 da old		1.057(1.052-1.062)[b3]	CBA strain; falling drop method[5]	6
45		Erythrocytes	Electrical charge			-17.9 mv	In M/15 phosphate buffer at pH 7.4	1
46			Electrophoretic mobility			1.40 sq cm/volt sec x 10^{-4}		
47	Rabbit	Whole blood	Specific gravity, at 25/4°C			1.050(1.048-1.052)[b3]	Falling drop method[5]	6
48		Erythrocytes	Electrical charge			-7.0 mv	In M/15 phosphate buffer at pH 7.4	1
49			Electrophoretic mobility			0.55 sq cm/volt sec x 10^{-4}		
50			Specific gravity			1.098(1.093-1.104)	Gravimetric method	14
51		Plasma or serum	Colloid osmotic pressure			290(230-350) mm H_2O		13
52			Freezing point depression			0.592°C		7
53			Specific gravity			1.025(1.018-1.031)[b]	Gravimetric method	14
54	Rat	Whole blood	Relative viscosity, at 20°C	♂	5	4.49(3.72-5.05)	Hirudin anticoagulant	16
55				♀	5	4.55(4.41-4.73)		
56			Specific gravity, at 25/4°C	200-250 g		1.056(1.054-1.058)[b3]	Sprague-Dawley strain; falling drop method[5]	6
57				♂, 100-300 g		1.054(1.046-1.061)[b3]	Mixed strains; copper sulfate method[4]	5
58				♀, 100-300 g		1.054(1.046-1.061)[b3]		
59		Erythrocytes	Electrical charge			-18.6 mv	In M/15 phosphate buffer at at pH 7.4	1
60			Electrophoretic mobility			1.45 sq cm/volt sec x 10^{-4}		
61		Plasma or serum	Colloid osmotic pressure			260(220-290) mm H_2O		13
62			Relative viscosity At 13-14°C	♂	5	1.63(1.56-1.68)	Hirudin anticoagulant	16
63			At 13-16°C	♀	5	1.65(1.50-1.80)		
64			Specific gravity		8	1.0262(1.0249-1.0281)	Falling drop method; heparin anticoagulant	17
65			At 25/4°C	♂, 100-300 g		1.023(1.017-1.028)[b3]	Mixed strains; copper sulfate method[4]	5
66				♀, 100-300 g		1.022(1.018-1.027)[b3]		
67	Sheep	Whole blood	Specific gravity, at 20/4°C	♂, castrated; ♀		1.051(1.041-1.061)[b3]	Cheviot, black-faced, gray-faced strains; benzene-chloroform method	11
68		Erythrocytes	Specific gravity			1.084(1.080-1.087)	Gravimetric method	14
69		Serum	Colloid osmotic pressure			300(290-340) mm H_2O		13

/3/ Values in literature converted to standard reference temperature of water at 4°C. /4/ Consult reference 19 for details. /5/ Consult reference 12 for details.

Part II: MAMMALS OTHER THAN MAN (Concluded)

	Animal	Blood	Property	Subjects Specification	No. of Observations	Value	Remarks	Reference
	(A)	(B)	(C)	(D)	(E)	(F)	(G)	(H)
70	Sheep (con-cluded)	Serum (con-clud-ed)	Freezing point depression			$0.619^{o}C$		7
71			Relative viscosity, at 25°C		10	1.60(1.382-1.818)		8
72			Specific gravity, at 25/4°C		10	1.0273(1.0258-1.0288)	Gravimetric method	8
73	Swine	Whole blood	Specific gravity, at 25/4°C	♂, young		1.047(1.038-1.055)[b3]	Duroc-Jersey, Poland-China, Chester-White strains; copper sulfate method[4]	5
74				♀, young		1.043(1.035-1.052)[b3]		
75		Plasma or serum	Colloid osmotic pressure			330(300-350) mm H_2O		13
76			Freezing point depression			$0.615^{o}C$		7
77			Relative viscosity, at 25°C		40	1.55(1.432-1.668)		8
78			Specific gravity, at 25/4°C	♂, young		1.022(1.021-1.025)[b3]	Duroc-Jersey, Poland-China, Chester-White strains; copper sulfate method[4]	5
79				♀, young		1.023(1.020-1.027)[b3]		
80					40	1.0272(1.0249-1.0295)	Gravimetric method	8

/3/ Values in literature converted to standard reference temperature of water at 4°C. /4/ Consult reference 19 for details.

Contributors: (a) Hendry, E. B., (b) Dole, Vincent P., (c) Keys, Ancel, (d) Holman, H. H., (e) Cronkite, Eugene P., (f) Hill, Robert M.

References: [1] Abramson, H. A., and L. S. Moyer. 1936. J. Gen. Physiol. 19:601. [2] Barbour, H. G., and W. F. Hamilton. 1926. J. Biol. Chem. 69:625. [3] Braun, W. 1946. Am. J. Vet. Res. 7:451. [4] Collins, D. A., and F. H. Scott. 1932. J. Biol. Chem. 97:189. [5] Cronkite, E. P. Unpublished. [6] Dougherty, T. F., and A. White. 1944. Endocrinology 35:3. [7] Dukes, H. H. 1937. The physiology of domestic animals. Comstock, Ithaca. [8] Eder, H. 1953. Biochem. Zschr. 325:36. [9] Ederstrom, H. E., and B. de Boer. 1946. Anat. Rec. 94:663. [10] Hepp, O. 1936. Zschr. ges. exp. Med. 99:709. [11] Holman, H. H. 1944. J. Comp. Path., Lond. 54:26. [12] Kazan, B. M. 1941. J. Laborat. Clin. M. 26:1681. [13] Keys, A., and R. M. Hill. 1934. J. Exp. Biol., Lond. 11:28. [14] MacLeod, J. 1932. Q. J. Exp. Physiol., Lond. 22:275. [15] Malorny, G. 1952. Arch. exp. Path., Berl. 215:619. [16] Moll, K. 1943-44. Pflügers Arch. 247:74. [17] Siegel, P. S., I. E. Alexander, and H. L. Stuckey. 1947. Am. J. Physiol. 150:729. [18] Stewart, J., and H. H. Holman. 1940. Vet. Rec., Lond. 52:157. [19] Van Slyke, D. D., R. A. Phillips, V. P. Dole, P. B. Hamilton, R. M. Archibald, and J. Plazin. 1950. J. Biol. Chem. 183:349. [20] Windle, W. F., M. Sweet, and W. H. Whitehead. 1940. Anat. Rec. 78:321.

3. BLOOD PHYSICAL PROPERTIES OTHER THAN VOLUMES: VERTEBRATES (Continued)

Part III: BIRDS

Values in parentheses are ranges, estimate "c" (cf. Introduction).

	Animal	Blood	Property	Subjects Specification	No. of Observations	Value	Remarks	Reference
	(A)	(B)	(C)	(D)	(E)	(F)	(G)	(H)
1	Chicken	Whole blood	Relative viscosity	N. Hamp. breed ♂, fasted 24 hr	15	4.6(4.0-5.2)	Hellige viscosimeter; pooled samples	3
2				♀, fasted 24 hr	36	3.4(3.1-3.9)		
3			Specific gravity	N. Hamp. breed ♂, fasted 24 hr	15	1.0511 (1.0507-1.0515)	Pyknometric method; pooled samples	3
4				♀, fasted 24 hr	36	1.0450 (1.0418-1.0480)		
5				White Leghorn	19	1.04495 (1.0365-1.0510)	Copper sulfate method	4
6		Plasma or serum	Colloid osmotic pressure	♂		150(140-160) mm H$_2$O		1
7			Refractive index, at 28°C	N. Hamp. breed ♂, fasted 24 hr	15	1.3423 (1.3422-1.3423)	Abbé refractometer method; pooled samples	3
8				♀, fasted 24 hr	36	1.3458 (1.3446-1.3471)		
9			Relative viscosity	N. Hamp. breed ♂, fasted 24 hr	15	1.7(1.6-1.8)	Hellige viscosimeter method; heparin anticoagulant; pooled samples	3
10				♀, fasted 24 hr	36	1.5(1.2-1.9)		
11			Specific gravity	N. Hamp. breed ♂, fasted 24 hr	15	1.0193 (1.0178-1.0207)	Pyknometric method; pooled samples	3
12				♀, fasted 24 hr	36	1.0203 (1.0185-1.0228)		
13			Specific gravity	White Leghorn	21	1.01904 (1.0175-1.0210)	Copper sulfate method	4
14	Dove	Serum	Colloid osmotic pressure			110(80-120) mm H$_2$O		1
15	Duck	Whole blood	Relative viscosity, at 20°C	♂	5	4.03(3.54-4.79)	Hirudin anticoagulant	2
16				♀	5	3.87(3.44-4.42)		
17			Specific gravity			1.056		5
18		Plasma or serum	Relative viscosity At 10-14°C	♂	5	1.49(1.40-1.55)	Hirudin anticoagulant	2
19			At 8-14°C	♀	5	1.76(1.59-1.94)		
20			Specific gravity			1.020		5
21	Goose	Whole blood	Relative viscosity, at 20°C	♂	5	4.58(4.03-5.55)	Hirudin anticoagulant	2
22				♀	5	4.50(3.64-5.16)		
23			Specific gravity			1.050		5
24		Plasma or serum	Relative viscosity At 12-17°C	♂	5	1.48(1.25-1.63)	Hirudin anticoagulant	2
25			At 13-18°C	♀	5	1.63(1.43-1.82)		
26			At 14-17°C	♀	5	1.73(1.70-1.82)	Hirudin anticoagulant	
27			Specific gravity			1.021		5
28	Guinea fowl	Whole blood	Specific gravity			1.057		5
29		Serum	Specific gravity			1.021		
30	Ostrich	Whole blood	Specific gravity			1.063		5
31		Plasma	Specific gravity			1.022		

Contributors: (a) Schechtman, A. M., (b) Hendry, E. B., (c) Keys, Ancel

References: [1] Keys, A., and R. M. Hill. 1934. J. Exp. Biol., Lond. 11:28. [2] Moll, K. 1943-44. Pflügers

Arch. 247:74. [3] Schechtman, A. M., W. G. Heim, P. F. Knight, E. Levi, A. E. S. Smith, and E. M. Weller. Unpublished. [4] Sturkie, P. D. 1947. Am. J. Physiol. 148:610. [5] Sturkie, P. D. 1954. Avian physiology. Comstock, Ithaca.

4. PHYSICAL PROPERTIES OF SERUM: REPTILES, AMPHIBIANS, FISHES

Values in parentheses are ranges, estimate "c" (cf. Introduction).

Animal	Property	Value	Reference
(A)	(B)	(C)	(D)
Reptiles			
1 Turtle (Malacoclemmys sp)	Colloid osmotic pressure	58(48-68) mm H_2O[1]	1, 6
2		96(81-112) mm H_2O[2]	
Amphibians			
Frog			4
3 Rana catesbeiana	Colloid osmotic pressure	103(96-115) mm H_2O	
4 R. temporaria	Colloid osmotic pressure	70 mm H_2O	
5 Toad (Bufo vulgaris)	Colloid osmotic pressure	133(83-242) mm H_2O	3, 6
Fishes			
6 Bass (Labrax lupus)	Colloid osmotic pressure	(174-250) mm H_2O	2, 5
7 Carp, common (Cyprinus carpio)	Colloid osmotic pressure	(100-113) mm H_2O	2, 5
8 Cod (Gadus morhua)	Colloid osmotic pressure	113(112-114) mm H_2O	4
9	Freezing point depression	0.765°C	7
10	Refractive index, at 17.5°C[3]	1.34215(1.34182-1.34249)	4
Dogfish			2, 5
11 Acanthias vulgaris	Colloid osmotic pressure	(42-43) mm H_2O	
12 Mustelus hinnulus	Colloid osmotic pressure	(57-64) mm H_2O	
13 Scyllium canicula	Colloid osmotic pressure	(31-36) mm H_2O	
Eel			2, 5
14 Anguilla vulgaris	Colloid osmotic pressure	225 mm H_2O	
15 Conger vulgaris	Colloid osmotic pressure	(146-173) mm H_2O	
16 Gurnard (Trigla lucerna)	Colloid osmotic pressure	(195-213) mm H_2O	2, 5
17 Mackerel (Scomber scombrus)	Colloid osmotic pressure	(196-198) mm H_2O	2, 5
18 Pike (Esox lucius)	Colloid osmotic pressure	(112-146) mm H_2O	2, 5
19	Freezing point depression	0.514°C	4
20 Plaice (Pleuronectes platessa)	Colloid osmotic pressure	115(107-126) mm H_2O	4
21	Freezing point depression	0.732°C	
22	Refractive index, at 17.5°C[3]	1.34165(1.34052-1.34237)	
23 Ray, electric (Torpedo marmorata)	Colloid osmotic pressure	(42-52) mm H_2O	2, 5
24 Scorpion fish (Scorpaena scrofa)	Colloid osmotic pressure	(181-186) mm H_2O	2, 5
25 Tench (Tinca vulgaris)	Colloid osmotic pressure	101(93-109) mm H_2O	4
26	Freezing point depression	0.523°C	
27	Refractive index, at 17.5°C[3]	1.34089(1.34082-1.34094)	
28 Turbot (Rhombus maximus)	Colloid osmotic pressure	174 mm H_2O	2, 5

/1/ In spring, fasting. /2/ In fall, fed. /3/ Zeiss Pulfrich refractometer, calibrated with distilled water and standard salt solution at same temperature.

Contributors: (a) Hill, Robert M., (b) Keys, Ancel, (c) Dole, Vincent P., (d) Mendlowitz, Milton, (e) Wise, John P.

References: [1] Campbell, M. L., and A. H. Turner. 1937. Biol. Bull. 73:504. [2] Cardot, H., and P. Meyer. 1936. Ann. physiol., Par. 12:665. [3] Horikawa, T. 1932. J. Exp. M. 19:233. [4] Keys, A., and R. M. Hill. 1934. J. Exp. Biol., Lond. 11:28. [5] Krogh, A., and P. Meyer. 1932. Erg. Physiol. 34:18. [6] Krogh, A., and F. Nakazawa. 1927. Biochem. Zschr. 188:241. [7] Macallum, A. B. 1910. Proc. R. Soc., Lond., Ser. B, 82:602.

5. BLOOD WATER AND SOLIDS: MAMMALS

Values in parentheses are ranges, estimate "c" (cf. Introduction).

	Animal	Blood	Water %	Total Solids %	Reference
	(A)	(B)	(C)	(D)	(E)
	Man				
1	Children	Whole blood	(78.9-80.8)	17.4(16.2-18.3)	C, 11; D, 4
2	Adults	Whole blood	(80.5-80.8)	22.4(20.0-24.9)	C, 5; D, 4
3		Erythrocytes	72(70-75)	37(34-39)	8
4		Plasma or serum	94(93-95)	8.6(7.9-9.1)	7, 10
5	Cat	Whole blood	79.6	20.4	6
6		Erythrocytes	62.4	37.6	
7		Serum	92.7	7.3	
	Cattle				6
8	Bull	Whole blood	81.5	18.5	
9		Erythrocytes	61.9	38.1	
10		Serum	91.3	8.7	
11	Cow	Whole blood	80.9	19.1	
12		Erythrocytes	59.2	40.8	
13		Serum	91.4	8.6	
14	Dog	Whole blood	(79.2-81.0)	(19.0-20.8)	6
15		Erythrocytes	(62.7-64.4)	(35.6-37.3)	6
16		Plasma or serum	93(91-95)	(7.6-7.7)	2, 6
17	Goat	Whole blood	80.4	19.6	6
18		Erythrocytes	60.9	39.1	
19		Serum	90.8	9.2	
20	Horse	Whole blood	(74.9-79.5)	(20.5-25.1)	6
21		Erythrocytes	61.3	38.7	
22		Serum	(90.2-91.5)	(8.5-9.8)	
23	Rabbit	Whole blood	81.7	18.3	6
24		Erythrocytes	63.4	36.6	6
25		Serum	93(92-94)	6.7(6.0-7.8)	9
26	Rat	Whole blood	81.6(79.7-82.5)	18.4(17.5-20.3)	1, 2
27		Plasma	92.9	7.1	3
28	Sheep	Whole blood	(82.2-82.5)	(17.5-17.8)	6
29		Erythrocytes	(60.5-62.8)	(37.2-39.5)	
30		Serum	91.7	8.3	
31	Swine	Whole blood	79.1	20.9	6
32		Erythrocytes	62.6	37.4	
33		Serum	91.8	8.2	

Contributors: (a) Manery, J. F., (b) Allison, James B., (c) Luckey, T. D., and Cohagen, D. L., (d) Mirsky, I. Arthur, and Erdoes, Ervin, (e) Bacchus, Habeeb

References: [1] Allison, J. B., W. H. Cole, J. H. Holmes, and W. S. Root. 1947. Am. J. Physiol. 149:422. [2] Allison, J. B. Unpublished. [3] Bacchus, H., C. A. Toompas, and M. H. Heiffer. 1951. Unpublished. [4] Courtney, A. M., and H. L. Fales. 1917. Am. J. Dis. Child. 14:202. [5] Davis, F. E., K. Kenyon, and J. Kirk. 1953. Science 118:276. [6] Dukes, H. H. 1947. The physiology of domestic animals. Ed. 6. Comstock, Ithaca. [7] Hald, P. M. 1946. J. Biol. Chem. 163:429. [8] Hald, P. M., M. Tulin, T. S. Danowski, P. H. Lavietes, and J. P. Peters. 1947. Am. J. Physiol. 149:340. [9] Manery, J. F. Unpublished. [10] Miller, A. T., Jr. 1942. J. Biol. Chem. 143:65. [11] Ujsághy, P. 1941. Zschr. Kinderh. 62:266.

II. Blood Electrolytes

6. BLOOD ELECTROLYTES: MAN

Values in parentheses are ranges, estimate "c" unless otherwise indicated (cf. Introduction).

	Constituent	Value	Reference
	(A)	(B)	(C)
	Whole Blood		
1	Aluminum	(21-94) μg/100 ml	67
2	Bicarbonate	20.9(19.1-22.7)[b] mEq/L	64
3	Bromine	0.81(0.33-1.73) mg/100 ml	65
4	Calcium	9.7 mg/100 ml	2
5	Chloride	295 mg/100 ml	19
6	Chromium	3.5 μg/100 ml	22
7	Copper	98(72-124) μg/100 ml	66
8	Fluorine	(11-45) μg/100 ml	38
9	Gold	0.012 mg/100 g	32
	Iodine		
10	Total I	9.7(2.5-16.9) μg/100 ml	11
11	Protein-bound I	(4.0-8.5) μg/100 ml	47, 62
12	Thyroxine I	4.35(3.9-4.8) μg/100 ml	15
13	Iron	(45.5-52.3) μg/100 ml	39
14	Lead	29(18-49) μg/100 ml	32
15	Lithium	1.9(0.9-3.0) μg/100 ml	4
16	Magnesium	4.04(3.58-4.50) mg/100 ml	34
17	Manganese	13(0-25) μg/100 ml	32
18	Mercury	0.385(0.16-0.51) μg/100 ml	60
19	Phosphate	2.95(2.4-3.5) mg/100 ml	68
	Phosphorus		
20	Total P	34.982 mg/100 ml	51
21	Inorganic P	3.3(2.4-3.76) mg/100 ml	7
22	Total acid-soluble P	23.5(20.8-25.8) mg/100 ml	33
23	Organic acid-soluble P	23.1(18.6-28.6) mg/100 ml	28
24	Adenosine triphosphate P	4.6(1.8-6.2) mg/100 ml	28
25	Diphosphoglycerate P	12.4(8.1-16.7) mg/100 ml	28
26	Hexosephosphate P	3.2(1.4-5.0) mg/100 ml	28
27	Lipid P	13.7(12.5-15.4) mg/100 ml	57
28	Nucleoprotein P	2.65 mg/100 ml	31
29	Nucleotide P	2.8(2.2-3.4) mg/100 ml	33
30	Potassium	45.5 mEq/L	37
31	Rubidium	0.303(0.260-0.345) mg/100 ml	5
32	Silicon	8.3 μg/ml	69
33	Silver	Trace	32
34	Sodium	94.0(91.8-96.2)[b] mEq/L	46
	Sulfate		
35	Total SO$_4$	0.75(0.5-1.0) mg/100 ml	12
36	Inorganic SO$_4$	0.45 mg/100 ml	13
37	Ethereal SO$_4$	3.80 mg/100 ml	13
	Sulfur		
38	Total S	1928(1648-2314) g/L	14
39	Inorganic S	0.45(0.28-0.65) mg/100 ml	48
40	Neutral S	3.80(3.19-5.20) mg/100 ml	48
41	Tin	0.013 mg/100 g	32
42	Zinc	880(480-1280)[b] μg/100 ml	63
	Erythrocytes		
43	Aluminum	7 μg/100 ml	32
44	Bromine	0.98(0.92-1.40) mg/100 ml	30
45	Calcium	(0.6-1.4) mEq/L	56
46	Chloride	78 mEq/L	3
47	Cobalt	1.20 μg/100 ml	29
48	Copper	115(84-159) μg/100 ml	36
49	Fluorine	25(9-40) μg/100 ml	38
50	Iodine, protein-bound	(4.9-5.2) μg/100 ml	41

Constituent	Value	Reference
(A)	(B)	(C)
Erythrocytes (concluded)		
51 Iron, non-hemoglobin	2.48(1.58-5.30) μg/100 ml	1
52 Lead	57(29-86) μg/100 ml	32
53 Magnesium	(3.4-5.6) mg/100 ml	58
54 Manganese	19 μg/100 ml	32
Phosphorus		
55 Inorganic P	2.41(0.9-3.3) mg/100 ml	28
56 Organic acid-soluble P	49.7(38.5-58.7) mg/100 ml	28
57 Adenosine triphosphate P	10.6(4.2-15.1) mg/100 ml	28
58 Diphosphoglycerate P	29.2(19.0-40.4) mg/100 ml	28
59 Hexosephosphate P	7.5(3.5-10.7) mg/100 ml	28
60 Lipid P	11.9 mg/100 ml	17
61 Nucleotide P	6.2(5.1-7.1) mg/100 ml	33
62 Potassium	437(425-444) mg/100 ml	42
63 Silver	Trace	32
64 Sodium	14(Trace-31) mg/100 ml	42
65 Sulfur, ethereal	0.015 mg/100 ml	48
66 Tin	26 μg/100 ml	32
67 Zinc	1440(900-1980)[b] μg/100 ml	63
Plasma or Serum		
68 Aluminum	46 μg/100 ml	32
69 Bicarbonate	(24-31) mEq/L	25
70 Bromine	(0.7-1.0) μg/100 ml	21
71 Calcium	9.8(8.4-11.2)[a] mg/100 ml	10, 23, 55
72 Chloride	369(337-400)[a] mg/100 ml	23, 55, 59, 70
73 Cobalt	0.85 μg/100 ml	29
74 Copper	119(94-144)[a] μg/100 ml	9
75 Fluorine	27(10-44) μg/100 ml	38
Iodine		
76 Total I	7.1(4.8-8.6) μg/100 ml	49
77 Organic I	(2.2-5.1) μg/100 ml	16
78 Precipitable I	5.0(3.8-7.1) μg/100 ml	26, 27, 44
79 Protein-bound I	7.0(6.0-8.4) μg/100 ml	61
80 Thyroxine I	(4-8) μg/100 ml	50
81 Iron	105(39-170)[a] μg/100 ml	9
82 Lead	2.9 μg/100 ml	32
83 Magnesium	2.1(1.6-2.6)[a] mg/100 ml	23, 53, 55, 59
84 Manganese	8 μg/100 ml	32
85 Phosphate	(3.1-4.9) mg/100 ml	52
Phosphorus		
86 Total P	11.4(10.7-12.1) mg/100 ml	17
87 Inorganic P	3.5(2.7-4.3)[a] mg/100 ml	6, 18
88 Organic P	8.2(7-9) mg/100 ml	20
89 Adenosine triphosphate P	0.16(0.0-0.64) mg/100 ml	28
90 Diphosphoglycerate P	0.03(0.0-0.36) mg/100 ml	28
91 Hexosephosphate P	0.04(0.0-0.22) mg/100 ml	28
92 Lipid P	9.2(6.4-12.0)[a] mg/100 ml	43
93 Nucleic acid P	0.54(0.44-0.65) mg/100 ml	40
94 Potassium	16.0(13.1-18.9)[a] mg/100 ml	24, 54, 59
95 Rubidium	0.114 mg/100 ml	5
96 Silicon	0.79 mg/100 ml	35
97 Sodium	325(312-338) mg/100 ml	10, 54
Sulfate		
98 Total SO$_4$	3.3(2.7-3.9) mg/100 ml	8
99	1.22(0.97-1.58) mg/100 ml	45
100 Inorganic SO$_4$	3.7(2.4-5.0) mg/100 ml	8
101	1.28(0.94-1.49) mg/100 ml	45
102 Ethereal SO$_4$	0.67 mg/100 ml	13
103	0.076(0.00-0.19) mg/100 ml	45
Sulfur		
104 Inorganic S	0.9(0.8-1.1) mg/100 ml	8
105 Organic S	1.7(1.37-2.57) mg/100 ml	8
106 Ethereal S	0.1(0.00-0.19) mg/100 ml	45

Constituent	Value	Reference
(A)	(B)	(C)
Plasma or Serum (concluded)		
Sulfur (concluded)		
107 Neutral S	1.95 mg/100 ml	13
108 Non-protein S	2.8(2.4-3.6) mg/100 ml	8
109 Sulfate S	1.1(0.9-1.3) mg/100 ml	8
110 Tin	4 μg/100 ml	32
111 Zinc	300(0-613) μg/100 ml	63

Contributors: (a) Luckey, T. D., and Cohagen, D. L., (b) Mirsky, I. Arthur, and Erdoes, Ervin, (c) West, Clark D., (d) Freeman, Smith, (e) Largent, Edward J., (f) Levine, Victor E., (g) Cartwright, G. E., (h) Kerr, Stanley E., (i) Lewis, Howard B., (j) Ponder, Eric

References: [1] Alcuin-Arens, M. 1940-41. Q. J. M. Techn. 6-7:203. [2] Baumann, R., and R. Herrmann. 1953. Zschr. ges. exp. Med. 120:172. [3] Bernstein, R. E. 1954. Science 120:459. [4] Bertrand, D. 1951. Bull. Soc. chim. biol., Par. 33:829. [5] Bertrand, G., and D. Bertrand. 1951. Bull. Acad. nat. méd., Par. 135:27. [6] Bodansky, A., and H. L. Jaffe. 1934. Arch. Int. M. 54:88. [7] Brain, R. T., H. D. Kay, and P. G. Marshall. 1928. Biochem. J., Lond. 22:628. [8] Brown, B. H., and H. B. Lewis. 1941. J. Biol. Chem. 138:705. [9] Cartwright, G. E., C. M. Huguley, H. Ashenbrucker, J. Fay, and M. M. Wintrobe. 1948. Blood, N. Y. 3:501. [10] Consolazio, W. V., and J. H. Talbott. 1940. J. Biol. Chem. 132:753. [11] Curtis, G. M., and M. B. Fertman. 1947. Arch. Surg. 54:541. [12] Denis, W. 1921. J. Biol. Chem. 49:316. [13] Denis, W., G. R. Hermann, and L. Reed. 1928. Arch. Int. M. 41:385. [14] Dezani, S. 1931. Biochim. ter. sper. 18:34. [15] Elmer, A. W., Z. Luczynski, and M. Scheps. 1934. C. rend. Soc. biol. 115:1714. [16] Fazio, B., V. Costa, and G. Asserto. 1954. Arch. Maragliano pat. clin. 9:511. [17] Ferranti, F., and O. Giannetti. 1933. Diagn. tecn. laborat., Nap. 4:664. [18] Gibbs, E. L., W. G. Lennox, L. F. Nims, and F. A. Gibbs. 1942. J. Biol. Chem. 144:325. [19] Gigli, G. 1939. Boll. Soc. ital. biol. sper. 14:343. [20] Grassheim, K., and E. Lucas. 1928. Zschr. klin. Med. 107:172. [21] Gray, M. G., and M. Moore. 1942. J. Laborat. Clin. M. 27:680. [22] Grushko, Y. M. 1948. Biokhimiia, Moskva 13:124. [23] Hald, P. M. 1933. J. Biol. Chem. 103:471. [24] Hald, P. M. 1946. Ibid. 163:429. [25] Hald, P. M., A. J. Heinsen, and J. P. Peters. 1947. J. Clin. Invest. 26:983. [26] Heinemann, M., C. L. Johnson, and E. B. Man. 1948. Ibid. 27:91. [27] Heinemann, M., C. L. Johnson, and E. B. Man. Unpublished. [28] Helve, O. 1946. Acta med. scand. 125:505. [29] Heyrovský, A. 1952. Čas. lék. česk. 91:680. [30] Hunter G. 1955. Biochem. J., Lond. 60:261. [31] Javillier, M., and M. Fabrykant. 1931. Bull. Soc. chim. biol., Par. 13:685. [32] Kehoe, R. A., J. Cholak, and R. V. Story. 1940. J. Nutrit. 19:579. [33] Kerr, S. E., and L. Daoud. 1935. J. Biol. Chem. 109:301. [34] Kunkel, H. O., P. B. Pearson, and B. S. Schweigert. 1947. J. Laborat. Clin. M. 32:1027. [35] Kvorning, S. A., and E. Kirk. 1949. J. Geront. 4:16. [36] Lahey, M. E., C. J. Gubler, G. E. Cartwright, and M. M. Wintrobe. 1953. J. Clin. Invest. 32:322. [37] Lans, H. S., I. F. Stein, and K. A. Meyer. 1952. Am. J. M. Sc. 223:65. [38] Largent, E. J., and J. Cholak. Unpublished. [39] Makarovskaya, T. D. 1950. Klin. med., Moskva 28:85. [40] Mandel, P., and P. Metais. 1948. C. rend. Soc. biol. 142:241. [41] McClendon, J. F., and W. C. Foster. 1944. Am. J. M. Sc. 207:549. [42] Overman, R. R., and A. K. Davis. 1947. J. Biol. Chem. 168:641. [43] Peters, J. P., and E. B. Man. 1943. J. Clin. Invest. 22:707. [44] Peters, J. P., E. B. Man, and M. Heinemann. 1948. Obst. Gyn. Survey 3:647. [45] Power, M. H., and E. G. Wakefield. 1938. J. Biol. Chem. 123:665. [46] Prytz, B. 1953. Bull. S. Francis Sanat., Roslyn 10:27. [47] Reals, W. J., J. A. Jarman, and R. T. Beattie. 1953. Mil. Surgeon 113:478. [48] Reed, L., and W. Denis. 1927. J. Biol. Chem. 73:623. [49] Sachs, A., et al. 1943. Arch. Int. M. 71:489. [50] Salter, W. T., and I. Rosenbloom. 1951. J. Endocr., Lond. 7:180. [51] Sehra, K. B., and B. Ahmad. 1945. Ann. Biochem. Exp. M., Calc. 5:145. [52] Simonsen, D. G., M. Wertman, L. M. Westover, and J. W. Mehl. 1946. J. Biol. Chem. 166:747. [53] Simonsen, D. G.,

L. M. Westover, and M. Wertman. 1947. Ibid. 169:39. [54] Smith, R. G., P. Craig, E. J. Bird, A. J. Boyle, L. T. Iseri, S. D. Jacobson, and G. B. Myers. 1950. Am. J. Clin. Path. 20:263. [55] Snyder, R., and S. Katzenelbogen. 1942. J. Biol. Chem. 143:223. [56] Sobel, A. E., G. Kraus, and B. Kramer. 1941. Ibid. 140:501. [57] Sokolovitch, M. 1931. Arch. Dis. Childh., Lond. 6:183. [58] Streef, G. M. 1939. J. Biol. Chem. 129:667. [59] Sunderman, F. W. 1931. J. Clin. Invest. 9:615. [60] Szép, Ö. 1940. Biochem. Zschr. 307:79. [61] Talbot, N. B., A. M. Butler, A. H. Saltzman, and P. M. Rodriguez. 1944. J. Biol. Chem. 153:486. [62] Tommasino, P. O., and J. J. Staffieri. 1953. Rev. As. méd. argent. 67:489. [63] Vallee, B. L., and J. G. Gibson, II. 1948. J. Biol. Chem. 176:445. [64] West, C. D. Unpublished. [65] Wikoff, H. L., R. A. Brunner, and H. W. Allison. 1940. Am. J. Clin. Path. 10:234. [66] Wintrobe, M. M., G. E. Cartwright, and C. J. Gubler. 1953. J. Nutrit. 50:395. [67] Wolff, H. 1948. Biochem. Zschr. 319:1. [68] Wootten, I. D. P., and E. J. King. 1953. Lancet, Lond. 264:470. [69] Worth, G., and G. Campen. 1951. Hoppe Seyler Zschr. 288:155. [70] Wu, H. 1922. J. Biol. Chem. 51:21.

7. BLOOD ELECTROLYTES: CATTLE

Part I: WHOLE BLOOD

Values in parentheses are ranges, estimate "c" or "d" (cf. Introduction).

	Animal	Constituent	No. of Subjects	No. of Observations	Age of Subjects	Value mg/100 ml	Reference
	(A)	(B)	(C)	(D)	(E)	(F)	(G)
1	Bull	Potassium[1]	4	16	2-4 yr	73(53-101)	2
2			18	68	5-7 yr	69(37-112)	
3			17	68	$7\frac{1}{2}$-10 yr	61(46-100)	
4			8	34	11-13 yr	59(46-91)	
5			3	9	$13\frac{1}{2}$-15 yr	111(53-179)	
6		Sodium[1]	4	16	2-4 yr	267(255-284)	
7			18	68	5-7 yr	260(220-293)	
8			17	68	$7\frac{1}{2}$-10 yr	264(246-289)	
9			8	34	11-13 yr	267(250-285)	
10			3	9	$13\frac{1}{2}$-15 yr	240(186-282)	
11	Angus	Potassium	1	15	4 yr	66(59-77)	
12		Sodium	1	15	4 yr	256(241-265)	
13	Ayrshire	Potassium	2	8	6-8 yr	48(46-50)	
14		Sodium	2	8	6-8 yr	273(265-278)	
15	Brown Swiss	Potassium	4	16	6-8 yr	63(40-87)	
16		Sodium	4	16	6-8 yr	262(248-288)	
17	Guernsey	Potassium	12	48	$4-13\frac{1}{2}$ yr	63(53-91)	
18		Sodium	12	48	$4-13\frac{1}{2}$ yr	267(245-293)	
19	Holstein	Potassium	13	55	6-15 yr	53(40-65)	
20		Sodium	13	55	6-15 yr	269(246-289)	
21	Jersey	Potassium	10	40	2-14 yr	92(55-178)	
22		Sodium	10	40	2-14 yr	250(186-275)	
23	Red Dane	Potassium	6	23	5-12 yr	79(57-95)	
24		Sodium	6	23	5-12 yr	256(245-275)	
25	Shorthorn,	Potassium	2	5	5-6 yr	85(54-90)	
26	milking	Sodium	2	5	5-6 yr	249(236-267)	
	Ox	Phosphorus					4
27		Inorganic P				5.2(3.3-7.6)[2]	
28		Total acid-soluble P				8.6(6.6-11.1)[2]	
29		Organic acid-soluble P				3.4(2.1-4.9)[2]	
30		Nucleotide P				0.8(0.6-1.1)[2]	
31	Heifer	Potassium	12	12	At birth	174(106-199)	2
32					1 wk	147(107-185)	

/1/ Modified Hunter technique [3], using Perkins-Elmer flame photometer and internal standard. /2/ Defibrinated blood.

Part I: WHOLE BLOOD (Concluded)

	Animal	Constituent	No. of Subjects	No. of Observations	Age of Subjects	Value mg/100 ml	Reference
	(A)	(B)	(C)	(D)	(E)	(F)	(G)
33	Heifer (con-	Potassium (concluded)	12	12	2 wk	125(68-142)	2
34	cluded)				4 wk	110(100-115)	
35					6 wk	90(75-102)	
36					8 wk	80(60-98)	
37					10 wk	61(38-84)	
38					12 wk	56(50-60)	
39		Sodium	12	12	At birth	231(212-286)	
40					1 wk	233(212-258)	
41					2 wk	222(195-250)	
42					4 wk	257(251-263)	
43					6 wk	269(230-273)	
44					8 wk	269(258-288)	
45					10 wk	275(261-289)	
46					12 wk	282(274-296)	
47	Cow	Copper				(0.82-1.40)	1
48	Lactating	Potassium	100	200	3-6 yr	51(40-68)	2
49		Sodium	100	200	3-6 yr	283(255-310)	
50	Permanently	Potassium	13	130	$2\frac{1}{2}$-7 yr	92(31-149)	2
51	sterile	Sodium	13	130	$2\frac{1}{2}$-7 yr	266(220-296)	
52	Male, female	Copper				(0.129-0.153)	6
53		Magnesium				2.04(1.95-2.09)	5

Contributors: (a) Duncan, C. W., and Huffman, C. F., (b) Kerr, Stanley E., (c) Levine, Victor E., (d) Mirsky, I. Arthur, and Erdoes, Ervin.

References: [1] Beck, A. 1940-42. Austral. J. Exp. Biol. 19-20:145. [2] Duncan, C. W., C. F. Huffman, and G. C. Gerritsen. 1959. Michigan Agr. Exp. Sta. Unpublished. [3] Hunter, F. R. 1951. J. Biol. Chem. 192:701. [4] Kerr, S. E., and L. Daoud. 1935. Ibid. 109:301. [5] Kunkel, H. O., P. B. Pearson, and B. S. Schweigert. 1947. J. Laborat. Clin. M. 32:1027. [6] Sahai, K., and N. D. Kehar. 1951. Ind. J. Vet. Sc. 21:235.

Part II: ERYTHROCYTES

Values in parentheses are ranges, estimate "c" or "d" (cf. Introduction).

	Animal	Constituent	No. of Subjects	No. of Observations	Age of Subjects	Value mg/100 ml	Reference
	(A)	(B)	(C)	(D)	(E)	(F)	(G)
1	Bull	Potassium[1]	4	16	2-4 yr	138(97-196)	3
2			18	68	5-7 yr	117(83-218)	
3			17	68	$7\frac{1}{2}$-10 yr	102(74-201)	
4			8	34	11-13 yr	100(84-154)	
5			3	9	$13\frac{1}{2}$-15 yr	200(88-330)	
6		Sodium[1]	4		2-4 yr	180(163-214)	
7			18		5-7 yr	185(174-233)	
8			17		$7\frac{1}{2}$-10 yr	192(183-233)	
9			8		11-13 yr	193(173-233)	
10			3		$13\frac{1}{2}$-15 yr	145(65-215)	
11	Angus	Potassium	1	15	4 yr	113(105-126)	
12		Sodium	1	15	4 yr	166(135-204)	
13	Ayrshire	Potassium	2	8	6-8 yr	76(74-80)	
14		Sodium	2	8	6-8 yr	212(200-227)	
15	Brown Swiss	Potassium	4	16	6-8 yr	106(60-150)	
16		Sodium	4	16	6-8 yr	189(160-236)	

/1/ Modified Hunter technique [6], using Perkins-Elmer flame photometer and internal standard.

Part II: ERYTHROCYTES (Concluded)

	Animal	Constituent	No. of Subjects	No. of Observations	Age of Subjects	Value mg/100 ml	Reference
	(A)	(B)	(C)	(D)	(E)	(F)	(G)
	Bull (concluded)						
17	Guernsey	Potassium	12	48	4-13½ yr	106(58-153)	3
18		Sodium	12	48	4-13½ yr	194(151-222)	
19	Holstein	Potassium	13	55	6-15 yr	89(66-115)	
20		Sodium	13	55	6-15 yr	198(172-234)	
21	Jersey	Potassium	10	40	2-14 yr	167(83-247)	
22		Sodium	10	40	2-14 yr	156(45-202)	
23	Red Dane	Potassium	6	23	5-12 yr	133(79-135)	
24		Sodium	6	23	5-12 yr	184(162-220)	
25	Shorthorn,	Potassium	2	5	5-6 yr	158(84-170)	
26	milking	Sodium	2	5	5-6 yr	160(140-180)	
	Ox	Phosphorus					
27		Organic acid-soluble P				$9.1(5.1-13.3)^2$	7
28		Adenosine triphosphate P				(4.2-6.0)	8
29		Diphosphoglycerate P				(<0.4-<0.7)	8
30		Nucleotide P				$2.0(1.5-2.6)^2$	7
31	Heifer	Potassium	12	12	At birth	359(177-415)	3
32					1 wk	363(306-401)	
33					2 wk	316(158-408)	
34					4 wk	303(253-360)	
35					6 wk	250(200-326)	
36					8 wk	211(157-292)	
37					10 wk	140(78-165)	
38					12 wk	107(92-116)	
39		Sodium	12	12	At birth	66(24-110)	
40					1 wk	57(24-92)	
41					2 wk	53(20-110)	
42					4 wk	77(20-148)	
43					6 wk	110(64-148)	
44					8 wk	115(89-160)	
45					10 wk	155(133-177)	
46					12 wk	185(174-204)	
	Cow	Sulfur					2,9
47		Inorganic S				1.45	
48		Ethereal S				0.21	
49	Lactating	Potassium	100	200	3-6 yr	106(90-135)	3
50		Sodium	100	200	3-6 yr	181(140-215)	
51	Permanently	Potassium	13	130	2½-7 yr	141(32-306)	3
52	sterile	Sodium	13	130	2½-7 yr	146(72-215)	
53	Male, female	Chloride				302	1
54		Magnesium				1.5(0.5-2.9)	4,5
55		Potassium				137	1
56		Sodium				239	1

/2/ Defibrinated blood.

Contributors: (a) Duncan, C. W., and Huffman, C. F., (b) Mirsky, I. Arthur, and Erdoes, Ervin, (c) Kerr, Stanley E., (d) Ponder, Eric, (e) Cotlove, Ernest

References: [1] Bernstein, R. E. 1954. Science 120:459. [2] Denis, W., and L. Reed. 1926-27. J. Biol. Chem. 71:191. [3] Duncan, C. W., C. F. Huffman, and G. C. Gerritsen. 1959. Michigan Agr. Exp. Sta. Unpublished. [4] Eveleth, D. F. 1937. J. Biol. Chem. 119:289. [5] Greenberg, D. M., S. P. Lucia, M. A. Mackey, and E. V. Tufts. 1933. Ibid. 100:139. [6] Hunter, F. R. 1951. Ibid. 192:701. [7] Kerr, S. E., and L. Daoud. 1935. Ibid. 109:301. [8] Rapoport, S., and G. M. Guest. 1941. Ibid. 138:269. [9] Reed, L., and W. Denis. 1927. Ibid. 73:623.

Part III: PLASMA OR SERUM

Values are mg/100 ml, unless otherwise specified. Values in parentheses are ranges, estimate "c" or "d" (cf. Introduction).

	Animal	Plasma or Serum	Constituent	No. of Subjects	No. of Observations	Age of Subjects	Value	Reference
	(A)	(B)	(C)	(D)	(E)	(F)	(G)	(H)
1	Bull	Plasma	Calcium[1]	8	63	3 yr	10.6(8.5-11.5)	8
2				24	173	6 yr	10.2(8.5-12.3)	
3				11	80	9 yr	10.3(8.5-11.8)	
4				4	25	12 yr	10.0(8.3-11.0)	
5			Magnesium[2]	8	63	3 yr	2.04(1.48-2.99)	
6				24	173	6 yr	1.96(1.44-2.59)	
7				11	80	9 yr	1.93(1.46-2.65)	
8				4	25	12 yr	1.91(1.45-3.16)	
9			Phosphorus[3]	8	63	3 yr	5.33(3.60-7.35)	
10				24	173	6 yr	5.16(2.62-7.76)	
11				11	80	9 yr	5.01(3.23-7.02)	
12				4	25	12 yr	4.98(3.90-6.25)	
13		Serum	Potassium[4]	4	16	2-4 yr	22(20-25)	4
14				18	68	5-7 yr	23(17-25)	
15				17	68	$7\frac{1}{2}$-10 yr	23(18-26)	
16				8	34	11-13 yr	23(20-26)	
17				3	9	$13\frac{1}{2}$-15 yr	24(21-26)	
18			Sodium[4]	4		2-4 yr	336(315-350)	
19				18		5-7 yr	332(309-360)	
20				17		$7\frac{1}{2}$-10 yr	330(315-348)	
21				8		11-13 yr	335(313-358)	
22				3		$13\frac{1}{2}$-15 yr	335(316-392)	
23	Angus	Serum	Potassium[4]	1	15	4 yr	24(21-28)	4
24			Sodium	1	15	4 yr	337(315-374)	
25	Ayrshire	Serum	Potassium	2	8	6-8 yr	23(21-25)	
26			Sodium	2	8	6-8 yr	326(313-340)	
27	Brown Swiss	Serum	Potassium	4	16	6-8 yr	22(17-26)	
28			Sodium	4	16	6-8 yr	332(320-341)	
29	Guernsey	Serum	Potassium	12	48	4-$13\frac{1}{2}$ yr	23(18-28)	
30			Sodium	12	48	4-$13\frac{1}{2}$ yr	334(315-392)	
31	Holstein	Serum	Potassium	13	55	6-15 yr	23(19-26)	
32			Sodium	13	55	6-15 yr	330(313-355)	
33	Jersey	Serum	Potassium	10	40	2-14 yr	23(20-28)	
34			Sodium	10	40	2-14 yr	334(315-390)	
35	Red Dane	Serum	Potassium	6	23	5-12 yr	24(18-26)	
36			Sodium	6	23	5-12 yr	332(315-361)	
37	Shorthorn,	Serum	Potassium	2	5	5-6 yr	21(17-25)	
38	milking		Sodium	2	5	5-6 yr	328(323-340)	
39	Ox	Serum	Copper				(0.0328-0.0352)	14
40	Heifer	Plasma	Calcium[1]	144	1387	Birth-6 mo	11.5(9.3-14.2)	7
41				92	1023	7-12 mo	11.4(9.3-14.1)	
42				59	551	13-18 mo	11.3(9.3-14.1)	
43			Carbon dioxide[5]	66	684	Birth-6 mo	61.2(44.9-82.2) vol %	7
44				52	638	7-12 mo	60.8(46.2-74.9) vol %	
45				35	343	13-18 mo	58.9(47.1-71.7) vol %	
46			Chloride[6]	66	684	Birth-6 mo	320(294-354)	7
47				52	638	7-12 mo	325(294-363)	
48				35	343	13-18 mo	331(294-360)	
49			Magnesium[2]	90	1329	Birth-6 mo	2.37(1.62-3.67)	6
50				43	605	7-12 mo	2.48(1.66-3.75)	
51				23	352	13-18 mo	2.48(1.83-3.83)	

/1/ Modified Kramer-Tisdall method [10]. /2/ Modified Briggs method [5]. /3/ Modified Briggs method [2]. /4/ Modified Hunter technique [9], using Perkins-Elmer flame photometer and internal standard. /5/ Van Slyke method [15]. /6/ Van Slyke method [16].

Part III: PLASMA OR SERUM (Continued)

	Animal	Plasma or Serum	Constituent	No. of Subjects	No. of Observations	Age of Subjects	Value	Reference
	(A)	(B)	(C)	(D)	(E)	(F)	(G)	(H)
52	Heifer (concluded)	Plasma (concluded)	Phosphorus[3]	144	1387	Birth-6 mo	7.67(5.02-10.40)	7
53				92	1023	7-12 mo	7.56(4.92-10.00)	
54				59	551	13-18 mo	7.07(4.16-10.24)	
55		Serum	Potassium	12	12	At birth	32(24-40)	4
56						1 wk	26(25-29)	
57						2 wk	27(24-29)	
58						4 wk	26(24-27)	
59						6 wk	25(24-25)	
60						8 wk	24(22-26)	
61						10 wk	23(22-23)	
62						12 wk	23(20-27)	
63			Sodium	12	12	At birth	351(341-381)	
64						1 wk	336(306-352)	
65						2 wk	334(321-345)	
66						4 wk	339(330-354)	
67						6 wk	333(324-341)	
68						8 wk	331(326-343)	
69						10 wk	330(327-333)	
70						12 wk	336(331-344)	
71	Cow	Plasma	Calcium[1]	62	978	3 yr	10.8(8.0-14.5)	7
72				48	791	6 yr	10.8(8.8-13.3)	
73				15	306	9 yr	10.8(8.7-12.6)	
74				4	87	12 yr	10.7(9.3-12.7)	
75			Carbon dioxide[5]	40	112		59.2(41.4-75.8) vol %	13
76			Chloride[6]	40	110		329(294-357)	13
77			Magnesium[2]	47	705	3 yr	2.31(1.55-3.89)	7
78				25	508	6 yr	2.45(1.40-3.77)	
79				15	306	9 yr	2.37(1.48-3.55)	
80				4	87	12 yr	2.36(1.50-3.33)	
81			Phosphorus[3]	67	1021	3 yr	5.69(2.27-9.62)	7
82				53	866	6 yr	4.80(2.19-7.91)	
83				20	413	9 yr	4.42(2.19-8.33)	
84				6	163	12 yr	4.79(2.35-6.44)	
85		Serum	Potassium				23	11
86			Sodium				349	
87	Lactating	Serum	Potassium	100	200	3-6 yr	22(18-27)	4
88			Sodium	100	200	3-6 yr	342(325-365)	
89	Permanently sterile	Serum	Potassium	13	130	$2\frac{1}{2}$-7 yr	21(9-29)	4
90			Sodium	13	130	$2\frac{1}{2}$-7 yr	337(311-362)	
91	Holstein	Plasma	Calcium[1]	3	73	13 yr	10.6(9.1-12.3)	7
92				2	43	14 yr	11.2(9.7-12.5)	
93			Magnesium[2]	3	73	13 yr	2.50(1.93-3.50)	
94				2	43	14 yr	2.58(1.83-3.77)	
95			Phosphorus[3]	4	89	13 yr	4.76(2.35-7.40)	
96				2	43	14 yr	4.12(2.31-6.95)	
97	Male, female	Serum	Bicarbonate	13			163.5(145.2-179.9)	1
98			Calcium	15			11.2(9.2-12.4)	1
99			Chloride	31			391(369-415)	1
100			Magnesium	8			2.19(1.94-2.67)	1
101			Phosphate				(5.6-6.5)	3, 12
102			Phosphorus	15			6.8(4.3-9.3)	1
103			Potassium	6			21.1(17.2-23.0)	1
104			Sodium	6			359(343-386)	1

/1/ Modified Kramer-Tisdall method [10]. /2/ Modified Briggs method [5]. /3/ Modified Briggs method [2].
/5/ Van Slyke method [15]. /6/ Van Slyke method [16].

Contributors: (a) Duncan, C. W., and Huffman, C. F., (b) Manery, J. F., (c) Mirsky, I. Arthur, and Erdoes, Ervin, (d) Levine, Victor E.

Part III: PLASMA OR SERUM (Concluded)

References: [1] Bauer, W., M. W. Ropes, and H. Waine. 1940. Physiol. Rev. 20:272. [2] Briggs, A. P. 1922. J. Biol. Chem. 53:13. [3] Drago, G. R. 1951. Rev. Fac. med. vet., Lima 5:61. [4] Duncan, C. W., C. F. Huffman, and G. C. Gerritsen. 1959. Michigan Agr. Exp. Sta. Unpublished. [5] Duncan, C. W., C. F. Huffman, and C. S. Robinson. 1935. J. Biol. Chem. 108:35. [6] Duncan, C. W., C. C. Lightfoot, and C. F. Huffman. 1938. J. Dairy Sc. 21:689. [7] Duncan, C. W., C. C. Lightfoot, and C. F. Huffman. Michigan Agr. Exp. Sta. Unpublished. [8] Duncan, C. W., C. C. Lightfoot, C. F. Huffman, W. W. Snyder, and A. J. Rykala. Ibid. Unpublished. [9] Hunter, F. R. 1951. J. Biol. Chem. 192:701. [10] Kramer, B., and F. F. Tisdall. 1921. Ibid. 47:475. [11] Martin, F. N., Jr. 1946-47. N. Orleans M. & S. J. 99:103. [12] Ogasawara, K. 1953. Igaku to Seibutsugaku 29:250. [13] Robinson, C. S., and C. F. Huffman. 1926. J. Biol. Chem. 67:245. [14] Sarata, U. 1934. Jap. J. M. Sc., Ser. 2, 2:305. [15] Van Slyke, D. D. 1917. J. Biol. Chem. 30:347. [16] Van Slyke, D. D. 1923. Ibid. 58:523.

8. BLOOD ELECTROLYTES: MAMMALS OTHER THAN MAN, CATTLE

Part I: WHOLE BLOOD

All values from reference 7 are for defibrinated blood. Values in parentheses are ranges, estimate "c" unless otherwise indicated (cf. Introduction).

	Animal	Constituent	Value	Reference
	(A)	(B)	(C)	(D)
1	Armadillo (Dasypus sixcinctus)	Phosphorus, inorganic	4.6 mg/100 ml	12
	Ass (Equus asinus)	Phosphorus		7
2		Inorganic P	3.3(1.8-5.4) mg/100 ml	
3		Total acid-soluble P	16.4(14.4-20.2) mg/100 ml	
4		Organic acid-soluble P	13.1(11.9-14.8) mg/100 ml	
5		Nucleotide P	0.5(0.4-0.5) mg/100 ml	
	Buffalo (Bos bubalis)	Phosphorus		7
6		Inorganic P	4.4(4.1-4.7) mg/100 ml	
7		Total acid-soluble P	7.6(7.0-8.0) mg/100 ml	
8		Organic acid-soluble P	3.2(2.9-3.7) mg/100 ml	
9		Nucleotide P	0.5(0.5-0.6) mg/100 ml	
	Camel			
10	Camelus bactrianus	Phosphorus, inorganic	5.6 mg/100 ml	12
	C. dromedarius	Phosphorus		7
11		Inorganic P	4.6(3.6-5.5) mg/100 ml	
12		Total acid-soluble P	19.9(16.2-22.8) mg/100 ml	
13		Organic acid-soluble P	15.3(12.6-18.1) mg/100 ml	
14		Nucleotide P	1.4(1.1-1.7) mg/100 ml	
	Cat (Felis domestica)	Phosphorus		7
15		Inorganic P	6.2(5.2-6.9) mg/100 ml	
16		Total acid-soluble P	12.1(11.3-12.5) mg/100 ml	
17		Organic acid-soluble P	5.9(4.4-7.3) mg/100 ml	
18		Nucleotide P	0.8(0.7-1.0) mg/100 ml	
19	Deer, sambar (Cervus hippelaphus)	Phosphorus, inorganic	4.2 mg/100 ml	12
20	Dog (Canis familiaris)	Calcium	(2.10-2.65) mEq/kg	4
21		Chloride	87.0(76.0-98.0)[b] mM/L	3
22		Magnesium	(2.47-2.58) mM/L	4
		Phosphorus		7
23		Inorganic P	4.1(2.3-4.9) mg/100 ml	
24		Total acid-soluble P	23.8(16.8-28.7) mg/100 ml	
25		Organic acid-soluble P	19.8(14.5-24.2) mg/100 ml	
26		Nucleotide P	1.3(0.9-1.7) mg/100 ml	
27		Potassium	6.5(5.3-7.7)[b] mM/L	3
28		Silicon	23 µg/100 ml	9
29		Sodium	121.2(108.2-134.2)[b] mM/L	3

Part I: WHOLE BLOOD (Continued)

	Animal	Constituent	Value	Reference
	(A)	(B)	(C)	(D)
30	Dolphin (Tursiops truncatus)	Chloride	88.0(80.7-105.0) mM/L	3
31		Potassium	44.1(41.7-47.9) mM/L	
32		Sodium	94.7(91.8-99.3) mM/L	
33	Elephant (Elephus indicus)	Phosphorus, inorganic	3.4 mg/100 ml	12
	Goat			
34	Capra hircus	Phosphorus, inorganic	(6.8-8.4) mg/100 ml	12
	C. hircus syriaca	Phosphorus		7
35		Inorganic P	5.6(1.1-8.4) mg/100 ml	
36		Total acid-soluble P	9.1(7.3-12.0) mg/100 ml	
37		Organic acid-soluble P	3.5(3.0-4.0) mg/100 ml	
38		Nucleotide P	0.8(0.5-0.9) mg/100 ml	
39	Guinea pig (Cavia domestica)	Calcium	(8.60-11.29) mg/100 ml	17
40		Iodine, total	7.2 µg/100 ml	6
		Phosphorus		7
41		Inorganic P	4.9(3.5-6.1) mg/100 ml	
42		Total acid-soluble P	28.1(23.6-32.2) mg/100 ml	
43		Organic acid-soluble P	23.4(20.0-27.8) mg/100 ml	
44		Nucleotide P	2.0(1.6-2.3) mg/100 ml	
45	Horse (Equus caballus)	Copper	36(34-37) µg/100 ml	14
		Phosphorus		7
46		Inorganic P	2.3(2.1-2.4) mg/100 ml	
47		Total acid-soluble P	21.3(18.0-24.6) mg/100 ml	
48		Organic acid-soluble P	19.1(15.9-22.2) mg/100 ml	
49		Nucleotide P	0.6 mg/100 ml	
50		Silicon	129 µg/100 ml	8
	Hyena (Hyaena striata)	Phosphorus		7
51		Inorganic P	2.9 mg/100 ml	
52		Total acid-soluble P	5.7 mg/100 ml	
53		Organic acid-soluble P	2.8 mg/100 ml	
54		Nucleotide P	0.45 mg/100 ml	
	Jackal (Canis aureus)	Phosphorus		7
55		Inorganic P	6.2 mg/100 ml	
56		Total acid-soluble P	17.5 mg/100 ml	
57		Organic acid-soluble P	11.3 mg/100 ml	
58		Nucleotide P	1.0 mg/100 ml	
59	Kangaroo (Macropus rufus)	Phosphorus, inorganic	4.3 mg/100 ml	12
60	Monkey	Chloride	93(83-110) mEq/L	11
61		Potassium	53(46-62) mEq/L	5, 11, 15
62		Sodium	99(86-109) mEq/L	5, 11, 15
	Macacus sp	Phosphorus		7
63		Inorganic P	3.6 mg/100 ml	
64		Total acid-soluble P	19.4 mg/100 ml	
65		Organic acid-soluble P	15.8 mg/100 ml	
66		Nucleotide P	1.3 mg/100 ml	
67	M. cynomolgus	Phosphorus, inorganic	(3.1-4.1) mg/100 ml	12
68	M. rhesus	Phosphorus, inorganic	3.6 mg/100 ml	12
69	Mouse (Mus musculus)	Phosphorus, inorganic	(7.4-7.9) mg/100 ml	12
	Mule (Equus sp)	Phosphorus		7
70		Inorganic P	2.3(2.0-2.5) mg/100 ml	
71		Total acid-soluble P	13.4(12.9-13.9) mg/100 ml	
72		Organic acid-soluble P	11.2(10.9-11.4) mg/100 ml	
73		Nucleotide P	0.5 mg/100 ml	
74	Opossum (Didelphys virginiana)	Phosphorus, inorganic	3.3 mg/100 ml	12
75	Rabbit	Copper	(73.9-98.6) µg/100 ml	13
76		Lead	39 µg/100 ml	16
77		Magnesium	5.23(4.72-5.73) mg/100 ml	10
78		Silicon	100 µg/100 ml	9
	Lepus cuniculus	Phosphorus		7
79		Inorganic P	4.5(3.6-5.5) mg/100 ml	
80		Total acid-soluble P	41.3(37.0-49.6) mg/100 ml	
81		Organic acid-soluble P	36.7(33.1-44.1) mg/100 ml	
82		Nucleotide P	3.5(3.1-4.2) mg/100 ml	
83	Raccoon (Procyon lotor)	Phosphorus, inorganic	4.3 mg/100 ml	12

Part I: WHOLE BLOOD (Concluded)

	Animal	Constituent	Value	Reference
	(A)	(B)	(C)	(D)
84	Rat	Manganese	0.17 mg/L	14
85		Sulfate, inorganic	3.0 mg/100 ml	2
86		Sulfur, inorganic	1.0 mg/100 ml	2
	Mus norvegicus albinus	Phosphorus		7
87		Inorganic P	4.0(3.2-4.8) mg/100 ml	
88		Total acid-soluble P	27.5(25.8-29.2) mg/100 ml	
89		Organic acid-soluble P	23.5(22.6-24.4) mg/100 ml	
90		Nucleotide P	2.4(2.0-2.7) mg/100 ml	
91	Sheep	Copper	(730-1450) µg/100 ml[1]	1
92		Magnesium	2.79(2.61-2.92) mg/100 ml	10
93	Ovis aries	Phosphorus, inorganic	6.5 mg/100 ml	12
	O. aries crassicandus	Phosphorus		7
94		Inorganic P	5.1(5.0-5.1) mg/100 ml	
95		Total acid-soluble P	9.4(9.2-9.5) mg/100 ml	
96		Organic acid-soluble P	4.3(4.1-4.5) mg/100 ml	
97		Nucleotide P	1.2(1.1-1.2) mg/100 ml	
98	O. platyora	Phosphorus, inorganic	3.3 mg/100 ml	12
99	Swine (Sus scrofa)	Magnesium	5.26(5.03-5.60) mg/100 ml	10
100		Phosphorus, inorganic	(6.9-7.3) mg/100 ml	12
	S. scrofa melitensis	Phosphorus		7
101		Inorganic P	5.0(4.3-6.1) mg/100 ml	
102		Total acid-soluble P	40.6(38.0-43.2) mg/100 ml	
103		Organic acid-soluble P	35.6(33.7-37.1) mg/100 ml	
104		Nucleotide P	3.9(3.7-4.3) mg/100 ml	
	Wolf (Canis lupus)	Phosphorus		7
105		Inorganic P	4.3(4.1-4.5) mg/100 ml	
106		Total acid-soluble P	26.8(26.3-27.3) mg/100 ml	
107		Organic acid-soluble P	22.5(21.8-23.2) mg/100 ml	
108		Nucleotide P	1.5 mg/100 ml	

/1/ Females.

Contributors: (a) Kerr, Stanley E., (b) Levine, Victor E., (c) Overman, R. R., (d) Lewis, Howard B., (e) Eichelberger, Lillian

References: [1] Deck, A. 1940 42. Austral. J. Exp. Biol. 19 20.145. [2] Brown, D. H., and H. D. Lewis. 1941. J. Biol. Chem. 138:705. [3] Eichelberger, L., E. S. Fetcher, Jr., E. M. K. Geiling, and B. J. Vos, Jr. 1940. Ibid. 133:145. [4] Eichelberger, L., and F. C. McLean. 1942. Ibid. 142:467. [5] Flanagan, J. B., A. E. Davis, and R. R. Overman. 1950. Am. J. Physiol. 160:89. [6] Hinton, J. E., B. Eckerson, and M. Bruger. 1942. Ann. Surg. 115:206. [7] Kerr, S. E., and L. Daoud. 1935. J. Biol. Chem. 109:301. [8] King, E. J. 1939. Biochem. J., Lond. 33:944. [9] King, E. J., and H. Stantial. 1933. Ibid. 27:990. [10] Kunkel, H. O., P. B. Pearson, and B. S. Schweigert. 1947. J. Laborat. Clin. M. 32:1027. [11] Overman, R. R. 1948. Am. J. Physiol. 152:113. [12] Rapoport, S., and G. M. Guest. 1941. J. Biol. Chem. 138:269. [13] Sarata, U. 1933-34. Jap. J. M. Sc., Ser. 2, 2:305. [14] Skinner, J. T., W. H. Peterson, and H. Steenbock. 1931. J. Biol. Chem. 90:65. [15] Stern, J. 1940. Am. J. Hyg. 31(C):32. [16] Tompsett, S. L. 1941. Biochem. J., Lond. 36:48. [17] Van Wagtendoux, W. J., and A. M. Freed. 1947. J. Biol. Chem. 167:225.

Part II: ERYTHROCYTES

All values from reference 10 are for defibrinated blood. Values in parentheses are ranges, estimate "c" (cf. Introduction).

	Animal	Constituent	Value		Reference
	(A)	(B)	(C)		(D)
1	Armadillo (Dasypus sixcinctus)	Phosphorus Organic acid-soluble P	96.7 mg/100 ml		12
2		Adenosine triphosphate P	43.7 mg/100 ml		
3		Diphosphoglycerate P	26.6 mg/100 ml		
4	Ass (Equus asinus)	Phosphorus Organic acid-soluble P	40.0(38.1-41.8) mg/100 ml		10
5		Nucleotide P	1.5(1.3-1.7) mg/100 ml		
	Camel				
6	Camelus bactrianus	Phosphorus Organic acid-soluble P	54.1 mg/100 ml		12
7		Adenosine triphosphate P	10.9 mg/100 ml		
8		Diphosphoglycerate P	29.1 mg/100 ml		
9	C. dromedarius	Phosphorus Organic acid-soluble P	62.8(53.7-70.6) mg/100 ml		10
10		Nucleotide P	5.7(4.7-7.6) mg/100 ml		
11	Cat (Felis domestica)	Chloride	84 mEq/L		1
12		Magnesium	4.4 mEq/L		6, 8
13		Phosphorus Organic acid-soluble P	20.7(19.2-22.7) mg/100 ml		10
14		Adenosine triphosphate P	(9.4-10.2) mg/100 ml		12
15		Diphosphoglycerate P	(3.5-4.4) mg/100 ml		12
16		Nucleotide P	3.0(2.8-3.1) mg/100 ml		10
17		Potassium	8 mEq/L		1
18		Sodium	142 mEq/L		1
19	Deer, sambar (Cervus hippelaphus)	Phosphorus Organic acid-soluble P	11.6 mg/100 ml		12
20		Adenosine triphosphate P	6.1 mg/100 ml		
21	Dog (Canis familiaris)	Chloride	87 mEq/L		1
22		Copper	98 mg/100 ml		9
23		Fluoride	17(9-24) μg/100 ml		15
24		Phosphorus Organic acid-soluble P	56.5(55.8-57.1) mg/100 ml		10
25		Adenosine triphosphate P	9.9 mg/100 ml		12
26		Diphosphoglycerate P	31.0 mg/100 ml		12
27		Nucleotide P	3.8(3.5-4.0) mg/100 ml		10
28		Potassium	10 mEq/L		1
29		Sodium	135 mEq/L		1
30		Sulfur Inorganic S	1.35 mg/100 ml		3, 13
31		Ethereal S	0.54 mg/100 ml		
32	Dolphin (Tursiops truncatus)	Chloride	57.5(48.2-82.6) mEq/L		5
33		Magnesium	9.8(8.0-11.6) mEq/L		
34		Potassium	99.4(94.8-103.5) mEq/L		
35		Sodium	13.2(7.7-15.8) mEq/L		
36	Elephant (Elephas indicus)	Phosphorus Organic acid-soluble P	47.9 mg/100 ml		12
37		Adenosine triphosphate P	12.5 mg/100 ml		
38		Diphosphoglycerate P	18.7 mg/100 ml		
39	Goat	Sulfur Inorganic S	1.5 mg/100 ml		3, 13
40		Ethereal S	0.15 mg/100 ml		
41	Capra hircus	Phosphorus Organic acid-soluble P	(10.8-11.8) mg/100 ml		12
42		Adenosine triphosphate P	7.3 mg/100 ml		
43		Diphosphoglycerate P	<0.2 mg/100 ml		
44	C. hircus syriaca	Phosphorus Organic acid-soluble P	12.1(11.1-13.0) mg/100 ml		10
45		Nucleotide P	3.2(3.1-3.3) mg/100 ml		
46	Guinea pig (Cavia domestica)	Magnesium	8.1 mEq/L		7

	Animal	Constituent	Value	Reference
	(A)	(B)	(C)	(D)
	Guinea pig (Cavia domestica)	Phosphorus		
47	(concluded)	Organic acid-soluble P	64.6(61.5-69.2) mg/100 ml	10
48		Adenosine triphosphate P	(10.4-11.2) mg/100 ml	12
49		Diphosphoglycerate P	(28.4-34.8) mg/100 ml	12
50		Nucleotide P	5.5(5.2-5.7) mg/100 ml	10
51	Hamster (Cricetus sp)	Magnesium	8.3 mEq/L	11
52	Horse (Equus caballus)	Chloride	85 mEq/L	1
53		Magnesium	5.6(4.0-7.2) mEq/L	7, 8
		Phosphorus		
54		Organic acid-soluble P	46.7(45.5-47.9) mg/100 ml	10
55		Adenosine triphosphate P	(3.2-3.7) mg/100 ml	12
56		Diphosphoglycerate P	(31.5-33.4) mg/100 ml	12
57		Nucleotide P	1.5(1.2-1.8) mg/100 ml	10
58		Potassium	140 mEq/L	1
59		Sodium	16 mEq/L	1
	Hyena (Hyaena striata)	Phosphorus		10
60		Organic acid-soluble P	8.4 mg/100 ml	
61		Nucleotide P	1.4 mg/100 ml	
	Jackal (Canis aureus)	Phosphorus		10
62		Organic acid-soluble P	42.8 mg/100 ml	
63		Nucleotide P	3.8 mg/100 ml	
	Kangaroo (Macropus rufus)	Phosphorus		12
64		Organic acid-soluble P	53 mg/100 ml	
65		Adenosine triphosphate P	9.2 mg/100 ml	
66		Diphosphoglycerate P	18.6 mg/100 ml	
67	Monkey	Chloride	78 mEq/L	1
68		Potassium	145 mEq/L	
69		Sodium	24 mEq/L	
	Macacus sp	Phosphorus		10
70		Organic acid-soluble P	44.5 mg/100 ml	
71		Nucleotide P	3.7 mg/100 ml	
	M. cynomolgus	Phosphorus		12
72		Organic acid-soluble P	(47.0-49.3) mg/100 ml	
73		Adenosine triphosphate P	(11.3-11.4) mg/100 ml	
74		Diphosphoglycerate P	(28.9-32.0) mg/100 ml	
	M. rhesus	Phosphorus		12
75		Organic acid-soluble P	56.6 mg/100 ml	
76		Adenosine triphosphate P	13.4 mg/100 ml	
77		Diphosphoglycerate P	31.0 mg/100 ml	
78	Mouse	Magnesium	9.8 mEq/L	7
	Mus musculus	Phosphorus		12
79		Organic acid-soluble P	(84.1-85.8) mg/100 ml	
80		Adenosine triphosphate P	(12.1-16.0) mg/100 ml	
81		Diphosphoglycerate P	(51.8-54.0) mg/100 ml	
	Mule (Equus sp)	Phosphorus		10
82		Organic acid-soluble P	45.5(37.0-54.0) mg/100 ml	
83		Nucleotide P	2.1(1.6-5.4) mg/100 ml	
	Opossum (Didelphys virginiana)	Phosphorus		12
84		Organic acid-soluble P	50.9 mg/100 ml	
85		Adenosine triphosphate P	12.1 mg/100 ml	
86		Diphosphoglycerate P	22.8 mg/100 ml	
87	Rabbit	Copper	(51.2-85.5) μg/100 ml	14
88		Chloride	80 mEq/L	1
89		Magnesium	6.0 mEq/L	7, 8
90		Potassium	142 mEq/L	1
91		Sodium	22 mEq/L	1
	Lepus cuniculus	Phosphorus		
92		Organic acid-soluble P	87.8(81.9-93.7) mg/100 ml	10
93		Adenosine triphosphate P	21.1 mg/100 ml	12
94		Diphosphoglycerate P	45.3 mg/100 ml	12
95		Nucleotide P	7.7(7.6-7.7) mg/100 ml	10

Part II: ERYTHROCYTES (Concluded)

	Animal	Constituent	Value	Reference
	(A)	(B)	(C)	(D)
	Raccoon (Procyon lotor)	Phosphorus		12
96		Organic acid-soluble P	61.6 mg/100 ml	
97		Adenosine triphosphate P	4.0 mg/100 ml	
98		Diphosphoglycerate P	27.4 mg/100 ml	
99	Rat	Chloride	82 mEq/L	1
100		Magnesium	7.1(5.8-8.4) mEq/L	7
101		Potassium	135 mEq/L	1
102		Sodium	28 mEq/L	1
	Mus norvegicus albinus	Phosphorus		
103		Organic acid-soluble P	66.8 mg/100 ml	12
104		Adenosine triphosphate P	14.4 mg/100 ml	12
105		Diphosphoglycerate P	34.1 mg/100 ml	12
106		Nucleotide P	4.1 mg/100 ml	10
107	Seal, elephant (Mirounga sp)	Potassium	6.8 mEq/L	4
108		Sodium	95 mEq/L	
109	Sheep	Chloride	78 mEq/L	1
110		Magnesium	2.0(0.9-2.6) mEq/L	7, 8
111		Potassium	46 mEq/L	1
112		Sodium	98 mEq/L	1
	Ovis aries	Phosphorus		12
113		Organic acid-soluble P	15.4 mg/100 ml	
114		Adenosine triphosphate P	8.4 mg/100 ml	
115		Diphosphoglycerate P	<0.8 mg/100 ml	
	O. aries crassicandus	Phosphorus		10
116		Organic acid-soluble P	13.9(13.8-13.9) mg/100 ml	
117		Nucleotide P	3.8(3.4-4.1) mg/100 ml	
	O. platyora	Phosphorus		12
118		Organic acid-soluble P	10.0 mg/100 ml	
119		Adenosine triphosphate P	6.5 mg/100 ml	
120	Swine (Sus scrofa)	Iron	(105-124) µg/100 ml	2
121		Magnesium	8.4(6.8-9.2) mEq/L	7, 8
		Phosphorus		12
122		Organic acid-soluble P	(95.0-98.7) mg/100 ml	
123		Adenosine triphosphate P	(20.8-22.4) mg/100 ml	
124		Diphosphoglycerate P	(43.7-45.0) mg/100 ml	
	S. scrofa melitensis	Phosphorus		10
125		Organic acid-soluble P	94.5(93.7-95.3) mg/100 ml	
126		Nucleotide P	10.8(10.3-11.3) mg/100 ml	
	Wolf (Canis lupus)	Phosphorus		10
127		Organic acid-soluble P	57.1 mg/100 ml	
128		Nucleotide P	3.8(3.7-3.9) mg/100 ml	

Contributors: (a) Kerr, Stanley E., (b) Mirsky, I. Arthur, and Erdoes, Ervin, (c) Cotlove, Ernest, (d) Ponder, Eric, (e) Levine, Victor E., (f) Largent, Edward J., (g) Platner, W. S., (h) Eichelberger, Lillian

References: [1] Bernstein, R. E. 1954. Science 120:459. [2] Cartwright, G. E., and M. M. Wintrobe. 1948. J. Biol. Chem. 176:571. [3] Denis, W., and L. Reed. 1926-27. Ibid. 71:191. [4] Eadie, J., and R. L. Kirk. 1952-53. Austral. J. Sc. 15:26. [5] Eichelberger, L., E. S. Fetcher, Jr., E. M. K. Geiling, and B. J. Vos, Jr. 1940. J. Biol. Chem. 133:145. [6] Eichelberger, L., and F. C. McLean. 1942. Ibid. 142:467. [7] Eveleth, D. F. 1937. Ibid. 119:289. [8] Greenberg, D. M., S. P. Lucia, M. A. Mackey, and E. V. Tufts. 1933. Ibid. 100:139. [9] Gubler, C. J., M. E. Lahey, H. Ashenbrucker, G. E. Cartwright, and M. M. Wintrobe. 1952. Ibid. 196:209. [10] Kerr, S. E., and L. Daoud. 1935. Ibid. 109:301. [11] Platner, W. S. 1949. Univ. Michigan Microfilm Pub. 1231. p. 289. [12] Rapoport, S., and G. M. Guest. 1941. J. Biol. Chem. 138:269. [13] Reed, L., and W. Denis. 1927. Ibid. 73:623. [14] Sarata, U. 1933-34. Jap. J. M. Sc., Ser. 2, 2:305. [15] Smith, F. A., and D. E. Gardner. (AECD 2161c, 1948.) In C. Voegtlin and H. C. Hodge, ed. 1953. Nat. Nucl. En. Ser. VI-1, pt. 3. McGraw-Hill, New York. p. 1179.

Part III: PLASMA OR SERUM

Values in parentheses are ranges, estimate "c" unless otherwise indicated (cf. Introduction).

	Animal	Constituent	Value	Reference
	(A)	(B)	(C)	(D)
1	Cat	Chloride	112 mEq/L	3
2		Magnesium	2.2 mEq/L	14,15
3		Potassium	(4.6-6.0) mEq/L	3, 25
4		Sodium	(156-158) mEq/L	3, 25
5	Dog	Bicarbonate	20.5(18.0-24.0) mEq/L	32
6		Calcium	5.3(4.7-6.1) mEq/L	37
7		Chloride	112 mEq/L	3
8		Fluoride	25(12-35) μg/100 ml	35
		Iodine		
9		Total I	29(14-52) μg/100 ml	40
10		Protein-bound I	2.6 μg/100 ml	28
11		Magnesium	(1.9-2.5) mg/100 ml	18
12		Phosphate	1.6(1.3-2.0) mEq/L	1
13		Phosphorus, lipid	(9.75-14.2) mg/100 ml	34
14		Potassium	(4.8-5.5) mEq/L	3, 25
15		Sodium	(150-153) mEq/L	3, 25
		Sulfur		
16		Inorganic S	3.2 mg/100 ml	30
17		Ethereal S	0.54 mg/100 ml	11, 31
18	Dolphin	Calcium	2.3(2.0-2.6) mM/L	13
19		Chloride	110.2(105.1-125.4) mM/L	
20		Magnesium	1.1(1.0-1.4) mM/L	
21		Phosphorus, inorganic	1.9(1.1-2.8) mM/L	
22		Potassium	4.3(3.5-5.4) mM/L	
23		Sodium	153.3(149.1-164.7) mM/L	
24	Goat	Calcium	10.3 mg/100 ml	26
25		Chloride	437 mg/100 ml	
26		Magnesium	2.5 mg/100 ml	
27		Phosphate	6.5 mg/100 ml	
28		Potassium	14.1 mg/100 ml	
29		Sodium	431 mg/100 ml	
30	Guinea pig	Calcium	10.7(7.4-13.6) mg/100 ml	27, 36
31		Magnesium	2.3 mg/100 ml	27
32		Phosphate	5.3 mg/100 ml	27
33		Potassium	(23.7-27.3) mg/100 ml	21
34	Hamster	Magnesium	2.1 mEq/L	29
35	Hedgehog	Magnesium	2.7 mEq/L	38
36	Horse	Calcium	(12.3-12.4) mg/100 ml	17, 27
37		Chloride	108 mEq/L	3
38		Copper	(35.6-39.1) μg/100 ml	33
39		Magnesium	(1.8-2.5) mg/100 ml	17, 27
40		Phosphate	(3.1-5.6) mg/100 ml	17, 27
41		Potassium	(5.2-6.1) mEq/L	3, 25
42		Silicon	118 μg/100 ml[1]	19
43		Sodium	(152-156) mEq/L	3, 25
44		Sulfur, inorganic	3.4 mg/100 ml	30
45	Monkey	Chloride	115 mEq/L	3
46		Potassium	4.7 mEq/L	
47		Sodium	151 mEq/L	
48	Mouse	Calcium	8.4 mg/100 ml	27
49		Magnesium	1.3 mg/100 ml	
50		Phosphate	5.6 mg/100 ml	
51	Rabbit	Bicarbonate	28 mEq/L	7
52		Calcium	3.84(2.6-5.0) mM/L	7
53		Chloride	(100-110) mEq/L	3, 24
54		Copper	(28.0-32.7) μg/100 ml	33
55		Lead	15 μg/100 ml	41
56		Magnesium	2.45(2.05-2.97) mg/100 ml	22

/1/ Defibrinated blood.

Part III: PLASMA OR SERUM (Continued)

	Animal	Constituent	Value	Reference
	(A)	(B)	(C)	(D)
57	Rabbit (con-	Phosphate	2.8 mEq/L	2
58	cluded)	Potassium	(5.5-6.0) mEq/L	3, 25
59		Silicon	18 µg/100 ml	20
60		Sodium	(142-150) mEq/L	3, 39
		Sulfate		4
61		Total SO$_4$	16.2(12-21) mg/100 ml	
62		Inorganic SO$_4$	14.4(10.8-27) mg/100 ml	
63		Ethereal SO$_4$	1.2(0.3-3.0) mg/100 ml	
		Sulfur		4
64		Inorganic S	5.0(3.6-6.1) mg/100 ml	
65		Organic S	1.6(1.0-2.1) mg/100 ml	
66		Ethereal S	0.4(0.1-1.0) mg/100 ml	
67		Non-protein S	7.0(6.0-8.3) mg/100 ml	
68		Sulfate S	5.4(4.0-6.9) mg/100 ml	
69	Rat	Bicarbonate	20.9(16.1-25.3) mEq/L	10
70		Calcium	6.2(5.4-7.2) mEq/L	7
71		Chloride	118 mEq/L	3
72		Copper	320 µg/100 ml	16
73		Iodine	3.4(3.3-3.5) µg/100 ml	40
74		Iron	143 µg/100 ml	9
75		Magnesium	1.6 mg/100 ml	27
76		Phosphate	7.0(5.8-8.2) mEq/L	8
77		Potassium	5.9 mEq/L	3
78		Sodium	152 mEq/L	3
79	Seal, elephant	Potassium	4.5 mEq/L	12
80		Sodium	142 mEq/L	
81	Sheep	Calcium	11.4 mg/100 ml	27
82		Chloride	116 mEq/L	3
83		Magnesium	2.27(2.02-2.47) mg/100 ml	22
84		Phosphate	6.9 mg/100 ml	27
85		Potassium	(4.8-5.9) mEq/L	3, 25
86		Sodium	(151-160) mEq/L	3, 25
87	Swine	Calcium	(10.99-11.3) mg/100 ml	23, 27, 42
88		Copper	206(133.4-278.6)[b] µg/100 ml	5
89		Iron	(152-200) µg/100 ml	6
90		Magnesium	1.6 mg/100 ml	27
91		Phosphate	(5.29-9.6) mg/100 ml	23, 27, 42
92		Potassium	6.2 mEq/L	25
93		Sodium	149 mM/L	25

Contributors: (a) Mirsky, I. Arthur, and Erdoes, Ervin, (b) Levine, Victor E., (c) Eichelberger, Lillian, (d) Cole, Warren H., (e) Cotlove, Ernest, (f) Lewis, Howard B., (g) Ponder, Eric, (h) Platner, W. S., (i) Allison, James B.

References: [1] Allison, J. B., W. H. Cole, J. H. Holmes, and W. S. Root. 1947. Am. J. Physiol. 149:422. [2] Behrndt, H. 1942. Am. J. Dis. Child. 64:789. [3] Bernstein, R. E. 1954. Science 120:459. [4] Brown, B. H., and H. B. Lewis. 1941. J. Biol. Chem. 138:705. [5] Cartwright, G. E., and M. M. Wintrobe. 1948. Ibid. 172:557. [6] Cartwright, G. E., and M. M. Wintrobe. 1948. Ibid. 176:571. [7] Cole, W. H., J. B. Allison, T. J. Murray, A. A. Boyden, J. A. Anderson, and J. H. Leathem. 1944. Am. J. Physiol. 141:165. [8] Conway, E. J., and D. Hingerty. 1946. Biochem. J., Lond. 40:561. [9] Craft, R. C., and B. C. Walker. 1947. Endocrinology 40-41:340. [10] Darrow, D. C., H. E. Harrison, M. Taffel. 1939. J. Biol. Chem. 130:487. [11] Denis, W., and L. Reed. 1926-27. Ibid. 71:191. [12] Eadie, J., and R. L. Kirk. 1952. Austral. J. Sc. 15:26. [13] Eichelberger, L., E. S. Fetcher, Jr., E. M. K. Geiling, and B. J. Vos, Jr. 1940. J. Biol. Chem. 133:145. [14] Eichelberger, L., and F. C. McLean. 1942. Ibid. 142:467. [15] Greenberg, D. M., S. P. Lucia, M. A. Mackey, and E. V. Tufts. 1933. Ibid. 100:139. [16] Greenstein, J. P., and J. W. Thompson. 1942-43. J. Nat. Cancer Inst. 3:405. [17] Jennings, F. W., and W. Mulligan. 1953. J. Comp. Path. 63:286. [18] Jetter, W. W., and A. R. Moritz.

1943. Arch. Path., Chic. 35:601. [19] King, E. J. 1939. Biochem. J., Lond. 33:944. [20] King, E. J., and H. Stantial. 1933. Ibid. 27:990. [21] Kinsell, L. W., and R. L. Zwemer. 1941-42. J. Laborat. Clin. M. 27:206. [22] Kunkel, H. O., P. B. Pearson, and B. S. Schweigert. 1947. Ibid. 32:1027. [23] Luque, J. M. S. 1951. An. fac. vet. univ. Madrid 3:187. [24] Manery, J. F., I. S. Danielson, and A. B. Hastings. 1938. J. Biol. Chem. 124:359. [25] Martin, F. N., Jr. 1946-47. N. Orleans M. & S. J. 99:103. [26] Murty, V. N., and N. D. Kehar. 1951. Ind. J. Physiol. Allied Sc. 5:71. [27] Ogasawara, K. 1953. Igaku to Seibutsugaku 29:250. [28] O'Neal, L. W., and P. Heinbecker. 1954. Endocrinology 53:60. [29] Platner, W. S. 1949. Univ. Michigan Microfilm Pub. 1231. p. 289. [30] Power, M. H., and E. G. Wakefield. 1938. J. Biol. Chem. 123:669. [31] Reed, L., and W. Denis. 1927. Ibid. 73:623. [32] Root, W. S., J. B. Allison, W. H. Cole, J. H. Holmes, W. W. Walcott, and M. I. Gregersen. 1947. Am. J. Physiol. 149:52. [33] Sarata, U. 1933-34. Jap. J. M. Sc., Ser. 2, 2:305. [34] Sinclair, R. G. 1948. J. Biol. Chem. 174:343. [35] Smith, F. A., and D. E. Gardner. (AECD 2161c. 1948.) In C. Voegtlin and H. C. Hodge, ed. 1953. Nat. Nucl. En. Ser. VI-1, pt. 3. McGraw-Hill, New York. p. 1179. [36] Snyder, L. H., and W. D. Tweedy. 1941. Proc. Soc. Exp. Biol., N. Y. 47:234. [37] Sobel, A. C., G. Kraus, and B. Kramer. 1941. J. Biol. Chem. 140:511. [38] Soumalainen, P. 1938. Nature, Lond. 141:471. [39] Stedman, L. T., J. Ariel, and S. L. Warren. 1943. Cancer Res. 3:471. [40] Taurog, A., and I. L. Chaikoff. 1946. J. Biol. Chem. 163:313. [41] Tompsett, S. L. 1941. Biochem. J., Lond. 36:48. [42] Wilwerth, A. M. 1949. Arq. Esc. sup. vet. Minas Gerais 2:89.

9. BLOOD ELECTROLYTES: BIRDS

All values from reference 2 are for defibrinated blood. Values in parentheses are ranges, estimate "c" (cf. Introduction).

	Bird	Blood	Constituent	Value mg/100 ml	Reference
	(A)	(B)	(C)	(D)	(E)
1	Canary	Serum	Potassium	(21-25)	10
2	Serinus canarius	Whole blood	Phosphorus, inorganic	5.6[1]	7
3		Erythrocytes	Phosphorus Organic acid-soluble P	131.4[1]	
4			Adenosine triphosphate P	53.2[1]	
5			Phytic acid P	55.6[1]	
6	Chicken	Erythrocytes	Magnesium	9.4	1
7			Potassium	464(413-558)	8
8		Plasma	Iodine, total	0.0072	9
9			Magnesium	2.8	1
10			Potassium	23.4(17.9-25.3)	8
11		Serum	Calcium	(13.2-23.7)	5
12			Copper	0.014[2]	3
13			Magnesium	(1.4-2.0)	5
14			Phosphate	(6.2-7.9)	6
15			Potassium	22	10
16	Gallus bankiva	Whole blood	Phosphorus Inorganic P	2.5(1.4-2.9)	2
17			Total acid-soluble P	33.0(25.5-39.4)	
18			Organic acid-soluble P	31.5(22.3-36.6)	
19			Nucleotide P	1.7(1.4-2.3)	
20		Erythrocytes	Phosphorus Organic acid-soluble P	98.6(95.8-101.4)	2
21			Adenosine triphosphate P	(9.2-11.9)	7
22			Nucleotide P	5.5(4.2-7.3)	2
23			Phytic acid P	(61.2-68.1)	7

/1/ Pooled blood samples. /2/ Females.

	Bird	Blood	Constituent	Value mg/100 ml	Reference
	(A)	(B)	(C)	(D)	(E)
24	Crane, demoiselle (Anthropoides virgo)	Whole blood	Phosphorus, inorganic	4.9	7
		Erythrocytes	Phosphorus		
25			Organic acid-soluble P	117.8	
26			Adenosine triphosphate P	28.7	
27			Phytic acid P	66.2	
28	Duck	Serum	Potassium	(18-20)	10
	Anas boscas	Whole blood	Phosphorus		2
29			Inorganic P	6.7(6.1-7.3)	
30			Total acid-soluble P	44.8(44.1-45.5)	
31			Organic acid-soluble P	38.1(36.8-39.4)	
32			Nucleotide P	4.8	
		Erythrocytes	Phosphorus		
33			Organic acid-soluble P	110.5(108.8-112.2)	2
34			Adenosine triphosphate P	(19.2-25.9)	7
35			Nucleotide P	14.0(13.3-14.7)	2
36			Phytic acid P	(63.6-73.9)	7
	Goose (Anser domesticus)	Whole blood	Phosphorus		2
37			Inorganic P	5.2(5.1-5.4)	
38			Total acid-soluble P	53.0(49.8-57.2)	
39			Organic acid-soluble P	47.8(44.4-52.1)	
40			Nucleotide P	5.3(5.2-5.3)	
		Erythrocytes	Phosphorus		
41			Organic acid-soluble P	100.9(93.2-111.0)	2
42			Adenosine triphosphate P	(19.0-27.4)	7
43			Nucleotide P	12.1(10.9-13.3)	2
44			Phytic acid P	(65.5-80.0)	7
45	Heron, night (Nycticorax nycticorax)	Whole blood	Phosphorus, inorganic	6.1	7
		Erythrocytes	Phosphorus		
46			Organic acid-soluble P	126.1	
47			Adenosine triphosphate P	49.0	
48			Phytic acid P	49.0	
49	Macaw (Ara macao)	Whole blood	Phosphorus, inorganic	6.4	7
		Erythrocytes	Phosphorus		
50			Organic acid-soluble P	113.1	
51			Adenosine triphosphate P	22.6	
52			Phytic acid P	76.3	
53	Parakeet (Psittacula spengeli)	Whole blood	Phosphorus, inorganic	8.3[1]	7
		Erythrocytes	Phosphorus		
54			Organic acid-soluble P	115.3[1]	
55			Adenosine triphosphate P	26.4[1]	
56			Phytic acid P	77.3[1]	
57	Pigeon	Erythrocytes	Magnesium	44	6
58		Plasma	Calcium	10.5	4
59			Magnesium	2.4	6
60	Columba livia	Whole blood	Phosphorus, inorganic	(5.2-7.1)	7
		Erythrocytes	Phosphorus		
61			Organic acid-soluble P	(110.6-134.1)	
62			Adenosine triphosphate P	(30.6-39.7)	
63			Phytic acid P	(67.4-86.8)	
64	Stork (Ciconia alba)	Whole blood	Phosphorus, inorganic	5.6	7
		Erythrocytes	Phosphorus		
65			Organic acid-soluble P	111.2	
66			Adenosine triphosphate P	26.5	
67			Phytic acid P	63.5	
68	Swan, black (Cygnus atratus)	Whole blood	Phosphorus, inorganic	3.9	7
		Erythrocytes	Phosphorus		
69			Organic acid-soluble P	97.8	
70			Adenosine triphosphate P	21.2	
71			Phytic acid P	67.8	
	Turkey (Meleagris gallopavo)	Whole blood	Phosphorus		2
72			Inorganic P	4.0(3.3-5.4)	
73			Total acid-soluble P	40.8(35.0-44.7)	

/1/ Pooled blood samples.

	Bird	Blood	Constituent	Value mg/100 ml	Reference
	(A)	(B)	(C)	(D)	(E)
74	Turkey (Meleagris gallopavo) (concluded)	Whole blood (concluded)	Phosphorus (concluded) Organic acid-soluble P	36.8(31.5-40.3)	2
75			Nucleotide P	3.7(2.8-4.3)	
76		Erythrocytes	Phosphorus Organic acid-soluble P	93.7(91.9-95.4)	2
77			Adenosine triphosphate P	(16.2-16.8)	7
78			Nucleotide P	9.9	2
79			Phytic acid P	74.2	7

Contributors: (a) Kerr, Stanley E., (b) Levine, Victor E., (c) Mirsky, I. Arthur, and Erdoes, Ervin, (d) Platner, W. S., (e) Overman, R. R.

References: [1] Eveleth, D. F. 1937. J. Biol. Chem. 119:289. [2] Kerr, S. E., and L. Daoud. 1935. Ibid. 109:301. [3] Locke, A., E. R. Main, and D. O. Rosbach. 1932. J. Clin. Invest. 11:527. [4] MacDonald, W. R., and O. Riddle. 1945. J. Biol. Chem. 159:445. [5] Ogasawara, K. 1953. Igaku to Seibutsugaku 29:250. [6] Platner, W. S. 1949. Univ. Michigan Microfilm Pub. 1231. p. 289. [7] Rapoport, S., and G. M. Guest. 1941. J. Biol. Chem. 138:269. [8] Stern, T. N., V. V. Cole, A. C. Bass, and J. H. Tomlinson, Jr. 1950. Fed. Proc., Balt. 9:1. [9] Taurog, A., and I. L. Chaikoff. 1946. J. Biol. Chem. 163:313. [10] Velick, S. F., and J. Scudder. 1940. Am. J. Hyg. 31(C):92.

10. PLASMA ELECTROLYTES: REPTILES

Values in parentheses are ranges, estimate "c" (cf. Introduction).

	Reptile	No. of Subjects	Constituent	Value mM/L	Reference
	(A)	(B)	(C)	(D)	(E)
	Crocodile				
1	Alligator mississipiensis[1]	50	Bicarbonate	18(16-20)[2]	1, 4-7
2		50	Calcium	3.6	
3		50	Chloride	114(102-121)[3]	
4		50	Magnesium	1.1	
5		50	Phosphate	1.1	
6		50	Potassium	3.5(3.3-3.9)	
7		50	Sodium	142(133-145)	
8		50	Sulfate	0.5	
9	Caiman latirostris		Chloride	108	5
10			Potassium	3.8	
11			Sodium	140	
12	Crocodilus acutus	1	Bicarbonate	11	13
13		1	Calcium	3.4	
14		1	Chloride	117	
15		1	Magnesium	1.9	
16		1	Potassium	7.9	
17		1	Sodium	149	
	Lizard				
18	Anolis carolinensis	25	Bicarbonate	15(10-23)	9
19		20	Calcium	2.9(2.0-4.2)	
20		30	Chloride	127(113-133)	
21		19	Phosphate	2.6(1.7-3.2)	
22		15	Potassium	4.6(2.8-5.9)	
23		41	Sodium	157(139-186)	

/1/ Immature animals, 2-5 feet long. /2/ Wide variation following feeding; maximum = 106 mM/L [8]. /3/ Wide variation following feeding; minimum = 7 mM/L [8].

	Reptile	No. of Subjects	Constituent	Value mM/L	Reference
	(A)	(B)	(C)	(D)	(E)
	Lizard (concluded)				
24	Ctenosaura acanthura	5	Bicarbonate	15(10-22)	18
25		5	Calcium	2.9(2.3-3.5)	
26		5	Chloride	133(128-137)	
27		5	Magnesium	1.0(0.9-1.1)	
28		5	Phosphate	2.3(1.8-3.4)	
29		5	Potassium	2.9(2.4-3.2)	
30		5	Sodium	159(158-163)	
31	Heloderma suspectum		Bicarbonate	18	16
32			Chloride	129	
33	Iguana iguana	9	Bicarbonate	24(15-33)	18
34		9	Calcium	2.7(2.6-2.8)	
35		9	Chloride	118(110-124)	
36		9	Magnesium	0.8(0.7-1.1)	
37		9	Phosphate	2.0(1.6-2.4)	
38		9	Potassium	3.5(2.9-4.3)	
39		9	Sodium	157(142-165)	
40	Ophisaurus ventralis	1	Bicarbonate	2	12
41	Sauromalus obesus		Chloride	127	14
	Snake				
42	Agkistrodon piscivorus	5	Calcium	3.4(2.3-5.0)	19
43		5	Chloride	88.5(80.9-102.0)	
44		4	Magnesium	1.1(1.0-1.2)	
45		6	Phosphorus	1.7(0.7-2.8)	
46		6	Sodium	141(125-157)	
47	Ancistrodon contortrix	1	Bicarbonate	12	12
48		2	Calcium	3.5(3.2-3.7)	
49		2	Chloride	138(129-147)	
50		2	Magnesium	2.3(1.8-2.8)	
51		2	Phosphate	1.3(1.1-1.6)	
52		2	Potassium	5.1(5.0-5.2)	
53		2	Sodium	156(147-161)	
54	A. piscivorus	2	Bicarbonate	6(5-7)	12
55		3	Calcium	3.7(2.5-4.5)	
56		5	Chloride	143(117-160)	
57		3	Magnesium	2.2(1.4-2.4)	
58		3	Phosphate	1.8(1.7-1.9)	
59		3	Potassium	5.0(4.5-5.6)	
60		3	Sodium	171(169-173)	
61	Coluber constrictor	3	Bicarbonate	14(8-22)	12
62		4	Calcium	3.1(2.0-4.3)	19
63		8	Chloride	132(124-144)	12
64		2	Magnesium	(1.1-1.9)	12, 19
65		4	Phosphorus	3.9(2.6-5.8)	19
66		4	Potassium	4.1(3.3-4.8)	12
67		4	Sodium	162(159-167)	12
68	Crotalus atrox	1	Calcium	3.7	12, 21
69		5	Chloride	135(128-137)	
70		1	Magnesium	1.8	
71		1	Phosphate	1.0	
72		1	Potassium	3.7	
73		1	Sodium	154	
74	C. horridus	1	Calcium	2.2	3
75		1	Magnesium	1.0	
76		1	Phosphate	2.3	
77	C. viridis	1	Chloride	123	12
78		1	Potassium	3.6	
79		1	Sodium	146	
80	Elaphe obsoleta	2	Calcium	3.6(3.1-4.2)	12
81		2	Chloride	131(119-143)	
82		1	Magnesium	2.5	
83		1	Phosphate	2.5	
84		2	Potassium	4.9(4.5-5.3)	
85		2	Sodium	162(153-168)	

	Reptile	No. of Subjects	Constituent	Value mM/L	Reference
	(A)	(B)	(C)	(D)	(E)
	Snake (continued)				
86	Farancia abacura	1	Calcium	3.3	12
87		1	Chloride	115	
88		1	Potassium	5.4	
89		1	Sodium	147	
90	Heterodon platyrhinos	2	Bicarbonate	8(3-12)	12
91		2	Chloride	126(124-127)	
92		2	Potassium	4.4(4.2-4.5)	
93		2	Sodium	155(152-158)	
94	Homalopsis buccata		Calcium	4.2	2
95			Potassium	4.8	
96			Sodium	162	
97	Lampropeltis getulus	5	Bicarbonate	7(2-10)	12
98		3	Calcium	3.7(3.6-3.9)	12
99		9	Chloride	129(121-133)	12
100		2	Magnesium	(0.9-2.0)	12, 19
101		5	Phosphorus	2.4(1.3-5.4)	19
102		7	Potassium	4.5(3.4-5.6)	12
103		7	Sodium	165(156-171)	12
104	Masticophis flagellum	2	Calcium	3.4(3.3-3.7)	12
105		2	Chloride	120(111-128)	
106		1	Magnesium	2.1	
107		1	Phosphate	1.2	
108		2	Potassium	3.9(3.4-4.4)	
109		2	Sodium	(155-156)	
110	Natrix cyclopion	4	Chloride	138(128-149)	12
111		1	Phosphate	1.9	
112		2	Potassium	4.8(4.6-4.9)	
113		2	Sodium	159(158-160)	
114	N. grahamii	1	Calcium	3.8	12
115		1	Chloride	120	
116		1	Potassium	3.5	
117		1	Sodium	156	
118	N. rhombifera	1	Bicarbonate	7	12
119			Calcium	3.9[4]	
120		2	Chloride	129(126-132)	
121		2	Potassium	4.0(3.9-4.0)	
122		2	Sodium	155(150-160)	
123	N. sipedon	4	Bicarbonate	7(?-11)	11, 12
124		10	Calcium	4.3(2.6-5.1)[4]	11, 12
125		10	Chloride	136(132-140)	11, 12
126		10	Magnesium	1.4(0.8-2.8)[4]	11, 12
127		3	Phosphorus	1.7(1.6-1.9)	19
128		10	Potassium	4.4(3.6-4.7)	11, 12
129		10	Sodium	159(151-168)	11, 12
130	Pituophis catenifer	1	Calcium	3.6	12
131		1	Chloride	136	
132		1	Potassium	5.9	
133		1	Sodium	176	
134	Thamnophis elegans	3	Bicarbonate	6(2-15)	11, 12
135		12	Calcium	3.3(3.0-4.1)[4]	
136		8	Chloride	133(123-143)	
137		12	Magnesium	1.3(0.8-1.8)[4]	
138		2	Phosphate	2.6	
139		8	Potassium	4.4(3.8-4.8)	
140		8	Sodium	159(149-169)	
141	T. ordinoides	1	Bicarbonate	6	12
142		2	Chloride	126(123-128)	
143		2	Potassium	5.4(4.0-6.7)	
144		2	Sodium	159(151-167)	
145	T. sauritus	2	Bicarbonate	7(5-8)	10-12
146		12	Calcium	2.7(1.5-4.4)	

/4/ Greatly elevated in females during follicle development.

	Reptile	No. of Subjects	Constituent	Value mM/L	Reference
	(A)	(B)	(C)	(D)	(E)
	Snake (concluded)				
147	Thamnophis sauritus (concluded)		Calcium	90[5]	10-12
148		2	Chloride	125(123-127)	
149		12	Magnesium	2.0(1.1-2.7)	
150			Magnesium	15.9[5]	
151		12	Phosphate	1.6(1.4-2.0)	
152			Phosphate	17.6[5]	
153		2	Potassium	5.4(5.1-5.6)	
154		2	Sodium	159(157-161)	
155	T. sirtalis	1	Bicarbonate	2	11, 12
156		17	Calcium	3.0(2.7-4.2)[4]	
157		6	Chloride	130(124-137)	
158		17	Magnesium	1.5(0.6-2.2)[4]	
159		2	Phosphate	0.7	
160		6	Potassium	5.9(4.1-7.2)	
161		6	Sodium	152(143-159)	
	Turtle				
162	Caretta caretta	1	Bicarbonate	36	23
163			Calcium	3.1	23
164			Chloride	113	15, 23
165			Magnesium	2.9	23
166		1	Phosphate	3.0	23
167			Potassium	3.8	15, 23
168			Sodium	158	15, 23
169	C. kempi	5	Bicarbonate	29(23-32)	23
170		1	Calcium	5.2	
171		1	Chloride	108	
172		1	Magnesium	1.4	
173		1	Phosphate	3.5	
174		1	Potassium	6.6	
175		1	Sodium	163	
176		1	Sulfate	0.3	
177	Chelydra serpentina		Bicarbonate	38	17
178		2	Calcium	2.9(2.5-3.2)	12
179		2	Chloride	86(82-90)	12
180		1	Magnesium	1.5	12
181		6	Phosphate	1.3(1.1-1.7)	24
182		2	Potassium	3.2(2.5-3.8)	12
183		2	Sodium	(123-141)	12, 23
184			Sulfate	0.3	23
185	Chrysemys picta	7	Bicarbonate	47(44-49)	23
186		2	Calcium	5.5(4.8-6.1)	
187		2	Chloride	85(81-89)	
188		2	Magnesium	4.8(1.6-7.9)	
189		2	Phosphate	1.0(0.9-1.0)	
190		2	Potassium	3.3(3.0-3.6)	
191		2	Sodium	135(120-149)	
192		1	Sulfate	0.8	
193	Emys blandingii	5	Bicarbonate	39(36-43)	23
194		1	Calcium	3.3	
195		1	Chloride	91	
196		1	Magnesium	2.1	
197		1	Phosphate	1.3	
198		1	Potassium	3.9	
199		1	Sodium	130	
200		1	Sulfate	1.3	
201	Graptemys geographica	6	Bicarbonate	39(33-48)	23
202		1	Calcium	3.4	
203		1	Chloride	87	
204		1	Magnesium	0.5	
205		1	Phosphate	1.2	
206		1	Potassium	2.4	

/4/ Greatly elevated in females during follicle development. /5/ Females, during follicle development.

	Reptile	No. of Subjects	Constituent	Value mM/L	Reference
	(A)	(B)	(C)	(D)	(E)
	Turtle (concluded)				
207	Graptemys geographica	1	Sodium	124	23
208	(concluded)	1	Sulfate	0.4	
209	Kinosternon subrubrum	1	Bicarbonate	30	23
210		2	Calcium	3.5(2.7-4.3)	12
211		2	Chloride	97(86-109)	12
212		2	Magnesium	1.0(0.9-1.1)	12
213		2	Phosphate	1.7(1.5-2.0)	12
214		2	Potassium	4.2(3.5-5.0)	12
215		2	Sodium	121(108-133)	12
216	Pseudemys scripta	15	Bicarbonate	26	25
217		15	Calcium	1.5	25
218		9	Chloride	81(76-85)	20, 26
219		15	Magnesium	2.2	25
220		15	Phosphate	1.1	25
221		7	Potassium	4.2(3.3-5.1)	20
222		7	Sodium	120(100-134)	20
223		6	Sulfate	0.17(0.1-0.2)	20
224	Stenotherus odoratus	1	Bicarbonate	25	12
225		1	Calcium	3.0	
226		1	Chloride	84	
227		1	Magnesium	1.0	
228		1	Phosphate	1.8	
229		1	Potassium	3.8	
230		1	Sodium	126	
231	Terrapene carolina	4	Calcium	2.7(1.7-3.7)	12
232		4	Chloride	122(114-128)	12
233		1	Magnesium	1.7	12
234		1	Phosphate	1.1	12
235		4	Potassium	4.6(4.1-5.2)	12
236		4	Sodium	140(126-156)	12
237		3	Sulfate	0.6(0.4-0.9)	20
238	T. ornata	1	Calcium	1.7	12
239		1	Chloride	104	
240		1	Magnesium	2.0	
241		1	Phosphate	1.0	
242		1	Potassium	4.6	
243		1	Sodium	115	
244	Testudo graeco		Calcium	4.0	15
245			Chloride	100	15, 22
246			Potassium	7.8	15
247	Trionyx ferox	7	Calcium	1.7(0.6-2.9)	12
248		7	Chloride	90(85-102)	
249		4	Magnesium	1.5(1.4-1.6)	
250		5	Phosphate	2.0(1.3-3.2)	
251		6	Potassium	6.8(4.4-7.1)	
252		7	Sodium	113(109-120)	

Contributors: (a) Dessauer, Herbert C., (b) Hutton, Kenneth E., (c) Musacchia, X. J.

References: [1] Austin, J. H., F. W. Sunderman, and J. G. Camack. 1927. J. Biol. Chem. 72:677. [2] Bergman, R. A. M. 1951. Proc. Akad. wet. Amsterdam, Ser. C, 54:511. [3] Carmichael, E. B., and P. W. Petcher. 1945. J. Biol. Chem. 161:693. [4] Coulson, R. A., and T. Hernandez. 1955. Proc. Soc. Exp. Biol., N. Y. 88:682. [5] Coulson, R. A., and T. Hernandez. Unpublished. [6] Coulson, R. A., T. Hernandez, and J. L. Beebe. 1957. Proc. Soc. Exp. Biol., N. Y. 96:606. [7] Coulson, R. A., T. Hernandez, and F. G. Brazda. 1950. Ibid. 73:203. [8] Coulson, R. A., T. Hernandez, and H. C. Dessauer. 1950. Ibid. 74:866. [9] Dessauer, H. C. 1952. Ibid. 80:742. [10] Dessauer, H. C., and W. Fox. 1959. Am. J. Physiol. 197:360. [11] Dessauer, H. C., W. Fox, and N. L. Gilbert. 1956. Proc. Soc. Exp. Biol., N. Y. 92:299. [12] Dessauer, H. C., W. Fox, and D. E. Sutton.

10. PLASMA ELECTROLYTES: REPTILES (Concluded)

Unpublished. [13] Dill, D. B., and H. T. Edwards. 1931. J. Biol. Chem. 90:515. [14] Dill, D. B., H. T. Edwards, A. V. Bock, and J. H. Talbott. 1935. J. Cellul. Physiol. 6:37. [15] Drilhon, A., and F. Marcoux. 1942. Bull. Soc. chim. biol., Par. 24:103. [16] Edwards, H. T., and D. B. Dill. 1935. J. Cellul. Physiol. 6:21. [17] Henderson, L. J. 1928. Blood. A study in general physiology. Yale University Press, New Haven. [18] Hernandez, T., and R. A. Coulson. 1951. Proc. Soc. Exp. Biol., N. Y. 76:175. [19] Hutton, K. E. 1958. J. Cellul. Physiol. 52:319. [20] Hutton, K. E., and C. J. Goodnight. 1957. Physiol. Zool. 30:198. [21] Luck, J. M., and L. Keeler. 1929. J. Biol. Chem. 82:703. [22] Nera, M. C. D. 1925. Boll. Ist. zool. Roma 3:71. [23] Smith, H. W. 1929. J. Biol. Chem. 82:651. [24] Vars, H. M. 1934. Ibid. 105:135. [25] Williams, J. K. Unpublished. [26] Wilson, J. W. 1939. J. Cellul. Physiol. 13:315.

11. PLASMA ELECTROLYTES: AMPHIBIANS

Values in parentheses are ranges, estimate "c" (cf. Introduction).

	Amphibian	No. of Subjects	Constituent	Value mM/L	Reference
	(A)	(B)	(C)	(D)	(E)
1	Congo snake (Amphiuma means)	5	Bicarbonate	18(14-21)	9
2		1	Calcium	3.1	9
3		11	Chloride	85(77-95)	9
4		1	Magnesium	1.1	9
5			Phosphate	3.5	7
6		7	Potassium	4.3(3.3-5.6)	9
7		11	Sodium	109(95-116)	9
8	Frog		Bicarbonate	25	4
9			Calcium	2.0	4
10				2.5	2
11			Chloride	74	4
12			Magnesium	2.9	4
13			Phosphate	3.1	4
14			Potassium	2.5	4
15			Sodium	104	4
16	Rana areolata		Calcium	1.5	6
17			Chloride	75	
18			Magnesium	0.6	
19			Potassium	5.8	
20			Sodium	86	
21	R. catesbeiana		Calcium	1.6	3
22		4	Chloride	70(55-82)	
23			Magnesium	3.8	
24			Phosphate	2.2	
25		3	Potassium	4.8(4.4-5.0)	
26		3	Sodium	105(101-113)	
27	R. esculenta		Calcium	2.3	10
28			Chloride	70	
29			Magnesium	1.6	
30			Potassium	5.1	
31			Sodium	96	
32	R. pipiens	36	Chloride	70	5
33		30	Potassium	1.7	
34		30	Sodium	111	
35	Toad		Calcium	1.8	8
36			Calcium, dialyzable	0.5	
37			Magnesium	1.0	
38			Magnesium, dialyzable	0.4	
39			Phosphate	1.9	
40	Bufo woodhousii	7	Chloride	80(66-107)	3
41		2	Potassium	4.0	
42		2	Sodium	107	

	Amphibian	No. of Subjects	Constituent	Value mM/L	Reference
	(A)	(B)	(C)	(D)	(E)
	Toad (concluded)				
43	Microhyla carolinensis	1	Bicarbonate	5	3
44		1	Potassium	7.4	
45		1	Sodium	128	
46	Xenopus laevis	9	Calcium	2.0	1
47		7	Magnesium	0.8	

Contributor: Dessauer, Herbert C.

References: [1] Charles, E. 1930. Proc. R. Soc., Lond., Ser. B, 107:504. [2] Clark, A. J., M. G. Eggleton, P. Eggleton, R. Gaddie, and C. P. Stewart. 1938. Metabolism of the frog's heart. Oliver and Boyd, Edinburgh and London. [3] Dessauer, H. C., W. Fox, and D. E. Sutton. Unpublished. [4] Fenn, W. O. 1936. Physiol. Rev. 16:450. [5] Gibbons, L. V., and H. M. Kaplan. 1959. Copeia 2:176. [6] Macallum, A. B. 1926. Physiol. Rev. 6:316. [7] McCay, C. M. 1931. J. Biol. Chem. 90:497. [8] Ogasawara, K. 1954. Chem. Abstr. 48:2797g. [9] Pearson, J. Unpublished. [10] Urano, F. 1908. Zschr. Biol. 50:212.

12. BLOOD ELECTROLYTES: FISHES

Values in parentheses are ranges, estimate "c" (cf. Introduction).

	Fish	Blood	Constituent	Value	Reference
	(A)	(B)	(C)	(D)	(E)
1	Buffalo fish, black (Ictiobus niger)	Serum	Magnesium	2.58(2.1-3.1) mg/100 ml	5
2	Carp	Whole blood	Chloride	401(347-446) mg/100 ml	2
3			Manganese	(5.8-7.2) μg/100 ml	
4			Potassium	169.5(154.0-176.5) mg/100 ml	
5		Serum	Calcium	11.50(9.45-14.77) mg/100 ml	2
6				21.6 mg/100 ml	4
7			Iron	25(16-33) μg/100 ml	2
8			Magnesium	3.32(2.52 3.00) mg/100 ml	2
9				1.3 mg/100 ml	4
10			Phosphate	9.0 mg/100 ml	4
			Phosphorus		2
11			Total P	49.0(37.3-60.6) mg/100 ml	
12			Inorganic P	8.69(6.79-12.10) mg/100 ml	
13			Potassium	24.6(17.5-26.9) mg/100 ml	2
14			Sodium	300(292-316) mg/100 ml	2
15			Sulfur, inorganic	0.944(0.765-1.172) mg/100 ml	2
16	German (Cyprinus carpio)	Serum	Magnesium	4.72(4.6-6.0) mg/100 ml	5
17	Silver (Caysiodes velifer)	Serum	Magnesium	4.52(4.15-4.97) mg/100 ml	5
	Catfish				5
18	Bullhead (Ameiurus erebennus)	Serum	Magnesium	6.32(5.8-7.8) mg/100 ml	
19	Channel (Ictalurus punctatus)	Serum	Magnesium	5.46(4.40-7.02) mg/100 ml	
20	Chub, Columbia River (Mylocheilus lateralis)	Serum	Magnesium	4.36(3.88-4.66) mg/100 ml	5
21	Goldfish (Carassius auratus)	Whole blood	Magnesium	12.27(11.5-12.8) mg/100 ml	5
22		Serum	Magnesium	2.02(1.42-2.70) mg/100 ml	
23	Goosefish (Lophius piscatorius)	Plasma	Calcium	0.55 mEq/100 ml	1
24			Chloride	16 mEq/100 ml	
25			Magnesium	0.5 mEq/100 ml	
26			Phosphate	2.1 mEq/100 ml	
27			Potassium	0.51 mEq/100 ml	
28			Sodium	20.0 mEq/100 ml	

Fish	Blood	Constituent	Value	Reference
(A)	(B)	(C)	(D)	(E)
29 Skate (Raja erinacea)	Whole blood	Calcium	(9.8–14.2) mEq/L	3
30		Chloride	(236–279) mEq/L	
31		Magnesium	(1.4–6.2) mEq/L	
32		Potassium	(4.8–11.9) mEq/L	
33		Sodium	(230–287) mEq/L	
34 Squaremouth (Acrochelius alutaceus)	Serum	Magnesium	3.48(3.14–3.82) mg/100 ml	5
35 Sucker, Moogadee or Snake River (Catostomus pocatello)	Serum	Magnesium	3.22(2.92–3.58) mg/100 ml	5
Trout				5
36 Brook (Salvelinus fontinalis)	Serum	Magnesium	2.69(1.33–3.87) mg/100 ml	
37 Brown (Salmo trutta)	Serum	Magnesium	4.78(3.7–6.1) mg/100 ml	
38 Rainbow (S. irideus)	Serum	Magnesium	4.16(3.3–5.7) mg/100 ml	
39 Whitefish, Rocky Mountain (Prosopium williamsonii)	Serum	Magnesium	2.95(1.8–4.3) mg/100 ml	5

Contributors: (a) Wilber, Charles G., (b) Platner, W. S., (c) Mirsky, I. Arthur, and Erdoes, Ervin

References: [1] Brull, L., and E. Nizet. 1953. J. Marine Biol. Ass. U. K. 32:321. [2] Field, J. B., C. A. Elvehjem, and C. Juday. 1943. J. Biol. Chem. 148(2):261. [3] Hartman, F. A., L. A. Lewis, K. A. Brownell, F. F. Sheldon, and R. F. Walther. 1941. Physiol. Zool. 14(4):476. [4] Ogasawara, K. 1953. Igaku to Seibutsugaku 29:250. [5] Platner, W. S. 1949. Univ. Michigan Microfilm Pub. 1231. p. 289.

III. Blood Nitrogenous Substances

13. PHYSICAL PROPERTIES OF PLASMA PROTEINS: CATTLE, HORSE, RABBIT, SWINE

Adapted from Phelps, R. A., and F. W. Putnam, "Molecular Parameters of Proteins," in F. W. Putnam, ed., 1960, "The Plasma Proteins," Academic Press, New York, v. 1. Property (column C): sedimentation constant ($S_{20, w}$) given in Svedberg units (10^{-13} cm/sec/dyne/g) and reduced to water at 20°C; diffusion constant ($D_{20, w}$) given in Fick units (10^{-7} sq cm/sec) and reduced to water at 20°C; electrophoretic mobility (veronal buffer pH = 8.6, ionic strength = 0.1) given in units of 10^{-5} sq cm/volt/sec. Values in parentheses are ranges, estimate "c" (cf. Introduction).

	Animal	Protein	Property	Method	Value	Reference
	(A)	(B)	(C)	(D)	(E)	(F)
1	Cattle	Albumin	Sedimentation constant, $S_{20, w}$		4.41	19
2			Diffusion constant, $D_{20, w}$		5.9	33
3			Molecular weight	Calculated from S_{20} and D_{20}	69,200	19
4				Archibald	70,300	11
5				Osmotic pressure	67,500	26
6				Light-scattering	73,000	7
7					77,000	5
8			Electrophoretic mobility	Tiselius	6.6	20
9			Isoelectric point	Determined from electrophoretic mobility in 0.1 M sodium acetate buffer	pH 4.7	20
10			Partial specific volume		0.734 ml/g	3
11			Reduced specific viscosity		0.0413	19
12			Frictional ratio	Calculated from S_{20} and D_{20}	1.30	2
13		Fetuin	Sedimentation constant, $S_{20, w}$		2.86	4
14					3.52	31
15			Diffusion constant, $D_{20, w}$		5.2	4
16			Molecular weight	Calculated from S_{20} and D_{20}	45,000	4
17			Electrophoretic mobility	Tiselius	5.1	18
18					5.6	31
19			Isoelectric point	Determined from electrophoretic mobility	pH 3.4	4
20					pH 3.3	31
21			Partial specific volume		0.712 ml/g	4
22		Prothrombin	Sedimentation constant, $S_{20, w}$	In 1% protein solution	4.85	15
23			Diffusion constant, $D_{20, w}$		6.24	
24			Molecular weight	Calculated from S_{20} and D_{20}	62,700	
25			Isoelectric point		pH 4.2	
26			Partial specific volume		0.70 ml/g	
27			Reduced specific viscosity		0.041	
28			Frictional ratio		1.32	
29		Fibrinogen	Sedimentation constant, $S_{20, w}$		7.8	29
30			Diffusion constant, $D_{20, w}$		2.02	10
31			Molecular weight	Calculated from S_{20} and D_{20}	330,000	29
32				Osmotic pressure	441,000	21
33				Light-scattering	340,000	9
34			Isoelectric point	In 0.001 M phosphate buffer	pH 5.8	28
35			Partial specific volume		0.718 ml/g	27
36			Reduced specific viscosity		0.25	29
37		γ-Globulin	Sedimentation constant, $S_{20, w}$		(7.28-7.31)	14
38			Diffusion constant, $D_{20, w}$		4.1	30
39			Molecular weight	Osmotic pressure	169,000	31
40			Partial specific volume		0.725 ml/g	13
41		γ-Pseudo-globulin	Sedimentation constant, $S_{20, w}$		6.85	24
42			Molecular weight	Osmotic pressure	147,000	
43			Reduced specific viscosity		0.059	
44	Horse	Albumin	Sedimentation constant, $S_{20, w}$		4.50	10
45			Diffusion constant, $D_{20, w}$		6.1	10
46			Molecular weight	Calculated from S_{20} and D_{20}	70,000	10
47				Osmotic pressure	73,000	1
48				Light-scattering	(72,200-76,500)	25
49			Partial specific volume		0.748 ml/g	32
50			Reduced specific viscosity		0.062	6
51			Frictional ratio	Calculated from S_{20} and D_{20}	1.27	10

	Animal (A)	Protein (B)	Property (C)	Method (D)	Value (E)	Reference (F)
52	Horse (concluded)	γ-Globulin, T-component	Sedimentation constant, $S_{20,w}$		6.9	16
53			Diffusion constant, $D_{20,w}$		4.87	
54			Molecular weight	Calculated from S_{20} and D_{20}	135,000	
55			Isoelectric point	In succinate buffer, ionic strength 0.045	pH 5.6	
56			Frictional ratio	Calculated from S_{20} and D_{20}	1.28	
57	Rabbit	γ-Globulin	Sedimentation constant, $S_{20,w}$		7.05	22
58			Diffusion constant, $D_{20,w}$		4.1	
59			Molecular weight	Calculated from S_{20} and D_{20}	160,000	
60	Swine	Albumin	Molecular weight	Light-scattering	72,000	25
61		Ceruloplasmin	Molecular weight	Calculated	151,000	23
62			Isoelectric point	In 0.02 M sodium acetate + 0.18 M sodium chloride	pH 4.4	8
63		Transferrin	Sedimentation constant, $S_{20,w}$		5.8	17
64			Diffusion constant, $D_{20,w}$		5.8	
65			Molecular weight	Calculated from S_{20} and D_{20}	88,000	
66			Isoelectric point		pH 4.4	
67			Frictional ratio	Calculated from S_{20} and D_{20}	1.25	
68		γ-Globulin	Sedimentation constant, $S_{20,w}$		7.28	12
69			Partial specific volume		0.744 ml/g	13

Contributor: Edsall, John T.

References: [1] Adair, G. S., and M. E. Robinson. 1930. Biochem. J., Lond. 24:1864. [2] Creeth, J. M. 1952. Ibid. 51:10. [3] Dayhoff, M. O., G. E. Perlmann, and D. A. MacInnes. 1952. J. Am. Chem. Soc. 74:2515. [4] Deutsch, H. F. 1954. J. Biol. Chem. 208:669. [5] Edsall, J. T., H. Edelhoch, R. Lontie, and P. R. Morrison. 1950. J. Am. Chem. Soc. 72:4641. [6] Fahey, K. R., and A. A. Green. 1938. Ibid. 60:3039. [7] Halwer, M., G. C. Nutting, and B. A. Brice. 1951. Ibid. 73:2786. [8] Holmberg, C.-G., and C. B. Laurell. 1948. Acta chem. scand. 2:550. [9] Katz, S., K. Gutfreund, S. Shulman, and J. D. Ferry. 1952. J. Am. Chem. Soc. 74:5706. [10] Kekwick, R. A. 1938. Biochem. J., Lond. 32:552. [11] Klainer, S. M., and G. Kegeles. 1956. Arch. Biochem., N. Y. 63:247. [12] Koenig, V. L. 1949. Ibid. 23:229. [13] Koenig, V. L. 1950. Ibid. 25:241. [14] Koenig, V. L., and K. O. Pedersen. 1950. Ibid. 25:97. [15] Lamy, F., and D. F. Waugh. 1953. J. Biol. Chem. 203:489. [16] Largier, J. F. 1958. Arch. Biochem., N. Y. 77:350. [17] Laurell, C. B., and B. Ingleman. 1947. Acta chem. scand. 1:770. [18] Lieberman, I., F. Lamy, and P. Ove. 1959. Science 129:43. [19] Loeb, G. I., and H. A. Scheraga. 1956. J. Phys. Chem. 60:1633. [20] Longsworth, L. G., and C. F. Jacobsen. 1949. J. Phys. Colloid Chem. 53:126. [21] Nanninga, L. B. 1946. Arch. néerl. physiol. 28:241. [22] Nichol, J. C., and H. F. Deutsch. 1948. J. Am. Chem. Soc. 70:80. [23] Pedersen, K. O. In C. G. Holmberg and C. B. Laurell. 1948. Acta chem. scand. 2:550. [24] Phelps, R. A., and J. R. Cann. 1957. Biochim. biophys. acta, Amst. 23:149. [25] Putzeys, P., and J. Brosteaux. 1941. Meded. Koninkl. Vlaam. Acad. Wet., Belgie, v. 3, pt. 1. [26] Rowe, D. S., and M. E. Abrams. 1957. Biochem. J., Lond. 67:431. [27] Scheraga, H. A., W. R. Carroll, L. F. Nims, E. Sutton, J. K. Backus, and J. M. Saunders. 1954. J. Polymer Sc. 14:427. [28] Sheppard, E., and I. S. Wright. 1954. Arch. Biochem., N. Y. 52:414. [29] Shulman, S. 1953. J. Am. Chem. Soc. 75:5846. [30] Smith, E. L., and D. M. Brown. 1950. J. Biol. Chem. 183:241. [31] Spiro, R. G. 1959. Fed. Proc., Balt. 18:328. [32] Svedberg, T., and B. Sjögren. 1928. J. Am. Chem. Soc. 50:3318. [33] Wagner, M. L., and H. A. Scheraga. 1956. J. Phys. Chem. 60:1066.

14. PHYSICAL CHEMICAL PROPERTIES OF PLASMA GLYCOPROTEINS: MAN

Adapted from Schmid, K., "The Plasma Glycoproteins," in R. W. Jeanloz and E. A. Balazs, ed., 1961, "The Hexosamines," Academic Press, New York. Values are for man unless otherwise indicated. Values in parentheses are ranges, estimate "c" unless otherwise indicated (cf. Introduction).

	Protein	Method	Property	Value	Reference Specific	Reference General
	(A)	(B)	(C)	(D)	(E)	(F)
1	Prealbumin, tryptophan-rich	Homogeneity established by electrophoresis and ultracentrifuge	Molecular weight	61,000		65,69
2			Sedimentation constant, $S_{20,w}^{0\%}$	4.2		
3			Estimated amount in plasma or serum	30 mg/100 ml		
4			Electrophoretic mobility, pH 8.6	-9.0×10^{-5} sq cm/volt sec		
5			Extinction coefficient, $E_{278}^{1cm,1\%}$	14.4		
6	α_1-Acid glycoprotein (orosomucoid)[1]	Homogeneity established by electrophoresis and ultracentrifuge, pH 1-13; chromatography; C- and N-terminal amino acid analysis; immunochemical analysis; starch-gel electrophoresis	Molecular weight	41,000	65	11,16,17,52, 60,66,67, 72,78,79, 81
7				44,000	78	
8			Sedimentation constant, $S_{20,w}^{0\%}$	3.2		
9			Partial specific volume	0.688 ml/g	65	
10				0.675 ml/g	52	
11			Estimated amount in plasma or serum	50		
12			Electrophoretic mobility, pH 8.6	-5.3×10^{-5} sq cm/volt sec		
13			Approximate isoelectric point Phosphate buffer	pH 2.8		
14			TCA buffer	pH 1.8	78	
15			Isoionic point (phosphate buffer)	pH 3.4	16	
16			Optical rotation, $[\alpha]_D^{22}$	-22°		
17			Extinction coefficient, $E_{278}^{1cm,1\%}$	8.93		
18	α_1-Glycoprotein		Molecular weight	54,000		24,65,66
19			Sedimentation constant, $S_{20,w}^{0\%}$	3.5(0.8%)		
20			Estimated amount in plasma or serum	30 mg/100 ml		
21			Electrophoretic mobility, pH 8.6	-5.0×10^{-5} sq cm/volt sec		
22	Fetuin (cattle)[2]	Homogeneity established by electrophoresis and ultracentrifuge, pH 1-11.5[3]	Molecular weight	45,000	12,20	
23			Sedimentation constant, $S_{20,w}^{0\%}$	3.5	12,75	
24			Partial specific volume	0.712 ml/g	12	
25			Estimated amount in plasma or serum	500 mg/100 ml	12	
26			Electrophoretic mobility, pH 8.6	-5.6×10^{-5} sq cm/volt sec	75	
27				-5.1×10^{-5} sq cm/volt sec	47	
28			Approximate isoelectric point (Cl'-formate buffer)	pH 3.3	12,75	
29			Isoionic point (Cl'-formate buffer)	pH 4.0	75	
30			Extinction coefficient, $E_{278}^{1cm,1\%}$	4.1	75	
31	α_1-Lipoproteins	Heterogeneity established by ultracentrifuge	Molecular weight	(150,000-400,000)	48,50	2,5,7,9,22, 48,50,65
32			Sedimentation constant, $S_{20,w}^{0\%}$	(4-6)		
33			Partial specific volume	0.841 ml/g	50	
34			Estimated amount in plasma or serum	260 mg/100 ml		

/1/ For information on crystallization (Pb^{++} salt), consult reference 60. /2/ For information on crystallization, consult reference 47. /3/ Reference 75.

	Protein	Method	Property	Value	Reference Specific	Reference General
	(A)	(B)	(C)	(D)	(E)	(F)
35	α_1-Lipo-proteins (concluded)	Heterogeneity established by ultracentrifuge	Electrophoretic mobility, pH 8.6	-5.2 x 10^{-5} sq cm/volt sec		2,5,7,9,22, 48,50,65
36			Approximate isoelectric point	pH 5.2		
37	Zn-α_2-Glyco-protein	Homogeneity established by electrophoresis and ultracentrifuge, pH 4-10	Sedimentation constant, $S^{0\%}_{20,w}$	3.2		8,59,61
38			Estimated amount in plasma or serum	4 mg/100 ml		
39			Electrophoretic mobility, pH 8.6	-4.2 x 10^{-5} sq cm/volt sec		
40			Approximate isoelectric point	pH 3.8		
41			Extinction coefficient, $E^{1cm,1\%}_{278}$	16		
42	Ba-α_2-Glyco-proteins	Homogeneity established by ultracentrifuge; 2 components on electrophoresis, pH 4.0	Sedimentation constant, $S^{0\%}_{20,w}$	3.3		13,59,61,62
43			Estimated amount in plasma or serum	8 mg/100 ml		
44			Electrophoretic mobility, pH 8.6	-4.2 x 10^{-5} sq cm/volt sec		
45			Approximate isoelectric point	pH (4.1-4.3)		
46			Extinction coefficient, $E^{1cm,1\%}_{278}$	5.6		
47	Prothrombin	Homogeneity established by electrophoresis and starch-gel electrophoresis (heterogeneous in ultracentrifuge)	Estimated amount in plasma or serum	9 mg/100 ml		1,23,48,51
48			Electrophoretic mobility, pH 8.6	-4.0 x 10^{-5} sq cm/volt sec		
49	Prothrombin (cattle)	Homogeneity established by electrophoresis, ultra-centrifuge, and immuno-chemical analysis	Molecular weight	63,000		34,35,37, 39-43,64, 65,70,71
50			Sedimentation constant, $S^{0\%}_{20,w}$	4.8		
51			Partial specific volume	0.70 ml/g	70	
52			Approximate isoelectric point	pH 4.2		
53	Haptoglobin, type I-1	Homogeneity established by electrophoresis, ultra-centrifuge, and immuno-chemical analysis	Molecular weight	85,000[4]		10,30,36,46, 65,73
54			Sedimentation constant, $S^{0\%}_{20,w}$	4.3		
55			Partial specific volume	0.72 ml/g		
56			Estimated amount in plasma or serum	100 mg/100 ml		
57			Electrophoretic mobility, pH 7.6	-3.3 x 10^{-5} sq cm/volt sec		
58			Approximate isoelectric point	pH 4.2		
59			Optical rotation, [α]	-50°		
60			Extinction coefficient, $E^{1cm,1\%}_{278}$	15.6		
61	Ceruloplas-min[5]	2 components on electro-phoresis	Molecular weight	151,000		4,6,27,31, 56,57,65, 74
62			Sedimentation constant, $S^{0\%}_{20,w}$	7.3		
63			Partial specific volume	0.70 ml/g		
64			Estimated amount in plasma or serum	30 mg/100 ml		
65			Stability	pH (4.4-10.0)[6]	4	
66			Electrophoretic mobility, pH 8.6	-4.6 x 10^{-5} sq cm/volt sec		
67			Approximate isoelectric point	pH 4.4		
68			Extinction coefficient, $E^{1cm,1\%}_{278}$	0.68 (610 mμ)		
69	α_2-19S-Gly-coprotein[7]	Homogeneity established by electrophoresis, ultra-centrifuge, immuno-chemical analysis[8], and starch-gel electro-phoresis	Molecular weight	900,000		32,44,45,54, 63,65
70			Sedimentation constant, $S^{0\%}_{20,w}$	19.6		
71			Estimated amount in plasma or serum	240 mg/100 ml		

/4/ Dimer of 170,000 molecular weight binds hemoglobin.   /5/ For information on crystallization (isoelectric), consult reference 27.   /6/ Reversible titration.   /7/ For information on crystallization (isoelectric), consult reference 44.   /8/ Reference 63.

	Protein (A)	Method (B)	Property (C)	Value (D)	Reference Specific (E)	Reference General (F)
72	α_2-19S-Gly-coprotein[7] (concluded)	Homogeneity established by electrophoresis, ultracentrifuge, immunochemical analysis[8], and starch-gel electrophoresis	Electrophoretic mobility, pH 8.6	-4.2×10^{-5} sq cm/volt sec		32,44,45,54, 63,65
73			Approximate isoelectric point	pH 5.4		
74			Extinction coefficient, $E_{278}^{1cm,1\%}$	6.9		
75	β_1-Transferrin[9]	Homogeneity established by electrophoresis and ultracentrifuge	Molecular weight	88,000		24,26,28,50, 65
76			Sedimentation constant, $S_{20,w}^{0\%}$	5.5		
77			Partial specific volume	0.725 ml/g	50	
78			Estimated amount in plasma or serum	200 mg/100 ml		
79			Electrophoretic mobility, pH 8.6	-3.0×10^{-5} sq cm/volt sec	42	
80				-3.3×10^{-5} sq cm/volt sec	65	
81			Approximate isoelectric point Fe-saturated buffer	50 pH 5.4	50	
82			Fe-free buffer	pH 5.8		
83			Optical rotation, $[\alpha]_D^{25}$	-27°		
84			Isomerization	pH 4-5	26	
85			Extinction coefficient, $E_{278}^{1cm,1\%}$	11.2		
86				0.57(465 mμ)		
87	β_1-Lipoproteins	Heterogeneity established by ultracentrifuge	Molecular weight	2,500,000		2,5,7,15,22, 38,49,50, 65
88			Sedimentation constant, $S_{20,w}^{0\%}$	(-1 to -8)		
89			Partial specific volume (anhydrous)	0.95 ml/g	50	
90			Estimated amount in plasma or serum	100 mg/100 ml		
91			Electrophoretic mobility, pH 8.6	-3.2×10^{-5} sq cm/volt sec		
92			Approximate isoelectric point	pH 5.4		
93			Extinction coefficient, $E_{278}^{1cm,1\%}$	(5.5-14.5)		
94				0.55 (460 mμ)		
95	β_2-Globulins		Molecular weight	150,000		5,15,48
96			Sedimentation constant, $S_{20,w}^{0\%}$	7		
97			Estimated amount in plasma or serum	200 mg/100 ml		
98	Fibrinogen	Homogeneity established by electrophoresis, ultracentrifuge, and clottability	Molecular weight	340,000		3,14,19,21, 25,50,53, 58,65,68, 76,77
99			Sedimentation constant, $S_{20,w}^{0\%}$	8.0		
100			Partial specific volume	0.724 ml/g		
101			Estimated amount in plasma or serum	270 mg/100 ml		
102			Stability	pH (5.0-11.8)		
103			Electrophoretic mobility, pH 8.6	(-2.1 to -2.6) x 10^{-5} sq cm/ volt sec		
104			Approximate isoelectric point	pH 5.9		
105			Extinction coefficient, $E_{278}^{1cm,1\%}$	15.9		
106	γ-Globulins 7S components	Heterogeneity established by electrophoresis	Molecular weight	150,000		18,29,48,50, 65
107			Sedimentation constant, $S_{20,w}^{0\%}$	7.0		
108			Partial specific volume	0.739 ml/g		

/7/ For information on crystallization (isoelectric), consult reference 44. /8/ Reference 63. /9/ For information on crystallization (isoelectric), consult reference 28.

	Protein	Method	Property	Value	Reference Specific	Reference General
	(A)	(B)	(C)	(D)	(E)	(F)
	γ-Globulins (concluded)					
109	7S components (concluded)	Heterogeneity established by electrophoresis	Estimated amount in plasma or serum	670 mg/100 ml		18,29,48,50,65
110			Electrophoretic mobility, pH 8.6	-1.2×10^{-5} sq cm/volt sec		
111				$(-0.5$ to $-1.5) \times 10^{-5}$ sq cm/volt sec		
112			Approximate isoelectric point	pH (6.3-7.3)		
113			Extinction coefficient, $E_{278}^{1cm,1\%}$	14.5		
114	19S components[10]	Heterogeneity established by electrophoresis	Molecular weight	$\sim$1,000,000		33,45,54
115			Sedimentation constant, $S_{20,w}^{0\%}$	19		
116			Estimated amount in plasma or serum	30 mg/100 ml		
117	Rheumatoid factor[11]		Sedimentation constant, $S_{20,w}^{0\%}$	22		55,80

/10/ Dissociation with mercaptoethanol in 7S subunits. /11/ Dissociation in presence of urea in 7S and 19S components.

Contributor: Schmid, Karl

References: [1] Alexander, B. In O. Hoffmann-Ostenhof, ed. 1959. Proc. 4th Internat. Congr. Biochem., Vienna, 1958. Pergamon Press, New York. v. 10, p. 37. [2] Avigan, J., R. Redfield, and D. Steinberg. 1956. Biochim. biophys. acta, Amst. 20:557. [3] Blombäck, B. 1958. Acta physiol. scand., Suppl. 148. [4] Brown, R. K. 1958. Klin. Wschr. 36:1. [5] Brown, R. K. Unpublished. [6] Brown, R. K., W. H. Baker, A. Peterkofsky, and D. L. Kaufman. 1954. J. Am. Chem. Soc. 76:4244. [7] Brown, R. K., R. E. Davis, B. Clark, and H. van Vunakis. 1956. Proc. 3rd Internat. Conf. Biochem. Probl. Lipids. Koninkl. Vlaam. Acad. Wetenschappen, Brussels. p. 104. [8] Bürgi, W., and K. Schmid. Unpublished. [9] Cohn, E. J., et al. 1946. J. Am. Chem. Soc. 68:459. [10] Connell, G. E., and O. Smithies. 1959. Biochem. J., Lond. 72:115. [11] Deiss, W. P., and L. B. Holmes. 1958. J. Clin. Invest. 37:51. [12] Deutsch, H. F. 1954. J. Biol. Chem. 208:669. [13] Dus, K., and K. Schmid. 1960. Biochim. biophys. acta, Amst. 37:172. [14] Edsall, J. T., J. F. Foster, and H. Scheinberg. 1947. J. Am. Chem. Soc. 69:2731. [15] Epstein, F. H., and W. D. Block. 1959. Proc. Soc. Exp. Biol., N. Y. 101:740. [16] Eylar, E. H. 1958. Thesis, Harvard University. [17] Eylar, E. H. Unpublished. [18] Fahey, J. L. 1959. Fed. Proc., Balt. 18:43. [19] Ferry, J. D. 1954. Physiol. Rev. 34:753. [20] Fisher, H. W., T. T. Puck, and G. Sato. 1958. Proc. Nat. Acad. Sc. U. S. 44:4. [21] Fitzgerald, J. E., N. S. Schneider, and D. F. Waugh. 1957. J. Am. Chem. Soc. 79:601. [22] Frederickson, D. S., and R. S. Gordon, Jr. 1958. Physiol. Rev. 38:585. [23] Goldstein, R., A. Le Belloc'h, B. Alexander, and E. Zonderman. 1959. J. Biol. Chem. 234:2857. [24] Göllner, I. 1955. Behringwerk Mitt., Heft 30, p. 42. [25] Hartley, R. W., Jr., and D. F. Waugh. In press. J. Am. Chem. Soc. [26] Heremans, J. F., M. T. Heremans, and H. E. Schultze. 1959. Clin. chim. acta, Amst. 4:96. [27] Holmberg, C. G., and C.-B. Laurell. 1948. Acta chem. scand. 2:550. [28] Inman, J. K. 1956. Thesis. Harvard University. [29] Isliker, H. 1957. Advance. Protein Chem., N. Y. 12:388. [30] Jayle, M. F., and G. Boussier. 1955. Exposés ann. biochim. med. 17:157. [31] Keltz, A. 1959. Fed. Proc., Balt. 18:258. [32] Koechlin, B. A. 1952. J. Am. Chem. Soc. 74:2649. [33] Kunkel, H. G., E. C. Franklin, and H. J. Müller-Eberhard. 1959. J. Clin. Invest. 38:424. [34] Laki, K., D. R. Kominz, P. Symonds, L. Lorand, and

W. H. Seegers. 1954. Arch. Biochem., N. Y. 49:276. [35] Lamy, F., and D. Waugh. 1953. J. Biol. Chem. 203:487. [36] Laurell, C.-B. 1959. Clin. chim. acta, Amst. 4:79. [37] Lorand, L., N. Alkjaersig, and W. H. Seegers. 1953. Arch. Biochem., N. Y. 45:312. [38] Lorand, L., and W. R. Middlebrook. 1952. Biochem. J., Lond. 52:196. [39] Magnusson, S. 1958. Acta chem. scand. 12:355. [40] Miller, K. D. 1958. J. Biol. Chem. 231:987. [41] Miller, K. D. In O. Hoffmann-Ostenhof, ed. 1959. Proc. 4th Internat. Congr. Biochem., Vienna, 1958. Pergamon Press, New York. v. 15, p. 22. [42] Miller, K. D., R. K. Brown, G. Casillas, and W. H. Seegers. 1959. Thromb. Diath. Haemorrh. 3:362. [43] Miller, K. D., and W. H. Seegers. 1956. Arch. Biochem., N. Y. 60:398. [44] Müller-Eberhard, H. J., and H. G. Kunkel. 1956. J. Exp. M. 104:253. [45] Müller-Eberhard, H. J., H. G. Kunkel, and E. C. Franklin. 1956. Proc. Soc. Exp. Biol., N. Y. 93:146. [46] Nyman, M. 1959. Scand. J. Clin. Lab. Invest., Suppl. 39. [47] O'Dea, J. Unpublished. [48] Oncley, J. L. In H. N. Antoniades, ed. In press. Hormones in human plasma. Little and Brown, Boston. [49] Oncley, J. L., and F. R. N. Gurd. In J. L. Tullis, ed. 1953. Blood cells and plasma proteins, their state in nature. Academic Press, New York. [50] Oncley, J. L., G. Scatchard, and A. Brown. 1947. J. Phys. Colloid. Chem. 51:184. [51] Pechet, L., B. Alexander, and G. H. Tishkoff. In press. Thromb. Diath. Haemorrh. [52] Popenoe, E. A., and R. M. Drew. 1957. J. Biol. Chem. 228:673. [53] Porter, R. R. In F. W. Putnam, ed. 1960. The plasma proteins. Academic Press, New York. [54] Poulik, M. D. 1959. J. Immun., Balt. 82:502. [55] Sanders, B. E., O. P. Miller, and M. N. Richard. 1959. Arch. Biochem., N. Y. 84:60. [56] Scheinberg, I. H. Unpublished. [57] Scheinberg, I. H., and A. G. Morell. 1957. J. Clin. Invest. 36:1193. [58] Scheraga, H. A., and M. Laskowski, Jr. 1957. Advance. Protein Chem., N. Y. 12:1. [59] Schmid, K. 1953. J. Am. Chem. Soc. 75:2532. [60] Schmid, K. 1953. Ibid. 75:60. [61] Schmid, K. 1954. Biochim. biophys. acta, Amst. 14:437. [62] Schmid, K., and W. Bürgi. Unpublished. [63] Schönenberger, M., R. Schmidtberger, and H. E. Schultze. 1958. Zschr. Naturforsch. 13b:741. [64] Schultze, H. E. 1957. Scand. J. Clin. Lab. Invest., Suppl. 31, p. 135. [65] Schultze, H. E. 1958. Deut. med. Wschr. 83:1742. [66] Schultze, H. E., I. Göllner, K. Heide, M. Schönenberger, and G. Schwick. 1955. Zschr. Naturforsch. 10b:463. [67] Schultze, H. E., R. Schmidtberger, and H. Haupt. 1957-58. Biochem. Zschr. 329:490. [68] Schultze, H. E., M. Schönenberger, and G. Schwick. 1958. Med. & Chem., Berl. 4:451. [69] Schultze, H. E., M. Schönenberger, and G. Schwick. 1956-57. Biochem. Zschr. 328:267. [70] Schwick, G., and H. E. Schultze. 1959. Clin. chim. acta, Amst. 4:26. [71] Seegers, W. H. 1955. Advance. Enzymol. 16:23. [72] Smith, E. L., D. M. Brown, H. E. Weimer, and R. J. Winzler. 1950. J. Biol. Chem. 185:569. [73] Smithies, O. In press. Advance. Protein Chem., N. Y. [74] Sober, H. A., F. J. Gutter, M. M. Wyckoff, and E. A. Peterson. 1956. J. Am. Chem. Soc. 78:756. [75] Spiro, R. G. 1959. Fed. Proc., Balt. 18:328. [76] Stary, Z., F. Bursa, and S. G. Anhegger-Lisie. 1953. Hoppe Seyler Zschr. 295:29. [77] Tristram, G. R. 1949. Advance. Protein Chem., N. Y. 5:142. [78] Weimer, H. E., J. W. Mehl, and R. J. Winzler. 1950. J. Biol. Chem. 185:561. [79] White, W. F., C. W. Gurney, E. Goldwasser, and L. O. Jacobson. In G. Pincus, ed. In press. Recent progress in hormone research. Academic Press, New York. [80] Williams, R. R., L. C. Stewart, and J. C. Jenkins. 1958. Proc. Soc. Exp. Biol., N. Y. 99:554. [81] Yamashima, I. 1956. Acta chem. scand. 10:1666.

15. CHEMICAL COMPOSITION OF PLASMA GLYCOPROTEINS: MAN

Adapted from Schmid, K., "The Plasma Glycoproteins," in R. W. Jeanloz and E. A. Balazs, ed., 1961, "The Hexosamines," Academic Press, New York. Values are for man unless otherwise indicated.

	Protein (A)	Constituent (B)	Value % (C)	Specific (D)	General (E)
1	Prealbumin, tryptophan-rich	Tryptophan	2.6		63,67
2		Sulfate	0		
3		Phosphate	0		
4		Polypeptide moiety	96		
5		Carbohydrate moiety	1.3		
6		Hexose	1.1		
7		Hexosamine	0.15		
8		Sialic acid	0		
9		Fucose	0		
10	a₁-Acid glyco-protein (orosomucoid)[1]	Sulfate	0		11,15, 16,49, 57,64, 65,70, 77,78, 80
11		Phosphate	0		
12		Free sulfhydryl groups	0		
13		Nitrogen	11		
14		Polypeptide moiety	66		
15		Carbohydrate moiety	40		
16		Hexose	16		
17		Galactose	9.8	63	
18			6.5	80	
19			7.5	16	
20		Mannose	4.7	63	
21			4.8	80	
22			6.5	16	
23		Glucosamine	12		
24		Galactosamine	0		
25		Sialic acid	11		
26		Fucose	1.0		
27	a₁-Glycoprotein[2]	Nitrogen	13.3		22,63, 64
28		Polypeptide moiety	84		
29		Carbohydrate moiety	14		
30		Hexose	6.8		
31		Hexosamine	3.6		
32		Sialic acid	3.3		
33	Fetuin (cattle)	Nitrogen	12.2	73	
34		Polypeptide moiety	74	73	
35		Hexose	8.3	73	
36		Hexosamine	5.6	73	
37		Galactosamine	0.6	73,74	
38		Sialic acid	8.7	73	
39	a₁-Lipoproteins[3]	Nitrogen	8.0	9	2,5,7,9, 20,45, 47,63
40		Polypeptide moiety	65		
41		Hexose	1.2		

	Protein (A)	Constituent (B)	Value % (C)	Specific (D)	General (E)
42	a₁-Lipoproteins[3] (concluded)	Galactose	0.4		2,5,7,9, 20,45, 47,63
43		Mannose	0.4		
44		Hexosamine	0.2		
45		Sialic acid	0.3		
46		Fucose	0.05		
47	Zn-a₂-Glycoprotein[4]	Nitrogen	12.6		8,56,58
48		Polypeptide moiety	80		
49		Carbohydrate moiety	16		
50		Hexose	5.0		
51		Hexosamine	3.5		
52		Sialic acid	7.0		
53	Ba-a₂-Glycoproteins[5]	Nitrogen	13.2		12,56, 58,60
54		Polypeptide moiety	80		
55		Hexose	6.0		
56		Hexosamine	5.0		
57		Galactosamine	0		
58		Sialic acid	4.6		
59		Fucose	0.2		
60	Prothrombin[6]	Carbohydrate moiety	16		1,21,45, 48
61		Hexose	6.8		
62		Hexosamine	4.0		
63		Galactosamine	0		
64		Sialic acid	5.0		
65		Fucose	0.2		
66	Prothrombin (cattle)[7,8]	Nitrogen	14.7		32,33, 35,37- 41,62, 63,68, 69
67		Polypeptide moiety	85		
68		Carbohydrate moiety	11		
69		Hexose	6.5		
70		Galactose	3.1		
71		Mannose	1.5		
72		Hexosamine	2.3		
73		Sialic acid	4.2		
74		Fucose	0.2		
75	Haptoglobin, type I-1	Nitrogen	12.9		10,28, 34,44, 63,71
76		Polypeptide moiety	83		
77		Carbohydrate moiety	23		
78		Hexose	11		
79		Galactose	5.5		
80		Mannose	5.5		
81		Hexosamine	5.7		
82		Sialic acid	5.5		
83		Fucose	0.2		

/1/ For amino acid composition, consult references 77 and 78; for C-terminal amino acids, reference 59 (N-terminal amino acids not reactive with dinitrofluorobenzene). /2/ For N-terminal amino acids, consult reference 63. /3/ For amino acid composition, consult reference 7; for C- and N-terminal amino acids, references 2, 7, and 20. /4/ For amino acid composition and C-terminal amino acids, consult reference 8 (N-terminal amino acids not reactive with dinitrofluorbenzene). /5/ For amino acid composition, consult reference 60; for C- and N-terminal amino acids, reference 12. /6/ 2600 units/mg protein (after starch-gel electrophoretic separation), assuming N-factor of 6.25. /7/ 2000 units/mg protein (chromatography on Amberlite IRC-50). /8/ For amino acid composition, consult references 32 and 40; for N-terminal amino acids, references 37 and 39.

15. CHEMICAL COMPOSITION OF PLASMA GLYCOPROTEINS: MAN (Continued)

	Protein (A)	Constituent (B)	Value % (C)	Reference Specific (D)	Reference General (E)
84	Cerulo-plasmin[9]	Nitrogen	13.8		4,6,25,
85		Polypeptide moiety	92		29,53,
86		Carbohydrate moiety	8		54,63,
87		Hexose	3		72
88		Galactose	2		
89		Mannose	1		
90		Hexosamine	3.2	4	
91		Sialic acid	2.0		
92		Fucose	0.2		
93	α_2-19S-Gly-	Nitrogen	14.5		30,42,
94	coprotein	Polypeptide moiety	92		43,51,
95		Carbohydrate moiety	11		61,63
96		Hexose	5.3		
97		Galactose	3.7		
98		Mannose	3.6		
99		Hexosamine	2.7		
100		Sialic acid	2.3		
101		Fucose	0.1		
102	β_1-Trans-	Nitrogen	14.7		22,24,
103	ferrin[10,11]	Polypeptide moiety	95		26,47,
104		Carbohydrate moiety	5.5		63
105		Hexose	2.4		
106		Galactose	1.8		
107		Mannose	0.6		
108		Hexosamine	1.6		
109		Sialic acid	1.4		
110		Fucose	0.1		
111	β_1-Lipopro-	Nitrogen	4.2		2,5,7,
112	teins[12]	Polypeptide moiety	23		14,20,
113		Hexose	0.9		36,46,
114		Hexosamine	0.8		47,63
115		Sialic acid	0.3		
116		Fucose	0.03		
117	Fibrinogen[13]	Nitrogen	16.7		3,13,18,
118		Polypeptide moiety	92		19,23,
119		Carbohydrate moiety	5.0		47,50,
120		Hexose	3.2		55,63,
121		Galactose	1.6		66,75,
122		Mannose	1.6		76
123		Hexosamine	1.0		
124		Glucosamine	1.0		
125		Galactosamine	0		
126		Sialic acid	0.8		
127		Fucose	0		
128	γ-Globulins 7S com-	Nitrogen	15.6		17,27,
129	ponents[14]	Polypeptide moiety	97		45,47,
130		Carbohydrate moiety	2.6		63
131		Hexose	1.2		
132		Galactose	0.3		
133		Mannose	0.7		
134		Hexosamine	1.4		
135		Sialic acid	0.3		
136		Fucose	0.2		
137	19S com-	Nitrogen	14.5		31,43,51
138	ponents	Carbohydrate moiety	10		
139		Hexose	5.2		
140		Hexosamine	2.9		
141		Sialic acid	1.7		
142		Fucose	0.6		
143	Rheumatoid	Nitrogen	14.5		52,79
144	factor	Carbohydrate moiety	10		
145		Hexose	5.3		
146		Hexosamine	2.4		
147		Sialic acid	1.8		

/9/ 8 M Cu++/M protein, or 1.34% Cu. /10/ 2 M Fe++/M protein. /11/ For N-terminal amino acids, consult reference 24. /12/ For amino acid composition, consult reference 7; for C- and N-terminal amino acids, reference 20. /13/ For amino acid composition, consult reference 13. /14/ For amino acid composition, consult references 17 and 27.

Contributor: Schmid, Karl

References: [1] Alexander, B. In O. Hoffmann-Ostenhof, ed. 1959. Proc. 4th Internat. Congr. Biochem., Vienna, 1958. Pergamon Press, New York. v. 10, p. 37. [2] Avigan, J., R. Redfield, and D. Steinberg. 1956. Biochim. biophys. acta, Amst. 20:557. [3] Blombäck, B. 1958. Acta physiol. scand., Suppl. 148. [4] Brown, R. K. 1958. Klin. Wschr. 36:1. [5] Brown, R. K. Unpublished. [6] Brown, R. K., W. H. Baker, A. Peterkofsky, and D. L. Kaufman. 1954. J. Am. Chem. Soc. 76:4244. [7] Brown, R. K., R. E. Davis, B. Clark, and H. van Vunakis. 1956. Proc. 3rd Internat. Conf. Biochem. Probl. Lipids. Koninkl. Vlaam. Acad. Wetenschappen, Brussels. p. 104. [8] Bürgi, W., and K. Schmid. Unpublished. [9] Cohn, E. J., et al. 1946. J. Am. Chem. Soc. 68:459. [10] Connell, G. E., and O. Smithies. 1959. Biochem. J., Lond. 72:115. [11] Deiss, W. P., and L. B. Holmes. 1958. J. Clin. Invest. 37:51. [12] Dus, K., and K. Schmid. 1960. Biochim. biophys. acta, Amst. 37:172. [13] Edsall, J. T., J. F. Foster, and H. Scheinberg. 1947. J. Am. Chem. Soc. 69:2731. [14] Epstein, F. H., and W. D. Block. 1959. Proc. Soc. Exp. Biol., N. Y. 101:740. [15] Eylar, E. H. 1958. Thesis. Harvard University.

[16] Eylar, E. H. Unpublished. [17] Fahey, J. L. 1959. Fed. Proc., Balt. 18:43. [18] Ferry, J. D. 1954. Physiol. Rev. 34:753. [19] Fitzgerald, J. E., N. S. Schneider, and D. F. Waugh. 1957. J. Am. Chem. Soc. 79:601. [20] Fredrickson, D. S., and R. S. Gordon, Jr. 1958. Physiol. Rev. 38:585. [21] Goldstein, R., A. LeBolloc'h, B. Alexander, and E. Zonderman. 1959. J. Biol. Chem. 234:2857. [22] Göllner, I. 1955. Behringwerk Mitt., Heft 30, p. 42. [23] Hartley, R. W., Jr., and D. F. Waugh. In press. J. Am. Chem. Soc. [24] Heremans, J. F., M. T. Heremans, and H. E. Schultze. 1959. Clin. chim. acta, Amst. 4:96. [25] Holmberg, C. G., and C.-B. Laurell. 1948. Acta chem. scand. 2:550. [26] Inman, J. K. 1956. Thesis. Harvard University. [27] Isliker, H. 1957. Advance. Protein Chem., N. Y. 12:388. [28] Jayle, M. F., and G. Boussier. 1955. Exposés ann. biochim. med. 17:157. [29] Keltz, A. 1959. Fed. Proc., Balt. 18:258. [30] Koechlin, B. A. 1952. J. Am. Chem. Soc. 74:2649. [31] Kunkel, H. G., E. C. Franklin, and H. J. Müller-Eberhard. 1959. J. Clin. Invest. 38:424. [32] Laki, K., D. R. Kominz, P. Symonds, L. Lorand, and W. H. Seegers. 1954. Arch. Biochem., N. Y. 49:276. [33] Lamy, F., and D. Waugh. 1953. J. Biol. Chem. 203:487. [34] Laurell, C.-B. 1959. Clin. chim. acta, Amst. 4:79. [35] Lorand, L., N. Alkjaersig, and W. H. Seegers. 1953. Arch. Biochem., N. Y. 45:312. [36] Lorand, L., and W. R. Middlebrook. 1952. Biochem. J., Lond. 52:196. [37] Magnusson, S. 1958. Acta chem. scand. 12:355. [38] Miller, K. D. 1958. J. Biol. Chem. 231:987. [39] Miller, K. D. In O. Hoffmann-Ostenhof, ed. 1959. Proc. 4th Internat. Congr. Biochem., Vienna, 1958. Pergamon Press, N. Y. v. 15, p. 32. [40] Miller, K. D., R. K. Brown, G. Casillas, and W. H. Seegers. 1959. Thromb. Diath. Haemorrh. 3:362. [41] Miller, K. D., and W. H. Seegers. 1956. Arch. Biochem., N. Y. 60:398. [42] Müller-Eberhard, H. J., and H. G. Kunkel. 1956. J. Exp. M. 104:253. [43] Müller-Eberhard, H. J., H. G. Kunkel, and E. C. Franklin. 1956. Proc. Soc. Exp. Biol., N. Y. 93:146. [44] Nyman, M. 1959. Scand. J. Clin. Lab. Invest., Suppl. 39. [45] Oncley, J. L. In H. N. Antoniades, ed. In press. Hormones in human plasma. Little and Brown, Boston. [46] Oncley, J. L., and F. R. N. Gurd. In J. L. Tullis, ed. 1953. Blood cells and plasma proteins, their state in nature. Academic Press, New York. [47] Oncley, J. L., G. Scatchard, and A. Brown. 1947. J. Phys. Colloid. Chem. 51:184. [48] Pechet, L., B. Alexander, and G. H. Tishkoff. In press. Thromb. Diath. Haemorrh. [49] Popenoe, E. A., and R. M. Drew. 1957. J. Biol. Chem. 228:673. [50] Porter, R. R. In F. W. Putnam, ed. 1960. The plasma proteins. Academic Press, New York. [51] Poulik, M. D. 1959. J. Immun., Balt. 82:502. [52] Sanders, B. E., O. P. Miller, and M. N. Richard. 1959. Arch. Biochem., N. Y. 84:60. [53] Scheinberg, I. H. Unpublished. [54] Scheinberg, I. H., and A. G. Morell. 1957. J. Clin. Invest. 36:1193. [55] Scheraga, H. A., and M. Laskowski, Jr. 1957. Advance. Protein Chem., N. Y. 12:1. [56] Schmid, K. 1953. J. Am. Chem. Soc. 75:2532. [57] Schmid, K. 1953. Ibid. 75:60. [58] Schmid, K. 1954. Biochim. biophys. acta, Amst. 14:437. [59] Schmid, K., W. L. Bencze, T. Nussbaumer, and J. O. Wehrmüller. 1959. J. Biol. Chem. 234:529. [60] Schmid, K., and W. Bürgi. Unpublished. [61] Schönenberger, M., R. Schmidtberger, and H. E. Schultze. 1958. Zschr. Naturforsch. 13b:741. [62] Schultze, H. E. 1957. Scand. J. Clin. Lab. Invest., Suppl. 31, p. 135. [63] Schultze, H. E. 1958. Deut. med. Wschr. 83:1742. [64] Schultze, H. E., I. Göllner, K. Heide, M. Schönenberger, and G. Schwick. 1955. Zschr. Naturforsch. 10b:463. [65] Schultze, H. E., R. Schmidtberger, and H. Haupt. 1957-58. Biochem. Zschr. 329:490. [66] Schultze, H. E., M. Schönenberger, and G. Schwick. 1958. Med. & Chem., Berl. 4:451. [67] Schultze, H. E., M. Schönenberger, and G. Schwick. 1956-57. Biochem. Zschr. 328:267. [68] Schwick, G., and H. E. Schultze. 1959. Clin. chim. acta, Amst. 4:26. [69] Seegers, W. H. 1955. Advance. Enzymol. 16:23. [70] Smith, E. L., D. M. Brown, H. E. Weimer, and R. J. Winzler. 1950. J. Biol. Chem. 185:569. [71] Smithies, O. In press. Advance. Protein Chem., N. Y. [72] Sober, H. A., F. J. Gutter, M. M. Wyckoff, and E. A. Peterson. 1956. J. Am. Chem. Soc. 78:756. [73] Spiro, R. G. 1959. Fed. Proc., Balt. 18:328. [74] Spiro, R. G. In press. J. Biol. Chem. [75] Stary, Z., F. Bursa, and S. G. Anhegger-Lisie. 1953. Hoppe Seyler Zschr. 295:29. [76] Tristram, G. R. 1949. Advance. Protein Chem., N. Y. 5:142. [77] Weimer, H. E., J. W. Mehl, and R. J. Winzler. 1950. J. Biol. Chem. 185:561. [78] White, W. F., C. W. Gurney, E. Goldwasser, and L. O. Jacobson. In G. Pincus, ed. In press. Recent progress in hormone research. Academic Press, New York. [79] Williams, R. R., L. C. Stewart, and J. C. Jenkins. 1958. Proc. Soc. Exp. Biol., N. Y. 99:554. [80] Yamashima, I. 1956. Acta chem. scand. 10:1666.

16. ELECTROPHORETIC ANALYSIS OF PLASMA PROTEINS: VERTEBRATES

The study of plasma proteins by electrophoresis depends on the existence of different charges on the several proteins, and may employ various methods of determination, i.e., the moving boundary, starch block, and paper electrophoresis. When an electrical current is passed through plasma in a U tube, the groups of proteins shift with different velocities and thus tend to separate. (The velocity of each component, in cm/sec, divided by the field strength, in v/cm, is defined as the mobility of the component.) By means of an ingenious optical system (Tiselius apparatus), the refractive index changes at separation boundaries can be photographed quantitatively (see charts). However, the quantitative interpretation of electrophoretic data in terms of plasma protein concentration is complicated by the interference of lipids and carbohydrates which migrate with the protein. Furthermore, the results obtained under different experimental conditions are not identical, and the protein fractions appear at times to be bound together so that clear separation is not possible, e.g., the α_1-globulin boundary, which separates from albumin at pH 8.6, moves with albumin at pH 7.8 or lower. In addition, the α-globulin groups include glycoproteins, mucoproteins, and lipoproteins, and the β-globulin group also includes lipoproteins.

Contributors: (a) Petermann, Mary L., (b) Deutsch, Harold F., (c) Moore, Dan H.

References: [1] Wiggers, C. J. 1949. Physiology in health and disease. Ed. 5. Lea and Febiger, Philadelphia. p. 359. [2] Putnam, F. W., ed. 1960. The plasma proteins. Academic Press, New York. v. 1.

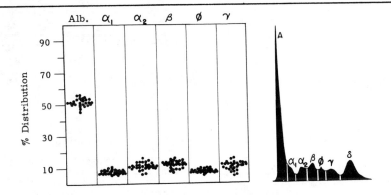

Electrophoretic Analysis of Whole Plasma

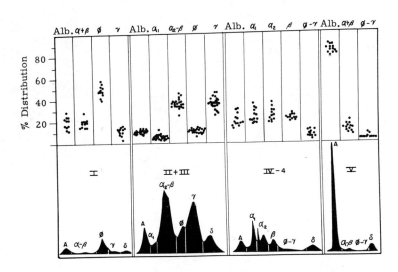

Electrophoretic Analysis of Plasma Fractions

Contributor: Chanutin, Alfred

Reference: Pearsall, H. R., and A. Chanutin. 1949. Am. J. Med. 7:297.

Part I: IN VERONAL BUFFER SOLUTION AT VARIOUS IONIC STRENGTHS AND PROTEIN CONCENTRATIONS: MAN

pH of buffer solution = 8.6.

	Ionic Strength M/L	Protein Concentration g/100 ml	Albumin %	Globulin, %			Fibrinogen %	γ-Globulin %
				Total α	α_1	β		
	(A)	(B)	(C)	(D)	(E)	(F)	(G)	(H)
1	0.05	1.0	55.9	13.9	4.2	15.0	6.3	8.9
2		2.0	57.7	12.5	3.6	14.3	6.5	9.0
3		2.5	57.9	10.7	4.4	14.0	6.3	11.1
4	0.10	1.0	53.7	14.8	5.4	14.2	7.0	10.3
5		1.5	55.4	13.2	5.4	13.6	6.6	11.2
6		2.0	55.1	14.2	5.0	12.3	7.8	10.6
7		2.3	57.3	11.2	4.0	14.7	6.7	10.1
8	0.20	1.0	51.4	15.0	5.6	14.3	6.9	12.4
9		2.0	52.3	14.9	4.7	13.8	7.3	11.7
10		2.5	53.4	12.3	6.6	15.1	6.6	12.6
11	0.30	1.0	51.0	15.4	6.8	14.5	6.7	12.4
12		1.5	50.4	15.8	8.3	14.8	6.3	12.7
13		2.0	51.3	14.4	5.7	16.3	5.8	12.2

Contributor: Koenig, Virgil L.

Reference: Armstrong, S. H., Jr., M. J. E. Budko, and K. C. Morrison. 1947. J. Am. Chem. Soc. 69:416.

Part II: IN VARIOUS BUFFER SOLUTIONS AND IONIC STRENGTHS: CATTLE

	Ionic Strength M/L	Molarity	Albumin %	Globulin, %						Fibrinogen %	γ-Globulin %
				Total α	α_1	α_2	β	β_1	β_2		
	(A)	(B)	(C)	(D)	(E)	(F)	(G)	(H)	(I)	(J)	(K)
				Veronal-Sodium Chloride Buffer (pH = 8.6)							
1	0.05		36.5		6.3	9.7		5.8	10.0	19.0	12.7
2	0.10		35.0		5.4	9.3		5.1	9.0	20.3	16.0
3		0.05[1]	35.5		6.3	9.2		4.9	9.1	19.7	15.6
4	0.15	0.05[1]	33.0		5.0	11.4		3.8	9.7	19.3	17.9
5		0.10[1]	33.7		5.1	10.1		4.4	8.5	20.6	17.8
6	0.20	0.10[1]	33.3		5.1	11.2		3.2	9.4	19.7	18.1
7	0.30	0.20[1]	32.4		6.0	10.4		3.7	8.5	20.3	18.8
				Phosphate Buffer (pH = 7.7)							
8	0.05		49.9	6.5			9.5			20.7	12.0
9	0.10		43.7	10.9			9.7			20.8	14.9
10	0.15		38.6	15.0			9.5			20.2	16.8
11	0.20		37.5	15.7			9.6			20.2	17.0
12	0.30		35.2	16.3			9.4			20.7	18.5
13	0.40		33.8	15.9			10.0			21.3	19.1
				Phosphate-Potassium Chloride Buffer (pH = 7.7)							
14	0.10	0.05[2]	45.4			11.4	9.1			21.2	12.9
15	0.15	0.10[2]	38.6		5.4	8.7	9.6			20.0	17.9
16	0.20	0.15[2]	35.6		6.1	8.8	9.8			20.5	19.4
17	0.30	0.25[2]	33.6		4.8	10.7	8.2			21.8	20.9

/1/ Sodium chloride. /2/ Potassium chloride.

Contributor: Koenig, Virgil L.

Reference: Koenig, V. L., J. D. Perrings, and K. R. Hogness. 1946. Arch. Biochem., N. Y. 11:345.

16. ELECTROPHORETIC ANALYSIS OF PLASMA PROTEINS: VERTEBRATES (Continued)

Part III: IN VERONAL-CITRATE BUFFER SOLUTION: MAMMALS, BIRDS, FISHES

pH of buffer solution = 8.6, ionic strength = 0.1. Mobility (m) = sq cm/sec/volt x 10^5.

	Animal	Measurement	Albumin Peak[1]	Albumin	Globulin α_1	Globulin α_2	Globulin α_3	Globulin β	Fibrinogen	γ-Globulin
	(A)	(B)	(C)	(D)	(E)	(F)	(G)	(H)	(I)	(J)
				Mammals						
1	Man	m		6.6	5.4	4.3		3.1	2.3	1.3
2		%		59.6	6.7	8.8		11.0	4.8	9.1
3	Cat	m		7.7	6.3	5.2	4.1	3.4	2.6	1.6
4		%		41.4	8.1	20.2	4.7	8.7	5.2	12.5
5	Cattle, ♀	m		7.0	5.5	4.7		3.7	2.6	1.4
6		%		40.6	10.7	8.3		13.7	16.3	11.0
7	Dog	m		6.8	5.7	4.4		3.3	2.4	1.2
8		%		39.6	16.9	8.0		13.0	13.3	9.3
9	Fox	m		7.5	6.4	5.2		3.2		1.3
10		%		47.1	10.2	7.8		31.2		3.9
11	Goat	m		7.3	5.6	4.1		3.1	2.5	1.5
12		%		49.2	13.7	12.7		3.9	7.6	12.9
13	Guinea pig	m		6.1	5.4	4.9	4.4	3.0	2.1	1.0
14		%		54.6	4.0	3.7	15.2	8.8	8.1	5.6
15	Horse	m	7.9	7.1	5.8	4.8		3.7	2.5	1.4
16		%	0.8	29.8	8.2	12.3		21.9	15.8	11.2
17	Mink	m		4.9	4.2	3.8		3.7	3.2	2.2
18		%		51.5	11.7	9.8		10.3	5.0	12.1
19	Monkey	m	7.4	6.6	5.4	4.8	4.2	3.3	2.2	1.4
20		%	0.5	50.0	5.9	5.2	4.7	16.1	8.4	9.0
21	Rabbit	m		6.8	5.1			3.5	2.4	1.4
22		%		63.3	11.5			13.0	7.9	4.3
23	Rat	m	7.1	6.1				2.7		1.6
24		%	1.3	59.1	15.4			19.4		4.8
25	Sheep	m		6.8	5.3	4.3		3.4	2.6	1.6
26		%		43.7	9.8	6.7		15.0	9.7	15.0
27	Swine	m	7.3	6.5	5.2	4.4		3.7	2.8	1.8
28		%	0.4	39.9	6.0	16.3		8.2	13.9	15.2
				Birds						
29	Chicken	m	8.1	7.3	6.1	4.6				2.9
30		%	0.5	38.2	15.8	7.7				37.5
31		m	7.5	6.8	5.4	4.1				2.5
32		%	0.6	40.4	14.9	11.3				32.8
33	Duck	m	7.6	6.7	5.8	4.9			3.7	2.5
34		%	2.6	47.8	21.9	6.1			15.5	6.0
35	Pheasant	m	6.1	5.2	4.2	3.6			2.9	1.7
36		%	0.4	58.5	14.0	6.5			16.3	4.3
37	Pigeon	m	7.8	6.4	5.2	4.5			3.3	1.7
38		%	3.1	64.1	7.2	4.5			17.4	7.7
39	Turkey	m	6.7	5.9	5.0	4.1			2.9	1.7
40		%	1.0	51.5	13.4	4.3			21.6	8.1
				Fishes						
41	Carp	m		6.8	4.0			3.4	2.6	1.8
42		%	2.1	67.7	6.8			14.1	7.1	2.1

/1/ A component on the leading shoulder of the albumin peak.

Contributor: Koenig, Virgil L.

Reference: Deutsch, H. F., and M. B. Goodloe. 1945. J. Biol. Chem. 161:1.

16. ELECTROPHORETIC ANALYSIS OF PLASMA PROTEINS: VERTEBRATES (Concluded)

Part IV: IN VARIOUS BUFFER SOLUTIONS: MAMMALS, BIRDS

Mobility (m) = sq cm/sec/volt x 10^5.

	Animal	Measurement	Albumin	Globulin α_1	α_2	β_1	β_2	Fibrinogen	Globulin γ_1	γ_2	Reference
	(A)	(B)	(C)	(D)	(E)	(F)	(G)	(H)	(I)	(J)	(K)
	Veronal Buffer (pH = 8.6; ionic strength = 0.1)										
1	Man	m	5.92	3.87[1]		2.88		2.06	1.15		1
2		%	55	5[1]		13		7	11		
3	Cattle	m	6.36	5.40	4.67	3.83	3.12	2.45	1.72		2
4		%	36	6	11	4	10	20	15.0		
5	Sheep Young	m	6.68	5.32	4.14	3.23		2.54	1.90	1.02	4
6		%	52	8	9	7		12	11	2	
7	Adult	m	6.68	5.32	4.14	3.23		2.54	1.90	1.02	
8		%	38	8	9	11		17	13	4	
9	Swine	m	6.28	5.22	4.20	3.45		2.68	1.81		3
10		%	34	4	19	8		21	14.7		
11	Chicken	m	5.90	4.70		3.50		2.50	2.00		7
12		%	47	18		11		14	19		
	Veronal-Sodium Chloride Buffer (pH = 8.5; ionic strength = 0.2)										
13	Cattle	m	5.28	4.47	3.72		2.89	2.31	1.52		2
14		%	34	4	13		12	21	16		
15	Sheep	m	5.48	4.30	3.36	2.71		2.18	1.63	0.75	4
16		%	35	9	9	10		18	15	5	
17	Swine	m	5.39	4.44	3.60	2.96		2.43	1.66		3
18		%	31	4	19	9		21	17		
	Phosphate Buffer (pH = 7.7; ionic strength = 0.2)										
19	Man[2]	m	6.90[3]		4.90	3.60		2.50	1.10		5,6
20		%	63[3]		7	13		5	12		
21	Cattle	m	5.74		4.27		3.50	2.64	1.84		2
22		%	39		16		10	20	15		
23	Dog	m	7.60	6.30	5.20	3.60		2.70	1.10		6
24		%	39	14	4	15		16	13		
25	Sheep Young	m	6.14	4.59		3.33		2.72	2.06	0.89	4
26		%	53	14		7		10	13	4	
27	Adult	m	6.14	4.59		3.33		2.72	2.06	0.89	
28		%	39	16		10		12	18	6	
29	Swine	m	5.31		3.94	3.15		2.60	1.75		3
30		%	38		19	13		12	18		

/1/ Total α-globulin: m = 4.85, % = 14.   /2/ Phosphate buffer pH = 7.8, ionic strength = 0.16.   /3/ Albumin plus α_1-globulin.

Contributors: (a) Koenig, Virgil L., (b) Petermann, Mary L.

References: [1] Armstrong, S. H., Jr., M. J. E. Budko, and K. C. Morrison. 1947. J. Am. Chem. Soc. 69:416. [2] Hogness, K. R., J. W. Giffee, and V. L. Koenig. 1946. Arch. Biochem., N. Y. 10:281. [3] Koenig, V. L., and K. R. Hogness. 1946. Ibid. 9:119. [4] Koenig, V. L., J. D. Perrings, and F. Mundy. 1949. Ibid. 22:377. [5] Lewis, L. A. 1947. J. Exp. M. 86:185. [6] Lewis, L. A., and E. P. McCullagh. 1944. Am. J. M. Sc. 208:727. [7] Sanders, E., I. F. Huddleson, and P. J. Schaible. 1944. J. Biol. Chem. 155:469.

17. ELECTROPHORETIC ANALYSIS OF SERUM PROTEINS: VERTEBRATES

Serum proteins differ from plasma proteins in that fibrinogen has been lost in the clotting process.

Part I: IN VERONAL BUFFER SOLUTION

pH of buffer solution = 8.6, ionic strength = 0.1.   Mobility (m) = sq cm/sec/volt x 10^5.

	Animal	Measurement	Albumin	Globulin							Reference
				α_1	α_2	β_1	β_2	γ	γ_1	γ_2	
	(A)	(B)	(C)	(D)	(E)	(F)	(G)	(H)	(I)	(J)	(K)
				Mammals							
1	Man	m	5.9	5.1	4.1	2.8		1.0			6
2		%	63	5	7	13		12			
3	Cat	m	7.6	6.0	4.7	3.2		1.8			6
4		%	46	12	11	12		5			
5	Cattle	m	6.18	5.25	4.58	3.65	2.85		2.36	1.67	3
6		%	38	8	12	7	9		7	18	
7	Dog	m	7.20	5.60	4.60	3.30	2.80		1.80		1
8		%	46	20		26·			8		
9	Goat	m	6.90	5.30	4.00	3.00			1.80		2
10		%	37	11	13	8			32		
11	Guinea pig	m	6.1	4.8	4.1	2.7		1.1			6
12		%	54	11	21	6		8			
13	Hamster	m	6.0	4.9	4.0	3.5	2.4	1.6			6
14		%	59	12	5	14	5	6			
15	Rabbit	m	6.4	5.3	4.6	3.2		1.3			6
16		%	64	5	8	12		12			
17	Rat	m	5.9	5.3	4.4	2.8		1.7			6
18		%	65	13	5	13		4			
19	Cotton-	m	6.3	5.0	4.1	3.0		1.0			
20		%	47	8	29	10		7			
	Sheep										5
21	Young	m	6.64	5.28	4.25	3.40			2.27	1.02	
22		%	54	7	10	8			18	3	
23	Adult	m	6.64	5.28	4.25	3.40			2.27	1.02	
24		%	39	8	9	9			32	4	
25	Swine	m	6.19	5.10	4.10	3.35	2.75		1.95		4
26		%	38	4	19	8	13		18		
27		m	4.9	4.4	3.1	2.4	2.0	1.5			6
28		%	45	4	13	8	12	8			
				Birds							
29	Chicken	m	5.70	4.50		3.50			1.90	17	7
30		%	58	16		9					
31	Pigeon	m	5.8	4.4	2.8		2.4	1.7			6
32		%	58	10	5		18	9			
				Fishes							
33	Carp	m	6.0		3.7	2.9		1.7			6
34		%	47		21	12		20			

Contributor: Koenig, Virgil L.

References: [1] Gjessing, E. C., S. Ludewig, and A. Chanutin. 1947. J. Biol. Chem. 170:551. [2] Gjessing, E. C., S. Ludewig, and A. Chanutin. 1948. Ibid. 174:683. [3] Hogness, K. R., J. W. Giffee, and V. L. Koenig. 1946. Arch. Biochem., N. Y. 10:281. [4] Koenig, V. L., and K. R. Hogness. 1946. Ibid. 9:119. [5] Koenig, V. L., J. D. Perrings, and F. Mundy. 1949. Ibid. 22:377. [6] Moore, D. H. 1945. J. Biol. Chem. 161:21. [7] Sanders, E., I. F. Huddleson, and P. J. Schaible. 1944. Ibid. 155:469.

Part II: IN PHOSPHATE BUFFER SOLUTION

Ionic strength of buffer solutions = 0.2. Mobility (m) = sq cm/sec/volt x 10^5.

	Animal	Buffer pH	Measurement	Albumin	Globulin α_1	α_2	β_1	β_2	γ	γ_1	γ_2	Reference
	(A)	(B)	(C)	(D)	(E)	(F)	(G)	(H)	(I)	(J)	(K)	(L)
					Mammals							
1	Man	7.4	m	5.1[1]		3.5	2.5		0.7			4
2			%	65[1]		9	16		11			
3	Cat	7.4	m	6.4	5.3	4.4	3.3		1.1			4
4			%	36	10	14	17		23			
5	Cattle	7.7	m	5.72		4.53		3.41		2.69	1.82	1
6			%	43		20		10		9	19	
7	Dog	7.4	m	5.5		3.8	2.6	2.0	0.7			4
8			%	50		10	16	14	5.5			
9	Guinea pig	7.4	m	4.2	3.6	3.1	1.7		0.6			4
10			%	65	15	5	6		9			
11	Hamster	7.4	m	4.3	3.5	2.6	1.6		0.6			4
12			%	60	14	6	10		10			
13	Monkey	7.4	m	5.4		3.9	3.1		1.5			4
14			%	52		8	16		24			
15	Rabbit	7.4	m	5.4		4.5	3.1		0.9			4
16			%	70		6	13		15			
17	Rat	7.4	m	4.6		3.0	2.1		0.9			4
18			%	74		8	13		8			
19	Cotton-	7.4	m	4.6		3.0	2.3		0.5			
20			%	52		27	12		10			
	Sheep											3
21	Young	7.7	m	6.13	4.61		3.45			2.29	0.92	
22			%	55	15		7			19	5	
23	Adult	7.7	m	6.13	4.61		3.45			2.29	0.92	
24			%	41	16		8			31	5	
25	Swine	7.4	m	4.7		3.2	2.5		1.0			4
26			%	47		19	15		20			
27		7.7	m	5.55		4.15	3.24			1.82		2
28			%	42		18	17			24		
					Birds							
	Chicken											4
29	Male, young	7.4	m	5.2	4.2	3.2	2.3		1.5			
30			%	44	15	10	14		14			
31	Female	7.4	m[2]	4.9	4.0	3.1	1.8		1.1			
32			%[2]	29	6	8	35		21			
33	Pigeon	7.4	m	4.1		2.2	1.6		0.3			4
34			%	57		19	16		8			
					Fishes							
35	Carp	7.4	m	4.2		3.4	2.5		0.9			4
36			%	48		16	13		23			

/1/ Albumin plus α_1-globulin. /2/ For leading shoulder of albumin peak, m = 5.8, % = 5.

Contributor: Koenig, Virgil L.

References: [1] Hogness, K. R., J. W. Giffee, and V. L. Koenig. 1946. Arch. Biochem., N. Y. 10:281. [2] Koenig, V. L., and K. R. Hogness. 1946. Ibid. 9:119. [3] Koenig, V. L., J. D. Perrings, and F. Mundy. 1949. Ibid. 22:377. [4] Moore, D. H. 1945. J. Biol. Chem. 161:21.

18. ELECTROPHORETIC ANALYSIS OF SERUM PROTEINS IN ORDER OF INCREASING MOBILITY: VERTEBRATES AND INVERTEBRATES

Blood samples were collected from severed artery in turtles and frogs, from main circulatory sinus in crabs and snails, and by heart puncture in snakes and fishes. No attempt was made to identify the protein components; instead, electrophoretic areas were assigned numbers in order of increasing electrophoretic mobility. pH of veronal buffer solution = 8.6, ionic strength = 0.1. Mobility (m) = sq cm/sec/volt x 10^5.

	Animal	No. of Subjects	Measurement	Component No. 1	2	3	4	5	6	7	8	9	10
	(A)	(B)	(C)	(D)	(E)	(F)	(G)	(H)	(I)	(J)	(K)	(L)	(M)
				Reptiles									
1	Snake Agkistrodon	1	m	1.0	1.8	2.8	3.9	4.5	5.0	5.7	6.4	6.8	7.4
2	piscivorus		%	2.5	15.8	18.8	13.5	5.4	5.3	11.3	6.4	5.4	15.6
3	Crotalus atrox	2	m	1.7	2.6	3.2	3.7	4.3	4.7	5.3	5.8	6.3	7.3
4			%	4.4	5.9	6.0	21.0	8.7	3.9	8.7	4.0	4.6	32.8
5	C. horridus	1	m	3.4	4.7	6.2	7.4	8.7	10.0	11.0	12.4	14.0	
6			%	3.8	3.5	19.7	9.4	8.8	13.3	10.3	28.4	2.8	
7	Lampropeltis	1	m	1.4	2.0	2.6	3.4	3.8	4.4	5.1	6.5	7.9	
8	triangulum		%	1.3	5.7	16.4	11.6	5.9	5.8	11.9	23.8	17.6	
9	Natrix sipedon	2	m	3.8	4.1	5.7	6.9	7.6	8.8	10.0	11.7		
10			%	16.6	17.9	30.7	5.0	10.3	3.5	6.6	9.4		
11	Turtle Amyda spinifera	3	m	1.4	2.5	3.5	4.4	5.8	6.9				
12			%	1.9	15.5	11.6	17.6	51.8	1.6				
13	Chelydra	8	m	1.1	1.8	3.8	3.6	4.5	5.3	6.1			
14	serpentina		%	5.3	20.5	31.5	16.6	7.5	16.2	2.4			
				Amphibians									
15	Bullfrog (Rana	5	m	1.5	2.3	3.1	3.7	4.3	4.9	5.6	6.5	7.2	
16	catesbeiana)		%	8.4	7.0	5.5	5.8	12.0	22.4	16.0	22.4	0.5	
				Fishes									
17	Bass, rock	20	m	2.3	3.0	3.6	4.3	5.4	6.1	7.0	7.9	8.8	
18	(Ambloplites rupestris)		%	1.3	5.7	2.9	9.3	24.2	17.3	10.7	27.9	0.7	
19	Buffalo fish (Ictiobus	1	m	1.4	2.5	3.1	3.9	4.7	5.4	6.2	6.9		
20	bubalus)		%	2.5	25.0	10.2	9.7	17.8	5.5	5.5	23.8		
21	Bullhead (Ameiurus	25	m	1.8	3.0	4.0	5.4	6.8	7.6	8.7	10.0		
22	sp)		%	0.6	4.7	8.5	15.8	7.3	9.3	30.6	23.2		
23	Carp (Cyprinus	7	m	2.3	3.7	4.7	5.7	7.1	8.6				
24	carpio)		%	4.1	8.2	14.3	15.0	21.5	36.9				
25	Catfish Ictalarus anguilla	4	m	1.7	2.3	3.1	3.7	4.4	5.6	6.7	7.7		
26			%	6.2	7.8	4.3	5.1	14.1	32.4	4.2	25.9		
27	I. lacustris	25	m	1.3	1.8	2.3	3.0	3.9	4.7	5.7	6.5		
28			%	2.9	3.8	3.2	6.6	6.6	11.2	20.6	45.1		
29		3	m	1.1	1.9	2.7	3.2	3.9	4.7	5.6	6.5		
30			%	1.9	5.2	4.5	7.4	5.3	10.8	36.0	28.9		
31	Herring, lake	25	m	1.4	2.4	3.2	3.8	4.3	4.8	5.3	6.1	6.8	7.7
32	(Leucichthys artedi arcturus)[1]		%	1.7	12.4	7.4	7.5	5.4	9.9	4.4	6.6	17.0	26.5
33	Perch Perca flavescens[2]	25	m	2.5	2.9	3.5	4.4	5.0	5.8	6.5	7.2	8.0	8.7
34			%	1.8	2.6	7.0	4.6	18.8	8.8	4.4	5.2	7.0	11.0
35	Stizostedion	8	m	2.7	3.8	4.7	5.4	5.9	6.7	7.6	7.8	10.0	11.0
36	vitreum[3]		%	1.1	4.1	5.6	3.0	4.0	13.0	4.7	13.2	9.5	8.0
37	Pike, northern (Esox	2	m	1.9	2.8	3.7	4.3	5.7	8.0	8.7			
38	lucius)		%	7.8	12.2	6.3	7.8	48.2	13.5	4.2			
39	Sturgeon (Acipenser	1	m	1.7	2.3	3.0	3.6	4.3	5.0	5.6	6.2	6.9	7.4
40	sp)		%	22.6	8.5	10.4	5.6	5.3	18.3	11.5	8.9	7.4	1.5
41		1	m	1.5	2.2	2.7	3.2	3.7	4.1	4.5	5.2	5.9	
42			%	17.9	18.2	7.6	2.9	6.0	15.0	6.5	25.1	0.8	
43	Sucker (Catostomus	8	m	1.4	2.1	3.0	3.8	4.9	5.5	6.4	7.4		
44	commersonii)		%	1.4	13.6	14.2	12.1	18.7	7.6	31.8	0.6		

/1/ 11th component: m = 8.5, % = 1.2. /2/ 11th component: m = 9.7, % = 29.8; 12th component: m = 10.8, % = 1.2.
/3/ 11th component: m = 11.9, % = 33.8.

Animal	No. of Subjects	Measure-ment	Component No.									
			1	2	3	4	5	6	7	8	9	10
(A)	(B)	(C)	(D)	(E)	(F)	(G)	(H)	(I)	(J)	(K)	(L)	(M)
Fishes (concluded)												
45 Trout Cristivomer	8	m	1.3	2.2	2.7	3.4	4.2	4.9	6.5	7.5		
46 namaycush		%	1.4	3.8	7.9	6.5	8.2	12.8	58.4	1.0		
47 Salmo gairdnerii	6	m	1.3	2.0	2.7	3.1	4.2	5.1	6.3	7.4		
48 irideus		%	1.2	1.6	3.4	4.0	34.7	6.7	45.6	2.8		
49 S. trutta fario[4]	4	m	1.4	1.9	2.5	3.2	4.2	5.1	5.5	6.0	6.5	7.4
50		%	1.1	3.2	7.2	15.0	20.2	7.6	11.0	16.9	9.6	7.4
51 Whitefish (Coregonus	25	m	1.3	2.7	3.0	3.5	4.1	4.8	5.7	5.9	7.0	7.7
52 clupeaformis)		%	0.5	7.5	11.7	12.7	8.1	14.6	12.1	17.6	14.7	0.5
Arthropods, Mollusks												
53 Crab, horseshoe	2	m	2.0	4.5	5.1	6.1	6.7					
54 (Limulus polyphemus)		%	4.0	7.5	10.7	24.5	53.3					
55 Snail, land	25	m	2.4	3.5	4.7	6.2	7.1	7.9	9.5			
56 (Polygyria sp)		%	2.7	2.0	4.8	7.0	13.6	62.3	7.6			

/4/ 11th component: m = 8.0, % = 0.8.

Contributor: Koenig, Virgil L.

Reference: Deutsch, H. F., and W. H. McShan. 1949. J. Biol. Chem. 180:219.

19. ULTRACENTRIFUGAL ANALYSIS OF SERUM LIPOPROTEINS AND PROTEINS: MAN

Lipoproteins are isolated from serum by the use of the preparative ultracentrifuge. The isolation is possible because lipoproteins have (1) high molecular weights (60,000-100,000,000,000), and (2) lower densities than serum proteins. If ultracentrifugation is carried out in a solution of density 1.063 g/ml (achieved by the addition of sodium chloride to serum), all lipoproteins of densities less than 1.063 g/ml undergo flotation in an intense centrifugal field (52,640 rpm, radius of 72.5 mm, at 26°C), whereas the serum proteins and lipoproteins of densities greater than 1.063 g/ml undergo sedimentation. In this process, all lipoproteins of density 1.04 g/ml and less are quantitatively recovered in the top layer of the solution in the ultracentrifuge tube.

The low-density lipoproteins occur in a series, or spectrum, of closely-spaced flotation rates, which are measured in terms of a unit known as the Svedberg of flotation, or the S_f unit. One S_f unit represents a flotation rate of 10^{-13} cm/sec/dynes/g. When the measurement has been corrected for the slowing effect of increased lipoprotein concentration, the unit is expressed as S_f^0. The close spacing of the flotation rates renders difficult the measurement of the serum level of lipoprotein of each flotation rate; hence, the system has been adopted of measuring the sum of the concentrations between arbitrarily-chosen flotation rate limits. The hydrated density of S_f^0 20-400 = <1.007 g/ml, and S_f^0 0-20 = 1.007-1.04 g/ml. There are differences of opinion with regard to the predictive value of the atherogenic index; these differences are set forth in reference 8. HDL is used to indicate the high-density lipoproteins. The hydrated density of HDL_1 = 1.05 g/ml, HDL_2 = 1.075 g/ml, and HDL_3 = 1.145 g/ml.

Contributors: (a) DeLalla, Oliver F., and Gofman, John W., (b) Mann, George V., (c) Page, Irvine H.

References: [1] DeLalla, O. F. 1958. Ph. D. Thesis. University of California, Berkeley. [2] DeLalla, O. F., H. A. Elliott, and J. W. Gofman. 1954. Am. J. Physiol. 179:333. [3] DeLalla, O. F., and J. W. Gofman. In D. Glick, ed. 1954. Methods of biochemical analysis. Interscience, New York. v. 1. [4] Gofman, J. W., F. Glazier, A. Tamplin, B. Strisower, and O. F. deLalla. 1954. Physiol. Rev. 34:589. [5] Gofman, J. W., B. Strisower, O. F. deLalla, A. Tamplin, H. Jones, and F. Lindgren. 1953. Mod. Med., Chic. 21:119. [6] Gofman, J. W., et al. 1956. Circulation, N. Y. 14:691. [7] Lewis, L. A., et al. 1957. Ibid. 16:227. [8] Lindgren, F. T., H. A. Elliott, and J. W. Gofman. 1951. J. Phys. Colloid Chem. 55:80.

Part I: CONCENTRATIONS: MALES

Subjects were clinically healthy and non-fasting. Values are mg/100 ml serum. Values in parentheses are ranges, estimate "b" (cf. Introduction).

	Specification	17-29 Years (585 Subjects)	30-39 Years (834 Subjects)	40-49 Years (399 Subjects)	50-65 Years (143 Subjects)
	(A)	(B)	(C)	(D)	(E)
	Low density lipoproteins				
1	S_f^o 0-12	322(236-408)	365(271-439)	380(296-464)	383(308-458)
2	S_f^o 12-20	40(19-61)	51(23-74)	57(34-80)	56(32-80)
3	S_f^o 20-100	75(34-116)	91(37-145)	107(41-173)	103(45-161)
4	S_f^o 100-400	37(0-80)	51(0-115)	66(0-157)	58(0-128)
5	Atherogenic index[1]	59(39-79)	69(45-93)	78(49-107)	76(50-102)
	High density lipoproteins				
6	HDL_1	23(16-30)	24(9-39)	25(10-40)	27(5-49)
7	HDL_2	37(9-65)	36(8-64)	37(9-65)	42(10-74)
8	HDL_3	217(177-257)	219(177-261)	226(176-276)	224(173-275)
	Proteins				
9	Macroglobulin	199(124-274)	169(105-233)	155(91-219)	152(91-213)
10	γ-Globulins	1322(1025-1619)	1345(1045-1645)	1369(1060-1678)	1431(1103-1759)
11	Albumin	4717(4237-5197)	4634(4175-5093)	4572(4084-5060)	4442(3935-4949)

/1/ Atherogenic index = (S_f^o 0-12 (mg %) x 0.1 + S_f^o 20-400 (mg %) x 0.175). /2/ Electrophoretic determination = (740-770) mg/100 ml [2, 3]. /3/ Electrophoretic determination = (4040-4090) mg/100 ml [2, 3].

Contributors: (a) DeLalla, Oliver F., and Gofman, John W., (b) Page, Irvine H.

References: [1] DeLalla, O. F. 1958. Ph. D. Thesis. University of California, Berkeley. [2] Dole, V. P. 1944. J. Clin. Invest. 23:708. [3] Lewis, L. A., and E. P. McCullagh. 1944. Am. J. M. Sc. 208:727.

Part II: CONCENTRATIONS: FEMALES

Subjects were clinically healthy and non-fasting. Values are mg/100 ml serum. Values in parentheses are ranges, estimate "b" (cf. Introduction).

	Specification	17-29 Years (190 Subjects)	30-39 Years (99 Subjects)	40-49 Years (37 Subjects)	50-65 Years (10 Subjects)
	(A)	(B)	(C)	(D)	(E)
	Low density lipoproteins				
1	S_f^o 0-12	283(215-351)	324(238-410)	346(279-413)	437(397-477)
2	S_f^o 12-20	30(14-46)	41(19-63)	42(21-63)	93(57-129)
3	S_f^o 20-100	44(15-73)	51(15-87)	65(14-116)	77(29-125)
4	S_f^o 100-400	9(0-23)	13(0-30)	18(0-42)	32(0-69)
5	Atherogenic index[1]	43(31-55)	51(33-69)	56(37-75)	79(57-101)
	High density lipoproteins				
6	HDL_1	21(14-28)	22(13-31)	23(18-28)	25(10-32)
7	HDL_2	80(39-121)	81(36-126)	89(36-142)	117(51-183)
8	HDL_3	228(190-266)	235(197-273)	241(198-284)	270(216-324)
	Proteins				
9	Macroglobulin	272(195-349)	218(139-297)	227(142-312)	198(147-249)
10	γ-Globulins	1347(1054-1640)	1319(962-1676)	1332(1088-1676)	1324(980-1668)
11	Albumin	4618(4074-5162)	4629(4070-5188)	4465(4020-4910)	4348(3838-4858)

/1/ Atherogenic index = (S_f^o 0-12 (mg%) x 0.1 + S_f^o 20-400 (mg %) x 0.175).

Contributors: DeLalla, Oliver F., and Gofman, John W.

Reference: DeLalla, O. F. 1958. Ph. D. Thesis. University of California, Berkeley.

19. ULTRACENTRIFUGAL ANALYSIS OF SERUM LIPOPROTEINS AND PROTEINS: MAN (Continued)

Part III: PEARSON PRODUCT-MOMENT CORRELATIONS: MALES

Subjects were clinically healthy and non-fasting.

	Specification	Pearson Coefficient			
		17-29 Years (803 Subjects)	30-39 Years (562 Subjects)	40-49 Years (387 Subjects)	50-65 Years (140 Subjects)
	(A)	(B)	(C)	(D)	(E)
	HDL$_1$ vs				
1	S$_f^o$ 0-12	0.21	0.06	-0.01	-0.01
2	S$_f^o$ 12-20	-0.03	0.02	-0.04	-0.02
3	S$_f^o$ 20-100	-0.03	0.22	0.15	0.31
4	S$_f^o$ 100-400	0.04	0.27	0.41	0.55
5	Atherogenic index	0.09	0.23	0.28	0.38
	HDL$_2$ vs				
6	S$_f^o$ 0-12	-0.27	-0.20	-0.25	-0.26
7	S$_f^o$ 12-20	-0.25	-0.17	-0.27	-0.25
8	S$_f^o$ 20-100	-0.28	-0.25	-0.26	-0.36
9	S$_f^o$ 100-400	-0.21	-0.21	-0.18	-0.29
10	Atherogenic index	-0.33	-0.29	-0.31	-0.39
11	HDL$_1$	-0.17	-0.08	-0.05	-0.11
	HDL$_3$ vs				
12	S$_f^o$ 0-12	0.01	-0.03	-0.10	-0.03
13	S$_f^o$ 12-20	-0.01	0.02	-0.04	0.01
14	S$_f^o$ 20-100	-0.12	-0.13	-0.18	-0.16
15	S$_f^o$ 100-400	-0.07	-0.14	-0.15	-0.08
16	Atherogenic index	-0.07	-0.12	-0.19	-0.11
17	HDL$_1$	-0.01	-0.02	-0.04	0.04
18	HDL$_2$	0.30	0.36	0.41	0.42
	Macroglobulin vs				
19	S$_f^o$ 0-12	-0.04	0.03	-0.02	0.21
20	S$_f^o$ 12-20	-0.08	0.01	-0.04	0.18
21	S$_f^o$ 20-100	-0.05	-0.04	0.00	0.11
22	S$_f^o$ 100-400	-0.05	-0.04	-0.05	0.02
23	Atherogenic index	-0.06	-0.02	-0.04	0.14
24	HDL$_1$	0.00	0.03	-0.03	0.08
25	HDL$_2$	0.11	0.05	0.16	0.02
26	HDL$_3$	-0.07	-0.06	-0.05	-0.01
	γ-Globulins vs				
27	S$_f^o$ 0-12	-0.07	-0.08	0.02	-0.11
28	S$_f^o$ 12-20	-0.09	-0.02	-0.06	-0.03
29	S$_f^o$ 20-100	-0.03	0.03	0.04	0.17
30	S$_f^o$ 100-400	0.00	0.05	0.03	0.05
31	Atherogenic index	-0.06	0.01	0.03	0.05
32	HDL$_1$	0.05	0.06	-0.08	-0.10
33	HDL$_2$	-0.03	-0.01	-0.03	-0.15
34	HDL$_3$	-0.02	-0.07	-0.02	-0.07
35	Macroglobulin	0.01	0.06	0.02	0.01
	Albumin vs				
36	S$_f^o$ 0-12	0.03	0.05	-0.01	0.13
37	S$_f^o$ 12-20	-0.02	0.01	0.03	0.20
38	S$_f^o$ 20-100	-0.03	0.02	0.03	0.09
39	S$_f^o$ 100-400	-0.01	0.02	0.03	0.14
40	Atherogenic index	0.00	0.04	0.03	0.17
41	HDL$_1$	0.02	-0.01	0.01	0.07
42	HDL$_2$	-0.03	0.06	0.05	0.00
43	HDL$_3$	0.00	0.04	0.05	0.17
44	Macroglobulin	0.21	0.19	0.36	0.30
45	γ-Globulins	-0.25	-0.20	-0.27	-0.29

Part III: PEARSON PRODUCT-MOMENT CORRELATIONS: MALES (Concluded)

Contributors: DeLalla, Oliver F., and Gofman, John W.

Reference: DeLalla, O. F. 1958. Ph. D. Thesis. University of California, Berkeley.

Part IV: PEARSON PRODUCT-MOMENT CORRELATIONS: FEMALES

Subjects were clinically healthy and non-fasting.

Specification	Pearson Coefficient 17-29 Years (188 Subjects)	Pearson Coefficient 30-49 Years (132 Subjects)		Specification	Pearson Coefficient 17-29 Years (188 Subjects)	Pearson Coefficient 30-49 Years (132 Subjects)
(A)	(B)	(C)		(A)	(B)	(C)
HDL$_1$ vs				**Macroglobulin vs (concluded)**		
1 S_f^o 0-12	0.35	0.24	22	S_f^o 100-400	-0.05	-0.04
2 S_f^o 12-20	0.04	0.12	23	Atherogenic index	-0.12	-0.04
3 S_f^o 20-100	0.06	0.15	24	HDL$_1$	-0.09	0.04
4 S_f^o 100-400	0.11	0.33	25	HDL$_2$	0.06	0.12
5 Atherogenic index	0.24	0.26	26	HDL$_3$	-0.01	-0.11
HDL$_2$ vs				**γ-Globulins**		
6 S_f^o 0-12	-0.09	-0.17	27	S_f^o 0-12	-0.03	-0.04
7 S_f^o 12-20	-0.05	-0.18	28	S_f^o 12-20	0.17	0.01
8 S_f^o 20-100	-0.27	-0.30	29	S_f^o 20-100	0.13	0.02
9 S_f^o 100-400	-0.22	-0.32	30	S_f^o 100-400	0.24	0.09
10 Atherogenic index	-0.21	-0.29	31	Atherogenic index	0.12	0.01
11 HDL$_1$	-0.23	-0.21	32	HDL$_1$	0.01	-0.06
HDL$_3$ vs			33	HDL$_2$	-0.14	-0.03
12 S_f^o 0-12	0.15	-0.02	34	HDL$_3$	-0.05	0.05
13 S_f^o 12-20	0.18	0.03	35	Macroglobulin	0.01	0.17
14 S_f^o 20-100	0.05	0.08		**Albumin vs**		
15 S_f^o 100-400	0.14	0.10	36	S_f^o 0-12	0.14	0.12
16 Atherogenic index	0.17	0.05	37	S_f^o 12-20	-0.05	0.07
17 HDL$_1$	0.12	-0.03	38	S_f^o 20-100	-0.11	0.07
18 HDL$_2$	0.25	0.27	39	S_f^o 100-400	-0.15	0.05
Macroglobulin vs			40	Atherogenic index	-0.01	0.11
19 S_f^o 0-12	-0.10	0.00	41	HDL$_1$	0.09	0.04
20 S_f^o 12-20	-0.17	-0.02	42	HDL$_2$	0.03	0.05
21 S_f^o 20-100	-0.04	-0.07	43	HDL$_3$	0.25	0.18
			44	Macroglobulin	0.36	0.20
			45	γ-Globulins	-0.32	-0.11

Contributors: DeLalla, Oliver F., and Gofman, John W.

Reference: DeLalla, O. F. 1958. Ph. D. Thesis. University of California, Berkeley.

20. ULTRACENTRIFUGAL ANALYSIS OF SERUM LIPOPROTEINS IN PREGNANCY AND POSTPARTUM: MAN

Nine subjects were followed through some or all of the gestation and postpartum periods of an uncomplicated pregnancy. Matched control values are the mean for clinically healthy individuals of the same age and sex as the pregnant and postpartum subjects.

	Condition	No. of Subjects	Lipoprotein	Mean Level mg/100 ml	Matched Controls mg/100 ml	Difference in Means	Significance Test[1,2]
	(A)	(B)	(C)	(D)	(E)	(F)	(G)
1	Pregnancy 2nd trimester	7	S_f^0 0–12	309.7	298.6	+11.1	NS
2			S_f^0 12–20	54.6	47.7	+6.9	NS
3			S_f^0 20–100	63.4	56.4	+7.0	NS
4			S_f^0 100–400	15.9	20.9	−5.0	NS
5			HDL$_1$	20.4	15.1	+5.3	0.02 > P > 0.01
6			HDL$_2$	168.3	121.0	+47.3	0.02 > P > 0.01
7			HDL$_3$	240.0	207.0	+33.0	0.05 > P > 0.01
8	3rd trimester	9	S_f^0 0–12	369.2	298.6	+70.6	0.05 > P > 0.01
9			S_f^0 12–20	105.2	47.7	+57.5	0.05 > P > 0.01
10			S_f^0 20–100	141.3	56.4	+84.9	0.05 > P > 0.01
11			S_f^0 100–400	34.2	20.9	+13.3	NS
12			HDL$_1$	21.7	15.1	+6.6	0.05 > P > 0.01
13			HDL$_2$	151.0	121.0	+30.0	NS
14			HDL$_3$	254.7	207.0	+47.7	P 0.01
15	Postpartum Delivery to 5 da	9	S_f^0 0–12	348.3	298.6	+49.7	0.05 > P > 0.01
16			S_f^0 12–20	76.8	47.7	+29.1	0.05 > P > 0.01
17			S_f^0 20–100	126.1	56.4	+69.7	0.05 > P > 0.01
18			S_f^0 100–400	41.8	20.9	+20.9	0.05 > P > 0.01
19			HDL$_1$	23.8	15.1	+8.7	P < 0.01
20			HDL$_2$	117.8	121.0	−3.2	NS
21			HDL$_3$	257.6	207.0	+50.6	0.02 > P > 0.01
22	5 da–6 mo	7	S_f^0 0–12	381.7	298.6	+83.1	0.05 > P > 0.01
23			S_f^0 12–20	65.7	47.7	+18.0	0.05 > P > 0.01
24			S_f^0 20–100	77.1	56.4	+20.7	0.05 > P > 0.01
25			S_f^0 100–400	31.6	20.9	+10.7	NS
26			HDL$_1$	22.0	15.1	+6.9	0.05 > P > 0.01
27			HDL$_2$	94.3	121.0	−26.7	NS
28			HDL$_3$	282.4	207.0	+75.4	P < 0.01
29	9 mo	3	S_f^0 0–12	269.3	298.6	−29.3	NS
30			S_f^0 12–20	34.7	47.7	−13.0	NS
31			S_f^0 20–100	67.3	56.4	+10.9	NS
32			S_f^0 100–400	24.7	20.9	+3.8	NS
33			HDL$_1$	17.0	15.1	+1.9	NS
34			HDL$_2$	52.2	121.0	−69.8	NS
35			HDL$_3$	220.5	207.0	+12.5	NS

/1/ Difference of Pearson product-moment coefficient from zero. /2/ NS = not significant at the 5% level or below.

Contributors: DeLalla, Oliver F., and Gofman, John W.

Reference: Gofman, J. W., et al. 1954. Plasma, Milano 2:413.

21. ULTRACENTRIFUGAL ANALYSIS OF SERUM LIPOPROTEINS IN PATHOLOGICAL CONDITIONS: MAN

Part I: LEVELS IN METABOLIC STATES

Matched control values are the mean for clinically healthy individuals of the same age and sex as the subjects with pathological conditions. Values in parentheses are ranges, estimate "c" (cf. Introduction).

Condition	Subjects Age, yr	Subjects No.	Lipoprotein	Level mg/100 ml	Matched Controls mg/100 ml	Difference in Means	Significance Test[1,2]
(A)	(B)	(C)	(D)	(E)	(F)	(G)	(H)
1 Chronic biliary obstruction	(24-52)	1♂, 5♀	S_f^o 0-12	910(579-1550)	346	+7.0[3]	P << 0.01
2			S_f^o 12-20	1053(575-2119)	70	+29.2[3]	P << 0.01
3			S_f^o 20-100	1265(150-3472)	78	+29.7[3]	P << 0.01
4			S_f^o 100-400	49(0-114)	39	+0.3[3]	NS
5	(20-49)	1♂, 4♀	HDL1	8.4(9-27)	15.4	-7.0	NS
6			HDL2	0.6(0-3)	101	-100.4	P < 0.01
7			HDL3	16.6(0-62)	195.8	-179.2	P < 0.01
8 Diabetes mellitus	(11-55)	2♂, 8♀	S_f^o 0-12	225(0-408)	324	-99	
9			S_f^o 12-20	74(0-155)	41	+33	
10			S_f^o 20-100	450(20-1120)	51	+399	
11			S_f^o 100-400	836(7-3739)	13	+823	
12		1♂, 6♀	HDL1	88(3-217)	22	+66	
13			HDL2	40(0-96)	81	-41	
14			HDL3	106(0-203)	235	-129	
15 Essential hyperlipemia	(29-68)	7♂, 2♀	S_f^o 0-12	229(130-320)	364	-1.6[3]	P < 0.01
16			S_f^o 12-20	66(18-92)	68	-0.1[3]	NS
17			S_f^o 20-100	450(184-1100)	109	+7.1[3]	P << 0.01
18			S_f^o 100-400	967(132-2937)	83	+11.5[3]	P << 0.01
19		4♂, 1♀	HDL1	80.0(30-102)	19.5	+60.5	P < 0.01
20			HDL2	54.0(14-71)	79.9	-25.9	NS
21			HDL3	144.2(61-300)	195.6	-51.4	NS
22 Glycogen storage disease	(27-33)	2♂	S_f^o 0-12	512(320-703)	321	+191	
23			S_f^o 12-20	186(69-293)	57	+129	
24			S_f^o 20-100	1019(623-1414)	94	+925	
25			S_f^o 100-400	1543(934-2151)	58	+1485	
26			HDL1	155(82-255)	20	+135	
27			HDL2	0	59	-59	
28			HDL3	117(93-140)	182	-65	
29 Nephrotic state	(3-41)	10♂, 3♀	S_f^o 0-12	787(455-1290)	276	+6.3[3]	P << 0.01
30			S_f^o 12-20	236(85-401)	41	+9.8[3]	P << 0.01
31			S_f^o 20-100	583(213-1219)	69	+14.7[3]	P << 0.01
32			S_f^o 100-400	355(37-748)	37	+11.0[3]	P << 0.01
33	(19-68)	5♂	HDL1	33.2(5-82)	20.6	-12.6	NS
34			HDL2	16.0(0-67)	71.2	-55.2	< 0.01
35			HDL3	157.0(21-396)	186.5	-29.5	NS
36 Spontaneous myxedema	(44-60)	2♀	S_f^o 0-12	779(730-827)	390	+389	
37			S_f^o 12-20	162(130-193)	65	+97	
38			S_f^o 20-100	108(103-112)	70	+38	
39			S_f^o 100-400	17(16-18)	25	-8	
40	60	1♀	HDL1	34	24	+10	
41			HDL2	53	105	-52	
42			HDL3	153	255	-102	

/1/ Difference of Pearson product-moment coefficient from zero. /2/ NS = not significant at the 5% level or below.
/3/ Standard score unit. (The standard score of differences in means between diseased and matched controls is equal to the difference in means divided by the standard deviation of the measurement.)

Part I: LEVELS IN METABOLIC STATES (Concluded)

	Condition	Subjects Age, yr	Subjects No.	Lipoprotein	Level mg/100 ml	Matched Controls mg/100 ml	Difference in Means	Significance Test[1,2]
	(A)	(B)	(C)	(D)	(E)	(F)	(G)	(H)
43	Xanthelasma	(33-70)	11♂, 32♀	S_f^o 0-12	444(258-979)	352	+1.1[3]	P < 0.01
44				S_f^o 12-20	112(36-405)	76	+1.2[3]	P < 0.01
45				S_f^o 20-100	105(36-267)	96	+0.2[3]	NS
46				S_f^o 100-400	54(7-179)	54	0.0[3]	NS
47			2♂, 3♀	HDL_1	19.4(12-23)	15.8	+2.7	NS
48				HDL_2	64.0(24-169)	91.0	-27.0	NS
49				HDL_3	204(132-258)	191.0	+13.0	NS
50	Xanthoma tendinosum	(14-52)	11♂, 7♀	S_f^o 0-12	793(452-1196)	336	+5.3[3]	P << 0.01
51				S_f^o 12-20	150(49-372)	65	+3.1[3]	P << 0.01
52				S_f^o 20-100	128(36-396)	92	+0.8[3]	P 0.01
53				S_f^o 100-400	36(0-85)	56	-0.4[3]	P 0.01
54			4♂, 5♀	HDL_1	25.8(18-36)	17.1	+8.7	P 0.01
55				HDL_2	14.9(3-51)	88.3	-73.4	P < 0.01
56				HDL_3	149.8(94-179)	193.2	-43.4	P < 0.01
57	X. tuberosum	(27-60)	17♂, 6♀	S_f^o 0-12	206(105-403)	358	-1.9[3]	P < 0.01
58				S_f^o 12-20	128(74-242)	74	+1.8[3]	P < 0.01
59				S_f^o 20-100	616(314-1832)	105	+9.1[3]	P << 0.01
60				S_f^o 100-400	650(74-2804)	72	+7.9[3]	P << 0.01
61			11♂, 5♀	HDL_1	25.6(3-88)	17.4	+8.2	NS
62				HDL_2	38.5(0-124)	75.6	-37.1	P < 0.01
63				HDL_3	165.9(85-249)	185.2	-19.3	NS

/1/ Difference of Pearson product-moment coefficient from zero. /2/ NS = not significant at the 5% level or below.
/3/ Standard score unit. (The standard score of differences in means between diseased and matched controls is equal to the difference in means divided by the standard deviation of the measurement.)

Contributors: DeLalla, Oliver F., and Gofman, John W.

Reference: Gofman, J. W., et al. 1954. Plasma, Milano 2:413.

Part II: PEARSON PRODUCT-MOMENT CORRELATIONS
FOR LIPOPROTEINS VS BLOOD PRESSURE IN HYPERTENSION

	Subjects Sex and Age	Subjects No.	Diastolic Pressure versus	Pearson Coefficient	Significance Test[1,2]
	(A)	(B)	(C)	(D)	(E)
	Males				
1	30-39 yr	83	HDL_1	+0.04	NS
2			HDL_2	-0.09	NS
3			HDL_3	-0.04	NS
4	40-49 yr	309	S_f^o 0-12	+0.093	NS
5			S_f^o 12-20	+0.005	NS
6			S_f^o 20-100	+0.153	P < 0.01
7			S_f^o 100-400	+0.208	P < 0.01
8		69	HDL_1	+0.09	NS
9			HDL_2	-0.17	NS
10			HDL_3	+0.07	NS

/1/ Difference of Pearson product-moment coefficient from zero. /2/ NS = not significant at the 5% level or below.

Part II: PEARSON PRODUCT-MOMENT CORRELATIONS
FOR LIPOPROTEINS VS BLOOD PRESSURE IN HYPERTENSION (Concluded)

	Subjects		Diastolic Pressure versus	Pearson Coefficient	Significance Test[1,2]
	Sex and Age	No.			
	(A)	(B)	(C)	(D)	(E)
	Males (concluded)				
11	50-59 yr	53	HDL_1	+0.08	NS
12			HDL_2	-0.18	NS
13			HDL_3	+0.13	NS
	Females				
14	30-39 yr	446	S_f^o 0-12	+0.125	P < 0.05
15			S_f^o 12-20	+0.051	NS
16			S_f^o 20-100	+0.136	P < 0.01
17			S_f^o 100-400	+0.147	P < 0.01
18		155	HDL_1	+0.04	NS
19			HDL_2	-0.15	P 0.05
20			HDL_3	-0.02	NS
21	40-49 yr	154	HDL_1	+0.01	NS
22			HDL_2	-0.09	NS
23			HDL_3	-0.29	P < 0.01
24	50-59 yr	78	HDL_1	+0.16	NS
25			HDL_2	-0.27	0.05 > P > 0.01
26			HDL_3	+0.03	NS

/1/ Difference of Pearson product-moment coefficient from zero. /2/ NS = not significant at the 5% level or below.

Contributors: DeLalla, Oliver F., and Gofman, John W.

Reference: Gofman, J. W., et al. 1954. Plasma, Milano 2:413.

Part III: PEARSON PRODUCT-MOMENT CORRELATIONS FOR LIPOPROTEINS VS OBESITY

Since no body fat values were available for the subjects, body fat content was crudely assessed by measurement of the variable designated as "relative weight," i.e., the ratio of actual to ideal weight for a particular height. (Ideal weights were taken from tables prepared by the Metropolitan Life Insurance Company.) There is a suggestion of a curvilinear regression of S_f^o 0-12 on relative weight, with a positive regression in the low relative weight range (up to relative weight of 1.1), and either zero or negative regression in the higher relative weight ranges. In all other cases, linear regression appears to be present.

	Subjects		Relative Weight versus	Pearson Coefficient	Significance Test[1,2]
	Sex and Age	No.			
	(A)	(B)	(C)	(D)	(E)
	Males				
1	30-39 yr	83	HDL_1	-0.16	NS
2			HDL_2	-0.06	NS
3			HDL_3	-0.23	0.05 > P > 0.01
4	40-49 yr	109	S_f^o 0-12	+0.107	NS
5			S_f^o 12-20	+0.140	0.05 > P > 0.01
6			S_f^o 20-100	+0.277	P < 0.01
7			S_f^o 100-400	+0.391	P < 0.01
8		69	HDL_1	+0.21	NS
9			HDL_2	-0.24	P 0.05
10			HDL_3	-0.04	NS
11	50-59 yr	53	HDL_1	+0.07	NS
12			HDL_2	-0.30	0.05 > P > 0.01
13			HDL_3	-0.11	NS

/1/ Difference of Pearson product-moment coefficient from zero. /2/ NS = not signigicant at the 5% level or below.

Part III: PEARSON PRODUCT-MOMENT CORRELATIONS FOR LIPOPROTEINS VS OBESITY (Concluded)

Subjects		Relative Weight versus	Pearson Coefficient	Significance Test[1,2]
Sex and Age	No.			
(A)	(B)	(C)	(D)	(E)
Females 30-39 yr	446	S_f^0 0-12	+0.112	0.05 > P > 0.01
		S_f^0 12-20	+0.101	0.05 > P > 0.01
		S_f^0 20-100	+0.208	P < 0.01
		S_f^0 100-400	+0.244	P < 0.01
	155	HDL$_1$	+0.04	NS
		HDL$_2$	-0.16	0.05 > P > 0.01
		HDL$_3$	-0.08	NS
40-49 yr	154	HDL$_1$	+0.04	NS
		HDL$_2$	-0.02	NS
		HDL$_3$	0.0	NS
50-59 yr	78	HDL$_1$	+0.14	NS
		HDL$_2$	-0.23	0.05 > P > 0.01
		HDL$_3$	+0.05	NS

/1/ Difference of Pearson product-moment coefficient from zero. /2/ NS = not significant at the 5% level or below.

Contributors: DeLalla, Oliver F., and Gofman, John W.

Reference: Gofman, J. W., et al. 1954. Plasma, Milano 2:413.

Part IV: LEVELS DURING DIABETIC ACIDOSIS THERAPY

This table illustrates (1) the restoration to normal of a grossly disturbed lipid metabolism by administration of insulin, and (2) the shift in distribution of lipoproteins from the higher S_f classes to the lower S_f classes during therapy.

Clinical State	Days After Hospital Admission	Lipoprotein Levels, mg/100 ml						
		S_f^0 0-12	S_f^0 12-20	S_f^0 20-100	S_f^0 100-400	HDL$_1$	HDL$_2$	HDL$_3$
(A)	(B)	(C)	(D)	(E)	(F)	(G)	(H)	(I)
1 Acidosis and coma	0	195	155	1120	3739	168	29	167
2 Acidosis relieved	4	444	352	1942	1530	141	7	179
3 Diabetes controlled	9	744	428	1277	685	66	7	179
4	14	939	338	670	139	34	14	172
5	29	614	134	493	228	41	33	203
6	43	531	148	432	132	25	33	219
7	50	616	150	332	152	19	19	192
8	56	549	108	150	31	Not analyzed		

Contributors: DeLalla, Oliver F., and Gofman, John W.

Reference: Gofman, J. W., et al. 1954. Plasma, Milano 2:413.

22. BLOOD NON-PROTEIN NITROGENOUS SUBSTANCES: MAN

Values are mg/100 ml blood, unless otherwise specified. Values in parentheses are ranges, estimate "c" unless otherwise indicated (cf. Introduction).

	Constituent (A)	Value (B)	Reference (C)
	Whole Blood		
1	Alloxan	0.02(0.015-0.025)	36
	Amino acids		
2	α-Alanine	(2.79-5.11)	23
3	Arginine	1.0(0.6-1.7)	26
4	Cystine	0.9(0.6-1.2)^b	29
5	Glutamine	10	39
6	Glycine	(1.8-2.5)	2,12,13,23
7	Histidine	1.214(1.09-1.38)	44
8	Isoleucine	1.3(0.9-1.5)	29
9	Leucine	1.7(1.4-2.0)^b	25
10	Lysine	2.2(1.3-3.0)	29
11	Methionine	0.426(0.392-0.457)	48
12	Phenylalanine	1.0(0.8-1.2)^b	29
13	Threonine	1.6(1.3-2.0)	29
14	Tryptophan	0.274(0.269-0.289)	15
15	Tyrosine	1.1(0.8-1.4)^b	29
16	Valine	2.4(2.0-2.9)	24
17	Ammonia	0.047	30
18	Bilirubin	(0.19-1.44)	14
19	Creatine	2.7	50
20	Creatinine	0.6	50
21	Ergothioneine	1.9(1.7-2.0)	37
	Glutathione		
22	Total	36.84(36.6-37.07)	11
23	Oxidized	4.02(3.99-4.06)	11
24	Reduced	(26.7-31.9)	40
25	Histamine	0.0043	41
26	Indican	(0.095-0.105)	4
27	Methylguanidine	<0.2	50
	Nucleotides		
28	Total	41(31-52)	27
29	Adenine	(21-36)	8
30	Polypeptides	<7	21
31	Porphyrin	0.0068	9
32	Protoporphyrin	0.014(0.011-0.017)	45
33	Urea	25.5(16.0-35.0)	58
34	Uric acid	2.75(1.6-3.9)	58
	Nitrogen		
35	Total N	(3000-4100)	22
36	Non-protein N	33.8(27-47)	28
37	Amide N	(134-144)	7
38	α-Amino N	4.24(3.44-4.93) mEq/L	23
39	Ammonia N	(0.015-0.116)	17
40	Nucleotide N	(3.2-5.0)	38
41	Polypeptide N	(2.7-7.5)	49
42	Residual N	(10-25)	20
43	Urea N	15.0(10.6-29.0)	28
44	Uric acid N	3.2(1.92-4.40)	28
	Erythrocytes		
	Amino acids		
45	α-Alanine	(2.5-5.6)	23,55
46	Arginine	0.3(0.1-0.6)	26
47	Cystine	0.4(0.3-0.5)	29
48	Glycine	(1.6-3.5)	2,12,13,23
49	Histidine	(2.2-2.8)	52
50	Isoleucine	0.9(0.5-1.4)	29

	Constituent (A)	Value (B)	Reference (C)
	Erythrocytes (concluded)		
	Amino acids (concluded)		
51	Leucine	1.5(1.0-1.8)	25
52	Lysine	1.4(0.9-1.8)	29
53	Methionine	0.5(0.3-0.8)	29
54	Phenylalanine	1.0(0.7-1.3)^b	29
55	Threonine	1.6(1.3-2.1)	29
56	Tryptophan	0.3	16,26,46
57	Tyrosine	1.1(0.7-1.5)^b	29
58	Valine	2.0(1.6-2.5)	24
59	Coproporphyrin, free	0.5(0-2.0) μg/100 ml	53
60	Creatine	8.1(6.0-10.2)^b	28,33
61	Creatinine	1.8(1.7-1.9)^b	28,33
	Glutathione		28,34
62	Total	87	
63	Oxidized	8.5	
64	Reduced	79	
65	Protoporphyrin, free	35(13-140) μg/100 ml	10
66	Uric acid	1.9(0.8-3.0)^b	18,19,28,33
	Nitrogen		
67	Non-protein N	49.30(39-61)	59
68	α-Amino N	5.95(4.89-6.59) mEq/L	23
69	Polypeptide N	7.02	31
70	Urea N	17.10(12-22)	59
	Plasma or Serum		
71	Allantoin	0.45(0.3-0.6)	6
	Amino acids		
72	Alanine	3.41(3.01-3.73)	47
73	Aminobutyric acid	0.30(0.22-0.35)	47
74	Arginine	1.51(1.22-1.93)	47
75	Asparagine	0.58(0.54-0.65)	47
76	Aspartic acid[1]	0.03(0.01-0.07)	47
77	Citrulline	0.50	6
78	Cysteine + cystine	1.18(1.08-1.30)	47
79	Glutamic acid	0.70(0.43-1.15)	47
80	Glutamine	8.30	5
81	Glycine	1.54(1.34-1.73)	47
82	Histidine	1.15(0.79-1.48)	47
83	Isoleucine	0.89(0.69-1.28)	47
84	Leucine	1.69(1.42-2.30)	47
85	Lysine	2.72(2.51-3.02)	47
86	Methionine	0.38(0.33-0.43)	47
87	1-Methylhistidine[1]	0.11(0.04-0.17)	47
88	3-Methylhistidine[1]	0.08(0.04-0.13)	47
89	Ornithine	0.72(0.62-0.80)	47
90	Phenylalanine	0.84(0.69-0.95)	47
91	Proline	2.36(2.01-3.34)	47
92	Serine	1.12(1.01-1.25)	47
93	Taurine	0.55(0.41-0.82)	47
94	Threonine	1.39(1.21-1.72)	47
95	Tryptophan	1.11	26
96	Tyrosine	1.03(0.81-1.45)	47
97	Valine	2.88(2.37-3.71)	47
98	Bilirubin	0.76(0.1-2.0)	56

/1/ Too low in concentration to permit unequivocal identification.

	Constituent	Value	Reference		Constituent	Value	Reference
	(A)	(B)	(C)		(A)	(B)	(C)
	Plasma or Serum (continued)				Plasma or Serum (concluded)		
99	Creatine	0.45(0.28-0.62)	3		Nitrogen		
100	Creatinine	1.1(0.7-1.5)	51	106	Total N	(1200-1430)	22
101	Histamine	0.005(0.002-0.008)	42	107	Non-protein N	(23-37)	35
102	Imidazoles	1.45(0-3.0)	32	108	α-Amino N	(3.37-4.97)	57
103	Indican	0.46(0.20-0.72)	43	109	Ammonia N	4.20	54
104	Urea	33(7-60)	1	110	Polypeptide N	2.21	31
105	Uric acid	(2.8-6.6)	51	111	Residual N	11.0	54
				112	Urea N	19.3(13 26)	59

Contributors: (a) Luckey, T. D., and Cohagen, D. L., (b) Beerstecher, Ernest, Jr., (c) Hamilton, Paul B., (d) West, Clark D., (e) Looney, Joseph M., (f) Bergeim, Olaf, (g) Hier, Stanley W., (h) Cartwright, G. E.

References: [1] Addis, T., E. Barrett, L. J. Poo, and D. W. Yuen. 1947. J. Clin. Invest. 26:869. [2] Alexander, B., G. Landwehr, and A. Seligman. 1945. J. Biol. Chem. 160:51. [3] Allinson, M. J. C. 1945. Ibid. 157:169. [4] Angostino, L. 1945. Boll. Soc. ital. biol. sper. 20:173. [5] Archibald, R. M. 1944. J. Biol. Chem. 154:643. [6] Archibald, R. M. 1944. Ibid. 156:121. [7] Bliss, S. 1929. Ibid. 81:129. [8] Buell, M. V. 1935. Ibid. 108:273. [9] Careddu, G. 1938. Atti Soc. med. chir. Padova 16:254. [10] Cartwright, G. E., C. M. Huguley, Jr., H. Ashenbrucker, J. Fay, and M. M. Wintrobe. 1948. Blood, N. Y. 3:501. [11] Ceresa, F., and P. Guala. 1940. Arch. Sc. med., Tor. 70:369. [12] Christensen, H. N., P. F. Cooper, Jr., R. D. Johnson, and E. L. Lynch. 1947. J. Biol. Chem. 168:191. [13] Christensen, H. N., and E. L. Lynch. 1946. Ibid. 163:741. [14] Delgado Febres, E. 1949. An. Fac. med. Lima 32:29. [15] Denko, C. W., W. E. Grundy, and J. W. Porter. 1947. Arch. Biochem., N. Y. 13:483. [16] Dunn, M. S., H. F. Schott, W. Frankl, and L. B. Rockland. 1945. J. Biol. Chem. 157:387. [17] Folin, O. 1932. Ibid. 97:141. [18] Folin, O., and H. Svedberg. 1930. Ibid. 88:85. [19] Folin, O., and H. Svedberg. 1930. Ibid. 88:715. [20] Gettler, A. O., and W. Baker. 1916. Ibid. 25:211. [21] Godfried, E. G. 1939. Biochem. J., Lond. 33:955. [22] Gram, H. C. 1924. Am. J. M. Sc. 168:511. [23] Gutman, G. E., and B. Alexander. 1947. J. Biol. Chem. 168:527. [24] Henderson, L. M., P. E. Schurr, and C. A. Elvehjem. 1949. Ibid. 177:815. [25] Hier, S. W. 1947. Ibid. 171:813. [26] Hier, S. W., and O. Bergeim. 1946. Ibid. 163:129. [27] Jackson, H., Jr. 1923. Ibid. 57:121. [28] Jellinek, E. M., and J. M. Looney. 1939. Ibid. 128(2):621. [29] Johnson, C. A., and O. Bergeim. 1951. Ibid. 188:883. [30] Labbé, M., F. Nepveux, and Hejda. 1929. C. rend. Acad. sc. 188:738. [31] Larizza, P. 1937. Arch. exp. Path., Lpz. 186:232. [32] Loeper, M., A. Lesure, and A. Thomas. 1934. Bull. Soc. chim. biol., Par. 16:1385. [33] Looney, J. M. 1924. Am. J. Psychiat. 4:34. [34] Looney, J. M., and H. M. Childs. 1934. J. Clin. Invest. 13:963. [35] Looney, J. M., and A. I. Walsh. 1939. J. Biol. Chem. 130:635. [36] Loubatieres, A., and P. Bouyard. 1951. Tunis. méd. 39:659. [37] Melville, D. B., and R. Lubschez. 1953. J. Biol. Chem. 200:275. [38] Niemer, H., and E. Stadler. 1949. Klin. Wschr. 27:278. [39] Örström, Å., and M. Örström. 1950. Acta med. scand. 138:108. [40] Pansini, R., and E. Pire. 1953. Boll. Soc. ital. biol. sper. 29:1629. [41] Peña y de la Peña, E., J. Kumate Rodríguez, P. Martinez Elizondo, and E. Téllez Girón. 1953. Bol. san. mil., Méx. 6:259. [42] Pettay, O. 1950. Acta paediat., Upps. 39:283. [43] Pinelli, L. 1935. Biochim. ter. sper. 22:563. [44] Schmidt, E. G., M. J. Schmulovitz, A. Szczpinski, and H. B. White. 1937. J. Biol. Chem. 120:705. [45] Schumm, O., and G. Knop. 1939. Zschr. ges. exp. Med. 106:252. [46] Steele, B. F., M. S. Reynolds, and C. A. Baumann. 1950. J. Nutrit. 40:145. [47] Stein, W. H., and S. Moore. 1954. J. Biol. Chem. 211:915. [48] Tamura, E., T. Tezuka, and T. Hayakawa. 1950-51. J. Jap. Soc. Food & Nutrit. 3:207. [49] Trovato, A. 1947. Atti Accad. peloritana Messina 48:75. [50] Van Pilsum, J. F., R. P. Martin, E. Kito, and J. Hess. 1956. J. Biol. Chem. 222:225. [51] Viergiver, E. 1954. Bull. Ayer Clin. Laborat. 4:61. [52] Von Euler, H., and L. Heller. 1947. Ark. kemi. mineral. geol. 25A:10. [53] Watson, C. J. 1950.

Arch. Int. M. 86:797. [54] Widal, F., and M. Laudat. 1926. C. rend. Soc. biol. 95:1233. [55] Wiss, O., and R. Kruger. 1948. Helvet. chim. acta 31:1774. [56] With, T. K. 1943. Acta med. scand. 115:542. [57] Woodruff, C. W., and E. B. Man. 1945. J. Biol. Chem. 157:95. [58] Wootton, I. D. P., and E. J. King. 1953. Lancet, Lond. 264:470. [59] Wu, H. 1922. J. Biol. Chem. 51:27.

23. BLOOD NON-PROTEIN NITROGENOUS SUBSTANCES: VERTEBRATES OTHER THAN MAN

Values are mg/100 ml blood, unless otherwise specified. Values in parentheses are ranges, estimate "c" unless otherwise indicated (cf. Introduction).

	Animal (A)	Blood (B)	Constituent (C)	Value (D)	Reference (E)
	Cat	Plasma[1]	Amino acids		28
1			Alanine	7.0	
2			Arginine	1.4	
3			Asparagine	0.9	
4			Aspartic acid	0.1	
5			Citrulline	<0.1	
6			Cystine	0.4	
7			Glutamic acid	1.8	
8			Glycine	2.3	
9			Histidine	1.4	
10			Isoleucine	0.8	
11			Leucine	1.6	
12			Lysine	2.8	
13			Methionine	0.4	
14			3-Methylhistidine	0.1	
15			Ornithine	0.2	
16			Phenylalanine	0.9	
17			Proline	2.3	
18			Serine	2.1	
19			Taurine	0.7	
20			Threonine	1.4	
21			Tryptophan	<0.2	
22			Tyrosine	0.7	
23			Valine	2.4	
24	Cattle	Plasma	Histamine	0.165 µg/ml	19
25	Cow	Whole blood	Creatinine	(1-2.07)	5
			Glutathione		18
26			Total	46	
27			Oxidized	6	
28			Reduced	40	
29			Uric acid	(0.05-2.08)	5
30		Plasma	Tryptophan	1.12(0.8-1.2)	27
	Dog	Whole blood	Amino acids		
31			Arginine	3.7(1.7-5.2)	13, 14
32			Histidine	1.33(1.0-2.0)	13
33			Isoleucine	1.76(1.2-2.2)	13
34			Leucine	2.51(1.2-3.6)	2
35			Lysine	2.54(1.6-3.6)	2
36			Methionine	1.18(0.8-1.7)	13
37			Phenylalanine	1.47(0.9-2.5)	13, 14
38			Threonine	2.4(1.2-3.3)	13
39			Tryptophan	1.17(0.6-2.4)	13
40			Tyrosine	1.2(0.7-2.0)	13
41			Valine	2.63(1.5-4.1)	13
42			Creatinine	(1-1.7)	5
			Glutathione		2
43			Total	31.3	
44			Reduced	29.2	

/1/ Blood obtained by heart puncture with heparinized syringe [25].

	Animal	Blood	Constituent	Value	Reference
	(A)	(B)	(C)	(D)	(E)
45	Dog (concluded)	Whole blood (con-cluded)	Uric acid	(0-0.5)	5
46		Erythrocytes	Arginine	4.2	13, 14
		Plasma	Amino acids		
47			Arginine	3.27(1.79-4.75)[b]	13, 14
48			Citrulline	(0.8-1.5)	1
49			Cystine	0.9(0.5-1.5)	13
50			Glutamic acid	<0.6	1
51			Glutamine	(7-13)	2
52			Histidine	1.24(0.90-1.58)[b]	13
53			Isoleucine	1.31(0.87-1.95)	13
54			Leucine	2.09(1.43-3.06)	13
55			Lysine	2.42(1.26-3.58)[b]	13
56			Methionine	(0.20-1.88)	13
57			Phenylalanine	1.16(0.58-1.74)[b]	13, 14
58			Threonine	2.58(1.5-3.5)	13
59			Tryptophan	1.20(0.8-1.5)	13
60			Tyrosine	1.06(0.58-1.54)[b]	13
61			Valine	2.22(1.5-3.0)	13
62			Uric acid	0.33	7
63	Goat	Whole blood	Creatinine	(0.9-1.82)	5
64			Uric acid	(0.33-1.0)	
		Plasma	Amino acids		21
65			Lysine	1.8(1.3-2.4)	
66			Tyrosine	1.2(1.0-1.5)	
67	Guinea pig	Whole blood	Glutathione, total	(80-175)	2
68		Plasma	Glycine	2.5	9
	Horse	Whole blood	Amino acids		
69			Cysteine	0.3	16
70			Cystine	1.25	2
71			Creatinine	(1.2-1.9)	5
			Glutathione		2
72			Total	60	
73			Reduced	50	
74			Uric acid	(0.90-1.09)	5
		Erythrocytes	Amino acids		
75			Cysteine	0.5	16
76			Cystine	0.6	2
		Plasma or serum	Amino acids		
77			Cysteine	0.2	16
78			Cystine	1.6	16
79			Tryptophan	1.2	22
80			Bilirubin	0.98	15
81			Urea	(28-58)	15
82	Mouse	Whole blood	Glutathione, total	(90-115)	2
		Plasma	Amino acids		24
83			Alanine	5.87(5.3-6.6)	
84			Arginine	0.97(0.9-1.0)	
85			Glutamic acid	3.33(2.9-3.6)	
86			Glycine	1.90(1.7-2.3)	
87			Histidine	1.57(1.4-1.7)	
88			Isoleucine	1.47(1.2-2.0)	
89			Leucine	2.40(2.2-2.8)	
90			Lysine	6.37(5.7-7.0)	
91			Methionine	1.9(1.7-2.2)	
92			Phenylalanine	2.4(2.0-3.2)	
93			Proline	1.83(1.6-2.1)	
94			Threonine	3.50(3.0-3.9)	
95			Tryptophan	1.23(1.1-1.4)	
96			Tyrosine	2.53(2.4-2.7)	
97			Valine	4.30(3.8-5.0)	
	Rabbit	Whole blood	Glutathione		2
98			Total	45(35-55)	
99			Reduced	35(26-40)	
100			Histamine	0.28	

	Animal	Blood	Constituent	Value	Reference
	(A)	(B)	(C)	(D)	(E)
	Rabbit (concluded)	Plasma	Amino acids		
101			Cystine	(0.9-1.1)	3
102			Glycine	4.0	9
	Rat	Whole blood	Glutathione		
103			Total	(75-165)	2
104			Reduced	40(30-45)	8
105			Uric acid	1.5(0.5-3.4)	4
106		Plasma	Urea	34	17
	Sprague-Dawley strain	Whole blood	Amino acids		
107			Alanine	$12.3(8.9-15.7)^b$	29
108			Tryptophan	1.57(1.5-2.0)	12
		Plasma	Amino acids		12
109			Arginine	$3.21(2.35-4.07)^b$	
110			Glycine	$2.27(1.85-2.69)^b$	
111			Histidine	$0.97(0.85-1.09)^b$	
112			Isoleucine	$1.32(0.96-1.68)^b$	
113			Leucine	$2.66(2.20-3.12)^b$	
114			Lysine	$5.8(4.4-7.2)^b$	
115			Methionine	$0.95(0.81-1.09)^b$	
116			Phenylalanine	$1.37(1.15-1.59)^b$	
117			Proline	$4.3(3.5-5.1)^b$	
118			Threonine	$4.4(3.4-5.4)^b$	
119			Tryptophan	$1.68(1.44-1.92)^b$	
120			Tyrosine	$2.23(1.73-2.73)^b$	
121			Valine	$2.67(2.27-3.07)^b$	
122	Sheep	Whole blood	Creatinine	(1.2-1.93)	5
123			Glutathione, total	26	2
124			Uric acid	(0.05-1.93)	5
125		Plasma	Tryptophan	1.1(0.8-1.3)	23
126	Swine	Whole blood	Creatinine	(1-2.7)	5
127			Glutathione, total	36	2
128			Uric acid	(0.05-1.95)	5
129		Erythrocytes	Ergothioneine	20.7(15.6-24)	20
		Plasma	Amino acids		
130			Cystine	(0.6-0.9)	3
131			Tryptophan	1.1(1.0-1.2)	23
132	Chicken[2]	Whole blood	Creatine	(0.90-1.85)	26
133			Urea	5.7	11
134			Uric acid	(2.47-8.08)	26
135	Turkey[2]	Whole blood	Creatinine	(0.86-0.94)	5
136			Uric acid	(3.41-5.19)	
137	Carp	Whole blood	Creatine	2.58	6
138			Creatinine	0.56	
139			Urea	7.6	
140			Uric acid	2.6	
141	Salmon	Whole blood	Glutathione, total	6.2	2
142	Skate (Raja erinacea)	Whole blood	Urea	(275-380) mEq/L	10
143	Trout	Whole blood	Creatine	1.32	6
144			Creatinine	0.72	
145			Urea	5.5	
146			Uric acid	8.6	

/2/ Non-laying.

Contributors: (a) Beerstecher, Ernest, Jr., (b) Lewis, Howard B., (c) Wilber, Charles G., (d) Steele, Betty F., (e) Mirsky, I. Arthur, and Erdoes, Ervin, (f) Hier, Stanley W., (g) Schweigert, B. S.

References: [1] Archibald, R. N. 1944. J. Biol. Chem. 154:643. [2] Beerstecher, E., Jr. Unpublished. [3] Brown, B. H., and H. B. Lewis. 1941. J. Biol. Chem. 138:705. [4] Byers, S. O., M. Friedman, and M. M. Garfield. 1947. Am. J. Physiol. 150:677. [5] Dukes, H. H. 1947. The physiology of domestic animals. Ed. 6. Comstock, Ithaca. p. 54. [6] Field, J. B., C. A. Elvehjem, and C. Juday. 1943. J. Biol. Chem. 148(2):261.

[7] Friedman, M., and S. O. Byers. 1948. Ibid. 175:727. [8] Grunert, R.,R., and P. H. Phillips. 1949. Ibid. 181:821. [9] Gutman, G. E., and B. Alexander. 1947. Ibid. 168:527. [10] Hartman, F. A., L. A. Lewis, K. A. Brownell, F. F. Shelden, and R. F. Walther. 1941. Physiol. Zool. 14:476. [11] Heller, V. G., and R. H. Thayer. 1948. Endocrinology 42:161. [12] Henderson, L. M., P. E. Schurr, and C. A. Elvehjem. 1949. J. Biol. Chem. 177:815. [13] Hier, S. W. 1947. Ibid. 171:813. [14] Hier, S. W., and O. Bergeim. 1946. Ibid. 163:129. [15] Jennings, F. W., and W. Mulligan. 1953. J. Comp. Path. 63:286. [16] Numata, I. 1940. Biochem. Zschr. 304:404. [17] Persike, E. C. 1948. Endocrinology 42:356. [18] Reid, J. T., G. M. Warn, and R. L. Salzburg. 1948. Am. J. Physiol. 152:633. [19] Romanelli, V. 1949. Atti Soc. ital. sc. vet. 3:232. [20] Salt, H. B. 1931. Biochem. J., Lond. 25:812. [21] Schweigert, B. S. Unpublished. [22] Schweigert, B. S., P. B. Pearson, and M. C. Wickering. 1947. Arch. Biochem., N. Y. 12:139. [23] Schweigert, B. S., H. E. Sauberlich, C. A. Elvehjem, and C. A. Baumann. 1946. J. Biol. Chem. 164:213. [24] Steele, B. F., M. S. Reynolds, and C. A. Baumann. 1950. Arch. Biochem., N. Y. 25:124. [25] Stein, W. H., and S. Moore. 1954. J. Biol. Chem. 211:915. [26] Sturkie, P. D. 1954. Avian physiology. Comstock, Ithaca. [27] Sutton, T. S., and G. C. Esh. 1948. J. Dairy Sc. 31:187. [28] Tallan, H. H., S. Moore, and W. H. Stein. 1954. J. Biol. Chem. 211:927. [29] Von Euler, H., and L. Heller. 1947. Ark. kemi mineral. geol. 25A:22.

24. BLOOD LIPIDS: MAN

Values in parentheses are ranges, estimate "c" unless otherwise indicated (cf. Introduction).

Lipid	Value mg/100 ml	Refer-ence		Lipid	Value mg/100 ml	Refer-ence
(A)	(B)	(C)		(A)	(B)	(C)
Whole Blood				**Plasma or Serum (concluded)**		
1 Lipids, total	652	23	26	Cephalin	9(0-29)	34
2 Cephalin	(90-110)	32	27		30(11-49)[b2]	1
Cholesterol			28		96.0(47.0-133.5)	37
3 Total	(140-215)	40	29	Cerebrosides	(0-167)	26
4 Free	86(66-110)	28		Cholesterol		
5 Cholic acid	0.5(0.1-0.9)	21	30	Total	197(189-205)[b]	24
Fat			31		(159-260)	25
6 Total	590[1]	17	32		(176-481)[3]	19
7 Neutral	(100-380)	20	33	Free	(96-99.7)	15, 16
Fatty acids			34	Ester	106(75-137)[b]	4
8 Total	364(283-442)	30	35		(96-237)	35
9 Unsaturated	143	10	36		(120.9-124.6)	15, 16
10 Lecithin	9.34(6.8-11.1)[1]	7	37	Cholic acid	(0.5-1.5)	38
Steroids				Fat		
11 Total	150	31	38	Total	559(369-620)	26
12 17-Keto-	(0.88-0.96)	12	39	Neutral	142(24-260)	4
Erythrocytes				Fatty acids		
13 Lipids, total	596(411-781)[b]	3	40	Total	(294-341)	33
14 Cephalin	117(38-191)	26	41	Glyceride-	123.5	22
15 Cerebrosides	(12-113)	26	42	Phospholipid-	110.8	22
Cholesterol			43	Saturated	182.4	22
16 Total	173(118-228)[b]	14	44	Lecithin	(60-115)	13
17 Free	140(119-161)[b]	6	45		156(106-200)	34
Fat			46		107.0(49.6-203.8)	37
18 Total	400(180-595)	26		Phospholipids		
19 Neutral	315.4	18	47	Total	235(172-269)	36
20 Lecithin	32(3-95)	26	48		221(153-263)	34
Phosphatides		26	49		226.0(198-272)	37
21 Total	196(26-297)		50	Acetal-	(2.38-2.71)	27
22 Ether-insoluble	47(13-157)		51	Choline-	122(94-150)[b]	1
Plasma or Serum			52	Spingomyelin	35.35	29
			53		56(43-80)	34
			54		23.0(13.8-33.9)	37
23 Lipids, total	589(521-730)[1]	2		Steroids		
24	657(433-810)	39	55	17-Keto-	0.171	9
25	622	11	56	Reducing	(0.022-0.052)	8
			57	Triglyceride	128	5

/1/ Females. /2/ Males. /3/ Males and females, ages 61-87.

Contributors: (a) Luckey, T. D., and Cohagen, D. L., (b) Best, Charles H., (c) Mirsky, I. Arthur, and Erdoes, Ervin, (d) Kirk, John E.

References: [1] Artom, C. 1941. J. Biol. Chem. 139:65. [2] Boyd, E. M. 1933. Ibid. 101:323. [3] Boyd, E. M. 1934. J. Clin. Invest. 13:347. [4] Boyd, E. M. 1942. J. Biol. Chem. 143:131. [5] Bragdon, J. H. 1951. Ibid. 190:513. [6] Brun, G. C. 1939. Acta med. scand., Suppl. 99. [7] Chatterjee, H. N., and S. M. Ghosh. 1940. J. Ind. Chem. Soc. 17:356. [8] Chen, C., S. M. Voegtli, and S. Freeman. 1955. J. Biol. Chem. 217:709. [9] Clayton, G. W., A. M. Bongiovanni, and C. Papadatos. 1955. J. Clin. Endocr. Metab. 15:693. [10] Csonka, F. A. 1918. J. Biol. Chem. 33:401. [11] De la Huerga, J., C. Yesinick, and H. Popper. 1953. Am. J. Clin. Path. 23:1163.

[12] Dumazert, C., and G. Valensi. 1952. C. rend. Soc. biol. 146:471. [13] Erickson, B. N., I. Avrin, D. M. Teague, and H. H. Williams. 1940. J. Biol. Chem. 135:671. [14] Foldes, F. F., and A. J. Murphy. 1946. Proc. Soc. Exp. Biol., N. Y. 62:215. [15] Gertler, M. M., S. M. Garn, and J. Lerman. 1950. Blood, N. Y. 2:205. [16] Ghose, C. 1953. Ind. M. Gaz. 88:363. [17] Hermann, E., and J. Neumann. 1912. Biochem. Zschr. 43:47. [18] Herzstein, J., J. Chun, I. Wang, and D. Adlersberg. 1954. Ann. Int. M. 40:290. [19] Hobson, W., A. Jordan, and C. Roseman. 1953. Lancet, Lond. 265:961. [20] Il'inskii, B. V. 1940. Klin. med., Moskva 18(1):55. [21] Irvin, J. L., C. G. Johnston, and J. Kopala. 1944. J. Biol. Chem. 153:439. [22] Izzo, A., and A. D. Marenzi. 1944. Pub. Centro invest. tisiol., B. Air. 8:163. [23] Kaufman, H. T., and H. G. Schwarz. 1954. Fette Seifen Anstrichmittel 56:17. [24] Kenny, A. P. 1952. Biochem. J., Lond. 52:611. [25] Kingsley, G. R., and R. R. Schaffert. 1949. J. Biol. Chem. 180:315. [26] Kirk, E. 1938. Ibid. 123:637. [27] Leupold, F., and H. Büttner. 1954. Klin. Wschr. 32:119. [28] Manrique, V. 1943. Actas 3º Congr. peru. quim. 2(2):310. [29] Marenzi, A. D., and C. E. Cardini. 1943. J. Biol. Chem. 147:371. [30] McClure, C. W., and M. E. Huntsinger. 1928. Ibid. 76:5. [31] Monasterio, G., and G. Berti. 1951-52. Gior. biochim. 1:157. [32] Nakamura, K. 1931. Med. Bull. Univ. Cincinnati 6:158. [33] Page, E., and L. Michaud. 1951. Canad. J. M. Sc. 29:239. [34] Petersen, V. P. 1950. Scand. J. Clin. Lab. Invest. 2:44. [35] Smith, R. M., and A. Marble. 1937. J. Biol. Chem. 117:673. [36] Taurog, A., C. Entenman, B. A. Fries, and A. L. Chaikoff. 1944. Ibid. 155:19. [37] Thannhauser, S. J., J. Benotti, and H. Reinstein. 1939. Ibid. 129:709. [38] Thannhauser, S. J., E. Ginsburg, S. Maddock, W. H. Blanchard, and H. Reinstein. 1942. Tr. Ass. Am. Physicians 57:290. [39] Wilson, W. R., and A. E. Hansen. 1936. J. Biol. Chem. 112:457. [40] Wootton, I. D. P., and E. J. King. 1953. Lancet, Lond. 264:470.

25. BLOOD LIPIDS: VERTEBRATES OTHER THAN MAN

Values in parentheses are ranges, estimate "b" unless otherwise indicated (cf. Introduction).

	Animal	Blood	Lipid	Value mg/100 ml	Reference
	(A)	(B)	(C)	(D)	(E)
1	Cat	Erythrocytes	Cholesterol, total	(218-246)[c]	7
2		Plasma	Lipids, total	376(145-607)	1
			Cholesterol		
3			Total	93(43-143)	1
4			Free	30(9-51)	4
5			Ester	73(25-121)	1
6			Fat, neutral	108	1
7			Fatty acids, total	228(56-400)	1
8			Phospholipids, total	132(21-243)	1
9	Cattle	Serum	Cephalin	3	4
10			Lecithin	54	
11			Phospholipids, total	80	
12			Spingomyelin	22	
13	Bull	Erythrocytes	Cholesterol, total	180	7
14	Ox	Erythrocytes	Cholesterol, total	340	7
15	Cow	Plasma	Lipids, total	348(185-511)	1
16			Fat, neutral	105	1
17			Fatty acids, total	202(26-378)	1
18			Phospholipids, total	84(17-151)	1
			Cholesterol		
19			Total	110(8-212)	1
20			Free	37	4
21			Ester	73(25-121)	1
22	Dog	Erythrocytes	Cholesterol, total	(213-216)[c]	7
23		Plasma or serum	Lipids, total	580(470-725)[c]	1
24			Cephalin	22	9

	Animal	Blood	Lipid	Value mg/100 ml	Reference
	(A)	(B)	(C)	(D)	(E)
25	Dog (con-cluded)	Plasma or serum (concluded)	Cholesterol Total	173(138-214)[C]	1
26			Free	134(103-159)[C]	1
27			Ester	39(35-55)[C]	4
28			Lecithin	370(300-470)[C]	1
29				288	4
30			Sphingomyelin	55	4
31	Goat	Erythrocytes	Cholesterol, total	170	7
32		Plasma	Lipids, total	300	4
33			Cholesterol, total	(46-95)[C]	
34			Phospholipids, total	(140-180)[C]	
35	Guinea pig	Plasma	Lipids, total	169(94-244)	1
36			Cholesterol Total	32(21-43)	4
37			Free	11(7-15)	4
38			Ester	21(12-30)	1
39			Fat, neutral	73	1
40			Fatty acids, total	116(92-140)	1
41			Phospholipids, total	51(25-77)	1
42	Horse	Erythrocytes	Cholesterol, total	110	7
43		Serum	Cholesterol Total	77	1
44			Free	47	4
45			Ester	30	4
46	Monkey	Serum	Cholesterol, total	118	4
47	Mouse	Whole blood	Cholesterol, total	(132-244)[C]	6
48	Mule	Erythrocytes	Cholesterol, total	(205-222)[C]	7
49	Rabbit	Erythrocytes	Cephalin	107(64-150)	2
50			Cholesterol Total	133(115-151)	
51			Free	133(115-151)	
52			Fat, neutral	41	
53			Lecithin	86(56-116)	
54			Phospholipids, total	240(191-289)	
55			Sphingomyelin	47(35-59)	
56		Plasma	Lipids, total	243(69-417)	1
57			Cephalin	27	4
58			Cholesterol Total	45(10-80)	1
59			Free	22	
60			Ester	22	
61			Fat, neutral	105(7-203)	1
62			Fatty acids, total	169(40-298)	1
63			Phospholipids, total	78(13-143)	1
64			Sphingomyelin	38	5
65	Rat	Plasma	Lipids, total	230(69-417)	1
66			Cholesterol Total	52(28-76)	
67			Free	21(5-37)	
68			Ester	31(11-51)	
69			Fat, neutral	85(26-144)	
70			Fatty acids, total	153(108-198)	
71			Phospholipids, total	83(36-130)	
72	Sheep	Erythrocytes	Cholesterol, total	240	7
73		Plasma	Phospholipids, total	90(24-123)[C]	8
74	Swine	Erythrocytes	Cholesterol, total	50	7
75		Plasma or serum	Cephalin	3	4
76			Cholesterol, total	(152-154)[C]	3
77			Lecithin	72	4
78			Phospholipids, total	96(80-130)[C]	1
79			Sphingomyelin	21	4
80	Chicken	Plasma or serum	Lipids, total	520(341-699)	1

	Animal	Blood	Lipid	Value mg/100 ml	Reference
	(A)	(B)	(C)	(D)	(E)
81	Chicken (concluded)	Plasma or serum (concluded)	Cholesterol Total	(58-94)[c1]	3
82				(23-121)[c2]	3
83				100(52-148)	1
84			Free	34(15-53)	4
85			Ester	66(26-106)	1
86			Fat, neutral	225(63-387)	1
87			Fatty acids, total	361(206-516)	1
88			Phospholipids, total	155(84-226)	1

/1/ Laying. /2/ Non-laying.

Contributors: (a) Best, Charles H., (b) Handler, Philip, (c) Ponder, Eric, (d) Mirsky, I. Arthur, and Erdoes, Ervin

References: [1] Boyd, E. M. 1942. J. Biol. Chem. 143:131. [2] Burt, N. S., and A. J. Rossiter. 1950. Biochem. J., Lond. 46:569. [3] Dukes, H. H. 1947. The physiology of domestic animals. Ed. 6. Comstock, Ithaca. [4] Handler, P. Unpublished. [5] Kirk, J. E. 1938. J. Biol. Chem. 123:637. [6] Lea, A. J. 1948. Endocrinology 42:477. [7] Ponder, E. 1948. Hemolysis and related phenomena. Grune and Stratton, New York. [8] Popjak, G. 1946. Biochem. J., Lond. 40:608. [9] Sinclair, R. G. 1948. J. Biol. Chem. 174:343.

26. BLOOD CARBOHYDRATES: MAN

Values in parentheses are ranges, estimate "c" unless otherwise indicated (cf. Introduction).

	Carbohydrate	Value mg/100 ml	Remarks	Reference
	(A)	(B)	(C)	(D)
			Whole Blood	
1	Fructose	(0-1)	Fetus	4
2		(0.5-5.0)		18
3	Glucosamine	(60-82)		8
4	Glucose	(36-116)	Fetus; calculated from fermentable sugar in cord blood	4
5		(20-30)	Newborn; zinc hydroxide filtrate, ferricyanide iodometric titration	6
6		90(80-100)[b]	Arterial blood, fasting subjects; zinc hydroxide filtrate, copper-iodometric titration	13, 14
7		85.5(75.5-95.5)[b]	Venous blood, fasting subjects; zinc hydroxide filtrate, copper-iodometric titration	13, 14
8		90(71-109)[b]	Fasting subjects	5
9	Glucuronic acid	6.7(4.1-9.3)[b]	Tungstate-sulfuric acid filtrate, color development with naphthoresorcinol	7
10	Glycogen	5.5(1.2-16.2)	Copper-iodometric titration	17
			Erythrocytes	
11	Glucose	74(46-102)[b]	Defibrinated blood; tungstic acid filtrate, fermentation	12
12	Glucuronic acid	0.6(0.0-2.0)	Color development with naphthoresorcinol, with preliminary hydrolysis but without deproteinization	1
			Plasma or Serum	
13	Fructose	7.5	Zinc hydroxide filtrate, fermentation, color development with diphenylamine	9
14	Glucosamine	48(42-55)	Fetus; color development with acetylacetone on hydrolysate of alcohol precipitate	10

	Carbohydrate	Value mg/100 ml	Remarks	Reference
	(A)	(B)	(C)	(D)
			Plasma or Serum (concluded)	
15	Glucosamine (concluded)	63(52-69)	Subjects, 3-8 yr; color development with acetylacetone on hydrolysate of alcohol precipitate	10
16		67(61-78)	Subjects, 21-49 yr; color development with acetylacetone on hydrolysate of alcohol precipitate	10
17		81(70-89)	Subjects, 61-85 yr; color development with acetylacetone on hydrolysate of alcohol precipitate	10
18		(76-110)		19
19	Acetyl-	(80-100)		15
20	Glucose	90(71-109)		5
21		97(61-133)[b]	Defibrinated blood; tungstic acid filtrate, fermentation	12
22	Glucuronic acid	0.8(0-1.6)	Color development with naphthoresorcinol, with preliminary hydrolysis but without deproteinization	1
23		1.71(1.13-2.29)[b]		16
24	Glycogen	6.8(4.8-8.9)		11
25	Lactose	(0-trace)	Males, females (pregnant and non-pregnant); destruction of non-lactose sugar by Bacillus proteus; tungstic acid filtrate, copper-molybdate color formation	3
26		(0-2)	During lactation, 3-8 da postpartum; destruction of non-lactose sugar by B. proteus; tungstic acid filtrate, copper-molybdate color formation	
	Pentose			2
27	Total	3.7(2.6-4.8)[b]	Trichloracetic acid filtrate, quantitative orcinol reaction	
28		2.55(1.75-3.35)[b]	Saline extract of acetone precipitate	
29	Phosphorylated	2.1	Trichloracetic acid filtrate	
30		2.2(1.6-2.8)[b]	Saline extract of acetone precipitate	
	Polysaccharides			
31	Non-glucosamine	80(62-103)	Fetus; absorption at 500 mμ by product of tryptophan reaction with acidified alcohol precipitate	10
32		105(94-118)	Subjects, 3-8 yr; absorption at 500 mμ by product of tryptophan reaction with acidified alcohol precipitate	
33		(93-126)	Subjects, 21-49 yr; absorption at 500 mμ by product of tryptophan reaction with acidified alcohol precipitate	
34		129(104-138)	Subjects, 61-85 yr; absorption at 500 mμ by product of tryptophan reaction with acidified alcohol precipitate	
35	Protein-bound	(170-220)		15

Contributors: (a) Mirsky, I. Arthur, (b) Luckey, T. D., and Cohagen, D. L., (c) West, Clark D.

References: [1] Deichmann, W. B., and M. Dierker. 1946. J. Biol. Chem. 163:753. [2] Green, H. M., H. B. Stoner, H. J. Whiteley, and D. Eglin. 1949. Clin. Sc., Lond. 8:65. [3] Hubbard, R. S., and H. J. Brock. 1935. J. Biol. Chem. 110:411. [4] Karvonen, M. J. 1949. Acta paediat., Upps. 37:68. [5] Lozner, E. L., A. W. Winkler, F. H. L. Taylor, and J. P. Peters. 1941. J. Clin. Invest. 20:507. [6] Pedersen, J. 1949. Acta paediat., Upps., Suppl. 77, p. 201. [7] Ratish, H. D., and J. G. M. Bullowa. 1943. Arch. Biochem., N. Y. 2:381. [8] Rivano, R., and G. Mannetti. 1950. Arch. Maragliano pat. clin. 5:1099. [9] Seibert, F. B., M. L. Pfaff, and M. V. Seibert. 1948. Arch. Biochem., N. Y. 18:279. [10] Shetlar, M. R., J. V. Foster, K. H. Kelly, and M. R. Everett. 1948. Proc. Soc. Exp. Biol., N. Y. 69:507. [11] Sikinami, Y., H. Hosokawa, and M. Oba. 1940. Tohoku J. Exp. M. 38:371. [12] Somogyi, M. 1928. J. Biol. Chem. 78:117. [13] Somogyi, M. 1948. Ibid. 174:189. [14] Somogyi, M. 1948. Ibid. 174:597. [15] Stary, Z., F. Bursa, Ō. Kaleoglu, and M. Bilen. 1950. Bull. Fac. méd. Istanbul 13:233. [16] Südhof, H. 1954. Deut. Arch. klin. Med. 201:89. [17] Wagner, R. 1946. Arch. Biochem., N. Y. 11:249. [18] Wallenfals, K. 1951. Naturwissenschaften 38:238. [19] West, R., and D. H. Clarke, 1938. J. Clin. Invest. 17:173.

27. BLOOD CARBOHYDRATES: VERTEBRATES OTHER THAN MAN

Values in parentheses are ranges, estimate "b" unless otherwise indicated (cf. Introduction).

	Animal	Blood	Carbohydrate	Value mg/100 ml	Remarks	Reference
	(A)	(B)	(C)	(D)	(E)	(F)
1	Antelope	Whole blood	Glucose	56	Somogyi-Shaffer-Hartman method	21
2	Cat	Whole blood	Glucose	74(64-84)	Fasting subjects; tungstic acid filtrate, color formation with ferric ferrocyanide	5
3		Erythrocytes	Glucose	76	Tungstic acid filtrate, fermentation	32
4		Serum		297	Tungstic acid filtrate, fermentation	32
5	Cattle	Whole blood	Glucose	46(36-47)^c		2
6	Calf	Erythrocytes	Glucose	48	Tungstic acid filtrate, fermentation	32
7		Serum	Glucose	118	Tungstic acid filtrate, fermentation	
8	Ox	Erythrocytes	Glucose	15	Tungstic acid filtrate, fermentation	32
9		Serum	Glucose	85	Tungstic acid filtrate, fermentation	
10	Deer	Whole blood	Glucose	54	Somogyi-Shaffer-Hartman method	21
11	Dog	Whole blood	Glucose	(96-106)^c		4, 25
12				77(67-87)	Fasting subjects; zinc hydroxide filtrate, ferrocyanide-iodometric titration	5
13		Erythrocytes	Glucose	41	Tungstic acid filtrate, fermentation	32
14		Serum	Glucose	132	Tungstic acid filtrate, fermentation	32
15	Dromedary	Whole blood	Glucose	85		21
16		Serum	Glucose	108		18
17	Fox	Whole blood	Glucose	104(70-138)		31
18	Goat	Whole blood	Glucose	75	Young animals	21
19				54	Adult animals	
20		Plasma	Glucose	83.5		24
21	Mountain-	Whole blood	Glucose	61	Somogyi-Shaffer-Hartman method	21
22	Guinea pig	Whole blood	Glucose	96(82-107)^c	Zinc hydroxide filtrate, copper-iodometric titration	17
23				95(60-125)^c	Fasting subjects; zinc hydroxide filtrate, copper-iodometric titration	
24		Erythrocytes	Glucose	53	Tungstic acid filtrate, fermentation	32
25		Serum	Glucose	155	Tungstic acid filtrate, fermentation	32
26	Hamster, Syrian	Plasma	Glucose	(88.9-97.3)^c		34
27	Horse	Whole blood	Glucose	73(54-95)^c		2
28	Llama	Whole blood	Glucose	90	Somogyi-Shaffer-Hartman method	21
29	Mink	Whole blood	Glucose	122(72-172)		31
30	Monkey	Erythrocytes	Glucose	119	Tungstic acid filtrate, fermentation	32
31		Serum	Glucose	148	Tungstic acid filtrate, fermentation	
32	Mouse, albino	Whole blood	Glucose	174(82-266)	Tungstic acid filtrate, color formation with ferric ferrocyanide	16
33				109(75-143)	Fasting subjects; tungstic acid filtrate, color formation with ferric ferrocyanide	
34	Opossum, Australian	Erythrocytes	Glucose	81(73-89)	Tungstic acid filtrate, color formation with ferric ferrocyanide	1
35				140[1]		
36		Plasma	Glucose	123(107-139)	Tungstic acid filtrate, color formation with ferric ferrocyanide	
37				241[1]		
38	Rabbit	Erythrocytes	Glucose	41	Tungstic acid filtrate, fermentation	32
39			Glucuronic acid	0.7(0.0-1.9)^c	Color development with naphtho-resorcinol, with preliminary hydrolysis but without deproteinization	10
40		Plasma or serum	Glucosamine	71(51-91)	Acetylacetone reaction	35
41			Glucose	145	Tungstic acid filtrate, fermentation	32
42				112		25
43			Glucuronic acid	1.4(0-3)^c	Color development with naphtho-resorcinol, with preliminary hydrolysis but without deproteinization	10

/1/ During lactation.

	Animal	Blood	Carbohydrate	Value mg/100 ml	Remarks	Reference
	(A)	(B)	(C)	(D)	(E)	(F)
44	Rabbit (con-cluded)	Plasma or serum (concluded)	Pentose Total	5.3(2.9-7.7)	Fasting subjects; saline extract of acetone precipitate	13
45			Phosphorylated	2.9(1.5-4.3)	Fasting subjects	
46	Albino	Whole blood	Glucose	87(67-107)	Fasting subjects; zinc hydroxide filtrate, color formation with copper-arsenomolybdate	6
47	Rat	Erythrocytes	Glucuronic acid	0.4(0-1.2)^c	Color development with naphtho-resorcinol, with preliminary hydrolysis but without depro-teinization	10
48		Plasma or serum	Glucuronic acid	0.9(0.5-1.3)	Color development with naphtho-resorcinol, with preliminary hydrolysis but without depro-teinization	10
49			Pentose, total	5.4(4.4-6.4)	Fasting subjects; saline extract of acetone precipitate	13
50			Polysaccharide, non-glucosamine	164	Tryptophan reaction	30
51	Albino Wistar strain	Whole blood	Glucose	66(56-76)	Fasting subjects; hydroxide filtrate, copper-iodometric titration	8
52	Yale strain	Whole blood	Glucose	85(77-93)	Fasting subjects; zinc hydroxide filtrate, copper-iodometric titration	
53	Sheep	Whole blood	Fructose	70(12-128)	Fetus; cadmium hydroxide filtrate, color development with FeCl$_3$-resorcinol	3
54			Glucose	40	Adults	21
55			Reducing sub-stance, ferment-able (as glucose)	20	Fetus	3
56		Erythrocytes	Glucose	10	Tungstic acid filtrate, fermentation	32
57		Plasma or serum	Glucose	(40-50)^c		28
58				80	Tungstic acid filtrate, fermentation	32
59	Squirrel	Whole blood	Glucose	85	Non-hibernating	20
60				67	Hibernating	
61	Swine	Serum	Glucose	90	Tungstic acid filtrate, fermentation	32
62	Chicken	Whole blood	Glucose	170(136-204)	Zinc hydroxide filtrate, copper-iodometric titration	29
63		Plasma	Glucose	(152-182.5)^c		23
64	Duck	Whole blood	Glucose	114(90-138)	Zinc hydroxide filtrate, color formation with copper-arsenomolybdate	22
65	Owl	Whole blood	Glucose	(200-350)^c	Zinc hydroxide filtrate, copper-iodometric titration	26
66	Pigeon	Whole blood	Glucose	152(117-187)	Fasting subjects; zinc hydroxide filtrate, color formation with copper-arsenomolybdate	33
67	Alligator	Whole blood	Glucose	99(21-205)^c	Fasting subjects; tungstic acid fil-trate, color formation with copper-molybdate (Folin-Wu)	9
68	Snake Bothrops sp	Whole blood	Glucose	67(26-108)	Males	27
69				60(22-98)	Females	
70	Philohydras sp	Whole blood	Glucose	63(25-101)		27
71	Rattle-	Whole blood	Glucose	63	Non-hibernating; tungstic acid filtrate	7
72				60	Hibernating; tungstic acid filtrate	
73	Frog	Whole blood	Glucose	42(36-48)		19
74		Plasma	Glucose	40.5		15
75	Carp, fresh-water	Whole blood	Glucose	111.2		11
76				(98-256)^c		12

	Animal	Blood	Carbohydrate	Value mg/100 ml	Remarks	Reference
	(A)	(B)	(C)	(D)	(E)	(F)
77	Eel	Whole blood	Glucose	(44-141)c		12
78	Skate (Raja erinacea)	Whole blood	Glucose	(28-75)c		14
79	Trout	Whole blood	Glucose	70.2		11

Contributors: (a) Mirsky, I. Arthur, and Erdoes, Ervin, (b) Wilber, Charles G., (c) Rodbard, Simon

References: [1] Anderson, D. 1937. Austral. J. Exp. Biol. 15:17. [2] Ayyar, M. A. R., and K. N. G. Nayar. 1941. Ind. Vet. J. 17:259. [3] Bacon, J. S. D., and D. J. Bell. 1948. Biochem. J., Lond. 42:397. [4] Balea, E., Y. López de Ytté, J. P. Segundo, M. A. Patetta Queirolo, and R. Arana. 1953. Arch. Soc. biol. Montevideo 20:64. [5] Bodo, R. C., F. W. Co Tui, and A. E. Benaglia. 1937. J. Pharm. Exp. Ther. 61:48. [6] Broh-Kahn, R. H., B. Simkin, and I. A. Mirsky. 1950. Arch. Biochem., N. Y. 25:157. [7] Carmichael, E. B., and P. W. Petcher. 1945. J. Biol. Chem. 161:693. [8] Cole, V. V., and B. K. Harned. 1938. Endocrinology 23:318. [9] Coulson, R. A., T. Hernandez, and F. Brazda. 1950. Proc. Soc. Exp. Biol., N. Y. 73:203. [10] Deichmann, W. B., and M. Dierker. 1946. J. Biol. Chem. 163:753. [11] Field, J. B., C. A. Elvehjem, and C. Juday. 1943. Ibid. 148:261. [12] Gon, S. K. 1939. J. Chosen M. Ass. 29:1925. [13] Green, H. N., H. B. Stoner, and M. Bielschowsky. 1949. J. Path. Bact., Lond. 61:101. [14] Hartman, F. A., L. A. Lewis, K. A. Brownell, F. F. Shelden, and R. F. Walther. 1941. Physiol. Zool. 14:476. [15] Hashimoto, K., and S. Nukata. 1951. Fol. pharm. jap. 47:9. [16] Hiestand, W. A., M. F. Hadley, S. E. Mercer, and B. K. Sandcock. 1947. Proc. Soc. Exp. Biol., N. Y. 65:324. [17] Johnson, D. D. 1950. Endocrinology 46:135. [18] Lazarev, G. I. 1939. Uchen. zapiski Kazan. gosudarst. zootekh. vet. Inst. Baumana 50:3. [19] Lundberg, E., and S. Thyselius-Lundberg. 1946. Acta med. scand., Suppl. 170, p. 513. [20] Lyman, R. A. 1943. J. Mammal. 24:467. [21] McCandless, E. L., and J. A. Dye. 1950. Am. J. Physiol. 162:434. [22] Mirsky, I. A. 1945. Proc. Soc. Exp. Biol., N. Y. 59:35. [23] Murray, H. C., and M. M. Rosenberg. 1953. Poult. Sc. 32:805. [24] Murty, V. N., and N. D. Kehar. 1951. Ind. J. Physiol. Allied Sc. 5:71. [25] Muzzo, J. P. 1949. Actas 3º Congr. peru. quim. 1:339. [26] Nelson, N., S. Elgart, and I. A. Mirsky. 1942. Endocrinology 31:119. [27] Prado, J. L. 1946. Mem. Inst. Butantan 19:59. [28] Reid, R. L. 1953. Austral. J. Agr. Res. 4:213. [29] Rodbard, S. 1947. Am. J. Physiol. 150:67. [30] Shetlar, M. R., C. P. Erwin, and M. R. Everett. 1950. Cancer Res. 10:445. [31] Smith, S. E. Unpublished. [32] Somogyi, M. 1933. J. Biol. Chem. 103:665. [33] Streicher, E., D. B. Hackel, and W. Fleischmann. 1950. Am. J. Physiol. 161:300. [34] Sullivan, R. E., and F. G. Everett. 1952. J. Dent. Res. 31:151. [35] Werner, I. 1949. Acta physiol. scand. 19:27.

Values in parentheses are ranges, estimate "c" unless otherwise indicated (cf. Introduction).

	Acid (A)	Value mg/100 ml (B)	Remarks (C)	Reference (D)
			Whole Blood	
1	Acetoacetic	0.31		23
2	Carbolic (phenol) Total	1.17(0.73-1.78)	7 subjects	21
3		(0.0553-0.1200)	6 subjects	19
4	Conjugated	(0.0400-0.0695)	6 subjects	19
5	Free	(0.0184-0.0630)	6 subjects	19
6	Citric	1.85(1.25-2.45)[b]	23 subjects	24
7	Formic	(1.120-8.449)		22
8	β-Hydroxybutyric	(0.6-60.5)	2 subjects, 6 observations	4
9	α-Ketoglutaric	0.6(0.11-0.86)	34 subjects	20
10	Lactic	(3-33)		12
11		10(4.8-15.2)[b]	Arterial blood; tungstic acid filtrate, oxidation by manganese to acetaldehyde, and titration of bound bisulfite with iodine	5
12		11.5(6.1-16.9)[b]	Cerebral venous blood; tungstic acid filtrate, oxidation by manganese to acetaldehyde, and titration of bound bisulfite with iodine	5
13	Oxalic	(0.4-0.6)		1
14	Pyruvic	1.77(1.15-3.15)	25 newborn	3
15		1.46(1.30-1.62)[b]		17
16		0.85(0.59-1.11)[b]	34 subjects	20
17	Silicic	0.83(0.35-1.31)[b]		25
			Erythrocytes	
18	Lactic	12	Tungstic acid filtrate, oxidation by manganese to acetaldehyde, and titration of bound bisulfite with iodine	9
19	Desoxyribonucleic	Trace	6.84 μg/million leukocytes; alkali treatment and precipitation by trichloracetic acid	B, 13; C, 15
20	Ribonucleic	135.5(101.5-169.5)[b]	Alkali treatment and precipitation by trichloracetic acid	13
			Plasma or Serum	
21	Citric	2.2(1.4-3.0)[b]	23 subjects	24
22		2.88(1.14-4.62)[b]	Newborn, 1 day old	6
23		2.4(1.6-3.2)[b]	Formation of pentabromoacetone, color formation with sodium sulfide	16
24	Guanidoacetic	(0.24-0.28)	5 males	7
25	α-Ketoglutaric	0.9	Oxidation to succinic acid, manometric measurement with succinic dehydrogenase	10
26	Lactic	36	Tungstic acid filtrate, oxidation by manganese to acetaldehyde, and titration of bound bisulfite with iodine	9
27	Malic	0.5(0.1-0.9)[b]	Formation of fluorescent compound with orcinol	8
28	Neurominic	(40-65)		2
29	Pyruvic	1.2(0.4-2.0)[b]	Color formation with diazo reagent	18
30	Salicylic	2(0.2-4.0)		14
31	Succinic	0.5		11

Contributors: (a) Luckey, T. D., and Cohagen, D. L., (b) Mirsky, I. Arthur

References: [1] Barber, H. H., and E. J. Gallimore. 1940. Biochem. J., Lond. 34:144. [2] Böhm, P., St. Dauber, and L. Baumeister. 1954. Klin. Wschr. 32:289. [3] Caffarena, G., and M. Merlini. 1953. Arch. Maragliano pat. clin. 8:987. [4] Crandall, L. A., Jr. 1940. J. Biol. Chem. 133:539. [5] Gibbs, E. L., W. G. Lennox, L. F. Nims, and F. A. Gibbs. 1942. Ibid. 144:325. [6] Gittleman, I. F., and J. B. Pincus. 1952. Pediatrics 9:38. [7] Hoberman, H. D. 1947. J. Biol. Chem. 167:721. [8] Hummel, J. P. 1949. Ibid. 180:1225. [9] Johnson, R. E., H. T. Edwards, D. B. Dill, and J. W. Wilson. 1945. Ibid. 157:461. [10] Krebs, H. A. 1938. Biochem. J., Lond. 32:108. [11] Krebs, H. A. 1950. Annual Rev. Biochem. 19:409. [12] Linko, E. 1950. Ann. med. int. fenn. 39:161. [13] Mandel, P., P. Metais, and R. Bieth. 1948. C. rend. Soc. biol. 142:241. [14] Mendioroz, B. A. 1949. Rev. As. bioquim. argent. 16(4):17. [15] Metais, P., and P. Mandel. 1950.

C. rend. Soc. biol. 144:277. [16] Natelson, S., J. B. Pincus, and J. K. Logovoy. 1948. J. Clin. Invest. 27:446. [17] Palomino, G. 1951. An. Fac. farm. bioquim. Univ. San Marcos 2:599. [18] Rosenthal, S. M. 1949. J. Biol. Chem. 179:1235. [19] Schmidt, E. G. 1943. Ibid. 150:769. [20] Shimizu, T. 1951. Igaku to Seibutsugaku 18:127. [21] Starr, M. P. 1949. Northwest M. 48:330. [22] Stepp, W., and H. Zumbusch. 1920. Deut. Arch. klin. Med. 134:112. [23] Walker, P. G. 1954. Biochem. J., Lond. 58:699. [24] Wolcott, G. H., and P. O. Boyer. 1948. J. Biol. Chem. 172:729. [25] Worth, G. 1952. Klin. Wschr. 30:82.

29. BLOOD MISCELLANEOUS ORGANIC ACIDS: VERTEBRATES OTHER THAN MAN

Values in parentheses are ranges, estimate "c" unless otherwise indicated (cf. Introduction).

	Animal	Blood	Acid	Value mg/100 ml	Remarks	Reference
	(A)	(B)	(C)	(D)	(E)	(F)
1	Cattle, ♀	Whole blood	Lactic	(5-20)		2
2	Dog	Whole blood	Lactic	11(2-13)	Oxidation to acetaldehyde, titration of bound bisulfite	10
3				18.9(10.3-30.7)	17 subjects; oxidation to acetaldehyde, titration of bound bisulfite	1
4		Plasma	Citric	2.9(1.7-3.9)		6
5			Lactic	22.5(12.6-36)	17 subjects; oxidation to acetaldehyde, titration of bound bisulfite	1
6	Guinea pig	Plasma	Pyruvic	2.3	Color formation with diazo reagent	8
7	Horse	Whole blood	Lactic	(10-16)		2
8	Rabbit	Plasma	Pyruvic	1.9	Color formation with diazo reagent	8
9	Rat	Whole blood	Fumaric	<0.3	Chromatographic separation in column of silica gel, titration with alkali	5
10			Lactic	13(5-21)	Oxidation to acetaldehyde, titration of bound bisulfite	7
11		Plasma	Pyruvic	1.85	Color formation with diazo reagent	8
12	Sheep	Whole blood	Lactic	(9-12)		2
13	Chicken	Whole blood	Lactic	(20-98)	Laying hens	2
14				(47-56)	Non-laying hens	
15		Erythrocytes	Desoxyribo-nucleic	3060(2782-3338)[b]	Alkali treatment and precipitation by tri-chloracetic acid	4
16			Ribonucleic	1156(772-1540)[b]		
17	Duck	Erythrocytes	Desoxyribo-nucleic	2590	Alkali treatment and precipitation by tri-chloracetic acid	4
18			Ribonucleic	1530		
19	Goose	Erythrocytes	Desoxyribo-nucleic	3760	Alkali treatment and precipitation by tri-chloracetic acid	4
20			Ribonucleic	1360		
21	Frog	Whole blood	Lactic	52.2		3
22	Carp (Cyprinus sp)	Whole blood	Lactic	13.5(9.1-17.9)[b]	Oxidation to acetaldehyde, titration of bound bisulfite	9
23	Tench (Tinca tinca)	Whole blood	Lactic	16(13.4-18.6)[b]	Oxidation to acetaldehyde, titration of bound bisulfite	9

Contributor: Mirsky, I. Arthur

References: [1] Baissett, A., L. Bugnard, and J. Rogeon. 1938. Bull. Soc. chim. biol., Par. 20:51. [2] Dukes, H. H. 1947. The physiology of domestic animals. Ed. 6. Comstock, Ithaca. p. 54. [3] Hashimoto, K., and S. Nukata. 1951. Fol. pharm. jap. 47:9. [4] Mandel, P., P. Metais, and R. Bieth. 1948. C. rend. Soc. biol. 142:1022. [5] Marshall, L. M., J. M. Orten, and A. H. Smith. 1949. J. Biol. Chem. 179:1127. [6] Miller, M., E. Bueding, R. O. Strauch, J. Owens, and H. Woodward. 1949. Proc. Am. Diabetes Ass. 9:85. [7] Newman, E. V. 1938. Am. J. Physiol. 122:359. [8] Rosenthal, S. M. 1949. J. Biol. Chem. 179:1235. [9] Secondat, M., and D. Diaz. 1942. C. rend. Acad. sc. 215:71. [10] Swan, M. H. 1943. Am. J. Physiol. 140:125.

V. Blood Vitamins, Hormones, Enzymes

30. BLOOD VITAMINS: MAN

Values are μg/100 ml, unless otherwise specified. Values in parentheses are ranges, estimate "c" unless otherwise indicated (cf. Introduction).

	Vitamin (A)	Value (B)	Remarks (C)	Reference (D)
			Whole Blood	
1	A	(60-70) I.U./100 ml		39
2	Carotene	120(20-300)		24
3	Carotenol	13(9-17)		21,24,48
4	B_1 (thiamine)	(5-13)	66 subjects	22
5		4.7(4.3-5.2)		9
6		8.0(4-11)		43
7	B_2 (riboflavin)	21.2(13.3-35.0)	8 subjects	7
8		(15-60)		2,7,45
9	B_6 (pyridoxine)	3	Newborn-18 months	6
10		(1.65-1.90)	Adults	30
11	B_{12} (cyanocobalamine)	0.08(0.06-0.14)	Oxalated blood; method of Skeggs, et al, using _Lactobacillus leichmannii_ as test organism	16
	B_c (folic acid)			
12	Total	3.53(2.30-5.28)	6 subjects; microbiological assay	17
13	Free	0.085(0.05-0.13)	Microbiological assay	42
14	B_t (carnitine)	(700-1400)		19
15	B_x (p-aminobenzoic acid)	3.4	Microbiological assay	36
16	C (ascorbic acid)	(200-1720)	Newborn	20
17		1300(700-1900)[b]	Reduction of dichlorophenol-indophenol observed colorimetrically	11
18	E (tocopherol)	(300-600)		31
19		600(300-1300)		3
20	H (biotin)	0.04	Infants	47
21		1.23(0.75-1.73)	6 subjects; chemical determination	17
22	Choline, free	1320(1030-1710)	8 subjects	18
23		2500(1000-4000)		3
24	Niacin (nicotinic acid)	610(450-770)		23
25		(260-573)	60 subjects	13
26	Niacinamide (nicotinamide)	(600-700)		5
27	Pantothenic acid	31(23-45)	6 subjects	17
28		19.4(12.0-26.8)		33
			Erythrocytes	
29	B_1 (thiamine)	8.0(6.6-9.4)	Leukocytes: 0.67(0.56-0.77)	9
30		4.45	Leukocytes: 0.50	52
31	B_2 (riboflavin)	22.4(18-26)	Burch-Bessey-Lowry fluorometric method	10
32	C (ascorbic acid)	1000(500-2800)		38
33		1100(500-1700)	Reduction of dichlorophenol-indophenol observed colorimetrically	11
34	Choline, free	(4.4-7.5)	Chemical determination	28,40
35	Niacin (nicotinic acid)	135		28
36	Pantothenic acid	25(15-30)	Microbiological assay	33
			Plasma or Serum	
37	A	108(69-158) I.U./100 ml	133 subjects	12
38		58(39-74)	10 subjects	4
39	Carotene	220(40-540)		24
40		138(14-262)[b]	71 subjects	14
41		141(89-198)	10 subjects	4
42	Carotenol	24(10-60)		21,24,48
43	B_1 (thiamine)	7(1-9)		43
44		7.6(1-15)	40 observations	29

	Vitamin	Value	Remarks	Reference
	(A)	(B)	(C)	(D)
		Plasma or Serum (concluded)		
45	B$_2$ (riboflavin)	3.2(2.6-3.7)	13 subjects; Burch-Bessey-Lowry fluoro-metric method	10
46		0.84	141 subjects	46
47	B$_{12}$ (cyanocobalamine)	19.5(12.2-46.0) μμg/100 ml	13 subjects	34
48		20(8-42) μμg/100 ml	24 subjects	37
49	B$_c$ (folic acid) Total	1.75(1.5-5.0)	Microbiological assay	17
50	Free	<0.05	Microbiological assay	42
51	C (ascorbic acid)	1500(300-2700)[b]	Fetus; titration with 2,6-dichloroben-zenone indophenol	20
52		700(0-1500)	Newborn; titration with 2,6-dichloroben-zenone indophenol	20
53		800		49
54		1100(100-2100)	Colorimetric measurement of dinitrophenyl-hydrazone	27
55	D$_2$ (calciferol)	2.75(1.25-4.13)	Animal assay	50
56	E (tocopherol)	980	188 subjects	15
57		1200(900-1590)	13 subjects	35
58		(361-412)	25 subjects	32
59		800(300-1600)	Chemical determination	3
60	H (biotin)	1.27(0.95-1.66)	6 subjects; microbiological assay	17
61	Choline Total	(7,000-14,000)	Newborn	8
62		(18,000-32,000)	Children and adults	8
63		(26,000-35,000)	Chemical determination	28
64	Free	440(250-990)	21 males	1
65		(50-2500)	Chemical determination	3,28,40
66	Inositol	500(370-760)	Microbiological assay with Neurospora	44
67	Niacin (nicotinic acid)	30	8 subjects	25
68	Pantothenic acid	15(6-35)	Microbiological assay	33,41,51

Contributors: (a) Luckey, T. D., and Cohagen, D. L., (b) Beerstecher, Ernest, Jr., (c) Mirsky, I. Arthur, and Erdoes, Ervin

References: [1] Appleton, H. D., B. N. LaDu, Jr., B. B. Levy, J. M. Steele, and B. B. Brodie. 1953. J. Biol. Chem. 205:803. [2] Axelrod, A. E., T. D. Spies, and C. A. Elvehjem. 1941. Proc. Soc. Exp. Biol., N.Y. 46:146. [3] Beerstecher, E., Jr. Unpublished. [4] Bessey, O. A., O. H. Lowry, M. J. Brock, and J. A. Lopez. 1946. J. Biol. Chem. 166:177. [5] Bisaz, S. 1952. Schweiz. med. Wschr. 82:1025. [6] Boxer, G. E., M. P. Pruss, and R. S. Goodhart. 1957. J. Nutrit. 63:623. [7] Bradford, E. A. M., and H. Coke. 1945. Biochem. J., Lond. 39:379. [8] Brante, G., and L. Söderhjelm. 1948. Acta paediat., Upps. 35:207. [9] Burch, H. B. 1952. J. Biol. Chem. 198:486. [10] Burch, H. B., O. A. Bessey, and O. H. Lowry. 1948. Ibid. 175:457. [11] Butler, A. M., and M. Cushman. 1940. J. Clin. Invest. 19:459. [12] Campbell, D. A., and E. Tonks. 1948. Brit. J. Ophth. 32:205. [13] Carter, C. W., and J. R. P. O'Brien. 1945. Q. J. Med., Oxf. 14:197. [14] Caveness, H. L., G. H. Satterfield, and W. J. Dunn. 1941. Arch. Ophth., Chic. 25:827. [15] Chieffi, M., and J. E. Kirk. 1951. J. Geront. 6:17. [16] Couch, J. R., O. Orcese, P. W. Witten, and R. W. Colby. 1950. Am. J. Physiol. 163:77. [17] Denko, C. W., W. E. Grundy, and J. W. Porter. 1947. Arch. Biochem., N. Y. 13:481. [18] Eagle, E. 1941. J. Laborat. Clin. M. 27:103. [19] Fraenkel, G. 1953. Biol. Bull. 104:359. [20] Hamil, B. M., B. M. Munko, E. Z. Moyer, M. Kaucher, and H. H. Williams. 1947. Am. J. Dis. Child. 74:417. [21] Hartzler, E. 1948. J. Nutrit. 36:381. [22] Hirosaki, T. 1954. Fukuoka acta med. 45:791. [23] Jännes, J. 1950. Acta med. scand., Suppl. 249. [24] Kirk, E., and M. Chieffi. 1948. J. Nutrit. 36:315. [25] Klein, J. R., W. A. Perlzweig, and P. Handler. 1942. J. Biol. Chem. 145:27. [26] Klein, J. R., W. A. Perlzweig, and P. Handler. 1945. Ibid. 158:561. [27] Lowry, O. H., J. A. Lopez, and O. A. Bessey. 1945. Ibid. 160:609. [28] Luecke, R. H., and P. B. Pearson. 1944. Ibid. 153:259.

[29] Magyar, I. 1940. Zschr. Vitaminforsch., Bern 10:32. [30] Marsh, M. E. 1955. J. Nutrit. 56:115. [31] Meunier, P., and A. Vinet. 1942. Bull. Soc. chim. biol., Par. 24:365. [32] Nair, P. P., and N. G. Magar. 1956. J. Biol. Chem. 220:157. [33] Pearson, P. B. 1941. Ibid. 140:423. [34] Pitney, W. R., M. F. Beard, and E. J. van Loon. 1954. Ibid. 207:143. [35] Quaife, M. L., and P. L. Harris. 1944. Ibid. 156:499. [36] Ritchey, M. G., L. F. Wicks, and E. L. Tatum. 1947. Ibid. 171:51. [37] Rosenthal, H. L., and H. P. Sarett. 1952. Ibid. 199:433. [38] Sargent, F. 1947. Ibid. 171:471. [39] Scalogne, H. W. 1942. Acta med. scand. 111:359. [40] Schlegel, J. U. 1949. Proc. Soc. Exp. Biol., N. Y. 70:695. [41] Schmidt, V. 1945. Nord. med. 25:137. [42] Schweigert, B. S., and P. B. Pearson. 1947. Am. J. Physiol. 148:319. [43] Smits, G., and E. Florijn. 1949. Biochim. biophys. acta, Amst. 3:44. [44] Sonne, S., and H. Sobotka. 1947. Arch. Biochem., N. Y. 14:93. [45] Strong, F. M., R. E. Feeney, B. Moore, and H. T. Parsons. 1941. J. Biol. Chem. 137:363. [46] Suvarnakich, K., G. V. Mann, and F. J. Stare. 1952. J. Nutrit. 47:105. [47] Švejcar, S., and J. Homolka. 1950. Ann. paediat., Basel 174:175. [48] Van Bruggen, J. T., and J. V. Straumfjord. 1948. J. Laborat. Clin. M. 33:67. [49] Waldo, A. L., and R. E. Zipf. 1955. Cancer, Phila. 8:187. [50] Warkany, J., and H. E. Mabon. 1940. Am. J. Dis. Child. 60:606. [51] Wright, L. D. 1943. J. Biol. Chem. 147:261. [52] Yamadori, M. 1949. Kitasato Arch. 22:281.

31. BLOOD VITAMINS: VERTEBRATES OTHER THAN MAN

Values in parentheses are ranges, estimate "c" unless otherwise indicated (cf. Introduction).

	Animal	Blood	Vitamin	Value µg/100 ml	Reference
	(A)	(B)	(C)	(D)	(E)
	Cattle	Whole blood	A		
1			Carotene	40(25-950)	30
2			Carotenol	14(6-17)	5, 29, 30, 34, 35
			B_1 (thiamine)		8
3			Total	8.0(5-11)	
4			Free	0.5(0-1)	
5			B_2 (riboflavin)	45(40-50)[1]	54
			B_c (folic acid)		52
6			Total	(2.1-3.0)	
7			Free	0.19(0.06-0.45)	
8			B_{12} (cyanocobalamine)	(0.04-0.05)	7
9			C (ascorbic acid)	500(200-1500)	4, 30
10			Choline, total	(11,000-31,000)	59
11			Niacin (nicotinic acid), free	180	3
12		Erythrocytes	D_2 (calciferol)	1.375	57
		Plasma or serum	A		
13			Carotene	(50-2000)	35
14			Carotenol	24(10-30)	5, 29, 30, 34, 35
			B_c (folic acid)		52
15			Total	(1.8-2.2)	
16			Free	<0.05	
17			C (ascorbic acid)	500(150-1500)	4, 30
18			D_2 (calciferol)	6.75	57
19			E (tocopherol)	400(200-500)	10, 11, 42
			Choline		27
20			Total	16,500	
21			Free	4000	
22	Dog	Whole blood	A, carotenol	1.5(0-3)	2, 6
23			B_1 (thiamine), total	7(5-9)	16
24			B_2 (riboflavin)	97(90-100)	54
25			B_{12} (cyanocobalamine)	0.09(0.05-0.11)	7

/1/ Young animals.

	Animal	Blood	Vitamin	Value μg/100 ml	Reference
	(A)	(B)	(C)	(D)	(E)
26	Dog (con-cluded)	Whole blood (concluded)	C (ascorbic acid)	500(200-2100)	26, 31
27			Niacin (nicotinic acid), total activity	800(500-1250)	1, 24, 36, 45
28			Pantothenic acid	25(15-35)	64
29		Erythrocytes	Niacin (nicotinic acid), total activity	1600	1, 24, 36, 45
30			Pantothenic acid	25(20-30)	64
31		Plasma or serum	A, carotenol	3(0-5)	2, 6
32			B_1 (thiamine), total	2.1(0.1-4.0)	16
33			C (ascorbic acid)	500(200-2100)	25, 26, 31
34			D_2 (calciferol)	1.374	58
35			E (tocopherol)	560	53
36			Choline Total	(12,000-15,000)	28
37			Free	(950-1100)	
38			Pantothenic acid	30(15-40)	64
39	Goat	Whole blood	B_{12} (cyanocobalamine)	0.07(0.05-0.09)	7
40		Plasma	C (ascorbic acid)	700(500-900)[b]	46
41			E (tocopherol)	16(5-25)[2]	3
42	Guinea pig	Whole blood	C (ascorbic acid)	120	33
43		Plasma or serum	C (ascorbic acid)	300	3
44			Choline, free	(2,000-12,000)	23
45	Horse	Whole blood	A		43
45			Carotene	65(13-114)	
46			Carotenol	8(6-10)	
47			B_{12} (cyanocobalamine)	0.21(0.12-0.34)	7
48			B_C (folic acid)	0.33(0.22-0.60)	52
49			C (ascorbic acid)	500(200-1500)	31, 43
50			Niacin (nicotinic acid), free	270	1, 36, 45
51			Pantothenic acid	45(35-55)	3
52		Erythrocytes	Pantothenic acid	52(45-60)	3
53		Plasma or serum	A Carotene	100(20-175)	43
54			Carotenol	12(9-16)	
55			B_C (folic acid)	0.35(0.25-0.48)	52
56			C (ascorbic acid)	500(200-1500)	31, 43
57				700	12
58			Choline Total	15,000	27
59			Free	4000	
60			Pantothenic acid	38(30-45)	3
61	Monkey, rhesus	Whole blood	B_6 (pyridoxine)	11(5-20)	17
62		Erythrocytes	B_6 (pyridoxine)	5(2-21)	
63		Plasma	B_6 (pyridoxine)	8(1-18)	
64	Mouse	Whole blood	B_6 (pyridoxine)	42	47
65			B_x (p-aminobenzoic acid)	29	
66			H (biotin)	1.25	
67			Choline, total	18,500	
68			Inositol	6600	
69	Albino Ameri-can	Whole blood	B_{12} (cyanocobalamine)	(0.22-0.23)	7
70	Swiss	Whole blood	B_{12} (cyanocobalamine)	0.12(0.09-0.14)	
71	Rabbit	Whole blood	B_1 (thiamine), total	(3-30)	48
72			B_{12} (cyanocobalamine)	1.01(0.64-1.50)	7
73			C (ascorbic acid)	(900-1400)	22
74			Pantothenic acid	20(15-35)	3
75		Plasma or serum	D_2 (calciferol)	1.3(1.1-1.8)	58
76			Choline, free	500	23
77			Pantothenic acid	(20-30)	3
78	Albino	Whole blood	A, carotenol	25(15-70)	18, 62
79		Plasma or serum	A, carotenol	45(30-130)	

/2/ 5 animals, 13 weeks old.

	Animal (A)	Blood (B)	Vitamin (C)	Value μg/100 ml (D)	Reference (E)
	Rat				
80	Albino	Whole blood	A, carotenol	6(4-7)	15
81			B_2 (riboflavin)	45(20-65)	54
82			C (ascorbic acid)	0.5(0.05-1.5)	55
83			H (biotin)	(1.5-3.5)	47
84		Plasma or serum	A, carotenol	10(6-12)	15
85			C (ascorbic acid)	500(50-1500)	55
86			E (tocopherol)	300(50-600)	49
87			Choline, free	(50-300)	23
88	Cotton-	Whole blood	B_{12} (cyanocobalamine)	0.36(0.33-0.38)	7
89	White	Whole blood	B_{12} (cyanocobalamine)	0.08(0.05-0.12)	7
	Sheep	Whole blood	A		39, 40
90			Carotene	7(0-14)	
91			Carotenol	24(14-31)	
92			B_1 (thiamine), total	5.8(3-15)	32
93			B_2 (riboflavin)	26.5(24-30)	37, 44
94			B_6 (pyridoxine)	12(10-15)	37, 44
95			B_{12} (cyanocobalamine)	0.07(0.06-0.09)	7
96			B_c (folic acid), total	4.6(3.5-5.5)	37, 44
97			C (ascorbic acid)	(400-800)	50
98			Niacin (nicotinic acid), total activity	1000(350-1400)	1, 36, 44, 45
99			Pantothenic acid	35(20-50)	37, 44
100		Erythrocytes	Pantothenic acid	30(20-40)	37, 44
101		Plasma or serum	A Carotene	10(0-20)	39, 40
102			Carotenol	(20-45)	21
103			B_1 (thiamine), total	5.8(3-15)	17, 60
104			C (ascorbic acid)	(400-800)	50
105				700(520-1260)[1]	41
106			D_2 (calciferol)	1.25(1.125-1.750)[3]	58
107			E (tocopherol)	20(10-30)[3]	61
108			Choline Total	10,000(8,000-15,000)	27
109			Free	3000(1000-4000)	
110			Pantothenic acid	25(20-30)	37, 44
111	Swine	Whole blood	A, carotenol	12(5-20)	19
112			B_1 (thiamine), total	20(17-30)	60
113			B_2 (riboflavin)	95	54
114			B_c (folic acid) Total	(2.3-3.1)	51
115			Free	0.66(0.45-0.99)	
116			B_{12} (cyanocobalamine)	0.10(0.08-0.13)	7
117			C (ascorbic acid)	0.4(0.2-1.2)	19
118			Niacin (nicotinic acid), total activity	475(450-600)	1, 36, 45
119			Pantothenic acid	35(30-40)	3
120		Erythrocytes	Pantothenic acid	30(25-35)	3
121		Plasma or serum	A, carotenol	20(10-35)	19
122			C (ascorbic acid)	400(200-1200)	19
123			D_2 (calciferol)	3.0(2.625-3.375)	58
124			Choline, free	2600	27
125			Pantothenic acid	35(30-40)	3
	Chicken	Whole blood	A		63
126			Carotene	24(20-200)[4]	
127			Carotenol	31(10-68)[4]	
128			B_2 (riboflavin)	15(12-18)	20
129			B_c (folic acid) Total	(2.2-4.3)	52
130			Free	0.87(0.44-1.65)	
131			C (ascorbic acid)	(600-2200)	51
132			Niacin (nicotinic acid), total activity	1100(1000-1200)	20
133			Pantothenic acid	45(40-50)	14, 38

/1/ Young animals. /3/ Very young animals. /4/ Females.

	Animal	Blood	Vitamin	Value $\mu g/100$ ml	Reference
	(A)	(B)	(C)	(D)	(E)
134	Chicken (con-	Plasma or serum	A		
	cluded)		Carotene	$(30-300)^4$	9, 63
135			Carotenol	$45(15-100)^4$	63
136			B$_2$ (riboflavin)	34(33-35)	20
			B$_c$ (folic acid)		52
137			Total	(3.0-4.2)	
138			Free	0.31(0.14-0.42)	
139			D$_2$ (calciferol)	2.5(2.125-3.375)	58
140			Pantothenic acid	50	3
141	Pigeon	Whole blood	B$_1$ (thiamine), total	29(21-40)	32
142		Plasma	B$_1$ (thiamine), total	(14-22)	
143	Turkey	Whole blood	B$_c$ (folic acid), free	1.68(1.02-2.76)	52
144			B$_{12}$ (cyanocobalamine)	0.53(0.45-0.60)	7
145	Snake	Whole blood	B$_2$ (riboflavin)	(0-310)	56
146		Plasma	B$_2$ (riboflavin)	$240(120-360)^b$	
147	Turtle	Whole blood	B$_{12}$ (cyanocobalamine)	0.66(0.59-0.69)	7
148	Carp	Whole blood	B$_2$ (riboflavin)	100	13
149			Niacin (nicotinic acid)	587	
150			Pantothenic acid	118	
151		Plasma	A	8.6	
152			Carotene	217	
153			C (ascorbic acid)	470	
154	Trout	Whole blood	B$_2$ (riboflavin)	54	13
155			Niacin (nicotinic acid)	290	
156			Pantothenic acid	165	
157		Plasma	A	17.5	
158			Carotene	44	
159			C (ascorbic acid)	230	

/4/ Females.

Contributors: (a) Beerstecher, Ernest, Jr., (b) Mirsky, I. Arthur, (c) Wilber, Charles G., (d) Levine, Victor E.

References: [1] Axelrod, A. E., and C. A. Elvehjem. 1939. J. Biol. Chem. 131:77. [2] Axelrod, A. E., T. D. Spies, and C. A. Elvehjem. 1941. Proc. Soc. Exp. Biol., N. Y. 46:146. [3] Beerstecher, E., Jr. Unpublished. [4] Bortree, A. L., C. F. Huffman, and C. W. Duncan. 1942. J. Dairy Sc. 25:983. [5] Boyer, P. D., P. H. Phillips, N. S. Lundquist, C. W. Jensen, and I. W. Rupel. 1942. Ibid. 25:433. [6] Boyer, P. D., P. H. Phillips, and J. K. Smith. 1944. J. Biol. Chem. 152:445. [7] Couch, J. R., O. Orcese, P. W. Witten, and R. W. Colby. 1950. Am. J. Physiol. 163:77. [8] De Jong, S. 1941. Acta brevia neerl. 11:176. [9] Deuel, H. J., Jr., M. C. Hrubetz, F. H. Mattson, M. G. Morehouse, and A. Richardson. 1943. J. Nutrit. 26:673. [10] Emmerie, A. 1942. Rec. tr. chim. Pays-Bas 61:305. [11] Emmerie, A., and C. Engel. 1939. Ibid. 58:895. [12] Errington, B. J., W. S. Hodgkiss, and E. P. Jayne. 1942. Am. J. Vet. Res. 3:242. [13] Field, J. B., C. A. Elvehjem, and C. Juday. 1943. J. Biol. Chem. 148:261. [14] Gillis, M. B., G. F. Heuser, and L. C. Norris. 1948. J. Nutrit. 35:351. [15] Glover, J. J., W. Goodwin, and R. A. Morton. 1947. Biochem. J., Lond. 41:97. [16] Govier, W. M. 1943. J. Pharm. Exp. Ther. 77:40. [17] Greenberg, L. D., and J. F. Rinehart. 1949. Proc. Soc. Exp. Biol., N. Y. 70:20. [18] Groth, H., and L. Skurnik. 1939. Acta med. scand. 101:333. [19] Grummer, R. H., C. K. Whitehair, G. Bohstedt, and P. H. Phillips. 1948. J. Animal Sc. 7:222. [20] Hertz, R., F. G. Dhyse, and W. W. Tullner. 1949. Endocrinology 44:283. [21] Hoefer, J. A., and W. D. Gallup. 1947. J. Animal Sc. 6:325. [22] Hökfelt, B. 1949. Acta endocr., Kbh. 2:347. [23] Kahane, E., and J. Levy. 1938. C. rend. Acad. sc. 207:642. [24] Klein, J. R., W. A. Perlzweig, and P. Handler. 1945. J. Biol. Chem. 158:561. [25] Knight, C. A., R. A. Dutcher, N. B. Guerrant, and S. I. Bechdel. 1941. J. Dairy Sc. 24:567. [26] Lacroix, J. V., S. E. Park, and A. E. Adler. 1942. North Am. Vet. 23:329. [27] Luecke, R. W., and P. B. Pearson. 1944. J. Biol. Chem. 153:259.

[28] Luecke, R. W., and P. B. Pearson. 1945. Ibid. 158:561. [29] Lundborg, A. 1933. Biochem. Zschr. 258:325. [30] Madsen, L. L., and I. P. Earle. 1947. J. Nutrit. 34:603. [31] Mannucci, G. 1943. Biochim. ter. sper. 30:13. [32] Meiklejohn, A. P. 1937. Biochem. J., Lond. 31:1441. [33] Møller-Christensen, E., and P. Fønss-Bech. 1941. Endokrinologie 23:393. [34] Moore, L. A., and M. H. Berry. 1945. J. Dairy Sc. 28:821. [35] Parrish, D. B., G. H. Wise, and J. S. Hughes. 1948. Analyt. Chem. 20:230. [36] Pearson, P. B. 1939. J. Biol. Chem. 129:491. [37] Pearson, P. B. 1941. Ibid. 140:423. [38] Pearson, P. B., V. H. Melass, and R. M. Sherwood. 1946. J. Nutrit. 32:187. [39] Pierce, A. W. 1945. Austral. J. Exp. Biol. 23:295. [40] Pierce, A. W. 1946. Ibid. 24:231. [41] Pope, A. L., P. H. Phillips, and G. Bohstedt. 1949. J. Animal Sc. 8:57. [42] Quaife, M. L., and P. L. Harris. 1944. J. Biol. Chem. 156:499. [43] Rasmussen, R. A., C. L. Cole, and M. J. Miller. 1944. J. Animal Sc. 3:346. [44] Ray, S. N., W. C. Weir, A. L. Pope, and P. H. Phillips. 1947. J. Nutrit. 34:595. [45] Regno, F. D. 1940. Boll. Soc. ital. biol. sper. 15:560. [46] Richmond, M. S., G. H. Satterfield, C. D. Grinnells, and W. J. Dann. 1940. J. Nutrit. 20:99. [47] Ritchey, M. G., L. F. Wicks, and E. L. Tatum. 1947. J. Biol. Chem. 171:51. [48] Ritsert, K. 1939. Klin. Wschr. 18:852. [49] Rosenberg, H. R. 1942. Chemistry and physiology of the vitamins. Interscience, New York. p. 85. [50] Satterfield, G. H., E. A. Bailey, Jr., J. E. Foster, and E. H. Hostetler. 1942. J. Nutrit. 24:121. [51] Schrimshaw, N. S., R. L. Goodland, and F. B. Hutt. 1949. Poult. Sc. 28:45. [52] Schweigert, B. S., and P. B. Pearson. 1947. Am. J. Physiol. 148:319. [53] Scudi, J. V., and R. P. Buhs. 1942. J. Biol. Chem. 146:1. [54] Strong, F. M., R. E. Feeney, B. Moore, and H. T. Parsons. 1941. Ibid. 137:363. [55] Todhunter, E. N., and T. J. McMillan. 1946. J. Nutrit. 31:573. [56] Villela, G. G., and J. L. Prado. 1945. J. Biol. Chem. 157:693. [57] Wallis, G. C. 1939. Proc. S. Dakota Acad. Sc. 19:55. [58] Warkany, J. 1937. Biochem. Zschr. 293:415. [59] Waugh, R. K., S. M. Haugh, and W. A. King. 1947. J. Dairy Sc. 30:641. [60] Westenbrink, H. G. K., E. P. Steyn Parvé, A. C. van der Linden, and W. A. van den Broeck. 1943. Zschr. Vitaminforsch., Bern 13:218. [61] Whiting, F., and J. K. Loosli. 1948. J. Nutrit. 36:721. [62] Williamson, M. B. 1947. Proc. Soc. Exp. Biol., N. Y. 66:621. [63] Wilson, W. O., F. R. Sampson, A. L. Moxon, and T. M. Paulsen. 1945. Poult. Sc. 24:237. [64] Wright, L. D. 1943. J. Biol. Chem. 147:261.

32. BLOOD HORMONES: MAN

Values are µg/100 ml, unless otherwise specified. Values in parentheses are ranges, estimate "c" unless otherwise indicated (cf. Introduction).

	Hormone	Value	Remarks	Reference
	(A)	(B)	(C)	(D)
	Whole Blood			
1	Adrenocorticotrophic hormone (ACTH)	<15	Determined by adrenal ascorbic acid depletion	29
2		40 milliunits/100 ml		28
3	Estrogen (as estradiol)	(0.03-0.06)	Non-pregnant women	19
4		0.22	Pregnant 3 months; determined by dialysis, modified Astwood assay	32
5		0.55	Pregnant $5\frac{1}{2}$ months; determined by dialysis, modified Astwood assay	
6	17-Hydroxycorticosterone	(0-14.5)		11
7	Insulin	0.8	$2\frac{1}{2}$ hours after eating	16
8	Pitocin (oxytocin)	1 unit/100 ml	1 unit equivalent to 0.5 mg postpituitary powder (USP XII)	27,30
9	Pitressin (vasopressin)	0.01 antidiuretic unit/100 ml		27
10	Thyrotrophic hormone (TSH)	0.09(0.05-0.15) Junkmann-Schoeller unit/100 ml	Determined by tadpole stasis method of D'Angelo and Gordon; cytological co-efficient = (3900-4900)	13

	Hormone	Value	Remarks	Reference
	(A)	(B)	(C)	(D)
		Plasma or Serum[1]		
	Androgens			20
11	Androsterone	25.0(14.3-35.7)	Males, 20-29 years old	
12		21.5(5.5-37.5)	Females, 21-29 years old	
13	Dehydroepiandrosterone	48.2(33.1-63.3)[b]	Males, 20-29 years old	
14		43.5(26.0-61.0)[b]	Females, 21-29 years old	
15	Chorionic gonadotrophic	(2,000-60,000) I.U./100 ml	Pregnant 60 days; peak value at 60-90 days	17
16	hormone[2]	(1000-1200) I.U./100 ml	Pregnant 100 days	17
17		(400-1000) I.U./100 ml	Pregnant 140 days to term	37
	Corticosteroids			
18	Conjugated corticoids	4.0(1.8-6.2)[b]	Children	18
19		(3.2-9.7)	Adults	8
20	Corticosterone	(0.4-2.0)		22
21	Hydrocortisone	6.25		22
22	17-Hydroxycorticoids	13(2-31)	Males	7
23		15(2-34)	Females	
24		12(3-24)	Aged subjects	
25	Epinephrin (adrenalin)	(0.001-0.007)	Venous plasma	9,10,25,36
26		(0.010-0.023)	Arterial plasma	25,36
	Estrogens			2,5,6,14, 23,26, 35
27	Total	2.7	Last trimester of pregnancy; determined by bioassay as estradiol equivalents	
	Estradiol			
28	Conjugates	(0.1-0.3)	Last trimester of pregnancy; determined by physical or chemical procedures as steroid	
29	Free	(1-5)[3]	Last trimester of pregnancy; determined by bioassay as estradiol equivalents, or by physical or chemical procedures as steroid	
	Estriol			
30	Conjugates	(0.1-1.0)	Last trimester of pregnancy; determined by bioassay as estradiol equivalents	
31		(4-20)	Last trimester of pregnancy; determined by physical or chemical procedures as steroid	
32	Free	(0.7-4.0)[3]	Last trimester of pregnancy; determined by bioassay as estradiol equivalents	
33		(1.5-13.0)	Last trimester of pregnancy; determined by physical or chemical procedures as steroid	
	Estrone			
34	Conjugates	(0.02-0.08)	Last trimester of pregnancy; determined by bioassay as estradiol equivalents	
35		(1-4)	Last trimester of pregnancy; determined by physical or chemical procedures as steroid	
36	Free	(0.05-0.15)	Last trimester of pregnancy; determined by bioassay as estradiol equivalents	
37		(1-3)	Last trimester of pregnancy; determined by physical or chemical procedures as steroid	
38	Insulin	21(0-66) micro-units/ml	30 fasting subjects; determined by immuno-assay	38
39	Norepinephrin (nor-	(0.030-0.040)	Venous plasma	9,10,25,36
40	adrenalin)	(0.020-0.031)	Arterial plasma	25,36
41	Progesterone	(10-28)	Late pregnancy; separated chromatographi-cally and measured by ultraviolet absorp-tion	31
42		(0-5)	Luteal phase	24
43	Thyroid hormone (as	5.5(4-7)	Children, 3-13 years old	33
44	protein-bound iodine)	5(4-8)	Adults	4

/1/ Consult references for information on: follicle-stimulating hormone (FSH) in pregnant women [21]; gonado-trophins in normal women during 9th-13th day of cycle, in surgical castrates, and in women at menopause [3,12,15]; growth hormone in male and female [27]; lactogenic hormone (luteotrophin, prolactin, LT) in postpartum women [34]; luteinizing hormone (LH) in pregnant women [21]; parathormone [27]; relaxin in pregnant women [1]. /2/ One international unit specific gonadotrophic activity of 100 μg urine preparation (pregnant female) kept at NIMR, London [30]. /3/ Concentration in erythrocytes approximately one-quarter that in plasma.

Contributors: (a) Bischoff, Fritz E., (b) Luckey, T. D., and Cohagen, D. L., (c) Zarrow, M. X., (d) Roberts, Sidney, (e) Forbes, Thomas R., (f) Catchpole, H. R., (g) Chaikoff, I. L., (h) Hansel, William, (i) Venning, Eleanor H., (j) Von Euler, U. S., (k) Samuels, Leo T., (l) Sayers, George, (m) Asdell, S. A.

References: [1] Abramson, D., E. Hurwitt, and G. Lesnick. 1937. Surg. Gyn. Obst. 65:335. [2] Aitken, E. H., and J. R. K. Preedy. 1957. Ciba Found. Colloquia Endocr. 11:331. [3] Albrieux, A. S. 1941. J. Clin. Endocr. 1:889. [4] Barker, S. B. 1948. J. Biol. Chem. 173:715. [5] Bischoff, F. E., and R. D. Stauffer. 1957. Am. J. Physiol. 191:313. [6] Bischoff, F. E., R. D. Stauffer, and C. L. Gray. 1954. Ibid. 177:65. [7] Bliss, E. L., A. A. Sandberg, D. H. Nelson, and K. Eik-Nes. 1953. J. Clin. Invest. 32:818. [8] Bongiovanni, A. M., and W. R. Eberlein. 1955. Proc. Soc. Exp. Biol., N. Y. 89:281. [9] Cohen, G., and M. Goldenberg. 1957. J. Neurochem., Lond. 2:58. [10] Cohen, G., and M. Goldenberg. 1957. Ibid. 2:71. [11] Cope, C. L., B. Hurlock, and C. Sewell. 1955. Clin. Sc., Lond. 14:25. [12] Day, F. T., and I. W. Rowlands. 1940. J. Endocr., Oxf. 2:255. [13] De Robertis, E. 1948. J. Clin. Endocr. 8:956. [14] Diczfolusy, E. 1958. Acta endocr., Kbh. 28:169. [15] Frank, R. T., and U. J. Salmon. 1936. Proc. Soc. Exp. Biol., N. Y. 34:363. [16] Gellhorn, E., A. Allen, and J. Feldman. 1941. Ibid. 46:572. [17] Jones, G. E. S., E. Delfs, and H. M. Stran. 1944. Bull. Johns Hopkins Hosp. 75:359. [18] Klein, R., C. Papadatos, J. Fortunato, and C. Byers. 1955. J. Clin. Endocr. 15:215. [19] Littrell, J. L., and J. Y. S. Tom. 1947. Endocrinology 40:292. [20] Migeon, C. J., A. R. Keller, B. Lawrence, and T. H. Sheppard. 1957. J. Clin. Endocr. 17:1051. [21] Nieburg, H. E., and R. B. Greenblatt. 1948. Ibid. 8:600. [22] Peterson, R. E. 1957. Ibid. 17:1150. [23] Preedy, J. R. K., and E. H. Aitken. 1956. Lancet, Lond. 272:191. [24] Preedy, J. R. K., E. H. Aitken, and R. V. Short. Unpublished. [25] Price, H. L., and M. L. Price. 1957. J. Laborat. Clin. M. 50:769. [26] Ray, E., and J. B. Brown. 1957. Ciba Found. Colloquia Endocr. 11:335. [27] Roberts, S. Unpublished. [28] Rossi, C. A., L. Montanari, M. Martinelli, and G. Moruzzi. 1953. Experientia, Basel 9:32. [29] Sayers, G. Unpublished. [30] Selye, H. 1950. Textbook of endocrinology. University of Montreal, Montreal. [31] Short, R. V., and B. Eton. 1959. J. Endocr., Lond. 18:418. [32] Szego, C., and S. Roberts. 1946. Proc. Soc. Exp. Biol., N. Y. 61:161. [33] Talbot, N. B., A. M. Butler, A. H. Saltzman, and P. M. Rodriguez. 1944. J. Biol. Chem. 153:479. [34] Tesauro, G. 1936. Pediatria (Arch.) Nap. 44:665. [35] Veldhuis, A. E. 1953. J. Biol. Chem. 202:167. [36] Vendsalu, A. 1960. Acta physiol. scand., v. 49, suppl. 173. [37] Venning, E. H. Unpublished. [38] Yallow, R. S., and S. A. Beison. 1960. J. Clin. Invest. 39:1157.

33. BLOOD HORMONES: VERTEBRATES OTHER THAN MAN

Values are µg/100 ml, unless otherwise specified. Values in parentheses are ranges, estimate "c" (cf. Introduction).

	Animal	Blood	Hormone	Value	Remarks	Reference
	(A)	(B)	(C)	(D)	(E)	(F)
1	Cattle, ♀	Whole blood	Estrogens Estradiol	0.3	Determined by acetone precipitation, modified Astwood assay	26
2				0.38	Pregnant 6 months; determined	
3			Protein-bound estradiol	0.23	by acetone precipitation, modified Astwood assay	
4			Progesterone	(0.9-4.0)	Pregnant, early to 8 months	20
5		Erythrocytes	Estrogen (as estradiol)	0.2	Pregnant	26
6		Plasma or serum	Estrogen (as estradiol)	<0.03	Non-pregnant	1, 7, 26
7				<0.07	Pregnant, all stages	

	Animal	Blood	Hormone	Value	Remarks	Reference
	(A)	(B)	(C)	(D)	(E)	(F)
8	Cattle, ♀ (con-cluded)	Plasma or serum (concluded)	Progesterone	(0.74-0.98)	Pregnant 32-256 days; amount of progesterone declines rapidly prior to parturition	25
9	Dog	Whole blood	Insulin	(0.35-0.45)	Fasted 24 hours	14
10		Plasma or serum	Thyroid hormone (as protein-bound iodine)	2.3(2-4)		13
11	Guinea pig	Plasma or serum	Relaxin	50 guinea pig units/ 100 ml	Pregnant	16, 27
12			Thyroid hormone (as protein-bound iodine)	(2.0-2.5)		2
13	Horse, ♀	Plasma or serum	Gonadotrophic hormone	(0.2-3.0) rat units/ 100 ml	Non-pregnant	3
14				(2,500-10,000) rat units/100 ml	Pregnant	3
15				15,000(4,300-35,200) I.U./100 ml	Pregnant	5, 6
16			Lactogenic hormone (luteo-trophin, prolactin, LT)	2 Riddle units/100 ml	Pregnant	18
17			Thyroid hormone (as protein-bound iodine)	(2.4-4.8)		22
18	Monkey	Plasma or serum	Progestins	600(10-900)	Luteal phase; determined by intrauterine assay on mice	10, 17
19			Thyroid hormone (as protein-bound iodine)	(4-8)		22
20	Mouse	Plasma or serum	Progestins Total	(500-1000)	Pregnant; determined by intra-uterine assay on mice	17
21			Free	(30-850)		
22			Protein-bound	(30-70)		
23			Thyroid hormone (as protein-bound iodine)	(3-4)		22
24	Rabbit	Whole blood	Insulin	(0.35-0.45)	Fasted 24 hours	14
25		Plasma or serum	Progestins	600	Pseudo-pregnant; determined by intrauterine assay on mice	17
26			Relaxin	1000 guinea pig units/100 ml	Pregnant	19
27	Rat	Whole blood	Adrenocorticotrophic hormone (ACTH)	<15	Determined by adrenal ascorbic acid depletion	23
28		Plasma or serum	Thyroid hormone (as protein-bound iodine)	3.2(3-4)		13
29			Thyrotrophic hormone (TSH)[1]	0.09 Junkmann-Schoeller unit/ 100 ml	Determined by tadpole stasis method of D'Angelo and Gordon	23
30	Sheep	Plasma or serum	Thyrotrophic hormone (TSH)[1]	0.09 Junkmann-Schoeller unit/ 100 ml	Determined by tadpole stasis method of D'Angelo and Gordon	23
31			Progesterone	180	Non-pregnant, 7th-16th day of estrous cycle; ovarian vein plasma	9, 24
32				(150-200)	Pregnant 1-18 weeks; ovarian vein plasma	8, 9, 21
33	Swine, ♀	Plasma or serum	Relaxin	200 guinea pig units/100 ml	Pregnant	15, 16
34	Chicken	Plasma or serum	Progestins	300	Rooster; determined by intra-uterine assay on mice	12
35				300	Ovulating hen; determined by intrauterine assay on mice	11
36			Thyroid hormone (as protein-bound iodine)	(3-4)		22
37	Pigeon	Plasma or serum	Thyrotrophic hormone (TSH)[1]	0.09 Junkmann-Schoeller unit/ 100 ml	Determined by tadpole stasis method of D'Angelo and Gordon	4

/1/ Also present in dog, rabbit; not detected in cattle, guinea pig, horse, turtle [4].

Contributors: (a) Zarrow, M. X., (b) Bischoff, Fritz E., (c) Paschkis, Karl E., (d) Hansel, William, (e) Forbes, Thomas R., (f) Chaikoff, I. L., (g) Asdell, S. A., (h) Roberts, Sidney, (i) Samuels, Leo T.

References: [1] Bitman, J., T. R. Wrenn, and J. F. Sykes. In F. X. Gassner, ed. 1958. Proc. 3rd Symposium Reproduction and Infertility. Pergamon Press, New York. pp. 141-156. [2] Chaikoff, I. L., A. Taurog, and W. O. Reinhardt. 1947. Endocrinology 40:47. [3] Cole, H. H., and H. Goss. 1939. Am. J. Physiol. 127:703. [4] D'Angelo, S. A., and H. S. Gordon. 1950. Endocrinology 46:39. [5] Day, F. T., and I. W. Rowlands. 1940. J. Endocr., Oxf. 2:255. [6] Day, F. T., and I. W. Rowlands. 1947. Ibid. 5:1. [7] Duncan, G. W., I. Casas, M. A. Emerson, and R. M. Melamphy. 1955. Fed. Proc., Balt. 14:40. [8] Edgar, D. G., D. S. Flax, and J. W. Ronaldson. 1959. J. Endocr., Lond. 19:44. [9] Edgar, D. G., and J. W. Ronaldson. 1957-58. Ibid. 16:378. [10] Forbes, T. R., C. W. Hooker, and C. A. Pfeiffer. 1950. Proc. Soc. Exp. Biol., N. Y. 73:177. [11] Fraps, R. M., C. W. Hooker, and T. R. Forbes. 1948. Science 108:86. [12] Fraps, R. M., C. W. Hooker, and T. R. Forbes. 1949. Ibid. 109:493. [13] Gaebler, O. H., and R. E. Strohmaier. 1942. Proc. Soc. Exp. Biol., N. Y. 51:343. [14] Gellhorn, E., A. Allen, and J. Feldman. 1941. Ibid. 46:572. [15] Hisaw, F. L., and M. X. Zarrow. 1948. Ibid. 69:395. [16] Hisaw, F. L., M. X. Zarrow, W. L. Money, R. V. N. Talmage, and A. A. Abramowitz. 1944. Endocrinology 34:122. [17] Hooker, C. W., and T. R. Forbes. 1949. Ibid. 44:61. [18] Leblond, C. P. 1937. C. rend. Soc. biol. 124:1062. [19] Marder, S. N., and W. L. Money. 1944. Endocrinology 34:115. [20] Melamphy, R. M., W. R. Hearn, and J. M. Rakes. 1959. J. Animal Sc. 18:307. [21] Neher, G. M., and M. X. Zarrow. 1954. J. Endocr., Oxf. 11:323. [22] Rawson, R. W., and W. T. Salter. In C. W. Emmons, ed. 1950. Hormone assay. Academic Press, New York. p. 228. [23] Roberts, S. Unpublished. [24] Short, R. V. 1958. J. Endocr., Lond. 16:415. [25] Short, R. V. 1958. Ibid. 16:426. [26] Szego, C., and S. Roberts. 1946. Proc. Soc. Exp. Biol., N. Y. 61:161. [27] Zarrow, M. X. 1947. Ibid. 66:488.

34. BLOOD ENZYMES: MAN

Values in parentheses are ranges, estimate "c" unless otherwise indicated (cf. Introduction).

	Enzyme	Value	Enzyme Activity Units	Remarks	Reference
	(A)	(B)	(C)	(D)	(E)
			Whole Blood		
1	Arginase	2000(800-3200)[b]	units/100 ml, as described by Kochakian	Males, females	17, 32, 33
2	Carbonic anhydrase[1]	(30-50)	units/100 ml at 37°C, as described by Altschule and Lewis	Premature infants	4, 5
3		(60-110)	units/100 ml at 37°C, as described by Altschule and Lewis	Full-term infants	4, 5
4		(130-160)	units/100 ml at 37°C, as described by Altschule and Lewis	Pregnant	4, 5
5		(130-260)	units/100 ml at 37°C, as described by Altschule and Lewis	Adult males	3, 4
6		(120-240)	units/100 ml at 37°C, as described by Altschule and Lewis	Adult females	3, 4
7	Cholinesterase	400(325-450)	μM acetylcholine hydrolyzed/min/100 ml	0.16 M acetylcholine substrate	2
8		540(446-684)	μM acetylcholine hydrolyzed/min/100 ml	0.012 M acetylcholine substrate	44
9		336(273-407)	μM acetylcholine hydrolyzed/min/100 ml	0.00025 M acetylcholine substrate	42
10	Glyoxalase	611.7(425-705)	ml CO_2/20 min/100 ml at 26°C and pH 7.2, in presence of glutathione	Methylglyoxal substrate	14

/1/ Activity due entirely to erythrocytes.

	Enzyme	Value	Enzyme Activity Units	Remarks	Reference
	(A)	(B)	(C)	(D)	(E)
	Whole Blood (concluded)				
11	Histaminase	36(30-40)	μg histamine destroyed/90 min/100 ml at 37°C	Increases during pregnancy	51
12	Lactic dehydrogenase	34,000(16,000-71,000)	$-\Delta D_{340}$/min/0.001 ml whole blood hemolysate at 24-27°C and pH 7.4		53
	Erythrocytes				
13	Adenylate kinase	124	μg glucose phosphorylated/hr/0.5 ml cell suspension at 37°C and with 5 mM added ADP	Washed, fresh cells	30
14	Arginase	5100(2500-7700)[b]	units/100 ml, as described by Kochakian	Males	17, 32, 33
15		4400(1800-7000)[b]	units/100 ml, as described by Kochakian	Females	
16	Carbonic anhydrase	73,000	Amount of erythrocytes that will halve the time of uncatalyzed reaction at 3°C under specified conditions	Less in newborn; parallels erythrocyte zinc concentration in all conditions in adults	6
17	Catalase	0.1	g/100 g dry weight		23
18	Cholinesterase	501(335-638)	μM acetylcholine hydrolyzed/min/100 ml	0.01 M acetylcholine substrate	13
19		876(725-1034)	μM acetylcholine hydrolyzed/min/100 ml	0.012 M acetylcholine substrate	44
20		1190(910-1370)	μM acetylcholine hydrolyzed/min/100 ml	0.002 M acetylcholine substrate	43
21		(600-790)	μM acetylcholine hydrolyzed/min/100 ml	Newborn; 0.0027 M acetylcholine substrate	43
22		(800-1300)	μM acetylcholine hydrolyzed/min/100 ml	Adults; 0.0027 M acetylcholine substrate	43
23		547(437-660)	μM acetylcholine hydrolyzed/min/100 ml	0.00025 M acetylcholine substrate	42
24		(90-142)	μM acetyl-β-methylcholine hydrolyzed/min/100 ml	Newborn; 0.135 M acetyl-β-methylcholine substrate	27
25		(141-287)	μM acetyl-β-methylcholine hydrolyzed/min/100 ml	Adults; 0.135 M acetyl-β-methylcholine substrate	27
26		116	μM acetyl-β-methylcholine hydrolyzed/min/100 ml	0.03 M acetyl-β-methylcholine substrate	40
27		4.5	μM benzoylcholine hydrolyzed/min/100 ml	0.006 M benzoylcholine substrate	40
28	Diphosphopyridine nucleotide nucleosidase	28(20-35)	μM DPN split/hr/100 ml blood at 37°C and pH 6.5		1, 28
29	Glutamic oxaloacetic transaminase	22.3	μM glutamate formed/hr/g cells at 37°C and pH 7.4		18
30	Glyoxalase	1398(1320-1500)	ml CO_2/20 min/100 ml at 26°C and pH 7.2, in presence of glutathione	Methylglyoxal substrate	14
31	Hexokinase	23	mg glucose phosphorylated/hr/100 ml blood at 37°C and pH 7.8	Whole cells	29
32		45	mg glucose phosphorylated/hr/100 ml blood at 37°C and pH 7.8	Whole hemolysate	
33	Lactic dehydrogenase	55.6(42.5-73.5)	mg DPNH/min/ml packed cells at 37°C and pH 7.2		24
34		230	μL O_2/100 min/g Hb at 37.5°C and pH 7.4		7
35		87	μL O_2/100 min/ml at 37.5°C and pH 7.4		34
36		30	μL O_2/30 min/ml at 38°C and pH 7.4		41
37		396	μL CO_2/30 min/ml at 38°C and pH 7.4		41

	Enzyme	Value	Enzyme Activity Units	Remarks	Reference
	(A)	(B)	(C)	(D)	(E)
			Erythrocytes (concluded)		
38	Pentose isomerase	3.6	μM ketopentose formed/hr/g Hb at 37°C and pH 7.4	Whole hemolysate	11
39	Phosphoglucose isomerase	3200(3100-3300)[b]	units/100 ml, as described by Bodansky		10
40	Phosphoglycerate kinase	24.6	μM 1,3-diphosphoglycerate utilized/hr/mg Hb at 37°C and pH 8.3	Dialyzed, stroma-free hemolysate	8
41	Phosphoglycerate mutase	0.33	μM 1,3-diphosphoglycerate utilized/hr/mg Hb at 37°C and pH 8.3	Dialyzed, stroma-free hemolysate	8
42	Pyrophosphatase, inorganic	212	μM inorganic phosphorus liberated/hr/ml at 37°C and pH 7.5	Dialyzed hemolysate	35
43		214	μM inorganic phosphorus liberated/hr/ml at 37°C and pH 7.5	Stroma-free hemolysate	
44		5.5	μM inorganic phosphorus liberated/hr/ml at 37°C and pH 7.5	Washed stroma	
45	Transaldolase	40	μM fructose-6-phosphate formed/hr/g Hb at 37°C and pH 7.4	Whole hemolysate	11
46	Transketalase	33	μM sedoheptulose-7-phosphate formed/hr/g Hb at 37°C and pH 7.4	Whole hemolysate	11
			Plasma or Serum		
	Adenosine polyphosphatase			Adenosine triphosphate substrate	37, 38
47	Acid	41(21-61)[b]	μM phosphorus/hr/100 ml at pH 4.8		
48	Alkaline	30(10-51)[b]	μM phosphorus/hr/100 ml at pH 8.9		
49	Aldolase	490(350-800)	μL fructose diphosphate/hr/100 ml at 38°C and pH 8.6	No change during pregnancy	46, 47
50	Amylase	(80-150)	mg dextrose or equivalent (by copper reduction)/100 ml under specified conditions	Starch substrate	48, 49
51	Catalase	690(420-950)	units/100 ml as described by Dille and Watkins		16
52	Cholinesterase	319(150-500)	μM acetylcholine hydrolyzed/min/100 ml	0.012 M acetylcholine substrate	44
53		398(228-572)	μM acetylcholine hydrolyzed/min/100 ml	0.01 M acetylcholine substrate	13
54		176(139-219)	μM acetylcholine hydrolyzed/min/100 ml	0.00025 M acetylcholine substrate	42
55		5.8	μM acetyl-β-methylcholine hydrolyzed/min/100 ml	0.03 M acetyl-β-methylcholine substrate	40
56		109	μM benzoylcholine hydrolyzed/min/100 ml	0.006 M benzoylcholine substrate	40
57		(183-261)	μM acetylcholine hydrolyzed/min/100 ml	Newborn; 0.135 M acetylcholine substrate	27
58		(302-378)	μM acetylcholine hydrolyzed/min/100 ml	Adults; 0.135 M acetylcholine substrate	27
59		(135-362)	μM acetylcholine hydrolyzed/min/100 ml	0.01 M acetylcholine substrate	22
60		316(152-522)	μM acetylcholine hydrolyzed/min/100 ml	0.009 M acetylcholine substrate	12
61		470(320-740)	μM acetylcholine hydrolyzed/min/100 ml	Children, 7-15 years old	36
62		350(230-540)	μM acetylcholine hydrolyzed/min/100 ml	Adults	36
63	Dehydropeptidase	359(191-527)	μM ammonia/30 min/100 ml at 37°C and pH 8.1	DL-Alanyldehydroalanine substrate	39
64	β-Glucuronidase	(0-181)	μg phenolphthalein/hr/100 ml at 38°C and pH 4.5	Males; phenolphthalein glucuronide substrate	19
65		(37-230)	μg phenolphthalein/hr/100 ml at 38°C and pH 4.5	Females; phenolphthalein glucuronide substrate	

	Enzyme	Value	Enzyme Activity Units	Remarks	Reference
	(A)	(B)	(C)	(D)	(E)
	Plasma or Serum (concluded)				
66	Histaminase	18(0–36)	μg histamine destroyed/90 min/100 ml at 37°C	Increases during pregnancy	51
67	Lactic dehydrogenase	49(34–68)	mg DPNH/min/100 ml at 37°C and pH 7.2	Children under 14 years	24
68		25(17–30)	mg DPNH/min/100 ml at 37°C and pH 7.2	Adults	24
69		15.1(7.5–22.7)	μM lactate/hr/ml at 32°C and pH 9.2	No significant variation with sex, race, fasting state, or exercise	25
70		181(80–250)	μM DPNH/30 min/100 ml at 37°C and pH 10.0		55
71		59(25–100)	+ΔD$_{340}$ 0.01/min/ml at 24–27°C and pH 8.8		50
72		440(200–680)	-ΔD$_{340}$ 0.001/min/ml at 23°C and pH 7.4		54
73	Lipase	(0–150)	ml nitrogen/20 NaOH/24 hr/100 ml	Standard olive-oil emulsion substrate	15
74	Phenolsulfatase	(30–1550)	units/100 ml	1 unit = amount of enzyme that produces color equivalent to 10 μg of p-nitrophenol from p-nitrophenyl sulfate	26
75	Phosphatase Acid	(1.0–4.0)	mg phenol/hr/100 ml at 37°C and pH 5.0	Disodiumphenylphosphate substrate	21
76	Alkaline[2]	(5.0–14.0)	mg phosphorus/hr/100 ml at 37°C and pH 8.6	Children; β-glycerophosphate substrate	9
77		(1.0–4.0)	mg phosphorus/hr/100 ml at 37°C and pH 8.6	Adults; β-glycerophosphate substrate	9
78		(10.5–13.0)	mg phenol/30 min/100 ml at 37.5°C and pH 9.0	Adults; disodiumphenylphosphate substrate	31
79		(2.8–8.6)	mg phosphorus/hr/100 ml	β-Glycerophosphate substrate	45
80	Phosphoglucose isomerase	20(8–40)	units/100 ml, as described by Bodansky		10
81	Profibrinolysin	(50–125)	units fibrinolysin/100 ml	1 unit of fibrinolysin will completely lyse a 0.1% fibrin clot in 120 seconds, at 28°C and pH 7.2, in isotonic saline buffered with imidazole	20
82	Vitamin B$_c$ conjugase	(80–100)	μg folic acid/90 min/100 ml at 37°C and pH 4.5	Yeast extract substrate	52

/2/ Increases during increased osteoblastic activity, biliary tract obstruction, and pregnancy.

Contributors: (a) Sabine, Jean C., (b) Lehninger, Albert L., (c) Morales, Daniel R., (d) Denstedt, Orville F., (e) Altschule, Mark D., (f) Stowe, Clarence M., Jr., (g) Dische, Zacharias, (h) Guest, M. Mason, (i) Sizer, Irwin W., (j) Meister, Alton, (k) Chance, Britton, (l) Gutman, Alexander B., (m) Rossiter, Roger J.

References: [1] Alivisatos, S. G. A., S. Kashket, and O. F. Denstedt. 1956. Canad. J. Biochem. Physiol. 34:46. [2] Alles, G. A., and R. C. Hawes. 1940. J. Biol. Chem. 133:375. [3] Altschule, M. D., and H. D. Lewis. 1949. Arch. Int. M. 83:547. [4] Altschule, M. D., and H. D. Lewis. 1949. J. Biol. Chem. 180:557. [5] Altschule, M. D., and C. A. Smith. 1950. Pediatrics 6:717. [6] Ashby, W. 1943. J. Biol. Chem. 151:521. [7] Blanchaer, M. C., P. Weiss, and D. E. Bergsogel. 1951. Canad. J. M. Sc. 29:108. [8] Blostein, R. 1960. Ph. D. Thesis. McGill

University, Montreal. [9] Bodansky, A. 1933. J. Biol. Chem. 101:93. [10] Bodansky, O. 1954. Cancer, Phila. 7:1191. [11] Brownstone, Y. S. 1958. Ph. D. Thesis. McGill University, Montreal. [12] Butt, H. R., M. W. Comfort, T. J. Dry, and A. E. Osterberg. 1942. J. Laborat. Clin. M. 27:649. [13] Callaway, S., D. R. Davies, and J. P. Rutland. 1951. Brit. M. J. 2:812. [14] Cohen, P. P., and E. K. Sober. 1945. Cancer Res. 5:631. [15] Comfort, M. W., and A. E. Osterberg. 1940. Med. Clin. N. America 24:1137. [16] Dille, R. S., and C. H. Watkins. 1948. J. Laborat. Clin. M. 33:480. [17] Edebacher, S., and H. Rothler. 1925. Hoppe Seyler Zschr. 148:264. [18] Fessler, A. 1959. M. Sc. Thesis. McGill University, Montreal. [19] Fishman, W. H., B. Springer, and R. Brunetti. 1948. J. Biol. Chem. 173:449. [20] Guest, M. M. 1954. J. Clin. Invest. 33:1553. [21] Gutman, E. B., and A. B. Gutman. 1940. J. Biol. Chem. 136:201. [22] Hall, G. E., and C. C. Lucas. 1937. J. Pharm. Exp. Ther. 61:10. [23] Herbert, D., and J. Pinsent. 1948. Biochem. J., Lond. 43:203. [24] Hill, B. R. 1956. Cancer Res. 16:460. [25] Hsieh, K. M., and H. T. Blumenthal. 1956. Proc. Soc. Exp. Biol., N. Y. 91:626. [26] Huggins, C., and D. R. Smith. 1947. J. Biol. Chem. 170:391. [27] Jones, P. E. H., and R. A. McCance. 1949. Biochem. J., Lond. 45:464. [28] Kashket, S. 1953. M. Sc. Thesis. McGill University, Montreal. [29] Kashket, S. 1956. Ph. D. Thesis. McGill University, Montreal. [30] Kashket, S., and O. F. Denstedt. 1958. Canad. J. Biochem. Physiol. 36:1057. [31] King, E. J., and A. R. Armstrong. 1934. Canad. M. Ass. J. 31:376. [32] Kochakian, C. D. 1944. J. Biol. Chem. 155:579. [33] Kochakian, C. D., E. H. Keutman, and E. E. Garber. 1948. Conf. Metab. Aspects Convalescence 17:187. [34] Kohn, H. I., and J. P. Klein. 1939. J. Biol. Chem. 130:1. [35] Malkin, A., and O. F. Denstedt. 1956. Canad. J. Biochem. Physiol. 34:121. [36] McArdle, B. 1940. Q. J. Med., Oxf. 9:107. [37] Meister, A. 1947. Science 106:167. [38] Meister, A. 1948. J. Clin. Invest. 26:263. [39] Meister, A., and J. Greenstein. 1948. J. Nat. Cancer Inst. 8:169. [40] Mendel, B., D. B. Mundell, and H. Rudney. 1943. Biochem. J., Lond. 37:473. [41] Quastel, J. H., and A. H. M. Wheatley. 1938. Ibid. 32:936. [42] Sabine, J. C. 1940. J. Clin. Invest. 19:833. [43] Sabine, J. C. 1955. Blood, N. Y. 10:1132. [44] Sawitsky, A., H. Fitch, and L. M. Meyer. 1948. J. Laborat. Clin. M. 33:203. [45] Shinowara, G. Y., L. M. Jones, and H. L. Reinhart. 1942. J. Biol. Chem. 142:921. [46] Sibley, J. A., and A. L. Lehninger. 1948-49. J. Nat. Cancer Inst. 9:303. [47] Sibley, J. A., and A. L. Lehninger. 1949. J. Biol. Chem. 177:859. [48] Somogyi, M. 1938. Ibid. 125:399. [49] Somogyi, M. 1941. Arch. Int. M. 67:665. [50] Wacker, W. E. C., D. D. Ulmer, and B. L. Vallee. 1956. N. England J. M. 255:450. [51] Werle, E., and G. Effkemann. 1940. Klin. Wschr. 19:717. [52] Wolff, R., L. Drouet, and R. Karlin. 1949. Science 109:612. [53] Wroblewski, F., and J. S. La Due. 1955. Proc. Soc. Exp. Biol., N. Y. 90:210. [54] Wroblewski, F., P. Ruegsegger, and J. S. La Due. 1956. Science 123:1122. [55] Zimmerman, H. J., and H. G. Weinstein. 1956. J. Laborat. Clin. M. 48:607.

35. BLOOD ENZYMES: VERTEBRATES OTHER THAN MAN

Values in parentheses are ranges, estimate "c" (cf. Introduction).

	Animal	Blood	Enzyme	Value	Enzyme Activity Units	Remarks	Reference
	(A)	(B)	(C)	(D)	(E)	(F)	(G)
1	Cat	Erythrocytes	Carbonic anhydrase	128,000	Amount of erythrocytes that will halve the time of un-catalyzed reaction at 3°C under specified conditions	Less in newborn; parallels erythrocyte zinc concentration in all conditions in adults	4
2			Cholinesterase	5.4	μM acetyl-β-methylcholine hydrolyzed/min/100 ml	0.03 M acetyl-β-methylcholine substrate	22
3		Plasma or serum	Cholinesterase	(64-140)	μM acetylcholine hydrolyzed/min/100 ml	0.01 M acetylcholine substrate	13, 20

	Animal	Blood	Enzyme	Value	Enzyme Activity Units	Remarks	Reference
	(A)	(B)	(C)	(D)	(E)	(F)	(G)
4	Cat (con-cluded)	Plasma or serum (con-cluded)	Cholinesterase (concluded)	8.9	μM acetyl-β-methylcholine hydrolyzed/min/100 ml	0.03 M acetyl-β-methyl-choline substrate	22
5				20.5	μM benzoylcholine hydrolyzed/min/100 ml	0.006 M benzoylcholine substrate	22
6	Cattle Calf	Erythro-cytes	Carbonic anhydrase	44,000	Amount of erythrocytes that will halve the time of un-catalyzed reaction at 3°C under specified conditions	Less in newborn; paral-lels erythrocyte zinc concentration in all conditions in adults	4
7	Ox	Erythro-cytes	Lactic dehy-drogenase	189	μL CO_2/30 min/ml at 38°C and pH 7.4		24
8		Serum	Cholinesterase	45	μM acetylcholine hydrolyzed/min/100 ml	0.01 M acetylcholine substrate	13
9	Cow	Whole blood	Catalase	202.8 (81.6-469.2)	g peroxide split/10 min/100 ml under conditions specified		7
10		Erythro-cytes	Cholinesterase	(127-243)	μM acetylcholine hydrolyzed/min/100 ml	0.01 M acetylcholine substrate	5, 32
11				238	μM acetylcholine hydrolyzed/min/100 ml	0.001 M acetylcholine substrate	33
12				226	μM acetylcholine hydrolyzed/min/100 ml	0.0001 M acetylcholine substrate	33
13			Lactic dehy-drogenase	0.58	$-\Delta D_{314}$/min/0.02 ml serum at 20°C and pH 8.3		14
14		Plasma or serum	Cholinesterase	7	μM acetylcholine hydrolyzed/min/100 ml	0.01 M acetylcholine substrate	5
15				6	μM acetylcholine hydrolyzed/min/100 ml	0.001 M acetylcholine substrate	33
16				2	μM acetylcholine hydrolyzed/min/100 ml	0.0001 M acetylcholine substrate	33
17			Lactic dehy-drogenase	0.28	$-\Delta D_{314}$/min/0.02 ml at 20°C and pH 8.3		12
18	Dog	Erythro-cytes	Carbonic anhydrase	84,000	Amount of erythrocytes that will halve the time of un-catalyzed reaction at 3°C under specified conditions	Less in newborn; paral-lels erythrocyte zinc concentration in all conditions in adults	4
19			Cholinesterase	27	μM acetyl-β-methylcholine hydrolyzed/min/100 ml	0.03 M acetyl-β-methyl-choline substrate	22
20		Plasma or serum	Cholinesterase	(121-302)	μM acetylcholine hydrolyzed/min/100 ml	0.01 M acetylcholine substrate	12, 13, 31
21				290	μM acetylcholine hydrolyzed/min/100 ml	0.002 M acetylcholine substrate	34
22				8	μM acetyl-β-methylcholine hydrolyzed/min/100 ml	0.03 M acetyl-β-methyl-choline substrate	22
23				79	μM benzoylcholine hydrolyzed/min/100 ml	0.006 M benzoylcholine substrate	22
24	Goat	Erythro-cytes	Cholinesterase	27	μM acetylcholine hydrolyzed/min/100 ml	0.01 M acetylcholine substrate	32
25		Plasma	Cholinesterase	11	μM acetylcholine hydrolyzed/min/100 ml	0.01 M acetylcholine substrate	14
26	Guinea pig	Erythro-cytes	Carbonic anhydrase	60,000	Amount of erythrocytes that will halve the time of un-catalyzed reaction at 3°C under specified conditions	Less in newborn; paral-lels erythrocyte zinc concentration in all conditions in adults	4
27			Cholinesterase	61	μM acetylcholine hydrolyzed/min/100 ml	0.01 M acetylcholine substrate	32
28		Plasma or serum	Cholinesterase	(100-300)	μM acetylcholine hydrolyzed/min/100 ml	0.01 M acetylcholine substrate	13, 32
29	Horse	Erythro-cytes	Cholinesterase	(45-79)	μM acetylcholine hydrolyzed/min/100 ml	0.01 M acetylcholine substrate	5, 32

	Animal	Blood	Enzyme	Value	Enzyme Activity Units	Remarks	Reference
	(A)	(B)	(C)	(D)	(E)	(F)	(G)
30	Horse (concluded)	Erythrocytes (concluded)	Cholinesterase (concluded)	40	μM acetylcholine hydrolyzed/min/100 ml	0.001 M acetylcholine substrate	33
31				54	μM acetylcholine hydrolyzed/min/100 ml	0.0001 M acetylcholine substrate	33
32		Plasma or serum	Cholinesterase	(200-310)	μM acetylcholine hydrolyzed/min/100 ml	0.01 M acetylcholine substrate	13, 31, 32
33				250	μM acetylcholine hydrolyzed/min/100 ml	0.001 M acetylcholine substrate	33
34				120	μM acetylcholine hydrolyzed/min/100 ml	0.0001 M acetylcholine substrate	33
35				16.5	μM acetyl-β-methylcholine hydrolyzed/min/100 ml	0.03 M acetyl-β-methyl-choline substrate	22
36				22.4	μM benzoylcholine hydrolyzed/min/100 ml	0.006 M benzoylcholine substrate	22
37	Monkey	Erythrocytes	Lactic dehydrogenase	0.87	cu mm CO_2/hr/10^6 cells at 38°C and pH 7.4		21
38	Mouse	Erythrocytes	Cholinesterase	50	μM acetylcholine hydrolyzed/min/100 ml	0.027 M acetylcholine substrate	27
39		Plasma or serum	Cholinesterase	(430-690)	μM acetylcholine hydrolyzed/min/100 ml	0.01 M acetylcholine substrate	13
40	Leaden	Plasma or serum	Lactic dehydrogenase	(25.4-41.4)	mM lactate/hr/L at 32°C and pH 9.2		15
41	Swiss	Plasma or serum	Lactic dehydrogenase	(92.6-145.6)	mM lactate/hr/L at 32°C and pH 9.2		15
42	Strain C57BL/6	Plasma or serum	Lactic dehydrogenase	1200 (940-1460)	$-\Delta D_{340}$ 0.001/min/ml at 24-27°C and pH 7.4		11
43	C58 by BALB	Plasma or serum	Lactic dehydrogenase	1100 (780-1420)	$-\Delta D_{340}$ 0.001/min/ml at 24-27°C and pH 7.4		11
44	Rabbit	Whole blood	Adenosine deaminase	415	μg nitrogen liberated/hr/100 ml		9
45			Muscle adenylic acid deaminase	41	μg nitrogen liberated/hr/100 ml in presence of 0.05% adenylic acid		
46		Erythrocytes	Cholinesterase	22	μM acetylcholine hydrolyzed/min/100 ml	0.01 M acetylcholine substrate	32
47				184 (129-246)	μM acetylcholine hydrolyzed/min/100 ml	0.002 M acetylcholine substrate	28
48				16	μM acetyl-β-methylcholine hydrolyzed/min/100 ml	0.03 M acetyl-β-methyl-choline substrate	22
49			Diphosphopyridine nucleotide nucleosidase	3200	μM DPN split/hr/100 ml blood at 37°C and pH 6.5		3, 16
50			Fumarase	600	Change in the optical density at 240 mμ, with a light path of 1 cm, at 25°C and pH 7.2 in presence of malate	Whole hemolysate	26
51			Glucose-6-phosphate dehydrogenase	0.6	mM glucose-6-phosphate oxidized/hr/100 ml blood at 25°C and pH 7.4	Stroma-free hemolysate	26
52			Glutamic oxaloacetic transaminase	11.9	μM glutamate formed/hr/g cells at 37°C and pH 7.4		10
53			Hexokinase	54	mg glucose phosphorylated/hr/100 ml blood at 37°C and pH 7.8	Whole hemolysate	17

	Animal	Blood	Enzyme	Value	Enzyme Activity Units	Remarks	Reference
	(A)	(B)	(C)	(D)	(E)	(F)	(G)
54	Rabbit (concluded)	Erythrocytes (concluded)	Isocitric dehydrogenase	0.35	mM isocitrate oxidized/hr/ 100 ml blood at 37.5°C and pH 7.4	Whole hemolysate	26
55			Lactic dehydrogenase	3.7	mM lactate oxidized/hr/ 100 ml blood at 37.5°C and pH 7.4	Stroma-free hemolysate	26
56				4.5	mM lactate oxidized/hr/ 100 ml blood at 37°C and pH 7.6	Stroma-free hemolysate	1
57			Malic dehydrogenase	0.75	mM malate oxidized/hr/ 100 ml blood at 37.5°C and pH 7.4	Stroma-free hemolysate	26
58			Pyrophosphatase, inorganic	3.5	mM pyrophosphate broken down/hr/100 ml blood at 37.5°C and pH 7.5	Stroma-free hemolysate	26
59				30	μM inorganic phosphorus liberated/hr/ml at 37°C and pH 7.5	Washed cells	19
60		Plasma or serum	Cholinesterase	(18-35)	μM acetylcholine hydrolyzed/min/100 ml	0.01 M acetylcholine substrate	13
61				50	μM acetylcholine hydrolyzed/min/100 ml	0.002 M acetylcholine substrate	34
62				41	μM acetylcholine hydrolyzed/min/100 ml	0.001 M acetylcholine substrate	18
63				13.8	μM acetyl-β-methylcholine hydrolyzed/min/100 ml	0.03 M acetyl-β-methyl-choline substrate	22
64				10.7	μM benzoylcholine hydrolyzed/min/100 ml	0.006 M benzoylcholine substrate	22
65			Lactic dehydrogenase	5.2	μL CO_2/hr/0.2 ml at 37°C and pH 7.4		1, 2
66				380	$-\Delta D_{340}$ 0.001/min/ml at 24-27°C and pH 7.4		35
67	Rat	Whole blood	Glyoxalase	861	ml CO_2/20 min/100 ml at 26°C and pH 7.2 in presence of glutathione	Methylglyoxal substrate	8
68		Erythrocytes	Aldolase	90 (70-110)	ml fructose diphosphate/ hr/100 ml at 38°C and pH 8.6	No change during pregnancy	29, 30
69			Carbonic anhydrase	144,000	Amount of erythrocytes that will halve the time of uncatalyzed reaction at 3°C under specified conditions	Less in newborn; parallels erythrocyte zinc concentration in all conditions in adults	4
70			Cholinesterase	253	μM acetylcholine hydrolyzed/min/100 ml	0.015 M acetylcholine substrate	23
71			Glyoxalase	2040	ml CO_2/20 min/100 ml at 26°C and pH 7.2 in presence of glutathione	Methylglyoxal substrate	8
72		Plasma or serum	Aldolase	6(4-9)	ml fructose diphosphate/ hr/100 ml at 38°C and pH 8.6	No change during pregnancy	29, 30
73			Lactic dehydrogenase	14	$-\Delta D_{340}$ 0.001/min/0.006 ml at 24-27°C and pH 7.4		6
74				3100	$-\Delta D_{340}$ 0.001/min/ml at 24-27°C and pH 7.4		35
75			Cholinesterase	58	μM acetylcholine hydrolyzed/min/100 ml	0.01 M acetylcholine substrate	20
76				16.1	μM acetyl-β-methylcholine hydrolyzed/min/100 ml	0.03 M acetyl-β-methyl-choline substrate	22
77				5.8	μM benzoylcholine hydrolyzed/min/100 ml	0.006 M benzoylcholine substrate	22
78	Sheep	Erythrocytes	Cholinesterase	64	μM acetylcholine hydrolyzed/min/100 ml	0.01 M acetylcholine substrate	32
79		Plasma	Cholinesterase	(0-7)	μM acetylcholine hydrolyzed/min/100 ml	0.01 M acetylcholine substrate	13, 32

	Animal	Blood	Enzyme	Value	Enzyme Activity Units	Remarks	Reference
	(A)	(B)	(C)	(D)	(E)	(F)	(G)
80	Swine	Erythrocytes	Carbonic anhydrase	59,000	Amount of erythrocytes that will halve the time of uncatalyzed reaction at 3°C under specified conditions	Less in newborn; parallels erythrocyte zinc concentration in all conditions in adults	4
81			Cholinesterase	93	μM acetylcholine hydrolyzed/min/100 ml	0.01 M acetylcholine substrate	32
82		Plasma or serum	Cholinesterase	(40-43)	μM acetylcholine hydrolyzed/min/100 ml	0.01 M acetylcholine substrate	13, 32
83	Chicken	Erythrocytes	Carbonic anhydrase	22,000	Amount of erythrocytes that will halve the time of uncatalyzed reaction at 3°C under specified conditions	Less in newborn; parallels erythrocyte zinc concentration in all conditions in adults	4
84			Isocitric dehydrogenase	168	μL CO_2 evolved/hr/100 mg dry weight	Whole hemolysate	25
85			Malic dehydrogenase	189	μL CO_2 evolved/hr/100 mg dry weight	Whole hemolysate	25
86			Succinic dehydrogenase	437	μL CO_2 evolved/hr/100 mg dry weight	Whole hemolysate	25
87			Pyrophosphatase, inorganic	201	μM inorganic phosphorus liberated/hr/ml at 37°C and pH 7.5	Dialyzed hemolysate	19
88				158	μM inorganic phosphorus liberated/hr/ml at 37°C and pH 7.5	Stroma-free hemolysate	
89				3.3	μM inorganic phosphorus liberated/hr/ml at 37°C and pH 7.5	Stroma	
90		Plasma or serum	Cholinesterase	(28-78)	μM acetylcholine hydrolyzed/min/100 ml	0.01 M acetylcholine substrate	13, 32

Contributors: (a) Sabine, Jean C., (b) Lehninger, Albert L., (c) Morales, Daniel R., (d) Stowe, Clarence M., Jr., (e) Denstedt, Orville F., (f) Altschule, Mark D., (g) Dische, Zacharias, (h) Koelle, George B.

References: [1] Alivisatos, S. G. A., and O. F. Denstedt. 1951. Science 114:281. [2] Alivisatos, S. G. A., and O. F. Denstedt. 1952. J. Biol. Chem. 199:493. [3] Alivisatos, S. G. A., S. Kashket, and O. F. Denstedt. 1956. Canad. J. Biochem. Physiol. 34:46. [4] Ashby, W. 1943. J. Biol. Chem. 151:521. [5] Augustinsson, K. B. 1948. Acta physiol. scand., Suppl. 52. [6] Bodansky, O., and J. Scholler. 1956. Cancer Res. 16:894. [7] Brody, S. 1949. Res. Bull. Univ. Missouri Agr. Exp. Sta. v. 433, p. 10. [8] Cohen, P. P., and E. K. Sober. 1945. Cancer Res. 5:631. [9] Conway, E. J., and R. Cooke. 1939. Biochem. J., Lond. 33:479. [10] Fessler, A. 1959. M. Sc. Thesis. McGill University, Montreal. [11] Friend, C., and F. Wroblewski. 1956. Science 124:173. [12] Hall, G. E., and C. C. Lucas. 1937. J. Pharm. Exp. Ther. 59:29. [13] Hall, G. E., and C. C. Lucas. 1937. Ibid. 61:10. [14] Hof, J., and I. Woller. 1956. Klin. Wschr. 34:98. [15] Hsieh, K. M., V. Suntzeff, and E. V. Cowdry. 1955. Proc. Soc. Exp. Biol., N. Y. 89:627. [16] Kashket, S. 1953. M. Sc. Thesis. McGill University, Montreal. [17] Kashket, S. 1956. Ph. D. Thesis. McGill University, Montreal. [18] Koelle, G. B. 1953. Biochem. J., Lond. 53:217. [19] Malkin, A., and O. F. Denstedt. 1956. Canad. J. Biochem. Physiol. 34:121. [20] McCance, R. A., A. O. Hutchinson, R. F. A. Dean, and P. E. H. Jones. 1949. Biochem. J., Lond. 45:493. [21] McKee, R. W., R. A. Ormsbee, C. B. Anfinsen, Q. M. Geiman, and E. G. Ball. 1946. J. Exp. M. 84:569. [22] Mendel, B., D. B. Mundell, and H. Rudney. 1943. Biochem. J., Lond. 37:473. [23] Pritchard, J. 1949. Am. J. Physiol. 158:72. [24] Quastel, J. H., and A. H. M. Wheatley. 1938. Biochem. J., Lond. 32:936. [25] Rubinstein, D., and O. F. Denstedt. 1953. J. Biol. Chem. 204:623. [26] Rubinstein, D., P. Ottolenghi, and O. F. Denstedt. 1956. Canad. J. Biochem. Physiol. 34:222. [27] Sabine, J. C. 1956. Am. J. Physiol. 187:275. [28] Sabine, J. C.

Unpublished. [29] Sibley, J. A., and A. L. Lehninger. 1948-49. J. Nat. Cancer Inst. 9:303. [30] Sibley, J. A., and A. L. Lehninger. 1949. J. Biol. Chem. 177:859. [31] Stedman, E., E. Stedman, and A. White. 1933. Biochem. J., Lond. 27:1055. [32] Stedman, E., E. Stedman, and A. White. 1935. Ibid. 29:2107. [33] Stowe, C. M., Jr. 1958. Cornell Vet. 48:241. [34] Wright, C. I., and J. C. Sabine. 1943. J. Pharm. Exp. Ther. 78:375. [35] Wroblewski, F., and J. S. La Due. 1955. Proc. Soc. Exp. Biol., N. Y. 90:210.

36. BLOOD COENZYMES: VERTEBRATES

Values in parentheses are ranges, estimate "c" unless otherwise indicated (cf. Introduction).

Animal	Blood	Coenzyme	Method	Value µg/100 ml	Reference
(A)	(B)	(C)	(D)	(E)	(F)
1 Man	Whole blood	Cocarboxylase[1,2]	Manometric determination of CO_2 evolved from pyruvate	7.0(2.8-11.2)[b]	2
2			Microbiological assay	8.9[3]	1
3				7.6[4]	
4		Pyridine nucleotide, total[5]	Alkaline acetone	3600(2400-4600)[b]	5
5	Erythrocytes	Cocarboxylase[1,2]	Microbiological assay	10.2(7.0-14.0)[3,6]	1
6				6.5(5.0-8.0)[4,6]	
7		Coenzyme A[7]	Acetylation of sulfanilamide	(210-280)	3
8		Flavin-adenine dinucleotide	Modification of alanine test of Warburg and Christian	75	4
9		Pyridine nucleotide, total[5,8]	Alkaline acetone	7700(6100-9300)[b]	5
10	Plasma	Flavin-adenine dinucleotide	Modification of alanine test of Warburg and Christian	10	4
11		Pyridine nucleotide, total[5]	Alkaline acetone	70(20-120)	5
Cattle					
12 Calf	Whole blood	Cocarboxylase[1,2]	Microbiological assay	(7.9-10.1)	1
13 Ox	Whole blood	Cocarboxylase[1,2]	Microbiological assay	(4.5-5.1)	1
14			Manometric determination of CO_2 evolved from pyruvate	5.7(2.7-8.7)[b]	2
15 Guinea pig	Whole blood	Cocarboxylase[1,2]	Microbiological assay	(45-80)	1
16 Horse	Whole blood	Cocarboxylase[1,2]	Microbiological assay	(1.1-1.7)	1
17 Rat, albino	Whole blood	Cocarboxylase[1,2]	Microbiological assay	20.5(10-25)	1
18		Flavin-adenine dinucleotide	Microbiological assay	(50-65)	1
19 Sheep	Whole blood	Cocarboxylase[1,2]	Microbiological assay	(4.0-4.7)	1
20 Swine	Whole blood	Cocarboxylase[1,2]	Microbiological assay	(12-20)	1
21 Chicken	Whole blood	Cocarboxylase[1,2]	Microbiological assay	6.0(5.6-11.0)	1
22 Pigeon	Whole blood	Cocarboxylase[1,2]	Manometric determination of CO_2 evolved from pyruvate	20.2(0.6-40.0)[b]	2
23 Frog	Whole blood	Cocarboxylase[1,2]	Microbiological assay	9.0	1

/1/ All blood cocarboxylase is intracellular. /2/ As bound thiamine. /3/ Males. /4/ Females. /5/ As diphosphopyridine nucleotide. /6/ Sex difference in erythrocyte cocarboxylase values is significant: males = 1.49 µg/100 billion erythrocytes; females = 1.28 µg/100 billion erythrocytes. /7/ As bound pantothenic acid. /8/ Ratio of diphosphopyridine nucleotide to triphosphopyridine nucleotide in erythrocytes is estimated at approximately 8:1; diphosphopyridine nucleotide is present almost entirely in erythrocytes.

Contributors: (a) Beerstecher, Ernest, Jr., and Spangler, S., (b) Granick, S., (c) Lehninger, Albert L.

References: [1] Beerstecher, E., Jr., and S. Spangler. Unpublished. [2] Goodhart, R. S., and H. M. Sinclair. 1939. Biochem. J., Lond. 33:1099. [3] Kaplan, N. O., and F. Lipmann. 1948. J. Biol. Chem. 174:37. [4] Klein, J. R., and H. I. Kohn. 1940. Ibid. 136:177. [5] Levitas, N., J. Robinson, F. Rosen, J. W. Huff, and W. A. Perlzweig. 1947. Ibid. 167:169.

VI. Blood Cells

37. ERYTHROCYTE AND HEMOGLOBIN VALUES: MAN

Part I: BIRTH TO MATURITY

Values are smoothed means and ranges from plotted curves. Values in parentheses are ranges, estimate "c" unless otherwise indicated (cf. Introduction).

	Age	Erythrocyte Count million/cu mm blood	Erythrocyte Packed Volume (Hematocrit) ml/100 ml blood	Erythrocyte Volume (Mean Corpuscular) cu μ	Hemoglobin Concentration		Erythrocyte Hemoglobin Content μμg	Reference
					g/100 ml blood	g/100 ml erythrocytes		
	(A)	(B)	(C)	(D)	(E)	(F)	(G)	(H)
1	At birth[1]	5.7(4.8-7.1)	56.6	106	21.5(18.0-27.0)	38.0	38	B,1,2,4-7,
2	1st da	5.6(4.7-7.0)	56.1	106	21.2(17.7-26.5)	37.8	38	9;C,4-
3	1st wk	5.3(4.5-6.4)	52.7	101	19.6(16.2-25.5)	37.2	37	6,9;D,9;
4	2nd wk	5.1(4.3-6.0)	49.6	96	18.0(14.5-24.2)	36.3	35	E-G,3-
5	3rd wk	4.9(4.1-6.0)	46.6	93	16.6(13.2-23.0)	35.6	34	7,9
6	4th wk	4.7(3.9-5.9)	44.6	91	15.6(12.0-21.8)	35.0	33	
7	2nd mo	4.5(3.8-5.8)	38.9	85	13.3(10.8-18.0)	34.2	30	
8	4th mo	4.5(3.8-5.3)	36.5	79	12.4(10.2-15.0)	34.0	27	
9	6th mo	4.6(3.9-5.3)	36.2	78	12.3(10.0-15.0)	34.0	27	
10	8th mo	4.6(4.0-5.4)	35.8	77	12.1(9.8-15.0)	33.8	26	
11	10th mo	4.6(4.0-5.5)	35.5	77	11.9(8.4-14.9)	33.5	26	
12	12th mo	4.6(4.0-5.5)	35.2	77	11.6(9.0-14.6)	33.0	25	
13	2nd yr	4.7(3.8-5.4)	35.5	78	11.7(9.2-15.5)	33.0	25	
14	4th yr	4.7(3.8-5.4)	37.1	80	12.6(9.6-15.5)	34.0	27	
15	6th yr	4.7(3.8-5.4)	37.9	80	12.7(10.0-15.5)	33.5	27	
16	8th yr	4.7(3.8-5.4)	38.9	80	12.9(10.3-15.5)	33.2	27	
17	10th yr	4.8(3.8-5.4)	39.0	80	13.0(10.7-15.5)	33.3	27	
18	12th yr	4.8(3.8-5.4)	39.6	81	13.4(11.0-16.5)	33.8	28	
	14 yr and over							8
19	♂	5.4(4.6-6.2)[b]	47	87	15.8(14.0-18.0)[b]	33.5	29	
20	♀	4.8(4.2-5.4)[b]	42	87	13.9(11.5-16.0)[b]	33.5	29	

/1/ When cord was clamped after placental separation rather than immediately after birth, erythrocyte count was 560,000/cu mm greater, and hemoglobin 2.6 g/100 ml greater, during first week of life. Erythrocyte and hemoglobin values were higher for heel blood (capillary) than for blood from superior sagittal sinus.

Contributors: (a) Bethell, Frank H., (b) DeMarsh, Q. B., (c) Glaser, Kurt, (d) Guest, George M., (e) Mayerson, H. S., (f) Osgood, Edwin E., (g) Windle, William F., (h) Wintrobe, M. M.

References: [1] DeMarsh, Q. B., H. L. Alt, and W. F. Windle. 1948. Am. J. Dis. Child. 75:860. [2] DeMarsh, Q. B., H. L. Alt, W. F. Windle, and D. S. Hillis. 1941. J. Am. M. Ass. 116:2568. [3] Elvehjem, C. A., W. H. Peterson, and D. R. Mendenhall. 1933. Am. J. Dis. Child. 46:105. [4] Guest, G. M. 1938. In Nutrition: newer diagnostic methods. Proc. 16th Conf. Milbank Mem. Fund, New York. [5] Guest, G. M., and E. W. Brown. 1957. A.M.A. J. Dis. Child. 93:486. [6] Guest, G. M., E. W. Brown, and M. Wing. 1938. Am. J. Dis. Child. 56:529. [7] Merritt, K. K., and L. T. Davidson. 1933. Ibid. 46:991. [8] Osgood, E. E. 1935. Arch. Int. M. 56:849. [9] Wintrobe, M. M. 1956. Clinical hematology. Ed. 4. Lea and Febiger, Philadelphia.

Part II: NON-PREGNANT, PREGNANT, AND POSTPARTUM FEMALES

Values in parentheses are ranges, estimate "c" (cf. Introduction).

	Condition	No. of Observations	Erythrocyte Count million/cu mm blood	Erythrocyte Packed Volume (Hematocrit) ml/100 ml blood	Hemoglobin Concentration g/100 ml blood
	(A)	(B)	(C)	(D)	(E)
1	Non-pregnant	42[1]	4.44(3.68-5.20)	41.5(37.5-45.0)	13.4(11.7-15.1)
	Pregnant[2]				
2	3rd mo	7	4.49(4.00-4.98)	40.6(35.0-46.2)	13.2(11.4-15.0)
3	4th mo	9	3.83(3.43-4.23)	37.0(32.0-42.0)	12.0(10.8-13.2)
4	5th mo	9	3.98(3.50-4.46)	34.8(31.0-38.6)	12.1(10.1-14.1)
5	6th mo	20	3.85(3.19-4.51)	36.0(30.0-42.0)	12.2(10.1-14.3)
6	7th mo	24	3.90(3.25-4.65)	36.0(31.0-41.0)	12.1(10.4-13.8)
7	8th mo	34	3.89(3.20-4.58)	36.4(31.5-41.3)	11.9(10.1-13.7)
8	9th mo	38	3.97(3.02-4.92)	37.5(31.5-43.5)	12.3(10.2-14.4)
9	Postpartum	16	4.14(3.23-5.05)	38.7(33.5-43.9)	12.7(10.4-15.0)

/1/ Number of subjects. /2/ 102 subjects.

Contributor: Battaglia, Frederick C.

Reference: Holly, R. G. 1953. Obst. Gyn., N. Y. 2:119.

Part III: ADULTS

Values in parentheses are ranges, estimate "b" unless otherwise indicated (cf. Introduction).

	Variable	Sex	Value	Remarks	Reference
	(A)	(B)	(C)	(D)	(E)
	Erythrocyte				
1	Count	♂	5.4(4.6-6.2) million/cu mm blood		3,16
2		♀	4.8(4.2-5.4) million/cu mm blood		
3	Packed volume	♂	47(40-54) ml/100 ml blood	Heparin or other isotonic antico-	16,18
4	(hematocrit)[1]	♀	42(37-47) ml/100 ml blood	agulant	
5		♂	45(40-50) ml/100 ml blood	Anticoagulant = 2 mg potassium	16
6		♀	41(36-45) ml/100 ml blood	oxalate/ml blood	
7	Volume (mean corpus-	♂	87(70-94) cu μ	Heparin or other isotonic antico-	16
8	cular)	♀	87(74-98) cu μ	agulant	
9		♂	82(70-94) cu μ	Anticoagulant = 2 mg potassium	
10		♀	86(74-98) cu μ	oxalate/ml blood	
11	Circulating volume	♂	28.3(20.3-36.3) ml/kg body wt		15
12		♀	24.2(19.0-29.4) ml/kg body wt		
13	Mass	♂	95(76-103) μμg	Calculated from mean corpuscular volume and specific gravity	20
	Diameter				
14	Dry	♂, ♀	7.5(7.2-7.8) μ	Determined by diffraction, or by 500 or more measurements with micrometer eyepiece	3,7
15	Wet	♂, ♀	8.4(7.4-9.4) μ		19
	Thickness				
16	Dry	♂, ♀	2.0(1.7-2.2) μ	Calculated from mean corpuscular volume and dry diameter	3,16
17	Wet	♂, ♀	2.4 μ		19
	Surface area				
18	Dry	♂, ♀	135(129-146) sq μ	Calculated from mean corpuscular volume and dry thickness	16
19	Wet	♂, ♀	163 sq μ		19

/1/ Centrifuged for 10 minutes at 3000 rpm or more, after attaining constant packed cell volume [16].

	Variable	Sex	Value	Remarks	Reference
	(A)	(B)	(C)	(D)	(E)
	Erythrocyte (concluded)				
20	Spherocytic index	♂, ♀	0.27		3,16
21	Electrophoretic mobility	♂, ♀	0.000128(0.000122-0.000134) sq cm/volt sec	In phosphate at pH 7.4	2
22		♂, ♀	0.000107(0.000103-0.000111) sq cm/volt sec	In 0.145 M sodium chloride	
23	pH	♂	7.24(7.21-7.26)		13
24	Specific gravity	♂	1.093(1.089-1.097)	At 25/4°C	10,20
25	Electrical charge	♂, ♀	5.21 electrostatic units x 10^3		1
26	Zeta potential	♂, ♀	16.8 millivolts		1
	Sedimentation rate				
27	Cutler method	♂	$(0-8)^c$ mm/hr		5
28		♀	$(0-10)^c$ mm/hr		
29	Westergren method	♂	$(0-15)^c$ mm/hr		21
30		♀	$(0-20)^c$ mm/hr		
31	Wintrobe method	♂	$(0-9)^c$ mm/hr		22
32		♀	$(0-15)^c$ mm/hr		
	Fragility				
33	Daland and Worthley	♂, ♀	$0.47(0.48-0.46)^c$ % NaCl solution	Initial hemolysis	6
34	method		$0.27(0.30-0.24)^c$ % NaCl solution	Final hemolysis	
35	Giffin and Sanford	♂, ♀	$(0.44-0.42)^c$ % NaCl solution	Initial hemolysis	12
36	method		$(0.34-0.32)^c$ % NaCl solution	Final hemolysis	
37	Parpart method	♂	$0.43(0.54-0.32)^c$ % NaCl solution	Mean hemolysis	17
38	Life span	♂, ♀	120(108-130) da		11
39	Production rate	♂	45,000 per cu mm blood/da		3,4,16
40		♀	40,000 per cu mm blood/da		
41		♂	3500 million/kg body wt/da		
42		♀	2630 million/kg body wt/da		
43	Iron content	♂, ♀	0.10(0.08-0.12) μμg	Calculated from hemoglobin content, using 0.339 as percent iron in hemoglobin	8,14,16
	Hemoglobin				
44	Whole blood concentra-	♂	16.3(14.5-18.1) g/100 ml blood		9
45	tion	♀	14.5(12.3-16.7) g/100 ml blood		
46	Erythrocyte concentra-	♂, ♀	33.5(30-40) g/100 ml erythrocytes	Heparin or other isotonic anticoagulant	3,16
47	tion	♂	35(30-40) g/100 ml erythrocytes	Anticoagulant - 2 mg potassium oxalate/ml blood	16
48		♀	34(30-40) g/100 ml erythrocytes		
49	Erythrocyte content	♂	29(25-34) μμg		16
50		♀	29(24-33) μμg		
51	Production rate	♂	0.13 g/100 ml blood/da		3,4,16
52		♀	0.11 g/100 ml blood/da		
53	Erythrocyte and hemoglobin replacement rate	♂, ♀	0.83% of total/da		3,4,16

Contributors: (a) Bethell, Frank H., (b) Carlsen, Elizabeth, (c) Collier, H. B., (d) Dole, Vincent P., (e) Ebaugh, Franklin G., Jr., (f) Gram, H. C., (g) Guest, George M., (h) Hirschboeck, John S., (i) Osgood, Edwin E., (j) Ponder, Eric, (k) Riser, William H., Jr., (l) Van Slyke, Donald D.

References: [1] Abramson, H. A. 1929. J. Gen. Physiol. 12:711. [2] Bangham, A. D., H. D. Heard, and D. G. King-Hele. 1958. Nature, Lond. 182:642. [3] Bethell, F. H. 1948. Clinical laboratory diagnosis and essentials of hematology. Edwards Letter Shop, Ann Arbor. [4] Callender, S. T., E. O. Powell, and L. J. Witts. 1945. J. Path. Bact., Lond. 57:129. [5] Cutler, J. W. 1932. Am. J. M. Sc. 183:643. [6] Daland, G. A., and K. Worthley. 1935. J. Laborat. Clin. M. 20:1122. [7] Donelson, E. G., J. M. Leichsenring, and L. M. Wall. 1940. Am. J. Physiol. 128:382. [8] Drabkin, D. L. 1945. Am. J. M. Sc. 209:268. [9] Drabkin, D. L. 1951. Physiol. Rev. 31:345. [10] Ebaugh, F. G., Jr., P. Levine, and C. P. Emerson. 1955. J. Laborat. Clin. M. 46:409.

[11] Ebaugh, F. G., Jr., G. P. Rodnan, and R. E. Peterson. Unpublished. [12] Giffin, H. Z., and A. H. Sanford. 1919. J. Laborat. Clin. M. 4:465. [13] Gram, H. C. 1924. Am. J. M. Sc. 168:521. [14] Grinstein, M., and C. V. Moore. 1949. J. Clin. Invest. 28:505. [15] Huff, R. L., and D. D. Feller. 1956. Ibid. 35:1. [16] Osgood, E. E. 1935. Arch. Int. M. 56:849. [17] Parpart, A. K., P. B. Lorenz, E. R. Parpart, J. R. Gregg, and A. M. Chase. 1947. J. Clin. Invest. 26:636. [18] Ponder, E. In O. Glaser, ed. 1944. Medical physics. Year Book Publishers, Chicago. [19] Ponder, E. 1948. Hemolysis and related phenomena. Grune and Stratton, New York. [20] Van Slyke, D. D., P. B. Hamilton, V. P. Dole, K. Emerson, Jr., and R. M. Archibald. 1950. J. Biol. Chem. 183:305. [21] Westergren, A. 1926. Am. Rev. Tuberc. 14:94. [22] Wintrobe, M. M., and J. W. Landsberg. 1935. Am. J. M. Sc. 189:102.

38. PROBABILITY DISTRIBUTION OF ERYTHROCYTE AND HEMOGLOBIN VALUES: MAN

Part I: ERYTHROCYTE COUNT

Erythrocyte count: 137♂ = 5.4(4.58-6.22) million/cu mm; 100♀ = 4.8(4.0-5.6) million/cu mm.

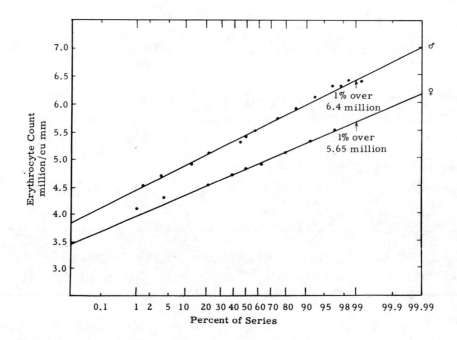

Contributor: Osgood, Edwin E.

38. PROBABILITY DISTRIBUTION OF ERYTHROCYTE AND HEMOGLOBIN VALUES: MAN (Concluded)

Part II: ERYTHROCYTE PACKED VOLUME

Erythrocyte packed volume (hematocrit): 94♂ = 44.8(39.2-50.4) ml/100 ml blood; 100♀ = 41.2(36.2-46.2) ml/100 ml blood.

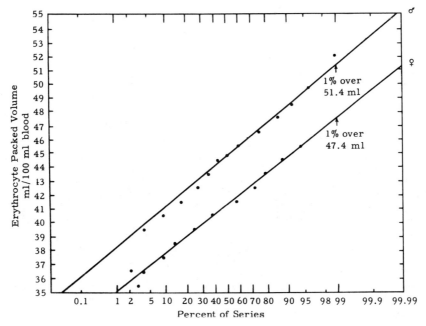

Contributor: Osgood, Edwin E.

Part III: HEMOGLOBIN CONCENTRATION

Hemoglobin concentration: 137♂ = 15.8(13.76-17.84) g/100 ml blood; 100♀ = 13.7(11.7-15.7) g/100 ml blood.

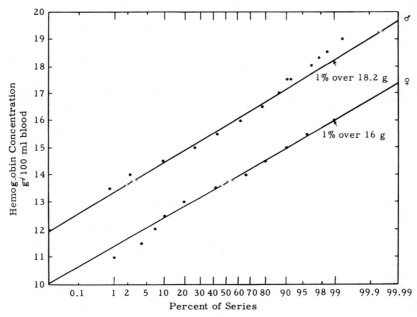

Contributor: Osgood, Edwin E.

113

39. ERYTHROCYTE AND HEMOGLOBIN VALUES FOR FETUS, NEWBORN, AND ADULT FEMALE: MAMMALS

Values for adult female are not necessarily those of the mother. Values in parentheses are ranges, estimate "c" unless otherwise indicated (cf. Introduction).

Animal	Age	Erythrocyte Count million/cu mm blood	Erythrocyte Packed Volume (Hematocrit) ml/100 ml blood	Erythrocyte Volume (Mean Corpuscular) cu μ	Hemoglobin Concentration g/100 ml blood	Erythrocyte Hemoglobin Content μμg	Reference
(A)	(B)	(C)	(D)	(E)	(F)	(G)	(H)
Man	Fetus (term = 280 da)						12
1	0.3 term	1.1(0.3-2.2)	27(23-33)	191(134-285)	9.3(8.0-10.9)	63(47-97)	
2	0.4 term	2.8(2.3-3.5)	33(29-44)	131(113-150)	10.7(6.0-13.1)	40(35-48)	
3	0.5 term	2.8(2.2-3.5)	36(30-41)	129(116-140)	11.5(8.7-14.6)	42(38-51)	
4	0.6 term	3.5(2.9-4.1)	44(36-52)	125(116-136)	13.6(11.0-14.7)	39(33-45)	
5	Newborn	4.8(3.8-6.0)[1]	51.3(41-61)[1]	113(90-124)	17.9(13.0-22.0)[1]	37.5(32-43)	4,11
6	Adult female	4.8(4.2-5.4)[b]	42(37-47)[b]	87(74-98)[b]	14.5(12.3-16.7)[b]	29(24-33)[b]	2,7
Cat	Fetus (term = 60 da)						13,14
7	0.6 term	2.2	28.0	134	7.9	36	
8	0.7 term	3.1(2.6-3.8)	30.5(26-36)	99(94-103)	9.1(7.5-10.7)	28(24-38)	
9	0.8 term	3.8(3.2-4.3)	34.3(30-41)	91(81-97)	10.1(9.3-11.2)	27(23-30)	
10	Newborn, 3-12 da	5.7(5.2-6.1)	39.3(35-48)	68(65-78)	12.4(9.6-15.1)	22(19-26)	
11	Adult female	6.6	34.2	51	11.8	18	
Cattle	Fetus (term = 280 da)						10
12	0.3 term	3.9(3.7-4.1)	37.7(34-40)	93(91-97)	8.5(7.7-9.1)	21.3(21-22)	
13	0.4 term	4.8(4.5-5.3)	43.0(40-47)	88(84-89)	10.9(10.3-11.4)	21.1(20-22)	
14	0.5 term	4.8(3.8-5.5)	36.7(28-45)	77(74-83)	8.5(6.9-9.7)	18.6(18-20)	
15	0.6 term	5.5(4.4-6.4)	40.4(32-50)	74(71-77)	9.6(7.7-11.2)	17.5(17-18)	
16	0.7 term	5.2(4.2-6.2)	37.0(32-44)	71(69-75)	9.7(8.3-12.1)	18.6(17-20)	
17	0.8 term	5.9(5.4-8.0)	39.7(35-47)	58(57-63)	9.8(8.8-11.5)	15.0(14-16)	
18	0.9 term	6.1(5.9-6.2)	31.0(30-32)	51(49-53)	8.4(8.3-8.5)	13.9(13-14)	
19	At term[2]	6.8(6.0-7.8)	35.9(32-42)	53(50-54)	9.6(8.5-10.8)	14.1(14-15)	
20	Adult female	8.1(6.1-10.7)	38.6(31-54)	50(47-54)	12.9(9.2-18.3)	15.7(14-19)	
Goat	Fetus (term = 147 da)						3
21	0.3 term		19		4.2		
22	0.5 term		31(29-33)		7.1(5.2-9.1)		
23	0.6 term		40		10.1		
24	0.7 term		22		9.0		
25	0.8 term		32		10.4		
26	0.9 term		28.5(28-29)		8.9(8.2-9.6)		
27	At term[3]		27		9.4		
28	Newborn, 24-48 hr		33(29-36)		11.0(9.9-12.4)		
29	Adult female		50		12.6		
Rabbit	Fetus (term = 31 da)						13,14
30	0.6 term	1.9(1.6-2.0)	22.3(21-23)	120(113-133)	7.3(7.1-7.7)	44(35-46)	
31	0.7 term	2.9(2.1-3.4)	34.4(23-38)	122(108-154)	9.6(7.7-11.1)	35(27-48)	
32	0.8 term	2.8(2.3-3.1)	32.0(28-37)	113(99-123)	10.1(8.8-11.0)	36(31-47)	
33	0.9 term	3.7(2.9-4.3)	30.5(24-34)	82(79-84)	10.0(8.5-11.3)	28(26-30)	
	Newborn						
34	2-18 hr	4.8(3.3-5.5)	44.1(32-50)	94(90-100)	14.2(11.0-15.7)	30(27-34)	
35	24-48 hr	5.2(4.4-5.8)	50.0(43-59)	97(89-102)	15.6(13.7-18.1)	33(27-34)	
36	Adult female	6.3	39.8	64	12.8	21	
Rat	Fetus (term = 21 da)						
37	0.6 term				5.1(5.0-5.3)		6
38	0.7 term				7.6(6.1-9.2)		6
39	0.8 term	1.0(0.7-1.2)	21.0	160	8.5(7.5-9.3)	52	5,6,13
40	0.9 term	1.8(1.5-2.1)	40.1	159(157-160)	8.2(7.4-9.1)	32.5(31-34)	5,6,13
	Newborn						13
41	1-7 da	2.0(1.4-2.9)	25.0(18-31)	126(96-172)	8.3(6.3-10.5)	43(31-60)	
42	8-14 da	2.2(1.6-2.8)	20.6(15-28)	92(77-110)	6.6(4.6-9.0)	31(24-36)	
43	Adult female	6.6	39.4	61	12.8	20	13
Sheep	Fetus (term = 147 da)						
44	0.2 term				4.0(2.8-4.8)		1
45	0.3 term				6.9(4.6-8.4)		1

/1/ Cord or venous blood; capillary blood values may increase as much as 20% during first week after birth [9].
/2/ Probably by cesarean section. /3/ Cesarean section.

39. ERYTHROCYTE AND HEMOGLOBIN VALUES FOR FETUS, NEWBORN, AND ADULT FEMALE: MAMMALS (Concluded)

	Animal	Age	Erythrocyte Count million/cu mm blood	Erythrocyte Packed Volume (Hematocrit) ml/100 ml blood	Erythrocyte Volume (Mean Corpuscular) cu μ	Hemoglobin Concentration g/100 ml blood	Erythrocyte Hemoglobin Content μμg	Reference
	(A)	(B)	(C)	(D)	(E)	(F)	(G)	(H)
	Sheep (concluded)	Fetus (term = 147 da) (concluded)						
46		0.4 term	1.8(1.6-2.1)	27(25-29)	151(119-184)	8.3(6.4-11.2)	40.5	1,15
47		0.5 term				9.2(7.9-10.3)		1
48		0.6 term	5.1	37	73	10.7(8.7-12.8)	20.5	1,15
49		0.7 term				11.2(8.8-13.4)		1
50		0.8 term	8.1	41.5	48	11.9(10.2-13.6)	13.1	1,15
51		0.9 term	9.9(8.3-11.8)	49(41-54)	49(43-55)	12.6(8.5-17.0)	12.8(12-13)	1,15
52		Adult female	11.6	34	30	11.0	13	8
	Swine	Fetus (term = 114 da)						13,14
53		0.2 term	0.3(0.1-0.5)	6.6(4-11)	244(204-361)			
54		0.3 term	0.6(0.2-1.3)	10.3(4-20)	173(131-278)	3.3(1.5-4.9)	56(38-87)	
55		0.4 term	2.5(0.7-3.9)	26.2(10-33)	100(80-149)	6.9(2.6-10.6)	27(19-40)	
56		0.5 term	2.9(2.0-4.0)	27.4(23-35)	94(84-114)	6.8(4.9-11.2)	23(17-29)	
57		0.6 term	3.0(2.1-4.0)	30.3(19-38)	101(85-112)	8.1(5.2-9.7)	27(21-35)	
58		0.7 term	4.0(3.0-4.4)	31.0(29-34)	101(95-107)	7.0(6.5-9.6)	25(19-31)	
59		0.8 term	3.9(3.0-4.4)	32.4(29-36)	80(77-96)	8.7(7.6-9.6)	22(20-28)	
60		0.9 term	4.2(4.0-4.3)	34.5(33-36)	83(83-83)	9.3(8.8-9.7)	22.5(22-23)	
		Newborn						
61		1-12 hr	5.7(5.5-5.9)	39.6(39-40)	69(68-71)	11.8(11.8-12.0)	21(20-22)	
62		1-10 da	3.9(2.6-5.3)	25.0(18-36)	64(59-69)	8.1(5.4-10.1)	20(16-22)	
63		Adult female	6.9	40.8	59	13.8	21	

Contributors: (a) Barron, Donald H., (b) Bethell, Frank H., (c) Osgood, Edwin E., (d) Young, I. Maureen

References: [1] Barcroft, J. 1946. Researches on prenatal life. Blackwell, Oxford. [2] Drabkin, D. L. 1951. Physiol. Rev. 31:345. [3] Elliott, R. H., F. G. Hall, and A. S. G. Huggett. 1934. J. Physiol., Lond. 82:160. [4] Guest, G. M., E. W. Brown, and M. Wing. 1938. Am. J. Dis. Child. 56:529. [5] Kindred, J. E., and E. L. Corey. 1930. Anat. Rec. 47:213. [6] Nicholas, J. S. 1927. Am. J. Physiol. 83:499. [7] Osgood, E. E. 1935. Arch. Int. M. 56:849. [8] Ponder, E. 1934. The mammalian red cell and properties of haemolytic systems. Gebruder Borntrager, Berlin. [9] Smith, C. A. 1950. The physiology of the newborn infant. C. C. Thomas, Springfield, Ill. [10] Von Deseö, D. 1929. Pflügers Arch. 221:321. [11] Waugh, T. R., F. T. Merchant, and G. B. Maugham. 1939. Am. J. M. Sc. 198:646. [12] Wintrobe, M. M. 1956. Clinical hematology. Ed. 4. Lea and Febiger, Philadelphia. [13] Wintrobe, M. M., and H. B. Schumacher. 1935. Am. J. Anat. 58:313. [14] Wintrobe, M. M., and H. B. Schumacher. 1935. J. Clin. Invest. 14:837. [15] Young, I. M. Unpublished.

40. ERYTHROCYTE AND HEMOGLOBIN VALUES: VERTEBRATES OTHER THAN MAN

Values in parentheses are ranges, estimate "c" unless otherwise indicated (cf. Introduction).

Animal	RBC Count million/cu mm blood	RBC Packed Volume (Hematocrit) ml/100 ml blood	RBC Volume (Mean Corpuscular) cu μ	Hemoglobin Concentration g/100 ml blood	g/100 ml RBC	RBC Hemoglobin Content μμg	RBC Dimensions[1] (Dry Film) μ	Reference
(A)	(B)	(C)	(D)	(E)	(F)	(G)	(H)	(I)
Mammals								
1 Buffalo, domestic	6.8	44.3 (38-52)	72.0	13.0 (11.0-15.2)	19.0	29.0	5.5	6
2 Cat	8.0 (6.5-9.5)	40 (28-52)	57 (51-63)	11.2 (7.0-15.5)	28 (23-31)	14 (12-16)	6.0 (5.0-7.0)	1
3 Chimpanzee	5.1 (3.4-6.0)	41.6 (24-51)	81.4 (70-91)	12.3 (6.5-15.1)	30.6 (29-34)	24.5 (20-27)	7.4	9
4 Cow	8.1 (6.1-10.7)	40 (33-47)[b]	50 (47-54)	11.5 (8.7-14.5)[b]	29.0		5.9	1
5 Dog	6.3 (4.5-8.0)	45.5 (38-53)	66 (59-68)	14.8 (11.0-18.0)	33 (30-35)	23 (21-25)	7.0 (6.2-8.0)	1
6 Goat	16.0 (13.3-17.9)	33 (27.0-34.6)	19.3	10.5 (8.8-11.4)	34 (33-36)	6.7	4.0	9
7 Guinea pig	5.6 (4.5-7.0)	42 (37-47)	77 (71-83)	14.4 (11.0-16.5)	34 (33-35)	26.0 (24.5-27.5)	7.4 (7.0-7.5)	1.
8 Hamster	6.96 (3.96-9.96)[b]	49 (39-59)[b]	70.0	16.0 (2.0-30.0)[b]	32.0	23.0	5.6 (5.4-5.8)[b]	5
9 Horse	9.3 (8.21-10.35)[b]	33.4 (28-42)[b]		11.1 (8-14)[b]	33.0		5.5	1
10 Monkey, rhesus	5.2 (3.6-6.8)[b]	42 (32-52)[b]		12.6 (10-16)[b]	30.0			1
11 Mouse	9.3 (7.7-12.5)	41.5	49 (48-51)	14.8 (10-19)	36 (33-39)	16 (15.5-16.5)	6.0	1
12 Rabbit	5.7 (4.5-7.0)	41.5 (33-50)	61 (60-68)	11.9 (8.0-15.0)	29 (27-31)	21 (19-23)	7.5 (6.5-7.5)	1
13 Rat	8.9 (7.2-9.6)	46 (39-53)	61 (57-65)	14.8 (12.0-17.5)	32 (30-35)	17 (15-19)	7.5 (6.0-7.5)	1
14 Sheep	10.3 (9.4-11.1)	31.7 (29.9-33.6)	31 (30-32)	10.9 (10.0-11.8)	34.5 (34-35)	11.0	4.8	9
15 Swine	6.4	39.0 (38.0-40.0)	61.1 (59-63)	13.7 (13.2-14.2)	35.0	21.5 (21-22)		9
Birds								
16 Chicken	2.8 (2.0-3.2)	35.6 (24.0-43.3)	127 (120-137)	10.3 (7.3-12.9)	29 (27-30)	36.6 (33-41)	11.2 x 6.8	9
17 Duck[2]	2.8	39.5		14.8 (9-21)	38.1	52.1 (32-71)	12.8 x 6.6	8
18 Goose	2.8 (2.6-3.0)	44.7 (43.1-46.2)	160 (145-174)	12.7 (11.9-13.4)	28.5 (28-29)	45.5 (40-51)	12.2 x 7.2	9
19 Pigeon	3.2	42.3	131.0	12.8	30.0	40.0	13.2 x 6.9	9
20 Turkey	2.3	38.0		11.2	23.5		15.5 x 7.5	8
Reptiles								
21 Alligator (Alligator mississippiensis)	0.67	30.0	450.0	8.2	27.0	123.0	23.2 x 12.1	9
Snake								9
22 Garter- (Eutania sirtalis)	1.05 (0.71-1.39)	28 (19-37)	267 (266-268)	8.5 (5.8-11.3)	31.0	82.0	18.1 x 10.3	
23 Hognose- (Heterodon contortrix)	0.57 (0.50-0.63)	18.7 (13.3-24.1)	324.5 (266-383)	5.6 (3.7-7.5)	29.5 (28-31)	95.5 (74-119)	16.0 x 9.5	
24 Water- (Natrix sipedon)	0.77	35.5	465.0	10.0	28.0	131.0	19.6 x 11.0	
25 Terrapin, fresh-water	0.74	21.0	284.0	6.2	30.0	84.0	17 x 12	9
26 Tortoise (Testudo carolina)	0.74	22.1	300.0	6.2	28.0	85.0	18.0 x 8.7	9

/1/ Dimensions for mammals are diameters; dimensions for other vertebrates are length x width. /2/ As ducks mature, hematological values progressively increase.

40. ERYTHROCYTE AND HEMOGLOBIN VALUES: VERTEBRATES OTHER THAN MAN (Continued)

	Animal	RBC Count million/cu mm blood	RBC Packed Volume (Hematocrit) ml/100 ml blood	RBC Volume (Mean Corpuscular) cu μ	Hemoglobin Concentration g/100 ml blood	g/100 ml RBC	RBC Hemoglobin Content μμg	RBC Dimensions[1] (Dry Film) μ	Reference
	(A)	(B)	(C)	(D)	(E)	(F)	(G)	(H)	(I)
	Reptiles (concluded)								
27	Turtle, box (Terrapene carolina)	0.65 (0.61-0.70)	24.7 (22.4-26.9)	442.0	5.9 (5.4-6.2)	29	91.0	19 x 9	2,3
	Amphibians								
28	Congo snake (Amphiuma means)	0.03	40 (39-41)	13,857 (13,200-14,513)	9.4 (7.7-11.0)	24 (21-27)	3287 (2750-3823)	62.5 x 36.3	9
29	Frog (Rana catesbeiana)	0.44 (0.43-0.45)	29.3 (26.6-32.0)	670 (625-716)	7.8 (7.4-8.2)	27 (26-28)	179 (174-184)	24.8 x 15.3	9
30	Hellbender (Cryptobranchus alleganiensis)	0.07	49.0	7425	13.3	27.0	2010	40.5 x 21.0	9
31	Mud puppy (Necturus maculatus)	0.02	21.4	10,070	4.6	22.0	2160	52.8 x 28.2	9
	Fishes								
32	Carp (Cyprinus carpio)	0.84 (0.65-1.13)	31.3 (21-40)	311 (278-340)	10.5 (9.4-12.4)	33.5	72 (63-78)		4
33	Catfish (Ameiurus catus)	2.65	15.4	123	9.2	28	35	10.4 x 8.7	9
34	Cod, rock (Gadus callarias)	1.55 (1.49-1.60)	29.1 (23.8-32.6)	186 (159-201)	5.9 (5.2-6.4)	20 (19-22)	38 (35-40)	12.2 x 9.0	9
35	Dogfish Smooth (Mustelus canis)	0.46	23.3	541.0	4.6			19.1 x 13.8	7
36	Spiny (Squalus acanthias)	0.24	18.9	820.0	3.8			22.7 x 15.2	
37	Eel, common (Anguilla rostrata)	2.48	37.9 (36.0-39.8)	156 (141-170)	9.0 (8.0-10.0)	23.5 (22-25)	36.5 (35-38)	13.0 x 8.0	9
38	Eelpout (Zoarces anguillaris)	2.04	20.8	102	4.0	19	20	10.6 x 5.9	9
39	Flounder Rusty- (Limanda ferruginea)	1.23 (0.78-1.61)	14.6 (8.4-18.2)	117.7 (107-138)	3.2 (2.1-4.2)	22.7 (19-25)	26.7 (26-28)	10.3 x 7.7	9
40	Witch- (Glyptocephalus cynoglossus)	2.48	34.9	141	5.1	15	21	12.5 x 7.1	
41	Goosefish (Lophius piscatorius)	1.09	16.8	241.0	4.3			13.3 x 9.6	7
42	Hagfish (Myxine glutinosa)	0.15 (0.12-0.19)	22.2 (19.3-27.6)	1530 (1470-1560)	4.6 (4.0-5.7)	21.0	318.3 (303-330)	26.4 x 18.3	9
43	Hake Mud- (Urophycis tenuis)	2.07	50.0	242	7.0	14	35	13.7 x 8.0	9
44	Silver (Merluccius bilinearis)	1.26	32.1	254	6.5	20	52	11.1 x 5.9	
45	Hammerhead (Sphyrna zygaena)	0.44	23.1	526	5.4			15.2 x 11.2	7
46	Lamprey, sea (Petromyzon marinus)	0.33	23.5	710.0	5.8			14.3 x 14.3	7
47	Mackerel (Scomber scombrus)	3.94 (3.68-4.20)	57.5 (56-59)	146 (140-152)	14.9 (14.5-15.2)	26.0	37.5 (36-39)	12.5 x 8.3	9
48	Perch, white (Morone americana)	3.17 (2.70-3.63)	35.3 (32.7-37.8)	112.5 (104-121)	8.2 (6.7-9.7)	23.5 (21-26)	26 (25-27)	10.3 x 7.2	9

/1/ Dimensions for mammals are diameters; dimensions for other vertebrates are length x width.

Animal	RBC Count million/cu mm blood	RBC Packed Volume (Hematocrit) ml/100 ml blood	RBC Volume (Mean Corpuscular) cu μ	Hemoglobin Concentration g/100 ml blood	g/100 ml RBC	RBC Hemoglobin Content μμg	RBC Dimensions[1] (Dry Film) μ	Reference
(A)	(B)	(C)	(D)	(E)	(F)	(G)	(H)	(I)
Fishes (concluded)								
49 Pollock (Pollachias virens)	2.64 (2.34-2.93)	37.4 (35.8-39.0)	143 (133-153)	7.8 (7.4-8.1)	21.0	30 (28-32)	11.4 x 8.1	9
Ray								7
50 Electric (Torpedo nobilianus)	0.15	23.5	1593	3.3			29.8 x 23.1	
51 Sting- (Dasyatis centrourus)	0.30	19.0	612	3.0			20.6 x 14.3	
52 Rosefish (Sebastes marinus)	1.88	56.0	298	7.8	14	42	12.4 x 8.2	9
Sculpin								9
53 Daddy- (Myoxocephalus scorpius)	0.95 (0.87-1.03)	20.2 (19.8-20.6)	213.5 (200-227)	4.4 (4.0-4.8)	21.5 (20-23)	46.0	12.4 x 9.5	
54 Longhorn (M. octodecimspinosus)	1.69 (1.34-2.04)	29.4 (24.6-34.2)	175 (167-183)	5.6 (5.0-6.2)	19 (18-20)	33.5 (30-37)	11.6 x 8.9	
55 Sea robin (Prionotus strigatus)	1.93	22.2	130.0	6.2			10.4 x 7.3	7
Skate								
56 Barndoor- (Raja stabuliforis)	0.27	20.0	727	3.6			21.9 x 15.6	7
57 Clearnose- (R. eglanteria)	0.30	24.0	823	4.5			23.7 x 14.4	7
58 Common (R. erinacea)	0.09 (0.07-0.11)	7.2 (4.7-9.6)	778 (646-910)	1.4 (0.9-1.8)	19.5 (19-20)	148.5 (125-172)	24.3 x 13.9	9
59 Spotted (R. diaphanes)	0.13	10.0	766	2.8	28	216	23.3 x 14.1	9
60 Sucker, shark (Echeneis naucrates)	3.75	34.0	91.0	10.5			10.9 x 7.0	7
61 Trout (Salvelinus fontinalis)	1.01 (0.74-1.50)	27.2 (22-36)	314 (284-348)	8.5 (6.2-11.5)	31.2	75 (61-82)		4
62 Wrymouth (Cryptacanthodes maculatus)	1.10 (0.71-1.48)	21.3 (15.4-27.2)	200.5 (184-217)	6.4 (4.6-8.1)	30.0	60.5 (55-66)	9.0 x 14.0	9

/1/ Dimensions for mammals are diameters; dimensions for other vertebrates are length x width.

Contributors: (a) Altland, Paul D., (b) Bonnycastle, Desmond D., (c) Broun, Goronwy O., (d) Cronkite, Eugene P., (e) Ferguson, John H., (f) Hart, J. Sanford, (g) Kisch, Bruno, (h) McCutcheon, F. Harold, (i) Musacchia, X. J., (j) Rekers, Paul E., (k) Root, Raymond W., (l) Young, I. Maureen

References: [1] Albritton, E. C. 1952. Standard values in blood. W. B. Saunders, Philadelphia. p. 42. [2] Altland, P. D., and M. Parker. Unpublished. [3] Altland, P. D., and E. C. Thompson. 1958. Proc. Soc. Exp. Biol., N. Y. 99:456. [4] Field, J. B., C. A. Elvehjem, and C. Juday. 1943. J. Biol. Chem. 148:261. [5] Fulton, G. P., D. L. Joftes, R. Kegan, and B. R. Lutz. 1954. Blood, N. Y. 9:622. [6] Hafez, E. S., and A. Anwar. 1954. Nature, Lond. 174:611. [7] Kisch, B. 1951. Exp. M. & S. 9:125. [8] Sturkie, P. D. 1954. Avian physiology. Comstock, Ithaca. [9] Wintrobe, M. M. 1934. Fol. haemat., Lpz. 51:32.

41. ERYTHROCYTE DIAMETERS: MAMMALS

Values are for dry erythrocytes.

	Animal (A)	Erythrocyte Diameter μ (B)		Animal (A)	Erythrocyte Diameter μ (B)
1	Man (Homo sapiens)	7.5	51	Gayal (Bos frontalis)	5.9
	Anteater		52	Gibbon, white-handed (Hylobates lar)	7.5
2	Giant (Myrmecophaga tridactyla)	9.2	53	Giraffe, Nubian (Giraffa camelopardalis)	5.5
3	Spiny (Tachyglossus aculeata)	6.6	54	Gnu, white-tailed (Connochaetes gnou)	5.3
	Ape		55	Goat (Capra hircus)	4.0
4	Barbary (Macaca sylvana)	7.6	56	Guinea pig (Cavia porcellus)	7.1
5	Celebes black (Cynopithecus niger)	7.1	57	Hare, snow (Lepus timidus)	7.1
6	Armadillo, six-banded (Euphractus sexcinctus)	7.5	58	Hippopotamus (Hippopotamus amphibius)	7.4
7	Ass (Equus asinus)	6.4	59	Horse (Equus caballus)	5.5
8	Babirusa (Babyrousa babyrussa)	5.8	60	Hyena, striped (Hyaena hyaena)	6.8
9	Baboon (Papio doguera)	7.4	61	Hyrax, large-toothed (Procavia capensis)	7.7
	Badger		62	Kangaroo, great gray (Macropus giganteus)	7.6
10	Honey (Mellivora capensis)	6.6			
11	European (Meles meles)	6.4	63	Langur (Presbytis cristatus)	7.3
12	Sand (Arctonyx collaris)	7.0	64	Lemur, ring-tailed (Lemur catta)	6.5
13	Bandicoot (Bandicota indica)	6.5	65	Leopard, African (Felis pardus)	5.9
14	Rabbit- (Thalacomys lagotis)	6.5	66	Leopard cat (Felis bengalensis)	5.7
	Bat		67	Lion, African (Felis leo)	5.8
15	Big-eared (Plecotus auritus)	5.7	68	Loris, slender (Loris tardigradus)	7.3
16	Frosted (Vespertilio murinus)	6.1	69	Marmoset (Callithrix jacchus)	7.0
17	Noctule (Nyctalus noctula)	5.8	70	Marmot, hoary (Marmota caligata)	7.3
18	Rousette (Rousettus aegyptiacus)	6.5	71	Mole, European (Talpa europaea)	5.4
	Bear		72	Mongoose, gray (Herpestes ichneumon)	5.4
19	Black (Ursus americanus)	6.9		Monkey	
20	European (Ursus arctos)	6.8	73	Black spider- (Ateles paniscus)	7.1
21	Grizzly (Ursus horribilis)	7.2	74	Capuchin (Cebus capucinus)	7.3
22	Polar (Thalarctos maritimus)	6.6	75	Red (Erythrocebus patas)	7.5
23	Sun (Helarctos malayanus)	7.1	76	Rhesus (Macaca mulatta)	7.4
24	Beaver, European (Castor fiber)	7.6	77	Squirrel- (Saimiri sciureus)	6.8
	Bison			Mouse	
25	American (Bison bison)	6.2	78	House- (Mus musculus)	6.6
26	European (Bison bonasus)	6.2	79	Old-world field- (Apodemus sylvaticus)	6.6
27	Black buck (Antilope cervicapra)	5.0			
28	Brocket (Mazama americana)	4.9	80	Nilgai (Boselaphus tragocamelus)	5.2
29	Capybara (Hydrochoerus hydrochoeris)	8.0	81	Ocelot (Felis pardalis)	5.5
30	Caracal (Felis caracal)	6.0		Opossum	
31	Cat (Felis domesticus)	5.8	82	Brush-tailed (Trichosurus vulpecula)	7.0
32	Cattle (Bos taurus)	5.9	83	Common (Didelphis marsupialis)	7.4
33	Chamois (Rupicapra rupicapra)	3.6	84	Orangutan (Pongo pygmaeus)	7.5
34	Chevrotain (Tragulus javanicus)	2.1	85	Otter, European (Lutra lutra)	7.2
35	Chimpanzee (Pan troglodytes)	7.4	86	Polecat, European (Mustela putorius)	6.1
	Civet		87	Porcupine, European (Hystrix cristata)	7.5
36	African (Viverra civetta)	6.0	88	Porpoise (Phocaena phocoena)	6.6
37	Palm (Paguma larvata)	6.0	89	Rabbit (Oryctolagus cuniculus)	7.0
38	Coati, red (Nasua nasua)	6.7	90	Raccoon (Procyon lotor)	6.4
	Deer		91	Rat, house (Rattus rattus)	6.8
39	Hog- (Axis porcinus)	4.7	92	Rhinocerus, great Indian (Rhinoceros unicornis)	6.7
40	Musk- (Moschus moschiferus)	3.6			
41	Red (Cervus elaphus)	5.9	93	Sambar (Cervus unicolor)	5.0
42	White-tailed (Odocoileus virginianus)	5.0	94	Seal, harbor (Phoca vitulina)	7.7
43	Dingo (Canis dingo)	7.5		Sheep	
44	Dog (Canis familiaris)	7.1	95	Barbary (Ammotragus lervia)	4.0
	Elephant		96	Domestic (Ovis aries)	4.8
45	African (Loxodonta africana)	9.2	97	Shrew, musk (Suncus murinus)	7.5
46	Indian (Elephas maximus)	9.2	98	Sloth, two-toed (Choloepus didactylus)	8.8
47	Elk, American (Cervus canadensis)	6.1		Squirrel	
	Fox		99	European (Sciurus vulgaris)	6.5
48	Big-eared (Otocyon megalotis)	7.0	100	Fox- (S. niger)	6.6
49	Flying (Pteropus dasymallus)	6.4			
50	European red (Vulpes vulpes)	6.1			

Animal	Erythrocyte Diameter μ		Animal	Erythrocyte Diameter μ
(A)	(B)		(A)	(B)
Squirrel (concluded)		109	Tiger cat or native cat (Dasyurus viverrinus)	6.3
101 Giant (Ratufa indica)	7.0	110	Vole, water (Arvicola amphibius)	6.7
102 Giant flying (Petaurista petaurista)	6.7	111	Wallaby, brush (Protemnodon rufogriseus)	7.2
103 Gray (Sciurus carolinensis)	6.4	112	Weasel, snow (Mustela nivalis)	6.0
104 Swine (Sus scrofa)	6.0	113	Whale, humpback (Megaptera novaeangliae)	8.2
105 Tamarin (Leontideus rosalia)	7.2			
106 Tapir, Malay (Tapirus indicus)	6.4	114	Wolf (Canis lupus)	7.1
107 Tenrec (Tenrec ecaudatus)	6.2	115	Wombat, Tasmanian (Phascolomis ursinus)	7.3
108 Tiger (Felis tigris)	6.0			

Contributors: (a) Handley, Charles O., Jr., (b) Ponder, Eric

Reference: Ponder, E. 1948. Hemolysis and related phenomena. Grune and Stratton, New York.

42. ERYTHROCYTE O₂ CONSUMPTION: VERTEBRATES

Values are calculated on the basis that water content of cells is 70% by weight.

Animal	Sample	Method	Temp. °C	O₂ Consumption μL/mg dry wt/hr In Serum	In Ringer's Solution[1]	Reference
(A)	(B)	(C)	(D)	(E)	(F)	(G)
1 Man	Defibrinated blood	Chemical	37		0.015	10
2		Manometric	37	0.018	0.017	2
3	Washed erythrocytes	Manometric	37		0.060	7
4					0.020	4
5	Washed erythrocytes; buffy coat removed	Manometric	37		0.020	5
6					0.042	1
7 Rabbit	Defibrinated blood	Chemical	37		0.049	10
8			25	0.220		8
9		Manometric	38	0.064	0.028	9
10			37	0.062		6
11	Erythrocyte suspension	Manometric	37		0.024	7
12			37		0.037	5
13			20		0.023	5
14 Chicken	Defibrinated blood	Chemical	25	0.260		8
15		Manometric	38	0.350	0.210	9
16	Washed erythrocytes	Manometric	37		0.180	7
17	Washed erythrocytes; buffy coat removed	Manometric	37		0.136	5
18			20		0.050	
19 Goose	Defibrinated blood	Chemical	39	0.670	0.440	10
20			25	0.250		8
21		Manometric	37	0.720	0.400	3
22 Alligator, American (Alligator mississippiensis)	Defibrinated blood	Manometric	25	0.113	0.067	9
Snake						9
23 Garter- (Elaps sp)	Washed erythrocytes	Manometric	25	0.154	0.081	
24 Water- (Ancistrodon sp)	Washed erythrocytes	Manometric	25	0.173	0.083	
Turtle						
25 Blanding's	Washed erythrocytes	Manometric	25	0.096	0.067	9
26 Box- (Testudo carolina)	Washed erythrocytes	Manometric	25	0.158	0.081	9
27 Snapper- (Chelydra serpentina)	Washed erythrocytes	Manometric	25	0.119	0.075	9
28 Pseudemys elegans	Washed erythrocytes	Manometric	25		0.060	7

/1/ Or isotonic saline solution.

| Animal | Sample | Method | Temp. °C | O_2 Consumption μL/mg dry wt/hr | | Reference |
				In Serum	In Ringer's Solution[1]	
(A)	(B)	(C)	(D)	(E)	(F)	(G)
Frog						
29 Bull- (Rana catesbeiana)	Washed erythrocytes	Manometric	25	0.111	0.051	9
30 Leopard- (R. pipiens)	Washed erythrocytes; buffy	Manometric	37		0.139	5
31	coat removed		20		0.068	
32 Grunt, white (Haemulon plumieri)	Washed erythrocytes; buffy	Manometric	37		0.141	5
33	coat removed		20		0.067	
34 Puffer (Gymnodontes sp)	Washed erythrocytes	Manometric	20	0.227		9
35 Sea robin (Prionotus carolinus)	Washed erythrocytes	Manometric	20		0.075	9
36 Stingray (Dasyatis sp)	Washed erythrocytes; buffy	Manometric	37		0.266	5
37	coat removed		20		0.127	
38 Toadfish (Lophius sp)	Washed erythrocytes	Manometric	20	0.112		9

/1/ Or isotonic saline solution.

Contributors: (a) Hunter, F. R., (b) Ponder, Eric, (c) Gabrio, Beverly W.

References: [1] Damble, K. 1933. Zschr. ges. exp. Med. 86:594. [2] Harrop, G. A., and E. S. Barron. 1928. J. Exp. M. 48:207. [3] Horn, Z. 1930. Biochem. Zschr. 226:297. [4] Huennekens, F. M., L. Liu, H. A. P. Myers, and B. W. Gabrio. 1957. J. Biol. Chem. 227:253. [5] Hunter, A. S., and F. R. Hunter. 1957. J. Cellul. Physiol. 49:479. [6] Nagelein, E. 1925. Biochem. Zschr. 158:121. [7] Ramsey, R., and C. O. Warren, Jr. 1930. Q. J. Exp. Physiol., Lond. 20:213. [8] Roche, J., and E. Siegler-Soru. 1929. Arch. internat. physiol., Liége 31:413. [9] Tipton, S. R. 1933. J. Cellul. Physiol. 3:313. [10] Warburg, O. 1909. Zschr. physiol. Chem. 59:112.

43. ERYTHROCYTE CARBOHYDRATE METABOLISM: CAT, DOG, RABBIT

Values for rate of lactic acid formation are CO_2/hr/4 ml of a 50% erythrocyte suspension in Krebs-Ringer bicarbonate buffer under anaerobic conditions. Values for rate of methemoglobin reduction are grams of reduced hemoglobin/hr/100 ml of a 50% suspension of methemoglobin corpuscles (cells treated with nitrite and washed with 0.9% NaCl solution) in the presence of excess substrate. Erythrocytes are unable to utilize succinic acid in converting malic or fumaric acids to lactic acid. Values in parentheses are ranges, estimate "b" (cf. Introduction).

Animal	Substrate	Rate of Lactic Acid Formation	Rate of Methemoglobin Reduction	Probable Enzyme Involved in Utilization[1]
(A)	(B)	(C)	(D)	(E)
1 Cat	Control[2]	-2.6(-6.1 to +0.9)	0.06	
2	Glucose	25.8(12.1-39.5)	0.77	Glycolytic enzymes and possibly zwischenferment
3	Fructose	24.5(1.8-47.2)	0.79	
4	Mannose	19.6(4.7-34.5)	0.47	
5	Galactose	-0.5(-4.0 to +3.0)	0.15	Galactokinase, gal-1-p uridyl transferase, UDP gal-4-epimerase
6	Malate	4.3(-2.8 to +11.4)	1.07	Malic dehydrogenase, oxaloacetic acid decarboxylase
7	Fumarate	8.9(1.1-16.7)	1.12	Malic dehydrogenase, oxaloacetic acid decarboxylase, fumarase
8	Lactate		1.15	Lactic dehydrogenase
9 Dog	Control[2]	3.8(-0.1 to +7.1)	0.00	
10	Glucose	21.0(13.9-28.1)	0.78	Glycolytic enzymes and possibly zwischenferment
11	Fructose	20.5(11.1-29.9)	0.86	
12	Mannose	22.0(14.2-29.8)	0.69	

/1/ Exclusive of methemoglobin reductase and of pyridine nucleotide coenzymes which are probably utilized in methemoglobin reduction. /2/ Free or endogenous.

	Animal	Substrate	Rate of Lactic Acid Formation	Rate of Methemoglobin Reduction	Probable Enzyme Involved in Utilization[1]
	(A)	(B)	(C)	(D)	(E)
13	Dog (concluded)	Galactose	1.2(-0.6 to +3.0)	0.26	Galactokinase, gal-1-p uridyl transferase, UDP gal-4-epimerase
14		Malate	17.4(4.5-30.3)	1.19	Malic dehydrogenase, oxaloacetic acid decarboxylase
15		Fumarate	33.8(19.1-48.5)	1.20	Malic dehydrogenase, oxaloacetic acid decarboxylase, fumarase
16		Lactate		1.27	Lactic dehydrogenase
17	Rabbit	Control[2]	3.5(-0.4 to +7.4)	0.46	
18		Glucose	48.7(28.3-69.1)	2.92	Glycolytic enzymes and possibly zwischenferment
19		Fructose	59.3(36.4-82.2)	3.07	
20		Mannose	56.8(32.7-80.9)	2.80	
21		Galactose	13.5(7.4-19.6)	1.21	Galactokinase, gal-1-p uridyl transferase, UDP gal-4-epimerase
22		Malate	38.3(24.2-52.4)	2.08	Malic dehydrogenase, oxaloacetic acid decarboxylase
23		Fumarate	44.5(29.4-59.6)	1.82	Malic dehydrogenase, oxaloacetic acid decarboxylase, fumarase
24		Lactate		5.92	Lactic dehydrogenase

/1/ Exclusive of methemoglobin reductase and of pyridine nucleotide coenzymes which are probably utilized in methemoglobin reduction. /2/ Free or endogenous.

Contributor: Spicer, Samuel S.

References: [1] Spicer, S. S. 1950. J. Pharm. Exp. Ther. 99:185. [2] Spicer, S. S., and A. M. Clark. 1949. J. Biol. Chem. 179:987.

44. ERYTHROCYTE SEDIMENTATION RATE: VERTEBRATES

Sedimentation rates increase with increase in plasma globulins, with hemodilution, during infections, in diseases associated with inflammation, and with tissue injury; rates decrease with hemoconcentration. Rates were measured at end of first hour of observation; rates in succeeding hours usually decreased asymptotically. Values in parentheses are ranges, estimate "c" (cf. Introduction).

	Animal	Sex	Method	Rate mm/hr	Reference		Animal	Sex	Method	Rate mm/hr	Reference
	(A)	(B)	(C)	(D)	(E)		(A)	(B)	(C)	(D)	(E)
	Man[1]					15	Cat		Linzenmeier-Raunert	3	16
1	Child		Cutler	8.6(4-13)	12	16			Reichel	7.30(4-13)	9
2	12 da-14 yr		Smith	9.1(3-13)[2]	12	17	Cattle		Linzenmeier-Raunert	1	16
3	Adult	♂	Cutler	(0-8)	2	18			Reichel	1.17(1.0-1.8)	9
4		♀	Cutler	(0-10)		19	Dog		Linzenmeier-Raunert	2	16
5		♂	Landau	(0-6)	5	20			Reichel	4(2.5-5.0)	9
6		♀	Landau	(0-9)		21		♂, ♀	Wintrobe	(1-4)	11
7		♂	Smith	(0-10)	12	22		♀[3]	Wintrobe	(1-52)	
8		♀	Smith	(0-10)		23	Goat		Reichel	0.50	9
9		♂	Walton	(0-8)	13	24	Guinea pig[4]		Linzenmeier-Raunert	1.5	16
10		♀	Walton	(0-8)		25			Reichel	1.67(1.25-2.00)	9
11		♂	Westergren	(0-15)	14						
12		♀	Westergren	(0-20)							
13		♂	Wintrobe	(0-9)	15						
14		♀	Wintrobe	(0-15)							

/1/ Sedimentation time = 6-10 hours (Linzenmeier method) [6]. /2/ Capillary blood. /3/ 11-56 days pregnant. /4/ Sedimentation time = 60 hours (Linzenmeier method) [3].

	Animal	Sex	Method	Rate mm/hr	Reference		Animal	Sex	Method	Rate mm/hr	Reference
	(A)	(B)	(C)	(D)	(E)		(A)	(B)	(C)	(D)	(E)
26	Guinea pig[4] (concluded)		Westergren	1.06(0.75-1.75)	7	35	Sheep		Linzenmeier-Raunert	0.5	16
27	Horse		Cutler	18	4	36			Reichel	0.55(0.50-0.75)	9
28			Linzenmeier-Raunert	69	16	37	Swine		Linzenmeier-Raunert	5	16
29			Reichel	127(119-136)	9	38			Reichel	5.35(3-8)	9
30	Rabbit[5]		Linzenmeier-Raunert	2	16	39	Fowl		Linzenmeier-Raunert	4	16
31			Reichel	2(1.5-2.5)	9	40			Reichel	3.75(2-6)	9
32			Wintrobe	1.05[6]	10	41	Goose		Reichel	3.42(2.75-4.00)	9
33	Rat	♂	Cutler	0.7	1						
34		♀	Cutler	1.8							

/4/ Sedimentation time = 60 hours (Linzenmeier method) [3]. /5/ Sedimentation time = 17-42 hours (Linzenmeier method) [8]. /6/ No change after thyroidectomy.

Contributors: (a) Hirschboeck, John S., (b) Riser, William H., Jr.

References: [1] Creskoff, A. J., T. Fitz-Hugh, Jr., and E. J. Farris. In J. Q. Griffith and E. J. Farris, ed. 1942. The rat in laboratory investigation. J. B. Lippincott, Philadelphia. p. 358. [2] Cutler, J. W. 1932. Am. J. M. Sc. 183:643. [3] Frola, G. 1928. Arch. biol., Genova 5:47. [4] Hammersland, H. L., H. S. Herrin, and C. F. Haynes. 1938. J. Am. Vet. M. Ass. 93:320. [5] Landau, A. 1933. Am. J. Dis. Child. 45:691. [6] Linzenmeier, G. In J. Halban and L. Seitz. 1927. Biologie und Pathologie des Weibes. Urban and Schwarzenberg, Berlin. [7] Nicolle, P., and H. Simons. 1939. Sang, Par. 13:401. [8] Rix, E. 1936. Zschr. ges. exp. Med. 99:178. [9] Schappes, H. 1937. Fol. haemat., Lpz. 58:160. [10] Sharpe, J. C., and J. D. Bisgard. 1936. J. Laborat. Clin. M. 21:347. [11] Simms, B. T. 1940. J. Am. Vet. M. Ass. 96:77. [12] Smith, C. H. 1936. Am. J. M. Sc. 192:73. [13] Walton, A. C. R. 1933. J. Laborat. Clin. M. 18:711. [14] Westergren, A. 1926. Am. Rev. Tuberc. 14:94. [15] Wintrobe, M. M., and J. W. Landsberg. 1935. Am. J. M. Sc. 189:102. [16] Zott, F. 1931. Wien. tierärztl. Mschr. 18:570.

45. ERYTHROCYTE FRAGILITY: VERTEBRATES

The fragility of erythrocytes is tested by observing the beginning and completion of hemolysis when erythrocytes are placed in saline solutions of variable concentrations.

Part I: MAN

Blood dilution values are ratios of blood volume to mixture of blood and hemolyzing solution.

	Blood	No of Observations	Anticoagulant	Blood Dilution	Duration of Hemolysis	Sodium Chloride Concentration g NaCl/100 ml solution			Reference
						For 10% Hemolysis	For 50% Hemolysis	For 90% Hemolysis	
	(A)	(B)	(C)	(D)	(E)	(F)	(G)	(H)	(I)
1	Cutaneous	50	None	1:200	30 min	0.47[1]	0.43[1]	0.40[1]	1
2			Heparin	1:3	1 hr	0.42[2]		0.33[3]	2
3	Oxygenated	25	Waxed tube	1:26	20 min	0.43[1]	0.38[1]	0.34[1]	3
4		50	Heparin	1:23	30 min	0.40[1]	0.37	0.30[1]	4
5		20	Oxalate; heparin	1:20	1-2 hr	0.40	0.37	0.33	5

/1/ Estimated from graphs. /2/ Initial hemolysis. /3/ Complete hemolysis.

45. ERYTHROCYTE FRAGILITY: VERTEBRATES (Concluded)

Part I: MAN (Concluded)

	Blood	No. of Obser- vations	Anticoagulant	Blood Dilution	Duration of Hemolysis	Sodium Chloride Concentration g NaCl/100 ml solution			Ref- er- ence
						For 10% Hemolysis	For 50% Hemolysis	For 90% Hemolysis	
	(A)	(B)	(C)	(D)	(E)	(F)	(G)	(H)	(I)
6	Venous	12	Oxalate	1:201	30 min	0.46[1]	0.41[1]	0.37[1]	6
7		35[4]	Oxalate	1:41	30 min	0.46[1]		0.22[1]	7
8		38	Oxalate	1:20	5 hr	0.47	0.43	0.38	10
9		20[4]	Oxalate	1:37	1 hr	0.47		0.27	8
10		15	Unspecified	1:26	3 hr	0.43[2]	0.38	0.32[3]	9

/1/ Estimated from graphs. /2/ Initial hemolysis. /3/ Complete hemolysis. /4/ Washed cells.

Contributor: Hendry, E. B.

References: [1] Bohr, D. F. 1946. J. Laborat. Clin. M. 31:1179. [2] Creed, E. 1938. J. Path. Bact., Lond. 46:331. [3] Dacie, J. V., and J. M. Vaughan. 1938. Ibid. 46:341. [4] Daland, G. A., and K. Worthley. 1935. J. Laborat. Clin. M. 20:1122. [5] Hendry, E. B. 1948. Edinburgh M. J. 55:427. [6] Hunter, F. T. 1940. J. Clin. Invest. 19:691. [7] Kato, K. 1941. J. Laborat. Clin. M. 26:703. [8] Olbrich, O. 1947. Edinburgh M. J. 54:649. [9] Whitby, L. E. H., and M. Hynes. 1935. J. Path. Bact., Lond. 40:219. [10] Wieczorowski, E., and H. R. Fishback. 1942. J. Laborat. Clin. M. 27:542.

Part II: VERTEBRATES OTHER THAN MAN

	Animal	Sodium Chloride Concentration g NaCl/100 ml solution		Ref- er- ence		Animal	Sodium Chloride Concentration g NaCl/100 ml solution		Ref- er- ence
		For Initial Hemolysis	For Complete Hemolysis				For Initial Hemolysis	For Complete Hemolysis	
	(A)	(B)	(C)	(D)		(A)	(B)	(C)	(D)
1	Baboon		0.18	11	13	Marmoset		0.40	11
2	Camel		0.26	9	14	Mouse	0.54	0.33	7
	Cat				15	Ox	0.59	0.42	2
3	Young	0.58	0.47	4	16	Rabbit	0.57	0.45	7
4	Adult	0.69	0.50	3	17	Rat	0.48	0.38	7
5	Chimpanzee		0.28	11		Sheep			
6	Dog	0.45	0.36	7	18	Young	0.69	0.48	6
7	Dromedary	0.17	0.07	10	19	Adult	0.60	0.45	7
8	Goat	0.62	0.48	7	20	Swine	0.74	0.45	8
9	Guinea pig	0.45	0.33	7		Chicken			
10	Horse	0.59	0.39	1	21	♂	0.40	0.32	6
11	Lemur		0.42	11	22	♀	0.41	0.28	5
12	Llama	0.17	0.03	10					

Contributor: Hendry, E. B.

References: [1] Ashby, W. 1924. Am. J. Physiol. 68:611. [2] Demmel, M. In H. H. Dukes. 1942. The physiology of domestic animals. Ed. 5. Comstock, Ithaca. [3] Hacek, E. 1936. Wien. tierärztl. Mschr. 23:682. [4] Hammon, W. D. 1940. Anat. Rec. 76:259. [5] Hogan, A. G., and E. M. Parrott. 1940. J. Biol. Chem. 132:507. [6] Hunter, F. T. 1940. J. Clin. Invest. 19:691. [7] Kato, K. 1941. J. Laborat. Clin. M. 26:703. [8] Lyon, M. W. 1918. J. Infect. Dis. 22:49. [9] Ponder, E., G. Saslow, and J. F. Yeager. 1930. Biochem. J., Lond. 24:805. [10] Ponder, E., J. F. Yeager, and H. A. Charipper. 1928-29. Q. J. Exp. Physiol., Lond. 19:115. [11] Ponder, E., J. F. Yeager, and H. A. Charipper. 1928-29. Ibid. 19:181.

46. BLOOD LEUKOCYTE VALUES: MAN

Part I: BIRTH TO MATURITY

Values were derived from smoothed curves plotted from data given in the references. Unless designated percent (of total leukocytes), values are thousands/cu mm blood. Values in parentheses are ranges, estimate "c" (cf. Introduction).

	Age	Leukocytes, Total[1]	Neutrophils			Eosinophils	Basophils	Lymphocytes	Monocytes
			Total	Band[2]	Segmented				
	(A)	(B)	(C)	(D)	(E)	(F)	(G)	(H)	(I)
1	At	18.1(9.0-30.0)[3]	11.0(6.0-26.0)	1.65	9.4	0.40(0.02-0.85)	0.10(0-0.64)	5.5(2.0-11.0)	1.05(0.40-3.1)
2	birth		61%	9.1%	52%	2.2%	0.6%	31%	5.8%
3	12 hr	22.8(13.0-38.0)	15.5(6.0-28.0)	2.33	13.2	0.45(0.02-0.95)	0.10(0-0.50)	5.5(2.0-11.0)	1.20(0.40-3.6)
4			68%	10.2%	58%	2.0%	0.4%	24%	5.3%
5	24 hr	18.9(9.4-34.0)	11.5(5.0-21.0)	1.75	9.8	0.45(0.05-1.00)	0.10(0-0.30)	5.8(2.0-11.5)	1.10(0.20-3.1)
6			61%	9.2%	52%	2.4%	0.5%	31%	5.8%
7	1 wk	12.2(5.0-21.0)	5.5(1.5-10.0)	0.83	4.7	0.50(0.07-1.10)	0.05(0-0.25)	5.0(2.0-17.0)	1.10(0.30-2.7)
8			45%	6.8%	39%	4.1%	0.4%	41%	9.1%
9	2 wk	11.4(5.0-20.0)	4.5(1.0-9.5)	0.63	3.9	0.35(0.07-1.00)	0.05(0-0.23)	5.5(2.0-17.0)	1.00(0.20-2.4)
10			40%	5.5%	34%	3.1%	0.4%	48%	8.8%
11	4 wk	10.8(5.0-19.5)	3.8(1.0-9.0)	0.49	3.3	0.30(0.07-0.90)	0.05(0-0.20)	6.0(2.5-16.5)	0.70(0.15-2.0)
12			35%	4.5%	30%	2.8%	0.5%	56%	6.5%
13	2 mo	11.0(5.5-18.0)	3.8(1.0-9.0)	0.49	3.3	0.30(0.07-0.85)	0.05(0-0.20)	6.3(3.0-16.0)	0.65(0.13-1.8)
14			34%	4.4%	30%	2.7%	0.5%	57%	5.9%
15	4 mo	11.5(6.0-17.5)	3.8(1.0-9.0)	0.45	3.3	0.30(0.07-0.80)	0.05(0-0.20)	6.8(3.5-14.5)	0.60(0.10-1.5)
16			33%	3.9%	29%	2.6%	0.4%	59%	5.2%
17	6 mo	11.9(6.0-17.5)	3.8(1.0-8.5)	0.45	3.3	0.30(0.07-0.75)	0.05(0-0.20)	7.3(4.0-13.5)	0.58(0.10-1.3)
18			32%	3.8%	28%	2.5%	0.4%	61%	4.8%
19	8 mo	12.2(6.0-17.5)	3.7(1.0-8.5)	0.41	3.3	0.30(0.07-0.70)	0.05(0-0.20)	7.6(4.5-12.5)	0.58(0.08-1.2)
20			30%	3.3%	27%	2.5%	0.4%	62%	4.7%
21	10 mo	12.0(6.0-17.5)	3.6(1.0-8.5)	0.40	3.2	0.30(0.06-0.70)	0.05(0-0.20)	7.5(4.5-11.5)	0.55(0.05-1.2)
22			30%	3.3%	27%	2.5%	0.4%	63%	4.6%
23	12 mo	11.4(6.0-17.5)	3.5(1.5-8.5)	0.35	3.2	0.30(0.05-0.70)	0.05(0-0.20)	7.0(4.0-10.5)	0.55(0.05-1.1)
24			31%	3.1%	28%	2.6%	0.4%	61%	4.8%
25	2 yr	10.6(6.0-17.0)	3.5(1.5-8.5)	0.32	3.2	0.28(0.04-0.65)	0.05(0-0.20)	6.3(3.0-9.5)	0.53(0.05-1.0)
26			33%	3.0%	30%	2.6%	0.5%	59%	5.0%
27	4 yr	9.1(5.5-15.5)	3.8(1.5-8.5)	0.27 (0-1.0)	3.5(1.5-7.5)	0.25(0.02-0.65)	0.05(0-0.20)	4.5(2.0-8.0)	0.45(0-0.8)
28			42%	3.0%	39%	2.8%	0.6%	50%	5.0%
29	6 yr	8.5(5.0-14.5)	4.3(1.5-8.0)	0.25 (0-1.0)	4.0(1.5-7.0)	0.23(0-0.65)	0.05(0-0.20)	3.5(1.5-7.0)	0.40(0-0.8)
30			51%	3.0%	48%	2.7%	0.6%	42%	4.7%
31	8 yr	8.3(4.5-13.5)	4.4(1.5-8.0)	0.25 (0-1.0)	4.1(1.5-7.0)	0.20(0-0.60)	0.05(0-0.20)	3.3(1.5-6.8)	0.35(0-0.8)
32			53%	3.0%	50%	2.4%	0.6%	39%	4.2%
33	10 yr	8.1(4.5-13.5)	4.4(1.8-8.0)	0.24 (0-1.0)	4.2(1.8-7.0)	0.20(0-0.60)	0.04(0-0.20)	3.1(1.5-6.5)	0.35(0-0.8)
34			54%	3.0%	51%	2.4%	0.5%	38%	4.3%
35	12 yr	8.0(4.5-13.5)	4.4(1.8-8.0)	0.24 (0-1.0)	4.2(1.8-7.0)	0.20(0-0.55)	0.04(0-0.20)	3.0(1.2-6.0)	0.35(0-0.8)
36			55%	3.0%	52%	2.5%	0.5%	38%	4.4%
37	14 yr	7.9(4.5-13.0)	4.4(1.8-8.0)	0.24 (0-1.0)	4.2(1.8-7.0)	0.20(0-0.50)	0.04(0-0.20)	2.9(1.2-5.8)	0.38(0-0.8)
38			56%	3.0%	53%	2.5%	0.5%	37%	4.7%
39	16 yr	7.8(4.5-13.0)	4.4(1.8-8.0)	0.23	4.2	0.20(0-0.50)	0.04(0-0.20)	2.8(1.2-5.2)	0.40(0-0.8)
40			57%	3.0%	54%	2.6%	0.5%	35%	5.1%
41	18 yr	7.7(4.5-12.5)	4.4(1.8-7.7)	0.23	4.2	0.20(0-0.45)	0.04(0-0.20)	2.7(1.0-5.0)	0.40(0-0.8)
42			57%	3.0%	54%	2.6%	0.5%	35%	5.2%
43	20 yr	7.5(4.5-11.5)	4.4(1.8-7.7)	0.23 (0-0.7)	4.2(1.8-7.0)	0.20(0-0.45)	0.04(0-0.20)	2.5(1.0-4.8)	0.38(0-0.8)
44			59%	3.0%	56%	2.7%	0.5%	33%	5.0%
45	21 yr	7.4(4.5-11.0)	4.4(1.8-7.7)	0.22 (0-0.7)	4.2(1.8-7.0)	0.20(0-0.45)	0.04(0-0.20)	2.5(1.0-4.8)	0.30(0-0.8)
46			59%	3.0%	56%	2.7%	0.5%	34%	4.0%

/1/ Mean value is sum of means in columns C, F-I. /2/ Includes a small percentage of myelocytes during first few days after birth. /3/ Approximately 3 nucleated erythrocytes per 100 leukocytes have been found at birth.

Part I: BIRTH TO MATURITY (Concluded)

Contributors: (a) Broun, Goronwy O., (b) Diggs, L. W., (c) Glaser, Kurt, and Limarzi, Louis R., (d) Hamre, Christopher J., (e) Harrell, George T., (f) Osgood, Edwin E., (g) Smith, Clement A., (h) Wintrobe, M. M., (i) Zwemer, Raymund L.

References: [1] Broun, G. O. Unpublished. [2] Glaser, K., L. R. Limarzi, and H. G. Poncher. 1950. Pediatrics 6:789. [3] Hamre, C. J., and K. K. L. Wong. 1940. Am. J. Dis. Child. 60:22. [4] Hutaff, L. W., and G. T. Harrell. 1946. N. Carolina M. J. 7:641. [5] Lippman, H. S. 1924. Am. J. Dis. Child. 27:473. [6] Lucas, W. P. 1921. Ibid. 22:525. [7] Osgood, E. E., R. L. Baker, I. E. Brownlee, M. W. Osgood, D. M. Ellis, and W. Cohen. 1939. Ibid. 58:61. [8] Osgood, E. E., R. L. Baker, I. E. Brownlee, M. W. Osgood, D. M. Ellis, and W. Cohen. 1939. Ibid. 58:282. [9] Osgood, E. E., R. L. Baker, I. E. Brownlee, M. W. Osgood, D. M. Ellis, and W. Cohen. 1939. Arch. Int. M. 64:105. [10] Osgood, E. E., R. L. Baker, I. E. Brownlee, M. W. Osgood, D. M. Ellis, and W. Cohen. 1939. J. Laborat. Clin. M. 24:905. [11] Smith, C. A. 1950. The physiology of the newborn infant. C. C. Thomas, Springfield, Ill. [12] Sturgis, C. C., and F. H. Bethell. 1943. Physiol. Rev. 23:279. [13] Sunderman, F. W., and F. Boerner. 1949. Normal values in clinical medicine. W. B. Saunders, Philadelphia. [14] Washburn, A. H. 1935. Am. J. Dis. Child. 50:413. [15] Wegelius, R. 1948. Acta med. scand., Suppl. 4. [16] Wintrobe, M. M. 1946. Clinical hematology. Ed. 2. Lea and Febiger, Philadelphia.

Part II: DISTRIBUTION OF COUNTS

Graph represents absolute number of leukocytes/cu mm blood. Neutrophils = 3,800(1,900-7,800)/cu mm; lymphocytes = 2,500(1,300-5,000)/cu mm; total leukocytes = 7,200(4,400-11,600)/cu mm. 269 subjects, 19-38 years of age.

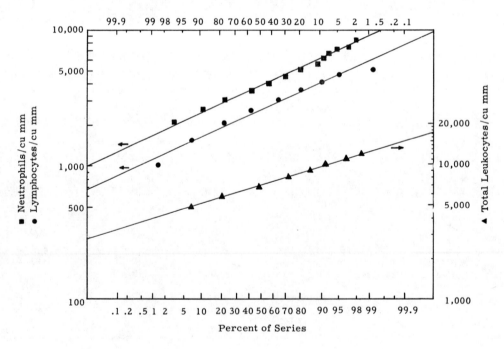

Contributor: Osgood, Edwin E.

Reference: Osgood, E. E. 1957. Brookhaven Symposium Biol. 10:33.

46. BLOOD LEUKOCYTE VALUES: MAN (Concluded)

Part III: PREGNANT AND POSTPARTUM FEMALES

All values are for venous blood. Values in parentheses are ranges, estimate "c" (cf. Introduction).

	Condition	No. of Subjects	Leukocytes, Total thousands/cu mm	Polymorphonuclear Cells %	Eosinophils %	Lymphocytes %	Monocytes %
	(A)	(B)	(C)	(D)	(E)	(F)	(G)
	Pregnant						
1	2 mo	12	9.5(6.8-15.0)	68(56-71)	1.7(0.6-7.8)	28(23-39)	2(0-6)
2	3 mo	13	10.5(6.6-14.1)	71(57-76)	1.5(0.6-4.8)	23(17-33)	4(1-8)
3	4 mo	9	10.3(7.5-14.6)	71(65-76)	1.3(0.2-2.5)	23(17-30)	2.5(0-4)
4	5 mo	16	10.6(8.9-14.8)	76(67-88)	1.1(0.2-2.8)	18(8-26)	3(1-7)
5	6 mo	15	11.1(6.9-17.1)	73(67-81)	1.3(0.3-2.9)	21(10-33)	3.5(0-8)
6	7 mo	18	10.5(6.8-20.3)	77(69-92)	1.3(0.3-4.1)	18(3-25)	2.3(0-8)
7	8 mo	17	10.1(7.5-15.3)	76(61-88)	1.3(0.06-3.80)	19(9-28)	3(0-8)
8	9 mo	9	10.8(5.9-14.7)	75(68-81)	1.2(0.2-2.2)	18(12-24)	3.5(0-8)
9	Labor	11	12.7(9.8-17.8)	82(72-88)	0.21(0.01-0.60)	14(8-20)	2.5
	Postpartum						
10	1 wk	7	16.4(9.7-25.7)	83(70-94)	0.35(0-1.5)	13(5-30)	2
11	1-2 mo	12	8.5(6.4-11.8)	63(52-79)	2.42(0.9-7.3)	29(17-44)	4

Contributors: (a) Caton, William L., (b) DeMarsh, Q. B.

Reference: Rath, C. E., W. Caton, D. E. Reid, C. A. Finch, and L. Conroy. 1950. Surg. Gyn. Obst. 90:320.

47. BLOOD LEUKOCYTE VALUES: VERTEBRATES OTHER THAN MAN

Unless designated percent (of total leukocytes), values are thousands/cu mm blood. Values in parentheses are ranges, estimate "c" (cf. Introduction).

	Animal	Leukocytes, Total	Neutrophils	Eosinophils	Basophils	Lymphocytes	Monocytes	Reference
	(A)	(B)	(C)	(D)	(E)	(F)	(G)	(H)
1	Cat	16.0(9.0-24.0)	9.5(5.5-16.5)	0.85(0.2-2.5)	0.02(0-0.1)	5.0(2.0-9.0)	0.65(0.05-1.40)	1
2			59.5(44-82) %	5.4(2-11) %	0.1(0-0.5) %	31(15-44) %	4(0.5-7.0) %	
3	Cattle	9.2(6.0-12.0)	2.9(1.9-3.7)	0.7(0.3-1.3)	0.06(0-0.09)	5.09(4.1-6.9)	0.48(0.27-1.40)	10
4			31.9(20-40) %	7.7(3-15) %	0.62(0-1) %	55.4(45-65) %	5.2(3-15) %	
5	Dog	12.0(8.0-18.0)	8.2(6.0-12.5)	0.6(0.2-2.0)	0.085(0-0.3)	2.5(0.9-4.5)	0.65(0.3-1.5)	1
6			68(62-80) %	5.1(2-14) %	0.7(0-2) %	21(10-28) %	5.2(3-9) %	
7	Goat	(5.0-14.0)	(2.10-3.35)	(0-1.1)	(0-0.6)	(2.10-11.25)	(0.05-0.60)	5
8	Guinea	10.0(7.0-19.0)	4.2(2.0-7.0)	0.4(0.2-1.3)	0.07(0-0.3)	4.9(3.0-9.0)	0.43(0.25-2.00)	1
9	pig		42(22-50) %	4(2-12) %	0.7(0-2) %	49(37-64) %	4.3(3-13) %	
10	Horse	(5.0-11.0)	(3.0-6.9)	(0.05-0.60)	(0-0.1)	(1.2-4.8)	(0.10-1.45)	5
11	Monkey	16.2(8.0-25.0)	6.8(4.9-8.1)	0.5(0.16-0.81)	0.05(0.002-0.080)	8.6(6.4-9.7)	0.24(0.16-1.90)	10
12			42.2(30-50) %	3.7(1-5) %	0.32(0.1-0.5) %	52.8(40-60) %	1.5(1-12) %	
13	Mouse	8.0(4.0-12.0)	2.0(0.7-4.0)	0.15(0-0.5)	0.05(0-0.1)	5.5(3.0-8.5)	0.3(0-1.3)	1
14			25.5(12-44) %	2(0-5) %	0.5(0-1) %	68(54-85) %	4(0-15) %	
15	Rabbit	9.0(6.0-13.0)	4.1(2.5-6.0)	0.18(0-0.4)	0.45(0.15-0.75)	3.5(2.0-5.6)	0.725(0.3-1.3)	1
16			46(36-52) %	2(0.5-3.5) %	5(2-7) %	39(30-52) %	8(4-12) %	
17	Rat	14.0(5.0-25.0)	3.1(1.1-6.0)	0.3(0-0.7)	0.1(0-0.2)	10.2(7.0-16.0)	0.3(0-0.65)	1
18			22(9-34) %	2.2(0-6) %	0.5(0-1.5) %	73(65-84) %	2.3(0-5) %	
19	Sheep	7.8(5-10)	2.8(1.6-3.5)	0.19(0.08-0.50)	0.03(0-0.15)	4.4(3.9-5.5)	0.47(0.08-0.60)	10
20			35.7(20-45) %	2.5(1-7) %	0.4(0-2) %	56.9(50-70) %	6(1-8) %	
21	Swine	(7.0-20.0)	(2.4-10.0)	(0.05-2.00)	(0-0.8)	(3.2-12.0)	(0.05-2.00)	5
22	Chicken	32.6(9.1-56.0)	9.1(3.0-18.2)[1]	0.05(0-0.23)[2]	0.9(0-2.6)	17.6(7.8-27.3)	4.4(0-9.7)	12
23			27.8 (9.1-56.0) %	1.5(0-7) %	2.7(0-8) %	54(24-84) %	13.7(0-30) %	

/1/ Heterophils with rod-shaped eosinophilic bodies. /2/ Heterophils with granular eosinophilic bodies.

	Animal	Leukocytes, Total	Neutrophils	Eosinophils	Basophils	Lymphocytes	Monocytes	Reference
	(A)	(B)	(C)	(D)	(E)	(F)	(G)	(H)
24	Duck	23.4			1.0(0-4.5)	45.8(13.0-73.5)	4.4(0.5-11.5)	8
25			24.3%	2.1%				11
26	Turkey	19.0(16.0-25.5)	44.5(35-65)[3, 4]	7.5(1-24)[3, 5]	6.9(3-11)[3]	36.3(22-46)[3]	7.3(2-11)[3]	6
27			45.4(39-52)[4, 6]	2.3(0-5)[5, 6]	5.1(1-9)[6]	40.9(35-48)[6]	6.5(3-10)[6]	
28	Snake	50.2[7]	2.7[1, 2]		0.01	19.7	3.4	9
29			5.4%		0.2%	39.4%	6.9%	
30	Turtle	37.5(24.0-48.0)	0.01[7]	4.1	3.0	21.0	3.5	2, 3
31			0.3%	10.8%	8%	56.1%	9.4%	
32	Frog	18.3	1.3	4.9	1.3	10.8		7, 10
33			7%	27%	7%	59%		
34	Fish	34.7(23.1-46.5)	1.6(1.0-2.0)		0.01(0.003-0.020)[8]	10.4(6.9-13.8)		4
35			4.5(3-6) %		0.3(0.1-0.5) %	30(20-40) %		

/1/ Heterophils with rod-shaped eosinophilic bodies. /2/ Heterophils with granular eosinophilic bodies. /3/ Supravital stain. /4/ Polymorphic myelocytes with eosinophilic rods. /5/ Polymorphic myelocytes with pseudoeosinophilic granules. /6/ Wright's stain. /7/ Includes thrombocytes. /8/ Includes occasional coarse acidophilic granules.

Contributors: (a) Altland, Paul D., (b) Craige, A. H., Jr., (c) Dunlap, J. S., (d) Endicott, Kenneth M., (e) Rekers, Paul E., (f) Rigdon, R. H.

References: [1] Albritton, E. C. 1951. Standard values in blood. W. B. Saunders, Philadelphia. p. 53. [2] Altland, P. D. 1955. Am. J. Physiol. 180:421. [3] Bernstein, R. E. 1938. S. Afr. J. Sc. 35:327. [4] Catton, W. T. 1951. Blood, N. Y. 6:39. [5] Craige, A. H., Jr. Unpublished. [6] Dunlap, J. S. Unpublished. [7] Goodale, P. 1910. J. Path. Bact., Lond. 14:195. [8] Hewitt, R. 1942. Am. J. Hyg. 36:6. [9] Ryerson, D. L. 1949. J. Entom. Zool. 41:49. [10] Scarborough, R. A. 1931-32. Yale J. Biol. v. 4. [11] Sturkie, P. D. 1954. Avian physiology. Comstock, Ithaca. [12] Twisselmann, N. M. 1939. Poult. Sc. 18:151.

48. LEUKOCYTE MORPHOLOGY: MAN

Part I: MYELOID SERIES

	Specification	Myeloblasts	Myelocytes	Metamyelocytes	Neutrophils, Polymorphonuclear	Eosinophils	Basophils
	(A)	(B)	(C)	(D)	(E)	(F)	(G)
				Supravital Stain			
1	Size	14-20 μ	16-24 μ	12-18 μ	12-15 μ	12-15 μ	12-15 μ
2	Contour	Smooth, sharp	Distinct, smooth	Irregular	Irregular; repeated pseudopod formation	Irregular; repeated pseudopod formation	Irregular; repeated pseudopod formation
3	Physical state	Gel	Gel; sol in C type	Sol	Sol	Sol	Sol
4	Motility	None	None	Slightly ameboid	Actively ameboid	Less active than neutrophils	Active
5	Phagocytosis	None	None	Slight to moderate	Active on bacteria, debris, etc.		
6	Cytoplasm Quantity	Scanty	Moderate	Plentiful	Plentiful	Plentiful	Plentiful
7	Color	Slightly yellow	Gray	Gray	Clear	Clear	Clear

Part I: MYELOID SERIES (Continued)

	Specification	Myeloblasts	Myelocytes	Meta-myelocytes	Neutrophils, Polymorpho-nuclear	Eosinophils	Basophils
	(A)	(B)	(C)	(D)	(E)	(F)	(G)
	Supravital Stain (concluded)						
8	Cytoplasm (concluded) Vacuoles, neutral red	None	Refractile, bright red; 3-10 in A myelocytes; 30-100 in B myelocytes	Streaming	Very small, refractile, yellowish-pink	Large, oval, re-fractile, bright yellow	Streaming, non-refractile, deep maroon
9	Mitochon-dria	Slender, numerous, diffuse	Fine, diffuse; few in C type	Fine, few	Fine, rarely present	Fine, rarely pres-ent	Fine, rarely pres-ent
10	Nucleus Shape	Round or oval	Round or oval	Reniform or "horseshoe"	Lobulated	Lobulated	Lobulated
11	Chromatin	Loose net-work	More dense with age	Moderately dense	Coarse	Coarse	Coarse
12	Nucleoli	2-5	Gradually disappear	None	None	None	None
	Wright's Stain						
13	Size	10-18 μ	12-18 μ	10-18 μ, juven-ile form	10-15 μ	10-15 μ, poly-morphonuclear type	10-15 μ, poly-morphonuclear type
14	Cytoplasm Quantity	Scanty	Moderate	Plentiful in juvenile form	Plentiful	Plentiful	Plentiful in poly-morphonuclear type
15	Color	Blue	Bluish-pink	Juvenile form pink	Faint pink	Polymorphonuclear type bluish-pink	Polymorphonuclear type faint pink
16	Granules	None or few azurophilic	Neutrophilic, eosinophilic, basophilic, none or few azurophilic; fine, diffuse, or clumped; red or blue-black	Neutrophilic, eosinophilic, or basophilic in juvenile form	Small, pink or violet-pink, numerous	Polymorphonuclear type large, coarse, refractile, uni-form in size, reddish orange, numerous	Polymorphonuclear type large, coarse, irregular in size and number, reddish-purple to blue-black
17	Perinuclear clear zone	None	None	None	None	None	None
18	Nucleus Position	Centric or eccentric	Eccentric	Centric or eccentric in juvenile form	Centric or eccentric	Centric or eccen-tric in polymor-phonuclear type	Centric in poly-morphonuclear type
19	Shape	Round or oval	Oval or slightly indented	"Horseshoe" or "sausage" in juvenile form	2-5 lobes or more	2-3 lobes or more in polymorphonu-clear type	Not always lobu-lated; 2-3 lobes or more in poly-morphonuclear type
20	Color	Light red-dish purple	Reddish-purple	Juvenile form light pur-plish-blue	Deep pur-plish-blue	Polymorphonuclear type purplish-blue	Polymorphonuclear type pale pur-plish-blue
21	Chromatin	Very fine network	Fine; coarser with age	Basi- and oxy-chromatin clearly dis-tinguished in juvenile form	Coarse	Coarse in poly-morphonuclear type	Coarse but smudg-ed, and overlaid with granules, in polymorphonu-clear type
22	Membrane	Very fine, indistinct	Fine, distinct	Present in juvenile form	Present	Present in poly-morphonuclear type	Present in poly-morphonuclear type

Part I: MYELOID SERIES (Concluded)

	Specification	Myeloblasts	Myelocytes	Meta-myelocytes	Neutrophils, Polymorpho-nuclear	Eosinophils	Basophils
	(A)	(B)	(C)	(D)	(E)	(F)	(G)
	Wright's Stain (concluded)						
23	Nucleus (concluded) Nucleoli	2-5	Smaller and fewer than in myeloblasts	None	None	None	None

Contributors: (a) Wintrobe, M. M., (b) Sundberg, R. Dorothy, (c) Tompkins, Edna H.

Reference: Wintrobe, M. M. 1956. Clinical hematology. Lea and Febiger, Philadelphia. pp. 216-217.

Part II: LYMPHOID SERIES

	Specification	Lymphoblasts	Lymphocytes		
			Young	Mature	Old
	(A)	(B)	(C)	(D)	(E)
	Supravital Stain				
1	Size	10-20 μ	9-18 μ	7-18 μ	7-15 μ
2	Contour	Sharp	Sharp	Sharp	Sharp
3	Physical state	Gel	Sol	Sol	Sol
4	Motility	None	By constriction rings; nucleus anterior	By constriction rings; nucleus anterior	By constriction rings; nucleus anterior
5	Phagocytosis	None	None	None	None
6	Cytoplasm Quantity	Scanty	More than in lympho-blasts	Usually plentiful	Usually scanty
7	Color	Yellow	Grayish-yellow	Gray	Colorless
8	Vacuoles, neutral red	None	None to many; any dis-tribution	None to many; any dis-tribution	None to many; any distribution
9	Mitochondria	Short, plump, rod-shaped; numerous especially near nucleus	Short, plump, rod-shaped; numerous, especially at one side of nucleus	Short, plump, rod-shaped; 10-20	Smaller than in earlier stages of lymphocyte development; 0-10
10	Nucleus Shape	Round or oval	Round or indented	Round or indented	Usually round
11	Chromatin	Sparse	Slight	Moderate	Coarse
12	Nucleoli	1-2	0-1	None	None
	Wright's Stain				
13	Size	10-18 μ		7-18 μ	
14	Cytoplasm Quantity	Scanty		Scanty or plentiful	
15	Color	Blue		Sky-blue, deep blue, or very pale blue	
16	Granules	None or few azurophilic	None or few azurophilic	None or few azurophilic	
17	Perinuclear clear zone	Present		Present when cytoplasm is dark	
18	Nucleus Position	Centric or eccentric		Eccentric	
19	Shape	Round or oval		Round or slightly indented	
20	Color	Light reddish-purple		Deep purplish-blue	

Part II: LYMPHOID SERIES (Concluded)

	Specification	Lymphoblasts	Lymphocytes		Old
			Young	Mature	
	(A)	(B)	(C)	(D)	(E)
		Wright's Stain (concluded)			
21	Nucleus (con-cluded) Chromatin	Moderately coarse particles; stippled		Moderate or large masses; poor distinction between basi- and oxy-chromatin	
22	Membrane	Fairly dense, fine but distinct		Dense	
23	Nucleoli	1-2 or more		None	

Contributors: (a) Wintrobe, M. M., (b) Sundberg, R. Dorothy, (c) Tompkins, Edna H.

Reference: Wintrobe, M. M. 1956. Clinical hematology. Lea and Febiger, Philadelphia. pp. 216-217.

Part III: MONOCYTIC SERIES

	Specification	Monoblasts	Monocytes		Clasmatocytes
			Young	Mature	
	(A)	(B)	(C)	(D)	(E)
		Supravital Stain			
1	Size	12-18 μ	12-18 μ	16-20 μ	15-80 μ
2	Contour	Sharp or slightly irregular	Irregular, lacy	Irregular, lacy	Irregular
3	Physical state	Gel	Sol	Sol	Sol
4	Motility	None	Surface film; bleblike pseudopodia	Surface film; bleblike pseudopodia	Surface film; bleblike pseudopodia
5	Phagocytosis	None	Uncommon	Uncommon	Usually for particle or cell
6	Cytoplasm Quantity	Scanty	Moderate	Abundant	Usually abundant
7	Color	Slightly yellow, turbid	Colorless, turbid	Colorless, turbid	Colorless
8	Vacuoles, neutral red	When present, very fine and located in centrosphere	Numerous; small, rosette arrangement	Very numerous; vary in size, occasionally rosette arrangement	Often many; vary in size and color
9	Mitochondria	Fine spheres or slender rods	Fine, dustlike rods	Fine, dustlike rods	Delicate, filamentous rods
10	Nucleus Shape	Round or oval	Indented	Markedly indented	Elongated, indented, or oval
11	Chromatin	Very sparse	Slight	Moderate; loose network	Moderate
12	Nucleoli	1-2	0-1	0	0-1
		Wright's Stain			
13	Size		12-20 μ	12-20 μ	15-80 μ
14	Cytoplasm Quantity			Abundant	Usually abundant
15	Color			Grayish- or cloudy-blue	Opaque sky blue
16	Granules		Variable in number, fine, lilac or reddish-blue, "azurophilic dust"	Abundant, fine, lilac or reddish-blue	Numerous, moderately coarse, azure
17	Perinuclear clear zone			None	None

Part III: MONOCYTIC SERIES (Concluded)

	Specification	Monoblasts	Monocytes		Clasmatocytes
			Young	Mature	
	(A)	(B)	(C)	(D)	(E)
	Wright's Stain (concluded)				
	Nucleus				
18	Position		Centric or eccentric	Centric or eccentric	Centric
19	Shape		Round, oval, notched, or "horseshoe"	Round, oval, notched, or "horseshoe"	Elongated, indented, or oval
20	Color		Pale bluish-violet	Pale bluish-violet	Pale bluish-violet
21	Chromatin		Fine; reticulated, skein-like, or lacy	Fine; reticulated, skein-like, or lacy	Spongy
22	Membrane		Present	Present	Distinct
23	Nucleoli			None	None

Contributors: (a) Wintrobe, M. M., (b) Sundberg, R. Dorothy, (c) Tompkins, Edna H.

Reference: Wintrobe, M. M. 1956. Clinical hematology. Lea and Febiger, Philadelphia. pp. 216-217.

49. BLOOD PLATELET COUNT: MAN

Part I: INFANTS

Values are for cutaneous blood [1] and were obtained by direct method of Wood, Vogel, and Famulener [2]. Values in parentheses are ranges, estimate "c" (cf. Introduction).

	Age	No. of Observations	Platelets thousands/cu mm		Age	No. of Observations	Platelets thousands/cu mm
	(A)	(B)	(C)		(A)	(B)	(C)
1	At birth	73	227(140-290)	9	5 mo	51	345(200-470)
2	1 wk	69	233(160-320)	10	6 mo	47	350(200-480)
3	2 wk	19	242(170-370)	11	7 mo	34	330(200-460)
4	3 wk	23	269(160-380)	12	8 mo	28	346(220-480)
5	1 mo	48	277(200-370)	13	9 mo	19	333(200-440)
6	2 mo	59	320(200-470)	14	10 mo	23	340(200-450)
7	3 mo	58	348(200-480)	15	11 mo	15	361(220-480)
8	4 mo	56	324(180-450)	16	1 yr	15	339(250-470)

Contributor: Mayerson, H. S.

References: [1] Merritt, K. K., and L. T. Davidson. 1933. Am. J. Dis. Child. 46:1008. [2] Wood, F. C., K. M. Vogel, and L. W. Famulener. 1929. Laboratory technique. Ed. 3. T. Dougherty, New York. p. 26.

Part II: ADULTS

Values in parentheses are ranges, estimate "c" unless otherwise indicated (cf. Introduction).

	Blood	No. of Subjects	Direct Method of:	Platelets thousands/cu mm	Reference
	(A)	(B)	(C)	(D)	(E)
1	Arterial	40♂	Tocantins	350(322-378)[b]	11
2	Venous	13♂[1]	Brecher	248(138-428)	6
3		50♂	Brecher-Cronkite	257(140-440)	5
4		138♂	Kristenson	294(204-395)	7, 10
5		20♀	Kristenson	291(214-360)	7, 10
6		40♂	Tocantins	310(150-690)	11
7	Cutaneous	100	Björkman	259(155-365)	4
8		13♂[1]	Brecher	242(122-408)	6
9		25	Lampert	246(134-358)[b]	3
10		100, ♂♀	Masure	269(162-376)	9
11		64, ♂♀	Rees-Ecker	409(273-545)[b]	1, 2, 8
12		80, ♂♀	Rees-Ecker-Sloan	241(140-340)	9
13		40♂	Tocantins	250(180-358)	11

/1/ 4 determinations on each subject.

Contributors: (a) Brecher, George, and Cronkite, Eugene P., (b) Diggs, L. W., and Dugdale, Marion, (c) Lewis, Jessica H.

References: [1] Aggeler, P. M., J. Howard, and S. P. Lucia. 1946. Blood, N.Y. 1:472. [2] Aggeler, P. M., and S. P. Lucia. 1949. Hemorrhagic disorders, a guide to diagnosis and treatment. University of Chicago Press, Chicago. [3] Biggs, R., and R. L. MacMillan. 1948. J. Clin. Path., Lond. 1:269. [4] Björkman, S. E. 1959. Acta haemat., Basel 22:377. [5] Brecher, G., and E. P. Cronkite. 1950. J. Appl. Physiol. 3:365. [6] Brecher, G., M. Schneiderman, and E. P. Cronkite. 1953. Am. J. Clin. Path. 23:15. [7] Kristenson, A. 1924. Studien über die Anzahl des Blutplättchen beim Menschen. Appelberg, Uppsala. [8] Rees, H. M., and E. E. Ecker. 1923. J. Am. M. Ass. 80:621. [9] Sloan, A. W. 1951. J. Clin. Path., Lond. 4:37. [10] Sunderman, F. W., and F. Boerner. 1949. Normal values in clinical medicine. W. B. Saunders, Philadelphia. [11] Tocantins, L. M. 1936. Am. J. M. Sc. 192:150.

50. BLOOD PLATELET COUNT: VERTEBRATES OTHER THAN MAN

Values in parentheses are ranges, estimate "c" (cf. Introduction).

	Animal	No. of Subjects	Platelets thousands/cu mm	Remarks	Reference
	(A)	(B)	(C)	(D)	(E)
1	Cat	7	345(164-500)	7 determinations	10
2			122		16
3		10	493(368-712)		1
4			519(356-760)		26
5	Cattle	10	684(542-975)		1
6	Calf		490	8 determinations	20
7	Dog	53	461(188-960)	173 determinations by direct method; venous blood from ear	23
8		17	467(353-535)	17 observations; femoral artery	2
9		10	492(298-793)		1
10	Guinea pig	55	104(15-415)		11
11		9	638(584-856)	12 determinations; blood from ear	17
12		10	719(550-880)	Determinations by direct method	25
13		4	783(525-900)	8 determinations by direct method; blood from ear	24

	Animal	No. of Subjects	Platelets thousands/cu mm	Remarks	Reference
	(A)	(B)	(C)	(D)	(E)
14	Horse	7	134(114-160)		3
15			335(249-461)		24
16		10	352(254-560)	10 determinations	13
17	Pony	255	(184-312)		3
18	Monkey, rhesus	6	267(155-424)	Determinations by direct method; blood from finger	15
19	Mouse		278(246-339)		6
20			987		14
21	Rabbit	148	533(170-1120)	991 determinations by direct method	5
22		11	536(424-586)	11 determinations; arterial and venous blood	2
23	Rat	15	390(320-440)		12
24		72	454(190-760)	Determinations by direct method	27, 28
25		13	477(232-641)		22
26		480	743(320-1210)	Determinations by direct method	4
27			754(702-796)		21
28		8	795(620-950)		18
29			800(500-1000)		7
30			823		19
31	Sheep		441(284-659)		9
32	Swine	5	403(296-616)	5 determinations	13
33	Turkey		66(58-77)		8

Contributors: (a) Tocantins, Leandro M., (b) Jaques, L. B., (c) Dunlap, J. S.

References: [1] Arndt, H. J. 1925. Arch. wiss. prakt. Tierh. 52:316. [2] Aynaud, M. 1909. Le globulin des mammifères. Steinheil, Paris. [3] Barkhan, P., S. C. Tomlin, and R. K. Archer. 1957. J. Comp. Path. 67:358. [4] Calaresu, F., and L. B. Jaques. 1960. Canad. J. Biochem. Physiol. 38:1275. [5] Casey, A. E., P. D. Rosahn, L. Hu, and L. Pearce. 1936. J. Exp. M. 64:453. [6] Copley, A. L., and T. P. Robb. 1942. Am. J. Clin. Path. 12:362. [7] Creskoff, A. J., T. Fitz-Hugh, Jr., and E. J. Farris. In J. Q. Griffith and E. J. Farris, ed. 1942. The rat in laboratory investigation. J. B. Lippincott, Philadelphia. ch. 14. [8] Dunlap, J. S. Blood and bone marrow of bronze turkeys. Unpublished. [9] Ercegovac, D. 1936. Sang, Par. 10:971. [10] Field, M. E. 1930. Am. J. Physiol. 93:245. [11] Giertz, H., and F. Hahn. 1955. Internat. Arch. Allergy, Basel. 6:23. [12] Hedinger, C., and H. Langemann. 1955. Schweiz. med. Wschr. 85:368. [13] Hikmet, P. 1927. Arch. wiss. prakt. Tierh. 55:222. [14] Jacobson, L. O. 1944. Endocrinology 34:240. [15] Krumbhaar, E. B., and J. H. Musser, Jr. 1920. J. Med. Res. 42:105. [16] Lawrence, J. S., and W. N. Valentine. 1947. Blood, N. Y. 2:40. [17] Ledingham, J. C. G., and S. P. Bedson. 1915. Lancet, Lond. 1:311. [18] Ma, W. C. 1932. Chin. J. Physiol. 6:359. [19] Machella, T. E., and G. M. Higgins. 1939. Am. J. M. Sc. 198:804. [20] Mariconda, G. 1933. Arch. fisiol., Fir. 32:387. [21] Olson, K. B. 1939. Proc. Soc. Exp. Biol., N.Y. 41:643. [22] Shechet, H. A., D. L. Friedman, and L. B. Nice. 1935. Ibid. 32:608. [23] Tocantins, L. M. 1936. Ann. Int. M. 9:838. [24] Tocantins, L. M. 1938. Medicine, Balt. 17:202. [25] Watabiki, T. 1917. Kitasato Arch. 1:195. [26] Weiser, R. 1922. Wien. tierärztl. Mschr. 9:153. [27] Yamamoto, S. 1933. Acta derm., Kyoto, Europ. ed. 21:94. [28] Yamamoto, S. 1933. Ibid. 21:133.

Part I: MODIFIED NEO-UNITARIAN (MONOPHYLETIC) THEORY (OF DOWNEY), O. P. JONES (1960)

Thick lines indicate the relation of blood cells in the normal adult, thin lines indicate the various possibilities in pathological and experimental conditions.

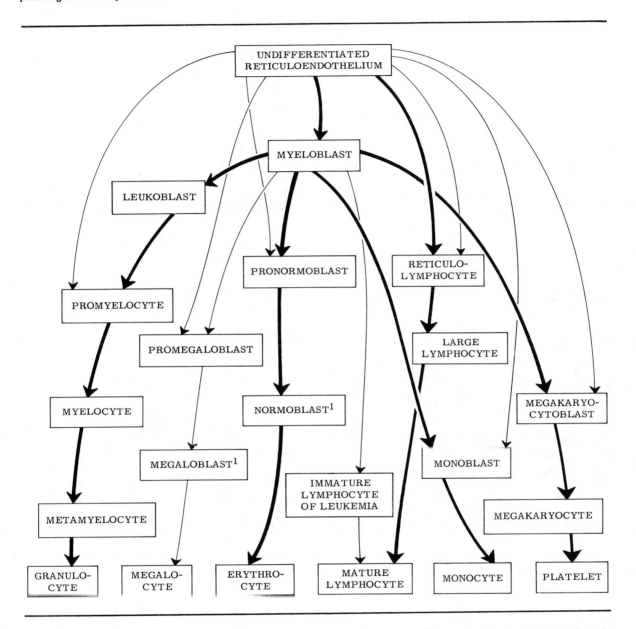

/1/ Megaloblast and normoblast each represent three consecutive forms: basophilic, polychromic, and orthochromic.

Contributor: Jones, Oliver P.

References: [1] Downey, H. 1938. Handbook of hematology. P. B. Hoeber, New York. v. 2, p. 1275. [2] Downey, H. 1938. Ibid. v. 3, p. 1965. [3] Jones, O. P. 1943. Arch. Path., Chic. 35:752. [4] Sundberg, R. D. and H. Downey. 1942. Am. J. Anat. 70:455.

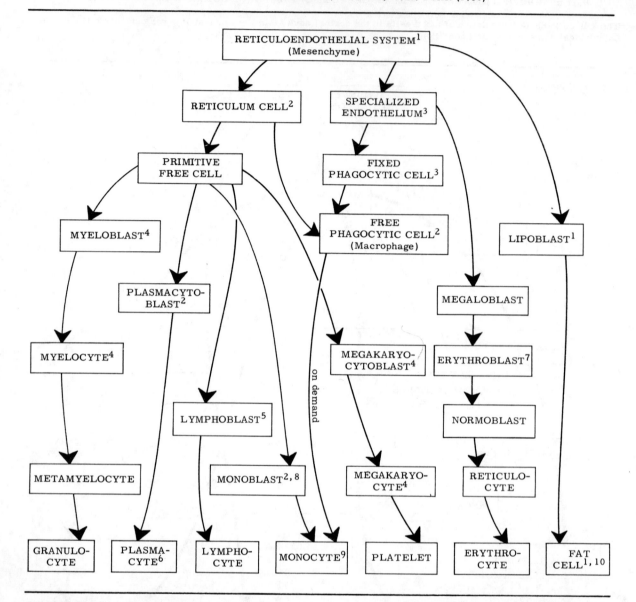

/1/ In special fat organs, diffuse connective tissue, and bone marrow. /2/ In diffuse connective tissue and organ parenchyma. /3/ In sinusoids of bone marrow, spleen, and lymph nodes; in Küpffer cells of liver. /4/ In bone marrow. /5/ In lymph nodes, spleen, liver, and connective tissue. /6/ Rare in blood, more common in connective tissue. /7/ Both early and late forms. /8/ May give rise to myeloblast in tissue culture. /9/ May give rise to fibroblast-like cell in tissue culture and may revert to monoblast on demand. Monocyte also may give rise to the epithelioid cell in fatty degeneration (of tuberculosis caseation), to Langhans giant cell, and to foreign body giant cell. /10/ There is evidence that the fat cell may give rise to macrophage (or the reverse).

Contributor: Doan, Charles A.

References: [1] Cunningham, R. S., F. R. Sabin, and C. A. Doan. 1925. Contr. Embryol. Carnegie Inst. 16:227. [2] Doan, C. A. 1931. Medicine, Balt. 10:323. [3] Doan, C. A. 1939. Bull. N. York Acad. M. 15:668. [4] Doan, C. A. 1940. J. Laborat. Clin. M. 26:89. [5] Doan, C. A., R. S. Cunningham, and F. R. Sabin. 1925. Contr. Embryol. Carnegie Inst. 16:163.

Values in parentheses are ranges, estimate "c" unless otherwise specified (cf. Introduction).

| Specification | Values from: | | | | |
| | Mulligan | Mulligan | Rekers and Coulter | Stasney and Higgins[1] | Van Loon and Clark |
(A)	(B)	(C)	(D)	(E)	(F)
1 Number of subjects	21	35	36	35	81
2 Age of subjects	0.5-2.5 da	Adult	19-24 mo	Adult	Adult
Cells, % of total cell count					
3 Proerythroblasts	1.3(0.4-3.2)[2]	0.5(0-1.4)[2]	0.3(0-1.3)[3]	59(40-78)	0.6(0.2-2.7)[2]
Normoblasts					
4 Early	5.8(3.0-9.5)[4]	1.5(0.4-3.8)[5]	28.2(8.0-53.9)[4]		7.8(6.4-10.0)[5]
5 Intermediate	45.1(33.0-56.6)[6]	38.1(18.6-63.6)[6]			16.4(11-26)[7]
6 Late			4.6(0-11.2)[6]		17.4(9-26)[8]
7 Myeloblasts		0.6(0-1.8)	1.9(0.2-3.7)	2.4(0-5.1)[9]	0.6(0.2-1.0)
8 Promyelocytes	0.8(0-2.2)	1.5(0.2-4.6)	0.7(0-3.3)	2.8(0-5.8)	1.6(0.7-2.8)
9 Myelocytes			2.7(0-9.5)		6.0(2.7-10.0)
10 Neutrophilic	4.3(2.0-6.6)	4.7(2.2-11.2)		8.9(2.8-15.0)	
11 Eosinophilic				1.2(0-2.4)	
12 Metamyelocytes	9.7(7.2-12.0)	10.5(5.6-20.0)	5.1(0-24.4)[10]	15.3(7.2-23.0)	3.4(1.1-4.6)
13 Band cells	20.6(14.8-28.4)[11]	31.0(16.8-53.8)[11]	42.4(16.5-62.9)[11]		11.7(6.8-17.0)
Segmented cells					
14 Neutrophilic	3.4(0.8-6.6)	3.9(0.2-8.6)	5.0(0.2-14.3)	5.1(0-12.5)	30.1(17-44)
15 Eosinophilic	2.4(0-5.2)	3.7(1.0-6.8)	4.7(0.2-19.3)	2.8(0-6.8)	2.0(0.4-3.8)
16 Basophilic			0.2(0-1.3)	0.1(0-0.3)	
17 Lymphocytes	3.3(1.6-6.0)	1.9(0-6.6)	0.7(0-8)	1.2(0.2-2.3)	0.9(0.2-2.7)
18 Monocytes					0.2(0-0.3)
19 Megakaryocytes			0.6(0-1.1)	0.1(0-0.5)	0.5(0-1.4)
20 Plasma cells			0.4(0-2.1)		
21 Reticulum cells				1.0(0-2.1)	
22 Unclassified cells	3.1(0.8-5.4)	2.1(0.8-6.1)	3.0(0-15.7)	0.2(0-0.7)[12]	
Reference	[1]	[2]	[3]	[4]	[5]

/1/ Ranges are estimate "b" (cf. Introduction). /2/ Pronormoblasts. /3/ Megaloblasts. /4/ Erythrocytes.
/5/ Basophilic normoblasts. /6/ Normoblasts. /7/ Polychromic normoblasts. /8/ Orthochromic normoblasts.
/9/ Includes leukoblasts. /10/ Juvenile cells. /11/ Stab cells. /12/ Includes heterophils.

Contributor: Rekers, Paul E.

References: [1] Mulligan, R. M. 1941. Anat. Rec. 79:101. [2] Mulligan, R. M. 1945. Ibid. 91:161. [3] Rekers, P. E., and M. Coulter. 1948. AECD 1925. Office of Technical Services, Department of Commerce, Washington, D. C. [4] Stasney, J., and G. M. Higgins. 1937. Am. J. M. Sc. 193:462. [5] Van Loon, E. J., and B. B. Clark. 1943. Clin. Med. 28:1575.

Values in parentheses are ranges, estimate

	Specification	Berman	Values from: Diggs	Israëls	Leitner
	(A)	(B)	(C)	(D)	(E)
1	Number of subjects	19♂♀			200♂♀
2	Marrow aspirated, ml	1.5	(0.1-0.2)	0.2	(0.1-0.3)
3	Nucleated cells, total, cells/cu mm				(60,000-100,000)
	Cells, % of total cell count				
4	Proerythroblasts	3[3,4]	(0-2)	(0.5-4.0)	0.8[5]
5	Normoblasts				
6	Early	10[3,9]	(1-4)[10]	(1-5)	3.2[5,11]
7	Intermediate	86[3,14]	(2-5)[15]	(12-20)	24.4[5,8]
8	Late	1[3,17]	(7-20)[8]	(6-10)	
9	Myeloblasts	3[19]	(0-3)	(0.3-2.0)	1.2
10	Promyelocytes	9	(1-5)[21]	(1-8)	2.2
11	Myelocytes				
12	Neutrophilic	6	(2-8)	(5-20)	12.6[22]
13	Eosinophilic				1.4
14	Basophilic				0.02
15	Metamyelocytes				
16	Neutrophilic	9	(3-12)[25]	(13-32)[26]	10.2
17	Eosinophilic				0.8
18	Band cells				
19	Neutrophilic	31	(20-40)		24
	Segmented cells				
20	Neutrophilic	17	(9-30)	(7-30)	28.4
21	Eosinophilic	2	(0-3)	(0.5-4.0)	1.8
22	Basophilic		(0-1)	(0-1)	0.02
23	Lymphocytes	14	(5-15)	(3-20)	7.6
24	Monocytes		(0-1)	(0.5-5.0)	1.4
25	Megakaryocytes	5		±[31]	0.8
26	Plasma cells	1	(0-1)	(0-2)	1.2
27	Reticulum cells	2		±[31]	0.4[32]
28	Unclassified cells				3.5
29	Disintegrated cells				
	Reference	[1]	[2]	[3]	[4]

/1/ Ranges are estimate "b" (cf. Introduction). /2/ Values are smoothed weighted means and calculated ranges. /8/ Normoblasts. /9/ Basophilic normoblasts. /10/ Early erythroblasts. /11/ Macroblasts. /12/ Erythroblasts. /17/ Orthochromic normoblasts. /18/ Metakaryocytes. /19/ Includes leukoblasts. /20/ Granuloblasts. /21/ /25/ Juvenile neutrophils. /26/ Includes band cells. /27/ Rhabdocytes. /28/ Polymorphonuclear cells. /29/

Contributors: (a) Diggs, L. W., (b) Osgood, Edwin E.

References: [1] Berman, L. 1949. Blood, N. Y. 4:511. [2] Diggs, L. W. In F. P. Parker, ed. 1948. Textbook pathology. William Heinemann, London. [4] Leitner, S. M. 1945. Die intravitale Knochenmarksuntersuchung. and A. J. Seaman. 1944. Physiol. Rev. 24:46. [7] Vaughan, S. L., and F. Brockmyre. 1947. Blood, N. Y., Spec. New York. [9] Wintrobe, M. M. 1956. Clinical hematology. Ed. 4. Lea and Febiger, Philadelphia.

DIFFERENTIAL CELL COUNTS: MAN

ADULTS

"c" unless otherwise specified (cf. Introduction).

Lucia and Hunt[1]	Osgood and Seaman[1,2]	Values from: Vaughan and Brockmyre	Whitby and Britton	Wintrobe	
(F)	(G)	(H)	(I)	(J)	
6♀	28♂, 24♀	42♂, 8♀			1
0.5	(0.5-10.0)	3.0	0.25	(1.0-2.0)	2
	35,000(10,000-100,000)	35,300(9,400-74,000)			3
0.6(0-3.4)[6]	0.2(0-1)[7]	9.5(1.5-24.0)[8]	(0-4)	4.0(1-8)[4]	4
				18.0(7-32)	5
8.0(0-20.4)[12]	2.0(0-4)[13]		(4-15)		6
	6.0(4-8)[16]				7
12.0(0-25)[8]	3.0(1-5)[18]		(7-19)		8
1.0(0-2.8)	0.4(0-1)[20]	1.3(0-3)	(0-2.5)	2.0(0.3-5.0)	9
4.0(1.2-6.8)	1.4(0-3)		(0.5-5.0)	5.0(1-8)	10
		8.9(2-16)			11
10.2(4.0-16.4)	4.2(0-12)[22]		(2-8)	12.0(5-19)	12
0.8(0-1.8)			(0-1)	1.5(0.5-3.0)	13
				0.3(0-0.5)	14
	6.5(3-10)[23]	8.8(3.5-18.0)[24]		22.0(13-32)	15
13.2(7.8-18.6)			(10-25)		16
1.3(0.5-2.1)			(0-2.5)		17
	24.0(17-33)[27]	23.9(12-34)			18
24.6(5.2-44.0)					19
10.0(0-22.4)[28]	15.0(5-25)[29]	18.5(6-36)[30]	(10-40)[26,28]	20.0(7-30)[28]	20
0.3(0-0.9)[28]	2.0(0-4)[29]	1.9(0-6.5)[30]	(0-4)[26,28]	2.0(0.5-4.0)[28]	21
	0.2(0-0.5)[29]	0.2(0-1.5)[30]	(0-1)[28]	0.2(0-0.7)[28]	22
10.3(1.5-19.1)	14.0(3-25)	16.2(7-35)	(5-20)	10.0(3-17)	23
0.5	2.0(0-4)	2.4(0-6)	(0-5)	2.0(0.5-5.0)	24
				0.4(0.03-3.00)	25
1.5(0-4.1)		0.3(0-1.5)	(0-1)	0.4(0-2)	26
		0.3(0-2.5)[33]		(0.2-2.0)	27
		0.02(0-0.5)			28
	19.0(10-30)	7.9(0-18)			29
[5]	[6]	[7]	[8]	[9]	

/3/ Percent of red series.   /4/ Pronormoblasts.   /5/ Per 100 leukocytes.   /6/ Megaloblasts.   /7/ Karyoblasts.
/13/ Prokaryocytes.   /14/ Polychromatophilic normoblasts.   /15/ Late erythroblasts.   /16/ Karyocytes.
Premyelocytes.   /22/ Includes early neutrophilic myelocytes.   /23/ Metagranulocytes.   /24/ Young forms.
Lobocytes. /30/ Filament cells.   /31/ Occasionally present.   /32/ Endothelial cells.   /33/ Reticuloendothelial cells.

of clinical pathology. Williams and Wilkins, Baltimore. [3] Israëls, M. C. G. 1955. An atlas of bone marrow Benno Schwabe Verlag, Basel. [5] Lucia, S. P., and M. L. Hunt. 1947. Am. J. M. Sc. 213:686. [6] Osgood, E. E., issue 1, p. 54. [8] Whitby, L. E. H., and C. J. C. Britton. 1957. Disorders of the blood. Ed. 8. Grune and Stratton,

Part II: NON-PREGNANT AND PREGNANT FEMALES

Bone marrow aspirated = 10 ml. Values in parentheses are ranges, estimate "c" (cf. Introduction).

	Cell Type	Non-pregnant[1]	Pregnant[2]		
			1st Trimester	2nd Trimester	3rd Trimester
	(A)	(B)	(C)	(D)	(E)
1	Nucleated cells, total, cells/cu mm	23,100 (7,500-46,000)	34,580 (14,400-65,700)	41,510 (15,700-125,000)	33,930 (16,900-70,000)
	Cells, % of total cell count				
2	Proerythroblasts	0.1(0-0.4)	0.2(0-0.4)	0.2(0-1)	0.2(0-0.5)
	Normoblasts				
3	Early	2.5(0.6-4.0)	2.1(0.6-3.2)	2.0(1-4)	2.8(0.3-6.2)
4	Intermediate	5.0(1.3-8.0)	3.2(1.6-5.0)	4.0(2.0-6.4)	5.3(0.3-13.6)
5	Late	1.9(0.4-3.2)	2.2(0.2-6.0)	2.2(0.4-7.0)	2.4(0.6-6.5)
6	Myeloblasts	0.3(0-0.8)	0.1(0-0.5)	0.3(0-1)	0.2(0-1)
7	Promyelocytes	1.0(0.1-2.2)	1.0(0.2-2.1)	0.9(0.4-2.0)	0.9(0-2.3)
	Myelocytes				
8	Early neutrophilic	0.5(0-1.4)	0.7(0-1.5)	0.7(0-2.8)	1.0(0.3-2.5)
9	Neutrophilic	6.0(1.4-11.0)	6.0(1.2-10.6)	7.0(4.0-11.2)	5.7(2.3-12.5)
10	Eosinophilic[3]	0.5(0-1.5)	0.7(0.2-2.6)	0.4(0-1.6)	0.4(0-1)
11	Metamyelocytes	5.6(1.4-9.4)	5.7(1.8-9.0)	5.4(1.6-8.6)	5.3(2-9)
12	Band cells	23.7(12.4-34.0)	30.2(15-46)	34.0(19.6-48.0)	34.5(23.5-45.0)
	Segmented cells				
13	Neutrophilic	16.6(10.4-31.0)	18.6(9-38)	15.3(8.0-21.6)	14.3(1.6-25.0)
14	Eosinophilic[4]	1.3(0.2-6.0)	1.3(0.2-6.0)	0.8(0.1-1.8)	0.7(0-1.6)
15	Basophilic	0.3(0-0.8)	0.3(0-1.0)	0.1(0-0.6)	0.2(0-0.6)
16	Lymphocytes	16.8(9.2-30.0)	13.5(4.5-28.0)	12.9(5.6-25.0)	12.0(5.5-23.3)
17	Monocytes	1.4(0-3.5)	1.1(0.1-3.0)	0.7(0-1.8)	0.7(0-2.4)
18	Disintegrated cells	16.2(10.5-24.0)	13.3(9.6-18.0)	12.4(6.0-23.5)	13.2(5.5-23.6)

/1/ 28 subjects. /2/ 40 subjects. /3/ Includes eosinophilic metamyelocytes. /4/ Includes band eosinophils.

Reference: Pitts, H. H., and E. A. Packham. 1939. Arch. Int. M. 64:471.

Part III: INFANTS AND CHILDREN

Values in parentheses are ranges, estimate "c" (cf. Introduction).

	Cell Type	Percent of Total Cell Count		
		1st Month	2nd-12th Month	2nd-20th Year
	(A)	(B)	(C)	(D)
1	Pronormoblasts	0.78(0-2.75)	0.59(0-1.5)	0.47(0-1.5)
	Normoblasts			
2	Basophilic	1.88(0-6.75)	2.08(0.25-4.25)	1.69(0.25-4.80)
3	Polychromatic	12.59(2.5-36.5)	14.49(5.0-24.0)	18.20(4.8-34.0)
4	Orthochromatic	1.57(0-4.75)	2.53(0-8.50)	2.72(0-7.75)
5	Myeloblasts	1.65	1.92(0.25-3.25)	1.23(0-3.25)
6	Leukoblasts	1.86(0.25-4.25)	1.11(0.33-2.50)	1.44(0-4.0)
7	Promyelocytes	3.77(0-13.75)	0.68	1.8(0-4.5)
8	Myelocytes	18.14(7.00-24.75)	16.73(12.0-26.5)	16.46(8.50-25.25)
9	Eosinophilic	0.74(0-3.0)	0.41(0-1.5)	0.48(0-2.25)
10	Metamyelocytes	25.64(10.75-40.00)	23.92	23.27(14.00-34.25)
11	Eosinophilic	1.74(0-4.25)	1.70(0-3.25)	2.21(0.25-6.25)
12	Polymorphonuclear cells	9.33(2.25-19.00)	7.25(2.5-15.5)	12.92(4.5-29.0)
13	Eosinophilic	1.2(0-2.75)	0.59(0-1.75)	0.84(0-3.5)
14	Lymphocytes	19.74	25.38	16.03(4.75-35.75)

Contributor: Limarzi, Louis R.

Reference: Glaser, K., L. R. Limarzi, and H. G. Poncher. 1950. Pediatrics 6:789.

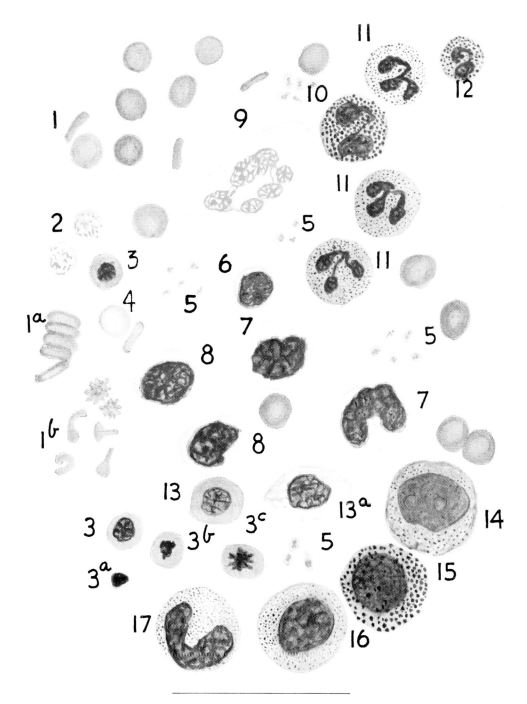

1	Erythrocytes	3c	Normoblast in mitosis	11	Neutrophil leukocytes
1a	Erythrocytes in rouleau	4	Ghost cells	12	Basophil leukocyte
1b	Deformed cells (poikilocytes), crenated forms	5	Platelets	13	Polychromatophil erythroblast
2	Reticulocytes stained with dilute solution of cresyl blue	6	Small lymphocyte	13a	Hemocytoblast
		7	Monocytes	14	Megaloblast
3	Early normoblasts	8	Large lymphocytes	15	Eosinophil myelocyte
3a	Extruded nucleus	9	Megakaryocyte	16	Neutrophil myelocyte
3b	Late normoblast	10	Eosinophil leukocyte	17	Neutrophil metamyelocyte

Reference: Best, C. H., and N. B. Taylor. 1961. The physiological basis of medical practice. Ed. 7. Williams and Wilkins, Baltimore.

VII. Blood Oxygen Dissociation

54. DATA FOR CONSTRUCTING BLOOD O_2 DISSOCIATION CURVES: VERTEBRATES AND INVERTEBRATES

The lowest O_2 tension (partial pressure), in mm Hg, at which respiratory pigment (hemoglobin, unless otherwise specified) is 95% or more saturated, is referred to as the tension of saturation. The tension at which the pigment is 50% saturated (i.e., when unoxygenated pigment equals oxygenated pigment) is called the tension of half saturation and is indicated as "t. $\frac{1}{2}$ sat." The tension of half saturation for a specific pigment establishes the upper limit of tissue O_2 tension and the lower limit of environmental oxygen for the function of that pigment. When percent saturation is plotted as ordinate against O_2 pressure as abscissa, the "position" (O_2 pressure required to produce 50% saturation) of the resultant dissociation curves differs from species to species, and varies greatly within the same species during development and with changes in pH, temperature, and dilution. The "shape" is not so affected, in that the curves may be superimposed upon each other after multiplying O_2 pressure (t. $\frac{1}{2}$ sat.) of the standard curve for man by a suitable factor "f" [1]. This is true for "shape" only as a first approximation, as recent investigation indicates the likelihood of small differences resulting from variations in pH, as well as from variations among individuals; it is only a rough approximation when applied to mammals other than man [2], and very rough for other vertebrates, e.g., certain fish show change in "shape" with changes in CO_2 pressure. The figure below illustrates dissociation curves for man and for four other animals, pigeon and crocodile with blood having a low affinity for oxygen (i.e., a high t. $\frac{1}{2}$ sat.) and <u>Arenicola</u> and eel with a high affinity and low t. $\frac{1}{2}$ sat. [3]. In the following tables, only the data for man (Part I) is given in full for constructing the curve.

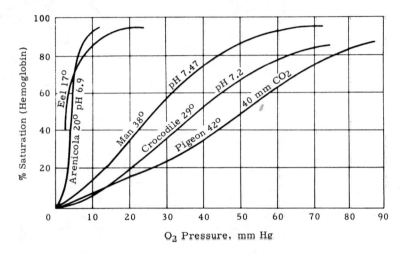

Contributors: (a) Forbes, William H., (b) McCutcheon, F. Harold.

References: [1] Allen, D. W., K. F. Guthe, and J. Wyman, Jr. 1950. J. Biol. Chem. 187:393. [2] Paul, W., and F. J. Roughton. 1951. J. Physiol., Lond. 113:23. [3] Redfield, A. C. 1933. Q. Rev. Biol. 8:31.

Part I: MAN

Normal whole blood from subjects at rest. Serum pH = 7.40, intracellular pH = 7.19, temperature = 37°C.

	Hemoglobin Saturation %	CO_2 Pressure mm Hg	O_2 Pressure mm Hg	Reference		Hemoglobin Saturation %	CO_2 Pressure mm Hg	O_2 Pressure mm Hg	Reference
	(A)	(B)	(C)	(D)		(A)	(B)	(C)	(D)
1	5.0	47.4	3.7	A, C, 1;	8	60.0	43.0	31.1	A, C, 1;
2	10.0	47.0	8.2	B, 2, 3	9	70.0	42.2	36.1	B, 2, 3
3	15.0	46.6	10.9		10	80.0	41.5	45.7	
4	20.0	46.2	13.4		11	85.0	41.1	51.7	
5	30.0	45.3	17.9		12	90.0	40.7	61.4	
6	40.0	44.6	22.0		13	95.0	40.3	80.0	
7	50.0[1]	43.8	26.3		14	98.0	40.0	113.0	

/1/ Standard reference condition with an "f" factor of 1.00.

Part I: MAN (Concluded)

Contributor: Forbes, William H.

References: [1] Dill, D. B. 1944. In Handbook of respiratory data in aviation. National Research Council, Washington, D. C. [2] Dill, D. B., H. T. Edwards, and W. V. Consolazio. 1937. J. Biol. Chem. 118:365. [3] Singer, R. B., and A. B. Hastings. 1948. Medicine, Balt. 27:223.

Part II: MAMMALS

	Animal	Temp. $^{\circ}$C	pH	CO_2 Pressure mm Hg	Calculated "f" Factor	t. $\frac{1}{2}$ sat. mm Hg	Reference
	(A)	(B)	(C)	(D)	(E)	(F)	(G)
1	Man	37.0	7.00	142	1.48	39.0[1,2]	A-C,E,F,5;D,9,26
2		37.0	7.10	110	1.35	35.5[1,2]	A-C,E,F,5;D,9,26
3		37.0	7.20	84	1.22	32.2	A-C,E,F,5;D,9,26
4		37.0	7.30	60	1.11	29.2	A-C,E,F,5;D,9,26
5		37.0	7.40	44	1.00	26.3	A-C,E,F,5;D,9,26
6		37.0	7.50	31	0.90	23.5	A-C,E,F,5;D,9,26
7		37.0	7.60	22	0.80	21.0	A-C,E,F,5;D,9,26
8		37.0	7.70	15	0.71	18.5[1,2]	A-C,E,F,5;D,9,26
9		10.0	7.40		0.29	7.4	11
10		20.0	7.40		0.47	12.4	11
11		30.0	7.40	48[1]	0.74	19.6	A-C,E,F,11;D,3,8,11
12		37.0	7.40	44[1,2]	1.00	26.3	A-C,E,F,11;D,3,8,11
13		40.0	7.40	42[1,2]	1.14	30.0	A-C,E,F,11;D,3,8,11
14	At work	37.5	7.40	34	1.00	26.5	2
15	At altitude, 5400 m	37.5	7.40	29	0.97	29.0	13,21,23
16	Terminal nephritis	37.5	7.11	7	1.14	30.0	19
17		37.5	6.83	40	1.79	47.0	
18	Pernicious anemia	37.5	7.40	48	1.18	31.0	7
19	Diabetic coma	37.5	7.40	2	1.03	27.0	6
20		37.5	6.86	40	1.25	33.0	
21		37.5	7.40	3	1.33	35.0	
22		37.5	6.92	40	1.52	40.0	
23	Cat	37.0	7.40		1.44	38.0	4
24		37.0	7.40	44	1.33	35.0	25
25			6.80			50.0	24
26	Dog	37.5	7.40	38	1.06	28.0	10
27		20.0	7.00			0.6	20
28		20.0	9.20			0.5	20
29		37.0	7.10			29.4	24
30	Fox (Vulpes fulva)			10		21	24
31		37.5		40		37.0	
	Goat (Capra hircus)						1
32	Fetus	38.0		50		25.0	
33	Mother	38.0		50		40	
34	Adult	38.0		50		28-33	
35	Horse	37.5	7.40	50	1.03	27.0	14
36		37.0[3]	7.00[3]			3.7[3]	27
37		37.0[3]	7.20[3]			3.4[3]	27
38		37.0[3]	7.40[3]			3.2[3]	27
39		30.0[3]	7.40[3]			1.5[3]	27
40		27.0[3]	7.40[3]			1.1[3]	27
41		20.0[3]	7.40[3]			0.5[3]	27
42		17.0[3]	7.40[3]			0.3[3]	27

/1/ Calculated. /2/ In calculations at 37°C, $pH = 6.15 + \log\dfrac{(\text{total } CO_2) - 0.0290\, CO_2 \text{ pressure}}{0.0290\, CO_2 \text{ pressure}}$, where 6.15 and 0.0290 are the pK' and CO_2 factors, respectively, for whole blood. /3/ Myoglobin (myohemoglobin, muscle hemoglobin). O_2 dissociation curves for myoglobin are rectangular hyperbolas.

Part II: MAMMALS (Continued)

	Animal	Temp. °C	pH	CO$_2$ Pressure mm Hg	Calculated "f" Factor	t. ½ sat. mm Hg	Reference
	(A)	(B)	(C)	(D)	(E)	(F)	(G)
	Llama						
43	Lama huanachus	39.0	7.40		0.76	20.0	18
44	L. peruana	38.0		43		22.0	24
45	Marmot	38.0		40		23.8	24
46	Mouse (Mus musculus)	38.0		40		72.0	24
47	Ox	37.0	7.40[1,2]	29.8	1.13	29.8	12
48		19.0[3]	7.00[3]			0.6[3]	20
49		19.0[3]	9.20[3]			0.5[3]	20
50	Peccary	37.0	7.40		1.10	29.0	12
51	Porpoise (Phocaena phocaena)	38.0		46	1.14	30.0	17
52	Rabbit	38.6	7.40	32	1.20	31.6	18
53	Rat	37.0	7.40		1.52	40.0	4
54	Kangaroo- (Dipodomys spectabilis)	37.0		40	1.93	51.0	16
55	White (Rattus norvegicus)	37.0		40	2.13	56.0	16
56	Sea lion (Eumetopiaes stelleri)	38.0		44	1.52	40.0	15
57	Seal (Phoca vitulina)			10		25	24
58		38.0		40		31	24
59		37.0		40	1.06	28.0	22
60	Sheep	37.0	7.40[1,2]		1.48	39.0	12
61		19.0[4]	9.30[4]	0.015[4]		3.0[4]	25
62		20.0[3]	9.20[3]			0.5[3]	20
63		39.0		40		37.0	24
64	Swine	37.0	7.40[1,2]		1.28	33.7	12
65	Vicuña (Lama vicugna)	39.0	7.40		0.69	18.0	18
66	Viscacha (Lagostomus sp)	38.6	7.40	28	0.99	26.0	18

/1/ Calculated. /2/ In calculations at 37°C, pH = $6.15 + \log\dfrac{\text{(total CO}_2\text{)} - 0.0290\ \text{CO}_2\ \text{pressure}}{0.0290\ \text{CO}_2\ \text{pressure}}$, where 6.15 and 0.0290 are the pK' and CO$_2$ factors, respectively, for whole blood. /3/ Myoglobin (myohemoglobin, muscle hemoglobin). O$_2$ dissociation curves for myoglobin are rectangular hyperbolas. /4/ Diluted blood and hemoglobin.

Contributors: (a) Forbes, William H., (b) McCutcheon, F. Harold, (c) Oberholzer, R.

References: [1] Barcroft, J., R. H. Elliott, L. B. Flexner, F. G. Hall, W. Herkel, E. F. McCarthy, T. McClurin, and M. Talaat. 1934. J. Physiol., Lond. 83:192. [2] Christensen, E. H., and D. B. Dill. 1935. J. Biol. Chem. 109:443. [3] Cullen, G. E., H. R. Keeler, and H. W. Robinson. 1925. Ibid. 66:301. [4] Harvard Medical School, Dept. of Biochemistry. 1948-53. Unpublished. [5] Dill, D. B. 1944. In Handbook of respiratory data in aviation. National Research Council, Washington, D. C. [6] Dill, D. B., A. V. Bock, J. S. Lawrence, J. H. Talbott, and L. J. Henderson. 1929. J. Biol. Chem. 81:551. [7] Dill, D. B., A. V. Bock, C. van Caulaert, A. Folling, L. M. Hurxthal, and L. J. Henderson. 1928. Ibid. 78:191. [8] Dill, D. B., C. Daly, and W. H. Forbes. 1937. Ibid. 117:569. [9] Dill, D. B., H. T. Edwards, and W. V. Consolazio. 1937. Ibid. 118:655. [10] Dill, D. B., H. T. Edwards, M. Florkin, and R. W. Campbell. 1932. Ibid. 95:143. [11] Dill, D. B., and W. H. Forbes. 1941. Am. J. Physiol. 132:685. [12] Dill, D. B., and J. H. Talbott, 1929. Ibid. 90:328. [13] Dill, D. B., J. H. Talbott, and W. V. Consolazio. 1937. J. Biol. Chem. 118:649. [14] Dill, D. B., C. van Caulaert, L. M. Hurxthal, J. L. Stoddard, A. V. Bock, and L. J. Henderson. 1927. Ibid. 73:251. [15] Florkin, M., and A. C. Redfield. 1931. Biol. Bull. 61:422. [16] Gjonnes, B., and K. Schmidt-Nielsen. 1952. J. Cellul. Physiol. 39:147. [17] Green, A. A., and A. C. Redfield. 1933. Biol. Bull. 64:44. [18] Hall, F. G., D. B. Dill, and E. S. Guzman Barron. 1936. J. Cellul. Physiol. 8:301. [19] Henderson, L. J., A. V. Bock, D. B. Dill, L. M. Hurxthal, and C. van Caulaert. 1927. J. Biol. Chem. 75:305. [20] Hill, R. 1936. Proc. R. Soc., Lond., Ser. B, 120:472. [21] Hurtado, A. 1953. In Edward K. Dunham lectures. Harvard University Press, Cambridge. [22] Irving, L.,

54. DATA FOR CONSTRUCTING BLOOD O_2 DISSOCIATION CURVES: VERTEBRATES AND INVERTEBRATES (Continued)

Part II: MAMMALS (Concluded)

O. M. Solandt, D. Y. Solandt, and K. C. Fisher. 1935. J. Cellul. Physiol. 6:393. [23] Keys, A., F. G. Hall, and E. S. Guzman Barron. 1936. Am. J. Physiol. 115:292. [24] Prosser, C. L. 1950. Comparative animal physiology. W. B. Saunders, Philadelphia. [25] Roughton, F. J. In F. J. Roughton and J. C. Kendrew, ed. 1949. Haemoglobin. Interscience, New York. p. 85. [26] Singer, R. B., and A. B. Hastings. 1948. Medicine, Balt. 27:223. [27] Theorell, H. 1934. Biochem. Zschr. 268:73.

Part III: BIRDS

	Animal	Temp. °C	pH	CO_2 Pressure mm Hg	Calculated "f" Factor	t. ½ sat. mm Hg	Reference
	(A)	(B)	(C)	(D)	(E)	(F)	(G)
	Chicken (Gallus domesticus)						
	Embryo						3
1	10 da	37.0[1]	7.38[1]			11.0[1]	
2	17 da	37.0[1]	7.38[1]			12.5[1]	
3	21 da	37.0[1]	7.38[1]			16.0[1]	
	Young						3
4	5 da	37.0[1]	7.38[1]			18.0[1]	
5	65 da	37.0[1]	7.38[1]			27.0[1]	
6	100 da	37.0[1]	7.38[1]			25.0[1]	
7	Adult	40.0	7.14	37	1.98	51	6
8		38.0		31		58	8
9		37.0[1]	7.10[1]		2.35	62.0[1]	1
10		37.0[1]	7.40[1]		1.58	41.7[1]	1
11		37.0[1]	7.70[1]		1.12	29.5[1]	1
12		37.5	7.10			52	1
13	Crow	42.0		40		53.0	10, 11
14	Duck	37.5	7.10			45	1, 8
15		37.5		40		42.0	7, 10, 11
16		37.0			1.71	45	1
17	Muscovy	37.0			1.48	39.0	1
18		37.0[1]	7.10[1]		2.20	58.0[1]	
19	Goose	42.0		50		37.5	10, 11
20		37.5	7.10			45.0	7
21				10		24[2]	7
22				40		35.7	7
23		20.0[3]	9.20[3]			0.7[3]	5
24		37.0			1.64	43.0	1
25	Huallata (Chloephaga melanoptera)	40.0	7.35			33.0	4
26	Ostrich (Rhea americana)	40.0	7.35			26.0	4
27	Pheasant	37.5	7.10			50.0	7
28	Ringnecked	37.0			1.82	48.0	1
29	Pigeon	37.5		40		35.0	2, 9
30		37.5	7.10			40.0	7
31		37.0			1.48	39.0	1
32		40.0				44.0	1

/1/ Hemoglobin solution. /2/ Calculated. /3/ Myoglobin (myohemoglobin, muscle hemoglobin). O_2 dissociation curves for myoglobin are rectantular hyperbolas.

Contributors: (a) Forbes, William H., (b) Lucas, Miriam Scott, (c) McCutcheon, F. Harold, (d) Oberholzer, R.

References: [1] Christensen, E. H., and D. B. Dill. 1935. J. Biol. Chem. 109:443. [2] Drastich, L. 1928. Pflügers Arch. 219:227. [3] Hall, F. G. 1934. J. Physiol., Lond. 83:222. [4] Hall, F. G., D. B. Dill, and E. S. Guzman Barron. 1936. J. Cellul. Physiol. 8:301. [5] Hill, R. 1936. Proc. R. Soc., Lond., Ser. B, 120:472.

Part III: BIRDS (Concluded)

[6] Morgan, V. E., and D. F. Chichester. 1935. J. Biol. Chem. 110:285. [7] Prosser, C. L. 1950. Comparative animal physiology. W. B. Saunders, Philadelphia. [8] Rostorfer, H. H., and R. H. Rigdon. 1947. Biol. Bull. 92:23. [9] Roughton, F. J. In F. J. Roughton and J. C. Kendrew, ed. 1949. Haemoglobin. Interscience, New York. p. 85. [10] Wastl, H., and G. Leiner. 1931. Pflügers Arch. 227:367. [11] Wastl, H., and G. Leiner. 1931. Ibid. 227:421.

Part IV: REPTILES

Animal	Temp. °C	pH	CO$_2$ Pressure mm Hg	Calculated "f" Factor	t. $\frac{1}{2}$ sat. mm Hg	Reference
(A)	(B)	(C)	(D)	(E)	(F)	(G)
1 Alligator (Alligator mississippiensis)			10		11	8
2			40		28	8
3	29.0	7.60	42.0	1.06	28.0	2
4 Chuckwalla (Sauromalus obesus)	20.0	7.60	37.0	0.91	24.0	3
5	37.0		55[1,2]	2.36	62.0	
6 Crocodile (Crocodilus acutus)	29.0	7.40[1]	50[1]	1.0	26.0	1
7	37.0	7.40[1,2]	45[1,2]	2.0	53.0	
8	29.0	7.20			38.0	
9 Gila monster (Heloderma suspectum)	20.0	7.40	36.0	1.22	32.0	4
10	37.0	7.40	32[1,2]	2.24	59.0	4
11	20.0	7.32	37.0		31.0	6
Turtle						
12 Caretta caretta	25.5[3]	7.40[3]			28.5[3]	8
13 Chelonis mydras	25.5[3]	7.40[3]			19.0[3]	8
14 Chelydra serpentina	25.5[3]	7.40[3]			14.0[3]	5, 7
15 Chrysemis picta	25.5[3]	7.40[3]			15.0[3]	8
16 Pseudemys concinna	25.0		40.0	0.77	20.0	9
17 P. elegans	25.0		27.0		28.0	8
18 P. scripta	25.5[3]	7.40[3]			15.8[3]	8
19 P. troostii	25.0		34.0		26.0	8, 10
20 Terrapene carolina	25.5[3]	7.40[3]			12.0[3]	8

/1/ Calculated. /2/ In calculations at 37°C, pH = 6.15 + log$\frac{(total\ CO_2) - 0.0290\ CO_2\ pressure}{0.0290\ CO_2\ pressure}$, where 6.15 and 0.0290 are the pK' and CO$_2$ factors, respectively, for whole blood. /3/ Hemoglobin solution.

Contributors: (a) Forbes, William H., (b) Lucas, Miriam Scott, (c) McCutcheon, F. Harold.

References: [1] Dill, D. B., and H. T. Edwards. 1931. J. Biol. Chem. 90:515. [2] Dill, D. B., and H. T. Edwards. 1935. J. Cellul. Physiol. 6:243. [3] Dill, D. B., H. T. Edwards, A. V. Bock, and J. H. Talbott. 1935. Ibid. 6:37. [4] Edwards, H. T., and D. B. Dill. 1935. Ibid. 6:21. [5] Henderson, L. J. 1928. Blood: a study in general physiology. Yale University Press, New Haven. [6] Lucas, M. S. Unpublished. [7] McCutcheon, F. H. 1947. J. Cellul. Physiol. 29:333. [8] Prosser, C. L. 1950. Comparative animal physiology. W. B. Saunders, Philadelphia. [9] Southworth, F. C., and A. C. Redfield. 1926. J. Gen. Physiol. 9:387. [10] Wilson, J. W. 1939. J. Cellul. Physiol. 13:315.

Part V: AMPHIBIANS

Values for lines 1 and 6-14 are for hemoglobin solution.

	Animal	Temp. °C	pH	CO$_2$ Pressure mm Hg	t. ½ sat. mm Hg	Reference
	(A)	(B)	(C)	(D)	(E)	(F)
	Congo snake					
1	Amphiuma sp	25.4	7.38		15.0	2, 5
2	A. tridactyla	26.0		43.0	30.0	5
	Frog					
3	Rana esculenta			1-2	11.0	3
4				10.0	17.0	
5				10.0	49.0	
	R. catesbeiana					
6	Adult	25.4	7.38		26.0	1
7		20.0	7.40		13.5	4
8	Tadpole	25.4	7.38		6.0	1
9		25.4	6.80		5.0	1
10		20.0	7.32		4.6	4
11		20.0	6.28		3.6	4
12	Hellbender (Cryptobranchus sp)	25.4	7.38		18.0	2, 3
13	Newt (Triturus sp)	25.4	7.38		7.5	2, 3
	Toad					2, 3
14	Bufo sp	25.4	7.38		30.0	
15	Desmognathus sp	25.4	7.38		5.0	

Contributors: (a) Forbes, William H., (b) Lucas, Miriam Scott, (c) McCutcheon, F. Harold, (d) Oberholzer, R.

References: [1] McCutcheon, F. H. 1936. J. Cellul. Physiol. 8:63. [2] McCutcheon, F. H., and F. G. Hall. 1937. Ibid. 9:191. [3] Prosser, C. L. 1950. Comparative animal physiology. W. B. Saunders, Philadelphia. [4] Riggs, A. F. 1951. J. Gen. Physiol. 35:23. [5] Scott, W. J. 1931. Biol. Bull. 61:211.

Part VI: FISHES

	Animal	Temp. °C	pH	CO$_2$ Pressure mm Hg	t. ½ sat. mm Hg	Reference
	(A)	(B)	(C)	(D)	(E)	(F)
1	Baiara (Hydrolycus scomberoides)	28.0		0	8.0	7, 13
2				25.0	22.0	
3	Bom-bom (Pterodoras granulosis)	28.0		0	11.0	7, 13
4				25.0	13.0	
5	Bowfin (Amia calva)	15.0		1-2	4.0	7
6				10.0	9.0	
7	Carp (Cyprinus carpio)			10.0	8.0	7
8		18.0		30.0	13.0	12
9		15.0		1-2	5.0	7
10	Catfish (Ictalurus sp)			1-2	1.4	7
11				10.0	5.0	
12		15.0		0-1	1.4	
13	Cod (Gadus sp)	14.0		<0.3	15.0	7
	Dogfish					
14	Smooth (Mustelus canis)	25.0[1]	7.40[1]		7.0[1]	2
15		25.0[1]	6.80[1]		12.0[1]	
	Spiny (Squalus suckleyi)					4
16	Embryo	25.0	7.53		12.7	
17	Adult	25.0	7.53		16.8	

/1/ Hemoglobin solution.

Part VI: FISHES (Continued)

	Animal	Temp. °C	pH	CO_2 Pressure mm Hg	t. $\frac{1}{2}$ sat. mm Hg	Reference
	(A)	(B)	(C)	(D)	(E)	(F)
	Eel					
18	American (Anguilla rostrata)	20.0[1]	7.3[1]		11.3[1]	9
19	Salt-water (A. bostoniensis)	17.0		0.3	4.0	7
20	Electric (Electrophorus	28.0		0	12.0	7, 13
21	electricus)			25.0	18.0	
22	Hagfish (Polistotrema stouti)	18.0	6.7-9.0		3-4	3
23		18.0[1]	6.7-9.0[1]		1.8[1]	
24	Haimara (Hoplias malabaricus)	28.0		0	8.0	7, 13
25	Hassa (Hoplosternum littorale)	28.0		0	11.0	7, 13
26				25.0	20.0	
27	Mackerel (Scomber scombrus)			10.0	52.0	7, 10
28		20.0	8.0	1.0	17.0	10
29		25.0[1]	7.38[1]		18.0[1]	7
30	Paku (Myleus setiger)	28.0		0	12.0	7, 13
31				25.0	55.0	
32	Plaice (Pleuronectes sp)	16.5		0.3	12.0	7
	Ray					
33	Raja sp	25.0[1]	7.38[1]		26.0[1]	2
34		25.0		1.0	45.0	
	R. binoculata					5
35	Embryo	10.0[1]	6.5[1]		10.0[1]	
36	Adult	10.0[1]	6.5[1]		15.0[1]	
37	R. oscillata	10.4	7.80	1.0	20.0	1
38		25.0		1.0	45.0	
39		37.0		1.0	98.0	
40		0.2		1.0	11.0	
41	Remora (Echeneis naucrates)	25.0[1]	7.38[1]		11.0[1]	2
42			6.80[1]		53.0[1]	
	Salmon, Atlantic (Salmo salar)					
43	In brackish water	15.0		1-2	23.0	7
44	In fresh water	15.0		1-2	21.0	8
45		15.0		10.0	35.0	7, 8
46	Scup (Stenotomus chrysops)	25.0[1]	7.38[1]		6.4[1]	2
47	Sea lamprey (Petromyzon marinus)	20.0[1]	6.6[1]		34[1]	11
48	Sea robin (Prionotus carolinus)	25.0[1]	7.38[1]		21.0[1]	2
49		20.0	7.70	1.0	17.0	10
50	Shark (Hypoprion brevirostris)	25.0[1]	7.40[1]		7.6[1]	6
51	Stingray (Dasyatis sp)	25.0[1]	7.40[1]		13-15[1]	6
52	Sucker (Catostomus sp)	15.0		1-2	12.0	7
53				10.0	43.0	
54	Tautog (Tautoga onitus)	25.0[1]	7.38[1]		6.0[1]	2
55	Toadfish (Opsanus tau)	20.0		1-2	14.0	7
56				10.0	33.0	7
57		25.0[1]	7.38[1]		3-4.4[1]	2
58		20.0	7.70	1.0	13.0	10
	Trout					7
59	Brook (Salvelinus fontinalis)	15.0		1-2	17.0	
60		15.0		10.0	42.0	
61	Brown (Salmo trutta)	15.0		1-2	17.0	
62		15.0		10.0	39.0	
63	Rainbow (S. gairdneri)	15.0		1-2	18.0	
64		15.0		10.0	35.0	

/1/ Hemoglobin solution.

Contributors: (a) Forbes, William H., (b) McCutcheon, F. Harold, (c) Oberholzer, R.

References: [1] Dill, D. B., H. T. Edwards, and M. Florkin. 1932. Biol. Bull. 62:23. [2] Hall, F. G., and F. H. McCutcheon. 1938. J. Cellul. Physiol. 11:205. [3] Manwell, C. 1958. Biol. Bull. 115:227. [4] Manwell, C.

Part VI: FISHES (Concluded)

1958. Physiol. Zool. 31:93. [5] Manwell, C. 1958. Science 128:419. [6] McCutcheon, F. H. 1947. J. Cellul. Physiol. 29:333. [7] Prosser, C. L. 1950. Comparative animal physiology. W. B. Saunders, Philadelphia. [8] Redfield, A. C. 1933. Q. Rev. Biol. 8:31. [9] Riggs, A. 1951. J. Gen. Physiol. 35:41. [10] Root, R. W. 1931. Biol. Bull. 61:427. [11] Wald, G., and A. Riggs. 1951. J. Gen. Physiol. 35:45. [12] Wastl, H. 1928. Biochem. Zschr. 197:363. [13] Willmer, E. N. 1934. J. Exp. Biol., Lond. 11:283.

Part VII: INVERTEBRATES

	Genus	Blood (Hemolymph) Pigment	Temp. °C	pH	CO_2 Pressure mm Hg	t. ½ sat. mm Hg	Reference
	(A)	(B)	(C)	(D)	(E)	(F)	(G)
1	Anadara	Hemoglobin				10.0	2
2	Arenicola	Hemoglobin		7.3		1.8	2
3			17.0		0	1.8	
4	Busycon	Hemocyanin	23.0		13.5	6.0	3
5	Cancer	Hemocyanin	23.0		0	12.0	2
6	Ceriodaphnia	Hemoglobin	17.0		0	0.8	2
7	Chironomus	Hemoglobin	17.0		0	0.2	2
8			17.0		0	0.6	
9	Daphnia	Hemoglobin	17.0		0	3.1	2
10	Gasterophilus	Hemoglobin, concentrated	39.0			4.9	2
11		Hemoglobin, dilute	39.0			0.02	
	Helix						
12	In summer	Hemocyanin	20.0		0	12.0	2,3
13	In winter	Hemocyanin	20.0	8.20		11.0	2
14	Homarus	Hemocyanin		7.20		90.0	2
15	Limulus	Hemocyanin			0	11.0	2
16				7.70		13.0	
17	Loligo	Hemocyanin	23.0		0	36.0	2, 4, 5
18	Nippostrongylus	Hemoglobin	19.0			<0.1	2
19	Octopus	Hemocyanin	25.0		0.6	3.0	1, 2, 6, 7
20	Phascolosoma	Hemerythrin	19.0			8.0	2
21	Planorbis	Hemoglobin	17.0		0	1.9	2
22			20.0		0	7.0	
23	Sipunculus	Hemerythrin	19.0		0.07–80.00	8.0	2
24	Spirographis	Chlorocruorin	20.0	7.70		27.0	2
25	Tubifex	Hemoglobin	17.0		0	0.6	2
26	Urechis	Hemoglobin	19.0		8.6	12.3	2

Contributor: Lucas, Miriam Scott

References: [1] Dhere, C. 1919. J. Physiol., Par. 18:221. [2] Prosser, C. L. 1950. Comparative animal physiology. W. B. Saunders, Philadelphia. [3] Redfield, A. C. 1934. Biol. Rev. Cambridge Philos. Soc. 9:175. [4] Redfield, A. C., T. Coolidge, and A. C. Hurd. 1926. J. Biol. Chem. 69:475. [5] Redfield, A. C., and R. Goodkind. 1929. J. Exp. Biol., Lond. 6:340. [6] Winterstein, H. 1909. Biochem. Zschr. 19:384. [7] Wolvekamp, H. P. 1938. Zschr. vergl. Physiol. 25:541.

O$_2$ dissociation is the relation between the amount of oxygen that remains chemically combined with hemoglobin, and the O$_2$ tension of the blood at definite temperature and pH. Blood is exposed to oxygen, carbon dioxide, and nitrogen in tonometers containing gas mixtures, and after sufficient time the O$_2$ content is determined. The amount of the physically dissolved oxygen is calculated from O$_2$ pressure and solubility to obtain the amount of oxygen combined with hemoglobin. At a definite O$_2$ pressure, the proportion of hemoglobin-bound oxygen (HbO$_2$) to the maximum binding capacity of hemoglobin for oxygen (O$_2$ capacity) equals the percent of O$_2$ saturation of hemoglobin:

$$\frac{HbO_2 \text{ (vol \%)}}{O_2 \text{ capacity (vol \%)}} \times 100 = \text{\% } O_2 \text{ saturation of hemoglobin.}$$ If percent O$_2$ saturations are to be compared at different O$_2$ pressures, the pH for all O$_2$ saturations must be the same. Therefore the pH values of the individual blood tests must be determined, and the O$_2$ pressure of the blood calculated according to pH value. Conversion factor for blood of man: log O$_2$ pressure = -0.48 per unit of serum pH (serum pH = 0.1 pH units).

Part I: BLOOD OBSERVATIONS

In adaptation to altitude there were no significant changes, other than a very small shift to right, in the O$_2$ dissociation curves [19]. A definite shift to right was seen in sickle cell anemias [5], and in congenital cyanotic heart disease [23]. Anticoagulant (column C): H = heparin, PO = potassium oxalate, SF = sodium fluoride, SO = sodium oxalate. Technique (column E): IVt = in vitro, IVv = in vivo. Method (columns F and H): K = Kugel tonometer [21], Bt = Barcroft tonometer [1], Gs = glass syringes, M = manometric [24], VS = Van Slyke and Stadie [30], F = ferrocyanide modification [22] of Haldane [13], Sh = Scholander [27], Bm = Barcroft differential manometer, Sp = spectrophotometric [18]. t. $\frac{1}{2}$ sat. = tension of half saturation (pressure at which hemoglobin is 50% saturated with oxygen).

| | Subjects | | Anti-coagulant | Equilibration | | | O$_2$ Capacity Estimated from | | Estimated Serum pH or CO$_2$ Pressure mm Hg | t. $\frac{1}{2}$ sat.[1] mm Hg | Reference |
	Animal	No.		Temp. °C	Technique	Method	O$_2$ Pressure mm Hg	Method			
	(A)	(B)	(C)	(D)	(E)	(F)	(G)	(H)	(I)	(J)	(K)
1	Man	14[2]	H, PO, SF	37.0	IVt	K	~200	M	pH = 7.40	26.8	3
2		1[3]	PO	37.5	IVt	Bt	~150	VS	40 mm Hg	25.0	6
3		3		37.0	IVt				M	pH = 7.40	26.3	7, 9
4		6	H	37.0	IVt	Bt	220	M	40 mm Hg	26.3	11
5	Cat[4]	8	PO, SF	37.0	IVt	K	~200	M	pH = 7.40	36.3	2
6	Dog	5	PO, SF	37.0	IVt	K	~200	M	pH = 7.40	29.1	2
7	Pig	8	PO, SF	37.0	IVt	K	~200	M	pH = 7.40	30.6	2
8	Sea lion	1	PO	38.0	IVt			M	~44 mm Hg	41.0	12
9	Guinea pig	12	PO, SF	37.0	IVt	K	~200	M	pH = 7.40	27.3	2
10	Rabbit	6	PO, SF	37.0	IVt	K	~200	M	pH = 7.40	30.7	2
11		4	H	38.6	IVt, IVv	Bt		M	pH = 7.40[5]	31.0	14
12	Rat Albino	37[6]		38.0	IVt	Bt		F	pH = 7.40	45.4	17
13	Kangaroo-	12		37.0	IVt	Gs		Sh	~40 mm Hg	52.5	10
14	Cow	6	PO, SF	37.0	IVt	K	~200	M	pH = 7.40	30.8	2
15		6		38.0	IVt	Bt		Bm	40-42 mm Hg	32.0	25
16	Goat	3[7]	H, PO, SF	37.0	IVt	K	~200	M	pH = 7.40	30.0	4
17			PO, SF	38.0	IVt	Bt	~150	M	pH = 7.40	30.2	15
18	Horse			38.0					pH = 7.40	29.0	31
19	Llama	4	H	39.0	IVt, IVv	Bt		M	pH = 7.40[5]	22.0	14
20		1	H, PO, SF	37.0	IVt	K	~200	M	pH = 7.40	23.4	4
21	Vicuña	1	H	39 and 40[8]	IVt	Bt		M	pH = 7.40[5]	20.0	14
22	Sheep	5	H	39.3	IVt, IVv	Bt		M	pH = 7.40[5]	40.6	14
23		7	H, PO, SF	37.0	IVt	K	~200	M	pH = 7.40	33.7	2
24	Argali	1		37.0	IVt	Bt		Sp	pH = 7.39	14.2	16
25	Mouflon	5		37.0	IVt	Bt		Sp	pH = 7.39	18.5	16
26	Dutch			37.0	IVt	Bt		Sp	pH = 7.39	28.0	16
27	Porpoise	1	SO	38.0	IVt			M	~46 mm Hg	31.0	12

/1/ Additional estimations of t. $\frac{1}{2}$ sat.: man = 26.5 mm Hg [29], 24 mm Hg [26]; cat = 39 mm Hg [26]; dog = 29 mm hg [8], 31 mm Hg [26]; pig = 32.5 mm Hg [26]; guinea pig = 25.4 mm Hg [28], 34 mm Hg [26]; cow = 25 mm Hg [26]; goat = 28.5 mm Hg [26]; horse = 23 mm Hg [26]; sheep = 27 mm Hg [26]. /2/ Curve is average of 54 dissociation curves with 207 single points. Significant differences among individuals, with maximum differences between two individuals at t. $\frac{1}{2}$ sat. of 5.8 mm Hg. /3/ Curve nearly identical with in vivo O$_2$ dissociation curve of Lambertsen, et al [20] (not shown). /4/ Chloralose-urethane used as anesthetic. /5/ Serum pH calculated from intracellular pH with factors in reference 19. /6/ Number of determinations. /7/ 14 dissociation curves with 42 determinations. /8/ At altitude of 2.81 and 4.71 kilometers, respectively.

Part I: BLOOD OBSERVATIONS (Concluded)

Contributors: Bartels, Heinz; Hilpert, Peter; and Riegel, Klaus

References: [1] Barcroft, J. 1928. The respiratory function of the blood. Pt. 2. Cambridge University Press, London. [2] Bartels, H., and H. Harms. 1959. Pflügers Arch. 268:334. [3] Bartels, H., H. Harms, P. Hilpert, O. Niemeyer, and K. Riegel. 1960. Ibid. In press. [4] Bartels, H., P. Hilpert, and K. Riegel. 1960. Ibid. In press. [5] Becklake, M. R., S. B. Griffith, M. McGregor, H. I. Goldman, and J. P. Shreve. 1955. J. Clin. Invest. 34:751. [6] Bock, A. V., H. Field, Jr., and G. S. Adair. 1924. J. Biol. Chem. 59:353. [7] Dill, D. B. 1944. In Handbook of respiratory data in aviation. National Research Council, Washington, D. C. [8] Dill, D. B., H. T. Edwards, M. Florkin, and R. W. Campbell. 1932. J. Biol. Chem. 95:143. [9] Dill, D. B., and W. H. Forbes. 1941. Am. J. Physiol. 132:685. [10] Gjönnes, B., and K. Schmidt-Nielsen. 1952. J. Cellul. Physiol. 39:147. [11] Gordon, E. E., R. C. Darling, and E. Shea. 1948-49. J. Appl. Physiol. 1:476. [12] Greene, A. A., and A. C. Redfield. 1933. Biol. Bull. 64:44. [13] Haldane, J. S. 1920. J. Path. Bact., Lond. 23:443. [14] Hall, F. G., D. B. Dill, and E. S. Guzman Barron. 1936. J. Cellul. Physiol. 8:301. [15] Hellegers, A. E., G. Meschia, H. Prystowsky, A. S. Wolkoff, and D. H. Barron. 1959. Q. J. Exp. Physiol., Lond. 44:215. [16] Huisman, T. H. J., G. van Vliet, and T. Sebens. 1958. Nature, Lond. 182:171. [17] Jones, E. S., B. G. Maegraith, and H. H. Sculthorpe. 1950. Ann. Trop. M. Parasit., Liverp. 44:168. [18] Jonxis, J. H. P., and H. W. Boeve. 1956. Acta med. scand. 115:157. [18] Keys, A. B., F. G. Hall, and E. S. Guzman Barron. 1936. Am. J. Physiol. 115:292. [20] Lambertsen, C. J., P. L. Bruce, D. L. Drabkin, and C. F. Schmidt. 1952. J. Appl. Physiol. 4:873. [21] Laué, D. 1951. Pflügers Arch. 254:142. [22] Maegraith, B. G., E. S. Jones, and H. H. Sculthorpe. 1950. Ann. Trop. M. Parasit., Liverp. 44:101. [23] Morse, M., D. E. Cassels, and M. Holder. 1950. J. Clin. Invest. 29:1098. [24] Peters, J. P., and D. D. Van Slyke. 1932. Quantitative clinical chemistry methods. Williams and Wilkins, Baltimore. [25] Roos, J., and C. Romijn. 1938. J. Physiol., Lond. 92:249. [26] Schmidt-Nielsen, K., and J. L. Larimer. 1958. Am. J. Physiol. 194:424. [27] Scholander, P. F., S. C. Flemister, and L. Irving. 1947. J. Biol. Chem. 169:173. [28] Valtis, D. J., and A. G. Baikie. 1955. Brit. J. Haemat. 1:146. [29] Valtis, D. J., and A. C. Kennedy. 1953. Glasgow M. J. 34:521. [30] Van Slyke, D. D., and W. C. Stadie. 1921. J. Biol. Chem. 49:1. [31] Van Slyke, D. D., H. Wu, and F. C. McLean. 1923. Ibid. 56:765.

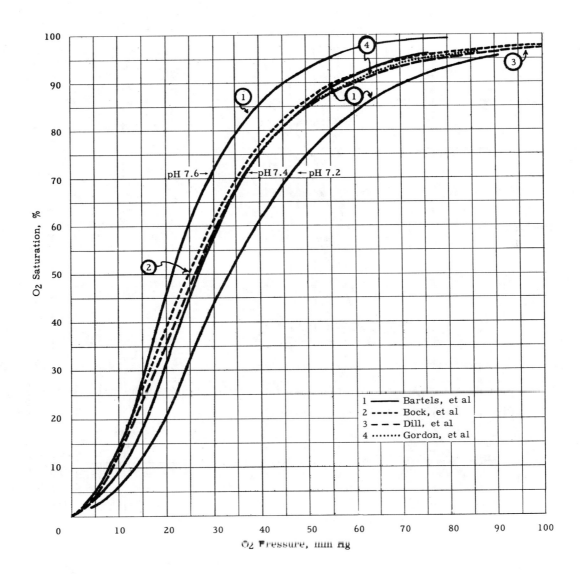

Contributors: Bartels, Heinz; Hilpert, Peter; and Riegel, Klaus

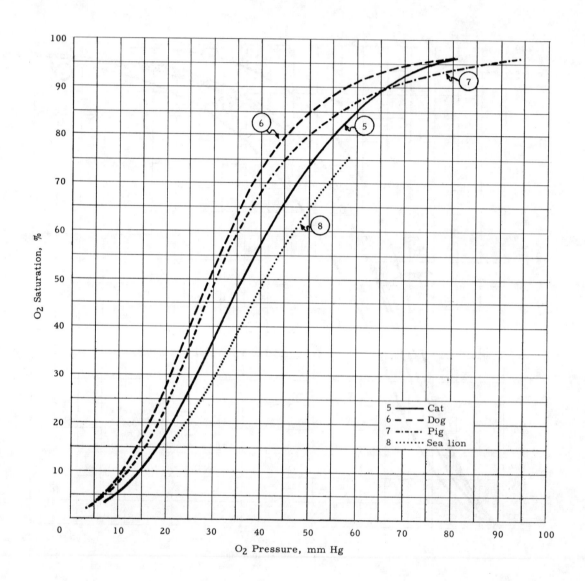

Contributors: Bartels, Heinz; Hilpert, Peter; and Riegel, Klaus

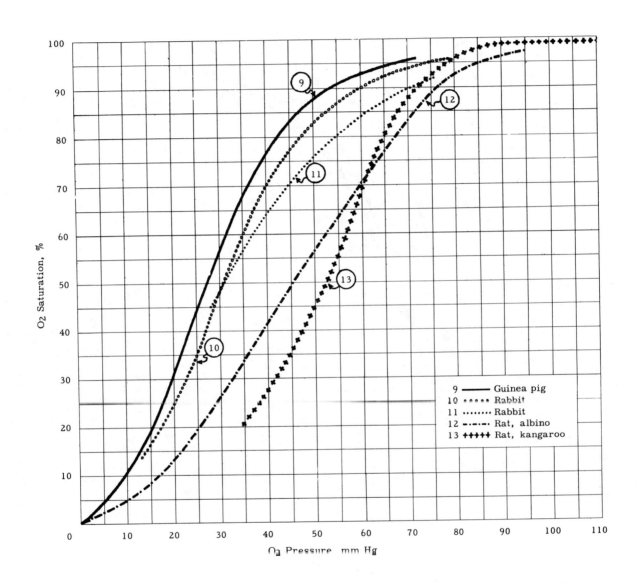

Contributors: Bartels, Heinz; Hilpert, Peter; and Riegel, Klaus

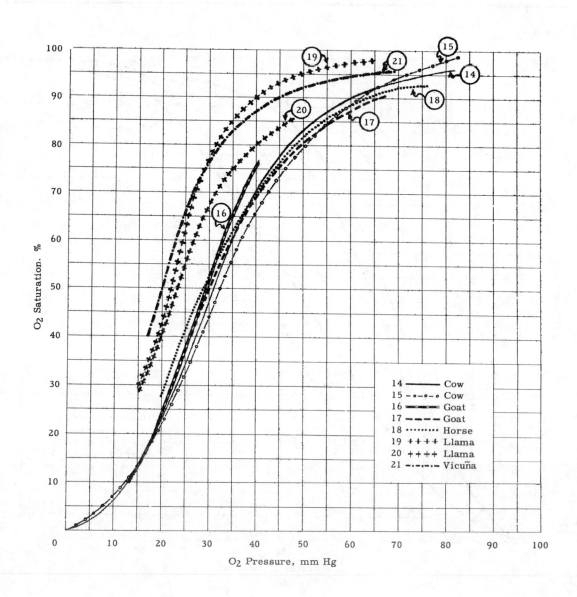

14	————	Cow
15	–o–o–o	Cow
16	✕✕✕✕	Goat
17	– – –	Goat
18	··········	Horse
19	++++	Llama
20	++++	Llama
21	–·–·–·–	Vicuña

Contributors: Bartels, Heinz; Hilpert, Peter; and Riegel, Klaus

154

Part VI: SHEEP

Numbers in legend refer to item numbers in Part I: BLOOD OBSERVATIONS

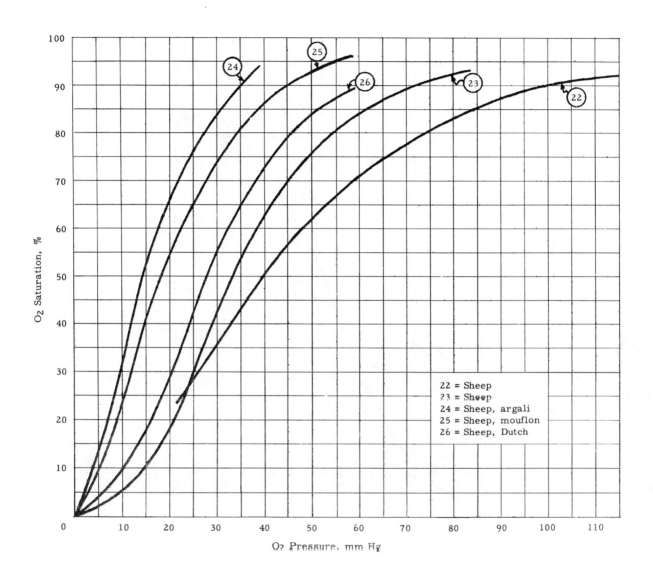

22 = Sheep
23 = Sheep
24 = Sheep, argali
25 = Sheep, mouflon
26 = Sheep, Dutch

O$_2$ Saturation, %

O$_2$ Pressure, mm Hg

Contributors: Bartels, Heinz; Hilpert, Peter; and Riegel, Klaus

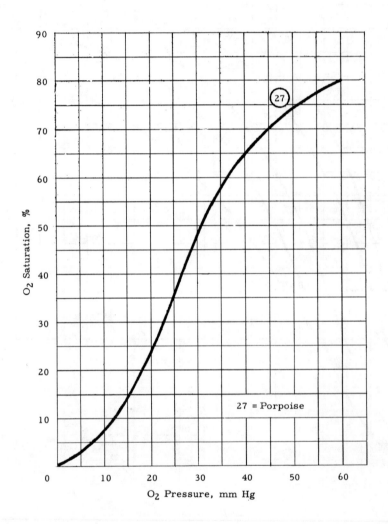

27 = Porpoise

Contributors: Bartels, Heinz; Hilpert, Peter; and Riegel, Klaus

Part I: BLOOD OBSERVATIONS

Since the alkali reserve in fetal blood differs from the alkali reserve in maternal blood, and differs among species, curves showing equal CO_2 pressures may have various pH values. In man the affinity for oxygen of infant blood is higher than that of adult blood [10], and therefore the pH values for fetal blood should be standardized by using the conversion factor for adult blood of man: log O_2 pressure = -0.48 per unit of serum pH (serum pH = 0.1 pH units). This factor is also used for other species [6]. Fetal age is quite important as there is a possibility of change in the dissociation curve with increase in age of the fetus. Anticoagulant (column D): H = heparin, PO = potassium oxalate, SF = sodium fluoride. Method (columns F and G): Bt = Barcroft tonometer [2], K = Kugel tonometer [12], M = manometric [15], B = Barcroft [1], C = colorimetric hemoglobin estimation.

| Subjects | | Age | Anti-coagulant | Equilibration[1] | | Method of Estimating O_2 Capacity[2] | Estimated Serum pH or CO_2 Pressure mm Hg | Refer-ence |
Animal	No.			Temp. °C	Method			
(A)	(B)	(C)	(D)	(E)	(F)	(G)	(H)	(I)
1 Man	10[3]	At birth	H	37.0	Bt	M	pH = 7.40	9
2	12[4]	5 da	H, PO, SF	37.0	K	M	pH = 7.40	13
3	11	61 da	H, PO, SF	37.0	K	M	pH = 7.40	13
4	12	81 da	H, PO, SF	37.0	K	M	pH = 7.40	13
5 Cow	1	Fetus, approximately 36 wk		38.5	Bt	B	43-45 mm Hg	14
6 Goat	8	Fetus, 103-141 da	PO, SF	38.0	Bt	M	pH = 7.40	11
7	1	At birth	PO	38.0	Bt	M	50 mm Hg	3
8 Rabbit		Fetus, 30 da		38.0	Bt	M, C[5]	Electrometric	5
9 Sheep	6	Fetus, 60-120 da and 120-150 da	H, SF	38.0	Bt	M	40 mm Hg	4
10 Goat	6	1, 11, 42, and 121 da	H, PO, SF	37.0	K	M	pH = 7.40	8
11 Sheep	1	4, 11, 22, 35, and 50 da	H, PO, SF	37.0	K	M	pH = 7.40	7

/1/ In vitro. /2/ From O_2 pressure. /3/ 8 full-term infants and 2 before term; no significant difference between the 2 groups. /4/ 10 premature infants. /5/ Calculated on basis of colorimetric hemoglobin estimation.

Contributors: Bartels, Heinz; Hilpert, Peter; and Riegel, Klaus

References: [1] Barcroft, J. 1908. J. Physiol., Lond. 37:12. [2] Barcroft, J. 1928. The respiratory function of the blood. Pt. 2. Cambridge University Press, London. [3] Barcroft, J., et al. 1934. J. Physiol., Lond. 83:192. [4] Barron, D. H. 1951. Yale J. Biol. 24:169. [5] Barron, D. H., and G. Meschia. 1954. Sympos. Quant. Biol. 19:93. [6] Bartels, H., and H. Harms. 1959. Pflügers Arch. 268:334. [7] Bartels, H., and K. Riegel. 1959. Beitr. Silikoseforsch. 60:19. [8] Bartels, H., K. Riegel, and P. Hilpert. 1960. Pflügers Arch. In press. [9] Darling, R. C., C. A. Smith, E. Asmussen, and F. M. Cohen. 1941. J. Clin. Invest. 20:739. [10] Eastman, N. J., E. M. Geiling, and A. M. DeLawder. 1933. Bull. Johns Hopkins Hosp. 53:246. [11] Hellegers, A. E., G. Meschia, H. Prystowsky, A. S. Wolkoff, and D. H. Barron. 1959. Q. J. Exp. Physiol., Lond. 44:215. [12] Laué, D. 1951. Pflügers Arch. 254:142. [13] Riegel, K., H. Bartels, and J. Schneider. 1959. Zschr. Kinderh. 83:209. [14] Roos, J., and C. Romijn. 1938. J. Physiol., Lond. 92:249. [15] Van Slyke, D. D., and J. M. Neill. 1924. J. Biol. Chem. 61:523.

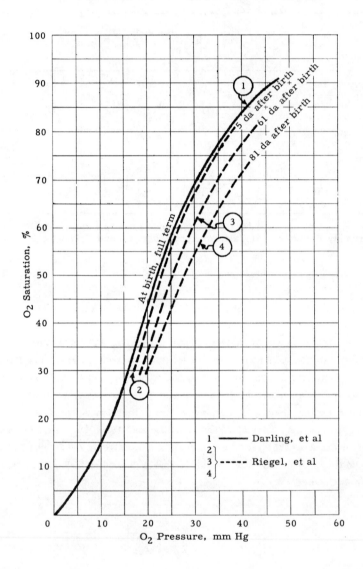

Contributors: Bartels, Heinz; Hilpert, Peter; and Riegel, Klaus

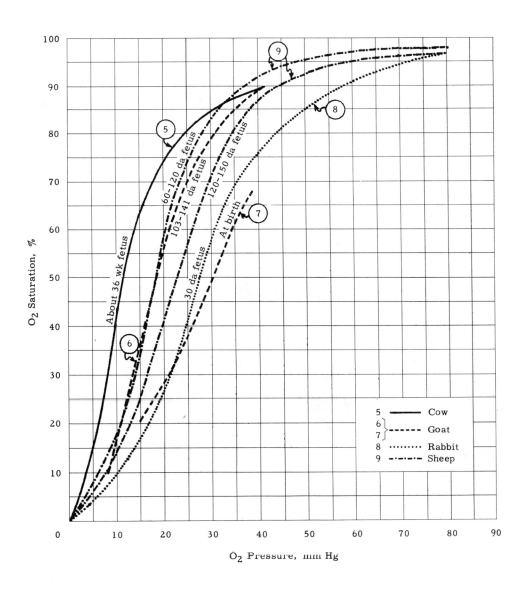

Contributors: Bartels, Heinz; Hilpert, Peter; and Riegel, Klaus

Part IV: GOAT, 1-121 DAYS AFTER BIRTH

Number in legend refers to item number in Part I: BLOOD OBSERVATIONS

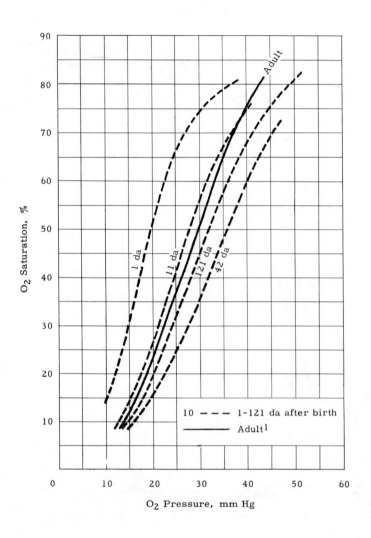

/1/ See table 55, page 154.

Contributors: Bartels, Heinz; Hilpert, Peter; and Riegel, Klaus

Part V: SHEEP, 4-50 DAYS AFTER BIRTH

Number in legend refers to item number in Part I: BLOOD OBSERVATIONS

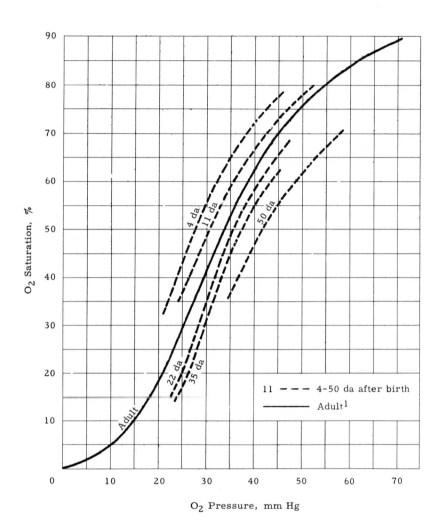

O$_2$ Saturation, %

O$_2$ Pressure, mm Hg

Legend:
11 – – – 4-50 da after birth
——— Adult[1]

/1/ See table 55, page 155.

Contributors: Bartels, Heinz; Hilpert, Peter; and Riegel, Klaus

57. O_2 DISSOCIATION RELATIONSHIPS OF FETAL AND MATERNAL BLOOD: MAN, COW, GOAT

Based upon the O_2 pressure at half saturation (t. $\frac{1}{2}$ sat.), an approximate curve can be drawn for the O_2 pressure values ranging from 15-80 mm Hg. The curve, however, is not necessarily valid above and below these pressures. In man, a decrease in t. $\frac{1}{2}$ sat. of 9 mm Hg for maternal blood and 2 mm Hg for fetal blood occurs with the separation of hemoglobin at pH 6.8 and 37°C; the relative position of the two curves may then be reversed [4]. Values in parentheses are ranges, estimate "b" (cf. Introduction).

	Animal	Duration of Pregnancy	No. of Subjects	t. $\frac{1}{2}$ sat., at 38°C mm Hg	No. of Subjects	t. $\frac{1}{2}$ sat., at 38°C mm Hg	Reference
				Fetal		Maternal	
	(A)	(B)	(C)	(D)	(E)	(F)	(G)
1	Man[1]	Term	16	21.86(21.26-22.46)[2]	6	27.27(26.37-28.17)[2]	2
2		Term	8	22.1[2]		26.3[2]	1
3		Term	42	21[2]			7
4		Term		19.0[2]	19	24[2,3]	5
5	Cow[4]	3.5 mo	3	18	3	34	6
6		5.5 mo	2	23	2	33	
7		7-8 mo	7	20	7	32	
8		Term	6	22.5	6	31.5	
9	Goat[1]	103-141 da	8	22.4	8	30.2	3

/1/ pH = 7.4. /2/ Corrected for Δ log O_2 pressure by factor of -0.048. /3/ Estimated from published curve. /4/ CO_2 pressure = 43(41-45) mm Hg.

Contributor: Kaiser, Irwin H.

References: [1] Beer, R., H. Bartels, and H. A. Raczkowski. 1955. Pflügers Arch. 260:306. [2] Darling, R. C., C. A. Smith, E. Asmussen, and F. M. Cohen. 1941. J. Clin. Invest. 20:739. [3] Hellegers, A., G. Meschia, H. Prystowsky, A. S. Wolkoff, and D. H. Barron. 1959. Q. J. Exp. Physiol., Lond. 44:215. [4] McCarthy, E. F. 1943. J. Physiol., Lond. 102:55. [5] Prystowsky, H., A. Hellegers, and P. Bruns. 1959. Am. J. Obst. 78:489. [6] Roos, J., and C. Romijn. 1940. Proc. Koninkl. Ned. Akad. Wetenschap. 43:1212. [7] Rooth, G., S. Sjöstedt, and F. Caligara. 1959. Biol. Neonat. 1:61.

58. O_2 AND CO_2 PRESSURE IN UMBILICAL BLOOD: MAN

Values in parentheses are ranges, estimate "c" unless otherwise indicated (cf. Introduction).

	Condition	Method	No. of Subjects	Specification	Pressure mm Hg	Reference
	(A)	(B)	(C)	(D)	(E)	(F)
			Oxygen			
	Cesarean section					
1	Mother breathing 21% O_2	Polarographic, using	4	Intervillous space	23.3(17.9-28.9)	4
2		Bloor-Beckman	4	Umbilical vein	16.8(8.3-21.6)	
3		electrode	4	Gradient[1]	6.4(2.9-9.6)	
4	Mother breathing 100% O_2	Polarographic, using	4	Intervillous space	39.2(32.0-56.4)	4
5		Bloor-Beckman	4	Umbilical vein	26.1(22.0-29.1)	
6		electrode	4	Gradient[1]	13.1(4.5-28.9)	
7	Normal pregnancy	Interpolation from O_2	5	Intervillous space	38.4(24.0-53.0)	1, 2
8		dissociation curves	5	Umbilical vein	20.8(6.5-31.0)	
9			5	Umbilical artery	12.4(5.0-18.0)	
10			5	Gradient[1]	21.7(17.7-29.5)	
11	Abnormal pregnancy	Interpolation from O_2	4	Intervillous space	19.1(10.0-32.0)	1, 2
12		dissociation curves	4	Umbilical vein	16.3(8.0-22.0)	
13			1	Umbilical artery	4.2	
14			4	Gradient[1]	3.2(-1.7 to +10.0)	

/1/ Gradient = partial pressure in maternal circulation minus partial pressure in fetal circulation.

	Condition	Method	No. of Subjects	Specification	Pressure mm Hg	Reference
	(A)	(B)	(C)	(D)	(E)	(F)
	Oxygen (concluded)					
15	Vaginal delivery Mother breathing 21% O$_2$	Polarographic, using Bloor-Beckman electrode	5	Umbilical vein	26.3(17.0-32.8)	4
16			5	Umbilical artery	11.8(8.8-16.5)	
17	Mother breathing 100% O$_2$	Polarographic, using Bloor-Beckman electrode	8	Umbilical vein	33.8(14.5-46.5)	4
18			8	Umbilical artery	17.5(9.6-31.0)	
19	Normal pregnancy	Interpolation from O$_2$ dissociation curves	6	Intervillous space	41.4(26.5-72.0)	1
20			6	Umbilical vein	20.9(12.2-39.0)	
21			1	Umbilical artery	11.0	
22			6	Gradient[1]	20.9(14.3-33.0)	
23	Abnormal pregnancy	Interpolation from O$_2$ dissociation curves	3	Intervillous space	16.8(15.8-18.5)	1
24			3	Umbilical vein	11.9(10.0-13.9)	
25			2	Umbilical artery	6.9(6.8-7.0)	
26			3	Gradient[1]	6.1(1.9-9.4)	
27	Cord clamped immediately after birth Spontaneous, uncomplicated delivery	Polarographic	68	Umbilical vein	28.9(16.3-41.5)[b]	6
28			51	Umbilical artery	16.9(5.1-28.7)[b]	
29		Polarographic, using Clark electrode	128	Umbilical vein	29(6-49)	5
30			96	Umbilical artery	18(6-32)	
31	Slightly asphyxiated infants	Polarographic, using Clark electrode	49	Umbilical vein	28(6-45)	5
32			32	Umbilical artery	16(6-27)	
33	Severely asphyxiated infants	Potentiometric, using dropping-mercury electrode	20	Umbilical vein	7(1-12)	7
34			19	Umbilical artery	4(1-11)	
35	Infants with meconium-stained amniotic fluid but without other signs of asphyxia	Polarographic, using Clark electrode	18	Umbilical vein	29(19-46)	5
36			12	Umbilical artery	15(8-20)	
	Carbon Dioxide					
37	Normal pregnancy		4	Intervillous space	37.1(31.0-42.1)	3
38			4	Umbilical vein	42.1(37.0-49.1)	
39			4	Umbilical artery	46.4(41.4-52.8)	
40			4	Gradient[1]	7.1(4.5-8.4)	
41	Abnormal pregnancy		3	Intervillous space	(37.1-32.1)	3
42			2	Umbilical vein	(46.5-47.9)	
43			1	Umbilical artery	52.7	
44			2	Gradient[1]	(17.5-20.5)	

/1/ Gradient = partial pressure in maternal circulation minus partial pressure in fetal circulation.

Contributors: (a) Nesbitt, Robert E. L., Jr., (b) Rooth, Gösta

References: [1] Prystowsky, H. 1957. Bull. Johns Hopkins Hosp. 101:48. [2] Prystowsky, H., A. Hellegers, and P. Bruns. 1960. Surg. Gyn. Obst. 110:495. [3] Prystowsky, H., A. Hellegers, and P. Bruns. Unpublished. [4] Quilligan, E. J., et al. 1960. Am. J. Obst. 79:1048. [5] Rooth, G., S. Sjöstedt, and F. Caligara. Unpublished. [6] Sjostedt, S., G. Rooth, and F. Caligara. 1960. Acta obst. gyn. scand. 39:34. [7] Wulf, H. 1958. Klin. Wschr. 36:234.

59. BLOOD O$_2$ DISSOCIATION LINE CHARTS: MAN

USE OF CHARTS

Changes in temperature and serum pH alter the position but not the shape of the O$_2$ dissociation curve. Dissociation curves for various values of serum pH and temperature for man may be computed from the one standard curve for normal human blood at 37°C, serum pH 7.4, by multiplying all the O$_2$ pressure values by factors for temperature and serum pH. The far left line gives factors for temperature, the next line factors for serum pH. The two lines at the right give the standard O$_2$ dissociation curve in a form more easily read than the usual graph. Computation is based on

$$P_{t, pH} = P \times f_t \times f_{pH}$$

where $P_{t, pH}$ is the O$_2$ pressure at temperature t and pH; P is the O$_2$ pressure at 37°C (serum pH 7.4 for the same percent saturation) given on the standard curve; and f_t and f_{pH} are the multipliers obtained from the line charts.

Examples of the use of these charts follow:

1) Problem: Prepare a complete O$_2$ dissociation curve for 30°C, pH 7.6.

   Method: The factor for 30°C is 0.74 and for pH 7.6 is 0.80. Their product is 0.59. Multiply all O$_2$ pressure values in the standard curve by 0.59; i.e., for 50% saturation, O$_2$ pressure in the new curve = 15.6 mm Hg (26.4 x 0.59).

2) Problem: Arterial blood taken during surgery had 88% saturation by Van Slyke manometric methods. pH was 7.56 at body temperature of 33.8°C. What is the O$_2$ pressure?

   Method: From the standard dissociation curve, right line, at 88% saturation, O$_2$ pressure = 57 mm Hg. The factors are 0.84 for pH and 0.87 for temperature. O$_2$ pressure = 41.6 mm Hg (57 x 0.84 x 0.87) in the patient.

To convert pressure to saturation, factors are used as divisors:

3) Problem: Arterial blood from a febrile subject had an O$_2$ pressure of 73 mm Hg, determined at body temperature of 40°C, using a Roughton-Scholander syringe. Serum pH, corrected to 40°C, was 6.98. What is the percent saturation?

   Method: Factors are 1.14 for temperature and 1.52 for serum pH. $\dfrac{73}{1.14 \times 1.52}$ = 42.1 mm Hg. From the dissociation curve, this equals 77% saturation.

4) Problem: Blood taken from a heart-lung by-pass machine was found to have an O$_2$ pressure by polarograph of 65 mm Hg and serum pH of 7.72, both having been measured at 37°C. The blood in the machine was at 30°C. What is the percent saturation and the O$_2$ pressure in the machine?

   Method: Since the blood was warmed anaerobically to 37°C for serum pH and O$_2$ pressure measurement, its saturation was unchanged, and the only correction needed to calculate saturation is that for serum pH. This for 7.72 is 0.70. $\dfrac{65}{0.70}$ = 93 mm Hg, which from dissociation curve reads 96.4% saturation.

   To find O$_2$ pressure at 30°C, first the serum pH at 30°C must be computed from the whole blood serum pH factor, -0.0147 units per degree [4]. -7° x -0.0147 = +0.103. Inasmuch as serum pH rises as temperature falls, 0.103 is added to 7.72 (= 7.82). The factor for pH 7.82 is 0.63 and for 30°C is 0.74. 93 x 0.63 x 0.74 = 43.3 mm Hg O$_2$ pressure in the machine. A simpler method of correcting the O$_2$ pressure from 37°C to 30°C is given in the line chart on page 166 (correction of O$_2$ pressure and CO$_2$ pressure of blood in vitro for temperature changes).

The standard dissociation curve and the serum pH and temperature factors were taken from curves published by Dill and Forbes [1, 2]. Pressures at the high end of the curves were taken from Nahas, et al [3]. These are assumed to be average curves, subject to some variation in normal conditions and perhaps to great variation in disease, particularly in diabetes and anemia. The chief reason for variation is failure of intracellular pH, which actually determines the affinity of hemoglobin for oxygen, to be related constantly to serum pH.

Contributor: Severinghaus, John W.

References: [1] Dill, D. B. 1944. In Handbook of respiratory data in aviation. National Research Council, Washington, D. C. [2] Dill, D. B., and W. H. Forbes. 1941. Am. J. Physiol. 132:685. [3] Nahas, C. G., E. H. Morgan, and E. H. Wood. 1952. J. Appl. Physiol. 5:169. [4] Rosenthal, T. B. 1948. J. Biol. Chem. 173:25.

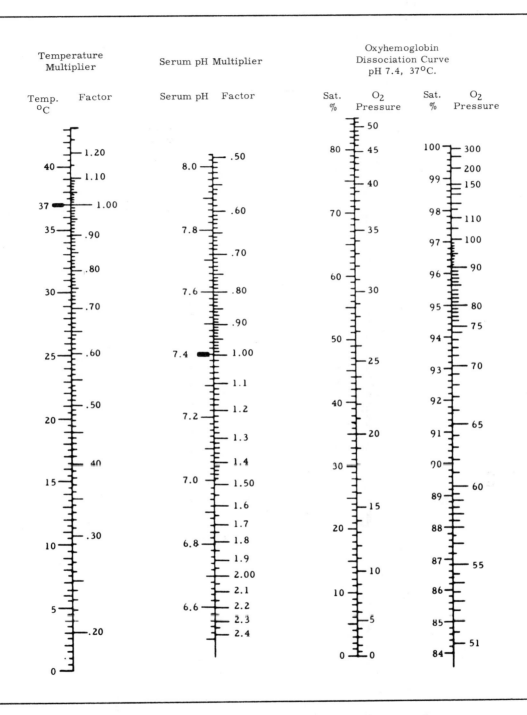

Contributor: Severinghaus, John W.

60. EFFECT OF TEMPERATURE CHANGE ON BLOOD O_2 AND CO_2 PRESSURES: MAN, DOG

These line charts illustrate the effect of changes in temperature on O_2 and CO_2 pressures in human or dog blood sealed in an anaerobic environment. Error increases progressively as pH and temperature deviate from standard values of 7.4 and 37°C, respectively. The values, which are applicable to either _in vitro_ or _in vivo_ conditions, have subsequently been reconfirmed using the O_2 and CO_2 electrodes. It should be pointed out that the oxygen factors do not apply to blood that is fully saturated with oxygen, and will not be accurate if the partial pressure of oxygen is above 100 mm Hg. When the partial pressure of oxygen is 600 mm Hg, the change with temperature was found to be approximately 2% per degree instead of 5.7% per degree. ΔT = temperature change in °C.

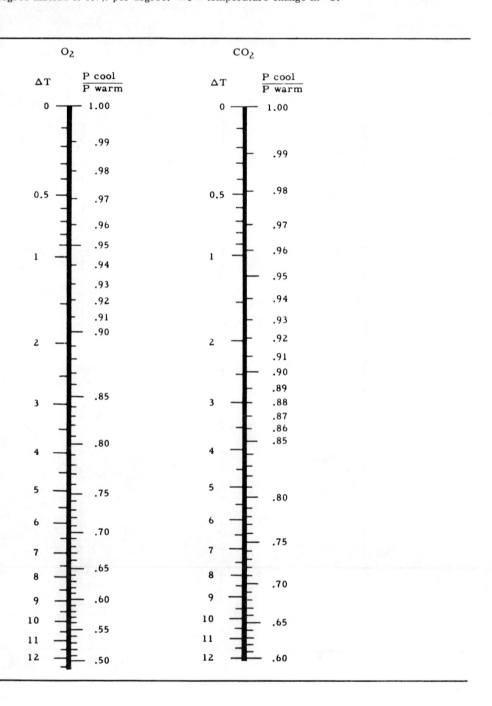

Contributor: Severinghaus, John W.

61. NOMOGRAM FOR DETERMINING SERUM pK': MAN, DOG

When temperature and pH are known, serum pK' for carbonic acid in man and dog may be determined from the nomogram. At 37.5°C and pH 7.4, mean pK' = 6.09. The exact value for pK' depends, among other things, on the plasma water content (the latter determines the solubility factor in the Henderson-Hasselbalch equation). The solubility factor used in the above determination was 0.0308 at 37°C or 0.0304 at 37.5°C. If Dill's solubility factors are used, a difference of approximately 2% is encountered and an additive factor of 0.01 should be applied to all pK' values (e.g., using the factor of 0.0310 at 37.5°C, pK' = 6.10 at pH 7.4)[1].

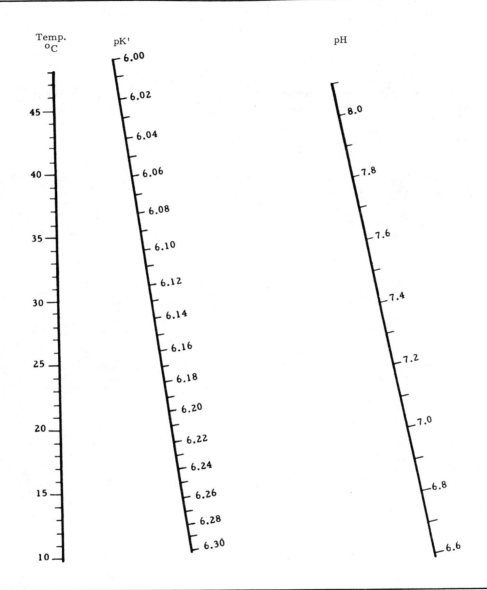

Contributor: Severinghaus, John W.

References: [1] Dill, D. B., and W. H. Forbes. 1941. Am. J. Physiol. 132:685. [2] Severinghaus, J. W., M. Stupfel, and A. F. Bradley. 1956. J. Appl. Physiol. 9:197.

62. BLOOD H$_2$CO$_3$ DISSOCIATION CONSTANTS: MAN, DOG, OX

The first apparent dissociation constants of H$_2$CO$_3$ are the same for man, dog, and ox. Methods used were gasometric or glass electrode. Values in parentheses are ranges, estimate "c" (cf. Introduction).

	Blood	Temp., °C	Dissociation Constant	Reference
	(A)	(B)	(C)	(D)
	Serum			
1	Normal	20	6.183(6.163-6.208)	1
2		38	6.11(6.097-6.122)	1-3
3	Nephritis	38	(6.108-6.134)	1-3
	Plasma			4
4	At pH 7.1	37	6.098	
5	At pH 7.4	37	6.09	
6	At pH 7.6	37	6.088	
	Erythrocytes			2
7	Reduced	37	5.98[1]	
8	Oxidized	37	6.04[2]	

/1/ Variation with pH: pK' = 7.275 minus 0.18 pH.   /2/ Variation with pH: pK' = 7.120 minus 0.18 pH.

Contributors: Bartels, Heinz, and Opitz, E.

References: [1] Cullen, G. E., H. R. Keeler, and H. W. Robinson. 1925. J. Biol. Chem. 66:301. [2] Dill, D. B., C. Daly, and W. H. Forbes. 1937. Ibid. 117:569. [3] Hastings, A. B., J. Sendroy, Jr., and D. D. Van Slyke. 1928. Ibid. 79:183. [4] Wiesinger, K., P. H. Rossier, E. Saboz, and G. Sampholo. 1949. Helvet. physiol. pharm. acta, Suppl. C, 7:28.

VIII. Blood Arteriovenous Differences

63. ARTERIAL AND VENOUS BLOOD GASES, NEWBORN AND ADULT: MAN

Values in parentheses are ranges, estimate "c" (cf. Introduction).

	Age	Variable	Method	No. of Subjects	Blood Type	Blood Source	Value	Reference
	(A)	(B)	(C)	(D)	(E)	(F)	(G)	(H)
1	New born[1]	pH	Calculated from Henderson-Hasselbalch equation, using 6.10 for pK'	11	Arterial	Vena umbilicalis	7.32(7.23-7.41)	3
2				9	Venous	Arteria umbilicalis	7.25(7.14-7.37)	
3		O_2 capacity	Van Slyke-Neill manometric	24	Arterial	Vena umbilicalis	22.2(17.2-26.2) vol %	3
4				18	Venous	Arteria umbilicalis	7.2(2.1-12.5) vol %[2]	
5		O_2 content	Van Slyke-Neill manometric	24	Arterial	Vena umbilicalis	10.6(5.6-17.9) vol %	3
6				19	Venous	Arteria umbilicalis	2.9(0.4-8.4) vol %	
7		O_2 saturation	Van Slyke-Neill manometric	24	Arterial	Vena umbilicalis	47.7(25.7-73.8) %	3
8				18	Venous	Arteria umbilicalis	13.9(2.4-37.6) %	
9		O_2 pressure	Potentiometric measurement with dropping-mercury electrode	50	Arterial	Vena umbilicalis	24.4(13.5-34.0) mm Hg	3
10				47	Venous	Arteria umbilicalis	10.4(1.2-19.0) mm Hg	
11		CO_2 content	Van Slyke-Neill manometric	23	Arterial	Vena umbilicalis	40.9(31.2-51.8) vol %	3
12				19	Venous	Arteria umbilicalis	48.0(37.4-55.2) vol %	
13		CO_2 pressure	Calculated from alkali reserve, Henderson nomogram, and CO_2 content	11	Arterial	Vena umbilicalis	44.9(35.0-60.0) mm Hg	3
14				9	Venous	Arteria umbilicalis	59.2(43.5-68.0) mm Hg	
15	Adult[3]	pH	Measurement with glass electrode	50	Arterial	Femoral or brachial artery	7.42(7.37-7.45)	5
16				50	Venous	Internal jugular vein	7.37(7.32-7.40)	
17		O_2 capacity	Van Slyke-Neill manometric with Roughton corrections for O_2 capacity	46	Arterial	Femoral or brachial artery	20.2(16.8-22.9) vol %	4
18			Van Slyke-Neill manometric	9	Mixed venous	Pulmonary artery	4.2(3.2-5.8) vol %[2]	1
19		O_2 content	Van Slyke-Neill manometric	50	Arterial	Femoral or brachial artery	19.6(17.3-22.3) vol %	5
20				50	Venous	Internal jugular vein	12.9(11.0-16.1) vol %	
21		O_2 saturation	Van Slyke-Neill manometric with Roughton corrections for O_2 capacity	46	Arterial	Femoral or brachial artery	96.2(93.5-97.5) %	4
22			Van Slyke-Neill manometric	50	Venous	Internal jugular vein	61.8(55.3-70.7) %	5
23		O_2 pressure	Potentiometric measurement with dropping-mercury electrode	59	Arterial	Femoral or brachial artery	93.0(80.0-104.0) mm Hg	2
24				9	Mixed venous	Pulmonary artery	39.4(29.5-48.5) mm Hg	1
25		CO_2 content	Van Slyke-Neill manometric	50	Arterial	Femoral or brachial artery	48.2(44.6-50.2) vol %	5
26				50	Venous	Internal jugular vein	54.8(51.0-57.7) vol %	
27		CO_2 pressure	Calculated from pH and arterial CO_2 content converted to plasma CO_2 content by use of Henderson-Hasselbalch equation	50	Arterial	Femoral or brachial artery	39.9(36.2-44.9) mm Hg	5
28				50	Venous	Internal jugular vein	49.9(46.9-54.3) mm Hg	

/1/ Before first breath, oxygenated blood goes from the placenta to the fetus via the umbilical vein. /2/ Arteriovenous O_2 difference. /3/ All values for males, under resting conditions.

Contributors: Bartels, Heinz, and Opitz, E.

References: [1] Bartels, H., et al. 1955. Pflügers Arch. 261:99. [2] Bartels, H., and G. Rodewald. 1952. Ibid. 256:113. [3] Beer, R., H. Bartels, and H. A. Raczkowski. 1955. Ibid. 260:306. [4] Douglas, J. C., and O. G. Edholm. 1949. J. Appl. Physiol. 2:307. [5] Gibbs, E. L., W. G. Lennox, L. F. Nims, and F. A. Gibbs. 1942. J. Biol. Chem. 144:325.

64. ARTERIOVENOUS O_2 AND CO_2 DIFFERENCES: MAN, DOG, MONKEY

All blood gases measured by manometric method of Van Slyke and Neill [13], unless otherwise specified. Values in parentheses are ranges, estimate "c" unless otherwise indicated (cf. Introduction).

Animal	Specification	No. of Subjects	No. of Observations	Arterio-venous O_2 Difference vol %	Veno-arterial CO_2 Difference vol %	Metabolic Rate ml O_2/100 g/min	Remarks	Reference
(A)	(B)	(C)	(D)	(E)	(F)	(G)	(H)	(I)
				Systemic[1]				
1 Man	Rest	24♂	24	4.4 (3.0-5.8)[b]			13 normal subjects and 11 patients with normal cardio-vascular function; venous samples from right atrium or ventricle, by catheter	1
2		6♀	6	3.9			Patients with normal cardio-vascular function; venous samples from right atrium or ventricle, by catheter	1
3		3♂	3	3.8 (3.6-4.2)		126 (111-147)[2]	Venous samples from pulmo-nary artery by catheter	10
4	Exercise, mild	3♂	3	7.3 (6.2-7.6)		406 (269-512)[2]	Exertion indicated by metabolic rate; venous samples from pulmonary artery by catheter	10
5		3♂	3	10.2 (9.2-11.6)		812 (700-912)[2]		
6 Dog	Pentobarbital	9	9	4.1 (2.3-6.3)			Venous samples from pulmo-nary artery by catheter	3
7	Pentothal, light	20	20	4.2 (3.4-5.0)[b]	4.1 (3.7-4.5)[b3]		Venous samples from pulmo-nary artery by catheter; A-V O_2 difference measured by method of Roughton and Scholander [11]	4
				Cerebral				
8 Man	Rest	14	34	6.3 (3.9-8.7)[b]	6.4	3.3 (2.4-4.2)[b]	Normal subjects; venous sam-ples from jugular bulb by needle puncture	6
9	Schizophrenia	21	30	6.2 (4.5-8.3)	6.1 (4.6-11.1)	3.4 (2.2-4.2)	Venous samples from jugular bulb by needle puncture	7
10	Hypoglycemia, insulin	6	7	4.4 (3.8-4.7)		2.6		
11	Coma, insulin	6	7	2.8 (1.5-5.6)		1.9		
12	Convulsion, electrical shock	7	7	8.3 (6.9-9.7)	7.9 (6.3-9.7)	3.1 (2.1-3.7)		
13	Pentothal semi-narcosis	8	8	6.2 (5.6-7.0)	6.1 (5.0-7.1)	Normal	Venous samples from jugular bulb by needle puncture	7

/1/ All arterial blood samples from brachial or femoral artery. /2/ ml O_2/min. /3/ For 10 observations.

	Animal	Specification	No. of Subjects	No. of Observations	Arterio-venous O_2 Difference vol %	Veno-arterial CO_2 Difference vol %	Metabolic Rate ml O_2/100 g/min	Remarks	Reference
	(A)	(B)	(C)	(D)	(E)	(F)	(G)	(H)	(I)
					Cerebral (concluded)				
14	Dog	Pentobarbital at 38°C	5	5	9.1 (5.3-15.1)			Venous samples from sagittal sinus by cannula	8
15		Hypothermia at 30°C	5	5	5.3 (4.8-5.7)			Hypothermia induced by surface cooling; venous samples from sagittal sinus by cannula	
16		Hypothermia at 25°C	5	5	4.0 (2.2-7.1)				
17	Monkey	Pentobarbital	11	11	8.0 (6.0-10.1)	8.0 (6.0-10.7)	3.7 (2.5-4.5)	Venous samples from internal jugular veins by cannula	12
					Coronary				
18	Dog	Pentobarbital	29	29	13.2			Venous samples from coronary sinus or great cardiac vein, by catheter	2
19			9	9	13.4 (12.1-15.8)		8.0 (5.6-14.4)	Venous samples from coronary sinus by catheter	3
20		Pentothal	20	20	13.1 (12.0-14.2)[b]	12.6 (11.2-14.0)[b]		Venous samples from coronary sinus by catheter	4
21		Pentothal at 38°C	8	8	13.7 (10.9-18.8)			Venous samples from great circumflex vein by needle puncture	9
22		Hypothermia at 20°C	13	13	12.6 (7.2-18.5)			Hypothermia induced by surface cooling; venous samples from great circumflex vein by needle puncture	9
23		Hypothermia at 17°C	7	7	12.3 (7.4-17.5)			Hypothermia induced by surface cooling; venous samples from great circumflex vein by needle puncture	5

Contributor: Hegnauer, A. H.

References: [1] Cournand, A., R. L. Riley, E. S. Breed, E. de F. Baldwin, and D. W. Richards, Jr. 1945. J. Clin. Invest. 24:106. [2] Eckenhoff, J. E., and J. H. Hafkenschiel. 1948. Am. Heart J. 36:893. [3] Eckenhoff, J. E., J. H. Hafkenschiel, E. L. Foltz, and R. L. Driver. 1948. Am. J. Physiol. 152:545. [4] Goodale, W. T., M. Lubin, J. E. Eckenhoff, J. H. Hafkenschiel, and W. G. Banfield, Jr. 1948. Ibid. 152:340. [5] Hegnauer, A. H., H. D'Amato, and J. Flynn. 1951. Ibid. 167:63. [6] Kety, S. S., and C. F. Schmidt. 1948. J. Clin. Invest. 27:476. [7] Kety, S. S., R. B. Woodford, M. H. Harmel, F. A. Freyhan, K. E. Appel, and C. F. Schmidt. 1947-48. Am. J. Psychiat. 104:765. [8] Lougheed, W. M., and D. S. Kahn. 1955. J. Neurosurg. 12:226. [9] Penrod, K. E. 1951. Am. J. Physiol. 167:79. [10] Riley, R. L., A. Himmelstein, H. L. Motley, H. M. Weiner, and A. Cournand. 1948. Ibid. 152:372. [11] Roughton, F. J. W., and P. F. Scholander. 1943. J. Biol. Chem. 148:541. [12] Schmidt, C. F., S. S. Kety, and H. H. Pennes. 1945. Am. J. Physiol. 143:33. [13] Van Slyke, D. D., and J. M. Neill. 1924. J. Biol. Chem. 61:523.

65. EFFECT OF RAPID DECOMPRESSION AND RECOMPRESSION ON ARTERIOVENOUS O_2 DIFFERENCES: DOG

Period: control = normal pressure; asphyxial = 9-43 minutes normal pressure following decompression in 5-6 seconds from 105-minute compression at 65 lb/sq in.; recompression = 84-minute compression at 30 lb/sq in. following asphyxial period; post-recompression = normal pressure following decompression over 30-minute period from 30 lb/sq in. Values in parentheses are ranges, estimate "c" (cf. Introduction).

	Period	Inhalation	Arterial O_2 Capacity vol %	O_2 Content			O_2 Saturation		
				Arterial vol %	Venous vol %	Arteriovenous Difference vol %	Arterial %	Venous %	Arteriovenous Difference %
	(A)	(B)	(C)	(D)	(E)	(F)	(G)	(H)	(I)
1	Control	Air	19.97 (15.7-23.1)	18.43 (14.6-20.9)	13.27 (7.3-17.0)	4.17 (2.6-5.8)	89.3 (86-92)	68.8 (57-75)	20.5(15-33)
2	Asphyxial[1]	Air	24.1 (18.7-26.7)	13.4 (5.4-23.5)	7.9 (0.5-17.1)	6.6 (4.1-9.7)	55 (24-88)	30.2 (2-64)	24.8(22-30)
3	Recompression	Air	18.55 (16.8-20.3)	19.4 (16.0-25.8)	10.7 (7.9-12.0)	8.7 (4.7-14.3)	91.5 (88-95)	54.5 (39-70)	37(25-49)
4		Oxygen	30.55 (29.6-31.5)	30.3 (29.0-31.7)	18.8 (15.9-20.5)	11.9 (11.7-12.1)	97.5 (95-100)	59 (54-64)	38.5(36-41)
5	Post-recompression[2]	Air	25.9 (22.8-29.0)	13.6 (5.9-24.3)	5.55 (2.3-8.8)	9.55 (3.6-15.5)	55 (26-84)	20 (10-30)	31.7(16-54)
6		Oxygen	27.6 (24.5-29.8)	25.2 (22.0-26.9)	11.9 (7.3-16.9)	13.3 (9.8-19.6)	91.3 (90-94)	43.3 (24-59)	48(35-66)

/1/ Blood samples taken immediately prior to recompression period. /2/ Blood samples taken 1 hour after subjects were returned to normal pressure.

Contributor: Behnke, Albert R.

Reference: Behnke, A. R., L. A. Shaw, A. C. Messer, R. M. Thompson, and E. P. Motley. 1936. Am. J. Physiol. 114:526.

66. ARTERIOVENOUS POSTABSORPTIVE GLUCOSE DIFFERENCES: MAN

Values are mg glucose/100 ml blood. Values in parentheses are ranges, estimate "c" (cf. Introduction).

	Blood	No. of Observations	Arterial	Venous	Arteriovenous Difference	Reference
	(A)	(B)	(C)	(D)	(E)	(F)
1	Fingertip[1]	100	88.4(78-97)	83.9(74-95)	4.5(1-13)	3
2	Radial artery	6	91.5(72-121)	89(67-121)	2.5(0-4)	2
3	Radial artery	10	85(68-108)	77(66-89)	9(-1 to +34)	2
4	Radial artery[2]	16	99(93-105)	98(87-105)	1(-2 to +7)	1

/1/ Copper-iodometric analysis of zinc sulfate-barium hydroxide filtrate; anticoagulant = potassium oxalate-sodium fluoride; accuracy = 1 mg/100 ml. /2/ Analysis by Folin-Wu method (1920).

Contributor: Hegnauer, A. H.

References: [1] Foster, G. L. 1923. J. Biol. Chem. 55:291. [2] Rabinowitch, I. M. 1927. Brit. J. Exp. Path. 8:76. [3] Somogyi, M. 1948. J. Biol. Chem. 174:189.

67. ARTERIOVENOUS GLUCOSE DIFFERENCES DURING ALIMENTARY HYPERGLYCEMIA: MAN

Non-glucose reducing substances reported as glucose, with the exception of lines 23-28 in which the analytical method employed excluded non-glucose reducing substances. Values in lines 1-11, 18-22, 29-32 obtained from plotted curves of the original data. Values in parentheses are ranges, estimate "c" (cf. Introduction).

	Ingested Nutrient	Quantity g	No. of Subjects	Method	Hour of Observation[1]	Arterial Blood mg/100 ml	Venous Blood mg/100 ml	Arterio-venous Difference	Reference
	(A)	(B)	(C)	(D)	(E)	(F)	(G)	(H)	(I)
1	Fructose	100	4	Folin-Wu (1920)	0.0	99(93-103)	98(87-105)	+1.1(-2 to +6)	1
2					0.5	122(107-139)	101(76-130)	22(9-45)	
3					1.0	118(112-125)	97(79-116)	21(9-33)	
4					2.0	112(109-114)	103(96-109)	9(5-13)	
5					2.5	105(98-109)	90(84-100)	15(8-25)	
6	Galactose	100	3	Folin-Wu (1920)	0.0	96(95-96)	95(93-97)	+1(-1 to +2)	1
7					0.5	148(126-174)	133(117-153)	15(9-21)	
8					1.0	182(152-218)	162(142-182)	20(12-36)	
9					2.0	238(212-278)	221(195-261)	17(16-17)	
10					3.0	186(180-197)	187(173-215)	-2(-18 to +9)	
11					4.0	110	109	+1	
12	Glucose	25	6[2]		0.0	91.5(72-121)	89(67-121)	2.5(0-5)	3
13					0.5	218(188-258)	165(149-180)	53(32-80)	
14		50	10	Modification of Benedict (1925)	0.0	85(68-108)	77(66-89)	+9(-1 to +34)	2
15					0.5	126(98-158)	106(78-128)	21(8-50)	
16					1.0	101(74-144)	88(63-128)	+13(-1 to +30)	
17					2.0	86(68-124)	79(62-125)	+7(-7 to +17)	
18		100	7	Folin-Wu (1920)	0.0	101(94-105)	101(93-105)	0(-1 to +4)	1
19					0.5	183(147-214)	140(110-163)	43(27-81)	
20					1.0	158(118-190)	109(81-134)	49(28-81)	
21					2.0	120(106-144)	86(61-107)	34(26-45)	
22					3.0	103(94-108)	87(80-98)	16(10-28)	
23		100	16[3]	Copper-iodometric analysis of zinc sulfate-barium hydroxide precipitates of whole blood[5]	0.0	91(83-102)[4]	86(75-98)	5(1-13)	4
24					0.5	160(133-189)[4]	126(96-150)	34(20-53)	
25					1.0	142(95-190)[4]	108(71-140)	34(18-55)	
26					2.0	122(100-165)[4]	96(70-142)	26(11-34)	
27					3.0	102(64-144)[4]	85(50-131)	17(3-35)	
28					4.0	82(57-119)[4]	73(53-94)	9(1-25)	
29	Starch	70-100	2	Folin-Wu (1920)	0.0	98(95-100)	95(93-96)	+3(-1 to +7)	1
30					0.5	158(151-166)	119(118-120)	35(23-46)	
31					1.0	146(140-152)	102(98-107)	44(42-45)	
32					2.0	105(91-119)	81(76-86)	24(15-33)	

/1/ After ingestion. /2/ Glycosuric but without clinical symptoms of diabetes. /3/ Normal. Subjects with the following were excluded: arterial peaks exceeding 190 mg/100 ml; venous peaks exceeding 150 mg/100 ml; glucose rise continuing into second hour. /4/ Blood from fingertip; demonstrated to be arterial with respect to glucose content. /5/ Anticoagulant = potassium oxalate-sodium fluoride; accuracy to 1 mg/100 ml.

Contributor: Hegnauer, A. H.

References: [1] Foster, G. L. 1923. J. Biol. Chem. 55:291. [2] Friedenson, M., M. K. Rosenbaum, E. J. Thalheimer, and J. P. Peters. 1928. Ibid. 80:269. [3] Rabinowitch, I. M. 1927. Brit. J. Exp. Path. 8:76. [4] Somogyi, M. 1948. J. Biol. Chem. 174:189.

68. VENOUS BLOOD LACTATE IN CONDITIONS OF REST, EXERCISE, HYPERVENTILATION, AND HYPOXIA: MAN

Method: TA = tungstic-acid filtrate via $KMnO_4$ oxidation to aldehyde and titration of bound iodine; A = conversion to aldehyde by concentrated H_2SO_4 and color formation with p-phenylphenol; O = oxidation with $KMnO_4$ and measured as CO_2 manometrically in Van Slyke apparatus. Values in parentheses are ranges, estimate "c" (cf. Introduction).

	Condition	No. of Observations	Method	Lactate mg/100 ml	Remarks	Reference
	(A)	(B)	(C)	(D)	(E)	(F)
1	Rest, at	26	TA	12(8.4-16.6)	9 subjects; daily variations may be as great as 25% of mean	2
2	sea level	6	TA	10.1(8.1-13.6)		1
3		11	TA	11.7(9.0-16.0)	3 subjects in good physical condition	1
4		6	TA	12.5(10.0-16.9)		2
5		1	TA	10.7		3
6		1	TA	8.2		3
7		6	A	19(5.0-45.0)		5
8		6	O	13.2(5.2-21.6)		6
9	Exercise	16		8.3(5.5-13.1)	16 males (basal), climbing and descending 21 ordinary steps twice in 1 minute	4
10		11	TA	12.6(8.6-25.4)	3 subjects in good physical condition, walking 3.5-8.6 mi/hr	1
11		6	TA	17.8(11.8-22.0)	Increase in 3 subjects walking 4.5-5.25 mi/hr	2
12		1	TA	38.7	Jogging at 6.48 mi/hr	3
13		1	TA	139.5	Running at 8.8 mi/hr	3
14		6	A	77(53.0-86.0)		5
15		6	O	157(145-174)	Untrained subjects, 4-10 minutes after 440-yard run	6
16	Hyperventilation	6	TA	27.6(21.3-35.7)	Hyperventilation to alveolar CO_2 pressure of 11-15 mm Hg	1
17	Hypoxia	1	TA	16.2	Simulated altitude reached in 1 hour (no acclimatization), without supplementary oxygen; rise in blood lactate approximately linear starting at 10,000 ft	3

Contributors: (a) Hegnauer, A. H., (b) Beatty, Clarissa H.

References: [1] Bock, A. V., D. B. Dill, and H. T. Edwards. 1932. J. Clin. Invest. 11:775. [2] Cook, L. C., and R. H. Hurst. 1933. J. Physiol., Lond. 79:443. [3] Friedemann, T. E., G. E. Haugen, and T. C. Kmieciak. 1945. J. Biol. Chem. 157:673. [4] Horwitt, M. K., O. W. Hills, and O. Kreisler. 1949. Am. J. Physiol. 156:92. [5] Hummel, J. P. 1949. J. Biol. Chem. 180:1225. [6] Laug, E. P. 1934. Am. J. Physiol. 107:687.

69. ARTERIOVENOUS LACTATE DIFFERENCES DURING CONDITIONS OF REST, EXERCISE, AND HYPERVENTILATION: MAN

Arteriovenous difference given as zero, unless statistically significant or greater than the analytical error. Daily variations in venous level may range from 7% to 25% of mean. Values in parentheses are ranges, estimate "c" (cf. Introduction).

	Condition	No. of Observations	Arterial Blood		Venous Blood		Arteriovenous Difference	Reference
			Artery	Lactate mg/100 ml	Vein	Lactate mg/100 ml		
	(A)	(B)	(C)	(D)	(E)	(F)	(G)	(H)
1	Rest	7	Femoral	12.6(9.7-16.3)	Femoral	12.5(9.0-14.7)	0	2
2		6	Femoral	14.1(11.7-16.2)	Jugular bulb	14.4(10.2-18.0)	0	
3	Exercise[1]	2[2]	Femoral	65.2(58.6-71.8)	Femoral	68.5(62.1-74.8)	-3.3	2
4		1[3]	Femoral	75.8	Femoral	74.8	0[4]	
5	Hyperventilation[5]	6	Radial	21.5(11.9-27.7)	Arm	27.6(21.3-35.7)	-6.1(0 to -15.7)	1

/1/ Standing-run for 1 minute, with maximal energy expenditure. /2/ Blood samples taken within 3 minutes after exercise. /3/ Blood samples taken 5 minutes after exercise. /4/ 1 mg difference may indicate that removal rate at 5 minutes exceeds production. /5/ Alveolar CO_2 pressure of 11-15 mm Hg.

Contributor: Hegnauer, A. H.

References: [1] Bock, A. V., D. B. Dill, and H. T. Edwards. 1932. J. Clin. Invest. 11:775. [2] Cook, L. C., and R. H. Hurst. 1933. J. Physiol., Lond. 79:443.

70. ARTERIAL AND VENOUS LACTATE AND PYRUVATE CONCENTRATIONS: MAN

Subjects at rest. Values in parentheses are ranges, estimate "b" (cf. Introduction).

	Specification	Blood Vessel	Collection Technique	Method	Value	Reference
	(A)	(B)	(C)	(D)	(E)	(F)
1	Lactate, mM/L	Artery	Delayed	Distillation, non-specific	1.10	B,E,11;C,D,6,7
2			Greatly delayed	Colorimetry, highly specific	0.887	B,E,2;C,D,1
3			Fairly rapid	Colorimetry, highly specific	0.667	B,E,5;C,D,1,8
4			Fairly rapid	Colorimetry, highly specific	0.670	B,E,8;C,D,1,8
5			Extremely rapid	Colorimetry, highly specific	0.618 (0.464-0.772)	B,E,15;C,D,1, 14
6		Arm vein	Delayed	Distillation, non-specific	1.11	B,E,3;C,D,6,7
7			Delayed	Distillation, non-specific	1.45	B,E,17;C,D,6,7
8			Delayed	Distillation, non-specific	1.54	B,E,12;C,D,6,7
9			Delayed	Distillation, non-specific	1.13	B,E,10;C,D,6,7
10			Fairly rapid	Colorimetry, highly specific	1.222 (0.514-1.930)	B,E,15;C,D,1,8
11	Pyruvate, mM/L	Artery	Moderately rapid	Specific	0.144	B,E,13;C,D,8,9
12			Extremely rapid	Very specific	0.142 (0.044-0.240)	B,E,15;C,D,14
13		Arm vein	Moderately rapid	Specific	0.088	B,E,10;C,D,8,9
14			Extremely rapid	Fairly specific	0.116	4
15			Unknown	Chromatography, completely specific	0.073 (0.041-0.105)	16
16			Moderately rapid	Specific	0.119 (0.021-0.217)	B,E,15;C,D,8,9
17	Lactate:Pyruvate (ratio)	Artery	Extremely rapid	Colorimetry, highly specific: Very specific (ratio)	4.24 (3.36-5.12)	B,E,15;C,D,1, 8,14
18		Arm vein	Delayed:Moderately rapid (ratio)	Distillation, non-specific: Specific (ratio)	13.2	B,E,10;C,D,6-9
19			Delayed:Moderately rapid (ratio)	Distillation, non-specific: Specific (ratio)	11.3	B,E,10;C,D,6-9
20			Extremely rapid	Fairly specific	9.3	4
21			Moderately rapid: Fairly rapid (ratio)	Specific:Colorimetry, highly specific (ratio)	10.12 (8.18-12.06)	B,E,15;C,D,1, 8,9

Contributor: Huckabee, William E.

References: [1] Barker, S. B., and W. H. Summerson. 1941. J. Biol. Chem. 138:535. [2] Bay, E., E. S. G. Barron, W. Adams, T. Gase, W. C. Halstead, and H. T. Ricketts. 1944. Com. M. Res., Off. Sc. Res. Develop. Rep. 344. [3] Bock, A. V., D. B. Dill, and H. T. Edwards. 1932. J. Clin. Invest. 11:775. [4] Bueding, E., and W. Goldfarb. 1941. J. Biol. Chem. 141:539. [5] Decker, D. G., and J. D. Rosenbaum. 1942. Am. J. Physiol. 138:7. [6] Edwards, H. T. 1938. J. Biol. Chem. 125:571. [7] Friedemann, T. E., M. Cotonio, and P. A. Shaffer. 1927. Ibid. 73:335. [8] Friedemann, T. E., and G. E. Haugen. 1942. Ibid. 144:67. [9] Friedemann, T. E., and G. E. Haugen. 1943. Ibid. 147:415. [10] Friedemann, T. E., G. E. Haugen, and T. C. Kmieciak. 1945. Ibid. 157:673. [11] Gibbs, E. L., W. G. Lennox, L. F. Nims, and F. A. Gibbs. 1942. Ibid. 144:325. [12] Hallock, P. 1939. J. Clin. Invest. 18:385. [13] Himwich, W. A., and H. E. Himwich. 1946. J. Neurophysiol. 9:133. [14] Huckabee, W. E. 1956. J. Appl. Physiol. 9:163. [15] Huckabee, W. E. Unpublished. [16] Seligson, D., G. J. McCormick, and V. Sborov. 1952. J. Clin. Invest. 31:661. [17] Weiss, S., and L. B. Ellis. 1935. Arch. Int. M. 55:665.

71. ARTERIOVENOUS LACTATE AND PYRUVATE DIFFERENCES IN VARIOUS STRUCTURES: MAN

Subjects at rest. Values in parentheses are ranges, estimate "b" (cf. Introduction).

	Specification	Structure or Body Region	Collection Technique	Method	Arteriovenous Difference[1]	Reference
	(A)	(B)	(C)	(D)	(E)	(F)
1	Lactate, mM/L	Brain	Delayed	Distillation, non-specific	-0.178 (-0.288 to -0.068)	B,E,6;C,D,2,5
2		Forearm	Fairly rapid	Colorimetry, highly specific	-0.110 (-0.154 to -0.066)	B,E,3;C,D,1,3
3			Extremely rapid	Colorimetry, highly specific	-0.164 (-0.238 to -0.090)	B,E,10;C,D,1,9
4		Heart	Fairly rapid	Colorimetry, highly specific	+0.30	B,E,7;C,D,1,3
5			Extremely rapid	Colorimetry, highly specific	+0.574 (-0.406 to +1.554)	B,E,10;C,D,1,9
6		Leg	Extremely rapid	Colorimetry, highly specific	-0.237 (-0.405 to -0.069)	B,E,10;C,D,1,9
7		Splanchnic		Colorimetry, highly specific	-0.28[2]	B,E,11;D,1
8		Uterus, pregnant	Extremely rapid	Colorimetry, highly specific	+0.350	B,E,10;C,D,1,9
9	Pyruvate, mM/L	Brain	Moderately rapid	Specific	-0.025 (-0.063 to +0.013)	B,E,8;C,D,3,4
10		Forearm	Extremely rapid	Very specific	-0.025 (-0.139 to +0.089)	B,E,10;C,D,9
11		Heart	Moderately rapid	Specific	+0.045	B,E,7;C,D,3,4
12			Extremely rapid	Very specific	+0.054 (-0.020 to +0.128)	B,E,10;C,D,9
13		Leg	Extremely rapid	Very specific	-0.030 (-0.158 to +0.098)	B,E,10;C,D,9
14		Splanchnic		Specific	+0.05[2]	B,E,11;D,4
15		Uterus, pregnant	Extremely rapid	Very specific	+0.072	B,E,10;C,D,9
16	Lactate:Pyruvate (ratio)	Forearm	Extremely rapid	Colorimetry, highly specific:Very specific (ratio)	-0.44 (-0.74 to -0.14)	B,E,10;C,D,1,9
17		Heart	Extremely rapid	Colorimetry, highly specific:Very specific (ratio)	+0.54 (+0.32 to +0.76)	B,E,10;C,D,1,9
18		Leg	Extremely rapid	Colorimetry, highly specific:Very specific (ratio)	-0.49 (-1.01 to +0.03)	B,E,10;C,D,1,9
19		Splanchnic		Colorimetry, highly specific:Specific (ratio)	-6.51[2]	B,E,11;D,1,4
20		Uterus, pregnant	Extremely rapid	Colorimetry, highly specific:Very specific (ratio)	+2.40	B,E,10;C,D,1,9

/1/ Venous concentration subtracted algebraically from arterial concentration, i.e., negative values indicate output by the various structures. /2/ Directional value only; arm vein concentration minus hepatic vein concentration.

Contributor: Huckabee, William E.

References: [1] Barker, S. B., and W. H. Summerson. 1941. J. Biol. Chem. 138:535. [2] Edwards, H. T. 1938. Ibid. 125:571. [3] Friedemann, T. E., and G. E. Haugen. 1942. Ibid. 144:67. [4] Friedemann, T. E., and G. E. Haugen. 1943. Ibid. 147:415. [5] Friedemann, T. E., M. Cotonio, and P. A. Shaffer. 1927. Ibid. 73:335. [6] Gibbs, E. L., W. G. Lennox, L. F. Nimms, and F. A. Gibbs. 1942. Ibid. 144:325. [7] Goodale, W. T., R. E. Olson, and D. B. Hackel. 1950. Fed. Proc., Balt. 9:49. [8] Himwich, W. A., and H. E. Himwich. 1946. J. Neurophysiol. 9:133. [9] Huckabee, W. E. 1956. J. Appl. Physiol. 9:163. [10] Huckabee, W. E. Unpublished. [11] Mendeloff, A. I. 1954. J. Clin. Invest. 33:1298.

IX. Blood Acid-Base Balance

72. DEFINITIONS OF ACID-BASE TERMINOLOGY

For a thorough consideration of the physicochemical laws, physiological regulations, and pathological states pertaining to acid-base disturbances in man, consult the classic works of Henderson [4], Peters and Van Slyke [5], and material of more recent date [3, 6, 7, 8].

Term	Definition
(A)	(B)
1 Acid	A chemical compound capable of dissociating in solution to form H^+ ions and negatively charged ions (anions), e.g., HCl (strong acid), H_2CO_3 (weak acid).
2 Base	A chemical compound capable of neutralizing an acid or dissociating in solution to form OH^- ions and positively charged ions (cations), e.g., NaOH (strong base), NH_4OH (weak base), $NaHCO_3$ (buffer salt, neutralizes strong acids). This definition avoids the undesirable past usage in acid-base literature of "base" as synonymous with "cation," and also the more modern but confusing Bronsted definition of base as an H^+ acceptor (e.g., the anion HCO_3^- would be called a "base") [1].
3 Buffer base	Biological buffer salts capable of neutralizing strong acids; in blood, the appropriate fraction of total cation and equivalent buffer anions, chiefly bicarbonate, hemoglobinate, and proteinate.
4 Acidosis	An abnormal condition caused by the accumulation in the body of an excess of acid or loss from the body of base [5].
5 Alkalosis	An abnormal condition caused by the accumulation in the body of an excess of base or loss from the body of acid [5].
6 Respiratory factor	If the acid concerned in the disturbance is H_2CO_3, the acidosis or alkalosis may be called "respiratory." The best index for this factor is the CO_2 pressure of arterial or cutaneous blood, which is normally equal to the CO_2 pressure of alveolar air. It can be calculated from plasma pH and total CO_2 by the Henderson-Hasselbalch equation (Table 73, Line 5), or measured directly. Venous CO_2 pressure is less desirable because of the variability of arteriovenous difference of 2-10 mm or more (Table 74, Parts I and III).
7 Metabolic factor	If a base or some acid other than H_2CO_3 is concerned in the disturbance, the acidosis or alkalosis may be called "metabolic." A satisfactory quantitative index for this factor is the whole blood buffer base concentration [8], or the plasma bicarbonate concentration at pH 7.4 [5]. The total CO_2 or bicarbonate concentration is not satisfactory because it also varies with CO_2 pressure, the respiratory factor [4, 5, 8]. The plasma CO_2 combining power, still widely used, is even less satisfactory because it does not measure directly any variable in blood or plasma [2, 5, 8]. Buffer base can be calculated from pH, total CO_2, hemoglobin, and plasma protein (Table 73, Line 7), or taken from a nomogram [8].
8 Compensation	In blood, CO_2 pressure and buffer base can be regarded as independent variables sufficient to define the state of acid-base balance. The pH and total CO_2 or bicarbonate, usually the variables determined, are better regarded as dependent variables. A primary disturbance in one factor, CO_2 pressure or buffer base, usually results in compensation, one manifestation of which is a change in the other factor in such a way that the pH is returned toward, but not necessarily to, the normal range (Table 78).

Contributor: Singer, Richard B.

References: [1] Clark, W. M. 1948. Topics in physical chemistry. Williams and Wilkins, Baltimore. [2] Davenport, H. W. 1950. The abc of acid-base chemistry. University of Chicago Press, Chicago. [3] Elkinton, J. R., and T. S. Danowski. 1955. The body fluids. Williams and Wilkins, Baltimore. [4] Henderson, L. J. 1928. Blood, a study in general physiology. Yale University Press, New Haven. [5] Peters, J. P., and D. D. Van Slyke. 1931. Quantitative clinical chemistry. Ed. 1. Williams and Wilkins, Baltimore. v. 1. [6] Shock, N. W., and A. B. Hastings. 1935. J. Biol. Chem. 112:239. [7] Shohl, A. T. 1939. Mineral metabolism. Reinhold, New York. [8] Singer, R. B., and A. B. Hastings. 1948. Medicine, Balt. 27:223.

Temperature corrections for pH measurements (lines 12-16) have been used in an attempt to reduce to a comparable basis some of the experimental values cited in Table 74, Parts I-III.

	Specification	Factor or Value	Constant, Formula, or Method	Reference
	(A)	(B)	(C)	(D)
1	Volume, at 0°C and 760 mm Hg, occupied by 1 gM of O_2. In the case of hemoglobin, grams may be related to O_2 capacity.	22.41 L	1 mM Hb O_2 = 22.4 ml (STP)	4
2	Volume, at 0°C and 760 mm Hg, occupied by 1 gM of CO_2	22.26 L	CO_2, mM/L = $\dfrac{CO_2 \text{ vol } \%}{2.226}$	4
3	Standard body temperature, man	37°C		9
4	Solubility factor of CO_2 in normal human plasma at 37°C	0.0314 mM/L/mm CO_2 pressure	For plasma or serum water = 940 g/L	3, 15, 17
5	First apparent dissociation constant, carbonic acid in human serum or plasma, 37°C	6.10	$pK'_1 = pH - \log \dfrac{CO_2 - (0.0314) CO_2 \text{ pressure}^1}{0.0314 \, CO_2 \text{ pressure}}$	5, 11, 13
6	Factor by which whole blood CO_2 content should be multiplied to obtain plasma CO_2 content, when hemoglobin content (or hematocrit value), pH, and O_2 saturation are given. Normally Hb = 9 mM/L or 15 g/100 ml or 20.2 vol %, pH = 7.40, O_2 saturation = 100%, and f = 1.217.	Approximately 1.217 in normal arterial blood	$(CO_2)p = f(CO_2)_b$	6, 16
7	Buffer base, $(BB)_b$, or cation and equivalent sum of blood bicarbonate, hemoglobin, and plasma protein anions. Normally $(HCO_3^-)_b$ = 21.0 mEq/L, oxygenated blood Hb = 9 mM/L, plasma protein = 39.8 g/L, pH = 7.40, then $(BB)_b$ = 21.0 + 9.0(2.01) + 39.8(0.24) = 49.1 mEq/L.	Approximately 49.1 mEq/L in normal arterial blood	$(BB)_b = (HCO_3^-)_b + Hb(f_1) + \text{plasma protein } (f_2)$	14
8	Temperature coefficients per °C increase: CO_2 solubility factor	-0.0007 mM/L/mm CO_2 pressure		7
9	Plasma carbonic acid pK'_1	-0.005		2
10	pH of whole blood or true plasma	-0.015		12
11	pH of separated plasma	-0.012		12
12	Temperature corrections for pH measurements: Correction to pH of separated plasma read at 38°C, centrifuged at average room temperature of 25°C, to obtain pH of true plasma at 37°C	-0.025	Change pH true plasma 37°C to 25°C = (-0.015) x (-12) = +0.180 Change pH separated plasma 25°C to 38°C = (-0.012) x (+13) = -0.155 Therefore, observed pH reads too high by +0.025	12
13	Correction to colorimetric pH read at 20°C on separated plasma to get pH at 38°C	-0.23		1, 8
14	Line 14 (correction) and line 15 (correction) combined to get pH of true plasma at 37°C	-0.255		1, 8, 12
15	Correction to colorimetric pH read at 20°C on separated serum to get pH at 38°C	-0.30		8
16	Line 14 (correction) and line 17 (correction) combined to get pH of true serum at 37°C	-0.325		8, 12
17	mEq/L ⇌ mg/100 ml, conversion		mEq/L = $\dfrac{(mg/100 \text{ ml}) \times 10 \times \text{valence}}{\text{gram ionic weight}}$	10

1/ Henderson-Hasselbalch equation.

73. ACID-BASE CONSTANTS, FACTORS, AND FORMULAS (Concluded)

Contributors: Singer, Richard B., and Hastings, A. Baird

References: [1] Cullen, G. E. 1922. J. Biol. Chem. 52:501. [2] Cullen, G. E., H. R. Keeler, and H. W. Robinson. 1925. Ibid. 66:301. [3] Dill, D. B., H. T. Edwards, and W. V. Consolazio. 1937. Ibid. 118:635. [4] Guye, A., and T. Batuecas. 1923. J. chim. phys., Par. 20:308. [5] Hastings, A. B., J. Sendroy, Jr., and D. D. Van Slyke. 1928. J. Biol. Chem. 79:183. [6] Hastings, A. B., and N. W. Shock. 1934. Ibid. 104:575. [7] Loomis, A. G. 1928. International critical tables. Nat. Acad. Sc.-Nat. Res. Counc., Washington, D. C. v. 3, p. 260. [8] Myers, V. C., E. Muntwyler, D. Binns, and W. H. Danielson. 1933. J. Biol. Chem. 102:19. [9] Pembrey, M. S. In E. A. Schaefer, ed. 1898. Textbook of physiology. Macmillan, New York. v. 1. [10] Peters, J. P., and D. D. Van Slyke. 1932. Quantitative clinical chemistry. Ed. 1. Williams and Wilkins, Baltimore. v. 2. [11] Robinson, H. W., J. W. Price, and G. E. Cullen. 1934. J. Biol. Chem. 106:7. [12] Rosenthal, T. B. 1948. Ibid. 173:25. [13] Rossier, P. H., and H. Mean. 1940. Rev. méd. Suisse rom. 60:633. [14] Singer, R. B., and A. B. Hastings. 1948. Medicine, Balt. 27:223. [15] Van Slyke, D. D. 1950. J. Biol. Chem. 183:331. [16] Van Slyke, D. D., and J. Sendroy, Jr. 1928. Ibid. 79:781. [17] Van Slyke, D. D., J. Sendroy, Jr., A. B. Hastings, and J. M. Neill. 1928. Ibid. 78:765.

74. ACID-BASE VALUES: MAN

Part I: ARTERIAL BLOOD

Diagram showing ionic patterns of arterial blood appears in Table 77. Hemoglobin concentration assumed to be 20 mM/L erythrocytes; 1 mM (single Fe-atom structure, molecular weight 16,500) combines with 22.4 ml of oxygen, STP when saturated. Handling of blood [18], column C: The four digits in the code number refer, successively, to anticoagulant, method of drawing blood, storage of sample, and centrifugation. Anticoagulant: (1) dry potassium oxalate, (2) mixture of dry oxalate and fluoride, (3) dry heparin, (4) heparin in 0.9% NaCl, (5) saline-heparin-fluoride solution. Drawing of blood: (1) oiled syringe, (2) syringe with dry anticoagulant, (3) syringe with dead space filled with heparin-saline solution. Storage (chilled to less than 5°C): (1) no storage period, (2) under oil, (3) over mercury, (4) syringe. Centrifugation: (1) no centrifugation, (2) special stoppered tube, (3) syringe. Method, column D: G = glass electrode, whole blood [9]; R = room temperature; CpH = calculation of pH by means of Henderson-Hasselbalch equation (cf. Table 73, line 5). Method, column G: X = gasometric Van Slyke, tonometer saturation with oxygen [18]; OC = O_2 capacity; Z = spectrophotometer, as oxyhemoglobin or cyanmethemoglobin [10, 11]; Y = gasometric Van Slyke, tonometer saturation plus corrections [4]. Method, column K: C = calculation of CO_2 pressure by means of Henderson-Hasselbalch equation (Table 73, lines 4 and 5); I = interpolated CO_2 dissociation curve [12]; D = direct Van Slyke tonometric measurement of CO_2 pressure [18]. Average adult arterial O_2 saturation = 98%. Values in parentheses are ranges, estimate "b" (cf. Introduction).

	Subjects		Han-dling of Blood	pH			Hemoglobin		CO_2 Content		CO_2 Pressure		Buffer Base[5] mEq/L	Ref-erence
	Age yr	No.		Meth-od	Observed	Adjust-ed[1]	Meth-od[2]	Concen-tration mM/L	Whole Blood[3] mM/L	Plas-ma[4] mM/L	Meth-od	Whole Blood or Plasma mm Hg		
	(A)	(B)	(C)	(D)	(E)	(F)	(G)	(H)	(I)	(J)	(K)	(L)	(M)	(N)
1	3-11	5♂, 4♀	434?	G, R		7.38		7.4 (6.4-8.4)	20.9 (18.7-23.1)	24.5	C	39.0 (32.4-45.6)	45.0	16
2	8-15	11♂	3132	CpH	7.38	7.38	X	8.2	21.5	25.6	I	40.4 (33.0-47.8)	46.3	19
3	16-48	35♂	3132	CpH	7.39	7.39	X	9.0	22.5	27.4	I	42.5 (35.4-49.6)	48.5	19
4	17-37	9♂	4341	G, 38°C	7.42 (7.38-7.46)	7.42				28.3	C	41.3 (36.1-46.5)	50.0	2

/1/ Values for pH adjusted to temperature of 37°C in accordance with lines 10, 11, and 12-16, Table 73. /2/ O_2 capacity of hemoglobin: Gasometric determinations of hemoglobin by saturation with oxygen or carbon monoxide in a tonometer may give results 1-2% high because of drainage errors, and also because of conversion of a small amount of an unidentified, inactive CO combining compound to an active form when the blood stands $\frac{1}{2}$-2 hours. Most older determinations of saturation with oxygen are thus too low by 1-3% [20]. /3/ Method: gasometric, manometric Van Slyke (later i factor) [22]. /4/ Calculated from whole blood CO_2 content (cf. Table 73, line 6). /5/ Calculated by method in Table 73, line 7.

Part I: ARTERIAL BLOOD (Continued)

	Subjects		Handling of Blood	pH			Hemoglobin		CO2 Content		CO2 Pressure		Buffer Base5 mEq/L	Reference
	Age yr	No.		Method	Observed	Adjusted1	Method2	Concentration mM/L	Whole Blood3 mM/L	Plasma4 mM/L	Method	Whole Blood or Plasma mm Hg		
	(A)	(B)	(C)	(D)	(E)	(F)	(G)	(H)	(I)	(J)	(K)	(L)	(M)	(N)
5	18-29	50♂	11?1	G, 38°C	7.42 (7.39-7.44)	7.43	X	9.3 (8.1-10.5)	21.6 (20.4-22.8)	26.6	C	37.0	48.4	13
6	18-38	12♂, 1♀	4111	G, 33°C	7.35	7.37	OC	8.7	21.2	25.6	C	42.0	47.0	21
7	18-39	36♂	4241	G, R	7.39 (7.34-7.44)	7.39	Z	8.7 (7.7-9.7)	22.5 (20.7-24.3)	27.1	C	42.0	48.6	17
8	21-52	10♂	2321, 4241	G?	7.42 (7.40-7.44)	7.42	X	8.3 (7.1-9.5)	22.2 (20.8-23.6)	26.7	C	39.0 (37.4-40.6)	48.3	5
9	23-24	3♂	4341	G, 38°C	7.40	7.40				27.1	C	41.2	49.0	1
10	23-49	12♂	4341	G, 25°C	7.39 (7.35-7.43)	7.39	OC	9.3	21.2 (19.2-23.2)	25.9	C	40.0 (34.0-46.0)	48.0	14
11	24-43	3♀	4341	G, 38°C	7.43	7.43				25.9	C	38.4	47.0	2
12	24.5[6]	12♂	434?	G, R	7.40 (7.33-7.47)	7.40		8.9 (8.1-9.7)	22.4 (19.8-25.0)	27.3	C	41.5 (37.3-45.7)	49.0	16
13	31.1[6]	11♂	4341	G, 37.5°C	7.41 (7.37-7.45)	7.41	OC	8.5	20.6 (18.2-23.0)	24.8	C	36.8 (30.8-42.8)	47.0	23
14	48-76	14♂	3132	CpH	7.38	7.38	X	8.9	22.1	26.8	I	42.8 (38.0-46.6)	47.4	19
15	50-77	22♀	4241	G, R	7.42 (7.34-7.50)	7.42	Y	7.8 (6.2-9.4)	21.1 (17.7-24.5)	25.0	C	36.3 (28.3-44.3)	45.3	3
16	50-81	27♂	4241	G, R	7.42 (7.36-7.48)	7.42	Y	7.7 (5.7-9.7)	21.5 (18.1-24.9)	25.4	C	37.0 (28.8-45.2)	45.6	3
17	Adult	12♂	3132	CpH	7.39 (7.34-7.44)	7.39	X	9.0 (7.8-10.2)	21.9 (20.9-22.9)	26.4[7]	I	41.0 (38.2-43.8)	48.5	7
18	Adult	10♂	3132	CpH	7.38 (7.34-7.42)	7.38	X	8.9	22.1 (20.5-23.7)	26.5	I	42.8	48.0	8
19	Adult	106♂	3132	CpH	7.37 (7.31-7.43)	7.37			22.2 (20.2-24.2)	26.9	I	43.3		8
20	Adult	18♂	3131	CpH	7.38 (7.37-7.39)	7.38				27.0[7]	I	43.1 (40.1-46.1)		6
21	25-26	5♂	5343	G, 37°C	7.37	7.37				26.5	C, D	43.1	48.0	15

/1/ Values for pH adjusted to temperature of 37°C in accordance with lines 10, 11, and 12-16, Table 73. /2/ O2 capacity of hemoglobin: Gasometric determinations of hemoglobin by saturation with oxygen or carbon monoxide in a tonometer may give results 1-2% high because of drainage errors, and also because of conversion of a small amount of an unidentified, inactive CO combining compound to an active form when the blood stands ½-2 hours. Most older determinations of saturation with oxygen are thus too low by 1-3% [20]. /3/ Method: gasometric, manometric Van Slyke (later i factor) [22]. /4/ Calculated from whole blood CO2 content (cf. Table 73, line 6). /5/ Calculated by method in Table 73, line 7. /6/ Mean age. /7/ Not calculated; actual value.

Contributors: Singer, Richard B., and Hastings, A. Baird

References: [1] Alexander, J. K., H. F. Spalter, and J. R. West. 1955. J. Clin. Invest. 34:533. [2] Alexander, J. K., J. R. West, J. A. Wood, and D. R. Richards. 1955. Ibid. 34:511. [3] Comroe, J. H., Jr., and F. Greifenstein. Unpublished. [4] Comroe, J. H., Jr., and P. Walker. 1948. Am. J. Physiol. 152:365. [5] Cournand, A., R. L. Riley, E. S. Breed, E. de F. Baldwin, and D. W. Richards, Jr. 1945. J. Clin. Invest. 24:106. [6] D'Elseaux, F. C., F. C. Blackwood, L. E. Palmer, and K. G. Sloman. 1942. J. Biol. Chem. 144:529. [7] Dill, D. B., H. T. Edwards, and W. V. Consolazio. 1937. Ibid. 118:635. [8] Dill, D. B., J. W. Wilson, F. G. Hall, and S. Robinson. 1940. Ibid. 136:449. [9] Dole, M. W. 1941. The glass electrode. J. Wiley and Sons, New York. [10] Drabkin, D. L., and J. H. Austin, Jr. 1932. J. Biol. Chem. 98:719. [11] Drabkin, D. L., and J. H.

Part I: ARTERIAL BLOOD (Concluded)

Austin, Jr. 1935-36. Ibid. 112:51. [12] Eisenman, A. J. 1926-27. Ibid. 71:611. [13] Gibbs, E. L., W. G. Lennox, L. F. Nims, and F. A. Gibbs. 1942. Ibid. 144:325. [14] Hickam, J. B., W. P. Wilson, and R. Frayser. 1956. J. Clin. Invest. 35:601. [15] Holaday, D. A., D. Ma, and E. M. Papper. 1957. Ibid. 36:1121. [16] Kennedy, C., and L. Sokoloff. 1957. Ibid. 36:1130. [17] Lambertsen, C. J., G. L. Emmel, D. Y. Cooper, H. H. Loeschke, and R. H. Kough. 1950. Fed. Proc., Balt. 9:73. [18] Peters, J. P., and D. D. Van Slyke. 1932. Quantitative clinical chemistry. Ed. 1. Williams and Wilkins, Baltimore. v. 2. [19] Robinson, S. 1938. Arbeitsphysiologie 10:251. [20] Roughton, F. J. 1944. Am. J. Physiol. 142:708. [21] Scheinberg, P., L. I. Blackburn, M. Rich, and M. Saslaw. 1954. Am. J. Med. 16:549. [22] Van Slyke, D. D., and J. Sendroy, Jr. 1927. J. Biol. Chem. 73:127. [23] Wilson, R. H., C. W. Borden, R. V. Ebert, and H. S. Wells. 1950. J. Laborat. Clin. M. 36:119.

Part II: CUTANEOUS BLOOD

Cutaneous blood is equivalent to arterial blood in acid-base properties [6]. Blood, from fingertip of warmed hand, collected and analyzed by microtechnique of Shock and Hastings [2]. Values in parentheses are ranges, estimate "b" (cf. Introduction).

| Subjects | | pH[1] | Erythrocyte Volume % | CO$_2$ Content | | CO$_2$ Pressure[3] mm Hg | Buffer Base[4] mEq/L | Reference |
Age	No.			Whole Blood mM/L	Plasma[2] mM/L			
(A)	(B)	(C)	(D)	(E)	(F)	(G)	(H)	(I)
1	4-6 da[5]	27♂♀	7.420(7.314-7.526)	50.8(50.7-50.9)	18.2(14.8-21.6)	22.8	34.2(26.8-41.6)	47.1	5
2	4-6 da[6]	18♂♀	7.380(7.262-7.498)	50.1(50.0-50.2)	15.3(10.7-19.9)	19.0	31.1(22.3-39.9)	43.1	5
3	17-22 yr	123♂	7.415(7.350-7.480)	46.6(44.4-48.8)	22.9(20.5-25.3)	28.0	41.2(34.1-48.3)	50.5	1
4	18-28 yr[7]	39♂	7.415(7.362-7.468)	47.5(41.8-53.2)	22.3(19.9-24.7)	27.4	40.3(33.0-47.6)	50.1	3
5	18-28 yr[8]	8♂	7.370(7.324-7.416)	46.6(42.4-50.8)	21.9(21.1-22.7)	26.8	43.5(37.9-49.1)	48.1	3
6	18-28 yr[7]	17♀	7.430(7.380-7.480)	41.0(35.2-46.8)	21.9(19.1-24.7)	26.1	37.1(32.5-41.7)	48.4	3
7	18-28 yr[8]	7♀	7.390(7.360-7.420)	38.0(35.0-41.0)	21.9(19.9-23.9)	26.0	40.4(37.5-43.3)	46.9	3
8	40-49 yr	10♂	7.400(7.360-7.440)	47.8(34.4-61.2)	22.6(19.4-25.8)	27.8	42.2(34.0-50.4)	50.0	4
9	50-59 yr	26♂	7.395(7.323-7.467)	44.1(36.9-51.3)	22.2(18.6-25.8)	26.8	41.2(32.2-50.2)	48.7	4
10	60-69 yr	54♂	7.395(7.348-7.442)	44.8(38.7-50.9)	22.3(18.0-26.6)	27.0	41.5(32.7-50.3)	49.0	4
11	70-79 yr	45♂	7.385(7.312-7.458)	43.4(37.1-49.7)	22.3(19.4-25.2)	26.8	42.0(34.7-49.3)	48.5	4
12	80-89 yr	17♂	7.385(7.307-7.463)	41.5(35.7-47.3)	22.2(17.8-26.6)	26.4	41.5(33.1-49.9)	47.9	4

/1/ Observed at 38°C, but adjusted to 37°C by adding 0.015 (cf. Table 73, line 10). /2/ Calculated from whole blood CO$_2$ content (cf. Table 73, line 6). /3/ Calculated from Henderson-Hasselbalch equation with constants from Table 73, lines 4 and 5. /4/ Calculated by method in Table 73, line 7. /5/ Breast-fed infants. /6/ Infants on evaporated-milk formula. /7/ Subjects seated and at rest; samples drawn at any time of day without control of previous activity. /8/ Subjects studied by successive daily samples drawn before breakfast and after $\frac{1}{2}$ hour of physical rest.

Contributors: Singer, Richard B., and Hastings, A. Baird

References: [1] Hamilton, J. A., and N. W. Shock. 1936. Am. J. Psychol 48·467 [2] Shock, N. W., and A. B. Hastings. 1934. J. Biol. Chem. 104:565. [3] Shock, N. W., and A. B. Hastings. 1934. Ibid. 104:585. [4] Shock, N. W., and M. J. Yiengst. 1950. J. Geront. 5:1. [5] Singer, R. B. Unpublished. [6] Singer, R. B., J. Shohl, and D. B. Bluemle. 1955. Clin. Chem. 1:287.

Part III: VENOUS BLOOD

Hemoglobin concentration assumed to be 20 mM/L erythrocytes; 1 mM (single Fe-atom structure, molecular weight 16,500) combines with 22.4 ml of oxygen, STP when saturated. Handling of blood [16], column D: The four digits in the code number refer, successively, to anticoagulant, method of drawing blood, storage of sample, and centrifugation. Anticoagulant: (1) none used (serum sample), (2) dry potassium oxalate, (3) mixture of dry oxalate and fluoride, (4) heparin in 0.9% NaCl. Drawing of blood: (1) oiled syringe, (2) syringe with dry anticoagulant, (3) syringe with dead space filled with heparin-saline solution, (4) oil tube. Storage (at room temperature): (1) under oil, (2) over mercury; (chilled to less than 5°C): (3) under oil, (4) syringe. Centrifugation: (1) no centrifugation, (2) oil tube, (3) special stoppered tube, (4) tube, under paraffin. Blood: J = jugular, A = antecubital, M = mixed venous. Method, column E: S = colorimetric, serum [14]; H = hydrogen electrode, serum or plasma [19]; G = glass electrode, whole blood [5]; C = calculated; P = colorimetric, plasma [2]. Method, column J: O = gasometric, manometric Van Slyke (original i factor) [20]; I = gasometric, manometric Van Slyke (later i factor) [21]; V = gasometric, volumetric Van Slyke [16]. Values in parentheses are ranges, estimate "b" (cf. Introduction). For additional information on internal jugular blood, consult references 9, 11, 18.

| | Subjects | | Blood | Handling of Blood | pH | | | Hb Concentration^{2,3} mM/L | O$_2$ Saturation^4 % | CO$_2$ Content | | CO$_2$ Pressure^5 mm Hg | Reference |
	Age	No.			Method	Observed	Adjusted^1			Method	Plasma mM/L		
	(A)	(B)	(C)	(D)	(E)	(F)	(G)	(H)	(I)	(J)	(K)	(L)	(M)
1	1-9 da	40♂♀	J	1112	S	7.400 (7.322-7.478)^6	7.375	10.3	87	O	23.6 (19.7-27.5)^7	37.7	13
2	16-34 yr	30♀^{8}	A	1112	H	7.405 (7.355-7.455)^6	7.380			I	27.3 (24.5-30.1)	42.6	15
3	20-39 yr	6♂	A	1112	S	7.710 (7.660-7.760)^9	7.385				28.3 (23.7-32.9)	44.4	3
4	21-52 yr	10♂	M	3331, 4241	G	7.390 (7.370-7.410)	7.390	8.3	72	I	28.6^{10}	45.7	1
5	22-31 yr	4♀	A	1112	S	7.685 (7.665-7.705)^9	7.360			I	27.8 (27.0-28.6)	46.0	3
6	Young adult	8♀	A	11?2	C	7.380				I	27.7	44.1^{11}	10
7	Adult	7♂	A	3124	H, P	7.410 (7.356-7.464)^6	7.385			I	30.8 (26.6-35.0)^{12}	48.3	22
8	Adult	21♂	A	2113	P	7.585 (7.513-7.657)^9	7.330	9.3	55	O	30.9 (27.7-34.1)^{13}	54.6	4
9	Adult	74♂	A	1112	S	7.675 (7.607-7.753)^9	7.340				29.5 (26.4-32.6)	51.0	6
10	Adult	27♂	A	1412				9.2	70	V	23.7 (20.7-26.7)^{14}		8
11	Adult	60♂	A	??11				8.8	68		24.0^{14}		12

/1/ Values for pH adjusted to temperature of 37°C in accordance with lines 10, 11, and 12-16, Table 73. /2/ Method: gasometric Van Slyke, tonometer saturation with oxygen [16]. /3/ O$_2$ capacity of hemoglobin: Gasometric determinations of hemoglobin by saturation with oxygen or carbon monoxide in a tonometer may give results 1-2% high because of drainage errors, and also because of conversion of a small amount of an unidentified, inactive CO-combining compound to an active form when the blood stands $\frac{1}{2}$-2 hours. Most older determinations of saturation with oxygen are thus too low by 1-3% [17]. /4/ Method: gasometric, manometric apparatus [16], except for line 10. /5/ CO$_2$ pressure at 37°C calculated from adjusted pH and CO$_2$ content by the Henderson-Hasselbalch equation (cf. Table 73, line 5). /6/ At 38°C. /7/ Whole blood CO$_2$ content = 19.1 mM/L. /8/ Postpartum, 1-7 months. /9/ At 20°C. /10/ Calculated from whole blood CO$_2$ content of 24.0(22.8-25.2) mM/L. /11/ Derived from interpolated CO$_2$ dissociation curve [7]. /12/ Whole blood CO$_2$ content = 26.2(22.4-30.0) mM/L. /13/ Whole blood CO$_2$ content = 26.1(23.5-28.7) mM/L. /14/ Values given are for whole blood CO$_2$ content.

Contributors: Singer, Richard B., and Hastings, A. Baird

References: [1] Cournand, A., R. L. Riley, E. S. Breed, E. de F. Baldwin, and D. W. Richards, Jr. 1945. J. Clin. Invest. 24:106. [2] Cullen, G. E. 1922. J. Biol. Chem. 52:501. [3] Cullen, G. E., and I. P. Earle. 1929. Ibid. 83:545. [4] Cullen, G. E., and H. W. Robinson. 1923. Ibid. 57:533. [5] Dole, M. W. 1941. The glass electrode. J. Wiley and Sons, New York. [6] Earle, I. P., and G. E. Cullen. 1929. J. Biol. Chem. 83:539. [7] Eisenman, A. J. 1926-27. Ibid. 71:611. [8] Goldschmidt, S., and A. B. Light. 1925. Am. J. Physiol. 73:127.

Part III: VENOUS BLOOD (Concluded)

[9] Kennedy, C., and L. Sokoloff. 1957. J. Clin. Invest. 36:1130. [10] Kydd, D. M. 1931. J. Biol. Chem. 91:63. [11] Lambertsen, C. J., R. H. Kough, D. Y. Cooper, G. L. Emmel, H. H. Loeschke, and C. F. Schmidt. 1953. J. Appl. Physiol. 5:471. [12] Lennox, W. G. 1930. Arch. Int. M. 46:630. [13] Marples, E., and V. W. Lippard. 1932. Am. J. Dis. Child. 44:31. [14] Myers, V. C., E. Muntwyler, D. Binns, and W. H. Danielson. 1933. J. Biol. Chem. 102:19. [15] Nice, M., J. W. Mull, E. Muntwyler, and V. C. Myers. 1936. Am. J. Obst. 32:375. [16] Peters, J. P., and D. D. Van Slyke. 1932. Quantitative clinical chemistry. Ed. 1. Williams and Wilkins, Baltimore. v. 2. [17] Roughton, F. J. 1944. Am. J. Physiol. 142:708. [18] Scheinberg, P., L. I. Blackburn, M. Rich, and M. Saslaw. 1954. Am. J. Med. 16:549. [19] Van Slyke, D. D., A. B. Hastings, C. D. Murray, and J. Sendroy, Jr. 1925. J. Biol. Chem. 65:701. [20] Van Slyke, D. D., and J. M. Neill. 1924. Ibid. 61:523. [21] Van Slyke, D. D., and J. Sendroy, Jr. 1927. Ibid. 73:127. [22] Van Slyke, D. D., and J. Sendroy, Jr. 1928. Ibid. 79:781.

Part IV: PROVISIONAL NORMAL VALUES, ADULTS

Values in parentheses are ranges, estimate "b" (cf. Introduction).

Blood	No. of Subjects	pH of Whole Blood or Plasma	Hematocrit Value[1] %	CO_2 Content				CO_2 Pressure mm Hg	Whole Blood Buffer Base mEq/L
				Whole Blood		Plasma			
				mM/L	vol %	mM/L	vol %		
(A)	(B)	(C)	(D)	(E)	(F)	(G)	(H)	(I)	(J)
1 Arterial[2]	153–277♂	7.39 (7.34–7.44)		22.2 (20–24)	49.5 (45–53)	26.9 (25–29)[3]	60.0 (56–64)[3]	41.6 (35–47)	48.4(46–52)
2 Cutaneous	180♂	7.41 (7.35–7.47)[4]	46.9(42–52)	22.7 (20–25)	50.5 (45–56)			41.3 (34–48)	50.1(47–53)
3	24♀	7.42 (7.36–7.48)[4]	40.1(34–46)	21.9 (19.5–24.5)	48.8 (43–55)			38.1 (33–43)	48.0(45–51)
4 Venous	118–125♂	7.35 (7.28–7.42)		24.4 (21–28)	54.4 (47–62)	29.6 (26–33)	66.0 (58–73)		
5	42♀	7.38 (7.31–7.45)				27.5 (25–32)	61.2 (56–71)		

/1/ Sitting position. /2/ Hemoglobin content (recumbent position) = 8.95(7.7-10.3) mM/L, or 15.0(13-17) g/100 ml; erythrocyte CO_2 content (calculated, in part, from whole blood CO_2 content) = 16.4(14.5-18.5) mM/L, or 36.5(32-41) vol %. /3/ Calculated, in part, from whole blood CO_2 content. /4/ Determined colorimetrically.

Contributors: Singer, Richard B., and Hastings, A. Baird

Part V: PHYSIOLOGICAL VARIABILITY

Change from control value indicated by +, -, ±, or 0.

	Control or Factor Varied	Subjects No. and Sex	Conditions of Observation	Hemo-globin mM/L	Adjusted pH	Whole Blood CO$_2$ mM/L	Adjusted CO$_2$ Pressure mm Hg	Calc. (BB)$_b$ mEq/L	Reference
	(A)	(B)	(C)	(D)	(E)	(F)	(G)	(H)	(I)
	Arterial Blood								
1	Control	259♂	15-50 years old; basal, supine; morning	9.0[1]	7.39	22.2	41.6	48.4	Page 183, line 1
	Posture								
2	Reclining	♂♀	Adults		?	?	-0.8	+	9
3	Sitting	4[2]♂♀	Adults	+0.3[3]	?	?	-2.7	+0.2[4]	8, 9
4	Standing	16[2]♂♀	Adults	+0.6	?	?	-3.7	+0.4[4]	9, 12
	Age								
5	0-13 da	♂♀	Supine; daytime	+1.8	?	-	-	-	3
6	3-45 da	12♂♀	Premature infants; supine; daytime	-0.5[5]	-0.09	-6	-4	-8	3, 13
7	2-13 wk	♂♀	Supine; daytime	-0.6	?	-	-	-	3
8	3 mo-2 yr	♂♀	Supine; daytime	-1.9	?	-	-	-	3
9	2-6 yr	♂♀	Supine; daytime	-1.5	?	-	-	-	3
10	8-15 yr	11♂♀	Basal, supine; daytime	0.9[6]	0	-1	-2.4	-2	3, 10
11	50-81 yr	41♂	Supine, after ½-hour rest; daytime	-0.8	+0.02	-0.4	-1.5	-2	1
	Cutaneous Blood								
12	Control	8♂	16-28 years old; sitting, after ½-hour rest; 8-9 a.m.	9.3[3]	7.37	21.9	43.5	48.1	11
13	Sex	7♀	16-28 years old; sitting, after ½-hour rest; 8-9 a.m.	-1.7[3]	+0.02	0	-3.1	-1.2	11
	Time of day								
14	9 a.m.-5 p.m.	39♂	16-28 years old; sitting, after uncontrolled activity	+0.2[3]	+0.04	+0.4	-3.2	+2.0	11
15	10 a.m.-4 p.m.	1♂	Adult; supine, after bed rest	±	+0.02	+2	±	+2	6
16	12 p.m.-6 a.m.	1♂	Adult; sleeping supine, after bed rest	±	-0.03	+2	+8	0	6
	Day-to-day variability								
17	Standard deviation[7]	8♂	16-28 years old; sitting, after ½-hour rest; 8-9 a.m.	±	±0.04[8]	±1.0[8]	±4.7[8]	±	11
18		7♀	16-28 years old; sitting, after ½-hour rest; 8-9 a.m.	±	±0.07[8]	±1.7[8]	±4.8[8]	±	
19	Before menstruation, 8-10 da	♀	27 years old; supine, after short rest; 8 a.m.		+0.03	?[9]	-4.7	-	2
20	After menstruation, 1-13 da	♀	27 years old; supine, after short rest; 8 a.m.		+0.01	?[9]	-2.7	-	

/1/ For 153 subjects. /2/ Hemoglobin only. /3/ Calculated from hematocrit value, assuming hemoglobin concentration of erythrocytes to be 20 mM/L. /4/ Calculated from the change in hemoglobin concentration by the formula $\Delta(BB)_b = 0.6\Delta(Hb)$, for average CO$_2$ pressure and pH. /5/ Change assumed from known variation of hemoglobin with age. /6/ Change for subjects 6-14 years old. /7/ Values in lines 17 and 18, columns E-G, are group means of the standard deviation values for all subjects. /8/ Standard deviation of the distribution of the group of standard deviations about the standard deviation: lines 17 and 18, column E = ±0.02; lines 17 and 18, column F = ±0.2; line 17, column G = ±0.7; line 18, column G = ±1.0. /9/ Possibly a negative change.

Part V: PHYSIOLOGICAL VARIABILITY (Concluded)

	Control or Factor Varied	Subjects No. and Sex	Conditions of Observation	Hemo-globin mM/L	Adjusted pH	Whole Blood CO_2 mM/L	Adjusted CO_2 Pressure mm Hg	Calc. $(BB)_b$ mEq/L	Reference
	(A)	(B)	(C)	(D)	(E)	(F)	(G)	(H)	(I)
				Venous Blood					
21	Control	60♂	Antecubital vein; supine, after ½-hour rest; daytime	68%[10]	7.36	23.9	50	49	7
22	Vein Internal jugular	60♂	18-50 years old; supine, after ½-hour rest; daytime	-5%[10]	-	+0.8	+	0	7
23	External jugular	40♂	16-50 years old; supine, after ½-hour rest; daytime	+19%[10]	+	-0.7	-	0	7
24	Femoral	14♂	16-50 years old; supine, after ½-hour rest; daytime	+2%[10]	0	+0.1	+	0	7
25	In dorsal surface of hand	33♂	Reclining, after ½-hour rest; daytime	+18%[10]	+	-1.4	-	0	4
26	Temperature 23°C	15♂	Antecubital vein; reclining, after ½-hour rest; daytime	-4%[10]	-	+0.2	+	0	4
27	28°C	15♂	Antecubital vein; reclining, after ½-hour rest; daytime	+5%[10]	+	-0.3	-	0	4
28	45°C	4♂	Adults; vein in dorsal surface of hand; reclining, after ½-hour rest; daytime	+30%[10]	+0.03	-2.2	-8	0	5

/10/ O_2 saturation.

Contributors: Singer, Richard B., and Hastings, A. Baird

References: [1] Comroe, J. H., Jr., and F. Greifenstein. Unpublished. [2] Döring, G. K. 1948. Pflügers Arch. 250:694. [3] Drabkin, D. L. Unpublished. [4] Goldschmidt, S., and A. B. Light. 1925. Am. J. Physiol. 73:127. [5] Goldschmidt, S., and A. B. Light. 1925. J. Biol. Chem. 64:53. [6] Hastings, A. B., and C. W. Eisele. 1940. Proc. Soc. Exp. Biol., N. Y. 43:308. [7] Lennox, W. G. 1930. Arch. Int. M. 46:630. [8] Maxfield, M. E., H. C. Bazett, and C. C. Chambers. 1941. Am. J. Physiol. 133:128. [9] Rahn, H. In J. H. Comroe, Jr., ed. 1950. Methods in medical research. Year Book Publishers, Chicago. v. 2, p. 223. [10] Robinson, S. 1938. Arbeitsphysiologie 10:251. [11] Shock, N. W., and A. B. Hastings. 1934. J. Biol. Chem. 104:585. [12] Waterfield, R. L. 1931. J. Physiol., Lond. 72:110. [13] Wilson, J. L., H. S. Reardon, and M. Murayama. 1948. Pediatrics 1:581.

pH adjusted to body temperature by applying correction of -0.015 per °C temperature difference (cf. Table 73, line 10). CO_2 pressure calculated by means of Henderson-Hasselbalch equation; value of pK'_1 increases 0.005 per °C decrease in temperature, and f_{CO_2} is assumed to increase proportionately as it does in pure water. The following values for pK'_1 and f_{CO_2} were used at temperatures other than 38°C: 5°C, 6.26 and 0.0864; 10°C, 6.24 and 0.0697; 20°C, 6.19 and 0.0508; 26°C, 6.16 and 0.0434; 34°C, 6.12 and 0.0357; 40°C, 6.09 and 0.0313; 42°C, 6.08 and 0.0303. Blood: A = arterial, M = mixed arterial and venous, V = venous, H = heart. Values in parentheses are ranges, estimate "c" unless otherwise indicated (cf. Introduction).

Animal	Body Temp. °C	Blood	Whole Blood pH	Erythrocytes Hb mM/L	Vol %	Plasma CO2 Content mM/L	CO2 Pressure mm Hg	Na+ mEq/L	Cl- mEq/L	H2O g/L	Protein g/L	Reference
(A)	(B)	(C)	(D)	(E)	(F)	(G)	(H)	(I)	(J)	(K)	(L)	(M)
Mammals[1]												
1 Man, adult male	37	A	7.39 (7.33-7.45)[b]	9.0	45	27.0 (25-29)[b]	42 (36-47)[b]	138 (132-144)[b]	102 (97-108)[b]	940	68	B-D,G-J,2;E,K,L,16
2 Cat	38.6	M	7.35 (7.24-7.40)			20.4 (17-24)[b]	36	153 (150-156)[b]	120 (117-123)[b]	941		B,17;C-K,39
3 Anesthetized	38.6	V	7.28 (7.18-7.35)	6.8	40	21.8 (19-25)	45 (34-52)		108 (105-111)	942	76	B,17;C,D,G-K,37;E,F,L,2
4 Cow	38.5	A	(7.35-7.50)[2]	7.0	40					930	83	B,C,17;D,28;E,F,L,2;K,31
5 Dog	38.9	A	7.36 (7.31-7.42)	9.0	46	21.4 (17-24)	38	147 (140-154)[b]	114 (108-119)[b]	941	67	B,15;C,D,G,H,4,15,21;E,F,L,2;I-K,30
6 Dolphin		H	7.38		44	30.9		153 (149-155)	110 (105-115)		78	18
7 Guinea pig	38.6	H; A	7.35 (7.17-7.55)	8.7	42	22.0 (16-26)[3]	40 (19-59)	141 (138-144)	104 (100-108)	954	47	B-D,G,H,23;E,F,L,2;I,J,25;K,31
8 Hamster Anesthetized	38	H; V	7.39 (7.37-7.44)	8.4	46	37.3 (35-39)	59 (54-61)	144 (140-151)	106 (103-108)	945		B-D,G,H,29;E,F,2;I,J,25;K,31
9 Hibernating	5	H; V	7.44 (7.34-7.56)			42.4 (35-50)	32 (26-42)					29
10 Horse	37.8	V	(7.20-7.55)	6.8	33	28.1 (24-32)	47	135	96	931	68	B-D,17;E,F,L,2;G,26;H,31;I-K,35
11 Rabbit	39.4	A	7.35 (7.21-7.57)	7.2		22.8 (13-33)[3]	40 (22-51)	140 (139-142)	102 (99-105)	944		B,C,17,23;D,G,H,23,40;E,F,I,J,40;K,31
12	39.6	H; A	7.32 (7.30-7.36)		42	18.0 (11-26)[3]	33 (20-48)	138 (122-144)	104 (84-110)		62	5
13 Rat[4]	38.2	A	7.35 (7.26-7.44)[b]	9.0	46	24.0 (20-28)[b]	42	144 (135-155)[b]	104 (99-112)[b]	946	60	B,23;C,D,G-J,6,7;E,F,L,2;K,7
14	38.0	A	7.38 (7.31-7.45)[b]			20.8 (14-28)[b]	34	135 (130-140)[b]	102 (97-107)[b]			33
15 Sheep	39.1	V	7.44 (7.32-7.54)	7.6	32	26.2 (21-28)	38	153 (146-161)	103 (98-109)	947	57	B,17;C,D,G-J,10;E,F,L,2;K,31
16 Squirrel, ground	38	H	7.43 (7.38-7.52)		53	20.5 (18-23)[5]						34
17 Hibernating	10	H	7.10 (7.01-7.20)		58	38.6 (33-40)[5]						

/1/ Homoiothermic body temperature relatively independent of environmental temperature except in hibernating animals. /2/ Venous blood. /3/ Calculated from whole blood CO_2 content, pH, and hemoglobin, by means of nomogram of Singer and Hastings [32]. /4/ The rat sometimes varies significantly in acid-base balance from one laboratory series to another. /5/ Values for whole blood.

75. ACID-BASE VALUES: VERTEBRATES (Continued)

	Animal	Body Temp. °C	Blood	Whole Blood pH	Erythrocytes Hb mM/L	Vol %	Plasma CO_2 Content mM/L	CO_2 Pressure mm Hg	Na^+ mEq/L	Cl^- mEq/L	H_2O g/L	Protein g/L	Reference
	(A)	(B)	(C)	(D)	(E)	(F)	(G)	(H)	(I)	(J)	(K)	(L)	(M)
	Birds[1]												
18	Chicken	41.7	V	7.54 (7.45-7.63)	6.8	32	23.0 (21-26)	26	154 (148-161)	117 (109-120)	960	36	B,C,17;D,27; E,F,L,2; G,1;H,K, 31;I,J,25
	Reptiles[6]												
19	Alligator[7]	5	H; M	7.74	4.2	25	36.1	15		110	958	41	B-J,L,13;K, 31
20		26	H; M	7.30 (6.87-7.66)	4.3	22	23.5 (15-40)	38	154 (146-162)	107 (83-128)	952	50	B-J,L,8;K,31
21		34	H; M	7.43	5.4		19.8	29		105	954	46	B-J,L,13;K, 31
22	Chameleon	26	H; M	7.26 (6.93-7.63)	4.2	28	15.4 (10-22)	27	157 (139-186)	127 (113-133)	958	41	B-J,L,11;K, 31
23	Iguana Black	26	H; M	7.22 (7.05-7.42)	3.6	35	14.5 (10-22)	28	159 (158-163)	133 (128-137)	940	68	B-J,L,24;K, 31
24	Common	26	H; M	7.48 (7.38-7.57)	4.2	30	24.4 (15-33)	27	157 (142-165)	118 (110-124)	952	50	
25	Snake	26	H	7.25 (7.12-7.50)		28	6.6 (3-16)		156 (143-169)	130 (122-143)		42	12
26	Turtle	26	H	7.65 (7.50-8.10)		25	24.4 (18-32)		125 (114-135)	92 (80-100)			38
	Fishes[6]												
27	Carp	20	H; V	7.39 (7.33-7.45)	6.4	31	17.7 (14-22)	22	130 (126-137)	107 (96-121)	957	42	B,C,H,K,31; D,G,3;E,F, I,L,20;J,36
28		15	V			39	13.5[5]	8.5[5]		147	951		19
29	Skate	10.4	A	7.82	2.7	20	3.5	1.3	254 (219-289)	255 (230-285)	967	27	B-H,L,14;I, J,22;K,31
30	Trout	15	V			35	9.5[5]	9.0[5]		140	955		19

/1/ Homoiothermic body temperature relatively independent of environmental temperature except in hibernating animals. /5/ Values for whole blood. /6/ Poikilothermic body temperature dependent on environmental tempera- ture. When temperature is decreased, pH and CO_2 solubility coefficient increase, and the O_2 dissociation curve is shifted to the left. /7/ The alligator shows a marked variation among individuals and in the same individual at different seasons, and a prolonged and extreme "alkaline tide" following meals [9].

Contributors: (a) Singer, Richard B., (b) Irvin, J. Logan, (c) Hernandez, Thomas

References: [1] Ackerson, C. W., M. J. Blish, and F. E. Mussehl. 1925. J. Biol. Chem. 63:75. [2] Albritton, E. C., ed. 1952. Standard values in blood. W. B. Saunders, Philadelphia. [3] Auvergnat, R., and M. Lecondat. 1942. C. rend. Acad. sc. 215:92. [4] Bennett, M. A. 1926. J. Biol. Chem. 69:675. [5] Cole, W. H., J. B. Allison, T. J. Murray, A. A. Boyden, J. A. Anderson, and J. H. Leathem. 1944. Am. J. Physiol. 141:165. [6] Cooke, R. E., F. R. Coughlin, Jr., and W. E. Segar. 1952. J. Clin. Invest. 31:1006. [7] Cotlove, E., M. A. Holiday, R. Schwartz, and W. M. Wallace. 1951. Am. J. Physiol. 167:665. [8] Coulson, R. A., T. Hernandez, and F. G. Brazda. 1950. Proc. Soc. Exp. Biol., N. Y. 73:203. [9] Coulson, R. A., T. Hernandez, and H. C. Dessauer. 1950. Ibid. 74:866. [10] Denton, D. A., W. Wynn, I. R. McDonald, and S. Simon. 1951. Acta med. scand., v. 140, suppl. 261. [11] Dessauer, H. C. 1952. Proc. Soc. Exp. Biol., N. Y. 80:742. [12] Dessauer, H. C., and W. Fox. Unpublished. [13] Dill, D. B., and H. T. Edwards. 1935. J. Cellul. Physiol. 6:243. [14] Dill, D. B., H. T. Edwards, and M. Florkin. 1932. Biol. Bull. 62:23. [15] Dill, D. B., H. T. Edwards, M. Florkin, and R. W. Campbell. 1932.

J. Biol. Chem. 95:143. [16] Dill, D. B., J. W. Wilson, F. G. Hall, and S. Robinson. 1940. Ibid. 136:449. [17] Dukes, H. H. 1947. The physiology of domestic animals. Ed. 6. Comstock, Ithaca. [18] Eichelberger, L., E. S. Fletcher, Jr., E. M. Geiling, and B. J. Vos, Jr. 1940. J. Biol. Chem. 133:145. [19] Ferguson, J. K., and E. C. Black. 1941. Biol. Bull. 80:139. [20] Field, J. B., C. A. Elvehjem, and C. Juday. 1943. J. Biol. Chem. 148:261. [21] Harkins, H. N., and A. B. Hastings. 1931. Ibid. 90:565. [22] Hartman, F. A., L. A. Lewis, K. A. Brownell, F. F. Shelden, and R. F. Walther. 1941. Physiol. Zool. 14:476. [23] Hawkins, J. A. 1924. J. Biol. Chem. 61:147. [24] Hernandez, T., and R. A. Coulson. 1951. Proc. Soc. Exp. Biol., N. Y. 76:175. [25] Hernandez, T., and R. A. Coulson. Unpublished. [26] Ijichi, N. 1922. J. Jap. Soc. Vet. Sc. 1:76. [27] Johnson, E. P., and W. B. Bell. 1936. J. Infect. Dis. 58:342. [28] Krapf, W. 1940. Jahrber. Vet. Med. 67:326. [29] Lyman, C. P., and A. B. Hastings. 1951. Am. J. Physiol. 167:633. [30] Mellors, R. C., E. M. E. Muntwyler, and F. R. Mantz. 1942. J. Biol. Chem. 144:773. [31] Singer, R. B. Unpublished. [32] Singer, R. B., and A. B. Hastings. 1948. Medicine, Balt. 27:223. [33] Smith, P. K., and A. H. Smith. 1934. J. Biol. Chem. 107:673. [34] Stormont, R. T., M. A. Foster, and C. Pfeiffer. 1939. Proc. Soc. Exp. Biol., N.Y. 42:56. [35] Van Slyke, D. D., A. B. Hastings, C. D. Murray, and J. Sendroy, Jr. 1925. J. Biol. Chem. 65:701. [36] Vars, H. M. 1934. Ibid. 105:135. [37] Wallace, W. M., and A. B. Hastings. 1942. Ibid. 144:637. [38] Williams, J. K. Unpublished. [39] Yannet, H. 1940. J. Biol. Chem. 136:265. [40] Young, I. M. 1952. Am. J. Physiol. 170:434.

76. CLASSIFICATION OF ACID-BASE DISTURBANCES: MAN

Ranges for acid-base variables, as reported in the literature or inferred from related observations, are for adult arterial or cutaneous blood. See also normal values (Table 74, Parts I and II) and Acid-Base Pathways (Table 78). Limits given are approximate. Underlined designation = the best index for existence of the particular condition.

Condition	Buffer Base[1] mEq/L	CO_2 Pressure mm Hg	Bicarbonate[2] mEq/L	pH at 37°C
(A)	(B)	(C)	(D)	(E)
1 Normal (arterial or cutaneous blood)	46-52	35-45	24-28	7.35-7.45
2 Metabolic acidosis (acid excess or base deficit)	Always low 20-46	Usually low 15-35	Usually low 4-24	Usually low 6.8-7.35
3 Respiratory acidosis (H_2CO_3 excess)	Normal or high 46-70	Always high 45-100+	Usually high 28-45	Usually low 7.0-7.35
4 Metabolic alkalosis (base excess or acid deficit)	Always high 52-75	Normal or high 35-55	Usually high 28-50	Usually high 7.45-7.65
5 Respiratory alkalosis (H_2CO_3 deficit)	Normal or low 40-52	Always low 10-35	Usually low 15-24	Usually high 7.45-7.70
6 Mixed acidosis (combination lines 2 and 3)	Always low 25-45	Always high 45-100	Variable 10-35	Always low 6.8-7.35
7 Mixed alkalosis (combination lines 4 and 5)	Always high 52-70	Always low 15-35	Variable 20-45	Always high 7.5-7.7
8 Mixed hypercapnia (combination of lines 3 and 4)	Always high 52-75	Always high 45-100	Always high 30-50	Variable 7.3-7.6
9 Mixed hypocapnia (combination of lines 2 and 5)	Always low 20-46	Always low 10-35	Always low 4-22	Variable 7.0-7.6

/1/ Buffer base for whole blood of normal hemoglobin concentration = 15 g/100 ml. A decrease in buffer base of whole blood is almost always accompanied by a decrease in plasma or extracellular Na^+ relative to Cl^- + X^-, e.g., decrease in plasma Na^+, increase in plasma Cl^- or plasma X^-, or any appropriate combination. An increase in buffer base of whole blood is accompanied by an increase in Na^+ relative to Cl^- + X^-, e.g., increase in plasma Na^+, decrease in plasma Cl^-, or any appropriate combination. See normal values in diagram on facing page. /2/ Comprises about 90-98% of total carbon dioxide in plasma; average, 95%.

Contributor: Singer, Richard B.

References: [1] Peters, J. P., and D. D. Van Slyke. 1931. Quantitative clinical chemistry. Ed. 1. Williams and Wilkins, Baltimore. v. 1. [2] Singer, R. B., and A. B. Hastings. 1948. Medicine, Balt. 27:223.

Diagram is included for use in conjunction with classification of acid-base disturbances (Table 76 on facing page). Values shown are for adult male, based on the literature. X^- = undetermined anion residue. "HbO_2" includes such other erythrocyte buffer anions as organic phosphate. B^+ = mEq total cation (Na^+, K^+, etc.) in 1 liter of blood, on the basis of a hematocrit value of 45%. Buffer base = the appropriate fraction of total cation and its equivalent amount, the labile fraction of total anions, i.e., proteinate, bicarbonate, oxyhemoglobinate, organic phosphate, and other erythrocyte buffer anions. CO_2 partial pressure or tension for plasma, erythrocytes, or whole blood = 41 mm Hg.

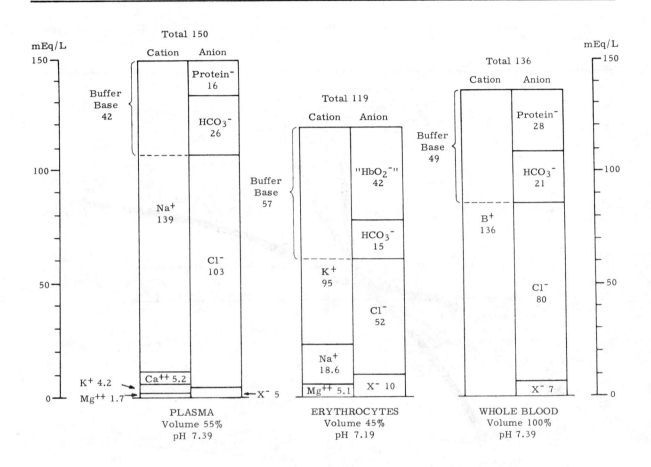

Contributor. Singer, Richard B.

78. PATHWAYS OF ACID-BASE DISTURBANCE: MAN

Any point on this acid-base diagram [3] gives simultaneously occurring values for four variables: (1) whole blood buffer base $(BB)_b$, the metabolic factor in the disturbance; (2) CO_2 pressure, the respiratory factor; (3) plasma CO_2 content; and (4) pH. The scale of $(BB)_b$ is strictly accurate only for oxygenated human blood at 37^oC, with a hematocrit value of 45% or hemoglobin concentration of 15 g/100 ml. The width of the buffer base bar corresponds to the "normal" range of arterial CO_2 pressure selected, namely, 35-45 mm Hg. Similarly, the width of the CO_2 pressure bar is the normal range for $(BB)_b$, from 46-52 mEq/L. The heavy arrows represent typical average pathways of the four principal types of acid-base disturbance (Table 76). They are based on observations of the contributor and colleagues [3-6], but are representative of similar clinical data in the literature. In metabolic acidosis, respiratory compensation is almost always present [4]; in metabolic alkalosis, respiratory compensation is frequently absent, especially under clinical conditions [5, 6]. In acute, experimental respiratory disturbances, the pathways are in the horizontal CO_2 pressure bar, with virtually no change in $(BB)_b$ [2]. The four mixed types of acid-base disturbance are not shown in the diagram, but the possible areas may be located from the classification in Table 76. Examples of these disturbances: mixed acidosis in thoracic surgery under ether anesthesia [1], mixed alkalosis in many dyspneic patients with congestive heart failure [7], mixed hypercapnia in some cases of cor pulmonale [5], and mixed hypocapnia in severe salicylate intoxication [4].

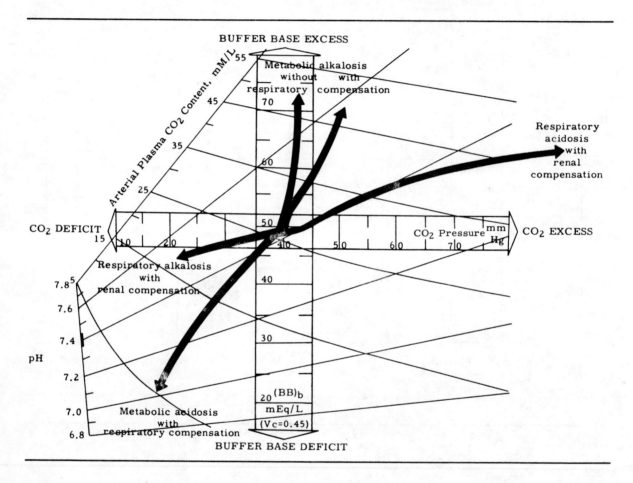

Contributor: Singer, Richard B.

References: [1] Beecher, H. K., and A. J. Murphy. 1950. J. Thorac. Surg. 19:50. [2] Shock, N. W., and A. B. Hastings. 1935. J. Biol. Chem. 112:239. [3] Singer, R. B. 1951. Am. J. M. Sc. 221:199. [4] Singer, R. B. 1954. Medicine, Balt. 33:1. [5] Singer, R. B. Unpublished. [6] Singer, R. B., R. C. Deering, and J. K. Clark. 1956. J. Clin. Invest. 35:245. [7] Squires, R. D., R. B. Singer, G. R. Moffit, Jr., and J. R. Elkinton. 1951. Circulation, N. Y. 4:697.

X. Blood Changes

79. EFFECT OF ALTITUDE ON BLOOD VALUES: MAN

Part I: ERYTHROCYTE COUNTS AND HEMOGLOBIN VALUES

All subjects were residents of the given locale. Values in parentheses are ranges, estimate "b" or "c" as indicated (cf. Introduction).

Altitude m	Country	Place	No. of Subjects	Erythrocyte Count million/cu mm blood	Blood Hemoglobin Concentration g/100 ml blood	Mean Corpuscular Hemoglobin[1] μμg	Reference
(A)	(B)	(C)	(D)	(E)	(F)	(G)	(H)
<395	United States	Kansas	350♂	5.11	15.0	29.4	19
		Kansas City	100♂	4.84	15.1	31.2	28
		New Orleans	115♂	5.26	15.6	29.7	7
			100♂	5.85	15.9	27.2	29
		Omaha	100♂	4.69	15.0	32.0	23
		Portland, Ore.	259♂	5.42	15.8	29.2	20
	Argentina	Buenos Aires	50♂	5.50	15.4	28.0	21
			50♂	5.30	14.8	27.9	26
	Denmark	Copenhagen	60♂	5.07	15.0	29.6	2
	Germany	Giessen	40♂	4.96	16.0	32.3	11
		Jena	52♂	5.06	16.0	31.6	10
	Hawaii	Honolulu	137♂	5.08	15.1	29.7	9
	India	Bombay	121♂	5.11	15.4	30.1	24
		Calcutta	50♂	5.36	14.8	27.6	18
	Norway	Oslo	50♂	5.52	16.2	29.3	15
	Peru	Lima	100♂	5.26	15.7	29.8	14
			175♂	5.14(4.46-5.82)[b]	16.0(14.4-17.6)[b]	31.1	13
			14♂	5.00(4.5-5.6)[c]	15.1(13.4-16.2)[c]	30.2	12
395	Argentina	Tucumán	153♂	5.31	16.1	30.3	17
500	Canada	Saskatchewan	20♂	5.52	15.6	28.3	6
	Switzerland	Zurich	139♂	5.00	15.0	30.0	3,4
1524	United States	Denver	40♂	5.42(4.83-6.07)[c]	16.5(15.0-18.3)[c]	30.4	1
			40♀	4.63(4.41-5.00)[c]	14.5(12.7-15.7)[c]	31.1	
1768	South Africa	Johannesburg	60♂	5.99	14.7	24.5	16
1830-1890	India	Coonoor and Wellington	80♂	5.33(3.95-6.04)[c]	15.9(13.1-20.3)[c]	29.8	22
2300	India	Ootacamund	20♂	5.38(4.75-6.02)[c]	15.8(14.8-16.8)[c]	29.4	22
	Mexico	Mexico City	23♂[2], 21♀[2]	5.26(4.37-6.14)[b]	14.2(13.1-15.3)[b]	27.0	27
			100♂	5.38(4.53-6.17)[c]	17.7(14.4-20.1)[c]	32.9	8
			100♀	5.01(4.27-6.01)[c]	15.2(12.8-17.7)[c]	30.3	
3730	Peru	Oroya	40♂	5.67(4.89-6.45)[b]	18.8(15.9-21.7)[b]	33.2	13
4540	Argentina	Mina Aguilar	81♂	6.46(5.07-9.43)[c]	19.4(15.7-24.9)[c]	30.0	5
	Peru	Morococha	32♂	6.15(5.01-7.29)[b]	20.8(17.3-24.2)[b]	33.8	13
			11♂	6.70(5.30-9.30)[c]	19.3(17.4-24.0)[c]	28.8	12
5340	Chile	Quilchua	6♂	7.37	22.6	30.7	25

/1/ $\dfrac{\text{Hemoglobin}}{\text{Erythrocytes}}$ x 10. /2/ Ages 4-6 years.

Contributors; (a) Dill, D. B., (b) Ebaugh, Franklin G., Jr., (c) Marbarger, John P.

References: [1] Andresen, M. I., and E. R. Mugrage. 1936. Arch. Int. M. 58:136. [2] Bierring, E., and G. Sørensen. 1936. Ugeskr. laeger 98:822. [3] Burgi, K. 1933. Schweiz. med. Wschr. 63:662. [4] Burgi, K. 1933. Ibid. 63:685. [5] Chiodi, H. 1950. J. Appl. Physiol. 2:431. [6] Fiddes, J., and C. Witney. 1936. Canad. M. Ass. J. 35:654. [7] Foster, F. C., and J. R. Johnson. 1931. Proc. Soc. Exp. Biol., N. Y. 28:929. [8] Gill, J. R., and D. G. Terán. 1948. Blood, N. Y. 3:660. [9] Hamre, C. J., and M. H. Au. 1942. J. Laborat. Clin. M. 27:1231. [10] Heilmeyer, L., and L. Hansold. 1936. Deut. Arch. klin. Med. 179:94. [11] Horneffer, L. 1928. Pflügers Arch. 220:703. [12] Huff, R. G., J. H. Lawrence, W. E. Sini, L. R. Wasserman, and T. G. Hennessy. 1951.

Medicine, Balt. 30:197. [13] Hurtado, A., C. Merino, and E. Delgado. 1945. Arch. Int. M. 75:284. [14] Hurtado, A., M. J. Pons, and C. Merino. 1938. La anemia de la enfermedad de carrión. Librerie e Imprenta Gil., Lima, Peru. [15] Jervell, O., and J. H. M. Waaler. 1934. Norsk mag. laegevid. 95:1141. [16] Liknaitzky, I. 1934. Q. J. Exp. Physiol., Lond. 24:161. [17] Moglia, J. L., and O. A. Fonio. 1944. Rev. Soc. argent. biol. 20:581. [18] Napier, L. E., and C. R. Das Gupta. 1935. Ind. J. M. Res. 23:305. [19] Nelson, C. F., and R. Stoker. 1937. Fol. haemat., Lpz. 58:333. [20] Osgood, E. E. 1935. Arch. Int. M. 56:849. [21] Parodi, A. S. 1930. Rev. Soc. argent. biol. 6:426. [22] Ramalingaswami, V., and P. S. Venkatachalam. 1950. Ind. J. M. Res. 38:17. [23] Sachs, A., V. E. Levine, and A. A. Fabian. 1935. Arch. Int. M. 55:226. [24] Sokhey, S. S., S. K. Gokhale, M. A. Malandkar, and H. S. Billimoria. 1937. Ind. J. M. Res. 25:505. [25] Talbott, J. H., and D. B. Dill. 1936. Am. J. M. Sc. 192:626. [26] Tenconi, J. 1931. C. rend. Soc. biol. 108:133. [27] Vázquez, J., R. Soto, O. Castrejón, and S. Dorantes. 1958. Bol. méd. Hosp. inf., Méx. 15:53. [28] Walters, O. S. 1934. J. Laborat. Clin. M. 19:851. [29] Wintrobe, M. M., and M. W. Miller. 1929. Arch. Int. M. 43:96.

Part II: HEMATOCRIT VALUES

All subjects were residents of the given locale. Values in parentheses are ranges, estimate "c" unless otherwise indicated (cf. Introduction).

	Altitude m	Country	Place	No. of Subjects	Hematocrit ml RBC/100 ml blood	Reference
	(A)	(B)	(C)	(D)	(E)	(F)
1	<395	Peru	Lima	14♂	45.0(40.0-49.0)	4
2				20♂	46.0(42.5-50.0)	6
3				15♀	39.8(26.0-41.0)	
4	1524	United States	Denver	40♂	48.4(43.8-53.6)	1
5				40♀	43.2(37.1-46.1)	
6	1830-1890	India	Coonoor and Wellington	80♂	49.0(38.0-65.0)	7
7	2300	India	Ootacamund	20♂	49.4(46.0-53.0)	7
8		Mexico	Mexico City	23♂[1], 21♀[1]	43.0(37.5-49.0)	8
9				100♂	51.2(45.0-58.5)	3
10				100♀	45.5(41.5-50.0)	
11	3730	Peru	Oroya	40♂	54.1(47.8-65.4)	5
12	4540	Argentina	Mina Aguilar	81	59.5(50.5-73.6)	2
13		Peru	Morococha	32	59.9(48.7-71.1)[b]	5
14				11	57.0(46.0-71.0)	4

/1/ Ages 4-6 years.

Contributors: (a) Ebaugh, Franklin G., Jr., (b) Marbarger, John P.

References: [1] Andresen, M. I., and E. R. Mugrage. 1936. Arch. Int. M. 58:136. [2] Chiodi, H. 1950. J. Appl. Physiol. 2:431. [3] Gill, J. R., and D. G. Terán. 1948. Blood, N. Y. 3:660. [4] Huff, R. G., J. H. Lawrence, W. E. Sini, L. R. Wasserman, and T. G. Hennessy. 1951. Medicine, Balt. 30:197. [5] Hurtado, A., C. Merino, and E. Delgado. 1945. Arch. Int. M. 75:284. [6] Monge, C. C., T. Cazorla, G. M. Whittenberry, B. Y. Sakota, and C. Razo-Patron. 1955. Acta physiol. lat. amer. 5:198. [7] Ramalingaswami, V., and P. S. Venkatachalam. 1950. Ind. J. M. Res. 38:17. [8] Vázquez, J., R. Soto, O. Castrejón, and S. Dorantes. 1958. Bol. méd. Hosp. inf., Méx. 15:53.

79. EFFECT OF ALTITUDE ON BLOOD VALUES: MAN (Concluded)

Part III: LEUKOCYTE COUNT

Values in parentheses are ranges, estimate "c" (cf. Introduction).

	Altitude m	Subject	Specification	Leukocytes thousands/cu mm	Reference
	(A)	(B)	(C)	(D)	(E)
1	Ground level	Resident		5.88	3
2	1830-2300	Resident		7.29(3.20-11.40)	5
3	2300	Resident	Ages 4-6 yr	7.88(4.33-15.05)	6
4	2400	Non-resident	On arrival	6.84	3
5	3140	Non-resident	On arrival	7.73	3
6	3475	Non-resident	7 da exposure	(11.30-12.70)	1
7	3730	Resident		6.50(3.40-9.60)	3
8	4175	Non-resident	On arrival	8.24	3
9	4510	Resident		6.74(4.10-12.10)	2
10	4540	Resident		6.90(4.70-10.90)	4
11		Non-resident	On arrival	6.51	3
12		Non-resident	1 da exposure	9.63	3
13		Non-resident	2 da exposure	7.16	3
14		Non-resident	3 da exposure	6.23	3
15		Non-resident	4 da exposure	5.91	3
16		Non-resident	5 da exposure	6.62	3
17		Non-resident	6 da exposure	5.73	3
18		Non-resident	7-21 da exposure	7.13	4
19	4845	Non-resident	On arrival	8.40	3

Contributors: (a) Marbarger, John P., (b) Ebaugh, Franklin G., Jr.

References: [1] Bähler, H. 1936. Schweiz. med. Wschr. 66:460. [2] Chiodi, H. 1950. J. Appl. Physiol. 2:431. [3] Hurtado, A., C. Merino, and E. Delgado. 1945. Arch. Int. M. 75:284. [4] Merino, C. 1950. Blood, N. Y. 5:1. [5] Ramalingaswami, V., and P. S. Venkatachalam. 1950. Ind. J. M. Res. 38:17. [6] Vázquez, J., R. Soto, O. Castrejón, and S. Dorantes. 1958. Bol. méd. Hosp. inf., Méx. 15:53.

Part IV: DIFFERENTIAL CELL COUNT

Values are percent of total leukocytes. Values in parentheses are ranges, estimate "c" (cf. Introduction).

	Altitude m	Subject	Neutrophils		Eosinophils	Basophils	Monocytes	Lymphocytes	Refer- ence
			Band	Segmented					
	(A)	(B)	(C)	(D)	(E)	(F)	(G)	(H)	(I)
1	1830-2300	Resident	46.2		4.4	0.14	3.1	45.5	3
2	2300	Resident[1]	1.8(0-6)	45.0(25-68)	6.9(2-18)	0.53(0-1.75)	5.6(1-11)	38.7(16-64)	4
3	2400	Non-resident[2]	1.8	57.3	4.8	0.4	5.4	30.3	2
4	3140	Non-resident[2]	2.1	61.9	2.4	0.8	4.8	28.0	2
5	3730	Resident	5.0	52.8(32-79)	2.5(0-10)	0.1(0-3)	4.9(0-9)	34.8(11-54)	2
6	4175	Non-resident[2]	1.8	57.1	4.6	0.5	6.8	30.0	2
7	4510	Resident	6.3(1-16)	44.1(13-69)	2.9(0-14)	0.8(0-3)	10.2(2-33)	35.6(8-55)	1
8	4540	Resident	3.0(0-6)	49.9(25-71)	2.2(0-5)	0.2(0-2)	5.5(1-13)	39.4(21-62)	2
9	4845	Non-resident[2]	2.8	62.0	3.3	0.6	3.1	28.3	2

/1/ Ages 4-6 years. /2/ On arrival.

Contributors: (a) Marbarger, John P., (b) Ebaugh, Franklin G., Jr.

References: [1] Chiodi, H. 1950. J. Appl. Physiol. 2:431. [2] Hurtado, A., C. Merino, and E. Delgado. 1945. Arch. Int. M. 75:284. [3] Ramalingaswami, V., and P. S. Venkatachalam. 1950. Ind. J. M. Res. 38:17. [4] Vázquez, J., R. Soto, O. Castrejón, and S. Dorantes. 1958. Bol. méd. Hosp. inf., Méx. 15:53.

80. EFFECT OF ALTITUDE ON BLOOD VALUES: VERTEBRATES OTHER THAN MAN

Values are for acclimatized animals.

Animal	Altitude m	Erythrocyte Count million/cu mm blood	Hematocrit ml RBC/100 ml blood	O₂ Capacity vol %	
				Blood	Erythrocytes
(A)	(B)	(C)	(D)	(E)	(F)
1 Llama	Sea level	11.4	38.6	23.5	60.9
2	2800	12.3	28.2	17.1	60.6
3	5300	11.0	25.8	14.9	57.8
4 Rabbit	Sea level	4.55	35.4	15.6	44.1
5 Sheep	Sea level	10.5	35.3	15.9	45.5
6	4700	12.05	50.2	18.9	37.6
7 Vicuña	4700	16.6	31.9	18.2	57.3
8 Viscacha	3700	7.12	31.8	14.8	46.6
9 Huallata	5300	3.27	59.1	23.6	40.1
10 Ostrich	3700	2.18	33.8	13.9	41.2

Contributor: Dill, D. B.

References: [1] Hall, F. G., D. B. Dill, and E. S. Barron. 1936. J. Cellul. Physiol. 8:301. [2] Prosser, C. L. 1950. Comparative animal physiology. W. B. Saunders, Philadelphia.

81. EFFECT OF ALTITUDE ON ARTERIAL BLOOD GASES: MAN

Part I: SIMULATED ALTITUDE

Subjects were adult males and females, resting during ascent to altitude. Method: T = tonometric analysis; Cal = calculated from observed saturation value and assumed O₂ capacity of 21.5 ml/100 ml blood (assumed O₂ capacity based on uniform, assumed hemoglobin content of 15.8 g/100 ml, where 15.8 g hemoglobin/100 ml blood x 1.36 = ml oxygen); VS = Van Slyke and spectrophotometric analyses; OR, 96-97 = oximeter readings, ground level setting of 96-97% saturation; OR, 100 = oximeter readings, ground level setting of 100% saturation; VM = Van Slyke mano-metric analysis; HB = arterial pressure from Hill-Barcroft formula; CC = $\dfrac{O_2\ \text{content - free } O_2}{O_2\ \text{capacity}}$; PA = arterial pressure assumed equal to alveolar pressure of alveolar samples; DC = determinations from CO₂ dissociation curves; V = Van Slyke analysis; HP = arterial pressure assumed equal to alveolar pressure, as determined by Haldane-Priestly method. Values in parentheses are ranges, estimate "b" (cf. Introduction).

	Altitude m	mm Hg[1]	No. of Subjects	Method	Variable	Value	Reference
	(A)	(B)	(C)	(D)	(E)	(F)	(G)
						Oxygen	
1	Sea level	760	>21	T	Pressure	96 mm Hg	3, 9, 14
2				Cal	Content	21.2 ml/100 ml blood	
3			51	VS	Saturation	98%	4, 10, 17
4	1524	632			Pressure	66 mm Hg	2
5				Cal	Content	19.6 ml/100 ml blood	
6			10	OR, 96-97	Saturation	91(87-95) %	12
7	2458	564			Pressure	60 mm Hg	2
8				Cal	Content	19.1 ml/100 ml blood	
9			10	OR, 96-97	Saturation	89(84.5-93.5) %	12
10	3048	523			Pressure	53 mm Hg	2
11				Cal	Content	18.4 ml/100 ml blood	
12			16	OR, 96-97	Saturation	85.4(79-92) %	12
13	3658	483			Pressure	52 mm Hg	2
14				Cal	Content	18.3 ml/100 ml blood	
15			11	OR, 96-97	Saturation	84.9(77-92.5) %	12

/1/ U. S. Standard Atmosphere.

Part I: SIMULATED ALTITUDE (Continued)

	Altitude		No. of Subjects	Method	Variable	Value	Reference
	m	mm Hg[1]					
	(A)	(B)	(C)	(D)	(E)	(F)	(G)
					Oxygen (concluded)		
16	4267	446			Pressure	44 mm Hg	2
17				Cal	Content	17.0 ml/100 ml blood	
18			17	OR, 96-97	Saturation	79.2(71-87.5) %	12
19	4877	412			Pressure	41 mm Hg	2
20				Cal	Content	16.4 ml/100 ml blood	
21			17	OR, 96-97	Saturation	76.2(65-87.5) %	12
22	5486	379			Pressure	36 mm Hg	2
23				Cal	Content	15.3 ml/100 ml blood	
24			13	OR, 96-97	Saturation	71.2(57-85.5) %	12
25	6069	349			Pressure	35 mm Hg	2
26				Cal	Content	15.2 ml/100 ml blood	
27			9	OR, 96-97	Saturation	70.8(57.5-84) %	12
28	10,668	179		Cal	Content	19.8 ml/100 ml blood	12
29			22	OR, 100	Saturation	92(84-100) %	
30	11,430	159	3		Pressure	74 mm Hg	6
31			4	Cal	Content	20.2 ml/100 ml blood	
32					Saturation	94%	
33	11,979	146	5	VM, HB	Pressure	57 mm Hg	1
34				Cal	Content	19.1 ml/100 ml blood	
35				VM, CC	Saturation	88.7%	
36	12,192	141	8		Pressure	55 mm Hg	6
37				Cal	Content	18.9 ml/100 ml blood	
38					Saturation	88.1(81-95) %	
39	12,497	134	3		Pressure	54 mm Hg	6
40				Cal	Content	18.6 ml/100 ml blood	
41					Saturation	86.4(85-88) %	
42	12,802	128	3		Pressure	49 mm Hg	6
43				Cal	Content	17.8 ml/100 ml blood	
44					Saturation	83(71-95) %	
45	13,106	122	2		Pressure	42 mm Hg	6
46			4	Cal	Content	16.9 ml/100 ml blood	
47			4		Saturation	78.5(65-92) %	
48	13,411	116	3		Pressure	36 mm Hg	6
49				Cal	Content	15.5 ml/100 ml blood	
50					Saturation	72.2(58-86) %	
51	13,716	111		Cal	Content	14.6 ml/100 ml blood	2
52					Saturation	68(53-83) %	
					Carbon Dioxide		
53	Sea level	760	341	T, PA, DC	Pressure	43 mm Hg	5, 7, 8, 11, 13-15
54			226	V, DC	Content	49 ml/100 ml blood	5, 7, 8, 13, 16, 17
55	1524	632	62[2]	HP	Pressure[3]	36.5 mm Hg	2
56	2458	564	10[2]	HP	Pressure[3]	37.4 mm Hg	2
57	3048	523	92[2]	HP	Pressure[3]	35.8 mm Hg	2
58	3658	483	61[2]	HP	Pressure[3]	34.8 mm Hg	2
59	4267	446	26[2]	HP	Pressure[3]	35.4 mm Hg	2
60	4877	412	9[2]	HP	Pressure[3]	33.8 mm Hg	2
61	5486	379	55[2]	HP	Pressure[3]	31.8 mm Hg	2
62	6069	349	81[2]	HP	Pressure[3]	29.4 mm Hg	2
63	11,430	159	3		Pressure	40.6 mm Hg	6
64					Content	46.3 ml/100 ml blood	
65	11,979	146	5	VM, DC	Pressure	39.4 mm Hg	1
66				VM	Content	50.0 ml/100 ml blood	
67	12,192	141	8		Pressure	35(26-44) mm Hg	6
68					Content	42.7(35-50) ml/100 ml blood	
69	12,497	134	3		Pressure	38.1 mm Hg	6
70					Content	44.8 ml/100 ml blood	

/1/ U. S. Standard Atmosphere.   /2/ Acclimatized to 305 meters.   /3/ Alveolar pressure.

Part I: SIMULATED ALTITUDE (Concluded)

	Altitude		No. of Subjects	Method	Variable	Value	Reference
	m	mm Hg[1]					
	(A)	(B)	(C)	(D)	(E)	(F)	(G)
				Carbon Dioxide (concluded)			
71	12,802	128	3		Pressure	40(36-44) mm Hg	6
72					Content	47.1(45-50) ml/100 ml blood	
73	13,106	122	3		Content	41.5(31-52) ml/100 ml blood	6
74	13,411	116	3		Pressure	33.2 mm Hg	6
75					Content	44.9 ml/100 ml blood	

/1/ U. S. Standard Atmosphere

Contributors: (a) Adler, Harry F., (b) Luft, Ulrich C., (c) Penrod, Kenneth E., (d) Stickney, J. Clifford

References: [1] Barach, A. L., M. Eckman, J. Eckman, E. Ginsburg, and C. C. Rumsey, Jr. 1947. J. Aviat. M. 18:139. [2] Committee on Aviation Medicine. 1944. Handbook of respiratory data in aviation. National Research Council, Washington, D. C. Charts A-1, B-1, B-3. [3] Comroe, J. H., Jr., and R. D. Dripps, Jr. 1944. Am. J. Physiol. 142:700. [4] Comroe, J. H., Jr., and P. Walker. 1948. Ibid. 152:365. [5] Dill, D. B., H. T. Edwards, and W. V. Consolazio. 1937. J. Biol. Chem. 118:635. [6] Dill, D. B., and F. G. Hall. 1942. J. Aeronaut. Sc. 9:220. [7] Dill, D. B., C. van Caulaert, L. M. Hurxthal, J. L. Stoddard, A. V. Bock, and L. J. Henderson. 1927. J. Biol. Chem. 73:251. [8] Dill, D. B., J. W. Wilson, F. J. Hall, and S. Robinson. 1940. Ibid. 136:449. [9] Drabkin, D. L. In F. J. W. Roughton and J. C. Kendrew, ed. 1949. Haemoglobin (symposium). Barcroft Mem. Conf., Cambridge, 1948. Interscience, New York. p. 35. [10] Drabkin, D. L., and C. F. Schmidt. 1945. J. Biol. Chem. 157:69. [11] Hamilton, J. A., and N. W. Shock. 1936. Am. J. Psychol. 48:467. [12] Henson, M., D. E. Goldman, H. R. Catchpole, E. P. Vollmer, B. G. King, and R. V. Whaley. 1947. J. Aviat. M. 18:149. [13] Hurtado, A., and H. Aste-Salazar. 1948. J. Appl. Physiol. 1:304. [14] Lilienthal, J. L., Jr., R. L. Riley, D. D. Proemmel, and R. E. Franke. 1946. Am. J. Physiol. 147:199. [15] Shock, N. W. 1941. Ibid. 133:610. [16] Shock, N. W., and A. B. Hastings. 1934. J. Biol. Chem. 104:585. [17] Wood, E. H. 1949. J. Appl. Physiol. 1:567.

Part II: INCOMPLETE ACCLIMATIZATION

Ten subjects, ages 29-44, unaccustomed to altitude. Method: DC = derived from O_2 dissociation curve by means of O_2 saturation and pH; VM = Van Slyke manometric analysis; $CC = \dfrac{O_2 \text{ content - free } O_2}{O_2 \text{ capacity}}$; Cal = calculated from Hasselbalch-Henderson equation by measurement of plasma CO_2 content and pH. Values in parentheses are ranges, estimate "c" unless otherwise indicated (cf. Introduction).

	Altitude		Method	Variable	Value	Reference
	m	mm Hg[1]				
	(A)	(B)	(C)	(D)	(E)	(F)
				Oxygen		
1	Sea level	760	DC	Pressure	94 mm Hg	1
2			VM	Content	21.1 ml/100 ml blood	
3			VM	Capacity	21.5 ml/100 ml blood	
4			CC	Saturation	98%	
5	2810	543	DC	Pressure	60(47.4-73.6)[b] mm Hg	3
6			VM	Content	20.0 ml/100 ml blood	
7			VM	Capacity	22.0 ml/100 ml blood	
8			CC	Saturation	91(86.8-95.2)[b] %	

/1/ U. S. Standard Atmosphere.

Part II: INCOMPLETE ACCLIMATIZATION (Concluded)

	Altitude		Method	Variable	Value	Reference
	m	mm Hg[1]				
	(A)	(B)	(C)	(D)	(E)	(F)
			Oxygen (concluded)			
9	3660	489	DC	Pressure	47.6(42.2-53.0) mm Hg	3
10			VM	Content	19.6 ml/100 ml blood	
11			VM	Capacity	23.0 ml/100 ml blood	
12			CC	Saturation	84.5(80.5-89.0) %	
13	4700	429	DC	Pressure	44.6(36.4-47.5) mm Hg	3
14			VM	Content	19.3 ml/100 ml blood	
15			VM	Capacity	24.2 ml/100 ml blood	
16			CC	Saturation	78(70.8-85.0) %	
17	5340	401	DC	Pressure	43.1(37.6-50.4) mm Hg	3
18			VM	Content	18.6 ml/100 ml blood	
19			VM	Capacity	24.4 ml/100 ml blood	
20			CC	Saturation	76.2(65.4-81.6) %	
21	6140	356	DC	Pressure	35(26.9-40.1) mm Hg	3
22			VM	Content	16.4 ml/100 ml blood	
23			VM	Capacity	25.0 ml/100 ml blood	
24			CC	Saturation	65.6(55.5-73.0) %	
			Carbon Dioxide			
25	Sea level	760	Cal	Pressure	41 mm Hg	1
26			VM	Content	49 ml/100 ml blood	
27	2810	543	Cal	Pressure	33.9(31.3-36.5)[b] mm Hg	2
28			VM	Content	42.3(39.3-45.3)[b] ml/100 ml blood	
29	3660	489	Cal	Pressure	29.5(23.5-34.3) mm Hg	2
30			VM	Content	40.7(36.9-44.1) ml/100 ml blood	
31	4700	429	Cal	Pressure	27.1(22.9-34.0) mm Hg	2
32			VM	Content	38.3(34.9-42.5) ml/100 ml blood	
33	5340	401	Cal	Pressure	25.7(21.7-29.7) mm Hg	2
34			VM	Content	35.0(30.9-40.0) ml/100 ml blood	
35	6140	356	Cal	Pressure	22.0(19.2-24.8) mm Hg	2
36			VM	Content	30.2(26.6-33.3) ml/100 ml blood	

/1/ U. S. Standard Atmosphere.

Contributor: Luft, Ulrich C.

References: [1] Committee on Aviation Medicine. 1944. Handbook of respiratory data in aviation. National Research Council, Washington, D. C. Charts A-1, B-1, B-3. [2] Dill, D. B., J. H. Talbott, and W. V. Consolazio. 1937. J. Biol. Chem. 118:649. [3] McFarland, R. A., and D. B. Dill. 1938. J. Aviat. M. 9:1.

Part III: COMPLETE ACCLIMATIZATION

Subjects were adult male residents, resting and fasting. Method: VM = Van Slyke manometric analysis; $CC = \dfrac{O_2 \text{ content - free } O_2}{O_2 \text{ capacity}}$; Cal = calculated from saturation value, serum pH and chart B-3 of reference 2; R = with 2% correction of Roughton, et al [6]; O_2C = calculated from O_2 content and O_2 dissociation curve; DC = determined from dissociation curves; T = tonometric analysis; CO_2C = calculated from CO_2 content and CO_2 dissociation curve. Values in parentheses are ranges, estimate "b" unless otherwise indicated (cf. Introduction).

	Altitude m	mm Hg[1]	No. of Subjects	Method	Variable	Value	Reference
	(A)	(B)	(C)	(D)	(E)	(F)	(G)
					Oxygen		
1	150[2]	746			Pressure	90 mm Hg	2
2					Content	20.7 ml/100 ml blood	
3					Capacity	21.7 ml/100 ml blood	
4					Saturation	95.4%	
5		750	80		Pressure	(95-97)[c] mm Hg	5
6				VM	Content	20.7(17.0-23.5)[c] ml/100 ml blood	
7				VM	Capacity	20.8(17.4-23.6)[c] ml/100 ml blood	
8				CC	Saturation	97.9(95.3-99.7)[c] %	
9	2390	568			Pressure	68 mm Hg	4
10			12	VM	Content	21.2(18.5-24) ml/100 ml blood	
11				VM	Capacity	23.1(19-27.5) ml/100 ml blood	
12				CC	Saturation	91.7(86.5-97) %	
13	3140	517			Pressure	66 mm Hg	2
14			11	VM	Content	21.9(19-25) ml/100 ml blood	4
15				VM	Capacity	24.0(22-26) ml/100 ml blood	
16				CC	Saturation	91.0(87-95) %	
17	3730	479			Pressure	57 mm Hg	2
18			15	VM	Content	21.9(18.5-25) ml/100 ml blood	4
19				VM	Capacity	25.0(21.5-28.5) ml/100 ml blood	
20				CC	Saturation	87.6(84.5-91.5) %	
21	3990	463	4	Cal	Pressure	55 mm Hg	1
22				VM	Content	21.1 ml/100 ml blood	
23				VM, R	Capacity	24.2 ml/100 ml blood	
24				CC	Saturation	86.9%	
25	4515	432	22	Cal	Pressure	49 mm Hg	1
26				VM	Content	21.6(18-25) ml/100 ml blood	
27				VM, R	Capacity	26.1(21-31) ml/100 ml blood	
28				CC	Saturation	82.8(75-90) %	
29	4540	431			Pressure	47 mm Hg	2
30			18	VM	Content	23.0(19.5-26.5) ml/100 ml blood	4
31				VM	Capacity	28.3(24-32.5) ml/100 ml blood	
32				CC	Saturation	81.4(75.5-87.0) %	
33		431	40	VM	Content	22.4(18.8-27.1)[c] ml/100 ml blood	5
34				VM	Capacity	27.3(22.3-33.0)[c] ml/100 ml blood	
35				CC	Saturation	81.0(75.6-86.7)[c] %	
36	4860	413			Pressure	46 mm Hg	2
37			12	VM	Content	23.4(20.5-26.5) ml/100 ml blood	4
38				VM	Capacity	29.0(25-33) ml/100 ml blood	
39				CC	Saturation	80.7(76-85) %	
40	5340	387	7	O_2C	Pressure	43 mm Hg	3
41				VM	Content	23.0 ml/100 ml blood	
42				VM	Capacity	30.2 ml/100 ml blood	
43				CC	Saturation	76.2 %	
					Carbon Dioxide		
44	150[2]	746			Pressure	41 mm Hg	2
45					Content	46 ml/100 ml blood	
46		750	80	DC	Pressure	40.1(35.3-46.0)[c] mm Hg	5
47				VM	Content	48.3(43.5-53.8)[c] ml/100 ml blood	
48	2390	568	12	DC	Pressure	37.8(34-42) mm Hg	4
49				VM	Content	41.1(37-45) ml/100 ml blood	

/1/ U. S. Standard Atmosphere. /2/ Approximately sea level values included for comparison purposes.

Part III: COMPLETE ACCLIMATIZATION (Concluded)

	Altitude		No. of Subjects	Method	Variable	Value	Reference
	m	mm Hg[1]					
	(A)	(B)	(C)	(D)	(E)	(F)	(G)
Carbon Dioxide (concluded)							

	m (A)	mm Hg[1] (B)	No. of Subjects (C)	Method (D)	Variable (E)	Value (F)	Reference (G)
50	3140	517	11	DC	Pressure	36.4(31-42) mm Hg	4
51				VM	Content	39.3(34.5-44) ml/100 ml blood	
52	3730	479	15	VM	Content	36.0(33-39) ml/100 ml blood	4
53	3990	463	4	T	Pressure	34.7 mm Hg	1
54				VM	Content	39.8 ml/100 ml blood	
55	4515	432	22	T	Pressure	33.8(28-40) mm Hg	1
56				VM	Content	37.9(33-43) ml/100 ml blood	
57	4540	431	18	T	Pressure	34.7(29-40) mm Hg	4
58				VM	Content	33.5(32-35) ml/100 ml blood	
59		431	40	DC	Pressure	33.0(28.5-37.1)[c] mm Hg	5
60				VM	Content	35.4(30.8-41.0)[c] ml/100 ml blood	
61	4860	413	12	T	Pressure	33.0(28-38) mm Hg	4
62				VM	Content	34.0(31-37) ml/100 ml blood	
63	5340	387	7	CO$_2$C	Pressure	29.3 mm Hg	3
64				VM	Content	31.8 ml/100 ml blood	

/1/ U. S. Standard Atmosphere.

Contributors: (a) Adler, Harry F., (b) Luft, Ulrich C., (c) Penrod, Kenneth E., (d) Stickney, J. Clifford, (e) Hurtado, Alberto

References: [1] Chiodi, H. 1957. J. Appl. Physiol. 10:81. [2] Committee on Aviation Medicine. 1944. Handbook of respiratory data in aviation. National Research Council, Washington, D. C. Charts A-1, B-1, B-3. [3] Dill, D. B., E. H. Christensen, and H. T. Edwards. 1936. Am. J. Physiol. 115:530. [4] Hurtado, A., and H. Aste-Salazar. 1948. J. Appl. Physiol. 1:304. [5] Hurtado, A., T. Velásquez, B. Reynafarje, and H. Aste-Salazar. 1956. School Aviat. M. Rep. 56-104. Randolph Air Force Base, Texas. [6] Roughton, F. J. W., R. C. Darling, and W. S. Root. 1944. Am. J. Physiol. 142:708.

82. EFFECT OF SHOCK ON BLOOD: MAMMALS

For a comprehensive review of the subject, consult reference 4, Part I.

Part I: MAN

Slight shock characterized by decreased blood pressure of 20% or less, cool skin temperature, pale skin color, definite slowing of circulation, and clear but distressed mental state. Severe shock characterized by weak-to-imperceptible pulse, decreased blood pressure of 40% to non-recordable, cold skin temperature, ashen-to-cyanotic (mottled) skin color, very sluggish circulation, severe thirst, apathetic-to-comatose mental state. Values in parentheses are ranges, estimate "c" unless otherwise indicated (cf. Introduction).

	Property or Constituent	Normal Value	Trauma without Shock		Slight Shock		Severe Shock		Reference
			No. of Subjects	Value	No. of Subjects	Value	No. of Subjects	Value	
	(A)	(B)	(C)	(D)	(E)	(F)	(G)	(H)	(I)
1	Arteriovenous O_2 difference, ml/L	45 (35-60)	8	46 (46-50)	4	71 (58-82)	4	84 (60-100)	3
	Blood pressure								3
2	Systolic, mm Hg	137 (122-149)	8	137 (102-167)	4	77 (48-113)	4	63 (46-80)	
3	Diastolic, mm Hg	74 (68-83)	8	69 (44-87)	4	40 (28-50)	4	32 (15-42)	
4	Mean arterial, mm Hg	97 (88-106)	8	94 (67-113)	4	54 (36-67)	4	44 (22-57)	
5	Atrial venous, mm H_2O	33	8	45 (12-70)	4	26 (10-47)	4	-8 (0 to -11)	
6	Peripheral venous, mm H_2O	74	8	86 (79-92)	4	77 (62-105)	4	90 (50-121)	
7	CO_2 combining power, mEq/L	27 (24-33)	13	27.9 (25.9-29.9)[b]	22	26.1 (24.7-27.5)[b]	25	22.1 (20.3-23.9)[b]	2
8	CO_2 content, arterial, vol %	49.1	8	44.1 (42.7-50.6)	4	35.8 (32.7-40.1)	4	28.0 (16.5-39.4)	3
	CO_2 pressure, mm Hg								3
9	Arterial	38.8	8	37.4 (30.4-42.8)	4	30.5 (27.0-33.4)	4	28.4 (17.4-39.4)	
10	Mixed venous	44.7	8	43.9 (38.3-48.2)	4	36.9 (32.0-39.5)	4	40.9 (31.4-46.7)	
11	O_2 content, arterial, vol %	16.6	8	15.6 (13.1-18.5)	4	12.3 (9.8-14.4)	4	11.8 (10.2-14.6)	3
	O_2 saturation, %								3
12	Arterial	96.0	8	94.2 (91.0-97.4)	4	90.8 (85.7-95.0)	4	94.6 (83.0-99.0)	
13	Mixed venous	67.7	8	66.7 (58.0-76.3)	4	38.4 (35.0-42.9)	4	28.2 (14.0-49.6)	
14	Hemoglobin, g/100 ml	16.0 (14.0-17.5)	14	12.1 (8.5-15.7)[b]	23	11.3 (8.1-14.5)[b]	24	8.8 (7.0-10.6)[b]	2
	pH								3
15	Arterial	7.42	8	7.39 (7.36-7.43)	4	7.38 (7.32-7.41)	4	7.28 (7.26-7.29)	
16	Mixed venous	7.39	8	7.36 (7.33-7.39)	4	7.32 (7.29-7.35)	4	7.22 (7.19-7.26)	
17	Peripheral vascular resistance, total dynes sec/cm^5	1290 (1100-1755)	8	1281 (952-1635)	4	1019 (738-1452)	4	1021 (567-1468)	3
	Volume								3
18	Whole blood, ml/sq m	2900	8	2791 (1910-3300)	4	2330 (1900-2500)	4	1670 (1540-1820)	
19	Plasma, ml/sq m	1600	8	1597 (1130-2070)	4	1532 (1376-1675)	4	1125 (1033-1310)	3
20	Erythrocyte (hematocrit), %	47 (42-52)	15	42.5 (39.1-45.9)[b]	26	38.4 (35.4-41.4)[b]	24	31.5 (28.5-34.5)[b]	2
21	Plasma Chloride, mEq/L	100 (97.5-104.0)	13	102 (96-108)[b]	24	101 (99.6-102.4)[b]	24	99.5 (97.7-101.3)[b]	1,2

Part I: MAN (Concluded)

	Property or Constituent	Normal Value	Trauma without Shock		Slight Shock		Severe Shock		Reference
			No. of Subjects	Value	No. of Subjects	Value	No. of Subjects	Value	
	(A)	(B)	(C)	(D)	(E)	(F)	(G)	(H)	(I)
	Plasma (concluded)								
22	Magnesium, mg/100 ml	1.8 (1.0-3.0)	11	1.7 (1.6-1.8)[b]	17	1.9 (1.8-2.0)[b]	16	2.5 (2.2-2.8)[b]	2
23	Phosphorus, mg/100 ml	3.0 (1.8-3.5)	14	3.3 (2.8-3.8)[b]	20	3.8 (3.5-4.1)[b]	21	5.8 (4.8-6.8)[b]	2
24	Protein, g/100 ml	6.5 (6.0-7.0)	15	6.6 (6.4-6.8)[b]	26	6.4 (6.2-6.6)[b]	25	6.0 (5.8-6.2)[b]	2
25	Creatinine, mg/100 ml	1.0 (0.5-1.2)	18	1.0 (0.9-1.1)[b]	24	1.3 (1.1-1.5)[b]	23	2.1 (1.8-2.4)[b]	2
26	Bilirubin, mg/100 ml	(0.1-0.5)	11	0.43 (0.27-0.59)[b]	23	0.68 (0.48-0.88)[b]	21	0.47 (0.46-0.48)[b]	2
27	Uric acid, mg/100 ml	3.0 (1.5-3.5)	10	4.0 (2.8-5.2)[b]	16	4.5 (3.7-5.3)[b]	16	5.2 (4.1-6.3)[b]	2
28	Nitrogen, non-protein, mg/100 ml	33 (25-40)	18	34.0 (31.0-37.0)[b]	24	35.0 (31.4-38.6)[b]	24	44.0 (39.8-48.2)[b]	2
29	Glucose, mg/100 ml	(80-90)	9	134 (116-152)[b]	14	149 (131-167)[b]	13	202 (150-254)[b]	2
30	Serum sodium, mEq/L	143 (139-149)			6	142.1	5	144.7	1,2

Contributors: (a) Wiggers, Carl J., (b) Engel, Frank L., (c) Page, Irvine H., (d) Fine, Jacob; Frank, Howard A.; and Korman, Henry

References: [1] Beecher, H. K., F. A. Simeone, C. H. Burnett, S. L. Shapiro, E. R. Sullivan, and T. B. Mallory. 1947. Surgery 22:672. [2] Board for the Study of the Severely Wounded. 1952. The physiologic effects of wounds. Office of the Surgeon General, Department of the Army, Washington, D. C. ch. 8, p. 201. [3] Cournand, A., et al. 1943. Surgery 13:964. [4] Wiggers, C. J. 1950. Physiology of shock. Harvard University Press, Cambridge.

Part II: CAT, DOG

Values in parentheses are ranges, estimate "c" (cf. Introduction).

	Animal	Blood	Property or Constituent	Control Value	Shock		Reference
					Traumatic	Hemorrhagic	
	(A)	(B)	(C)	(D)	(E)	(F)	(G)
1	Cat		CO_2 content, vol %	36.5	22.3		11
2		Arterial	O_2 saturation, %	(82-100)		(85-99)	4
3		Venous	O_2 saturation, %	(69-89)		(5-43)	4
4		Whole blood	Protein, total, g/100 ml	(4.7-5.5)	(4.7-7.4)		1
5			Nitrogen Creatine N, mg/100 ml	(1.2-1.9)	(1.3-6.0)		
6			Urea N, mg/100 ml	(26-32)	(25-49)		
7		Plasma	Nitrogen, amino acid, mg/100 ml	(4.2-7.6)		(4.8-11.8)	4
8	Dog		CO_2 pressure, mm Hg	(30.0-43.7)	(14.7-31.8)	(6.8-27.9)	11
9		Right heart	O_2 content, vol %	12.88	5.23	4.88	2
10		Jugular vein	O_2 content, vol %	13.86	4.68	6.00	2
11		Portal vein	O_2 content, vol %	12.32	7.50	4.59	2
12		Renal vein	O_2 content, vol %	14.54	10.83	7.62	2
13		Femoral vein	O_2 content, vol %	10.68	4.15	4.18	2
14		Femoral artery	O_2 content, vol %	17.14	16.11	13.84	2
15		Arterial	pH	(7.28-7.42)	(7.19-7.35)	(6.92-7.32)	11

Part II: CAT, DOG (Concluded)

	Animal	Blood	Property or Constituent	Control Value	Shock Traumatic	Shock Hemorrhagic	Reference
	(A)	(B)	(C)	(D)	(E)	(F)	(G)
16	Dog (concluded)	Whole blood	Phosphorus, inorganic, mg/100 ml	4.4	4.6	3.6	3
17			Ammonia, μg/ml	(0.7-1.2)		(1.8-4.1)	10
18			Creatinine, mg/100 ml	0.97	1.03		3
19			Nitrogen Non-protein N, mg/100 ml	15.1	19.7		3
20			Amino N, mg/100 ml	5.4	5.0		
21			Glucose, mg/100 ml	85.9	86.9		3, 9
22			Lactic acid, mg/100 ml	12.8	14.5		3
23			Lactate, mEq/L	(2.1-3.9)	(8.0-18.8)	(6.0-14.6)	11
24			Pyruvate, mEq/L	(0.1-0.2)	(0.4-0.5)	(0.4-0.5)	11
25		Plasma	Water, g/L	(912-946)	(911-919)	(917-957)	11
26			Anions, total, mEq/L	(146.6-160.7)	(154.3-162.0)	(148.6-151.8)	11
27			Cations, total, mEq/L	(160.9-172.1)	(169.2-170.8)	(164.5-177.9)	11
28			Base Total, mEq/L	(158.6-168.6)	(167.8-174.8)	(162.5-168.7)	11
29			Protein-bound, mEq/L	(12.8-20.7)	(12.2-16.3)	(11.0-14.9)	
30			Bicarbonate, mEq/L	(17.9-25.6)	(6.3-13.5)	(3.5-13.4)	11
31			Calcium, mEq/L	(5.1-6.6)	(5.1-5.4)	(5.4-5.8)	11
32			Iron, μg/100 ml	73		275	8
33			Iron-binding capacity, μg/100 ml	170		10	8
34			Magnesium, mEq/L	(1.4-2.2)	(2.6-3.2)	(2.7-2.9)	11
35			Phosphate, inorganic, mEq/L	(1.2-2.6)	(4.0-6.5)	(4.3-9.7)	11
36			Potassium, mEq/L	(4.4-6.2)	(5.1-6.5)	(7.6-7.7)	11
37				4.9	(5-12)		7
38			Sodium, mEq/L	(149-159)	(155-158)	(148-162)	11
39			Protein, %	100		(68-100)	5
40			Fibrinogen, %	100		(70-100)	5
41			Prothrombin, %	100		(2.5-80.0)	5
42			Uric acid, mg/100 ml	0.5		(4.0-5.0)	12,13
43			Nitrogen, amino acid, mg/100 ml	(2.6-5.0)		(5.0-7.5)	6
44		Serum	Chloride, mEq/L	(107.4-115.3)	(115.7-116.2)	(108.0-113.4)	11

Contributors: (a) Fine, Jacob; Frank, Howard A.; and Korman, Henry, (b) Engel, Frank L., (c) Baez, Silvio, (d) Page, Irvine H., (e) Wiggers, Carl J.

References: [1] Aub, J. C. 1920. Am. J. Physiol. 54:416. [2] Blalock, A., and H. Bradburn. 1930. Arch. Surg. 20:26. [3] Davis, H. A. 1948. Shock and allied forms of failure of the circulation. Grune and Stratton, New York. [4] Engel, F. L. 1944. J. Exp. M. 79:9. [5] Frank, E. D., H. A. Frank, and J. Fine. 1951. Am. J. Physiol. 167:499. [6] Kline, D. L. 1946. Ibid. 146:654. [7] Manery, J. F. 1943. Ibid. 138:499. [8] Mazur, A., S. Baez, and E. Shorr. 1955. J. Biol. Chem. 213:147. [9] McShan, W. H., V. R. Potter, A. Goldman, E. G. Shipley, and R. K. Meyer. 1945-46. Am. J. Physiol. 145:93. [10] Nelson, R. M., and D. Seligson. 1953. Surgery 34:1. [11] Root, W. S., J. B. Allison, W. H. Cole, J. H. Holmes, W. W. Walcott, and M. I. Gregersen. 1947. Am. J. Physiol. 149:52. [12] Van Slyke, D. D. 1948. Ann. N. York Acad. Sc. 49:593. [13] Zweifach, B. W., S. G. Hershey, E. A. Rovenstine, R. E. Lee, and R. Chambers. 1945. Surgery 18:48.

82. EFFECT OF SHOCK ON BLOOD: MAMMALS (Concluded)

Part III: RABBIT, RAT

Values in parentheses are ranges, estimate "c" (cf. Introduction).

Animal	Blood	Property or Constituent	Control Value	Shock Gravity	Shock Tourniquet	Reference
(A)	(B)	(C)	(D)	(E)	(F)	(G)
Rabbit	Erythrocytes	Phosphorus				1
		Inorganic P, mg/100 ml	(2.2-2.7)	(2.6-13.0)		
		Organic P, mg/100 ml	(70-89)	(68-98)		
	Plasma	Chloride, mEq/L	(107-114)	(95-110)		1
		Phosphorus				
		Inorganic P, mg/100 ml	(3.3-7.2)	(5.2-24.6)		
		Organic P, mg/100 ml	(0.1-0.8)	(0.4-8.6)		
	Serum	Glycerol				6
		Free, mM/L	1		(2.5-3.5)	
		Neutral fat, mM/L	1		(2.5-9.0)	
		Phospholipid, mg/100 ml	(90-100)		(180-350)	
Rat	Whole blood	Lymphocytes, %	72		2.43	12
		Uric acid, mg/100 ml	0.8	1.5[1]		8
		Nitrogen				
		Amino acid N, mg/100 ml	14	(13-23)[1]	(10-30)	7
		Creatine N, mg/100 ml	1.9	2.5[1]		8
		Glucose, mg/100 ml	(87-95)	(67-196)	(80-150)	3
		Lactic acid, mg/100 ml	(16-18)	(20-150)[1]	(20-43)	7
		Pyruvic acid, mg/100 ml	1.4	(1.5-5.0)[1]	(1.2-2.2)	7
		Ketones (as acetone) mg/100 ml	(3-6)		(0-6)[2]	2
	Erythrocytes	Volume (hematocrit), %	45.7	(25-30)[2]	(45.8-67.0)	4
		Nitrogen, amino acid, mg/100 ml	21		(21-24)[2]	10
	Plasma	Phosphate, inorganic, mg/100 ml	7.5	(6-13)[1]	(7.5-12.0)	7
		Uric acid, mg/100 ml	0.6	8.7[2]		5
		Nitrogen, amino acid, mg/100 ml	5.0		(6-12)	7
			7.0		(7-40)[2]	3
		Pentose, mg/100 ml	7.0	(4-17)[1]	(6-18)	7
		Aminopeptidase (glycyl-glycyl-glycine), μM hydrolyzed/0.1 ml plasma/hr	2.0		(4-11)[2]	11

/1/ Noble-Collip rotating-drum technique [9]. /2/ Hemorrhagic shock.

Contributors: (a) Fine, Jacob; Frank, Howard A.; and Korman, Henry, (b) Engel, Frank L., (c) Baez, Silvio, (d) Page, Irvine H., (e) Wiggers, Carl J.

References: [1] Allison, J. B., and W. H. Cole. 1944. Proc. Soc. Exp. Biol., N. Y. 57:21. [2] Engel, F. L., and K. Hewson. 1953. Ibid. 83:608. [3] Engel, F. L., M. G. Winton, and C. N. H. Long. 1943. J. Exp. M. 77:397. [4] Gray, J. L., A. L. Botkin, E. J. Moulden, and H. Jensen. 1950. Proc. Soc. Exp. Biol., N. Y. 75:189. [5] Green, S., and A. J. Mazur. 1958. J. Biol. Chem. 227:653. [6] Johnson, S. R., and L. B. Waldstrom. 1956. Scand. J. Clin. Lab. Invest. 8:323. [7] McShan, W. H., V. R. Potter, A. Goldman, E. G. Shipley, and R. K. Meyer. 1945-46. Am. J. Physiol. 145:93. [8] Neufeld, A. H., C. G. Toby, and R. L. Noble. 1943. Proc. Soc. Exp. Biol., N. Y. 54.249. [9] Noble, R. L., and J. D. Collip. 1941. Q. J. Exp. Physiol., Lond. 31:187 [10] Sayers, M. A., G. Sayers, M. G. Engel, F. L. Engel, and C. N. H. Long. 1945. Proc. Soc. Exp. Biol., N. Y. 60:20. [11] Schwartz, T. B., and F. L. Engel. 1953. Ibid. 83:568. [12] Wiedeman, M. P., and C. R. Lewis. 1949. Ibid. 71:467.

83. EFFECT OF IONIZING RADIATION ON HEMATOPOIETIC TISSUE: VERTEBRATES

Abbreviations and definitions: kv = kilovolt, a unit of electrical potential equal to 1000 volts; kvp = kilovolt peak, the crest value of the potential wave in kilovolts; c = curie, the quantity of radionuclide disintegrating at the rate of 3.7×10^{10} atoms per second; mc = millicurie, 1/1000 of a curie, or 3.7×10^7 disintegrations per second; μc = microcurie, 1/1,000,000 of a curie, or 3.7×10^4 disintegrations per second; r = roentgen, the amount of X ray that will produce 2.08×10^9 ion pairs in a cu cm of air under conditions of standard temperature and pressure, or the amount of radiation that dissipates 83.8 ergs/g of dry air; n = neutron dose that gives the same reading in a Victoreen Thimble Chamber as 1 roentgen of gamma rays from radium; single exposure = single or few closely-spaced exposures.

	Animal	Tissue	Radiation	Dose	Exposed Body Area or Administration	Effect	Manifestation[1]	Recovery[1]	Reference
	(A)	(B)	(C)	(D)	(E)	(F)	(G)	(H)	(I)
1	Man	Bone marrow	Atomic bomb, Japan	Severe; single exposure	Entire body	Decreased cellularity	Maximum decrease 6-30 da after exposure	7 da[2]	20
						Proliferation of reticuloendothelium; increased reticulum cells, plasma cells, macrophages, lymphocytes	6 da		
						Hyperplasia during recovery	6 wk	12-16 wk	
2			Radon	Atmosphere of 4×10^{-9} c/L air; 1 hr per treatment; 10 or more treatments		Erythroid hyperplasia; increased lymphocytes; decreased granulocytes; increase in basophil leukocytes in marrow			12
3		Lymphoid	Atomic bomb, Japan	Severe; single exposure	Entire body	Atrophy	3 da	5 da[3]	20
4		Sternal bone marrow	X ray 150-175 kv	100 r; single exposure	Localized	Decreased erythroblasts	2 da	Complete by 1 mo	5
						Decreased myeloid cells	3 da	Complete by 1 mo	
5				200 r; single exposure	Localized	Decreased erythroblasts	2 da		
						Decreased myeloid cells	2 da		
						Decreased erythroblast mitosis	2 da	4 da	
6				300 r; single exposure	Localized	Decreased mitosis, erythroid cells, myeloid cells	1 da	1-2 mo	
7				2000 r; single exposure	Localized	Transient aplasia			
8				3000 r or more; single exposure	Localized	Permanent aplasia			
9	Dog	Bone marrow	Gold[198]	244-504 mc	Intraperitoneal	Marked decrease in all cellular elements of marrow	Weeks		13
10			X ray 250 kvp	300 r; single exposure	Entire body	Decreased cellularity	As early as 2 da	24-28 da	22
						Decreased myeloid cells	2 da	24 da	
						Decreased erythroid cells	2 da	4 da	
						Reversed myeloid-erythroid ratio	7-9 da	40 da	

/1/ Initial observation; recorded as time following exposure. /2/ Some indication of recovery in all survivors.
/3/ Production of predominantly atypical mononuclear cells.

	Animal	Tissue	Radiation	Dose	Exposed Body Area or Administration	Effect	Manifestation[1]	Recovery[1]	Reference
	(A)	(B)	(C)	(D)	(E)	(F)	(G)	(H)	(I)
11	Dog (concluded)	Regional lymph	Gold[198]	2 mc	Interstitial, into anterior chest wall	Increased debris; decreased cellularity; abnormal mitosis; many abnormal plasma-cytoid cells (predominant cell type)	3 da		4
						Congestion of sinusoids by large phagocytic mononuclear cells			
12				5-10 mc	Interstitial, into anterior chest wall	Decreased cellularity; increased debris; areas of necrosis; many plasma-cytoid cells; thrombonecrosis of blood vessels	3 da		
13				30-85 mc	Interstitial, into anterior chest wall	Decreased cellularity; increased debris; necrosis of 90% or more of node; occasional islands of viable lymphoid tissue; numerous fibroblasts	3 wk (sacrificed)		
						Dense scar tissue	5-6 wk		
14	Guinea pig	Lymph nodes	X ray 200 kvp	175 r; single exposure	Entire body	Increased debris	3 hr	24 hr	1
						Slightly decreased cellularity	3-8 hr	By 4 da	
						Increased heterophils	3 hr	48 hr	
15	Mouse	Bone marrow	Fast neutrons (pile)	96 n; single exposure	Entire body	Increased debris	3 hr		1
						Decreased cellularity	3 hr	3 da	
16				117 n; single exposure	Entire body	Cell death	3 hr		
						Decreased cellularity	3 hr	5-9 da	
						Increased debris	3 hr		
						Cytological damage (megakaryocytes)	1 da		
						Increased spindle cells	9 da		
17			Mixed (detonation of nuclear device)	128 r[4]; single exposure	Entire body	Induction of myelogenous leukemia			9
18			Strontium[89]	2.0 μc	Intraperitoneal	Decreased hematopoiesis (all cell series)	3 da	Sustained	14
19			X ray 170 kv	200 r; single exposure	Entire body	Visible chromosome aberrations	18 hr		6
20			X ray 186 kv	400 r; single exposure	Entire body	Decreased lymphocytes	1 da		3
						Decreased normoblasts, cellularity	1 da	7 da	
						Decreased myelopoiesis	2 da	7-14 da	
						Shift to left present in myelocytic series	10 da		
21			X ray 200 kvp	50 r; single exposure	Entire body	Increased myeloid cells	8 hr		19
						Increased myeloblasts	12 hr		

/1/ Initial observation; recorded as time following exposure. /4/ Threshold dose.

	Animal	Tissue	Radiation	Dose	Exposed Body Area or Administration	Effect	Mani-festation[1]	Recovery[1]	Ref-er-ence
	(A)	(B)	(C)	(D)	(E)	(F)	(G)	(H)	(I)
22	Mouse (con-clud-ed)	Bone marrow (con-cluded)	X ray 200 kvp (con-cluded)	350 r; single exposure	Entire body	Increased debris	3 hr	5 da	1
						Decreased erythro-poiesis	3 hr	5-9 da	
						Decreased myelo-poiesis	3 hr	5 da	
23		Lymphoid	X ray 250 kvp	1/10 LD$_{50}$; single exposure	Entire body	Increased activity of adenosine triphos-phatase and 5-nu-cleotidase	Few hr	Few da	7
24		Lymph nodes	Fast neu-trons (pile)	96 n; single exposure	Entire body	Complete destruction of nodules	$\frac{1}{2}$ hr	3-9 da	1
25			X ray 186 kv	400 r; single exposure	Entire body	Decreased cellularity	2-3 hr	4 da	3
						Increased debris	2-3 hr		
						Cytological damage	2-3 hr	4 da	
						Disappearance of secondary nodules	48 hr	7-14 da	
						Increased extramed-ullary myelopoiesis	3-4 wk		
26		Lymph nodes and spleen	X ray 200 kvp	50 r; single exposure	Entire body	Occurrence of giant cells	4 hr		19
						Increased debris in follicles	4 hr		
						Necrotic foci in germinal follicles	8-12 hr		
27		Spleen	Strontium^{89}	2.0 μc	Intraperi-toneal	Greatly increased erythropoiesis and megakaryocytopoi-esis; decreased lymphocytopoiesis	3 da	Sustained	14
28			X ray 186 kv	400 r; single exposure	Entire body	Decreased mitosis	2-3 hr	7-10 da	3
						Cytological damage (lymphocytes)	2-3 hr	7-10 da	
						Increased debris	2-3 hr		
						Decreased erythro-poiesis	2-3 hr	7-10 da	
						Decreased mega-karyocytes	2-3 hr	10-14 da	
						Increased extramed-ullary myelopoiesis	10 da		
29			X ray 2000 kvp	625 r; single exposure	Entire body	Cellular injury (morphological) to lymphoid elements	1 hr	60 hr	15
						Cellular injury (morphological) to erythropoietic elements	1 hr	66 hr	
						Cellular injury (morphological) to myelopoietic elements	Subtle onset	80 hr	
30		Spleen and thymus	X ray	100-1000 r; single exposure	Entire body	Weight loss (propor-tional to dose)	120 hr		24
31		Thymus	X ray or thermal neutrons, plus γ rays	128-512 r; single exposure	Entire body	Induction of thymic lymphoma	1 yr (more common in ♀)		27
32				180 r; single exposure	Entire body	Involution	3 da		21

/1/ Initial observation; recorded as time following exposure.

	Animal	Tissue	Radiation	Dose	Exposed Body Area or Administration	Effect	Manifestation[1]	Recovery[1]	Reference
	(A)	(B)	(C)	(D)	(E)	(F)	(G)	(H)	(I)
33	Rabbit	Bone marrow	X ray 200 kvp	100 r; single exposure	Entire body	Decreased mitosis	Almost immediately after exposure	3 hr	10
						Abnormal mitosis	8 hr	14 hr	
34				400 r; single exposure	Entire body	Decreased mitosis	3 hr		
						Decreased erythropoiesis	3 hr	14 da	
						Increased debris	3 hr		
						Decreased granulocytopoiesis	1 da	Before 14 da	
35				800 r; single exposure	Entire body	Cessation of mitosis	½ hr	10 da	
						Decreased erythropoiesis	½ hr	10-14 da	
						Increased debris	3 hr		
						Decreased myelopoiesis	1 da	14 da	
						Decreased megaloblasts	2 da	21 da	
36		Lymph nodes	X ray 200 kvp	50 r; single exposure	Entire body	Increased debris	3 hr	10 hr	10
37				100 r; single exposure	Entire body	Increased debris	3 hr	24 hr	10
38				400 r; single exposure	Entire body	Increased debris	Within 3 hr		10
						Decreased cellularity of nodules	3 hr	24 hr	
						Decreased mitosis	3 hr	8 hr	
						Shift to left in lymphocytes	8-16 hr		
						Infiltration with heterophils	During first da		
39				800 r; single exposure	Entire body	Decreased mitosis	30 min	5 da	10
						Destruction of lymphocytes	30 min	5 da	10
						Increased debris (rapidly removed by phagocytes)	30 min	17 hr	10
						Disappearance of nodules	17-24 hr	21 da	10
						Increased spindle cells (reticulum cells)	24 hr		10
						Increased plasma cells	9 da		10
						Increased infiltration by heterophils (infiltration persisted several da)	1 da		28
40		Spleen	X ray 200 kvp	25 r; single exposure	Entire body	Increased debris	1 da		10
						Cytological damage	1 da		
41				50 r; single exposure	Entire body	Decreased mitosis	1 da		
						Cytological damage	1 da		
42				600 r; single exposure	Entire body	Cessation of mitosis	1 hr	8 hr	
						Increased debris	1 hr	8 hr	
						Cytological damage	1 hr		
						Decreased cellularity	1 hr	9 da	
43				800 r; single exposure	Entire body	Cessation of mitosis	½ hr	8 hr	
						Cytological damage (lymphocytes)	½ hr		
						Increased debris	½ hr	8 hr	
						Destruction of lymphocytes	3 hr	9 da	

/1/ Initial observation; recorded as time following exposure.

	Animal	Tissue	Radiation	Dose	Exposed Body Area or Administration	Effect	Manifestation[1]	Recovery[1]	Reference
	(A)	(B)	(C)	(D)	(E)	(F)	(G)	(H)	(I)
	Rabbit (concluded)	Spleen (concluded)	X ray 200 kvp (concluded)	800 r; single exposure (concluded)	Entire body	Decreased cellularity	3 hr	9 da	10
						Decreased erythroblasts	24 hr	14 da	
						Decreased size	1 da		
						Decreased myelocytes	2 da	14 da	
						Increased plasma cells	9 da		
44	Rat	Bone marrow	Fast neutrons (cyclotron)	56.4 n; single exposure	Entire body	Decreased cellularity, mitosis, megakaryocytes, erythroid and myeloid cells		16 da	16
45			Plutonium	300-3000 µc/kg body wt; single injection	Intravenous	Hypoplasia (femoral distal epiphysis and vertebra)	At autopsy, 14-260 da (depending upon dose)	30 da or more (with lower doses)[5]	8
46			Polonium	50-170 µc/kg body wt; single injection	Intravenous	Hypoplasia (extreme at 120-170 µc level, less severe at 50 µc level); hemorrhage	At autopsy, 7-300 da (depending upon dose)		8
47			Radium	17-8000 µc/kg body wt; single injection	Intravenous	Hypoplasia (femoral distal epiphysis and vertebra)	At autopsy, 11-407 da		8
48				10-50 µg	Intraperitoneal	Decreased megakaryocytes	3 da	9 da	23
49			X ray 200 kvp	550 r; single exposure	Entire body	Decreased lymphocytes	15 min	12 da	17
						Decreased megakaryocytes	3 hr	14 da	
						Decreased erythroid cells	6-15 hr	5 da	
						Decreased myeloid cells	30-45 hr	14 da	
50				600 r; single exposure	Entire body	Increased debris	3 hr		1
						Decreased erythropoiesis	3 hr	9 da	
						Decreased myelopoiesis	2 da	31 da	
51			X ray 100 kv	1000 r in 8 da at 125-200 r/da	Leg	Decreased cellularity, mitosis, myeloid-erythroid ratio; increased reticulum cells, phagocytic cells; relative increase in nucleated erythrocytes (absolute decrease)	1 da after last exposure (sacrificed)		11
52				2500 r in 20 da at 125-200 r/da	Leg	Almost no nucleated erythrocytes; mitosis abolished; decreased cellularity, myeloid-erythroid ratio; increased reticulum cells, phagocytes	1 da after last exposure (sacrificed)		
53		Lymph nodes	Plutonium	300-3000 µg/kg body wt; single injection	Intravenous	Hypoplasia (greater with larger doses)	At autopsy, 14-260 da		8

/1/ Initial observation; recorded as time following exposure. /5/ Signs of active marrow regeneration in femoral shaft in rats receiving lower doses and surviving 30 days or more.

	Animal	Tissue	Radiation	Dose	Exposed Body Area or Administration	Effect	Manifestation[1]	Recovery[1]	Reference
	(A)	(B)	(C)	(D)	(E)	(F)	(G)	(H)	(I)
54	Rat (concluded)	Lymph nodes (concluded)	Radium	17-8000 µc/kg body wt; single injection	Intravenous	Hypoplasia (more marked with greater doses); neoplastic changes in 3 of 20 rats examined	At autopsy, 11-407 da		8
55			X ray 200 kvp	400 r; single exposure	Entire body	Cytological damage (lymphocytes); degeneration of nodules	Within 16 hr	3 da	1
56				600 r; single exposure	Entire body	Cytological damage (lymphocytes)	$\frac{1}{2}$ hr	$14\frac{1}{2}$ hr	
						Infiltration by heterophils	8 hr		
						Degeneration of nodules	$14\frac{1}{2}$ hr	21 da	
						Disappearance of nodules	24 hr	21 da	
						Hemorrhage	Within 31 da		
57			X ray 240 kv	160 r; single exposure	Entire body	50% of lymphocytes showed nuclear pyknosis	5 hr		25
58		Spleen	Plutonium	300-3000 µc/kg body wt; single injection	Intravenous	Definite decrease in cellularity; hyperplasia of red pulp of spleen (extramedullary myelopoiesis)	At autopsy, 14-260 da		8
59			Radium	17-8000 µc/kg body wt; single injection	Intravenous	Complete or nearly complete atrophy of lymphoid elements at all dosage levels; marked extramedullary myelopoiesis with greater doses	At autopsy, 11-407 da		8
60			X ray 200 kvp	600 r; single exposure	Entire body	Decreased mitosis	$\frac{1}{2}$ hr	8 hr	1
						Decreased cellularity of nodules	3 hr	14 da	
						Destruction of lymphocytes	3 hr		
						Cytological damage (erythroblasts)	3 hr		
						Decreased erythropoiesis	8 hr	9 da	
						Decreased megakaryocytes	3 da	3 wk	
61			X ray 250 kvp	550 r; single exposure	Entire body	Increased debris	30 min	8 hr	17
						Destruction of lymphocytes	2 hr		
						Decreased cellularity	2 hr	9 da	
						Disappearance of nodules	30 hr	15 da	
62		Spleen and lymph nodes	Polonium	50-170 µc/kg body wt; single injection	Intravenous	Extreme decrease in cellularity	At autopsy, 7-300 da (depending upon dose)		8
63		Spleen, lymph nodes, and thymus	X ray 250 kvp	50-400 r (sublethal); single exposure	Entire body	Increased activity of adenosine triphosphatase and 5-nucleotidase	3 hr	72 hr	7

/1/ Initial observation; recorded as time following exposure.

209

	Animal	Tissue	Radiation	Dose	Exposed Body Area or Administration	Effect	Manifestation[1]	Recovery[1]	Reference
	(A)	(B)	(C)	(D)	(E)	(F)	(G)	(H)	(I)
64	Swine	Bone marrow	X ray 2000 kvp	600 r; single exposure	Entire body	Decreased erythroid elements	9 hr	None[6]	26
						Destruction of most nucleated erythrocytes	13 hr		
						Morphological damage to myeloid cells	13 hr		
						Almost complete absence of granulocytes	90 hr		
65		Lymphoid	X ray 2000 kvp	600 r; single exposure	Entire body	Fragmentation of lymphocytes	50 min		26
						Increased nuclear debris	50 min	3 hr	
						Increased phagocytosis of debris infiltration by granulocytes	3 hr		
						Destruction of almost all lymphocytes in central portion of nodules	13 hr	36-45 hr (recovery very gradual)	
						Destruction of almost all lymphocytes in nodules (only reticulum cells present)	29 hr	36-45 hr	
66	Chicken	Bone marrow	X ray 200 kvp	25 r; single exposure	Entire body	Cytological damage (lymphocytes)			18
67				100 r; single exposure	Entire body	Decreased mitosis	30 min	2 hr	
						Decreased cellularity	13 hr	12 da	
68				400 r; single exposure	Entire body	Decreased lymphocytes, myelocytes, erythroblasts	7 hr	13-48 hr	
69				800 r; single exposure	Entire body	Decreased mitosis	45 min		
						Erythropoiesis abolished	1 hr	2-4 da	
						Erythroblasts destroyed	1 hr	2-4 da	
						Small lymphocytes destroyed	1-2 hr		
						Increased debris	1-2 hr		
						Granulocytopoiesis destroyed	14 hr		
70		Spleen	X ray 200 kvp	25 r; single exposure	Entire body	Cytological damage (lymphocytes)			18
71				100 r; single exposure	Entire body	Debris and dead lymphocytes	$\frac{1}{2}$ hr	18 hr	
72				400 r; single exposure	Entire body	Decreased mitotic activity	$\frac{1}{2}$ hr	7 hr	
						Destruction of small lymphocytes	$\frac{1}{2}$ hr	3 da	
						3/4 of small lymphocytes killed	4 hr	3-5 da	
73				800 r; single exposure	Entire body	Cessation of mitosis	45 min	5 hr	
						Destruction of lymphocytes	45 min	9 da	
						Increased hemocytoblasts	45 min	1-3 da	
						Increased plasma cells	2 hr		

/1/ Initial observation; recorded as time following exposure. /6/ No evidence of regeneration during 164-hour period of observation.

	Animal	Tissue	Radiation	Dose	Exposed Body Area or Administration	Effect	Mani-festation[1]	Recovery[1]	Ref-erence
	(A)	(B)	(C)	(D)	(E)	(F)	(G)	(H)	(I)
74	Salmon	Kidney	X ray 200 kvp	500 r; single exposure	Entire body	Decreased hemato-poietic cells			2

/1/ Initial observation; recorded as time following exposure.

Contributor: Ingram, Marylou

References: [1] Bloom, W., ed. 1948. Nat. Nucl. En. Ser. IV-22I. McGraw-Hill, New York. [2] Bonham, K., L. R. Donaldson, R. F. Foster, A. D. Welander, and A. H. Seymour. 1948. Growth, Phila. 12:107. [3] Brecher, G., K. M. Endicott, H. Gump, and H. P. Brawner. 1948. Blood, N. Y. 3:1259. [4] Christoferson, W. M., and H. F. Berg. 1955. Cancer, Phila. 8:1261. [5] Denstad, T. 1943. Acta radiol., Stockh., Suppl. 52. [6] Devik, F., and F. Lothe. 1955. Ibid. 44:243. [7] DuBois, K. P., and D. F. Petersen. 1954. Am. J. Physiol. 176:282. [8] Fink, R. M., ed. 1950. Nat. Nucl. En. Ser. VI-3. McGraw-Hill, New York. [9] Furth, J., and A. C. Upton. 1954. Acta radiol., Stockh., Suppl. 116, p. 469. [10] Hagen, C. W., Jr., L. O. Jacobson, R. Murray, and P. Lear. 1944. MDDC-999. Office of Technical Services, Department of Commerce, Washington, D. C. [11] Hsü, C.-L., and W. C. Ma. 1940. Am. J. Cancer 39:319. [12] Inama, K. 1952. Wien. Zschr. inn. Med. 33:241. [13] Jackson, A. A., and P. F. Hahn. 1955. Cancer, Phila. 8:482. [14] Jacobson, L. O., E. L. Simmons, and M. H. Block. 1949. J. Laborat. Clin. M. 34:1640. [15] Lamson, B. G., and J. L. Tullis. 1951. Mil. Surgeon 109:281. [16] McDonald, E. 1947. Neutron effects on animals. Williams and Wilkins, Baltimore. [17] Metcalf, R. G., R. J. Blandau, and T. B. Barnett. 1950. UR 123. Office of Technical Services, Department of Commerce, Washington, D. C. (Also in H. A. Blair, ed. 1954. Nat. Nucl. En. Ser. VI-2. McGraw-Hill, New York.) [18] Murray, R., M. Pierce, and L. O. Jacobson. 1948. CH-3873. Office of Technical Services, Department of Commerce, Washington, D. C. [19] Nettleship, A. 1944. Radiology 42:64. [20] Oughterson, A. W., and S. Warren, ed. 1956. Nat. Nucl. En. Ser. VIII-8. McGraw-Hill, New York. [21] Patt, H. M., S. H. Mayer, R. L. Straube, and E. M. Jackson. 1953. J. Cellul. Physiol. 42:327. [22] Rekers, P. E. 1948. UR-11. Office of Technical Services, Department of Commerce, Washington, D. C. [23] Roofe, P. G., H. Bingham, R. Comer, and M. Madison. 1950. Anat. Rec. 108:537. [24] Storer, J. B., and W. H. Langham. 1954. AECU-3099. Office of Technical Services, Department of Commerce, Washington, D. C. [25] Trowell, O. A. 1952. J. Path. Bact., Lond. 64:687. [26] Tullis, J. L. 1951. Mil. Surgeon 109:271. [27] Upton, A. C., J. Furth, and K. W. Christenberry. 1954. Cancer Res. 14:682. [28] Zirkle, R. E., ed. 1956. TID-5220. Office of Technical Services, Department of Commerce, Washington, D. C.

84. EFFECT OF IONIZING RADIATION ON PERIPHERAL BLOOD: VERTEBRATES

Abbreviations and definitions: kv = kilovolt, a unit of electrical potential equal to 1000 volts; kvp = kilovolt peak, the crest value of the potential wave in kilovolts; mc = millicurie, 1/1000 of a curie, or 3.7×10^7 disintegrations per second (curie = the quantity of radionuclide disintegrating at the rate of 3.7×10^{10} atoms per second); μc = microcurie, 1/1,000,000 of a curie, or 3.7×10^4 disintegrations per second; r = roentgen, the amount of X ray that will produce 2.08×10^9 ion pairs in a cu cm of air under conditions of standard temperature and pressure, or the amount of radiation that dissipates 83.8 ergs/g of dry air; mr = milliroentgen, 1/1000 of a roentgen; megagram-r = megagram-roentgen, 10^6 gram-roentgens (gram-roentgen = the energy lost in 1 g of air by 1 roentgen-equivalent-physical of ionizing radiation or 83.8 ergs); n = neutron dose that gives the same reading in a Victoreen Thimble Chamber as 1 roentgen of gamma rays from radium; rad = a unit of absorbed dose, the energy absorption of 100 ergs/g of any medium; single exposure = single or few closely-spaced exposures; RBC = erythrocyte; WBC = leukocyte.

Part I: MAN

	Radiation	Dose	Exposed Body Area or Administration	Effect	Remarks	Reference
	(A)	(B)	(C)	(D)	(E)	(F)
				Single Exposure		
1	Atomic bomb detonation, Japan, 1945	Severe	Entire body	Leukopenia developed very rapidly; WBC almost absent from blood of many fatally injured victims		28
				Steadily decreasing RBC and hemoglobin; extremely severe anemia within 3-4 wk		
				Decreased platelets; purpura and other hemorrhagic manifestations common		
				Bizarre giant neutrophils, atypical lymphocytes, occasional plasma cells		
2		Moderately severe, or mild	Entire body	Leukopenia; minimal WBC counts during 4th wk; lowest WBC count = 1500-2500/cu mm hemoglobin		28
				Decreased RBC and hemoglobin; lowest RBC and hemoglobin levels 6-9 wk after exposure; tendency toward macrocytosis		
				Decreased platelets		
				Increased eosinophils; definite increase in absolute eosinophil count 8-12 wk after exposure		
3	Fall-out from detonation of nuclear device	175 r[1]	Surface deposition, inhalation, ingestion	Decreased lymphocytes; dropped to 55% of control level by 3rd da after exposure; remained stable at this level (greater depression in younger group)		7
				Decreased neutrophils; dropped to 70-80% of control level by 2nd wk; second decrease began 5th wk, with counts dropping to 50% of control level (greater depression in younger group)		
				Decreased platelets; reached minimum level (30% of control value) during 4th wk; second depression during 7th and 8th wk		
				Decreased hematocrit	First measured on 22nd da	
4	X ray Dental	35-315 r	Head, neck	Decreased absolute lymphocytes	Observed during 12-hr period after exposure	9

/1/ Calculated.

	Radiation	Dose	Exposed Body Area or Administration	Effect	Remarks	Reference
	(A)	(B)	(C)	(D)	(E)	(F)
			Single Exposure (concluded)			
5	X ray (concluded) 250 kv	300 r[2]	Sacroiliac joints, spine	Decreased lymphocytes, neutrophils, WBC count, venous hematocrit. Lymphocytes decreased 1-2 da after exposure; WBC count and venous hematocrit decreased 2nd da; neutrophils decreased 5th da after temporary increase.		4
			Repeated Exposure			
6	Occupational	100 mr/wk		WBC counts lower than in controls		25
7		125 mr/wk		WBC counts lower than in controls and in those individuals exposed to 100 mr/wk		25
8		0.02-0.05 r/da[3]		"In all probability, radiation quantities as low as 0.02-0.05 r/da can, after a comparatively short time, give rise to blood changes."	Based on data from Nordensen (1946) and Helde (1946)	13, 27, 32
9		0.05 r/da		Increased refractile neutral red bodies in lymphocytes	Study of 364 exposed employees	8
10	Cyclotron	Probably below maximum-permissible exposure; approximately $3\frac{1}{2}$ mo		Increased incidence of lymphocytes with bilobed nuclei	Blood picture returned to normal after extra shielding installed	17
11	Metallurgical laboratory	<0.1 r/da for 6 and 12 mo		Significant increase in lymphocyte count after 6 and 12 months of employment	The significant increase in lymphocyte count does not justify the inference that the rise was a result of occupational exposure alone. 453 employed 6 mo; 205, 12 mo.	29
12	Radiophysics institute			Hypersegmentation of polymorphonuclear leukocyte nuclei; pathological lymphocytes, granulocytopenia; left shift in granulocytes	Study of 1405 exposed employees; reported in 1946	13
13	Radium	0.2 μg[4]; repeated exposure during period 1941-1947		Almost all workers showed presence of abnormal early mononuclear cells; 22-40% of employees examined showed lymphocytosis without neutropenia	After individuals ceased luminizing, abnormal early mononuclear cells no longer present and lymphocyte counts returned to normal; several hundred luminizers examined each year.	6
14		Few weeks exposure		12 of 17 employees showed definite decrease of leukocytes, particularly of neutrophils; lymphocytosis; often a slight increase in eosinophils	Study of 17 exposed, new employees; reported in 1935	12

/2/ Mean surface dose. /3/ Estimated. /4/ Accumulated dose.

Part I: MAN (Continued)

	Radiation	Dose	Exposed Body Area or Administration	Effect	Remarks	Reference
	(A)	(B)	(C)	(D)	(E)	(F)
				Repeated Exposure (concluded)		
	Occupational (concluded)					
15	Radium (concluded)	6 mo-3 yr exposure		Blood picture same as that of new workers after several wk	Study of 15 employees; reported in 1935	12
16	Radium institute	1 mo-23 yr exposure		"Radiological blood picture," viz. high percentage of lymphocytes, normal RBC counts, and normal or high color index	15 employees observed in 1921; by 1923 all personnel showed counts differing very little from normal	1
17	Radium; X ray	Probably daily exposure		Persistent decrease in lymphocytes; less marked decrease in neutrophils	20 employees exposed to radium, 18 to X ray; reported in 1921	26
18	Predominantly X and γ rays (particle accelerator)	Tolerance range approximately 200 mr/wk		Increased incidence of lymphocytes with bilobed nuclei		10
19	γ ray, high energy	0.2 r/wk for 77 wk	Entire body	Decreased WBC, absolute lymphocytes, absolute neutrophils		18
20	X ray 55-60 kv (fluoroscope)	Approximately 800-1000 r (4 min) in 3 mo	Hands	Decreased absolute lymphocytes; increased percentage of lymphocytes in differential counts; many abnormal monocytes	Normal when blood re-examined 6 mo later	16
21	200, 400 kvp	Approximately 7 megagram-r; integral dose = 1-50 megagram-r, tumor dose = 3000-6000 r[5]	Tumor	Reduced absolute lymphocyte count to 25% of initial level	Injurious effect per megagram-r increased with decreasing integral dose per day	19
22	200, 400, 1000 kvp	40 r at 15-20 r/dose	Entire body	Decreased lymphocytes		21
23		200-300 r at 5-10 r/da	Entire body	Decreased lymphocytes		
24		88-300 r at 5-20 r/da	Entire body	Decreased lymphocytes, neutrophils, WBC, RBC, hemoglobin		
25	250 kv (30 x 30 cm or 45 x 45 cm fields)	50-75-100 r/da for 3-6 da		Transient increase in platelet count, followed by decrease; rate of decrease greater in patients with impaired hematopoiesis and greater with larger size of field		3
				Latent Effects		
26	Atomic bomb detonation Hiroshima, 1945	Approximately 400 r; single exposure	Entire body	Epilation		34
				Slight decrease in percentage of lymphocytes	1 yr after exposure	
				Slight increase in eosinophils	1 yr after exposure	
				Greater variability in blood picture of the 904 survivors than in blood picture of matched control groups	1 yr after exposure	

/5/ Integral dose specifies all of the radiation absorbed within the body; tumor dose refers to the average tissue dose absorbed in the region of the tumor.

Part I: MAN (Continued)

	Radiation	Dose	Exposed Body Area or Administration	Effect	Remarks	Reference
	(A)	(B)	(C)	(D)	(E)	(F)
	Latent Effects (continued)					
27	Atomic bomb detonation (concluded) Hiroshima, 1945 (concluded)	Single exposure		Increased incidence of leukemia among survivors at distance less than 2500 meters from impact area	Highest incidence among those exposed at distances less than 1500 meters from explosion. Peak incidence in period 1950-1952. More than 50% of cases acute or sub-acute. (Total number of cases, 92.)	22
28	Nagasaki	Single exposure at <1500 meters		Refractory hypoplastic anemia, characterized by anemia, leukopenia, thrombocytopenia	Latent period, 4-7 yr; 4 of 5075 survivors observed	20
29	Fall-out from detonation of nuclear device[6]	175 r[1]	Entire body	Decreased lymphocytes, monocytes, eosinophils, platelets	1 yr after exposure; blood picture of victims compared with that of carefully selected control groups	7
30	Laboratory accident	186 80 kv equivalent r, plus 10.7 r γ; single exposure		Decreased absolute lymphocyte count	Duration 1 yr	14
				Increased refractile neutral red bodies in lymphocytes	Present for 18 mo	
31		390 80 kv equivalent r, plus 26.4 r γ; single exposure		Decreased absolute lymphocytes; increased neutral red bodies in lymphocytes	2 yr after exposure	
32	Occupational X ray (physicians)	Probably repeated exposure, long duration		Incidence of death due to leukemia 1.75 times higher among physicians than among general male population; lower incidence due to cancer	Deaths occurred during period 1938-1942	11
33				Increased incidence of death due to leukemia	9354 physicians who died during period 1947-1951. Relatively short latent period (incidence increased within first 5 yr after exposure).	30
34		Many years exposure		Physician had mycosis fungoides for many years after working with X ray, and "temporary leukemia" from time to time throughout 14-year period	"Temporary leukemia" (WBC approximately 55,000/cu mm hemoglobin, 90% lymphocytes) responded well to X-ray therapy	2
35	X ray (physicians generally, and radiologists)			14 leukemic deaths per 299 deaths in radiologists; 344 leukemic deaths per 65,992 in physicians other than radiologists		23
36	Probably X ray and radium (physicians)	Repeated exposure, probably over many years		Incidence of death due to leukemia 1.6 times higher among physicians than among general male population		15

/1/ Calculated. /6/ Marshall Islands, spring, 1954.

Part I: MAN (Continued)

	Radiation (A)	Dose (B)	Exposed Body Area or Administration (C)	Effect (D)	Remarks (E)	Reference (F)
	Latent Effects (concluded)					
37	Occupational (concluded) Probably X ray and radium (dermatologists)	Repeated exposure, probably over many years		Increased incidence of leukemia	Deaths occurred in period 1935-1944	36
38	Radium	Chronic poisoning (fatal)	Internal deposition	Hyperplastic marrow showing regeneration of megaloblasts		24
39	Thorium X		Intravenous (tuberculosis of knee joint)	Myeloid leukemia developed 1 yr after administration of thorium X		31
40	Thorotrast	50 ml containing 2.5 g thorium/ 12 ml solution (890 r/yr/g thorium)[7]	Intravenous	Chronic myelosis	Injected in 1931; mild clinical course; paradoxical two-fold increase in WBC count when spleen irradiated with X ray	14
41	X ray		Spine (ankylosing spondylitis)	High incidence of death (7 of 64 deaths) due to leukemia		5
42				Deaths due to leukemia between 5 and 10 times expected number among patients receiving 1 course of therapy; at least 9 times expected number among patients receiving more than 1 course of therapy	Some, but not all, of increased incidence may reflect increased susceptibility of patients with ankylosing spondylitis to leukemia	
43		900-5950 r	Spine (ankylosing spondylitis)	7 patients developed blood dyscrasias after therapy; 5 instances of myeloid leukemia (1 had antecedent aplastic anemia); 2 instances of aplastic anemia	Latent period, $2\frac{1}{2}$ mo-6 yr	37
44		50-1500 r	Thymus (enlarged, in children)	Increased incidence of leukemia associated with doses less than 200 r; thyroid cancer associated with larger doses	Total incidence of neoplasma significantly higher than among non-irradiated siblings	33
45		Frequently >2.5 r	Prenatal, during X-ray examination of mother	Increased incidence of leukemia in children of irradiated mothers		35

/7/ Estimated total dose, 1780 r/yr for 25 yr.

Contributor: Ingram, Marylou

References: [1] Amundsen, P. 1924. Acta radiol., Stockh. 3:1. [2] Aub, J. C., S. B. Wohlback, B. J. Kennedy, and O. T. Bailey. 1955. A. M. A. Arch Path. 60:535. [3] Brown, W. M. C. 1949. Acta radiol., Stockh. 32:407. [4] Brown, W. M. C., and J. D. Abbatt. 1955. Brit. J. Haemat. 1:75. [5] Brown, W. M. C., and J. D. Abbatt. 1955. Lancet, Lond. 1:1283. [6] Browning, E. 1949. Brit. M. J. 1:428. [7] Cronkite, E. P., et al. 1955. J. Am. M. Ass. 159:430. [8] Dickie, A., and L. H. Hempelmann. 1947. J. Laborat. Clin. M. 32:1045. [9] Dobson, R. L., and M. M. Chupp. 1957. UCRL-3574. Office of Technical Services, Department of Commerce, Washington, D. C.

Part I: MAN (Concluded)

[10] Dobson, R. L., and M. M. Chupp. 1957. Proc. Soc. Exp. Biol., N. Y. 95:360. [11] Dublin, L. I., and M. Spiegelman. 1947. J. Am. M. Ass. 134:1211. [12] Goodfellow, D. R. 1935. Brit. J. Radiol. 8:669. [13] Helde, M. 1946. Acta radiol., Stockh. 27:308. [14] Hempelmann, L. H., H. Lisco, and J. G. Hoffman. 1952. Ann. Int. M. 36:279. [15] Henshaw, P. S., and J. W. Hawkins. 1944. J. Nat. Cancer Inst. 4:339. [16] Hultberg, S. 1949. Acta radiol., Stockh. 32:15. [17] Ingram, M., et al. 1952. Science 116:706. [18] Knowlton, N. P., Jr. 1948. AECU-1021. Office of Technical Services, Department of Commerce, Washington, D. C. [19] Kohn, H. I. 1955. Radiology 64:382. [20] Lange, R. D., and S. W. Wright. 1955. Blood, N. Y. 10:312. [21] Low-Beer, B. V. A., and R. S. Stone. 1948. AECD-2348. Office of Technical Services, Department of Commerce, Washington, D. C. (Also in R. S. Stone, ed. 1951. Nat. Nucl. En. Ser. IV-20. McGraw-Hill, New York.) [22] Maloney, W. C. 1955. N. England J. M. 253:88. [23] March, H. C. 1950. Am. J. M. Sc. 220:282. [24] Martland, H. S. 1929. J. Am. M. Ass. 92:466. [25] Mayneord, W. V. 1951. Brit. J. Radiol. 24:525. [26] Mottram, J. C. 1920-21. Arch. Radiol. Electrother., Lond. 25:368. [27] Nordenson, N. G. 1946. Acta radiol., Stockh. 27:416. [28] Oughterson, A. W., and S. Warren, ed. 1956. Nat. Nucl. En. Ser. VIII-8. McGraw-Hill, New York. [29] Pearlman, N., and G. Sacher. 1951. CH-3865. Office of Technical Services, Department of Commerce, Washington, D. C. (Also in R. S. Stone, ed. 1951. Nat. Nucl. En. Ser. IV-20. McGraw-Hill, New York.) [30] Peller, S., and P. Pick. 1951. J. Am. M. Ass. 147:893. [31] Schafer, E. L., and H. Grevel. 1952. Münch. med. Wschr. 94:158. [32] Sievert, R. M. 1947. Brit. J. Radiol. 20:306. [33] Simpson, C. L., L. H. Hempelmann, and L. M. Fuller. 1955. Radiology 64:840. [34] Snell, F. M., J. V. Neel, and K. Ishibashi. 1949. Arch. Int. M. 84:569. [35] Stewart, A., J. Webb, D. Giles, and D. Hewitt. 1956. Lancet, Lond. 271:447. [36] Ulrich, H. 1956. N. England J. M. 234:45. [37] Von Swaay, H. 1955. Lancet, Lond. 269:225.

Part II: VERTEBRATES OTHER THAN MAN

	Animal	Radiation	Dose	Exposed Body Area or Administration	Effect	Reference
	(A)	(B)	(C)	(D)	(E)	(F)
1	Bat	X ray 250 kv	500 r; single exposure (at room temp.)	Entire body	Decreased lymphocytes and granulocytes; no decrease in RBC	37
2	Burro	γ ray (cobalt⁶⁰)	400 r/da for 10 da	Entire body	Pronounced leukopenia (lymphocytes and granulocytes); lymphocytes less than 8% of normal 1 hr after exposure; minimal granulocyte count on 6th da. Decreased platelets; hyperferremia	41
3	Dog	Fast neutrons	1.7 n/da, 6 da/wk for 3-4 wk	Entire body	Decreased WBC, absolute lymphocytes, absolute neutrophils	9
4			1.7 n/da, 6 da/wk for 1 yr	Entire body	Decreased WBC, absolute lymphocytes, absolute neutrophils, platelets, RBC	
5		gold¹⁹⁸	Repeated injection	Intravenous	Aplastic anemia	20
6			250-500 mc; repeated injection	Intraperitoneal	Decreased WBC count; reached approximately 4800 WBC/cu mm hemoglobin; returned to normal 5-8 wk after initial injection	20
7			1 μc/kg body wt	Intravenous	Moderate leukopenia; decreased hemoglobin and hematocrit (depressed for several wk); increased RBC sedimentation rate	45
8			25.9-42.9 mc/kg body wt	Intravenous	Definite leukopenia; WBC in low normal range terminally	20

	Animal	Radiation	Dose	Exposed Body Area or Administration	Effect	Reference
	(A)	(B)	(C)	(D)	(E)	(F)
9	Dog (concluded)	Strontium[89]	2 or 7 mc	Parenteral	Decreased granulocytes, WBC count, hematocrit; hematocrit depression greater with 7 mc; minimal level, 21-25 da	29
10			20 mc	Parenteral	Decreased lymphocytes, granulocytes, WBC count, hematocrit; hematocrit depression greater than that following 2- or 7- mc dose	
11		X ray 175 kv	100 r/wk for life	Entire body[1]	Decreased fragility of RBC in 0.5% saline and alloxan (greater in splenectomized than in non-splenectomized dogs); severe anemia; increase in fragility in terminal stage of X-ray sickness	3
12		X ray 200 kvp	20 r; single exposure	Entire body	Decreased absolute lymphocytes	32
13			50 r; single exposure	Entire body	Decreased absolute lymphocytes, platelets, WBC, granulocytes	32
14			200 r; single exposure	Entire body	Decreased absolute lymphocytes, platelets, WBC, granulocytes, reticulocytes. Decrease in WBC and platelets more marked with increased doses.	32
15			10 r/da, 6 da/wk for 1 mo	Entire body	Decreased absolute lymphocytes, absolute neutrophils, WBC, RBC, hemoglobin, reticulocytes	18
16			1278 r at 12.5 r/da	Entire body	Aplastic anemia; absolute lymphocytes fell to 700/cu mm hemoglobin	31
17			900 r at 25 r/da	Entire body	Severe anemia; absolute lymphocytes reached level of 300/cu mm hemoglobin	47
18			900 r at 50 r/da	Entire body	Absolute lymphocytes reached level of about 100/cu mm hemoglobin	47
19		X ray 200 kvp, 1000 kvp	0.5 r/da, 6 da/wk for 2 yr	Entire body	Decreased lymphocytes	18
20			1.0 r/da, 6 da/wk for 1 yr	Entire body	Decreased lymphocytes, WBC, neutrophils	
21		X ray 250 kvp, 1000 kvp	3 r/da, 6 da/wk for 1-2 mo	Entire body	Decreased absolute lymphocytes, reticulocytes, platelets	18
22			6 r/da, 6 da/wk for 1-2 mo	Entire body	Decreased WBC, absolute lymphocytes, absolute neutrophils, platelets	
23		X ray 1000 kvp	5 r; single exposure		Increased incidence of lymphocytes with bilobed nuclei for 4 wk; peak incidence 2nd and 3rd wk after exposure	17
24	Goat	X ray 200 kvp	300 r; single exposure	Entire body	Decreased lymphocytes, neutrophils, WBC, RBC, hemoglobin	40
25	Guinea pig	γ ray (radium)	0.11 r/da for approximately 1 mo	Entire body	Decreased lymphocytes, WBC, heterophils	27
26			1.1 r/da for approximately 1 mo	Entire body	Decreased lymphocytes, WBC, heterophils	
27			1.1 r/da for approximately 1 yr	Entire body	Decreased lymphocytes, WBC, heterophils; decreased platelets in females only	
28			2.2 r/da for approximately 1 mo	Entire body	Decreased lymphocytes, WBC, heterophils	
29			2.2 r/da for approximately 1 yr	Entire body	Decreased lymphocytes, WBC, heterophils, platelets	

/1/ 5 splenectomized and 5 non-splenectomized dogs. Of the splenectomized animals, 4 lived 18 weeks, 1 lived 24 weeks; of the non-splenectomized animals, 4 succumbed in 15 weeks, 1 lived 26 weeks.

	Animal	Radiation	Dose	Exposed Body Area or Administration	Effect	Reference
	(A)	(B)	(C)	(D)	(E)	(F)
30	Guinea pig (concluded)	γ ray (radium) (concluded)	2.2 r/da for 79 wk	Entire body	Decreased lymphocytes, WBC, heterophils; decreased RBC, hemoglobin in males only	27
31			4.4 r/da for approximately 1 mo	Entire body	Decreased lymphocytes, WBC, heterophils	
32			4/4 r/da for approximately 1 yr	Entire body	Decreased lymphocytes, WBC, heterophils, platelets, RBC, hemoglobin	
33			8.8 r/da for 10 da	Entire body	Decreased lymphocytes, WBC	
34			8.8 r/da for approximately 1 mo	Entire body	Decreased lymphocytes, WBC, heterophils, platelets	
35			8.8 r/da for 19 wk	Entire body	Decreased lymphocytes, WBC, heterophils, RBC, hemoglobin (precipitous)	
36		X ray 200 kv	220 r; single exposure	Entire body	Decreased all leukocytes, RBC, hemoglobin	26
37	Hamster	X ray	600 r; single exposure	Entire body	Decreased lymphocytes, granulocytes, platelets, RBC, hemoglobin. Adhesiveness of WBC and platelets to endothelium not increased; RBC and hemoglobin decrease began approximately 9th da after exposure.	13
38			825 r; single exposure		Decreased granulocytes; maximum depression 5-7 da after exposure; returned to normal by 15th da	5
39	Monkey	Strontium^{90} (in equilibrium with Yttrium^{90})	0.1-0.2 mc/kg body wt; single injection	Intramuscular	Decreased lymphocytes, granulocytes, platelets, RBC. Lymphocytes decreased immediately after injection; granulocytes and platelets decreased 5 da after injection; minimal WBC levels in 3rd wk.	8
40			0.47-0.5 mc/kg body wt; single injection	Intramuscular	Decreased lymphocytes, granulocytes, platelets, RBC, reticulocytes. Reticulocytes normal 11-15 da after exposure; reduced but not absent 17th-20th da; RBC decreased 10th da after injection.	
41		X ray 250 kv	50-100 r; single exposure	Entire body	Decreased lymphocytes, granulocytes, platelets, RBC packed volume. WBC seldom less than 3000/cu mm hemoglobin; minimal levels about 15 da after exposure; reached normal levels only after 30 da.	12
42			260 r; single exposure	Entire body	Decreased lymphocytes, granulocytes, platelets, RBC, reticulocytes. Minimal WBC counts 14-17 da after exposure; marked reticulocytosis 16 da after exposure.	15
43			400 r; single exposure	Entire body	Decreased lymphocytes, granulocytes, platelets, RBC packed volume. WBC remained between 400 and 1600/cu mm hemoglobin from 5th to 8th da after exposure; returned to normal only after 30 da.	12
44			500-550 r; single exposure	Entire body	Decreased lymphocytes, granulocytes, platelets, RBC, reticulocytes. Rapid RBC decrease with minimal levels 20-26 da after exposure; reticulocytes absent 4th-17th da; reticulocytosis 18th-29th da.	15

	Animal	Radiation	Dose	Exposed Body Area or Administration	Effect	Reference
	(A)	(B)	(C)	(D)	(E)	(F)
45	Monkey (con-cluded)	X ray 250 kv (con-cluded)	600-650 r; single exposure	Entire body	Decreased lymphocytes, granulocytes, platelets, RBC, reticulocytes. Minimal RBC count on 17th da; 4 survivors had RBC counts above normal levels by 100th da; marked reticulocytosis and many circulating nucleated RBC after 18th da.	15
46			800 r; single exposure	Entire body	Decreased lymphocytes, granulocytes, platelets, RBC packed volume. WBC at levels below 500/cu mm hemoglobin 8th da after exposure; recovery trend began on 15th da; no survivors after 17 da.	12
47	Mouse	Fast neutrons (cyclotron)	30 n at 0.07 n/da, 5 da/wk	Entire body	Decreased WBC	10
48			230 n at 1.4 n/da, 5 da/wk	Entire body	Decreased absolute lymphocytes, WBC, RBC, hemoglobin; increased frequency of WBC below 15,000/cu mm; shift to left in heterophils	10
49			110 rad; 1 or 2 exposures		Increased incidence of myeloid leukemia; more common in males; peak incidence at 10-14 mo of age	43
50		Plutonium	0.0062 μc/g body wt	Intravenous or intramuscular	Moderately severe decrease in WBC counts; effect sustained	24
51			>0.0062 μc/g body wt	Intravenous or intramuscular	Decreased WBC counts, platelets, reticulocytes; anemia	
52		Radium	0.02-0.03 μg	Intravenous, intraperitoneal, or intracardial	Decreased WBC counts	24
53			0.1-0.2 μg	Intravenous, intraperitoneal, or intracardial	Macrocytic anemia	
54		Strontium^{89}	0.068 μc/g body wt	Intraperitoneal	Decreased heterophils observed in ABC male mice, not in CF-1 mice	36
55			0.068-14.5 μc/g body wt	Intraperitoneal	Decreased heterophils, lymphocytes. Both cell types decreased about equally; decrease greater with larger doses	
56			2.0 μc/g body wt	Intraperitoneal	Sustained anemia in splenectomized mice only; sufficient myeloid metaplasia in spleens of non-splenectomized mice to prevent anemia	
57		Thermal neutrons, plus γ ray (pile)	3.3-4.3 x 10^{12} n/sq cm plus 520 r γ; single exposure for 80 min	Entire body	Decreased leukocytes, erythrocytes, reticulocytes; recovery after approximately 2 wk	42
58		Thermal neutrons or X ray, plus γ ray (pile)	128 r or more; single exposure	Entire body	Increased incidence of myeloid leukemia; necrosis of bone marrow in more than 50% of mice with myeloid leukemia; peak incidence at 12-16 mo of age.	42
59		X ray	50-250 r; single exposure	Entire body	Decreased iron^{59} uptake by RBC; depression greater with larger doses	38
60		X ray 140 kv	400-600 r; single exposure	Entire body	Leukocytes simultaneously decreased to same minimal level in both high and low WBC strains 5-8 da after exposure	39
61		X ray 200 kvp	50 r; single exposure	Entire body	Decreased lymphocytes, WBC	30

	Animal	Radiation	Dose	Exposed Body Area or Administration	Effect	Reference
	(A)	(B)	(C)	(D)	(E)	(F)
62	Mouse (concluded)	X ray 250 kvp	100-500 r; single exposure		Increased incidence of leukemia. (After injection with virulent AK[4] leukemia cells, probit of percent leukemic deaths plotted against log of dose in r gives regression line of type Y = a + b log X.)	38
63			119 rad; 1 or 2 exposures	Entire body	Increased incidence of myeloid leukemia; more common in males; peak incidence 6-15 mo of age	43
64	LAF$_1$	γ ray (radium)	2.2 r/da for 29 wk	Entire body	Decreased WBC, lymphocytes	27
65			4.4 r/da for 29 wk	Entire body	Decreased WBC, lymphocytes	
66			4.4 r/da for 79 wk	Entire body	Decreased WBC, lymphocytes; decreased RBC, hemoglobin, platelets in males only	
67			8.8 r/da for 29 wk	Entire body	Decreased WBC, lymphocytes	
68			8.8 r/da for 79 wk	Entire body	Decreased WBC, lymphocytes, RBC, hemoglobin, platelets	
69	Rabbit	Fast neutrons (cyclotron)	15-45 n at 1.7 n/da, 6 da/wk	Entire body	Decreased absolute lymphocytes, WBC	9
70			50-75 n at 1.7 n/da, 6 da/wk	Entire body	Decreased absolute lymphocytes, absolute neutrophils, WBC	
71			325 n at 1.7 n/da, 6 da/wk	Entire body	Decreased absolute lymphocytes, absolute neutrophils, WBC, RBC, hemoglobin	
72		Fast neutrons (pile)	9 n; single exposure	Entire body	Decreased absolute lymphocytes	21
73			26 n; single exposure	Entire body	Decreased absolute lymphocytes, heterophils	
74			68-76 n; single exposure	Entire body	Decreased absolute lymphocytes, heterophils, platelets	
75			128 n; single exposure	Entire body	Decreased absolute lymphocytes, heterophils, platelets, RBC, hemoglobin, reticulocytes	
76		Plutonium	0.0062 μc/g body wt	Intravenous or intramuscular	Decreased WBC count (sustained)	24
77		Radium	0.1 μg	Intravenous, intramuscular, or intracardial	Decreased WBC count	24
78			0.1-0.2 μc	Intravenous, intramuscular, or intracardial	Macrocytic anemia	
79		Strontium^{89}	1.0 μc/g body wt	Intraperitoneal	Decreased heterophils	24
80			3.0 μc/g body wt	Intraperitoneal	Decreased heterophils, lymphocytes, RBC, hemoglobin; morphological changes in WBC, RBC; RBC and hemoglobin returned quickly to normal	36
81		X ray 200 kvp	25 r; single exposure	Entire body	Decreased lymphocytes; returned to normal by 48 hr after exposure	22,31
82			100 r; single exposure	Entire body	Decreased lymphocytes, heterophils, reticulocytes, platelets; leukocyte depression greater, recovery slower, with increasing doses	46

	Animal	Radiation	Dose	Exposed Body Area or Administration	Effect	Reference
	(A)	(B)	(C)	(D)	(E)	(F)
83	Rabbit (concluded)	X ray 200 kvp (concluded)	200 r; single exposure	Entire body	Decreased lymphocytes, heterophils, platelets, reticulocytes, morphological abnormalities; increased neutral red granules in lymphocytes; occasional phagocytic monocyte containing engulfed nuclear debris 12-24 hr after exposure	46
84			500 r; single exposure	Entire body	Decreased leukocytes, platelets, reticulocytes, RBC, hemoglobin; morphological abnormalities in leukocytes; decreased WBC migration in vitro; anemia maximal on 14th da after exposure; RBC returned to normal by 23rd da	35,46
85			800 r or more; single exposure	Entire body	Decreased lymphocytes, heterophils, reticulocytes, platelets, RBC, hemoglobin; increased number of nucleated RBC	46
86		X ray 250, 1000 kvp	60-120 r at 10 r/da, 6 da/wk	Entire body	Decreased absolute lymphocytes, absolute neutrophils, WBC	18
87			720-960 r at 10 r/da, 6 da/wk	Entire body	Decreased WBC, absolute lymphocytes, absolute neutrophils, RBC, platelets	
88	♀	γ ray (radium)	1.1 r/da for approximately 2 mo	Entire body	Decreased absolute lymphocytes	27
89			2.2 r/da for approximately 2 mo	Entire body	Decreased absolute lymphocytes	
90			2.2 r/da for approximately 9 mo	Entire body	Decreased absolute lymphocytes, platelets	
91			4.4 r/da for approximately 2 mo	Entire body	Decreased absolute lymphocytes	
92			4.4 r/da for approximately 9 mo	Entire body	Decreased absolute lymphocytes, platelets	
93			8.8 r/da for approximately 2 mo	Entire body	Decreased absolute lymphocytes	
94			8.8 r/da for approximately 9 mo	Entire body	Decreased absolute lymphocytes, platelets	
95	Rat	Fast neutrons	1.7 n/da, 6 da/wk for 1 mo	Entire body	Decreased absolute lymphocytes	9
96			1.7 n/da, 6 da/wk for 1 yr	Entire body	Decreased absolute lymphocytes, RBC, hemoglobin	
97		Phosphorus[32]	0.3-4.5 μc/g body wt; single injection	Intraperitoneal	Leukopenia with minimal leukocyte levels 12-14 da after exposure; minimal levels lower with greater doses; rate of WBC decrease per r greater with smaller doses	28
98		Plutonium	0.0062 μc/g body wt	Intravenous or intramuscular	Moderately sustained leukocyte decrease	24
99			>0.0063 μg/g body wt	Intravenous or intramuscular	Decreased leukocytes, RBC, reticulocytes, platelets; all decreases sustained	
100		Plutonium[2]	18.9 μc/kg body wt; single injection	Intravenous	Decreased lymphocytes, neutrophils, platelets	11

/2/ Injected in the form of plutonium citrate.

Part II: VERTEBRATES OTHER THAN MAN (Continued)

	Animal	Radiation	Dose	Exposed Body Area or Administration	Effect	Reference
	(A)	(B)	(C)	(D)	(E)	(F)
101	Rat (continued)	Plutonium[2] (concluded)	47 μc/kg body wt; single injection	Intravenous	Decreased leukocytes, platelets, RBC, hemoglobin	11
102			95 μc/kg body wt; single injection	Intravenous	Decreased leukocytes, platelets, RBC, hemoglobin, reticulocytes. With doses above 126 and 189 μc/kg, precipitous fall in RBC and hemoglobin, suggesting hemolytic process.	
103		Radium[3]	17 μc/kg body wt; single injection	Intravenous	Decreased leukocytes; slight decrease in platelets; lymphocyte depression more marked with greater doses; neutrophils reached minimal level of 4% normal 14 da after injection	11
104			300 μc/kg body wt; single injection	Intravenous	Decreased leukocytes, platelets; anemia; spiking reticulocytosis 160 da after injection	11
105			700 μc/kg body wt; single injection	Intravenous	Decreased leukocytes, platelets, RBC, reticulocytes. Maximal platelet depression approximately 7 da after injection; marked elevation between 15-50 da.	11
106			10-50 μg; single injection	Intraperitoneal	Transient increase in platelets 3rd da after injection, followed by progressive decrease	34
107			0.02-0.03 μg	Parenteral	Decreased leukocytes	24
108			0.1-0.2 μg	Parenteral	Macrocytic anemia	24
109		Strontium[89]	0.22-0.25 μc/g body wt; single injection	Intraperitoneal	Decreased neutrophils; more marked neutrophil decrease (also lymphopenia) with higher doses	36
110		X ray	5-100 r; single exposure	Entire body	Decreased iron[59] uptake by RBC; decrease greater with larger doses	16
111			50-250 r; single exposure	Entire body	Decreased iron[59] uptake by RBC depression varies as inverse function of radiation dose	
112		X ray 200 kv	85 r; single exposure	Entire body	Lymphocytes decreased by 12th hr after exposure; transient increase of neutrophils. Recovery commenced 2nd da after exposure; approached normal levels in 4 wk.	14
113			175 r; single exposure	Entire body	Lymphocytes decreased by 4th hr; all WBC decreased after 24 hr. Recovery commenced approximately 12-16 da after exposure.	14
114			600 r; single exposure	Entire body	Marked decrease in rate and extent of WBC migration in vitro 5 da after exposure (effect on WBC, not on plasma). Surface phagocytosis by WBC in vitro decreased 72 hr after exposure; returned to normal by 4th or 5th da after exposure. Extracts of leukocytes obtained 3 da after exposure had lost bactericidal activity against test organism Micrococcus aureus.	35
115		X ray 250 kvp	5 r; single exposure	Entire body	Decreased absolute lymphocytes	19
116			10 r; single exposure	Entire body	Decreased absolute lymphocytes, WBC	
117			50 r; single exposure	Entire body	Decreased neutrophils, WBC, absolute lymphocytes, reticulocytes	

/2/ Injected in the form of plutonium citrate. /3/ Injected in the form of radium chloride.

	Animal	Radiation	Dose	Exposed Body Area or Administration	Effect	Reference
	(A)	(B)	(C)	(D)	(E)	(F)
118	Rat (concluded)	X ray 250 kvp (concluded)	100 r; single exposure	Entire body	Decreased absolute lymphocytes, neutrophils, WBC, reticulocytes, platelets	19
119			300 r; single exposure	Entire body	Decreased absolute lymphocytes, neutrophils, WBC, reticulocytes, platelets, RBC, hemoglobin	
120		X ray 250-1000 kvp	0.5 r/da for 2 yr	Entire body	Decreased absolute lymphocytes	18
121			1 r/da for 1 yr	Entire body	Decreased absolute lymphocytes	
122		X or γ ray	2-75 r; single exposure	Entire body	Increased incidence of lymphocytes with bilobed nuclei; maximal incidence 1 wk after exposure	1
123		Yttrium^{91}	10 μc/g body wt	Gavage	Transient decrease in absolute lymphocytes	23
124			20 μc/g body wt	Gavage	Transient initial increase in RBC and hemoglobin, followed by severe anemia; maximal 20 da after administration	
125			0.3-2.0 μc/g body wt	Ingestion	Decreased lymphocytes; minimal level at 90 da. Returned rapidly to normal level after ingestion discontinued.	
126	Swine	Nuclear explosion, Bikini	Single exposure	Entire body	Macrocytic anemia; survived 17 mo; 1 of the 2 subjects also had achlorhydria	25
127			1300 r in 4 da, or 1500 r in 5 da; single exposure	Entire body	Decreased WBC count, platelets; many degenerating, abnormal leukocytes	4
128		X ray 1000 kv	200 r; single exposure	Entire body	Decreased WBC count	6
129	Chicken 6 da old	Phosphorus^{32}	235 μc; single injection	Subcutaneous	Decreased lymphocytes, WBC count, RBC. Maximal lymphocyte depression 4th da after injection; slow recovery; normal level reached on 55th da after injection; RBC normal 41 da after injection.	44
130	19 da old	Phosphorus^{32}	300 μc; single injection	Subcutaneous	Fatal anemia	7
131	28 da old	Phosphorus^{32}	760 μc; single injection	Subcutaneous	Fatal anemia (comparable to effect of 300 μc injection administered to 19-da-old chick)	7
132	1 da old	X ray 85 kv	360 r; single exposure	Entire body	Lymphocytes decreased with increased exposure	33
133		X ray 200 kvp	600 r; single exposure	Entire body	Decreased lymphocytes, heterophils, thrombocytes, RBC, hemoglobin, reticulocytes	47
134	Salmon	X ray 200 kv	750 r; single exposure	Entire body	Decreased nucleated cells	2

Contributor: Ingram, Marylou

References: [1] Bellack, S., and J. B. Storer. 1954. AMRL-162. Office of the Surgeon General, Ft. Knox, Kentucky. [2] Bonham, K., L. R. Donaldson, R. F. Foster, A. D. Welander, and A. H. Seymour. 1948. Growth, Phila. 12:107. [3] Constant, M. A., and P. H. Phillips. 1954. Am. J. Physiol. 178:367. [4] Cronkite, E. P. 1950. Blood, N. Y. 5:32. [5] Cronkite, E. P., and G. Brecher. 1955. Ann. N. York Acad. Sc. 59:815. [6] Cronkite, E. P., F. W. Ullrich, D. C. Eltzholtz, C. R. Sipe, and P. K. Schork. 1949. NM-007-039.21. U. S. Naval Medical Research Institute, Bethesda, Md. [7] Dixon, F. J. 1948. Proc. Soc. Exp. Biol., N.Y. 68:505. [8] Edington, G. M., A. H. Ward, J. M. Judd, and R. H. Mole. 1956. J. Path. Bact., Lond. 71:277. [9] Ely, J. O., M. J. Ross,

R. G. Metcalf, F. A. Inda, T. B. Barnett, and G. W. Casarett. 1950. UR-92. Office of Technical Services, Department of Commerce, Washington, D. C. [10] Evans, T. 1948. Radiology 50:811. [11] Fink, R. M., ed. 1950. Nat. Nucl. En. Ser. VI-3. McGraw-Hill, New York. [12] French, A. B., C. J. Migeon, L. T. Samuels, and J. Z. Bowers. 1955. Am. J. Physiol. 182:469. [13] Fulton, G. P., J. L. Joftes, R. Kagan, and B. R. Lutz. 1954. Blood, N. Y. 9:622. [14] Gershon-Cohen, J., and M. B. Hermel. 1954. Am. J. Roentg. 71:846. [15] Haigh, M. V., and E. Patterson. 1956. Brit. J. Radiol. 29:148. [16] Hennessey, T. G., and R. L. Huff. 1950. Proc. Soc. Exp. Biol., N. Y. 73:436. [17] Ingram, M. 1956. Proc. 1st Internat. Conf. Peaceful Uses Atomic Energy, Geneva, 1955. United Nations, New York. [18] Ingram, M., and W. B. Mason. 1950. UR-121. Office of Technical Services, Department of Commerce, Washington, D. C. (Also in H. A. Blair, ed. 1954. Nat. Nucl. En. Ser. VI-2. McGraw-Hill, New York.) [19] Ingram, M., and W. B. Mason. 1950. UR-122. Office of Technical Services, Department of Commerce, Washington, D. C. (Also in H. A. Blair, ed. 1954. Nat. Nucl. En. Ser. VI-2. McGraw-Hill, New York.) [20] Jackson, A. A., and P. F. Hahn. 1955. Cancer, Phila. 8:480. [21] Jacobson, L. O., and E. K. Marks. 1947. CH-3839. Office of Technical Services, Department of Commerce, Washington, D. C. [22] Jacobson, L. O., E. K. Marks, E. L. Simmons, C. W. Hagen, Jr., and R. E. Zirkle. 1947. CH-3798. Office of Technical Services, Department of Commerce, Washington, D. C. (Also in R. E. Zirkle, ed. 1954. Nat. Nucl. En. Ser. IV-22B. McGraw-Hill, New York. ch. 8, p. 265.) [23] Jacobson, L. O., and E. L. Simmons. 1946. AECD-2037. Office of Technical Services, Department of Commerce, Washington, D. C. [24] Jacobson, L. O., and E. L. Simmons. 1946. AECD-2372. Office of Technical Services, Department of Commerce, Washington, D. C. [25] Lawrason, F. D., and E. P. Cronkite. 1949. Yale J. Biol. 22:57. [26] Lorenz, E. 1951. J. chim. phys., Par. 48:264. [27] Lorenz, E., et al. 1947. Radiology 49:286. (Also in R. E. Zirkle, ed. 1954. Nat. Nucl. En. Ser. IV-22B. McGraw-Hill, New York. ch. 3.) [28] Mitra, S., K. L. Bhattacharya, A. Bose, and K. P. Chakraborty. 1953. Acta radiol., Stockh. 40:593. [29] Nelson, J. E., J. G. Gibson, II, B. L. Vallee, and M. A. van Dilla. 1949. Acta Unio internat. cancr., Brux. 6:819. [30] Nettleship, A. 1944. Radiology 42:64. [31] Prosser, C. L., H. Lisco, A. M. Brues, L. O. Jacobson, and M. N. Swift. 1947. MDDC-611, MDDC-1066. Office of Technical Services, Department of Commerce, Washington, D. C. (Also in Radiology 49:299, 1947.) [32] Prosser, C. L., E. E. Painter, and M. N. Swift. In R. E. Zirkle, ed. 1956. TID-5220 (CH-3738). Office of Technical Services, Department of Commerce, Washington, D. C. pp. 1-99. [33] Roberts, E., L. E. Card, and G. L. Clark. 1948. Biodynamica, Normandy 6:165. [34] Roofe, P. G., H. Bingham, R. Comer, and M. Madison. 1950. Anat. Rec. 108:537. [35] Schechmeister, I. C., and F. Fishman. 1950. J. Exp. M. 101:259. [36] Simmons, E. L., and L. O. Jacobson. 1946. MDDC-1387 (CH-3797). Office of Technical Services, Department of Commerce, Washington, D. C. [37] Smith, D. E., E. M. Jackson, and Y. Spiegel. 1952. ANL-4794. Q. Rep. Biol. M. Res. Div., Argonne National Laboratory, Chicago. [38] Storer, J. B., and W. H. Langham. 1954. AECU-3099. Office of Technical Services, Department of Commerce, Washington, D. C. [39] Swanson, H. D., C. A. Leone, and J. A. Weir. 1955. AECU-3130. Office of Technical Services, Department of Commerce, Washington, D. C. [40] Swift, M. N., C. L. Prosser, and E. S. Mika. 1946. AECU-108 (CH-3888). Office of Technical Services, Department of Commerce, Washington. D. C. [41] Trum, B. F., T. J. Haley, M. Bassin, J. Heglin, and J. H. Rust. 1953. Am. J. Physiol. 174:57. [42] Upton, A. C., J. Furth, and K. W. Christenberry. 1954. Cancer Res. 14:682. [43] Upton, A. C., G. S. Melville, Jr., M. Slater, F. P. Conte, and J. Furth. 1956. Proc. Soc. Exp. Biol., N. Y. 92:436. [44] Warren, S. L., and D. J. Dixon. 1949. Radiology 52:869. [45] Wheeler, B., M. A. Jackson, and P. F. Hahn. 1951. Am. J. Physiol. 166:323. [46] Zirkle, R. E., ed. 1954. Nat. Nucl. En. Ser. IV-22B. McGraw-Hill, New York. [47] Zirkle, R. E., ed. 1956. TID-5220. Office of Technical Services, Department of Commerce, Washington, D. C.

225

Values for plasma and blood volumes are percent of body weight.

Animal	No. of Subjects	Radiation and Dose	Measured Element (Method)	Control Plasma Volume	Control Total Blood Volume	Effect of Radiation Time after Exposure	Effect of Radiation Plasma Volume	Effect of Radiation Total Blood Volume	Reference
(A)	(B)	(C)	(D)	(E)	(F)	(G)	(H)	(I)	(J)
1 Dog	8	X ray 200-400 r	Plasma volume (T-1824)	5.5	9.1	16-24 hr	5.4	9.6	5
						4 da	5.5	8.7	
						7 da	5.7	9.0	
						10-12 da	6.1	9.1	
						14-20 da	6.3	8.6	
						21-40 da	6.0	9.4	
2	6	X ray 450-500 r	Erythrocyte mass (Phosphorus^{32})	4.2	7.8	4 da	4.7	7.8	6
						7 da	6.2	8.5	
						10-12 da	5.6	8.2	
						14-20 da	5.7	8.0	
3	1	α particles (plutonium^{239}); 0.287 μg/g, IV	Plasma volume (T-1824)	5.1	9.2	10-12 da	7.9	10.7	4
						21-40 da	6.7	8.4	
						Over 40 da	7.8	8.9	
4	1	α particles (plutonium^{239}); 0.358 μg/g, IV	Plasma volume (T-1824)	4.6	7.6	10-12 da	5.7	8.8	4
5	1	α particles (plutonium^{239}); 0.418 μg/g, IV	Plasma volume (T-1824)	5.3	9.0	10-12 da	6.0	8.4	4
6 Mouse	7	X ray 575 r	Erythrocyte mass (Phosphorus^{32}) Plasma volume (T-1824)	4.5[1]	7.2	4 da	4.6	7.2	10
						10-12 da	4.7	6.5	
						14-20 da	4.9	6.5	
7 Rabbit	1-3	X ray 800 r	Plasma volume (T-1824)	3.4	5.7	1-2 hr	3.6	5.2	3
						4 hr	4.2	6.8	
						6 hr	3.5	5.1	
8	2	X ray 1000 r	Erythrocyte mass (Phosphorus^{32}) Plasma volume (T-1824)	3.8[2]	5.7	16-24 hr	3.9	5.5	10
						4 da	3.5	5.3	
						7 da	3.0	4.6	
						10-12 da	3.2	4.6	
						14-20 da	3.7	4.9	
						21-40 da	3.8	5.0	
9 Rat	4-8	X ray 200 r	Plasma volume (T-1824)	4.4		30-48 hr	4.2		1
						10-12 da	4.5		
10	8-14	X ray 400 r	Plasma volume (T-1824)	4.4		30-48 hr	4.5		1
						10-12 da	4.4		
11	4-5	X ray 400 r	Erythrocyte mass (Phosphorus^{32})	2.5	4.8	30-48 hr	2.6	4.8	11
						4 da	2.8	5.2	
						7 da	2.7	4.5	
						10-12 da	3.2	5.1	
						14-20 da	3.0	4.5	
12	3-5	X ray 600 r	Erythrocyte mass (Phosphorus^{32})	2.5	4.8	30-48 hr	2.4	4.7	11
						4 da	2.7	5.3	
						7 da	2.6	4.4	
						10-12 da	3.4	4.7	
						14-20 da	3.8	5.0	
13	9-15	X ray 700 r	Plasma volume (T-1824)	4.4		30-48 hr	5.3		1
						14-20 da	6.4		
						21-40 da	4.5		
14	5	X ray 750 r	Erythrocyte mass (Phosphorus^{32})	2.5	4.8	30-48 hr	2.4	4.8	11
						4 da	2.8	5.2	
						7 da	3.1	4.7	
						10-12 da	3.7	4.5	
						14-20 da	3.5	4.8	
						21-40 da	3.9	4.8	
15	7-8	X ray 1500 r	Erythrocyte mass (Phosphorus^{32})	3.4	7.0	6 hr	3.5	6.7	2
						16-24 hr	3.2	5.6	
						30-48 hr	3.0	5.2	

/1/ Corrected by a factor of 1.2 for Evans' blue removed from blood. /2/ Corrected by a factor of 1.08 for Evans' blue removed from blood.

85. EFFECT OF IONIZING RADIATION ON TOTAL CIRCULATING PLASMA AND BLOOD VOLUMES: VERTEBRATES (Concluded)

| | Animal | No. of Subjects | Radiation and Dose | Measured Element (Method) | Control | | Effect of Radiation | | | Reference |
					Plasma Volume	Total Blood Volume	Time after Exposure	Plasma Volume	Total Blood Volume	
	(A)	(B)	(C)	(D)	(E)	(F)	(G)	(H)	(I)	(J)
16	Chicken 3-4 da	21	X ray 1000 r	Erythrocyte mass (Phosphorus^{32}) Plasma volume (Iodine^{131})	5.0	6.9	4 hr	2.9	4.6	7
17	6-8 mo	29♂	X ray 1200 r	Erythrocyte mass (Phosphorus^{32}) Plasma volume (Iodine^{131})	3.4	5.9	6 hr	2.2	4.8	8,9

Contributor: Stearner, S. Phyllis

References: [1] France, O. In R. E. Zirkle, ed. 1956. TID-5220. Office of Technical Services, Department of Commerce, Washington, D. C. pp. 411-427. [2] Montgomery, P. O. B., and S. Warren. 1951. Proc. Soc. Exp. Biol., N. Y. 77:803. [3] Painter, E. E., C. L. Prosser, and M. C. Moore. In R. E. Zirkle, ed. 1956. TID-5220. Office of Technical Services, Department of Commerce, Washington, D. C. pp. 147-181. [4] Painter, E. E., E. Russell, C. L. Prosser, M. N. Swift, W. Kisieleski, and G. Sacher. 1946. AECD-2042. Office of Technical Services, Department of Commerce, Washington, D. C. [5] Prosser, C. L., E. E. Painter, and M. N. Swift. In R. E. Zirkle, ed. 1956. TID-5220. Office of Technical Services, Department of Commerce, Washington, D. C. [6] Soberman, R. J., R. P. Keating, and R. D. Maxwell. 1951. Am. J. Physiol. 164:450. [7] Stearner, S. P., M. H. Sanderson, and E. J. Christian. 1957. ANL-5696. Q. Rep. Biol. M. Res. Div., Argonne National Laboratory, Chicago. pp. 31-34. [8] Stearner, S. P., M. H. Sanderson, E. J. Christian, and A. M. Brues. 1958. Am. J. Physiol. 192:620. [9] Stearner, S. P., et al. Unpublished. [10] Storey, R. H., L. Wish, and J. Furth. 1950. Proc. Soc. Exp. Biol., N. Y. 74:242. [11] Supplee, H., J. D. Hauschildt, and C. Entenman. 1952. Am. J. Physiol. 169:483.

86. EFFECT OF IONIZING RADIATION ON ORGAN BLOOD VOLUME: CHICKEN

	Animal	No. of Subjects	Organ	Condition	Organ Weight g	Erythrocyte Mass[1] % of organ weight Active	Inactive[3]	Plasma Volume[2] % of organ weight	Reference
	(A)	(B)	(C)	(D)	(E)	(F)	(G)	(H)	(I)
1	Chicken, 3-4 da	10	Duodenum	Control	0.257	1.14	0.46	6.64	1, 2
2				Irradiated[4]	0.205	1.87	1.16.	3.06	
3			Kidney	Control	0.245	7.9	1.2	24.7	
4				Irradiated[4]	0.259	5.2	7.5	9.4	
5			Liver	Control	1.69	7.4	4.0	15.7	
6				Irradiated[4]	1.52	3.6	9.2	7.2	
7			Lung	Control	0.210	17.1	2.1	40.3	
8				Irradiated[4]	0.217	18.0	2.1	20.9	
9			Proventriculus	Control	0.380	1.0	0	6.25	
10				Irradiated[4]	0.449	0.74	1.76	4.05	
11			Skeletal muscle	Control		0.91	0.19	2.85	
12				Irradiated[4]		0.94	0.31	1.70	
13			Spleen	Control	0.022	2.9	2.7	16.8	
14				Irradiated[4]	0.020	1.5	4.8	7.1	
15	Rooster	7-9	Duodenum	Control	3.69	2.86	0	7.40	2, 3
16				Irradiated[5]	3.53	2.83	0.12	4.10	
17			Kidney	Control	10.11	20.0	4.7	28.1	
18				Irradiated[5]	10.02	14.0	4.0	15.4	
19			Liver	Control	56.84	19.4	7.1	34.8	
20				Irradiated[5]	44.33	14.3	7.6	16.6	
21			Lung	Control	10.34	28.8	8.2	27.5	
22				Irradiated[5]	9.10	31.3	4.3	17.7	
23			Proventriculus	Control	4.44	2.63	0.03	6.80	
24				Irradiated[5]	4.91	1.64	0.15	3.80	
25			Skeletal muscle	Control		0.25	0.06	0.63	
26				Irradiated[5]		0.45	0.17	0.59	
27			Spleen	Control	4.68	16.5	6.4	22.1	
28				Irradiated[5]	1.79	6.5	12.7	8.4	

/1/ Method of measurement: lines 1-14, chromium^{51} and phosphorus^{32}; lines 15-28, chromium^{51}. /2/ Method of measurement: iodine^{131} human serum albumin. /3/ Erythrocyte mass that is pooled or inactively circulating and does not contribute to the actively circulating erythrocyte mass. /4/ 3-5 hours after irradiation with 1000 r X ray. /5/ 6-8 hours after irradiation with 1200 r X ray.

Contributor: Stearner, S. Phyllis

References: [1] Stearner, S. P., M. H. Sanderson, and E. J. Christian. 1957. ANL-5696. Q. Rep. Biol. M. Res. Div., Argonne National Laboratory, Chicago. pp. 31-34. [2] Stearner, S. P., M. H. Sanderson, E. J. Christian, and A. M. Brues. 1958. Am. J. Physiol. 192:620. [3] Stearner, S. P., et al. 1957. Unpublished.

Whole preserved blood was kept at 4°C and analyzed within 20 minutes after removal from storage. Blood changes occurring in eight days with preservative C were equivalent to those occurring in 18 days with CD and in 33 days with ACD. Preservative C = 3.2 g trisodium citrate-di-H$_2$O, in 100 ml aqueous solution, at pH 7.5 (effective tonicity of blood = 141%). Ten ml added to 100 ml blood increased blood citrate by 10 mM/L, and plasma citrate by 17 mM/L. Preservative CD = 2.13 g trisodium citrate-di-H$_2$O, plus 5 g glucose anhydrous, in 100 ml aqueous solution, at pH 7.5 (effective tonicity of blood = 94%). Fifteen ml added to 100 ml blood increased blood citrate by 11 mM/L, plasma citrate by 19 mM/L, and blood glucose by 650 mg/100 ml. Preservative ACD = 1.33 g trisodium citrate-di-H$_2$O, plus 470 mg citric acid and 3 g glucose anhydrous, in 100 ml aqueous solution, at pH 5.03 (effective tonicity of blood 66%). Twenty-five ml added to 100 ml blood increased blood citrate by 13 mM/L, plasma citrate by 21 mM/L, blood glucose by 600 mg/100 ml, and citric acid by 16.5 mEq/L. Values were obtained from smoothed curves in references.

	Property or Constituent	Method	Preservative	Storage Period, Days					Reference
				0	10	20	30	40	
	(A)	(B)	(C)	(D)	(E)	(F)	(G)	(H)	(I)
	Whole Blood								
1	pH	Measured at 37.5°C	C	7.4	7.1	7.1			1
2			CD	7.4	7.1	6.8	6.7	6.7	
3			ACD	7.1	6.7	6.6	6.6	6.6	
4	Glucose, mg/100 ml	Nelson's modification of Somogyi's method	C	70	10[1]	10[1]	10[1]		1
5			CD	720[2]	650	575	520		
6			ACD	670[2]	600	550	470		
7	Lactic acid, mg/100 ml	Friedman's modified aeration-titration	C	20	80				1
8			CD	10	135		210		
9			ACD	20	90		155	170	
10	Glycolysis rate, mg/100 ml/hr[3]	Blood incubated 90 minutes at 37°C	ACD					4	
	Erythrocytes								
11	Dimensions Diameter, μ	Stained film covered with 0.9% sodium chloride	C	7.69	6.92	6.25			1
12			CD	7.50	7.33	6.92	6.33	6.00	
13			ACD	7.42	7.33	7.17	6.83	6.50	
14	Thickness, μ	Mean corpuscular volume/πr^2. (Mean corpuscular volume = hematocrit/erythrocyte count/cu mm blood. Hematocrit determined by method of Guest and Star.)	C	1.80	2.32	3.05			
15			CD	2.08	2.30	2.58	3.23	3.65	
16			ACD	2.33	2.38	2.52	2.70	3.00	
	Hemolysis, % erythrocytes	Colorimetric % sodium chloride							1
17		0.9	C	0	2.5	9.8			
18		0.8	C	0	7.5	30			
19		0.7	C	0	34	61			
20		0.6	C	0	43	68	68		
21		0.5	C	0	60	80			
22		0.9	CD	0	0	2	6		
23		0.8	CD	0	0	7	30	50	
24		0.7	CD	0	2	16	48	60	
25		0.6	CD	0	3.6	25	64	76	
26		0.55	CD	5	16	56	80	85	
27		0.9	ACD	0	0	0	0.8	1.8	
28		0.8	ACD	0	0	0	2.2	15.5	
29		0.7	ACD	0	0	0	10	34	
30		0.6	ACD	0	4.2	13.7	28	65	
31		0.55	ACD	4.4	11.1	24.4	32.2	67.8	
	Glycolysis rate								1
32	Glucose lost, mg/100 ml/hr	Blood incubated 90 minutes at 37°C	C	50	10[4]	1[4]			
33	Lactic acid produced, mg/100 ml/hr	Blood incubated 90 minutes at 37°C	CD	40	20	6			
34			ACD	17	17	17	13		

/1/ Residual, non-fermentable reducing substances. /2/ Normal blood glucose, plus glucose in preservative. /3/ Lactic acid produced. /4/ Glycolysis measured by breakdown of added glucose, as glucose originally present had disappeared.

Property or Constituent	Method	Preservative	Storage Period, Days					Reference
			0	10	20	30	40	
(A)	(B)	(C)	(D)	(E)	(F)	(G)	(H)	(I)
Erythrocytes (concluded)								
35 Potassium, mEq/L		C	100	75	63			1
36		CD	100	74	65	60	53	
37		ACD	90	75	68	60	53	
38 Sodium, mEq/L		C	25	45	55			1
39		CD	21	40	47	52	58	
40		ACD	18	25	30	37	42	
41 Phosphorus, inorganic, mg/100 ml		C	0	35	35			1
42		CD	0	10	28	29	26	
43		ACD	5	18	25	25	25	
44 Adenosine triphosphate, mg/100 ml		C	15	5	2			1
45		CD	15	9	5	2	2	
46		ACD	15	14	12	9	6	
Plasma								
47 Hemoglobin present, mg/100 ml		C[5]	1	11				2
48 Potassium, mEq/L		C	5	23	32			1
49		CD	5	20	25	28	34	
50		ACD	5	12	19	23	27	
51 Sodium, mEq/L		C	166	149	142			1
52		CD	158	148	145	142	138	
53		ACD	160	152	148	142	137	
54 Phosphorus, inorganic, mg/100 ml		C	0	7	10			1
55		CD	2	3	6	10	12	
56		ACD	2	5	8	9	10	
57 Lactic acid, mg/100 ml	Friedman's modified aeration-titration	C		80				1
58		CD		185				
59		ACD		130				

/5/ 4% sodium citrate.

References: [1] Rapoport, S. 1947. J. Clin. Invest. 26:591. [2] Strumia, M. M., and J. J. McGraw. 1949. Blood and plasma transfusions. F. A. Davis, Philadelphia.

XI. Blood Coagulation

88. BLOOD COAGULATION THEORIES

Part I: ACCORDING TO F. C. MONKHOUSE AND W. W. COON (1960)

Synonymous terms for clotting factors: <u>Plasma thromboplastin component</u> = Christmas factor, platelet co-factor-2, autoprothrombin-2; <u>Antihemophilic factor</u> = antihemophilic globulin, thromboplastinogen; <u>Ac-globulin</u> = labile factor, factor V, proaccelerin; <u>Factor VII</u> = stable factor, autoprothrombin-1, proconvertin, cothromboplastin; <u>Plasminogen</u> = profibrinolysin; <u>Plasmin</u> = fibrinolysin.

Symbols: ———⟶ gives rise to; - - - - -⟶ acts on; ===⟹ inhibits or destroys; ☐ present in blood.

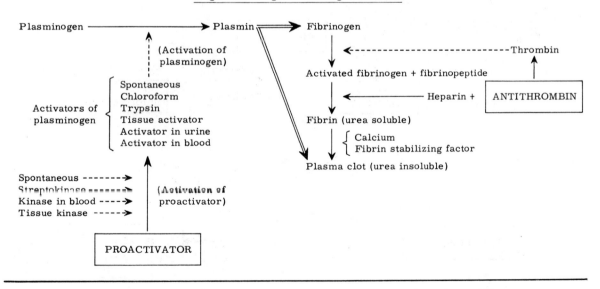

Stage I: Formation of Plasma Thromboplastin

Stage II: Formation of Thrombin

Stage III: Change of Fibrinogen to Fibrin

Contributors: (a) Monkhouse, Frank C., (b) Coon, William W.

References: [1] Astrup, T. 1956. Blood, N. Y. 11:781. [2] Lorand, L. 1954. Physiol. Rev. 34:742. [3] Sherry, S., W. Troll, and H. Glueck. 1954. Ibid. 34:736.

88. BLOOD COAGULATION THEORIES (Continued)

Part II: ACCORDING TO P. A. OWREN (1960)

System I: Intrinsic Blood Coagulation[1]

(1) CONTACT activates the inactive HAGEMAN FACTOR. Active HAGEMAN FACTOR interacts with PLASMA THROMBOPLASTIN ANTECEDENT, and an ACTIVATION PRODUCT is formed. (2) Reactions take place between the ACTIVATION PRODUCT and the following factors: FACTOR IX (antihemophilia factor B, Christmas factor), FACTOR VIII (antihemophilia factor A, antihemophilic globulin), FACTOR X (Stuart-Prower factor), lipoid factors with cephalin-like activity (from PLATELETS and possibly PLASMA LIPOID), and CALCIUM to form an intermediate complex termed BLOOD CONVERTIN. The sequence of reactions and the intermediates formed are not known. (3) BLOOD CONVERTIN brings about a minimal conversion of PROTHROMBIN to THROMBIN. (4) This initially-formed THROMBIN starts the accelerator system, i.e., the conversion of FACTOR V (proaccelerin) to ACCELERIN. (5) BLOOD CONVERTIN and ACCELERIN interact in the presence of calcium to form BLOOD PROTHROMBINASE. (6) BLOOD PROTHROMBINASE produces rapid conversion of PROTHROMBIN to THROMBIN. (7) THROMBIN is now formed in sufficient quantity to convert FIBRINOGEN to FIBRIN.

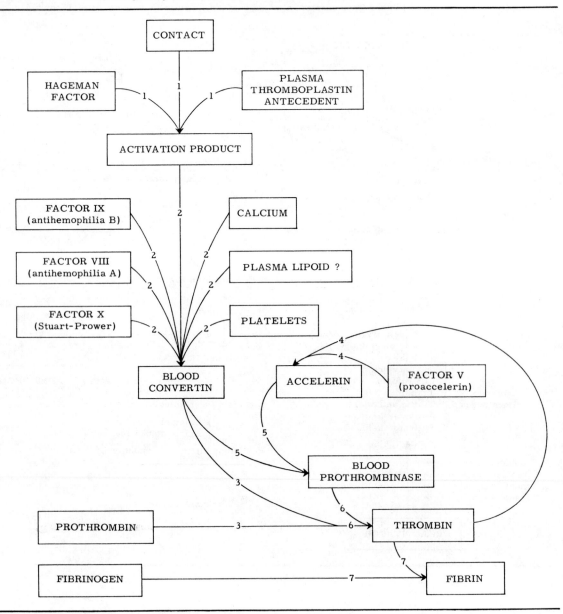

/1/ Factor VII (proconvertin) does not take part in the intrinsic blood coagulation system.

Part II: ACCORDING TO P. A. OWREN (1960) (Concluded)

System II: Extrinsic (tissue-blood) Coagulation[2]

(1) CONTACT (and/or TISSUE THROMBOPLASTIN) activates INACTIVE FACTOR VII (proconvertin) to ACTIVE FACTOR VII. (2) TISSUE THROMBOPLASTIN (liberated by tissue injury), ACTIVE FACTOR VII, CALCIUM, and FACTOR X (Stuart-Prower factor) interact to form TISSUE CONVERTIN. (3) TISSUE CONVERTIN brings about a minimal conversion of PROTHROMBIN to THROMBIN. (4) This initially-formed THROMBIN starts the accelerator system, i.e., the conversion of FACTOR V (proaccelerin) to ACCELERIN. (5) TISSUE CONVERTIN and ACCELERIN interact in the presence of calcium to form TISSUE PROTHROMBINASE. (6) TISSUE PROTHROMBINASE produces rapid conversion of PROTHROMBIN to THROMBIN. (7) THROMBIN is now formed in sufficient quantity to convert FIBRINOGEN to FIBRIN.

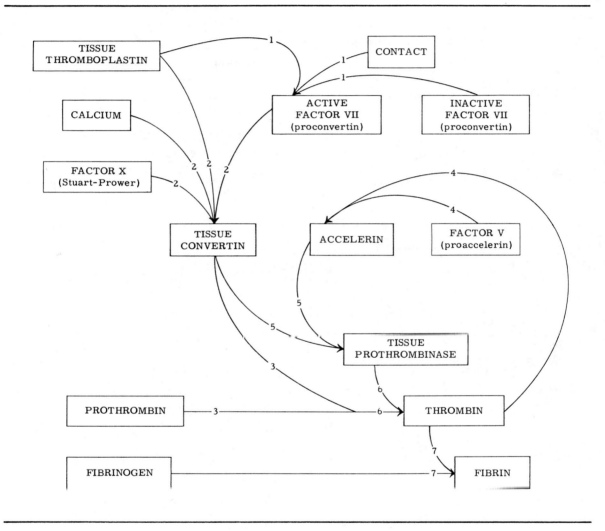

/2/ Platelets and antihemophilic factors do not take part in the extrinsic blood coagulation system.

Contributor: Owren, Paul A.

References: [1] Hjort, P. F. 1957. Scand. J. Clin. Lab. Invest., Suppl. 27. [2] Owren, P. A. 1947. Acta med. scand., Suppl. 194. [3] Waaler, B. A. 1959. Scand. J. Clin. Lab. Invest., Suppl. 37.

88. BLOOD COAGULATION THEORIES (Continued)

Part III: ACCORDING TO A. J. QUICK (1960)

(1) A plasma constituent, tentatively named PLATELET CO-FACTOR, after activation by thrombin, or by contact with glass, reacts with a PLATELET FACTOR to form ERYTHROCYTIN. (2) PLASMA THROMBOPLASTIN COMPONENT (factor IX) is inactive in plasma but is activated during coagulation. The activator mechanism is not known. (3) ERYTHROCYTIN, THROMBOPLASTINOGEN (factor VIII), and ACTIVATED PLASMA THROMBOPLASTIN COMPONENT interact to form INTRINSIC THROMBOPLASTIN. (4) INTRINSIC THROMBOPLASTIN, CALCIUM, and LABILE FACTOR (factor V) interact with PROTHROMBIN to form THROMBIN. In human blood, a large fraction of prothrombin is inactive but becomes activated during coagulation in glass. (5) When TISSUE THROMBOPLASTIN is utilized, STABLE FACTOR (factor VII) is required in addition to CALCIUM and LABILE FACTOR. (6) THROMBIN acts enzymatically on FIBRINOGEN to convert it to FIBRIN. (7) The prompt removal of THROMBIN by adsorption on FIBRIN holds in check the autocatalytic reaction mediated through the activating action of THROMBIN on the PLATELET CO-FACTOR.

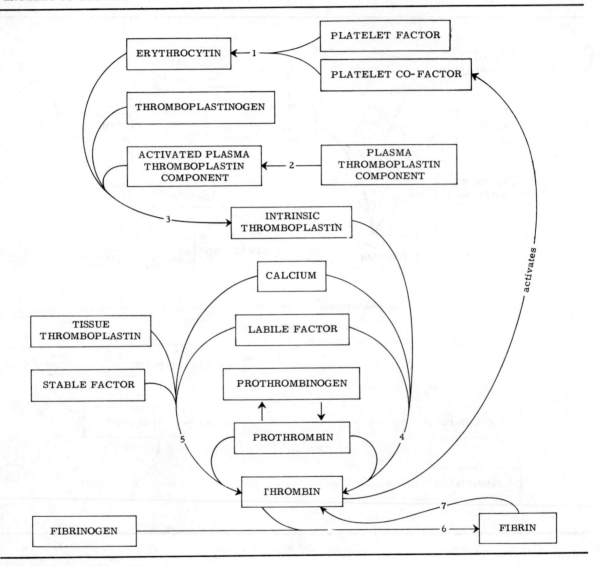

Contributor: Quick, Armand J.

References: [1] Quick, A. J. 1943. Am. J. Physiol. 140:212. [2] Quick, A. J. 1947. Am. J. M. Sc. 214:272. [3] Quick, A. J. 1958. Thromb. Diath. Haemorrh. 2:226. [4] Quick, A. J. 1960. Am. J. M. Sc. 239:51. [5] Quick, A. J., and J. E. Favre-Gilly. 1949. Am. J. Physiol. 158:387. [6] Quick, A. J., and C. V. Hussey. 1955. Brit. M. J. 1:934.

88. BLOOD COAGULATION THEORIES (Continued)

Part IV: ACCORDING TO W. H. SEEGERS (1960)

Prothrombin is found in the blood and may become activated in the presence of one or more procoagulants. Since prothrombin itself contains all the necessary material for the formation of thrombin, purified prothrombin can be activated to thrombin by placing it in 25% sodium citrate solution. Consequently the activators of prothrombin are catalysts and do not enter into stoichiometric combination with prothrombin to form thrombin. Anticoagulants inhibit the activation. Ordinarily the procoagulants and anticoagulants are present in balanced proportion. This balance is readily disturbed by the procoagulants from injured tissues. Contact with foreign surfaces also promotes prothrombin activation and platelet disintegration. With certain combinations of procoagulants, prothrombin is only partially activated and these derivatives of prothrombin themselves accelerate the conversion of prothrombin to thrombin. Thrombin, the only known enzyme in the blood coagulation mechanisms, functions as activator of prothrombin. It also functions with accelerator systems, such as plasma Ac-globulin which becomes serum Ac-globulin, and it further supports the dissolution of platelets. Plasma antithrombin eventually destroys thrombin activity. By proteolysis, thrombin splits peptides from fibrinogen and acts as a polymerase in the polymerization of the activated fibrinogen. In the presence of calcium ions and fibrin stabilizing factor, the fibrin of a normal clot forms. Vitamin K is needed for the metabolic production of prothrombin and its derivatives, whereas dicumarol may interfere with normal prothrombin metabolism.

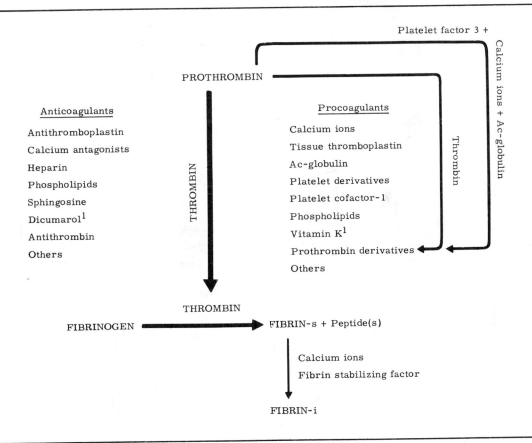

/1/ Related to prothrombin production.

Contributor: Seegers, Walter H.

References: [1] McClaughry, R. I., and J. L. Fahey. 1950. Blood, N. Y. 5:421. [2] Milstone, J. H. 1948. Proc. Soc. Exp. Biol., N. Y. 68:225. [3] Seegers, W. H. 1950. Circulation, N. Y. 1:2. [4] Seegers, W. H. In J. B. Sumner and K. Myrbäck, ed. 1950. The enzymes. Academic Press, N. Y. v. 1, pt. 1, ch. 35. [5] Ware, A. G., J. L. Fahey, and W. H. Seegers. 1948. Am. J. Physiol. 154:140. [6] Ware, A. G., and W. H. Seegers. 1948. Ibid. 152:567.

88. BLOOD COAGULATION THEORIES (Continued)

Part V: ACCORDING TO L. M. TOCANTINS (1960)

(1) CONTACT of the BLOOD with certain SURFACES (damaged blood vessel endothelium, glass) initiates the first changes in the inception of clotting. Blood PLATELETS adhere to the surface and to each other, swell and DISINTEGRATE, releasing among other substances PLATELET FACTOR 3 (cephalin-like factor) and PLATELET FACTOR 2 (a fibrinoplastic factor). Conjugation of PLATELET FACTOR 3 with PLATELET CO-FACTOR from plasma (factor IX, plasma thromboplastin component) leads, with the aid of FACTOR X (Stuart-Prower factor), to formation of PLASMA THROMBOPLASTIN. The plasma ANTITHROMBOPLASTIN slows or blocks formation of THROMBOPLASTIN and, less effectively, offsets the action of formed THROMBOPLASTIN. Antihemophilic globulin is considered to represent various stages of development of plasma thromboplastin, or various degrees of conjugation of the platelet lipid and its plasma co-factor. Plasma ANTITHROMBOPLASTIN is probably a lipid in conjugation with PLATELET PLASMA CO-FACTOR. (2) THROMBOPLASTIN (from TISSUES, or generated in PLASMA) brings about, with the aid of Ac-GLOBULIN (factor V) and CONVERTIN (factor VII), a minimal amount of conversion of PROTHROMBIN to THROMBIN. (3) This initial THROMBIN activates further transformation of PROTHROMBIN to THROMBIN, with the help of Ac-GLOBULIN. (4) Some of the THROMBIN may be inactivated by ANTITHROMBIN. The THROMBIN that escapes such inactivation acts, with the aid of PLATELET FACTOR 2, to convert FIBRINOGEN to FIBRIN. Some of the THROMBIN is removed from the plasma by adsorption on FIBRIN. (5) Adhesion of platelets to FIBRIN probably causes further PLATELET DISINTEGRATION.

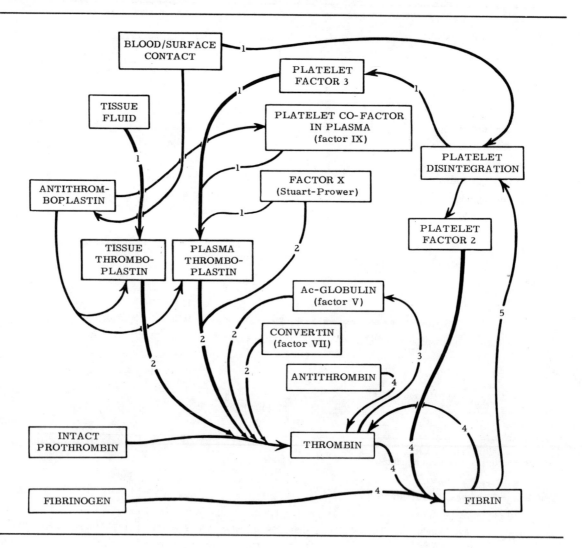

Contributor: Tocantins, Leandro M.

References: [1] Silver, M. J., D. L. Turner, and L. M. Tocantins. In L. M. Tocantins, ed. 1959. Progress in

Part V: ACCORDING TO L. M. TOCANTINS (1960) (Concluded)

hematology. Grune and Stratton, New York. v. 2. [2] Tocantins, L. M. 1943. Am. J. Physiol. 139:265.
[3] Tocantins, L. M. 1944. Proc. Soc. Exp. Biol., N. Y. 55:291. [4] Tocantins, L. M. 1944. Ibid. 57:211.
[5] Tocantins, L. M. 1946. Am. J. Physiol. 143:67. [6] Tocantins, L. M. 1946. Blood, N. Y. 1:56.
[7] Tocantins, L. M. 1949. Surg. Clin. N. America, Dec.:1835. [8] Tocantins, L. M. 1954. Blood, N. Y. 9:281.
[9] Tocantins, L. M. 1955. The coagulation of blood: methods of study. Grune and Stratton, New York.
[10] Tocantins, L. M., R. T. Carroll, and R. R. Holburn. 1951. Blood, N. Y. 6:720. [11] Tocantins, L. M.,
R. T. Carroll, and T. J. MacBride. 1948. Proc. Soc. Exp. Biol., N. Y. 68:110. [12] Tocantins, L. M., R. R.
Holburn, and R. T. Carroll. 1951. Ibid. 76:623.

89. INFANT BLOOD COAGULATION TESTS AND FACTORS: MAN

Values in parentheses are ranges, estimate "c" (cf. Introduction).

	Test or Factor	Method	Blood	No. of Obser- vations	Age of Subjects	Value	Reference
	(A)	(B)	(C)	(D)	(E)	(F)	(G)
1	Bleeding time	Puncture of heel; blood ab- sorbed every 30 seconds		136	1-4 da	2.5(0.5-8.0) min	19,26
2	Clotting time	Capillary tube	Capillary		1-2 da	3.5(1.5-5.0) min	20,26
3					3-6 da	4.5 min	
4		Lee-White	Venous	95	1-4 da	6.5(2-14) min	19,33
5		Recalcification of oxalated plasma	Venous plasma	240	1-6 da	2.5(1-6) min	3
6				40	3-6 da	1.5(1-3) min[1]	
7	Factor V (pro- accelerin)	One-stage (Stefanini and modifications)	Umbilical cord	47	Birth	(90-100) %	12,17,24,29
8			Venous plasma	175	1-2 da	80(30-160) %	2,3,15
9				90	3-6 da	95(60-160) %	
10		Two-stage (McClaughry and Seegers)	Umbilical cord; capillary	56	Birth-3 da	(13-160) %	9,12,31
11	Factor VII (procon- vertin)	Owren, Koller, et al	Umbilical cord; capillary	501	Birth-2 hr	32.9(1-100) %	8,10,11,13, 17,18,32
12			Capillary; ve- nous plasma	316	1-3 da	22(2-95) %	10,11,13, 18,22,32
13				30	4-6 da	26(13-65) %	32
14			Capillary		3 da	58(29-75) %[1]	32
15			Venous plasma		4-6 da	61(25-120) %[1]	3,9,21
16	Prothrombin, true	Two-stage (Iowa method)	Venous plasma	8	Birth	27(14-39) %	6
17				4	1-2 wk	38(27-44) %	
18				4	7-12 wk	51(41-61) %	
19				3	21-30 wk	74(68-79) %	
20				4	38-48 wk	93(85-100) %	
21		Two-stage (Iowa method and modifications)	Venous plasma	13	1-2 da	28(9-44) %	21,35
22				14	3-4 da	28(15-53) %	
23				8	5-6 da	34(23-42) %	
24				7	7-10 da	38(31-47) %	
25		Two-stage (Ware Seegers and modifications)	Umbilical cord	75	Birth	67(30-87) %	9,11
26			Venous plasma	21	3 da	42%	9
27				21	3 da	72%[1]	
28		One-stage (Owren and modifications)	Umbilical cord; venous plas- ma	288	Birth-2 hr	38(1-95) %	18
29			Capillary; ve- nous	103	3 hr-2 da	17(1-94) %	10,13
30				78	3 da	25(4-74) %[1]	10,13,31
31	Prothrombin activity	Quick and modifications	Umbilical cord	1693	Birth	80%	27
32			Venous	982	2-3 da	21.5%	
33					4-5 da	37.5%	
34					6-7 da	62.5%	

/1/ After administration of vitamin K.

Test or Factor	Method	Blood	No. of Observations	Age of Subjects	Value	Reference
(A)	(B)	(C)	(D)	(E)	(F)	(G)
35 Prothrombin activity (concluded)	Quick and modifications (concluded)	Venous (concluded)	711	1 da 3 da 5 da	65%[1] 38%[1] 68%[1]	27
38 Prothrombin consumption		Umbilical cord	32		83(55-95) %	12
39		Venous	66		77.5(1-95) %	19
40 Stuart-Prower		Venous	26		42%	2,3
41 Thrombo- plastin generation	Barium plasma	Venous	30		92%	1,2,3
42	Serum	Venous	77		20%	14
43			27		70%[1]	3
44 Thrombin time	0.2 ml plasma and 0.1 ml diluted thrombin solution	Venous plasma	188		28 sec	3,5
45 Fibrinogen[2]	Gravimetric	Venous	74		350(192-800) mg %	12,19
46	Kjeldahl, colorimetric, and turbidimetric	Venous	166		242(50-650) mg %	7,16,23,25, 28,30,34

/1/ After administration of vitamin K. /2/ Fibrinolytic activity (free and inhibitor) is decreased at birth and continues to diminish for several days [4, 23].

Contributors: (a) Diggs, L. W., and Aballi, Arturo J., (b) Owen, Charles A.

References: [1] Aballi, A. J., V. Lopez Banus, S. de Lamerens, and S. Rozengvaig. 1957. A. M. A. J. Dis. Child. 94:594. [2] Aballi, A. J., V. Lopez Banus, S. de Lamerens, and S. Rosengvaig. In press. The coagulation defect of the newborn. [3] Aballi, A. J., V. Lopez Banus, S. de Lamerens, and S. Rozengvaig. Unpublished.
[4] Berglund, G. 1958. Acta paediat., Upps. 47:511. [5] Biggs, R. 1951. Prothrombin deficiency. Blackwell Scientific Publications, Oxford. p. 55. [6] Brinkhous, K. M., H. P. Smith, and E. D. Warner. 1937. Am. J. M. Sc. 193:475. [7] Crane, M. M., and H. N. Sanford. 1936. Am. J. Dis. Child. 51:99. [8] De Nicola, P. 1952. Blood, N. Y. 8:947. [9] Douglas, A. S., and P. L. Davies. 1955. Arch. Dis. Childh., Lond. 30:509. [10] Dyggve, H. 1958. Acta paediat., Upps. 47:251. [11] Fresh, J. W., H. Adams, and F. M. Morgan. 1959. Obst. Gyn., N. Y. 13:37. [12] Fresh, J. W., J. H. Ferguson, and J. H. Lewis. 1956. J. Obst. Gyn. Brit. Empire 7:117. [13] Fresh, J. W., J. H. Ferguson, C. Stamey, F. M. Morgan, and J. H. Lewis. 1957. Pediatrics 19:241. [14] Hartmann, J. R., D. A. Howell, and L. K. Diamond. 1955. A. M. A. J. Dis. Child. 90:594. [15] Israels, L. G., A. Zipursky, and C. Sinclair. 1955. Pediatrics 150:180. [16] Landsberg, E. 1910. Arch. Gyn., Berl. 92:693. [17] Larrieu, M. J., J. P. Soulier, and A. Minkowski. 1952. Ét. néonatal. 1:39. [18] Loeliger, A., and F. Koller. 1952. Acta haemat., Basel 7:157. [19] Lopez Banus, V., and S. de Lamerens. 1956. Rev. cubana pediat. 28:381. [20] Merritt, K. K., and L. T. Davidson. 1933. Am. J. Dis. Child. 46:990. [21] Owen, C. A., and M. Hurn. 1953. J. Pediat., S. Louis 42:424. [22] Passaro, G. P. 1955. Arch. ital. pediat. 17:59. [23] Phillips, L. L., and V. Skraedelis. 1958. Pediatrics 22:715. [24] Quick, A. J. 1947. Am. J. Physiol. 151:63. [25] Rodda, F. C. 1920. Am. J. Dis. Child. 19:269. [26] Sanford, H. N. In J. Brennemann, ed. 1958. Practice of pediatrics. W. F. Prior, Hagerstown, Md. ch. 15. [27] Sanford, H. N., I. Schmigelsky, and J. M. Chapin. 1942. J. Am. M. Ass. 118:697. [28] Salazar de Sousa, C., J. Crespo Ferreira, A. Ferreira Gomez, and A. Estrella. 1953. Arch. fr. pédiat. 10:474.
[29] Stefanini, M. 1951. Lancet, Lond. 1:606. [30] Taylor, P. M. 1957. Pediatrics 19:233. [31] Van Creveld, S., M. M. P. Paulssen, and S. K. Teng. 1952. Ét. néonatal. 1:1. [32] Van Creveld, S., M. M. P. Paulssen, J. C. Vender Meig, and P. Versteeg. 1954. Ibid. 3:53. [33] Waddell, W. W., Jr., and D. Guerry, III. 1939. J. Pediat., S. Louis 15:802. [34] Waddell, W. W., Jr., and G. M. Lawson. 1940. J. Am. M. Ass. 115:1416. [35] Ziffren, S. E., C. A. Owen, G. R. Hoffman, and H. P. Smith. 1939. Proc. Soc. Exp. Biol., N. Y. 40:595.

Part I: SKIN BLEEDING TIME

Skin bleeding time varies with the temperature, circulation, and thickness of the skin, with the area punctured and the depth of the puncture, and with psychic influences. Values in parentheses are ranges, estimate "c" unless otherwise indicated (cf. Introduction).

	Method	Technique	Area Punctured	Wound Depth mm	Bleeding Time sec	Reference
	(A)	(B)	(C)	(D)	(E)	(F)
1	Duke	Blood absorbed every 15-30 seconds	Ear, finger	3	(60-180)	4, 8
2			Volar surface of forearm	3-4	147(0-450)[1]	7
3	Copley and Lalich	Wound immersed in physiological saline, 37°C	Finger	6	(17-340)[2]	2
4	Ivy	Sphygmomanometer cuff maintained at 40 mm Hg pressure; blood absorbed every 10 seconds	Volar surface of forearm	3	(0-240)	5
5		Sphygmomanometer cuff maintained at 40 mm Hg pressure; blood absorbed every 15-30 seconds	Volar surface of forearm	2	192(0-384)[b]	1
6				3-4	248(30-570)	6, 7
7				3	240(30-730)[3]	3, 6

/1/ Less than 374 seconds in 95% of population. /2/ Less than 180 seconds in 95% of population. /3/ Frank bleeding should stop within 360 seconds; blood-tinged oozing may last another 360 seconds.

Contributors: (a) Diggs, L. W., (b) Lewis, Jessica H.

References: [1] Aggeler, P. M., J. Howard, and S. P. Lucia. 1946. Blood, N. Y. 1:472. [2] Copley, A. L., and J. J. Lalich. 1942. J. Clin. Invest. 21:145. [3] Diggs, L. W. Unpublished. [4] Duke, W. W. 1910. J. Am. M. Ass. 55:1185. [5] Ivy, A. C., D. Nelson, and G. R. Bucher. 1941. J. Laborat. Clin. M. 26:1812. [6] Ivy, A. C., P. F. Shapiro, and P. Melnick. 1935. Surg. Gyn. Obst. 60:781. [7] Tocantins, L. M. 1946. Med. Clin. N. America 130:1361. [8] Wintrobe, M. M. 1946. Clinical hematology. Lea and Febiger, Philadelphia. p. 210.

Part II: CLOTTING TIME

Values in parentheses are ranges, estimate "c" unless otherwise indicated (cf. Introduction).

	Method	Technique	Surface	Temp. °C	No. of Subjects	Clotting Time min	Reference
	(A)	(B)	(C)	(D)	(E)	(F)	(G)
	Whole Blood						
1	Aggeler, et al	2 ml in each of 2 tubes (8 x 75 mm)	Glass	Room	64	8.9(3.5-14.3)[b]	1
2				37	64	7.5(4.7-10.4)[b]	
3	Allen and Attyah	2-syringe; 1 ml in each of 10 tubes, paired (9.5 x 40 mm)	Glass	37	52	(20-35)	2
4	Hirschboeck	1-syringe; 2 ml	Glass		12	6.33(4-10)	4
5			Collodion		12	22.2(12-31)	
6			Paraffin		12	16.7(10-26)	
7	Jaques, et al	Equivalent of 2-syringe	Silicone		7	182(138-245)	5
8	Kadish	1-syringe; 1 ml in 1 tube	Glass		50	(5-10)	6
9		2 ml in 1 tube (12.5 mm diameter)	Lusteroid		50	19(14-28)	
10	Lea and White	1 ml in 1 tube (8 mm diameter)	Glass	Room		6.5(5-8)	7
11	Margulies and Barker	Coagulochronometer	Glass	37	50	11.66(5-19)	9
12			Silicone	37	50	38.58(25-57)	
13	Mayer	2-syringe; venous blood in capillary tubes		21	40	11.9(10.0-13.7)[b]	10
14	Pohle and Taylor	1-syringe; 2 ml in each of 2 tubes (13 x 100 mm)		37.5		(6-12)	13

Part II: CLOTTING TIME (Concluded)

	Method	Technique	Surface	Temp. °C	No. of Subjects	Clotting Time min	Reference
	(A)	(B)	(C)	(D)	(E)	(F)	(G)
	Whole Blood (concluded)						
15	Quick, et al	1-syringe; 1 ml in each of 2 tubes					15
15		13 x 100 mm	Glass	37	6	(5-10)	
16		11 x 100 mm	Glass	37	6	(5.5-8.0)	
17		8 x 100 mm	Glass	37	6	(4.5-5.0)	
18		11 x 100 mm	Glass	22	6	(10.5-16.0)	
19		13 x 100 mm	Lusteroid	37	6	(10.5-16.5)	
20		11 x 100 mm	Collodion	37	6	(23-29)	
21		11 x 100 mm	Silicone	37	6	(36-52)	
22	Tocantins	1 ml in tube (13 mm in diameter)	Glass	37		11.5(8-16)	16
23			Paraffin	37		29.3(15-45)	
24	Wintrobe	2-syringe; 1 ml in each of 3 tubes (11 mm diameter)	Glass	37		(5-15)	17
	Plasma						
25	Cheney	0.2 ml oxalated plasma plus CaCl$_2$ in each of 2 tubes; plasma recalcified		23-26		5.3(3-8)	3
26	Jaques, et al	Native plasma; equivalent of 2-syringe	Glass		7	37(20-100)	5
27			Silicone		7	140(90-390)	
28	Lozner and Taylor	Native plasma; 1-syringe; 2 ml in each of 2 tubes (13 x 100 mm); all equipment oiled or siliconized	Glass	37.5		11	8
29			Collodion	37.5		64	
30			Paraffin	37.5		44	
31			Lusteroid	37.5		49	
32		Citrated, high-platelet plasma recalcified after 1 hour on specified surface	Glass	37.5		6	
33			Collodion	37.5		18	
34			Paraffin	37.5		20	
35			Lusteroid	37.5		20	
36	Nygaard	0.6 ml oxalated plasma plus CaCl$_2$ in tube; plasma recalcified		37		2.7(2.0-3.5)[1]	11
37	Owen, et al	0.2 ml oxalated, high-platelet plasma plus 0.2 ml CaCl$_2$ solution	Glass	37		(1.50-1.83)	12
38	Quick	0.1 ml oxalated plasma plus CaCl$_2$ in each of 2 tubes; plasma recalcified		37		(1.5-2.3)	14
39	Wintrobe	Oxalated, high-platelet plasma	Glass	37		(1.50-1.83)	18

/1/ Photoelectric end-point reading.

Contributors: Diggs, L. W., and Dugdale, Marion.

References: [1] Aggeler, P. M., J. Howard, and S. P. Lucia. 1946. Blood, N. Y. 1:472. [2] Allen, G. W., and A. M. Attyah. 1953. J. Laborat. Clin. M. 41:767. [3] Cheney, G. 1942. Am. J. M. Sc. 203:325. [4] Hirschboeck, J. S. 1940. Proc. Soc. Exp. Biol., N. Y. 45:122. [5] Jaques, L. B., E. Fidlar, E. T. Feldsted, and A. G. MacDonald. 1946. Canad. M. Ass. J. 55:26. [6] Kadish, A. H. 1947. Am. Heart J. 34:212. [7] Lee, R. I., and P. D. White. 1913. Am. J. M. Sc. 145:495. [8] Lozner, E. L., and F. H. L. Taylor. 1942. J. Clin. Invest. 21:241. [9] Margulies H., and N. W. Barker. 1949. Am. J. M. Sc. 218:42. [10] Mayer, G. A. 1957. J. Laborat. Clin. M. 49:938. [11] Nygaard, K. K. 1941. Hemorrhagic diseases. C. V. Mosby, St. Louis. [12] Owen, C. A., Jr., F. D. Mann, M. M. Hurn, and J. M. Stickney. 1955. Am. J. Clin. Path. 25:1417. [13] Pohle, F. J., and F. H. L. Taylor. 1937. J. Clin. Invest. 16:741. [14] Quick, A. J. 1942. The hemorrhagic diseases and the physiology of hemostasis. C. C. Thomas, Springfield, Ill. [15] Quick, A. J., R. Honorato, and M. Stefanini. 1948. Blood, N. Y. 3:1121. [16] Tocantins, L. M. 1946. Med. Clin. N. America 30:1361. [17] Wintrobe, M. M. 1956. Clinical hematology. Ed. 4. Lea and Febiger, Philadelphia. p. 286. [18] Wintrobe, M. M. 1956. Ibid. p. 290.

Part III: PLASMA PROTHROMBIN TIME

The results of different methods are not comparable, due to differences in concentration of the reacting substances. Values in parentheses are ranges, estimate "b" unless otherwise indicated (cf. Introduction).

	Method	Temp. °C	Source of Thromboplastin	Blood	Clotting Time sec	Ref- er- ence
	(A)	(B)	(C)	(D)	(E)	(F)
1	0.1 ml oxalated plasma plus CaCl$_2$	37	Rabbit brain, acetone-dehydrated	Venous	(11-12)^c	7
2				Venous	24(19-29)	8
3			Rabbit brain, dried at 37°C	Venous	(17-19)^c	4
4			Human brain, acetone-dehydrated	Venous	11.5(10-13)	1
5		38.5	Russell viper (Daboia) venom plus lecithin	Venous	10(8-12)	10
6	0.2 ml oxalated plasma plus CaCl$_2$	Room	Russell viper (Daboia) venom	Venous	23(16-30)^c	6
7	0.1 ml 10% plasma, plus pro-thrombin-free oxalated plasma, plus CaCl$_2$	37	Human brain, saline extract	Venous	35(30-40)	5
8	0.1 ml 10% plasma plus prothrom-bin-free oxalated plasma (CaCl$_2$ included in thromboplastin)	37	Human or rabbit brain, acetone-dehydrated	Venous	25(20-30)	9
9	0.1 ml 12.5% plasma, plus oxalated plasma[1], plus CaCl$_2$	37	Rabbit brain, acetone-dehydrated	Venous	41(34-48)	8
10	0.1 ml 25% plasma, plus oxalated plasma[1], plus CaCl$_2$	37	Human brain, acetone-dehydrated	Venous	28(21-35)	1
11	0.1 ml 50% plasma, plus oxalated plasma[1], plus CaCl$_2$	37	Human brain, acetone-dehydrated	Venous	16(13-19)	1
12	0.1 ml oxalated blood plus CaCl$_2$	Room	Rabbit brain, acetone-dehydrated	Cutaneous	20(18-22)	3
13	0.03-0.04 ml blood	Room	Beef lung or rabbit brain, fresh	Cutaneous	(20-30)^c	2
14	0.9 ml blood	Room	Beef lung or rabbit brain, acetone-dehydrated	Venous	(25-50)^c	11

/1/ Diluted with physiological saline.

Contributors: (a) Diggs, L. W., (b) Owen, Charles A., (c) Ware, Arnold G.

References: [1] Aggeler, P. M., J. Howard, S. P. Lucia, W. Clark, and A. Astaff. 1946. Blood, N. Y. 1:220. [2] Karabin, J. E., and E. R. Anderson. 1941. J. Laborat. Clin. M. 26:723. [3] Kato, K., and H. G. Poncher. 1940. J. Am. M. Ass. 114:749. [4] Magath, T. B. 1939. Am. J. Clin. Path., Techn. Suppl. 3, p. 107. [5] Owren, P. A. 1949. Scand. J. Clin. Lab. Invest. 1:81. [6] Page, R. C., and H. K. Russell. 1941. J. Laborat. Clin. M. 26:1366. [7] Quick, A. J. 1945. Am. J. Clin. Path. 15:560. [8] Shapiro, S., B. Sherwin, M. Redish, and H. A. Campbell. 1942. Proc. Soc. Exp. Biol., N. Y. 50:85. [9] Ware, A. G., and R. Stragnell. 1952. Am. J. Clin. Path. 22:791. [10] Witts, L. J., and F. C. G. Hobson. 1942. Brit. M. J. 1:575. [11] Ziffren, S. E., C. A. Owen, G. R. Hoffman, and H. P. Smith. 1940. Am. J. Clin. Path., Techn. Suppl. 4, p. 13.

Part IV: THROMBOELASTOGRAM VALUES

Values in parentheses are ranges, estimate "c" unless otherwise indicated (cf. Introduction).

	Investigator	No. of Subjects	Reaction Time min	Thrombus Formation Time min	Maximal Amplitude mm	Elasticity Values $\dfrac{100 \times \text{maximal amplitude}}{100 - \text{maximal amplitude}}$	Reference
	(A)	(B)	(C)	(D)	(E)	(F)	(G)
	Whole Blood						
1	Beller		(9-14)	(5-8)			1
2	Donner	30	(9-15)	(5-8)	(45-55)	(95-140)	5
3	Hartert		12	6	55	(90-150)	6, 7

Part IV: THROMBOELASTOGRAM VALUES (Concluded)

Investigator	No. of Subjects	Reaction Time min	Thrombus Formation Time min	Maximal Amplitude mm	Elasticity Values $\dfrac{100 \times \text{maximal amplitude}}{100 - \text{maximal amplitude}}$	Reference
(A)	(B)	(C)	(D)	(E)	(F)	(G)
Whole Blood (concluded)						
4 Hermansky		(8-15)	(4.5-8.5)	(45-60)	(80-150)	9
5 Leroux		(10.5-14.5)	(3-6)	50	(90-150)	10
6 Petersen	100	12	6			11
7 Walther	100	12.3(10.7-13.9)[b]	6.1(4.9-7.3)[b]		105(88.6-121.4)[b]	13
Plasma						
8 Bosson		(7-9)	(2.0-4.5)		(100-230)	2
9 Della Santa	42	8.8	3.7	54.9		3
10 De Nicola		(2.5-5.0)	(2.5-4.0)	(50-60)		4
11 Donner	30	(3-6)	(3.0-4.5)	(50-65)	(85-156)	5
12 Hartert		8.5	3.5	55	(90-150)	8
13 Leroux		(7.5-11.0)	(2.2-4.2)	(46.0-62.5)	(85.5-167.0)	10
14 Toledo	78	(5-9)	(2-4)	(50-72)	(100-257)	12

Contributors: Diggs, L. W., and Dugdale, Marion

References: [1] Beller, F. K. 1957. Die Gerrinungsverhältnisse bei der Schwangeren und beim Neugeborenen. Barth, Leipzig. [2] Bosson, P., and R. Dechamboux. 1958. La thrombélastographie de Hartert. Vigne, Paris. [3] Della Santa, R. 1954. Praxis, Bern 43:89. [4] De Nicola, P., and G. M. Mazzetti. 1956. Blood, N. Y. 11:71. [5] Donner, L. 1959. Probl. Hemat. Blood Transfusion 4:16. [6] Hartert, H. 1948. Klin. Wschr. 26:577. [7] Hartert, H. 1949. Schweiz. med. Wschr. 79:318. [8] Hartert, H. 1955. Zschr. klin. Med. 153:423. [9] Hermansky, F., V. Friedmann, and J. Vitek. 1958. Čas. lék. česk. 97:1581. [10] Leroux, M. 1957. La thrombélastographie. M. Garcia, Asnières. [11] Petersen, H., K. Breddin, and K. Röttger. 1954. Klin. Wschr. 32:328. [12] Toledo, B. F., and B. Milanés-López. 1958. Angiology 9:88. [13] Walther, G., and E. Volhard. 1955. Medizinische 17:65.

Part V: FIBRINOGEN LEVELS

Values in parentheses are ranges, estimate "c" unless otherwise indicated (cf. Introduction).

Method	No. of Subjects	Fibrinogen Level	Reference
(A)	(B)	(C)	(D)
1 Dilution of blood		100 mg %[1]	9
2 Gravimetric	1♂, 15♀	250(220-360) mg %	10
3 Gravimetric heat coagulation	6	(300-600) mg %	13
4	2	(290-360) mg %	5
5 Gravimetric CaCl$_2$ coagulation	4	335(316-364) mg %	4
6	25♂	270(200-360) mg %	5
7	25♀	290(210-380) mg %	5
8 Gravimetric thrombin coagulation	7	(350-600) mg %	12
9 Analysis by nitrogen CaCl$_2$ coagulation		(0.024-0.083) g fibrinogen N %	2
10	19♂	250(190-330) mg %	6
11	9♀	290(220-290) mg %	6
12	80	(0.028-0.233) g fibrinogen N %	7
13 Na$_2$SO$_4$ precipitation	80	(0.022-0.232) g fibrinogen N %	7
14 Na$_2$SO$_3$ precipitation	12	(400-731) mg %	1

/1/ >1:100 dilution.

Part V: FIBRINOGEN LEVELS (Concluded)

Method	No. of Subjects	Fibrinogen Level	Reference
(A)	(B)	(C)	(D)
15 Analysis by tyrosine	19♂	272(152-392)[b] mg %	8
16	14♀	294(173-415)[b] mg %	8
17 Pooled plasma		0.28% of plasma[2]	3
18 Electrophoresis		(0.2-0.4) % of plasma	11

/2/ Or 4% of total protein.

Contributors: Diggs, L. W., and Dugdale, Marion

References: [1] Campbell, W. R., and M. I. Hanna. 1937. J. Biol. Chem. 119:15. [2] Cullen, G. E., and D. D. Van Slyke. 1920. Ibid. 41:587. [3] Edsall, J. T., R. M. Ferry, and S. H. Armstrong. 1944. J. Clin. Invest. 23:557. [4] Foster, D. P., and G. H. Whipple. 1921. Am. J. Physiol. 58:407. [5] Gram, H. C. 1921. J. Biol. Chem. 49:279. [6] Ham, T. H., and F. C. Curtis. 1938. Medicine, Balt. 17:413. [7] Howe, P. E. 1923. J. Biol. Chem. 57:235. [8] Ratnoff, O. D., and C. Menzie. 1951. J. Laborat. Clin. M. 37:316. [9] Schneider, C. L. 1952. Am. J. Obst. 64:141. [10] Starlinger, W., and E. Winands. 1928. Zschr. ges. exp. Med. 60:138. [11] Stenhagen, E. 1938. Biochem. J., Lond. 32:714. [12] Von Szecsenyi-Nagy, L. 1944. Biochem. Zschr. 317:185. [13] Whipple, G. H. 1914. Am. J. Physiol. 33:50.

Part VI: BLOOD CLOT RETRACTION VOLUME AND TIME

Values in parentheses are ranges, estimate "c" unless otherwise indicated (cf. Introduction).

Method	Variable	Value	Remarks	Reference
(A)	(B)	(C)	(D)	(E)
1 Aggeler and Lucia	Extracorpuscular clot volume	7.9(-4.1 to +19.9)[b] % of volume of blood specimen[1]	Fluid volume of clot, exclusive of erythrocytes, leukocytes, and platelets, after clot retraction for 1 hour at 37°C	1
2 Diggs	Serum volume expressed from clot	(40-55) % of volume of blood specimen	After maximal clot retraction	2
3 Tocantins	Serum volume expressed from clot	78.1(62-94)[b] % of total serum present in blood specimen	Venous blood in paraffin tube, 13 mm diameter, 2 hours at 37°C; amount of serum initially present calculated from hematocrit	4
4 Diggs	Venous blood in test tube	(30-60) minutes	At room temperature	2
5 Hirschboeck	Drop of blood in castor oil	33(20-45) minutes		3

/1/ Negative values may occur owing to discrepancies between methods of measurement of formed elements and total clot volume.

Contributor: Diggs, L. W.

References: [1] Aggeler, P. M., J. Howard, and S. P. Lucia. 1946. Blood, N. Y. 1:472. [2] Diggs, L. W. Unpublished. [3] Hirschboeck, J. S. 1948. J. Laborat. Clin. M. 33:347. [4] Tocantins, L. M. 1946. Med. Clin. N. America 130:1361.

Part VII: SUMMARY OF NORMAL TEST VALUES

Values in parentheses are ranges, estimate "c" (cf. Introduction).

	Test	No. of Observations	Value	Reference
	(A)	(B)	(C)	(D)
1	Two-tube clotting time	50	11.35(7.45-15.0) min	2
2	Two-tube silicone clotting time	54	22.51(14.3-31.0) min	2
	One-stage prothrombin test			
3	Quick	53	11.68(9.7-13.0) sec	5
4	Owren	48	29.06(19.5-35.0) sec	3
5	Ware	45	22.38(19.0-30.0) sec	10
6	Two-stage prothrombin test		356(290-425) units	9
7	Factor V	45	18.5(15.6-20.8) sec	11
	Factor VII			
8	Serum	37	21.0(19.4-24.0) sec	8
9	Plasma	40	25.3(22.2-27.4) sec	8
10	Prothrombin consumption	50	96.5(74-100) %	4
11	Thromboplastin generation	50	17.02(9.0-21.2) sec	1
12	Partial thromboplastin time	206	76(64-98) sec	7
13	Fibrinogen	57	273.5(120-470) mg %	6

Contributors: (a) Coon, William W., (b) Brinkhous, K. M.

References: [1] Biggs, R., and A. S. Douglas. 1953. J. Clin. Path., Lond. 6:23. [2] Duff, I. F., R. H. Landaburu, J. Conrad, and J. A. Polhemus. Unpublished. [3] Owren, P. A. 1949. Scand. J. Clin. Lab. Invest. 1:81. [4] Quick, A. J. 1949. Blood, N. Y. 4:1281. [5] Quick, A. J. 1951. Physiology and pathology of hemostasis. Lea and Febiger, Philadelphia. [6] Ratnoff, O. D., and C. Menzie. 1951. J. Laborat. Clin. M. 37:316. [7] Rodman, N. F., Jr., E. M. Barrow, and J. B. Graham. 1958. Am. J. Clin. Path. 29:525. [8] Tocantins, L. M. 1955. The coagulation of blood: methods of study. Grune and Stratton, New York. p. 144. [9] Ware, A. G., and W. H. Seegers. 1949. Am. J. Clin. Path. 19:471. [10] Ware, A. G., and R. Stragnell. 1952. Ibid. 22:791. [11] Wolf, P. 1953. J. Clin. Path., Lond. 6:34.

91. RELATIVE LEVELS OF PLASMA PROTHROMBIN AND Ac-GLOBULIN: VERTEBRATES

Part I: PLASMA PROTHROMBIN

	Animal	No. of Observations	Plasma Prothrombin Level (Two-Stage Method)[1]	
			%[2]	units/ml[3]
	(A)	(B)	(C)	(D)
1	Man	11	84	294
2	Cat	9	91	319
3	Dog		100	350
4	Guinea pig	7	53	186
5	Rabbit, albino	5	89	312
6	Rat, albino	7	95	333
7	Chicken, white Leghorn	10	50	175
8	Turtle (Chrysemys picta)	4	42	147
9	Dogfish (Mustelus canis)	4	8	28
10	Sea bass (Centropristus striatus)	2	31	109
11	Stingray (Dasyatis centura)	2	27	95

/1/ Of Warner, Brinkhous, and Smith: oxalated, diluted venous plasma defibrinated with a small amount of thrombin; prothrombin converted to thrombin by use of thromboplastins, and thrombin assayed against a standard fibrinogen solution. [2] Somewhat different relative values are obtained by the Quick one-stage method [1].
/2/ Values expressed in terms of dog plasma, with prothrombin level arbitrarily set at 100. /3/ Values expressed in terms of dog plasma, which normally contains approximately 350 units prothrombin/ml plasma. A unit of prothrombin = amount required to form 1 unit of thrombin, which is the quantity that will cause clotting of 1 ml of standard fibrinogen solution in 15 seconds under standard conditions [2].

91. RELATIVE LEVELS OF PLASMA PROTHROMBIN AND Ac-GLOBULIN: VERTEBRATES (Concluded)

Part I: PLASMA PROTHROMBIN (Concluded)

Contributors: (a) Diggs, L. W., (b) Warner, E. D.

References: [1] Quick, A. J. 1941. Am. J. Physiol. 132:239. [2] Warner, E. D., K. M. Brinkhous, and H. P. Smith. 1939. Ibid. 125:296.

Part II: PLASMA Ac-GLOBULIN

Plasma Ac-globulin is also known as accelerator globulin, labile factor, proaccelerin (factor V), or plasma prothrombin conversion factor. Values in parentheses are ranges, estimate "c" (cf. Introduction).

Animal	Two-Stage Method[1]			One-Stage Method[2] %[5]	Reference
	No. of Observations	%[3]	units/ml[4]		
(A)	(B)	(C)	(D)	(E)	(F)
1 Man	12[6]	8.2	14.5(12-17)	2	B-D, 1; E, 2
2 Cat	3	79.4	140(123-170)		1
3 Cow	15[6]	73.9	130(120-140)	15	B-D, 1; E, 2
4 Dog	3	100	176(158-203)	20	B-D, 1; E, 2
5 Guinea pig	3	20.5	36.3(31-40)	10	B-D, 1; E, 2
6 Rabbit	4	94.5	166.3(92-310)	100	B-D, 1; E, 2
7 Rat	2	36.4	64(55-73)		1
8 Chicken	3	2.3	4.0(3.2-4.7)	5	B-D, 1; E, 2
9 Turtle	4[6]	1.7	3.0		1

/1/ Of Ware and Seegers [4]. /2/ Of Quick and Stefanini [2]. /3/ Values expressed in terms of dog plasma, with Ac-globulin level arbitrarily set at 100. /4/ A unit of plasma Ac-globulin = 1000 times the amount that, when present in 1 ml of a reacting mixture of prothrombin-thromboplastin-calcium, will reproduce a standard curve of thrombin production [1, 3]. /5/ Values expressed in terms of rabbit plasma, with Ac-globulin level arbitrarily set at 100. /6/ Number of specimens (pooled).

Contributors: (a) Seegers, Walter H., (b) Stefanini, Mario, (c) Owen, Charles A.

References: [1] Murphy, R. C., and W. H. Seegers. 1948. Am. J. Physiol. 154:134. [2] Quick, A. J., and M. Stefanini. 1948. J. Laborat. Clin. M. 33:819. [3] Ware, A. G., and W. H. Seegers. 1948. Am. J. Physiol. 152:567. [4] Ware, A. G., and W. H. Seegers. 1948. J. Biol. Chem. 172:699.

XII. Blood Groups

92. BLOOD GROUP SYSTEMS: MAN

To determine an individual's blood group, a battery of diagnostic reagents or antiserums is required. These reagents contain only antibodies specific for the blood factor in question and for no other antibodies. The blood factors detected by the use of the various antiserums are not all independent of one another, but fall naturally into sets which are known as blood group systems, corresponding to the different chemical substances or agglutinogens that go to make up the mosaic of the surface of the red blood cell (see diagram). In testing, the reaction is positive if the cells are agglutinated or clumped into large masses (generally visible to the naked eye); the reaction is negative if the cells remain evenly suspended (visible with the microscope).

The A-B-O, the Rh-Hr, and the M-N are the three most important of the blood group systems in man, and are the ones most used in the study of human linkage, in tests for zygosity of twins, and in medicolegal problems of disputed parentage. Other blood group systems have been reported after an antibody, giving reactions unrelated to previously described blood groups, has been encountered in the serum of certain individuals (mothers of erythroblastotic babies [Kell, Kidd], patients who had received blood transfusions [Duffy, Lutheran]).

The blood group systems in man depend on multiple allelic genes for their hereditary transmission. None of the blood-grouped genes is known to be sex-linked, and the genes of each blood group system appear to be located on different pairs of chromosomes, as is shown by their independent heredity.

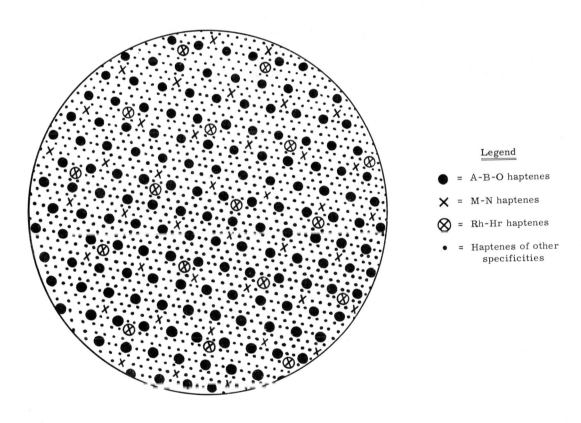

Legend

● = A-B-O haptenes

✕ = M-N haptenes

⊗ = Rh-Hr haptenes

· = Haptenes of other specificities

Distribution of Blood Group Agglutinogen Loci on Surface of Erythrocyte

Contributor: Wiener, Alexander S.

References: [1] Wiener, A. S., R. D. Owen, C. Stormont, and I. B. Wexler. 1957. J. Am. M. Ass. 164:2036.

[2] Wiener, A. S., and I. B. Wexler. 1958. Heredity of the blood groups. Grune and Stratton, New York.

Definitions: agglutinin = antibody that aggregates a particular antigen; agglutinogen = any substance that, acting as an antigen, stimulates the production of agglutinin; antiserum = a serum that contains antibody or antibodies; antibody = a modified serum globulin, synthesized by an animal in response to antigenic stimulus, that reacts specifically in vivo and in vitro with the homologous antigen; antigen = a high-molecular-weight substance, or complex, foreign to the blood stream of an animal, which, when gaining access to the tissues of the animal, stimulates the formation of a specific antibody and reacts specifically in vivo or in vitro with the homologous antibody; blood factors = the serological properties by which an agglutinogen is recognized; gene = the biologic unit of heredity, self-reproducing and located in a definite position (locus) on a particular chromosome; allelic genes = genes situated at corresponding loci in a pair of chromosomes; genotype = the fundamental hereditary constitution (or assortment of genes) of an individual; haptene = that portion of an antigenic molecule or antigenic complex that determines its immunological specificity; phenotype = the outward, visible expression of the hereditary constitution of an individual.

Symbols: (+) = factor produced by the gene, (-) = factor not produced by the gene, (±) = factor may be produced by such a gene.

Part I: PHENOTYPES AND GENOTYPES OF THE A-B-O SYSTEM

The A-B-O blood groups are determined by two agglutinogens on the red blood cells (agglutinogen A which occurs in two principal forms, A_1 and A_2, and agglutinogen B) and two corresponding, naturally-occurring iso-agglutinins in the serum (anti-A [alpha] and anti-B [beta]). The latter are regularly present in the serum when the corresponding agglutinogen is absent from the red cells, except during the neonatal period when the antibody-producing mechanism is immature. Tests include examination of the serum for iso-agglutinin content, as well as examination of the reaction of the red cells to anti-A and anti-B serums. Frequencies are for populations of European origin.

	Desig-nation	Frequency %	Phenotype					Genotype		
			Reaction with Antiserum[1]				Plasma Agglutinin	ABO Genes	Frequency %	Xx Genes[2]
			Anti-A	Anti-A_1	Anti-B	Anti-H				
	(A)	(B)	(C)	(D)	(E)	(F)	(G)	(H)	(I)	(J)
1	O	45.0	-	-	-	+	Anti-A, anti-B	OO	45.0	XX or Xx
2	A_1	31.0	+	+	-	-	Anti-B, occasionally anti-H	A_1A_1	3.5	
3								A_1A_2	2.6	
4								A_1O	25.0	
5	A_2	9.6	+	-	-	+	Anti-B, occasionally anti-A_1	A_2A_2	0.5	
6								A_2O	9.2	
7	B	10.0	-	-	+		Anti-A	BB	0.7	
8								BO	9.3	
9	A_1B	2.9	+	+	+	-	Occasionally anti-H	A_1B	2.9	
10	A_2B	1.1	+	-	+		Occasionally anti-A_1	A_2B	1.1	
11	"Bombay type"	Rare	-	-	-	-	Anti-A, anti-B, anti-H	BO^3	Rare	xx

/1/ Anti-A obtained from type-B subjects, and anti-B obtained from type-A subjects. /2/ Segregate independently of and modify ABO genes. /3/ Presumably other ABO genotypes would give the Bombay type, but have not been studied.

Contributor: Allen, Fred H., Jr.

References: [1] Race, R. R., and R. Sanger. 1958. Blood groups in man. Ed. 3. Blackwell, Oxford.
[2] Wiener, A. S., and I. B. Wexler. 1958. Heredity of the blood groups. Grune and Stratton, New York.

Part II: PHENOTYPES AND GENOTYPES OF THE Rh-Hr SYSTEM

The Rh-Hr system is the most complicated of the human blood systems. At the present time, four principal Rh blood factors (Rh_0, rh', rh'', and rh^W) and three principal Hr factors (hr', hr'', and hr) are recognized. However, antiserums for only four of these seven factors are readily available for routine clinical and medicolegal work (anti-Rh_0, anti-rh', anti-rh'', and anti-hr'). The Rh_0 factor is the most common source of clinical symptoms, as it is the most antigenic of the Rh-Hr factors. It appears to represent a special structure within the Rh-Hr agglutinogen, since red cells can be coated with the Rh_0-blocking antibody without interfering with the reactions of the red cells with other antibodies such as anti-rh', anti-rh'', anti-hr'. Frequencies are for white residents of New York City.

| | 2 Rh Phenotypes | | | 12 Rh Phenotypes | | | | | 28 Rh-Hr Phenotypes | | | | | 55 Genotypes |
| | Designation | Frequency % | Reaction with Anti-Rh_0 (or anti-rhesus) | Designation | Frequency %[1] | Reaction with Anti | | | Designation | Frequency %[1] | Reaction with anti | | | |
						rh'	rh''	rh^W			hr'	hr''	hr	
	(A)	(B)	(C)	(D)	(E)	(F)	(G)	(H)	(I)	(J)	(K)	(L)	(M)	(N)
1	Rh negative	15	-	rh	14.4	-	-	-	rh	14.4	+	+	+	rr
2				rh'	0.46	+	-	-	rh'rh	0.46	+	+	+	$r'r$
3									rh'rh'	0.0036	-	+	-	$r'r'$
4				rh'^w	0.004	+	-	+	rh'^Wrh	0.004	+	+	+	r'^Wr
5									rh'^Wrh'	0.00006	-	+	-	r'^Wr' or $r'^Wr'^W$
6				rh''	0.38	-	+	-	rh''rh	0.38	+	+	+	$r''r$
7									rh''rh''	0.0025	+	-	-	$r''r''$
8				rh^y	0.01	+	+	-	rh'rh''	0.006	+	+	-	$r'r''$
9									rh^yrh	0.008	+	+	+	r^yr
10									rh^yrh'	0.0001	-	+	-	r^yr'
11									rh^yrh''	0.0001	+	-	-	r^yr''
12									$rh^y rh^y$	0.000001	-	-	-	$r^y r^y$
13				rh_y^W	0.00005	+	+	+	rh'^Wrh''	0.00005	+	+	-	r'^Wr''
14									rh_y^Wrh	0.000001	-	+	-	$r'^W r^y$
15	Rh positive	85	+	Rh_0	2.1	-	-	-	Rh_0	2.1	+	+	+	R^0R^0 or R^0r
16				Rh_1	50.7	+	-	-	Rh_1rh	33.4	+	+	+	R^1r, R^1R^0, or R^0r'
17									Rh_1Rh_1	17.3	-	+	-	R^1R^1 or R^1r'
18				Rh_1^W	3.3	+	-	+	Rh_1^Wrh	1.6	+	+	+	$R^1{}^Wr$, $R^1{}^WR^0$, or $R^0r'^W$
19									$Rh_1^WRh_1$	1.7	-	+	-	$R^1{}^WR^1$, $R^1r'^W$, $R^1{}^Wr'$, $R^1{}^WR^1{}^W$, or $R^1{}^Wr'^W$
20				Rh_2	14.6	-	+	-	Rh_2rh	12.2	+	+	+	R^2r, R^2R^0, or R^0r''
21									Rh_2Rh_2	2.4	+	-	-	R^2R^2 or R^2r''
22				Rh_z	13.4	+	+	-	Rh_1Rh_2	12.9	+	+	-	R^1R^2, R^1r'', or R^2r'
23									Rh_zrh	0.2	+	+	+	R^Zr, R^ZR^0, or R^0r^y
24									Rh_zRh_1	0.2	-	+	-	R^ZR^1, R^Zr', or R^1r^y
25									Rh_zRh_2	0.07	+	-	-	R^ZR^2, R^Zr'', or R^2r^y
26									Rh_zRh_z	0.0004	-	-	-	R^ZR^Z or R^Zr^y
27				Rh_z^W	0.6	+	+	+	$Rh_1^WRh_2$	0.6	+	+	-	$R^1{}^WR^2$, $R^1{}^Wr''$, or $R^2r'^W$
28									$Rh_z^WRh_1$	0.008	-	+	-	$R^1{}^WR^Z$, $R^1{}^Wr^y$, or $R^Zr'^W$

/1/ Based on estimated gene frequencies: r = 38%, r' = 0.6%, r'' = 0.5%, r^y = 0.01%, r'^W = 0.005%, R^0 = 2.7%, R^1 = 41%, R^2 = 15%, R^Z = 0.2%, $R^1{}^W$ = 2%.

Contributor: Wiener, Alexander S.

Reference: Wiener, A. S., and I. B. Wexler. 1958. Heredity of the blood groups. Grune and Stratton, New York.

Part III: PARTIAL LIST OF ALLELIC GENES OF THE Rh-Hr SYSTEM

Frequencies are for populations of European origin.

Gene	Gene Frequency %	Agglutinogen	Blood Factor and Frequency												
			Rh_0 85%	Rh^A	rh' 70%	rh^{W1} 2%	rh^X Rare	rh_i 70%	rh'' 30%	rh^{W2} Rare	hr' 80%	hr'' 97%	hr 64%	hr^V Rare	Hr 99+%
(A)	(B)	(C)	(D)	(E)	(F)	(G)	(H)	(I)	(J)	(K)	(L)	(M)	(N)	(O)	(P)
1 r	38	rh	-	-	-	-	-	-	-	-	+	+	+	-	+
2 r^V	Rare[1]	rh^V	-	-	-	-	-	-	-	-	+	+	+	+	+
3 r'	0.6	rh'	-	-	+	-	-	+	-	-	-	+	-	-	+
4 r'^W	0.05	rh'w	-	-	+	+	-	+	-	-	-	+	-	-	+
5 r''	0.5	rh''	-	-	-	-	-	-	+	-	+	-	-	-	+
6 r^y	0.01	rh_y	-	-	+	-	-	-	+	-	-	-	-	-	+
7 R^0	2.7	Rh_o	+	+	-	-	-	-	-	-	+	+	+	-	+
8 R^{0V}	Rare[1]	Rh_o^V	+	+	-	-	-	-	-	-	+	+	+	+	+
9 $\bar{\bar{R}}^0$	Very rare	$\bar{\bar{R}}h_o$	+	+	-	-	-	-	-	-	-	-	-	-	-
10 $\bar{R}^{W1}$	Very rare	$\bar{R}h^{W1}$	+	+	-	+	-	-	-	-	-	-	-	-	-
11 R^{0a}	Very rare	Rh_o^a	+	-	-	-	-	-	-	-	+	+	+	-	+
12 R^1	41	Rh_1	+	+	+	-	-	+	-	-	-	+	-	-	+
13 R^{1W}	2	Rh_1^W	+	+	+	+	-	+	-	-	-	+	-	-	+
14 R^{1X}	Rare	Rh_1^X	+	+	+	-	+	+	-	-	-	+	-	-	+
15 R^2	15	Rh^2	+	+	-	-	-	-	+	-	+	-	-	-	+
16 R^{2W}	Rare	Rh_2^W	+	+	-	-	-	-	+	+	+	-	-	-	+
17 R^Z	0.2	Rh_z	+	+	+	-	-	-	+	-	-	-	-	-	+

/1/ Except in Negroes.

Contributor: Wiener, Alexander S.

Reference: Wiener, A. S. 1958. Science 128:849.

Part IV: KNOWN Rh-Hr BLOOD FACTORS AND CORRESPONDING ANTIBODIES

	Blood Factor	Year of Discovery	Antibody		Blood Factor	Year of Discovery	Antibody
	(A)	(B)	(C)		(A)	(B)	(C)
1	Rh_o ($\Re ho$)	1937 (1944)	Anti-rhesus, anti-Rh_o	10	rh^{W2}	1955	Anti-rh^{W2}
2	rh'	1941	Anti-rh'	11	rh^G	1956	Anti-rh^G
3	hr'	1941	Anti-hr'	12	rh_i	1958	Anti-rh_i
4	rh''	1943	Anti-rh''	13	Rh^A	1956	Anti-Rh^A
5	hr''	1945	Anti-hr''	14	Rh^B	1958	Anti-Rh^B
6	rh^{W1}	1946	Anti-rh^{W1}	15	Rh^C	1958	Anti-Rh^C
7	hr	1953	Anti-hr	16	Rh^D	1959	Anti-Rh^D
8	rh^X	1954	Anti-rh^X	17	Hr		Anti-Hr
9	hr^V	1955	Anti-hr^V	18	hr^S	1960	Anti-hr^S

Contributor: Wiener, Alexander S.

Reference: Wiener, A. S. 1960. J. Forensic M., S. Africa 7:93.

Part V: ALLELIC GENES OF THE M-N SYSTEM

So far as is known, the M-N phenotype of a person is exactly what would be expected from the genotype, no suppressing effect of any one M-N gene on any other having been demonstrated. In blood typing, anti-M is obtained from humans or immunized rabbits, anti-N from immunized rabbits or from seeds of Vicia graminea; anti-Hu and anti-He are obtained only from immunized rabbits, and other antiserums only from sensitized humans. Frequencies are for Europeans.

	Gene	Gene Frequency %	Blood Factor and Frequency										
			M 79%	Mg Rare	N 71%	S 55%	s 89%	U 99+%	Hu Rare[1]	He Rare[1]	Mi^a Rare[1]	Vw Rare[1]	Vr Rare[1]
	(A)	(B)	(C)	(D)	(E)	(F)	(G)	(H)	(I)	(J)	(K)	(L)	(M)
1	MS	25	+	−	+[2]	+	−	+	−	±	±	−	−
2	Ms	28	+	−	+[2]	−	+	+	−	±	−	−	±
3	MS^u	Rare	+	−	−	−	−	−	−	−	−	−	
4	NS	8	−	−	+	+	−	+	−	±	−	−	−
5	Ns	39	−	−	+	−	+	+	±	±	±	±	−
6	NS^u	Rare	−	−	+	−	−	−	−	−	−	−	
7	Mg	Rare	−	+		−			−	−	−	−	−
	Reference		[5]	[1, 2]	[5]	[9, 11]	[7]	[12]	[6]	[4]	[8]	[3]	[10]

/1/ Factors Hu, He, Mi^a, Vw, and Vr undoubtedly occur in other combinations than are shown here; there is, as yet, insufficient information about these factors to prepare a complete table of the M-N genes. /2/ These genes produce a small amount of N factor or something which cross-reacts with anti-N.

Contributor: Allen, Fred H., Jr.

References: [1] Allen, F. H., Jr., P. A. Corcoran, and F. R. Ellis. 1960. Vox Sang. 5:224. [2] Allen, F. H., Jr., P. A. Corcoran, H. B. Kenton, and N. Breare. 1958. Ibid. 3:81. [3] Graydon, J. J. 1946. Med. J. Australia 2:9. [4] Ikin, E. W., and A. E. Mourant. 1951. Brit. M. J. 1:456. [5] Landsteiner, K., and P. Levine. 1927. Proc. Soc. Exp. Biol., N. Y. 24:600. [6] Landsteiner, K., W. R. Strutton, and M. W. Chase. 1934. J. Immun. 27:469. [7] Levine, P., A. B. Kuhmichel, M. Wigod, and E. Koch. 1951. Proc. Soc. Exp. Biol., N. Y. 78:218. [8] Levine, P., A. H. Stock, A. B. Kuhmichel, and N. Bronikovsky. 1951. Ibid. 77:402. [9] Sanger, R., and R. R. Race. 1947. Nature, Lond. 160:505. [10] Van der Hart, M., M. van der Veer, J. J. van Loghem, R. Sanger, and R. R. Race. 1958. Vox Sang. 3:261. [11] Walsh, R. J., and C. Montgomery. 1947. Nature, Lond. 160:504. [12] Wiener, A. S., L. J. Unger, and E. B. Gordon. 1953. J. Am. M. Ass. 153:1444.

Part VI: ALLELIC GENES OF THE KELL SYSTEM

So far as is known, the Kell phenotype of an individual is exactly what would be expected from the genotype, e.g., k^{a}k^a has a weak k factor. None of the Kell genes has any suppressing effect on any other Kell gene, so far as has been demonstrated. Frequencies are for populations of European origin.

	Gene[1]	Gene Frequency %	Blood Factor and Frequency				
			K (Kell) 9%	k (Cellano) 99.8%	Kp^a (Penney) 2%	Kp^b (Rautenberg) 99.98%	Ku 99.99%
	(A)	(B)	(C)	(D)	(E)	(F)	(G)
1	K^a	Rare	+	−	+		
2	K^b	4.5	+	−	−	+	+
3	k^a	1.1	−	Weak	+	−	+
4	k^b	±92	−	+	−	+	+
5	K^o	±2	−	−	−	−	−

/1/ Only one example of K^a found; not, as yet, confirmed by family study.

Contributor: Allen, Fred H., Jr.

Part VI: ALLELIC GENES OF THE KELL SYSTEM (Concluded)

References: [1] Allen, F. H., Jr., S. J. Lewis, and H. Fudenberg. 1958. Vox Sang. 3:1. [2] Chown, B., M. Lewis, and H. Kaita. 1957. Nature, Lond. 180:711. [3] Levine, P., W. Wigod, A. M. Backer, and R. Ponder. 1949. Blood, N. Y. 7:869.

Part VII: ALLELIC GENES OF THE P SYSTEM

Frequencies are for populations of European origin.

Gene	Gene Frequency %	Blood Factor[1] and Frequency		
		P 100%	P_1 79%	P^k Rare
(A)	(B)	(C)	(D)	(E)
1 P_1	54	+	+	-
2 P_2	46	+	-	-
3 P^k	Rare	-	-	+
4 p	Rare	-	-	-

/1/ Anti-P = anti-Tj^a; anti-P_1 = antibody commonly known as anti-P.

Contributor: Allen, Fred H., Jr.

References: [1] Levine, P., O. Bobbitt, R. K. Waller, and A. Kuhmichel. 1951. Proc. Soc. Exp. Biol., N. Y. 77:403. [2] Matson, G. A., J. Swanson, J. Noades, R. Sanger, and R. R. Race. 1959. Am. J. Human Genet. 11:26. [3] Sanger, R. 1958. Proc. 6th Congr. Internat. Soc. Blood Transfusion. S. Karger, N. Y. p. 110.

Part VIII: GENOTYPES AND PHENOTYPES OF THE DUFFY SYSTEM

Frequencies are for populations of European origin.

Genotype		Phenotype Reaction with Antiserum[1]	
Designation	Frequency %	Anti-Fy^a	Anti-Fy^b
(A)	(B)	(C)	(D)
1 Fy^aFy^a	17	+	-
2 Fy^aFy	Rare	+	-
3 Fy^aFy^b	49	+	+
4 Fy^bFy^b	34	-	+
5 Fy^bFy	Rare	-	+
6 $FyFy$	Rare[2]	-	-

/1/ Antiserums found only in sensitized humans, and nearly always require the indirect antiglobulin technique when used as reagents. /2/ A common type in Negroes.

Contributor: Allen, Fred H., Jr.

References: [1] Cutbush, M., P. L. Mollison, and D. M. Parkin. 1950. Nature, Lond. 165:188. [2] Ikin, E. W., A. E. Mourant, H. J. Pettenkoffer, and G. Blumenthal. 1951. Ibid. 168:1077. [3] Sanger, R., R. R. Race, and J. Jack. 1955. Brit. J. Haemat. 1:370.

Part IX: GENOTYPES AND PHENOTYPES OF THE KIDD SYSTEM

Frequencies are for populations of European origin.

	Genotype		Phenotype Reaction with Antiserum[1]	
	Designation	Frequency %	Anti-Jk^a	Anti-Jk^b
	(A)	(B)	(C)	(D)
1	Jk^{a}Jk^a	27	+	-
2	Jk^{a}Jk	Rare	+	-
3	Jk^{a}Jk^b	50	+	+
4	Jk^{b}Jk^b	Rare	-	+
5	Jk^{b}Jk	23	-	+
6	JkJk	Rare[2]	-	-

/1/ Antiserums found only in sensitized humans, and nearly always require the indirect antiglobulin technique when used as reagents. /2/ Not so rare in some American Indians.

Contributor: Allen, Fred H., Jr.

References: [1] Allen, F. H., Jr., L. K. Diamond, and B. Niedziela. 1951. Nature, Lond. 167:482.

[2] Pinkerton, F. J., L. E. Mermod, B. A. Liles, J. A. Jack, Jr., and J. Noades. 1959. Vox Sang. 4:155.

[3] Plaut, G., E. Ikin, A. E. Mourant, R. Sanger, and R. R. Race. 1953. Nature, Lond. 171:431.

Part X: GENOTYPES AND PHENOTYPES OF THE LUTHERAN SYSTEM

Frequencies are for populations of European origin.

	Genotype		Phenotype Reaction with Antiserum[1]	
	Designation	Frequency %	Anti-Lu^a	Anti-Lu^b
	(A)	(B)	(C)	(D)
1	Lu^{a}Lu^a	0.2	+	-
2	Lu^{a}Lu^b	8	+	+
3	Lu^{b}Lu^b	92	-	+

/1/ Antiserums found only in sensitized humans, and are usually more active at 15°C than at 37°C.

Contributor: Allen, Fred H., Jr.

References: [1] Callender, S. T., and R. R. Race. 1946. Ann. Eugen., Lond. 13:102. [2] Greenwalt, T. J., and T. Sasaki. 1957. Blood, N. Y. 12:998.

92. BLOOD GROUP SYSTEMS: MAN (Continued)

Part XI: GENOTYPES AND PHENOTYPES OF THE LEWIS SYSTEM

The Lewis substances are primarily serum factors, and are only incidentally adsorbed onto the surface of the red cells. After a transfusion, the Lewis red cell type of an individual may change temporarily.

| | Genotype | | Secretion of ABH Substances in Saliva[2] | Phenotype | | Frequency % |
| | Secretor Genes[1] | Lewis Genes | | Reaction with Antiserum[3] | | |
				Anti-Le^a	Anti-Le^b	
	(A)	(B)	(C)	(D)	(E)	(F)
1	SeSe	LL or Ll	+	−	+	75
2	Sese	LL or Ll	+	−	+	
3	sese	LL or Ll	−	+	−	20
4	SeSe	ll	+	−	−	5
5	Sese	ll	+	−	−	
6	sese	ll	−	−	−	

/1/ Segregate independently of and modify Lewis genes (theory of Ceppellini). /2/ Substances secreted depend on A-B-O blood type of individual. /3/ Antiserums found in sensitized humans, and are commonly of "spontaneous" origin.

Contributor: Allen, Fred H., Jr.

Reference: Ceppellini, R. In R. R. Race and R. Sanger. 1958. Blood groups in man. Ed. 3. Blackwell, Oxford. p. 208.

Part XII: OTHER BLOOD SYSTEMS

Some or even all of the factors listed below may eventually prove to be related to one of the already-known blood group systems, and with further investigation duplications may even be found. At present, it is only possible to give some of the blood systems to which the factors do not belong. Frequencies are for populations of European origin.

	Blood Factor	Year of Discovery	Probable Frequency %	Unrelated Blood Group	Reference
	(A)	(B)	(C)	(D)	(E)
1	Levay	1946	<4	No information	1
2	Vel	1952	99.96	ABO, Lewis, Kidd	10
3	Ven	1952	<1	MN	12
4	Be^a	1953	<0.1	ABO, MN, Duffy	3
5	Wr^a (Ca)[1]	1953	0.08	ABO, MN, P, Rh, Kidd	7
6	Di^a	1954	<0.1	ABO, Rh, MN, P, Kidd, Kell, Duffy, Js	8
7	By	1954	0.007	No information	9
8	Rm	1954	<0.7	Rh	11
9	I	1956	99.98	No information	14
10	Yt^a	1956	99.7	ABO, MN, Rh	4
11	Js^a	1958	<0.3	ABO, MN, Rh, Di^a, Duffy, Kidd	6
12	Sw^a	1959	± 0.00014	ABO, MN, Rh, Kell, Lewis, Duffy, Kidd	2
13	Good	1960	Rare	No information	5

/1/ Cavaliere factor of Wiener and Brancato [13] is probably identical with Wright factor of Holman [7].

Contributor: Allen, Fred H., Jr.,

References: [1] Callender, S. T., and R. R. Race. 1946. Ann. Eugen., Lond. 13:102. [2] Cleghorn, T. E. 1959. Nature, Lond. 184:1324. [3] Davidsohn, I., K. Stern, E. R. Strausser, and W. Spurrier. 1953. Blood, N. Y. 8:747. [4] Eaton, B. R., J. A. Morton, M. M. Pickles, and K. E. White. 1956. Brit. J. Haemat. 2:333. [5] Frumin, A. M., M. M. Porter, and M. F. Eichman. 1960. Blood, N. Y. 15:681. [6] Giblett, E. R. 1959. Brit. J. Haemat. 5:319. [7] Holman, C. A. 1953. Lancet, Lond. 2:119. [8] Levine, P., E. A. Koch, R. T. McGee, and G. H. Hill. 1954. Am. J. Clin. Path. 24:292. [9] Simmons, R. T., and S. O. M. Were. 1955. Med. J. Australia 2:55. [10] Sussman, L. N., and E. B. Miller. 1952. Rev. hémat., Par. 7:368. [11] Van der Hart, M., H. Bosman, and

Part XII: OTHER BLOOD SYSTEMS (Concluded)

J. J. van Loghem. 1954. Vox Sang. 4:108. [12] Van Loghem, J. J., and M. van der Hart. 1950. Ned. tschr. geneesk. 11:748. [13] Wiener, A. S., and G. J. Brancato. 1953. Am. J. Human Genet. 5:350. [14] Wiener, A. S., L. J. Unger, L. Cohen, and J. Feldman. 1956. Ann. Int. M. 44:221.

93. HEREDITY OF BLOOD GROUPS AND TYPES: MAN

Because of the possibility of coincidence, it is considered an inconclusive finding when the blood type of the child matches the blood type of the putative parent. Therefore, in cases of disputed parentage, blood tests can be used only to exclude the claim of maternity or paternity.

Part I: A-B-O EXCLUSION

	Parental Phenotype Combination		Blood Group of Child that Refutes	
	Putative Mother	Putative Father	Putative Maternity	Putative Paternity
	(A)	(B)	(C)	(D)
1	O	O	AB	A, B
2		A	AB	B
3		B	AB	A
4		AB	AB	O
5	A	O	None	B, AB
6		A	None	B, AB
7		B	None	None
8		AB	None	O
9	B	O	None	A, AB
10		A	None	None
11		B	None	A, AB
12		AB	None	O
13	AB	O	O	AB
14		A	O	None
15		B	O	None
16		AB	O	None

Contributor: Wiener, Alexander S.

Reference: Wiener, A. S., and I. B. Wexler. 1958. Heredity of the blood groups. Grune and Stratton, New York.

Part II: M-N EXCLUSION

	Parental Phenotype Combination		Blood Type of Child that Refutes	
	Putative Mother	Putative Father	Putative Maternity	Putative Paternity
	(A)	(B)	(C)	(D)
1	M	M	N	MN
2		N	N	M
3		MN	N	None
4	N	M	M	N
5		N	M	MN
6		MN	M	None
7	MN	M	None	N
8		N	None	M
9		MN	None	None

Contributor: Wiener, Alexander S.

Reference: Wiener, A. S., and I. B. Wexler. 1958. Heredity of the blood groups. Grune and Stratton, New York.

Part III: Rh-Hr EXCLUSION

For convenience, the numbers 1 through 12 have been assigned in column C to the 12 Rh-Hr phenotypes listed in column B. Combinations of these numbers appear in columns D and E, which, when deciphered, give the blood type of the child. Thus, the blood type in line 1, column D = rh'rh', rhyrh', Rh_1Rh_1, Rh_ZRh_1.

	Parental Phenotype Combination		Assigned Pheno-type Number	Blood Type of Child that Refutes	
	Putative Mother	Putative Father		Putative Maternity	Putative Paternity
	(A)	(B)	(C)	(D)	(E)
1	rh	rh	1	3, 6, 9, 12	2, 4, 5, 7, 8, 10, 11
2		rh'rh	2	3, 6, 9, 12	4, 5, 7, 8, 10, 11
3		rh'rh'	3	3, 6, 9, 12	1, 4, 5, 7, 8, 10, 11
4		rh''	4	3, 6, 9, 12	2, 5, 7, 8, 10, 11
5		rh'rh''	5	3, 6, 9, 12	7, 8, 10, 11
6		rhyrh'	6	3, 6, 9, 12	1, 4, 7, 8, 10, 11
7		Rh_O	7	3, 6, 9, 12	2, 4, 5, 8, 10, 11
8		Rh_1rh	8	3, 6, 9, 12	4, 5, 10, 11
9		Rh_1Rh_1	9	3, 6, 9, 12	1, 4, 5, 7, 10, 11
10		Rh_2	10	3, 6, 9, 12	2, 5, 8, 11
11		Rh_1Rh_2	11	3, 6, 9, 12	None
12		Rh_ZRh_1	12	3, 6, 9, 12	1, 4, 7, 10
13	rh'rh	rh	1	None	3, 4, 5, 6, 7, 8, 9, 10, 11, 12
14		rh'rh	2	None	4, 5, 6, 7, 8, 9, 10, 11, 12
15		rh'rh'	3	None	1, 4, 5, 6, 7, 8, 9, 10, 11, 12
16		rh''	4	None	3, 6, 7, 8, 9, 10, 11, 12
17		rh'rh''	5	None	7, 8, 9, 10, 11, 12
18		rhyrh'	6	None	1, 4, 7, 8, 9, 10, 11, 12
19		Rh_O	7	None	3, 4, 5, 6, 9, 10, 11, 12
20		Rh_1rh	8	None	4, 5, 6, 10, 11, 12
21		Rh_1Rh_1	9	None	1, 4, 5, 6, 7, 10, 11, 12
22		Rh_2	10	None	3, 6, 9, 12
23		Rh_1Rh_2	11	None	None
24		Rh_ZRh_1	12	None	1, 4, 7, 10
25	rh'rh'	rh	1	1, 4, 7, 10	3, 5, 6, 8, 9, 11, 12
26		rh'rh	2	1, 4, 7, 10	5, 6, 8, 9, 11, 12
27		rh'rh'	3	1, 4, 7, 10	2, 5, 6, 8, 9, 11, 12
28		rh''	4	1, 4, 7, 10	3, 6, 8, 9, 11, 12
29		rh'rh''	5	1, 4, 7, 10	8, 9, 11, 12
30		rhyrh'	6	1, 4, 7, 10	2, 5, 8, 9, 11, 12
31		Rh_O	7	1, 4, 7, 10	3, 5, 6, 9, 11, 12
32		Rh_1rh	8	1, 4, 7, 10	5, 6, 11, 12
33		Rh_1Rh_1	9	1, 4, 7, 10	2, 5, 6, 8, 11, 12
34		Rh_2	10	1, 4, 7, 10	3, 6, 9, 12
35		Rh_1Rh_2	11	1, 4, 7, 10	None
36		Rh_ZRh_1	12	1, 4, 7, 10	2, 5, 8, 11
37	rh''	rh	1	3, 6, 9, 12	2, 5, 7, 8, 10, 11
38		rh'rh	2	3, 6, 9, 12	7, 8, 10, 11
39		rh'rh'	3	3, 6, 9, 12	1, 4, 7, 8, 10, 11
40		rh''	4	3, 6, 9, 12	2, 5, 7, 8, 10, 11
41		rh'rh''	5	3, 6, 9, 12	7, 8, 10, 11
42		rhyrh'	6	3, 6, 9, 12	1, 4, 7, 8, 10, 11
43		Rh_O	7	3, 6, 9, 12	2, 5, 8, 11
44		Rh_1rh	8	3, 6, 9, 12	None
45		Rh_1Rh_1	9	3, 6, 9, 12	1, 4, 7, 10
46		Rh_2	10	3, 6, 9, 12	2, 5, 8, 11
47		Rh_1Rh_2	11	3, 6, 9, 12	None
48		Rh_ZRh_1	12	3, 6, 9, 12	1, 4, 7, 10
49	rh'rh''	rh	1	None	3, 6, 7, 8, 9, 10, 11, 12
50		rh'rh	2	None	7, 8, 9, 10, 11, 12
51		rh'rh'	3	None	1, 4, 7, 8, 9, 10, 11, 12
52		rh''	4	None	3, 6, 7, 8, 9, 10, 11, 12
53		rh'rh''	5	None	7, 8, 9, 10, 11, 12
54		rhyrh'	6	None	1, 4, 7, 8, 9, 10, 11, 12
55		Rh_O	7	None	3, 6, 9, 12
56		Rh_1rh	8	None	None
57		Rh_1Rh_1	9	None	1, 4, 7, 10

	Parental Phenotype Combination		Assigned Phenotype Number	Blood Type of Child that Refutes	
	Putative Mother	Putative Father		Putative Maternity	Putative Paternity
	(A)	(B)	(C)	(D)	(E)
58	rh'rh''	Rh_2	10	None	3, 6, 9, 12
59	(con-	Rh_1Rh_2	11	None	None
60	cluded)	Rh_zRh_1	12	None	1, 4, 7, 10
61	rhyrh'	rh	1	1, 4, 7, 10	3, 6, 8, 9, 11, 12
62		rh'rh	2	1, 4, 7, 10	8, 9, 11, 12
63		rh'rh'	3	1, 4, 7, 10	2, 5, 8, 9, 11, 12
64		rh''	4	1, 4, 7, 10	3, 6, 8, 9, 11, 12
65		rh'rh''	5	1, 4, 7, 10	8, 9, 11, 12
66		rhyrh'	6	1, 4, 7, 10	2, 5, 8, 9, 11, 12
67		Rh_o	7	1, 4, 7, 10	3, 6, 9, 12
68		Rh_1rh	8	1, 4, 7, 10	None
69		Rh_1Rh_1	9	1, 4, 7, 10	2, 5, 8, 11
70		Rh_2	10	1, 4, 7, 10	3, 6, 9, 12
71		Rh_1Rh_2	11	1, 4, 7, 10	None
72		Rh_zRh_1	12	1, 4, 7, 10	2, 5, 8, 11
73	Rh_o	rh	1	3, 6, 9, 12	2, 4, 5, 8, 10, 11
74		rh'rh	2	3, 6, 9, 12	4, 5, 10, 11
75		rh'rh'	3	3, 6, 9, 12	1, 4, 5, 7, 10, 11
76		rh''	4	3, 6, 9, 12	2, 5, 8, 11
77		rh'rh''	5	3, 6, 9, 12	None
78		rhyrh'	6	3, 6, 9, 12	1, 4, 7, 10
79		Rh_o	7	3, 6, 9, 12	2, 4, 5, 8, 10, 11
80		Rh_1rh	8	3, 6, 9, 12	4, 5, 10, 11
81		Rh_1Rh_1	9	3, 6, 9, 12	1, 4, 5, 7, 10, 11
82		Rh_2	10	3, 6, 9, 12	2, 5, 8, 11
83		Rh_1Rh_2	11	3, 6, 9, 12	None
84		Rh_zRh_1	12	3, 6, 9, 12	1, 4, 7, 10
85	Rh_1rh	rh	1	None	3, 4, 5, 6, 9, 10, 11, 12
86		rh'rh	2	None	4, 5, 6, 10, 11, 12
87		rh'rh'	3	None	1, 4, 5, 6, 7, 10, 11, 12
88		rh''	4	None	3, 6, 9, 12
89		rh'rh''	5	None	None
90		rhyrh'	6	None	1, 4, 7, 10
91		Rh_o	7	None	3, 4, 5, 6, 9, 10, 11, 12
92		Rh_1rh	8	None	4, 5, 6, 10, 11, 12
93		Rh_1Rh_1	9	None	1, 4, 5, 6, 7, 10, 11, 12
94		Rh_2	10	None	3, 6, 9, 12
95		Rh_1Rh_2	11	None	None
96		Rh_zRh_1	12	None	1, 4, 7, 10
97	Rh_1Rh_1	rh	1	1, 4, 7, 10	3, 5, 6, 9, 11, 12
98		rh'rh	2	1, 4, 7, 10	5, 6, 11, 12
99		rh'rh'	3	1, 4, 7, 10	2, 5, 6, 8, 11, 12
100		rh''	4	1, 4, 7, 10	3, 6, 9, 12
101		rh'rh''	5	1, 4, 7, 10	None
102		rhyrh'	6	1, 4, 7, 10	2, 5, 8, 11
103		Rh_o	7	1, 4, 7, 10	3, 5, 6, 9, 11, 12
104		Rh_1rh	8	1, 4, 7, 10	5, 6, 11, 12
105		Rh_1Rh_1	9	1, 4, 7, 10	2, 5, 6, 8, 11, 12
106		Rh_2	10	1, 4, 7, 10	3, 6, 9, 12
107		Rh_1Rh_2	11	1, 4, 7, 10	None
108		Rh_zRh_1	12	1, 4, 7, 10	2, 5, 8, 11
109	Rh_2	rh	1	3, 6, 9, 12	2, 5, 8, 11
110		rh'rh	2	3, 6, 9, 12	None
111		rh'rh'	3	3, 6, 9, 12	1, 4, 7, 10
112		rh''	4	3, 6, 9, 12	2, 5, 8, 11
113		rh'rh''	5	3, 6, 9, 12	None
114		rhyrh'	6	3, 6, 9, 12	1, 4, 7, 10
115		Rh_o	7	3, 6, 9, 12	2, 5, 8, 11
116		Rh_1rh	8	3, 6, 9, 12	None
117		Rh_1Rh_1	9	3, 6, 9, 12	1, 4, 7, 10

Part III: Rh-Hr EXCLUSION (Concluded)

	Parental Phenotype Combination		Assigned Pheno-type Number	Blood Type of Child that Refutes	
	Putative Mother	Putative Father		Putative Maternity	Putative Paternity
	(A)	(B)	(C)	(D)	(E)
118	Rh_2 (con-cluded)	Rh_2	10	3, 6, 9, 12	2, 5, 8, 11
119		Rh_1Rh_2	11	3, 6, 9, 12	None
120		Rh_ZRh_1	12	3, 6, 9, 12	1, 4, 7, 10
121	Rh_1Rh_2	rh	1	None	3, 6, 9, 12
122		rh'rh	2	None	None
123		rh'rh'	3	None	1, 4, 7, 10
124		rh''	4	None	3, 6, 9, 12
125		rh'rh''	5	None	None
126		rhyrh'	6	None	1, 4, 7, 10
127		Rh_O	7	None	3, 6, 9, 12
128		Rh_1rh	8	None	None
129		Rh_1Rh_1	9	None	1, 4, 7, 10
130		Rh_2	10	None	3, 6, 9, 12
131		Rh_1Rh_2	11	None	None
132		Rh_ZRh_1	12	None	1, 4, 7, 10
133	Rh_ZRh_1	rh	1	1, 4, 7, 10	3, 6, 9, 12
134		rh'rh	2	1, 4, 7, 10	None
135		rh'rh'	3	1, 4, 7, 10	2, 5, 8, 11
136		rh''	4	1, 4, 7, 10	3, 6, 9, 12
137		rh'rh''	5	1, 4, 7, 10	None
138		rhyrh'	6	1, 4, 7, 10	2, 5, 8, 11
139		Rh_O	7	1, 4, 7, 10	3, 6, 9, 12
140		Rh_1rh	8	1, 4, 7, 10	None
141		Rh_1Rh_1	9	1, 4, 7, 10	2, 5, 8, 11
142		Rh_2	10	1, 4, 7, 10	3, 6, 9, 12
143		Rh_1Rh_2	11	1, 4, 7, 10	None
144		Rh_ZRh_1	12	1, 4, 7, 10	2, 5, 8, 11

Contributor: Wiener, Alexander S.

References: [1] Boyd, W. C. 1955. Vox Sang. 5:99. [2] Wiener, A. S., and I. B. Wexler. 1958. Heredity of the blood groups. Grune and Stratton, New York.

94. DISTRIBUTION OF BLOOD GROUPS AND TYPES IN VARIOUS POPULATIONS: MAN

Part I: A-B-O GROUPS

Population	Location	No. of Subjects	Frequency, %			
			Group O	Group A	Group B	Group AB
(A)	(B)	(C)	(D)	(E)	(F)	(G)
1 Ainu	Shizunai	504	36.7	44.5	14.7	5.1
American Indian						
2 Blackfoot	Montana	115	23.5	76.5	0	0
3 Navaho	Arizona	457	72.9	26.9	0.2	0.2
4 Pueblo	New Mexico	310	78.4	20.0	1.6	0
5 Ute	Utah	104	98.1	1.9	0	0
6 Armenian	Vicinity of Marash, Turkey	330	27.3	53.9	12.7	6.1
7 Australian aborigine	Australia	805	53.1	44.7	2.1	0
8 Australian white	Sydney	220	44.6	43.6	9.1	2.7
9 Basque	San Sebastian, Spain	91	57.2	41.7	1.1	0
Bedouin						
10 Iraqui	Vicinity of Baghdad	338	40.8	26.6	25.8	6.8
11 Rwala	Syrian desert	208	43.3	22.1	30.3	4.3
12 Belgian	Liége	3500	46.7	41.9	8.3	3.1
13 Burmese	Valleys of Upper Burma	229	36.2	26.2	29.7	7.9
14 Chinese	Peking	1000	30.7	25.1	34.2	10.0
15 Danish	Copenhagen	14,304	40.6	44.0	10.9	4.5
16 Dutch	Amsterdam	23,643	44.4	43.2	8.9	3.5
17 Egyptian	Cairo	502	27.3	38.5	25.5	8.8
18 English	Southern England	106,477	45.2	43.2	8.5	3.1
19 Eskimo	Southwest Greenland	1063	46.0	46.1	4.9	3.0
20 Estonian	Central, southern, and south-eastern Estonia	1844	32.3	36.6	22.4	8.7
21 Fijian	Fiji	160	43.8	43.1	9.4	3.8
22 Filipino	Philippine Islands	382	45.0	22.0	27.0	6.0
23 Finnish	Finland	23,200	34.1	41.0	18.0	6.9
24 French	Paris	14,303	42.7	45.6	8.3	3.3
25 German	Berlin	39,174	36.5	42.5	14.5	6.5
26 Greek	Athens	21,635	43.5	38.6	13.1	4.8
27 Hawaiian	Hawaiian Islands	413	36.5	60.8	2.2	0.5
28 Hindu	Calcutta	6247	32.4	24.1	36.2	7.3
29 Hungarian	Budapest	624	36.1	41.8	15.9	6.2
30 Indonesian	Djakarta	7129	39.2	26.8	27.3	6.7
31 Irish	Northern Ireland	10,784	52.0	34.7	10.4	2.9
32 Italian	Rome and vicinity	20,051	44.7	40.0	11.4	3.8
33 Japanese	Tokyo	33,834	31.2	38.4	21.8	8.6
34 Korean	South Korea (north of Seoul)	1000	27.0	32.0	29.0	12.0
35 Mambuti Pygmy	Belgian Congo	1032	30.6	30.3	29.1	10.0
36 Norwegian	Oslo	8292	37.8	50.0	8.2	4.0
37 Pakistani, Punjabi	Vicinity of Quetta, West Pakistan	10,000	30.6	24.5	34.8	10.0
38 Papuan	Papua	753	53.7	26.8	16.3	3.2
39 Polish	Warsaw	2886	33.1	38.9	20.1	7.9
40 Portugese	Lisbon	7502	41.8	47.9	7.6	2.7
41 Puerto Rican	Puerto Rico	429	48.7	38.7	9.6	3.0
42 Russian	Leningrad	1800	28.3	39.5	22.9	9.3
43 Scottish	Glasgow	456	47.6	38.4	9.0	5.0
44 Senegalese	Sierra Leone	635	47.4	25.0	24.1	3.5
45 Siamese	Bangkok	6267	37.3	21.8	33.1	7.8
46 Swedish	Kopparberg	10,732	38.5	44.7	10.9	5.8
47 Turkish	Balkans	500	36.8	38.0	18.6	6.6
48 Ukrainian	Kharkov	310	36.4	38.4	21.6	3.6
49 U. S. A. Negro	Iowa	6722	49.1	26.5	20.1	4.3
50 U. S. A. white	Rochester, New York	23,787	44.4	41.8	10.1	3.8
51 Welsh	North Wales	192	47.9	32.8	16.1	3.1
52 Yugoslavian	Yugoslavia	1527	32.8	42.7	17.9	6.6
53 Zulu	Northern Zululand	500	51.8	24.6	21.6	2.0

Contributors: (a) Levine, Philip, (b) Levine, Victor E., (c) Wiener, Alexander S.

References: [1] Boyd, W. C. 1939. Tabulae biol., Den Haag 17:113. [2] Boyd, W. C. 1950. Genetics and the

Part I: A-B-O GROUPS (Concluded)

races of man. Little and Brown, Boston. [3] Mourant, A. E., A. C. Kopeć, and K. Domaniewska-Sobczak. 1958. The ABO blood groups. Blackwell Scientific Publications, Oxford. [4] Wiener, A. S. 1943. Blood groups and transfusion. Ed. 3. C. C. Thomas, Springfield, Ill.

Part II: M-N TYPES

Population	Location	No. of Subjects	Frequency, %		
			Type M	Type N	Type MN
(A)	(B)	(C)	(D)	(E)	(F)
1 Ainu	Shizunai	504	17.9	31.9	50.2
American Indian					
2 Blackfoot	Montana	95	54.7	5.3	40.0
3 Navaho	New Mexico	361	84.5	1.1	14.4
4 Pueblo	New Mexico	140	59.3	7.9	32.8
5 Ute	Utah	104	58.7	6.7	34.6
6 Armenian	Vicinity of Marash, Turkey	332	32.8	20.2	47.0
7 Australian aborigine	Australia	730	3.0	67.4	29.6
8 Basque	Spain	91	23.1	25.3	51.6
Bedouin					
9 Iraqui	Vicinity of Baghdad	338	38.2	13.6	48.2
10 Rwala	Syrian desert	208	57.5	5.8	36.7
11 Belgian	Liége	3100	28.9	20.8	50.3
12 Chinese	Hong Kong	1029	33.2	18.2	48.6
13 Danish	Copenhagen	2023	29.1	21.4	49.5
14 Egyptian	Cairo	613	28.3	23.1	48.6
15 English	London	1522	30.5	21.4	48.2
16 Eskimo	East Greenland	569	83.5	0.9	15.6
17	Southwest Greenland	1063	66.2	2.9	31.0
18 Estonian	Estonia	310	34.8	15.5	49.7
19 Fijian	Fiji	200	11.0	44.5	44.5
20 Filipino	Philippine Islands	382	25.9	23.8	50.3
21 Finnish	Finland	6926	42.3	13.7	44.0
22 French	Paris	1400	30.1	19.8	50.1
23 German	Germany	40,255	30.2	19.7	50.0
24 Hindu	India	300	42.7	10.7	46.7
25 Hungarian	Budapest	624	33.5	18.6	47.9
26 Irish	Dublin	399	30.0	23.3	46.7
27 Italian	Modena and Sicily	736	28.9	17.1	53.9
28 Japanese	Japan	7551	29.0	21.1	49.9
29 Korean	Korea	836	27.9	20.8	51.4
30 Papuan	Papua	200	7.0	69.0	24.0
31 Polish	Poland	600	28.2	22.8	49.0
32 Russian	Leningrad	763	32.2	21.2	46.5
33 Scottish	Glasgow	456	35.0	17.1	47.9
34 Swedish	Sweden	1200	36.1	16.9	47.0
35 Ukrainian	Kharkov	310	36.1	19.6	44.3
36 U. S. A. Negro	New York City	278	28.4	21.9	49.6
37 U. S. A. white	New York City; Boston; Columbus, Ohio	6129	29.2	21.3	49.6
38 Welsh	North Wales	192	30.7	14.0	55.3
39 Yugoslavian	Yugoslavia	1527	30.3	17.9	51.8

Contributors: (a) Levine, Philip, (b) Wiener, Alexander S., (c) Levine, Victor E.

References: [1] Boyd, W. C. 1939. Tabulae biol., Den Haag 17:113. [2] Boyd, W. C. 1950. Genetics and the races of man. Little and Brown, Boston. [3] Wiener, A. S. 1943. Blood groups and transfusion. Ed. 3. C. C. Thomas, Springfield, Ill.

Part III: Rh-Hr TYPES

Population	No. of Sub- jects	Rh Positive Frequency, %						Rh Negative Frequency, %				Ref- er- ence
		Rho	Rh1		Rh2	Rh1Rh2	Rh1Rhz	rh	rh'	rh''	rh'rh''	
			Rh1Rh1	Rh1rh								
(A)	(B)	(C)	(D)	(E)	(F)	(G)	(H)	(I)	(J)	(K)	(L)	(M)
American Indian												
1 In Mexico	95	1.1	40.7	7.4	9.5	38.1	3.1	0	0	0	0	5
2 In Oklahoma	105	2.9	34.3	5.7	17.1	36.2	2.9	0	0.9	0	0	5
3 Ute	104	0	33.7		28.8	37.5		0	0	0	0	1
4 Asiatic Indian	156	1.9	70.5		5.1	12.8		7.1	2.6	0	0	5
5 Australian aborigine	100	4.0	39.0	14.0	21.0	15.0	6.0	0	1.0	0	0	5
6 Australian white	350	0.6	54.0		12.6	16.6		14.9	0.9	0.6	0	5
7 Basque	167	0.6	7.8	47.3	7.8	6.0	0	28.8	1.8	0	0	3
8 Chinese	132	0.9	60.6		3.0	34.1		1.5	0	0	0	5
9 Dutch	200	1.5	51.5		12.3	17.7		15.4	1.5	0	0	5
10 Egyptian		11.5	25.5	39.7	9.2	8.2		5.9				4
11 English	927	2.5	19.7	35.2	12.2	13.6	0.1	14.8	0.7	1.3	0	5
12 Eskimo	315	1.0	34.9		19.7	44.4		0	0	0	0	2
13 Filipino	100	0	87.0		2.0	11.0		0	0	0	0	5
14 German		2.0	19.5	35.6	13.0	13.9	0.4	14.4	0.5	0.8		4
15 Hindu		2.9	35.2	32.4	3.8	16.2	0	7.6	1.9			4
16 Indonesian	200	0.5	74.0		2.5	22.5	0	0	0	0	0.5	5
17 Italian		1.3	23.3	37.3	9.6	11.8	0.7	14.8	0.5	0.5	0.3	4
18 Japanese	150	0	37.4		13.3	47.3		1.3	0	0	0.7	5
19 Norwegian		1.5	15.9	35.6	13.8	14.7		16.2	0.7	1.2		4
20 Papuan	100	0	89.0	4.0	4.0		3.0	0	0	0	0	5
21 Puerto Rican	179	15.1	39.1		19.6	14.0		10.1	1.7	0.5	0	5
22 U. S. A. Negro	135	45.9	0.9	22.8	16.3	4.4	0	7.4	1.5	0.7	0	5
23	223	41.2	20.2		22.4	5.4		8.1	2.7	0	0	
24 U. S. A. white	766	2.2	20.9	33.8	14.9	13.9	0.1	12.5	0.9	0.5	0	5
25	7317	2.2	53.5		15.0	12.9		14.7	1.1	0.6	0.01	

Contributors: (a) Wiener, Alexander S., (b) Levine, Philip

References: [1] Matson, G. A., and C. L. Piper. 1947. Am. J. Phys. Anthrop. 5:357. [2] Matson, G. A., and H. J. Roberts. 1949. Ibid. 7:109. [3] Mourant, A. E. 1947. Nature, Lond. 160:505. [4] Mourant, A. E. 1954. The distribution of the human blood groups. Blackwell, Oxford. [5] Wiener, A. S. 1946. Am. J. Clin. Path. 16.477.

XIII. Hemolymph

95. PHYSICAL PROPERTIES OF HEMOLYMPH: INSECTS

For additional information, consult reference 6, Part I.

Part I: VOLUME

Hemolymph volume varies according to sex, stage of development, age, nutrition, rearing status, method of blood extraction, coagulability, and method of volume determination. Determinations were made on live or fresh-killed insects, unless otherwise specified. Values in parentheses are ranges, estimate "b" or "c" as indicated (cf. Introduction).

	Species	Stage	Method	Volume	Reference
	(A)	(B)	(C)	(D)	(E)
			Orthoptera		
1	Anabrus simplex	Adult	Exsanguination	$(0.05-0.10)^c$ ml/insect	21
2	Blattella germanica			20% body wt	12
3	Locusta migratoria	Nymph	Exsanguination	<0.2 ml/insect	15
4		Adult	Exsanguination	$(0-1)^c$ cu mm/insect	15
	Periplaneta americana	Nymph			27
5		♂	Dye dilution	$19.6(18.8-20.4)^b$ % body wt	
6			Chloride	$20(16.3-23.7)^b$ % body wt (individual)	
7				$16.8(14.8-18.8)^b$ % body wt (pooled)	
8			Cell dilution	$15.7(13.2-18.2)^b$ % body wt	
9		♀	Dye dilution	$19.8(19.1-20.5)^b$ % body wt	
10			Chloride	$18.6(14.5-22.7)^b$ % body wt (individual)	
11				$19.5(17.2-21.8)^b$ % body wt (pooled)	
12			Cell dilution	$16.8(12.3-21.3)^b$ % body wt	
13		Adult	Exsanguination	$(5-20)^c$ mg/insect	25
14				17% body wt	23
		Adult			27
15		♂	Dye dilution	$27.5(23.8-31.2)^b$ % body wt	
16			Chloride	$15.3(12.9-17.7)^b$ % body wt	
17		♀	Dye dilution	$20.9(18.8-23.0)^b$ % body wt	
18			Chloride	$16.9(11.9-21.9)^b$ % body wt	
19	P. fuliginosa	Nymph to adult	Cell dilution	$(4.7-6.9)^c$ % body wt	28
			Isoptera		
20	"Termite queen"	Adult, ♀	Exsanguination	17 ml/insect	24
			Neuroptera		
21	Sialis lutaria	Larva	Exsanguination	25% body wt	2
			Lepidoptera		
22	Agapema galbina	Pupa, ♂♀	Exsanguination	33% body wt (mean)	8
23	Bombyx mori	Larva	Exsanguination	$(0.15-0.22)^c$ ml/g body wt	4
24				0.35 ml/insect	10
25				$31.2(27.6-34.8)^b$ % body wt	22
26				$28.6(25.6-31.6)^b$ % body wt (dry)	
27		Pupa	Exsanguination	$(0.11-0.31)^c$ ml/g body wt	4
28				$(0.09-0.35)^c$ ml/insect	10
29		Adult	Exsanguination	0.05 ml/insect	10
30	Celerio euphorbiae	Larva, feeding	Exsanguination	$18.6(16.2-21.0)^b$ % body wt	14
31		Prepupa	Exsanguination	$(18.0-28.6)^c$ % body wt	14
32		Pupa	Exsanguination	$(18.3-42.6)^c$ % body wt	14
33				35% body wt	13
34				13% body wt (dry)	
35				$(0.6-0.7)^c$ ml/insect	24
36		Pupa (latent)	Exsanguination	$(26.7-38.0)^c$ % body wt	13
37		Pupa (subitan)	Exsanguination	$(3-30)^c$ % body wt	13
		Adult			14
38		♂	Exsanguination	$7.8(4.8-10.8)^b$ % body wt	
39		♀	Exsanguination	$7.2(2.8-11.6)^b$ % body wt	

Part I: VOLUME (Concluded)

	Species	Stage	Method	Volume	Reference
	(A)	(B)	(C)	(D)	(E)
	Lepidoptera (concluded)				
40	Galleria mellonella	Larva	Exsanguination	41(36.6-45.4)[b] % body wt (dry)	22
41	Hyalophora cecropia	Pupa	Exsanguination	0.25 ml/g body wt	7
42	Prodenia eridania	Larva	Exsanguination	0.12(0.07-0.20)[c] ml/insect	1
43			C^{14} inulin	0.19 ml/insect	18
	Coleoptera				
44	Dytiscus sp		Exsanguination	0.1 ml/insect	10
45	Hydrophilus sp		Exsanguination	0.3 ml/insect	10
46	Popillia japonica	Larva	Exsanguination	(0.9-25.4)[c] % body wt	3
47			Manganese	40.9(38.5-43.3)[b] % body wt	
48			Exsanguination	0.03 ml/insect	19
49	Tenebrio molitor	Larva	Dye dilution	10% body wt	17
50			Chloride	0.22 ml/g body wt	20
	Hymenoptera				
51	Apis mellifera	Larva	Exsanguination	(25-30)[c] % body wt	5
52				0.04 g/insect	
	Diptera				
53	Aedes aegypti	Larva	Exsanguination	(0.3-0.4)[c] cu mm/insect	26
54	Culex pipiens	Larva	Exsanguination	(0.3-0.4)[c] cu mm/insect	26
55	Phormia regina	Larva		20 µL/insect	9
56		Adult	Dye dilution	(6.6-10.2)[c] µL/insect	11
57				20% body wt	
58	Sarcophaga bullata	Larva	Dye dilution	(35.0-42.6)[c] % body wt	16
59		Pupa	Dye dilution	(23.0-33.4)[c] % body wt	

Contributors: (a) Jones, Jack Colvard, (b) Buck, John B.

References: [1] Babers, F. H. 1938. J. Agr. Res. 57:697. [2] Beadle, L. C., and J. Shaw. 1950. J. Exp. Biol., Lond. 27:96. [3] Beard, R. L. 1949. J. N. York Entom. Soc. 47:79. [4] Bialaszewicz, K., and C. Landau. 1938. Acta biol. exp., Warsz. 12:307. [5] Bishop, G. H. 1923. J. Biol. Chem. 58:567. [6] Buck, J. B. In K. D. Roeder, ed. 1953. Insect physiology. J. Wiley and Sons, New York. [7] Buck, J. B., and S. Friedman. 1958. J. Insect Physiol. 2:52. [8] Buck, J. B., and M. Keister. 1957-58. Ibid. 1:327. [9] Evans, D. R., and V. G. Dethier. 1957-58. Ibid. 1:3. [10] Florkin, M. 1937. Mém. couron. Acad. méd. Belgique 16:1. [11] Friedman, S. Unpublished. [12] Haber, V. R. 1926. Bull. Brooklyn Entom. Soc. 21:61. [13] Heller, J. 1932. Biochem. Zschr. 255:205. [14] Heller, J., and W. Swiechowska. 1948. Zool. Polonae 4:73. [15] Hoyle, G. 1954. J. Exp. Biol., Lond. 31:260. [16] Jones, J. C. 1956. J. Morph. 99:233. [17] Jones, J. C. 1957. J. Cellul. Physiol. 50:423. [18] Levenbook, L. 1961. J. Insect Physiol. v. 5. [19] Ludwig, D. 1951. Physiol. Zool. 24:329. [20] Munson, S. C., and J. F. Yeager. 1945. J. Econom. Entom. 38:634. [21] Pepper, J. H., F. T. Donaldson, and E. Hastings. 1941. Physiol. Zool. 14:470. [22] Richardson, C. H., R. C. Burdette, and C. W. Eagleson. 1931. Ann. Entom. Soc. America 24:503. [23] Smith, H. W. 1938. N. Hampshire Agr. Exp. Sta. Techn. Bull. 71:1. [24] Timon-David, J. 1945. Année biol. 21:134. [25] Tobias, J. M. 1948. J. Cellul. Physiol. 31:125. [26] Wigglesworth, V. B. 1938. J. Exp. Biol., Lond. 15:235. [27] Yeager, J. F., and S. C. Munson. 1950. Arthropoda 1:255. [28] Yeager, J. F., and O. E. Tauber. 1932. Ann. Entom. Soc. America 25:315.

Part II: pH

Values in parentheses are ranges, estimate "c" (cf. Introduction).

	Species	Stage	Method	pH	Reference
	(A)	(B)	(C)	(D)	(E)
	Orthoptera				
1	Chortophaga australior	Adult[1]	Colorimetric	6.8	5
2	C. viridifasciata	Nymph + adult	Hydrogen electrode	(6.43-7.05)	6
3		Adult[1]	Colorimetric	6.8	5
4	Dissosteira carolina	Adult[1]	Colorimetric	(6.8-6.9)	5
5	Melanoplus bivattatus	Adult[1]	Colorimetric	(6.0-6.7)	5
6	M. differentialis	Nymph	Hydrogen electrode	(6.42-6.98)	6
7		Adult	Colorimetric	(6.4-7.0)	5
8				(7.2-7.6)	10
9	M. femur-rubrum	Nymph + adult	Hydrogen electrode	(6.4-6.8)	6
10		Adult[1]	Colorimetric	(6.7-6.86)	5
11	M. scudderi	Adult[1]	Colorimetric	(6.6-6.9)	5
12	Periplaneta americana	Nymph + adult	Colorimetric	(7.5-8.0)	10
13	Romalea microptera	Nymph + adult	Hydrogen electrode	(6.4-6.8)	6
14	Schistocerca americana	Adult[1]	Colorimetric	6.6	5
	Trichoptera				
15	Anabolia nervosa	Larva	Quinhydrone electrode	(6.94-7.0)	17
16	Limnophilus flavicornis	Larva	Quinhydrone electrode	(7.04-7.18)	17
17	Phryganea obsoleta	Larva	Quinhydrone electrode	(6.8-6.98)	17
18	P. striata	Larva	Quinhydrone electrode	(6.71-6.81)	17
	Lepidoptera				
19	Anisota senatoria	Larva, last instar	Glass electrode	6.51(6.49-6.54)	13
20	Antherea polyphemus	Larva, last instar	Glass electrode	6.46(6.43-6.49)	13
21	Bombyx mori	Larva	Colorimetric	(6.4-7.2)	10
22		5th-6th instar	Glass electrode	6.77(6.70-6.83)	12
23		Pupa		6.51	1
24	Carpocapsa pomonella	Larva	Quinhydrone electrode	6.75	20
25	Choristoneura fumiferana	Larva[2]	Glass electrode	5.66(5.60-5.73)	13
26		Last instar	Glass electrode	6.98(6.96-7.02)	
27	Datana integerrima	Larva, last instar	Glass electrode	6.52(6.43-6.63)	13
28	D. ministra	Larva, last instar	Glass electrode	6.41(6.37-6.46)	13
29	Deilephila euphorbiae	Larva + pupa	Quinhydrone electrode	(6.36-6.64)	14
30	Eacles imperialis	Larva, last instar	Glass electrode	6.44(6.39-6.49)	13
31	Galleria mellonella	Pupa	Glass electrode	(5.8-6.4)	21
32	Hyphantria textor	Larva, last instar	Glass electrode	6.53(6.46-6.60)	13
33	Malacosoma disstria	Larva, 5th-6th instar	Glass electrode	(6.59-6.79)	12
34	M. pluviale	Larva, last instar	Glass electrode	6.55(6.52-6.58)	13
35	Nymphalis antiopa	Larva, last instar	Glass electrode	6.56(6.50-6.70)	13
36	Pieris brassicae	Pupa	Hydrogen electrode	(6.50-6.77)	7
37	P. rapae	Larva	Glass electrode	(6.76-7.56)	8
38		Pupa	Colorimetric	(5.9-6.4)	9
39	Prodenia eridania	Larva	Quinhydrone electrode	(6.40-6.67)	2
40	Schizura concinna	Larva, last instar	Glass electrode	6.32(6.29-6.35)	13
	Coleoptera				
41	Calosoma inquisitor	Adult	Colorimetric	(6.6-6.8)	16
42	Carabus cancellatus	Adult	Colorimetric	(6.6-7.5)	16
43	Dytiscus marginalis	Adult	Colorimetric	(6.8-7.3)	16
44	Hydrophilus piceus	Adult	Colorimetric	(6.7-7.0)	16
45	Leptinotarsus decemlineata	Larva + pupa	Colorimetric	(5.9-6.8)	11
46	Lucanus cervus	Adult	Colorimetric	(6.7-6.9)	16
47	Melolontha vulgaris	Adult	Colorimetric	(6.0-6.6)	16
48	Popillia japonica	Larva	Hydrogen electrode	7.07	19
49		Pupa	Hydrogen electrode	6.95	
50	Tenebrio molitor	Adult	Colorimetric	(6.2-7.3)	16

/1/ Stage not specified; probably adult. /2/ 2nd-last instar.

Part II: pH (Concluded)

	Species	Stage	Method	pH	Reference
	(A)	(B)	(C)	(D)	(E)
	Hymenoptera				
51	Apis mellifera	Larva	Hydrogen electrode	(6.77-6.93)	3
52		Adult	Colorimetric	6.70	15
53	Arge clavicornis[3]	Larva, last instar	Glass electrode	7.16(7.00-7.33)	13
54	A. pectoralis	Larva, last instar	Glass electrode	6.85(6.82-6.89)	13
55	Diprion hercyniae	Larva, 5th instar	Glass electrode	6.50(6.45-6.57)	12
56	D. similis	Larva, 6th instar	Glass electrode	6.70(6.65-6.73)	12
57	Hemichroa crocea	Larva, 5th instar	Glass electrode	6.69(6.66-6.73)	12
58	Monoctenus fulvus	Larva, last instar	Glass electrode	6.41(6.35-6.46)	13
59	Nematus ribesii	Larva, 6th instar	Glass electrode	6.67(6.63-6.69)	12
60	Neodiprion abietis	Larva, 6th instar	Glass electrode	6.49(6.47-6.53)	12
61	N. americanus	Larva, 5th instar	Glass electrode	6.54(6.50-6.57)	12
62	N. lecontei	Larva, 6th instar	Glass electrode	6.88(6.83-6.93)	12
63	N. sertifer	Larva, 6th instar	Glass electrode	6.81(6.77-6.83)	12
64	N. swainei	Larva, last instar	Glass electrode	6.48(6.43-6.54)	13
65	N. virginiana	Larva, 5th instar	Glass electrode	6.84(6.80-6.87)	12
66	Pikonema alaskensis	Larva, 5th instar	Glass electrode	6.55(6.42-6.58)	12
67	Pristiphora erichsonii	Larva, 4th instar	Glass electrode	6.49(6.45-6.57)	12
68		Larva, 5th instar	Glass electrode	6.64(6.58-6.72)	
	Diptera				
69	Chironomus tentans	Larva	Glass electrode	(7.23-7.72)	4
70	Drosophila melanogaster	Larva	Glass electrode	(7.03-7.15)	4
71	Gasterophilus intestinalis	Larva	Glass electrode	6.8	18
72	Musca domestica	Adult	Colorimetric	(7.2-7.6)	10
73	Prodiamesa praecox	Larva	Colorimetric	7.8	11
74	Sciara coprophila	Larva	Glass electrode	(7.03-7.25)	4

/3/ Species questionable.

Contributor: Buck, John B.

References: [1] Akao, A. 1931. J. Chosen M. Ass. 21:769. [2] Babers, F. H. 1938. J. Agr. Res. 57:697. [3] Bishop, G. H. 1923. J. Biol. Chem. 58:543. [4] Boche, R. D., and J. B. Buck. 1942. Physiol. Zool. 15:293. [5] Bodine, J. H. 1925. Biol. Bull. 48:79. [6] Bodine, J. H. 1926. Ibid. 51:363. [7] Brecher, L. 1925. Zschr. vergl. Physiol. 2:691. [8] Craig, R., and J. R. Clark. 1938. J. Econom. Entom. 31:51. [9] Fink, D. E. 1925. J. Gen. Physiol. 7:527. [10] Glaser, R. W. 1925. Ibid. 7:599. [11] Harnisch, O. 1929. Verh. Deut. zool. Ges. 33:57. [12] Heimpel, A. M. 1955. Canad. J. Zool. 33:99. [13] Heimpel, A. M. 1956. Ibid. 34:210. [14] Heller, J., and A. Moklowska. 1930. Biochem. Zschr. 219:473. [15] Hoskins, W. M., and H. S. Harrison. 1934. J. Econom. Entom. 27:924. [16] Kocian, V., and M. Špaček. 1934. Zool. Jahrb. 54:180. [17] Krey, J. 1937. Ibid. 58:201. [18] Levenbook, L. 1950. J. Exp. Biol., Lond. 27:158. [19] Ludwig, D. 1934. Ann. Entom. Soc. America 27:429. [20] Marshall, J. 1939. J. Econom. Entom. 32:838. [21] Taylor, I. R., J. H. Birnie, P. H. Mitchell, and J. L. Solinger. 1934. Physiol. Zool. 7:593.

Part III: SPECIFIC GRAVITY

Values in parentheses are ranges, estimate "c" (cf. Introduction).

Species	Stage	Specific Gravity	Reference	Species	Stage	Specific Gravity	Reference
(A)	(B)	(C)	(D)	(A)	(B)	(C)	(D)
Orthoptera				Lepidoptera (concluded)			
1 Acheta domestica	Nymph, ♂	1.0188	10	12 Galleria mellonella	Larva	1.0546	10
2	♀	1.0192		13 Prodenia sp	Larva	1.032	1
3	Adult, ♂	1.0215		Coleoptera			
4	♀	1.0195		14 Dytiscus sp	Adult	1.026	2
5 Periplaneta	Nymph	1.0182	11	15 Hydrophilus sp	Adult	1.012	2
6 americana	♂♀	1.0297	10	Hymenoptera			
7	Adult	1.0162	11	16 Apis sp	Larva	1.045	3
8 Leucophaea maderae	Nymph,♂♀	1.0293	10	Diptera			
Hemiptera				17 Calliphora sp	Larva	1.021	6
9 Oncopeltus fasciatus	Nymph,♂♀	1.0243	10	18 Gasterophilus sp	Larva	1.062	7
Lepidoptera				19 Musca domestica	Larva	1.0479	10
10 Bombyx sp	Larva	(1.032-1.041)	4, 9	20 Phormia sp	Larva	1.018	6
11 Deilephila sp	Larva	1.0307	5, 8				

Contributors: (a) Patton, Robert L., (b) Buck, John B.

References: [1] Babers, F. H. 1938. J. Agr. Res. 57:697. [2] Barratt, J. O., and G. Arnold. 1910. Q. J. Micr. Sc., Lond. 56:149. [3] Bishop, G. H. 1923. J. Biol. Chem. 58:543. [4] Ducceschi, V. 1902. Atti Accad. Georgofili, Fir. 80:365. [5] Heller, J., and A. Moklowska. 1930. Biochem. Zschr. 219:473. [6] Hopf, H. S. 1940. Biochem. J., Lond. 34:1396. [7] Levenbook, L. 1950. Ibid. 47:336. [8] Moklowska, A. 1929. Acta biol. exp., Warsz. 3:241. [9] Nazari, A. 1902. Atti Accad. Georgofili, Fir. 80:356. [10] Patton, R. L., et al. Unpublished. [11] Yeager, J. F., and R. W. Fay. 1935. Proc. Soc. Exp. Biol., N. Y. 32:1667.

Part IV: FREEZING POINT DEPRESSION

Values in parentheses are ranges, estimate "c" (cf. Introduction).

Species	Stage	Freezing Point Depression °C	Reference	Species	Stage	Freezing Point Depression °C	Reference
(A)	(B)	(C)	(D)	(A)	(B)	(C)	(D)
Odonata				Lepidoptera			
1 Aeschna sp	Larva	0.56	2	12 Bombyx mori	Larva	0.48	6,7,11,16
Orthoptera				13 Ephestia elutella	Larva	1.12	12
2 Acridia nasuta	Adult	0.99	9	14 Galleria mellonella	Larva	1.14	12
3 Blatta orientalis	Adult	0.75	12	15	Pupa	1.06	
4 Carausius morosus	Adult	0.56	12	16 Prodenia eridania	Larva	0.84	1
5 Decticus albifrons	Adult	0.71	12	17 Saturnia pyri	Larva	0.77	12
6 Gryllotalpa gryllotalpa	Adult	0.83	12	Coleoptera			
7 Locusta viridissima	Adult	0.74	12	18 Carabus intricatus	Adult[1]	0.94	12
Hemiptera				19 Dytiscus circumcinctus	Adult	0.56	3
				20 Hydrophilus pistaceus	Adult[1]	0.70	13
8 Nepa cinerea	Adult[1]	0.78	12	21 Melolontha vulgaris	Larva	0.81	12
9 Notonecta glauca	Adult[1]	0.59	12	22 Oryctes nasicornis	Larva	(0.76-0.77)	13
10 Pyrrhocoris apterus	Adult[1]	0.79	12	23 Popillia japonica	Larva	1.03	9
11 Ranatra linearis	Adult[1]	0.75	12	24 Silpha carinata	Adult[1]	0.88	12

/1/ Stage not specified; probably adult.

Part IV: FREEZING POINT DEPRESSION (Concluded)

	Species	Stage	Freezing Point Depression °C	Reference		Species	Stage	Freezing Point Depression °C	Reference
	(A)	(B)	(C)	(D)		(A)	(B)	(C)	(D)
	Coleoptera (concluded)					Diptera			
25	Tenebrio molitor	Larva	(1.16-1.34)	10,12	30	Aedes aegypti	Larva	(0.4-0.5)	14
26		Adult	0.97	12	31	A. detritus	Larva	(0.4-0.8)	4
27	Timarcha tenebricosa	Adult	0.74	12	32	Anopheles maculipennis	Larva, pupa, adult	(0.57-0.74)	15
	Hymenoptera				33	Culex pipiens	Larva	(0.4-0.5)	14
28	Apis mellifera	Larva	0.86	5	34	Gasterophilus intestinalis	Larva	0.872	8
29	Vespa crabro	Adult	0.87	12					

Contributor: Buck, John B.

References: [1] Babers, F. H. 1938. J. Agr. Res. 57:697. [2] Backman, E. L. 1911. Zbl. Physiol., Wien 25:835. [3] Backman, E. L. 1912. Pflügers Arch. 149:93. [4] Beadle, L. C. 1939. J. Exp. Biol., Lond. 16:346. [5] Bishop, G. H. 1923. J. Biol. Chem. 58:543. [6] Ducceschi, V. 1902. Atti Accad. Georgofili, Fir. 80:365. [7] Gamo, T., and S. Yamaguchi. 1927. J. Sc. Agr. Soc. 295:243. [8] Levenbook, L. 1950. Biochem. J., Lond. 47:336. [9] Ludwig, D. 1951. Physiol. Zool. 24:329. [10] Patton, R. L., and R. Craig. 1939. J. Exp. Zool. 81:437. [11] Polimanti, O. 1915. Biochem. Zschr. 70:74. [12] Rouschal, W. 1940. Zschr. wiss. Zool. Abt. A, p. 196. [13] Vialli, M. 1925. Arch. fisiol., Fir. 23:577. [14] Wigglesworth, V. B. 1938. J. Exp. Biol., Lond. 15:235. [15] Winogradskaja, O. N. 1936. Zschr. Parasitenk. 8:697. [16] Yagi, N. 1924. Zool. Mag. 36:319.

96. WATER CONTENT OF HEMOLYMPH: INSECTS

Estimates of water content of insect hemolymph were determined from the weighing of aliquots before and after drying to constant weight, usually at 105-110°C. Values in parentheses are ranges, estimate "c" (cf. Introduction).

	Genus	Stage	Water %	Reference		Genus	Stage	Water %	Reference
	(A)	(B)	(C)	(D)		(A)	(B)	(C)	(D)
	Lepidoptera					Coleoptera (concluded)			
1	Bombyx	Mature larva and pupa	(90-92)	1, 5	6	Hydrophilus (concluded)	Adult (concluded)	88	2
2			94	6	7	Popillia	Larva	91	8
3	Deilephila	Pupa	90	4		Diptera			
	Coleoptera				8	Gasterophilus	Larva	84	7
4	Hydrophilus	Larva	91	3	9	Lucilia	Larva	91	9
5		Adult	92	3					

Contributor: Buck, John B.

References: [1] Akao, A. 1935. Keijo J. M. 6:49. [2] Barratt, J. O., and G. Arnold. 1910. Q. J. Micr. Sc., Lond. 56:149. [3] Drilhon, A., and R.-G. Busnel. 1946. Bull. Soc. zool. France 71:185. [4] Heller, J. 1932. Biochem. Zschr. 255:205. [5] Kuroda, K. 1934. Keijo J. M. 5:151. [6] Kuwana, Z. 1937. Jap. J. Zool. 7:273. [7] Levenbook, L. 1950. Biochem. J., Lond. 47:336. [8] Ludwig, D. 1951. Physiol. Zool. 24:329. [9] Waterhouse, D. F. 1945. Counc. Sc. Indust. Res., Melbourne, Australia Bull. 191, p. 21.

Values in parentheses are ranges, estimate "c" (cf. Introduction).

Insect	Stage	Constituent	Value mg/100 ml	Reference
(A)	(B)	(C)	(D)	(E)
Odonata				
1 Aeschna sp	Naiad	Calcium	32.0	17
2		Magnesium	(7.30-14.96)	
3		Potassium	(16.81-21.11)	
4		Sodium	(309.81-412.39)	
5 Agrion sp	Naiad	Potassium	35.19	17
6		Sodium	363.4	6
7 Libellula sp	Naiad	Calcium	(15.1-32.0)	12, 17
8		Magnesium	5.8	12
9		Sodium	349.6	17
10 L. depressa	Naiad	Magnesium	14.6	17
11		Potassium	14.86	
12		Sodium	410.09	
Orthoptera				
13 Anabrus simplex	Adult	Calcium	12.0[1]	32
14		Magnesium	11.70	17
15			3.4[1]	32
		Phosphorus		32
16		Total P	101	
17		Inorganic P	61	
18		Potassium	(59.8-60.2)	17, 32
19		Sodium	50.4	32
20 Blabera fusca	Adult	Calcium	20.2	39
21		Magnesium	15.7	
22 Carausius morosus	Adult	Bicarbonate	30.5	41
23		Calcium	(15.0-32.4)	17, 41
24			7.0[1]	35
25		Chloride	358.0	41
26			308.4[1]	35
27		Magnesium	63.6	41
28			176.32	17
29			64.8[1]	35
30		Phosphorus, inorganic	123[2]	35
31		Potassium	(62.6-70.2)	34, 41
32			(97.75-107.53)	6, 17
33			70.2[1]	35
34		Sodium	(20.0-32.2)	17, 34
35			(34.5-48.3)	6, 41
36			25.3[1]	35
37 Chortophaga	Adult	Calcium	11.40	3
38 viridifasciata		Potassium	13.52	
39		Sodium	250.66	
40 Gryllotalpa	Adult	Calcium	56.0	17
41 gryllotalpa		Magnesium	12.65	17
42		Potassium	43.01	6
43		Sodium	(400.2-537.5)	6, 17
44 Leucophaea	Adult	Calcium	(26.0-40.0)	38
45 maderae		Magnesium	(4.2-4.7)	
46		Potassium	(13.0-20.0)	
47		Sodium	(236-262)	
48 Locusta	Nymph	Magnesium	30.16	17
49 migratoria		Potassium	46.92	
50		Sodium	138.00	
51	5th instar, 1-6 da before molt	Potassium	(101.4-282.0)	24
52		Sodium	(138.0-241.5)	
53	Nymph + adult	Potassium	35.19	17
54		Sodium	155.02	
55	Adult	Calcium	(148.0-204.0)	34
56		Magnesium	(18.24-26.75)	

/1/ Serum. /2/ Lowered to 40 mg/100 ml in serum (prepared by heating hemolymph).

	Insect	Stage	Constituent	Value mg/100 ml	Reference
	(A)	(B)	(C)	(D)	(E)
	Orthoptera (concluded)				
57	Locusta migratoria (concluded)	Adult (concluded) 6 hr-5 da after molt	Potassium	(78.0-234.0)	24
58			Sodium	(250.7-287.5)	
59	Periplaneta americana	Nymph	Calcium	6.6	37
60			Potassium	60.2[1]	39
61		Adult	Calcium	(17.0-17.8)	39
62			Magnesium	(13.5-27.5)	12, 39
63			Potassium	67.6[1]	37
64			Sodium	246[1]	37
65	P. australasiae	Adult	Calcium	19.4	39
66			Magnesium	14.8	
67	Romalea microptera	Adult	Potassium	70.4[1]	37
68			Sodium	147.2[1]	
69	Schistocerca gregaria	Nymph	Calcium	35.6	17
70			Magnesium	42.07	
71		5th instar	Potassium	20.72	
72			Sodium	186.99	
73	Stenobothrus stigmaticus	Adult	Potassium	242.42	6
74			Sodium	140.3	
75	Stenopelmatis longispina	Adult	Calcium	24.2	12
76			Magnesium	35.0	
77	Tettigonia viridissima	Adult	Potassium	199.41	6
78			Sodium	190.9	
	Dermaptera				
79	Forficula auricularia	Adult	Calcium	65.8	12
	Isoptera				
80	Zootermopsis augusticollis	Adult	Calcium	33.6	12
81			Magnesium	41.8	
	Thysanoptera				
82	Palomena prasina	Adult	Potassium	164.22	6
83			Sodium	50.6	
84	P. viridissima	Larva	Calcium	107.0	17
85		Larva + adult	Magnesium	97.04	
86			Sodium	8.05	
87		Adult	Calcium	107.0	
	Hemiptera				
88	Cimex lectularius	Adult	Potassium	35.19	6
89			Sodium	319.7	
90	Cinara cilicia	Adult	Calcium	42.9	12
91			Magnesium	36.5	
92	Gerris najas	Adult	Potassium	31.28	6
93			Sodium	326.6	
94	Notonecta kirbyii	Adult	Calcium	62.1	12
95			Magnesium	22.2	
96	Oncopeltus fasciatus	Larva	Chloride	91.2	36
97		Adult	Calcium	(22.1-27.9)	12, 31
98			Chloride	91.4	36
99			Magnesium	62.5	12
100			Potassium	80.2	31
101			Sodium	80.4	31
102	Rhodnius prolixus	Adult	Potassium	(15.64-23.46)	34
103			Sodium	363.4	
104	Triatoma infestans	Adult	Calcium	81.9	12
105			Magnesium	1.8	
106	T. megista	Adult	Potassium	19.55	6
107			Sodium	305.9	

/1/ Serum.

	Insect	Stage	Constituent	Value mg/100 ml	Reference
	(A)	(B)	(C)	(D)	(E)
	Hemiptera (concluded)				
108	Triatoma	Adult	Calcium	33.1	12
109	neotomae		Magnesium	1.2	
110	T. phyllosoma	Adult	Calcium	26.7	12
111			Magnesium	1.4	
112	T. protracta	Adult	Calcium	59.1	12
113			Magnesium	1.6	
	Neuroptera				
114	Myrmeleon	Larva	Calcium	24.2	17
115	formicarius		Magnesium	38.06	
116			Potassium	34.02	
117			Sodium	330.06	
	Trichoptera				
118	Chaetopteryx	Larva	Potassium	35.19	6
119	villosa		Sodium	146.96	
120	Phryganea sp	Larva	Calcium	28.8	17
121			Magnesium	62.02	
122			Potassium	26.59	
123			Sodium	211.6	
	Lepidoptera				
124	Actias selene	Larva	Calcium	51.0	17
125			Magnesium	72.96	
126			Potassium	200.58	
127			Sodium	11.04	
128	Aglais urticae	Larva	Potassium	168.13	6
129			Sodium	50.6	
130	Amathes	Larva	Calcium	80.8	17
131	xanthographa		Magnesium	126.71	
132			Potassium	114.17	
133			Sodium	55.43	
134	Antheraea mylitta	Larva	Calcium	43.8	17
135			Magnesium	45.84	
136			Potassium	194.33	
137			Sodium	2.99	
138	A. pornyi	Larva	Phosphorus, inorganic	13.8	18
139		Pupa	Calcium	33.0	13
140			Potassium	170.48	
141			Sodium	26.2	
142		Before diapause	Phosphorus, inorganic	16.5	
143	A. polyphemus	Pupa	Phosphorus, inorganic	35(12-67)	11
144	Apamea sordens	Larva	Calcium	34.2	17
145			Magnesium	69.07	
146			Potassium	151.32	
147	Bombyx mori	Larva	Chloride	51.5	33
148			Potassium	136.85	13
149				156.4[1]	37
150			Sodium	32.2	6
151				32.2[1]	37
152			Zinc	(1.056-1.281)	1
153		Day of 4th molt	Calcium	30.0	4
154			Magnesium	107.01	
155			Potassium	154.05	
156			Sodium	13.8	
		3rd-4th instar	Phosphorus		43
157			Total P	143(119-166)	
158			Inorganic P	11.2(10.1-14.6)	
159			Acid-soluble P	141(116-164)	

/1/ Serum.

	Insect	Stage	Constituent	Value mg/100 ml	Reference
	(A)	(B)	(C)	(D)	(E)
	Lepidoptera (continued)				
160	Bombyx mori (concluded)	Larva (concluded) 3rd-5th instar	Calcium	49.0	17
161			Magnesium	(98.25-122.82)	
162			Potassium	(163.44-180.25)	
163			Sodium	(7.82-33.58)	
164		5th instar	Phosphorus		
165			Total P	159(102-200)	43
166				75(55-122)	25
167			Inorganic P	6.7(4.7-13.5)	43
168				6.0(5.3-6.3)	25
169			Acid-soluble P	155(99-196)	43
170		In cocoon	Calcium	65(54-97)	25
				53.0	17
171			Magnesium	112.48	
172			Potassium	231.47	
173			Sodium	18.86	
174		Pupa	Phosphorus		
175			Total P	180	43
176				(120-210)	26
177			Inorganic P	13.7	43
178				(5-16)	26
179			Acid-soluble P	168	43
180				(90-175)	26
			Sodium	20.7	1
181		1st da	Calcium	59.0	17
182			Magnesium	106.40	
183			Potassium	214.66	
184			Sodium	49.91	
185		16th da after 4th molt	Calcium	48.0	4
186			Magnesium	84.39	
187			Potassium	166.27	
188			Sodium	25.99	
189		Adult	Calcium	29.0	4
190			Magnesium	54.23	
191			Phosphorus Total P	180	
192			Inorganic P	42	
193			Potassium	141.15	
194			Sodium	32.89	
195	B. rubi	Larva	Chloride	89.8	33
196	Celerio euphorbiae	Larva	Calcium	(41.25-72.00)	21, 30
197			Chloride	48.6	30
198			Iron	5.8	28, 30
199			Magnesium	43.5	30
200			Potassium	78.2	21
201		♂	Phosphorus Total P	77(71-82)	27
202			Inorganic P	9.9(9.0-11.0)	
203			Acid-soluble P	61(55-67)	
204		♀	Phosphorus Total P	81(76-89)	27
205			Inorganic P	10.9(9.4-12.3)	
206			Acid-soluble P	64(57-72)	
207		Pupa	Calcium	(32.0-64.0)	21
			Phosphorus		21, 27
208			Total P	64	
209			Inorganic P	(13.5-60.8)	
210			Acid-soluble P	58	
211			Potassium	(39.1-70.4)	21
212		Adult	Phosphorus, inorganic	10.8	21
213	Cossus cossus	Larva	Calcium	(55.4-103.0)	17
214			Chloride	6.69	33
215			Magnesium	(49.13-58.37)	17

	Insect	Stage	Constituent	Value mg/100 ml	Reference
	(A)	(B)	(C)	(D)	(E)
	Lepidoptera (continued)				
216	Cossus cossus	Larva (concluded)	Phosphorus, inorganic	11.5	18
217	(concluded)		Potassium	60.61	17
218			Sodium	42.32	17
219	Cucullia absinthii	Pupa	Calcium	65.0	17
220			Magnesium	62.26	
221			Potassium	190.42	
222			Sodium	22.54	
223	Dasychira	Pupa	Calcium	67.8	17
224	pudibunda		Magnesium	90.11	
225			Potassium	202.54	
226			Sodium	6.9	
227	Deilephila	Pupa	Calcium	82.0	17
228	elpenor		Magnesium	108.59	
229			Potassium	107.13	
230			Sodium	10.81	
231	Diataraxia	Larva	Calcium	63.8	17
232	oleracea		Magnesium	95.70	
233			Potassium	168.52	
234			Sodium	30.13	
235	Endromis	Pupa	Calcium	56.0	17
236	versicolora		Magnesium	53.50	
237			Potassium	128.25	
238			Sodium	2.99	
239	Ephestia	Larva	Calcium	82.4	17
240	kuehniella		Magnesium	62.14	17
241			Potassium	127.86	17
242				234.6	6
243				(183.7-254.1)	7
244			Sodium	39.1	6
245				74.98	17
246				(36.8-69.0)	7
247	Estigmene acraea	Larva	Calcium	10.2	12
248			Magnesium	12.3	
249	Eudia pavonia	Pupa	Calcium	28.4	13
250			Potassium	153.27	
251			Sodium	6.9	
252	Euproctis	Larva	Calcium	41.2	17
253	chrysorrhea		Magnesium	106.89	
254			Potassium	174.00	
255			Sodium	41.17	
256	Galleria	Larva	Calcium	48.8	17
257	mellonella		Magnesium	40.49	17
			Phosphorus		43
258			Total P	245	
259			Inorganic P	30.4	
260			Acid-soluble P	240	
261			Potassium	141.93	17
262			Sodium	60.95	17
263	Graellsia	Pupa	Calcium	35.0	17
264	isabellae		Magnesium	35.39	
265			Potassium	180.64	
266			Sodium	14.26	
267	Hesperocorixia	Adult	Calcium	15.6	12
268	larigata		Magnesium	4.2	
	Hyalophora	Larva, 5th instar	Phosphorus		42
269	cecropia		Inorganic P	7.8	
270			Acid-soluble P	88	
271		Pupa	Calcium	29.4	13
272			Potassium	195.50	
273			Sodium	16.1	
		Pupa[3]	Phosphorus		42
274			Inorganic P	15(7-27)	
275			Acid-soluble P	107(99-112)	

/3/ Includes pupa in diapause and developing adult.

	Insect	Stage	Constituent	Value mg/100 ml	Reference
	(A)	(B)	(C)	(D)	(E)
	Lepidoptera (continued)				
276	Hyloicus pinastri	Pupa	Calcium	30.0(29.6-33.3)	9
277			Magnesium	55.94	
278			Potassium	136.85	
279	Hypocrita	Larva	Calcium	50.0	17
280	jacobaeae		Magnesium	105.43	
281			Potassium	135.29	
282			Sodium	16.79	
283	Junonia coenia	Larva	Calcium	10.5	12
284			Magnesium	34.9	
285	Laphygma exigua	Larva	Calcium	10.9	12
286			Magnesium	67.3	
287	Mamestra	Larva	Calcium	35.8	17
288	brassicae		Magnesium	120.63	
289			Potassium	209.57	
290			Sodium	9.89	
291	Melanchra	Larva	Calcium	38.2	17
292	persicariae		Magnesium	96.06	
293			Potassium	157.57	
294			Sodium	24.84	
295	Mimas tiliae	Pupa	Calcium	259.4	17
296			Magnesium	18.97	
297			Potassium	153.27	
298			Sodium	7.36	
299	Papilio machaon	Larva	Calcium	66.8	17
300			Magnesium	72.72	
301			Potassium	117.12	
302			Sodium	31.28	
303	Peridroma	Larva	Calcium	17.5	12
304	margaritosa		Magnesium	102.2	
305	Phalera bucephala	Larva	Calcium	68.4	17
306			Magnesium	97.04	
307			Potassium	192.37	
308			Sodium	13.57	
309	Philosamia	Pupa	Calcium	57.0	17
310	cynthia		Magnesium	63.35	
311			Potassium	144.28	
312			Sodium	17.25	
313	Phlogophora	Larva	Calcium	71.0	17
314	meticulosa		Magnesium	83.17	
315			Potassium	136.46	
316			Sodium	28.29	
317	Phryganidia	Larva	Calcium	17.1	12
318	californica		Magnesium	62.5	
319	Pieris brassicae	Larva	Calcium	33.2(23.2-36.4)	9
320			Chloride	(69.5-93.0)	9
321			Magnesium	(48-112)	9
322			Phosphorus, total	77(63-101)	9
323			Potassium	(58-119)	9, 34
324			Sodium	(11.5-20.7)	34
325		Pupa	Calcium	21.2	9
326			Chloride	69.8	
327			Magnesium	64	
328			Phosphorus, total	136	
329			Potassium	(140-160)	
330	P. rapae	Larva	Calcium	82.0	17
331			Magnesium	80.99	17
332			Potassium	152.49	6
333				376.92	17
334				(289.3-312.8)	7
335			Sodium	25.3	6
336				(20.7-29.9)	7
337	Prodenia eridania	Larva	Calcium	36.75	2
338			Chloride	119.8	2

	Insect	Stage	Constituent	Value mg/100 ml	Reference
	(A)	(B)	(C)	(D)	(E)
			Lepidoptera (continued)		
339	Prodenia eridania (concluded)	Larva (concluded)	Copper		2
			Total	4.93	
340			In protein-free filtrate	2.94	
341			Magnesium	(17.2-17.4)	2, 17
342			Potassium	155	2
343			Sodium	51.2	2
344			Sulfur	44.4	2
		6th instar	Phosphorus		2
345			Total P	123	
346			Inorganic P	17.6	
347	P. praefica	Larva	Calcium	13.1	12
348			Magnesium	77.2	
349	Samia cynthia	Pupa	Calcium	(36.5-38.2)	20
350			Phosphorus, inorganic	11.0	
351			Potassium	(157.7-172.2)	
352			Sodium	(4.64-7.34)	
353	Saturnia carpini	Larva	Chloride	42.5	33
354	S. pavonia	Pupa	Potassium	153	13
355			Sodium	7.0	
356		Before diapause	Phosphorus, inorganic	27.5	
357	S. pyri	Pupa	Calcium	29.0	13
358			Chloride	62.5	33
359			Potassium	160.31	13
360			Sodium	8.97	13
361		Before diapause	Phosphorus, inorganic	23.9	13
362	Smerinthus ocellata	Pupa	Calcium	31.0	13
363			Potassium	136	
364			Sodium	12.42	
365		Before diapause	Phosphorus, inorganic	23.2	
366	Sphinx ligustri	Larva	Calcium	61.0	17
367			Magnesium	(59.83-69.92)	
368		Pupa	Calcium	(32.8-81.8)	17
369			Chloride	53.4	33
370			Potassium	(189.24-211.53)	13
371			Sodium	(5.98-9.89)	13, 17
372		Before diapause	Phosphorus, inorganic	22.0	13
373	S. pinastri	Larva	Magnesium	77	9
374		Pupa	Calcium	(29.6-33.3)	
375			Chloride	(57.6-62.9)	
			Phosphorus		
376			Total P	207	
377			Inorganic P	66	
378			Potassium	137.8	
379	Spilosoma lutea	Larva	Calcium	62.8	17
380			Magnesium	46.82	
381			Potassium	219.74	
382			Sodium	7.59	
383	Telea polyphemus	Pupa	Calcium	32.4	13
384				(16.4-31.2)	11
385			Chloride	(60.0-83.7)	11
386			Magnesium	(71.7-100.7)	11
387			Phosphorus, inorganic	(7.6-41.5)	11
388			Potassium	135.29	13
389				(176.5-305.2)	11
390			Sodium	(5.75-22.54)	13
391		Adult	Magnesium	(79.6-95.3)	11
392			Potassium	(172.8-295.9)	
393	Triphaena pronuba	Larva	Calcium	112.0	17
394			Magnesium	86.21	
395			Potassium	139.20	
396			Sodium	37.03	
397	Tropaea luna	Pupa	Calcium	62.8	17
398			Magnesium	59.34	

	Insect	Stage	Constituent	Value mg/100 ml	Reference
	(A)	(B)	(C)	(D)	(E)
			Lepidoptera (concluded)		
399	Tropaea luna	Pupa (concluded)	Potassium	206.45	17
400	(concluded)		Sodium	10.12	
401	Vanessa urticae	Larva	Potassium	168.1	7
402			Sodium	(48.3-133.4)	
403	Yponomeuta	Larva	Calcium	34.2	17
404	evonymella		Magnesium	36.12	
405			Potassium	91.10	
406			Sodium	7.36	
			Coleoptera		
407	Agelastica alni	Adult	Potassium	183.77	6
408			Sodium	39.1	
409	Cetonia aurata	Larva	Calcium	45.6	17
410			Magnesium	97.28	
411			Potassium	72.73	
412			Sodium	117.99	
413	Cicindela	Adult	Potassium	35.19	6
414	maritima		Sodium	372.6	
415	Coelocnemis	Adult	Calcium	54.2	12
416	dilaticollis		Magnesium	12.0	
417	Cybister sp	Adult	Calcium	76.4	17
418			Magnesium	62.99	
419			Potassium	28.54	
420			Sodium	330.05	
421	Dytiscus	Adult	Calcium	(45.0-52.0)	15, 17
422	marginalis		Chloride	224	33
423			Magnesium	45.60	17
424			Phosphorus, inorganic	10.5	18
425			Potassium	(19.6-39.1)	6, 17, 34
426			Sodium	(305.9-379.96)	6, 17, 34
427	Geotrupes	Adult	Calcium	35.6	17
428	stercorosus		Magnesium	60.56	
429			Potassium	62.56	
430			Sodium	273.93	
431	Hydrophilus	Larva	Phosphorus, inorganic	8.0	16
432	piceus	Adult	Calcium	(43.0-49.0)	14, 17, 19
433			Magnesium	(53.75-56.91)	17, 19
434			Phosphorus, inorganic	(10.5-14.0)	16
435			Potassium	(16.81-82.89)	14, 17, 19
436			Sodium	(277.61-284.51)	17, 19
437	Leptinotarsa	Larva	Calcium	(86.8-310.0)	17
438	decemlineata		Magnesium	(178.63-240.77)	
439			Potassium	(214.66-254.54)	
440			Sodium	(4.6-22.08)	
441		Adult	Potassium	111.44	14
442	Lytta molesta	Adult	Magnesium	223.0	12
443	Meloe strigulosus	Adult	Calcium	53.2	12
444			Magnesium	188.0	
445	Melolontha	Adult	Calcium	30.6	17
446	melolontha		Magnesium	50.22	17
447			Potassium	22.68	17
448				191.59	6
449			Sodium	13.8	6
450				259.9	17
451	Popillia japonica	Larva	Calcium	(31.2-31.9)	29
452			Chloride	(60.4-69.3)	
453			Magnesium	(46.9-47.4)	
454			Phosphorus, inorganic	15.2	
455			Sodium	(37.4-52.3)	
456	Scaphinotus sp	Adult	Calcium	21.8	12
457			Magnesium	22.4	
458	Tenebrio molitor	Larva	Calcium	(18.4-26.3)	10
459			Potassium	(102.5-146.7)	10
460				(125.12-207.23)	6, 34

	Insect	Stage	Constituent	Value mg/100 ml	Reference
	(A)	(B)	(C)	(D)	(E)
	Coleoptera (concluded)				
461	Tenebrio molitor	Larva (concluded)	Sodium	(142.3-202.3)	10
462	(concluded)			(124.2-177.1)	34
463		Pupa	Calcium	(6.5-8.8)	10
464			Potassium	(58.7-86.1)	
465			Sodium	(38.2-47.6)	
466		Adult	Calcium	(25.0-30.4)	10
467			Potassium	(90.1-97.4)	
468			Sodium	(80.1-86.3)	
469	Timarcha	Larva	Calcium	(92.8-144.4)	17
470	tenebricosa		Magnesium	200.64	
471			Potassium	(183.38-188.07)	
472			Sodium	3.68	
473		Larva + adult	Calcium	84.4	
474			Magnesium	142.88	
475			Potassium	158.75	
476		Adult	Magnesium	192.13	
	Hymenoptera				
477	Apis mellifera	Larva	Calcium	(14.0-36.4)	5, 17
478			Chloride	118	5
479			Magnesium	(22-25)	5, 17
480			Phosphorus, inorganic	31	5
481			Potassium	(119.26-175.95)	6, 17
482			Sodium	(23.0-25.1)	6, 17
483		Adult	Phosphorus, total	186	23
	Diprion hercyniae	Larva	Phosphorus		43
484			Total P	189	
485			Inorganic P	24.4	
486			Acid-soluble P	185	
487	Formica rufa	Pupa	Calcium	29.8	17
488			Magnesium	26.27	
489			Potassium	196.67	
490			Sodium	33.81	
491	Pteronidea ribesii	Larva	Calcium	35.0	17
492			Magnesium	81.47	
493			Potassium	169.69	
494			Sodium	3.68	
495	Tenthredinide sp	Larva	Potassium	215.05	6
496			Sodium	13.8	
497	Vespa crabro	Larva	Manganese	Trace	8
498	Vespula	Larva	Calcium	37.4	17
499	germanica		Magnesium	28.70	17
500			Potassium	(160.31-220.73)	6, 17
501			Sodium	(10.4-59.8)	6, 17
502		Pupa	Calcium	22.4	17
503			Magnesium	23.10	
504			Potassium	237.73	
505			Sodium	52.44	
506	V. pennsylvanica	Adult	Calcium	14.2	12
507			Magnesium	1.33	
	Diptera				
508	Aedes aegypti	Larva	Chloride	182	40
509	Calliphora	Larva	Potassium	(102.05-144.67)	6, 17
510	erythrocephala			(144.7-156.4)	7
511			Sodium	(340.4-363.3)	6, 7
512		3rd instar	Phosphorus		22
			Total P	97(92-102)	
513			Inorganic P	42(38-45)	
514			Acid-soluble P	74(71-76)	
515		Pupa	Calcium	41.6	17
516			Magnesium	41.71	
517			Sodium	321.08	

Insect	Stage	Constituent	Value mg/100 ml	Reference
(A)	(B)	(C)	(D)	(E)
		Diptera (concluded)		
518 Chironomus sp	Larva	Calcium	21.0	17
519		Magnesium	17.75	17
520		Potassium	(8.21-31.28)	6, 17
521		Sodium	(211.6-239.89)	6, 17
522 Culex pipiens	Larva	Chloride	170	40
523 Dictenidia	Larva	Calcium	27.6	17
524 bimaculata		Magnesium	17.63	
525		Potassium	14.47	
526		Sodium	91.08	
527 Eristalomyia	Larva	Calcium	24.0	17
528 tenax		Magnesium	16.17	
529		Potassium	30.89	
530		Sodium	203.0	
531 Gasterophilus	Larva	Bicarbonate	88.5	28
532 intestinalis		Calcium	11.4	
533		Chloride	48.6	
		Copper		
534		Total	0.55	
535		In protein-free filtrate	0.22	
536		Potassium	45	
537		Sodium	402.5	
538		Sulfur	9.7	
539		Zinc	0.88	
	3rd instar	Phosphorus		
540		Total P	109	
541		Inorganic P	12.5	
542		Acid-soluble P	81	
543 Pegomya sp	Larva	Potassium	226.78	6
544		Sodium	59.8	
Phormia terra-	Larva, 3rd instar	Phosphorus		22
545 novae		Total P	64(52-72)	
546		Inorganic P	26(22-30)	
547		Acid-soluble P	51(41-58)	
548 Stomoxys	Adult	Potassium	43.01	6
549 calcitrans		Sodium	294.4	
550 Tabanidae sp	Larva	Potassium	19.55	34
551		Sodium	347.3	
552 Tipula paludosa +	Larva	Calcium	24.6	17
553 T. oleracea		Magnesium	19.46	
554		Potassium	32.06	
555		Sodium	195.04	

Contributors: (a) Ludwig, Daniel, (b) Wyatt, Gerard R., (c) Babers, Frank H.

References: [1] Akao, A. 1935. Keijo J. M. 6:49. [2] Babers, F. H. 1938. J. Agr. Res. 57:697. [3] Barsa, M. C. 1954. J. Gen. Physiol. 38:79. [4] Bialaszewicz, K., and C. Landau. 1938. Acta biol. exp., Warsz. 12:307. [5] Bishop, G. H., A. P. Briggs, and E. Ronzoni. 1925. J. Biol. Chem. 66:77. [6] Bone, G. J. 1944. Ann. Soc. R. Zool. Belgique 75:123. [7] Bone, G. J. 1947. Nature, Lond. 160:679. [8] Bowen, V. T. 1950. J. Exp. Zool. 115:175. [9] Brecher, L. 1929. Biochem. Zschr. 211:40. [10] Butz, A. 1957. J. N. York Entom. Soc. 65:22. [11] Carrington, C. B., and S. M. Tenney. 1959. J. Insect Physiol. 3:402. [12] Clark, E. W., and R. Craig. 1953. Physiol. Zool. 26:101. [13] Drilhon, A. 1934. C. rend. Soc. biol. 115:1194. [14] Drilhon, A., and R. G. Busnel. 1937. Ibid. 124:806. [15] Drilhon, A., and R. G. Busnel. 1943. Bull. Soc. zool. France 68:21. [16] Drilhon, A., and R. G. Busnel. 1946. Ibid. 71:185. [17] Duchateau, G., M. Florkin, and J. Leclercq. 1953. Arch. internat. physiol., Liège 61:518. [18] Duval, M., and P. Portier. 1928. C. rend. Soc. biol. 99:1831.

[19] Florkin, M. 1943. Bull. Soc. R. Sc. Liége 12:301. [20] Gese, P. K. 1950. Physiol. Zool. 23:109. [21] Heller, J., and A. Moklowska. 1930. Biochem. Zschr. 219:473. [22] Hopf, H. S. 1940. Biochem. J., Lond. 34:1396. [23] Hoskins, W. M., and H. S. Harrison. 1934. J. Econom. Entom. 27:924. [24] Hoyle, G. 1956. Nature, Lond. 178:1236. [25] Ito, T., Y. Horie, and M. Tanaka. 1958. Proc. 10th Internat. Congr. Entom. 2:283. [26] Ito, T., H. Shigematsu, and Y. Horie. 1958. Nippon Sanshigaku Zasshi 27:217. [27] Karpiak, S. 1957. Prace Wrocław. Towarz. Nauk., Ser. B, v. 83. [30] Moklowska, A. 1950. Biochem. J., Lond. 47:336. [29] Ludwig, D. 1951. Physiol. Zool. 24:329. [30] Moklowska, A. 1929. Acta biol. exp., Warsz. 3:241. [31] Mullen, J. A. 1957. Nature, Lond. 180:813. [32] Pepper, J. H., F. T. Donaldson, and E. Hastings. 1941. Physiol. Zool. 14:470. [33] Portier, P., and M. Duval. 1927. C. rend. Soc. biol. 97:1605. [34] Ramsay, J. A. 1953. J. Exp. Biol., Lond. 30:358. [35] Ramsay, J. A. 1955. Ibid. 32:183. [36] Rapp, J. L. C. 1949. J. N. York Entom. Soc. 57:215. [37] Tobias, J. M. 1948. J. Cellul. Physiol. 31:143. [38] Todd, M. E. 1958. J. N. York Entom. Soc. 66:135. [39] Van Asperen, K., and I. van Esch. 1954. Nature, Lond. 174:927. [40] Wigglesworth, V. B. 1938. J. Exp. Biol., Lond. 15:235. [41] Wood, D. W. 1957. J. Physiol., Lond. 138:19. [42] Wyatt, G. R. In O. Hoffmann-Ostenhof, ed. 1959. Proc. 4th Internat. Congr. Biochem., Vienna, 1958. Pergamon Press, New York. v. 10, p. 161. [43] Wyatt, G. R., T. C. Loughheed, and S. S. Wyatt. 1956. J. Gen. Physiol. 39:853.

98. NITROGENOUS SUBSTANCES IN HEMOLYMPH: INSECTS

Part I: SUBSTANCES OTHER THAN AMINO ACIDS

Values are mg/100 ml hemolymph. Values in parentheses are ranges, estimate "c" (cf. Introduction).

| Species | Stage | Urea | Uric Acid | Nitrogen | | | | Refer-ence |
				Total N	Protein N	Non-protein N	Amino N	
(A)	(B)	(C)	(D)	(E)	(F)	(G)	(H)	(I)
Odonata								
1 Aeschna cyanea	Larva			529	311	218		26
Orthoptera								
2 Anabrus simplex	Adult			1302	693	608	262	22
3 Blatella germanica	Adult						56.4	24
4 Carausius morosus	Adult		4.5					25
5 Chortophaga viridi-fasciata	Adult			393.4	253.4	140		2
6 Leucophaea maderae	Adult	(16.0-19.5)	(9.7-15.6)	(658-1261)	(532.4-812.6)	(126.1-448.3)	(76.2-97.3)	28
7 Periplaneta americana	Adult	14.3 (9.1-17.6)		1028 (647-1760)	740 (476-1000)	228 (126-483)	78 (67-109)	D,F,H, 27·F G,29
Lepidoptera								
8 Antheraea polyphemus	Pupa, in diapause, ♂	7		1309	878	431	140	5,6
9 Bombyx mori	Larva 3rd-4th instar				224 (160-272)	460 (264-571)		31

Part I: SUBSTANCES OTHER THAN AMINO ACIDS (Continued)

	Species	Stage	Urea	Uric Acid	Nitrogen				Reference
					Total N	Protein N	Non-protein N	Amino N	
	(A)	(B)	(C)	(D)	(E)	(F)	(G)	(H)	(I)
	Lepidoptera (concluded)								
10	Bombyx mori (concluded)	Larva (concluded) 5th instar[1]	(57-77)	10.5	1421	(208-848)	527 (460-630)	223	C,16, 31;D, E,H, 11;F, G,11, 16,31
11		1-4 da			645 (586-749)	324 (272-404)			4
12		5-9 da			(879-1579)	(537-1368)			4
13		Prepupa		9.3 (8.2-10.8)	1380 (1356-1442)	894	448 (401-529)	168 (145-230)	11
14		Pupa 1-8 da		10.0 (6.8-12.6)	1242 (1092-1402)	701 (634-836)	550 (511-574)	234 (200-250)	11
15		9-15 da		12.9 (10.2-14.8)	987 (848-1070)	487 (416-558)	526 (505-557)	272 (250-290)	
16		Adult		13.6	1102	314	524	258	10
17	Celerio euphorbiae	Larva		20.4 (13.3-28.2)	1177 (1158-1206)	824 (808-835)	354 (318-398)	172 (166-182)	14
18		Pupa[2]		16.6 (10.5-32.0)	(380-1204)	(336-839)	361 (336-376)	173 (160-183)	
19		Adult		26.9		63		164	
20	Cossus cossus	Larva						234	7
21	Galleria mellonella	Larva				1360	580	199	24,31
22	Hyalophora cecropia	Larva[3], 4th-5th instar			(626-755)	(188-369)	412	212	6
		Pupa, in diapause							
23		♂			1354	826	527	178	
24		♀			1626	1140	486	140	
		Pupa → adult							
25		♂			(489-1104)	(108-727)	398 (377-443)	104 (70-137)	
26		♀			(349-1321)	(83-926)	365 (267-433)	105 (73-126)	
27	Prodenia eridania	Larva, 6th instar	6.2	14.8	568	167	401	235	1
28	Samia cynthia	Pupa			1070	629	441	327	2,7
29	S. carpini	Pupa						358	7
30	S. pyri	Pupa				384		285	7,8
31	Sphinx ligustri	Pupa						322	7
	Coleoptera								
32	Anomala orientalis	Larva			822.2	310.6	511.6	196.8	23
33	Dytiscus marginalis	Adult		18		508		106	8,9,12
34	Hydrous piceus	Adult	7.4	12.4 (10.7-14.5)		576 (500-720)		63 (40-80)	10,13

/1/ Glycerophosphorylethanolamine = 0.6 mg P/100 ml; phosphorylethanolamine = 2.2 mg P/100 ml [16].
/2/ Phosphagen = 5.5(4.9-6.6) mg P/100 ml [14].   /3/ Larva, 5th instar: phosphorylethanolamine = 1.9 mg P/100 ml; pupa in diapause and developing adult: phosphorylethanolamine = 7.5(1.9-15) mg P/100 ml [30].

Part I: SUBSTANCES OTHER THAN AMINO ACIDS (Concluded)

	Species	Stage	Urea	Uric Acid	Nitrogen				Reference
					Total N	Protein N	Non-protein N	Amino N	
	(A)	(B)	(C)	(D)	(E)	(F)	(G)	(H)	(I)
	Coleoptera (concluded)								
35	Popillia japonica	Larva, 3rd instar[4]	58 (45-87)	12 (9-15)	1302 (1170-1485)	(80-608)	(429-886)	238 (215-262)	18-20
36		Prepupa	32	8.1		637	342	248	19
37		Pupa	48 (28-111)	97 (79-112)	(714-2344)	562 (295-644)	502 (332-612)	207 (173-227)	19
38		Adult			1896	990	906		19
39	Tenebrio molitor	Larva			(1112-1477)	(738.3-990.5)	(304.1-486.2)	(100.1-151.1)[5]	15
	Hymenoptera								
40	Apis mellifera	Larva		5.3 (3.2-7.7)		1052 (1000-1110)	340 (306-385)	290 (250-308)	3
41	Diprion hercyniae	Larva				865	686		31
	Diptera								
42	Gasterophilus intestinalis	Larva, 3rd instar[6]	20.4	2.2	1850	1720	130	94	17

/4/ Allantoin = 93 [18-20]. /5/ 50.3 also reported [21]. /6/ Ammonia = 1.8 [17].

Contributors: (a) Wyatt, Gerard R., (b) Ludwig, Daniel

References: [1] Babers, F. H. 1938. J. Agr. Res. 57:697. [2] Barsa, M. C. 1954. J. Gen. Physiol. 38:79. [3] Bishop, G. R., A. P. Briggs, and E. Ronzoni. 1925. J. Biol. Chem. 66:77. [4] Bito, S. 1927. Nogeikagaku Kaishi 3:487. [5] Carrington, C. B., and S. M. Tenney. 1959. J. Insect Physiol. 3:402. [6] Chefurka, W. 1953. Ph. D. Thesis. Harvard University. [7] Duval, M., P. Portier, and A. Courtois. 1928. C. rend. Acad. sc. 186:652. [8] Florkin, M. 1935. C. rend. Soc. biol. 118:1224. [9] Florkin, M. 1937. Mém. Acad. Belgique 16:1. [10] Florkin, M. 1937. Arch. internat. physiol., Liége 45:6. [11] Florkin, M. 1937. Ibid. 45:17. [12] Florkin, M., and G. Duchateau. 1942. Bull. Acad. Belgique 28:373. [13] Florkin, M., and H. Renwart. 1939. C. rend. Soc. biol. 131:1274. [14] Heller, J., and A. Moklowska. 1930. Biochem. Zschr. 219:473. [15] Joseph, M. T. 1958. Ann. Entom. Soc. America 51:554. [16] Kondo, Y., and T. Watanabe. 1957. Nippon Sanshigaku Zasshi 26:298. [17] Levenbook, L. 1950. Biochem. J., Lond. 47:336. [18] Ludwig, D. 1951. Physiol. Zool. 24:329. [19] Ludwig, D. 1954. Ibid. 27:325. [20] Ludwig, D., and W. P. Cullen. 1956. Ibid. 29:153. [21] Marcuzzi, G. 1955. Rendic. Accad. Lincei 18:654. [22] Pepper, J. H., F. T. Donaldson, and E. Hastings. 1941. Physiol. Zool. 14:470. [23] Po-Chedley, D. S. 1958. J. N. York Entom. Soc. 66:171. [24] Pratt, J. J. 1950. Ann. Entom. Soc. America 43:573. [25] Ramsay, J. A. 1955. J. Exp. Biol., Lond. 32:183. [26] Raper, R., and J. Shaw. 1948. Nature, Lond. 162:999. [27] Todd, M. E. 1957. J. N. York Entom. Soc. 65:85. [28] Todd, M. E. 1958. Ibid. 66:135. [29] Van Asperen, K., and I. van Esch. 1956. Arch. néerl. zool. 11:342. [30] Wyatt, G. R., In O. Hoffmann-Ostenhof, ed. 1959. Proc. 4th Internat. Congr. Biochem., Vienna, 1958. Pergamon Press, New York. v. 12, p. 161. [31] Wyatt, G. R., T. C. Loughheed, and S. S. Wyatt. 1956. J. Gen. Physiol. 39:853.

Species	Stage	Method	Alanine	Arginine	Asparagine	Aspartic Acid	Glutamic Acid	Glutamine
(A)	(B)	(C)	(D)	(E)	(F)	(G)	(H)	(I)
Odonata								
1 Aeschna sp	Larva	Microbiological assay	47	23	6	8	20	43
Orthoptera								
2 Carausius morosus	Adult	Microbiological assay	35	18	10	4	9	69
3 Locusta migratoria	Larva	Microbiological assay	31	20	9	5	0	166
Lepidoptera								
4 Actias selene	Pupa, hibernating	Microbiological assay	116	155	28		145	
5 Amathes xylographa	Larva	Microbiological assay	79	63	84		268	
6 Antheraea pernyi	Pupa, hibernating	Microbiological assay	199	197	17		120	
7 Bombyx mori — Larva 3rd-4th instar[1]		Paper chromatography	13	22	47	11	17	228
8 5th instar, 7th da[2]		Ion-exchange column chromatography	15	21	0	3	85	56
9 Late 5th instar[3]		Paper chromatography	50	28	59	10	10	143
10 Late 5th instar		Microbiological assay	49	36	112		295	
11 Spinning		Microbiological assay	32	28	24		67	
12 Pupa[4]		Paper chromatography	21	21	24	14	20	115
13 Pupa[5]		Ion-exchange column chromatography	16	87	2	32	83	130
14 Celerio euphorbiae	Pupa, hibernating	Microbiological assay	132[6]	165	17		143[6]	
15 Citheronia regalis	Pupa, hibernating	Microbiological assay	27	233	27		203	
16 Cossus cossus	Larva	Microbiological assay	37	86	50		71	
17 Deilephila elpenor — Pupa, hibernating ♂		Microbiological assay	91	129	13		118	
18 ♀		Microbiological assay	115	128	15		103	
19 Eacles magnifica	Pupa, hibernating	Microbiological assay	31	235	7	3	27	115
20 Euproctis chrysorrhoea	Larva	Microbiological assay	33	51	16		323	
21	Pupa	Microbiological assay	38	107	29		315	
22 Galleria mellonella	Larva[7]	Paper chromatography	225	39	13	38	22	369
23 Hyalophora cecropia	Pupa, hibernating	Microbiological assay	66	149	5		83	
24 Imbrasia macrothyris	Larva	Microbiological assay	24	20	10		85	
25 Laothoe austati	Pupa, hibernating	Microbiological assay	16	131	19		95	
26 L. populi	Pupa, hibernating	Microbiological assay	100[6]	406	27		195	
27 Lasiocarpa quercus	Pupa, hibernating	Microbiological assay	407	194	9		462	
28 Papilio machaon	Pupa, hibernating	Microbiological assay	158	127	17		214	
29 Philosamia canningi	Pupa, hibernating	Microbiological assay	8	153	4		286	

/1/ β-Alanine = 35 mg/100 ml; cystine + cysteine = 0; tryptophan = 0. /2/ β-Alanine = 5 mg/100 ml; ornithine = 13
0; tryptophan = 0. /4/ Cystine + cysteine = 0; tryptophan = 0. /5/ β-Alanine = 2 mg/100 ml. /6/ Varies with

AMINO ACIDS

ml hemolymph.

Glycine	Histidine	Isoleucine	Leucine	Lysine	Methionine	Phenylalanine	Proline	Serine	Threonine	Tyrosine	Valine	Reference	
(J)	(K)	(L)	(M)	(N)	(O)	(P)	(Q)	(R)	(S)	(T)	(U)	(V)	
Odonata													
33	12	17	26	11	7	8	24	24	17	8	26	1	1
Orthoptera													
27	57	11	13	25	11	8	14		35	7	24	1	2
84	28	23	21	45	3	13	88	50	17	17	41	1	3
Lepidoptera													
51	112	46	44	258	51	23	302		76	9	94	1	4
48	114	34	18	68	3	16	161		43	0	31	1	5
75	173	55	49	172	38	24	377		136	4	70	1	6
69	104	16		115	6	3	14	93	19	9	19	8	7
18	276	8	10	82		7	13	49	28	6	16	7	8
73	273	29		164	14	11	36	111	36	31	23	8	9
69	280	13	16	79	9	10	35		68	4	22	2	10
57	261	19	23	85	58	13	32		38	11	23	2,4	11
116	239	51		117	73	17	64	69	35	71	43	8	12
56	159	21	24	34		9	24	42	120	34	34	6	13
50	113	67	76	285[6]	46	28	176[6]		77	58	90	3	14
82	121	36	47	471	115	27	136		85	22	60	1	15
23	79	36	63	153	?	25	123		27	124	41	1	16
												1	
54	80	53	55	313	60	26	125		60	79	94		17
45	86	64	70	271	60	29	121		57	115	103		18
46	124	15	15	345	65	8	81		8	40	35	1	19
76	134	24	18	78	8	12	143		42	3	39	1	20
55	55	38	39	164	11	15	112		43	13	55		21
51	136	42		68	27	11	520	47	62	76	29	8	22
31	86	46	53	199	34		422		63	3	99	1	23
102	43	10	6	64	3	6	10		9	86	19	1	24
5	4	21	15	64	25	9	28		21	40	22	1	25
41	78	47	36	287	59	16	77		54	18	77	1	26
48	119	68	59	172	44	32	421		57	181	125	1	27
48	80	48	68	363	143	34	202		52	5	111	1	28
67	61	43	53	271	57	26	151		49	11	75	1	29

mg/100 ml; taurine = 4 mg/100 ml; tryptophan = 5 mg/100 ml. /3/ β-Alanine = 39 mg/100 ml; cystine + cysteine = storage temperature of pupa. /7/ β-Alanine = 51 mg/100 ml; cystine + cysteine = 0; tryptophan = 0.

	Species	Stage	Method	Alanine	Arginine	Asparagine	Aspartic Acid	Glutamic Acid	Glutamine
	(A)	(B)	(C)	(D)	(E)	(F)	(G)	(H)	(I)
	Lepidoptera (concluded)								
30	Philosamia cynthia	Pupa, hibernating	Microbiological assay	253	166	8	4	14	81
31	P. ricini	Pupa, hibernating	Microbiological assay	49	137	36		426	
32	Pseudobunaea seydeli	Larva	Microbiological assay	9	16	17		100	
33	Saturnia atlantica	Pupa, hibernating	Microbiological assay	49	155	7		151	
34	S. pavonia	Pupa, hibernating	Microbiological assay	161[6]	135	11		238	
35	S. pyri	Pupa, hibernating	Microbiological assay	50	243	13		469	
36	Smerinthus ocellatus	Larva	Microbiological assay	28	19	28		202	
37	ocellatus	Pupa, hibernating	Microbiological assay	171	320	1		127	
38	Sphinx ligustri	Pupa, hibernating	Microbiological assay	294	262	2	7	13	209
39		Adult	Microbiological assay	14	20	25		421	
40	Triphaena pronuba	Larva	Microbiological assay	28	82	16		112	
	Coleoptera								
41	Hydrous piceus	Adult	Microbiological assay	61	10	18		163	
42	Leptinotarsa decemlineata	Adult	Microbiological assay	34	19	21		611	
	Hymenoptera								
43	Apis mellifera	Larva	Microbiological assay	58	63	33		328	
44	Diprion hercyniae	Larva[8]	Paper chromatography	99	20	63	12	17	146
	Diptera								
45	Calliphora augur	Larva[9]	Paper chromatography	118	Trace	35	14	48	109
46	augur	Pupa[10]	Paper chromatography	31	Trace	25	13	63	65
47	Gasterophilus sp	Larva	Microbiological assay		9	15		314	

/6/ Varies with storage temperature of pupa. /8/ β-Alanine = 0; cystine + cysteine = 43 mg/100 ml. /9/ β-Alanine = cystine + cysteine = trace; hydroxyproline = 0; ornithine = 0; taurine = trace; tryptophan = 0.

Contributor: Wyatt, Gerard R.

References: [1] Duchateau, G., and M. Florkin. 1958. Arch. internat. physiol. biochim. 66:573. [2] Florkin, M. Congr. Biochem., Vienna, 1958. Pergamon Press, New York. v. 14, p. 63. [4] Fukuda, T., et al. 1955. J. Sanshigaku Zasshi 26:341. [7] Kondo, Y., and T. Watanabe. 1957. Ibid. 26:298. [8] Wyatt, G. R., T. C. Loughheed,

ACIDS (Concluded)

Glycine	Histidine	Isoleucine	Leucine	Lysine	Methionine	Phenylalanine	Proline	Serine	Threonine	Tyrosine	Valine	Reference	
(J)	(K)	(L)	(M)	(N)	(O)	(P)	(Q)	(R)	(S)	(T)	(U)	(V)	
Lepidoptera (concluded)													
52	89	82	108	247	64	28	244		80	5	127	1	30
	41	28	38	114	12	16	63		1	42	38	1	31
98	106	14	6	43	4	5	9		32	230	21	1	32
40	72	63	70	234	115	16	313		37	7	91	1	33
46	66	64	74	253	113	41	380		64	41	74	1	34
65	80	57	57	166	98	47	390		106	65	84	1	35
53	83	13	8	78	8	10	24		35	30	84	1	36
38	64	54	49	316	79	24	242		55	16	90		37
44	112	54	69	367	65	32	176		81	9	/107	1	38
53	70	25	30	35	35	25	70		26	179	49	3	39
	202	17	21	139	0	20	143		46	481	45	1	40
Coleoptera													
22	11	17	8	23	4	7	203		15	6	16	1	41
17	43		12	42		9	637		21	0	25	1	42
Hymenoptera													
78	24	25	28	90	22	11	393		38	3	59	1	43
108	92	22		43	68	10	262	200	34	38	34	8	44
Diptera													
29	0	20		Trace	Trace	20	92	25	Trace	134	16	5	45
24	0	11		Trace	Trace	29	63	31	Trace	95	10		46
6	1	8	8	9	8	8	17		24	22	15	1	47

0; cystine + cysteine = trace; hydroxyproline = trace; ornithine = 0; taurine = trace; tryptophan = 0. /10/ β-Alanine = 0;

1954. Bull. Soc. zool. France 79:369. [3] Florkin, M. In O. Hoffmann-Ostenhof, ed. 1959. Proc. 4th Internat. Biochem., Tokyo 42:341. [5] Hackman, R. H. 1956. Austral. J. Biol. Sc. 9:400. [6] Kondo, Y. 1957. Nippon and S. S. Wyatt. 1956. J. Gen. Physiol. 39:853.

Part I: LIPIDS

Values in parentheses are ranges, estimate "c" (cf. Introduction).

Species	Stage	Constituent	Value mg/100 ml	Reference
(A)	(B)	(C)	(D)	(E)
Lepidoptera				
1 Bombyx mori	Larva, 5th instar	Phosphorylcholine	21(18-24)	11
2	Pupa	Phosphorylcholine	56	11
3		Phospholipid	(10-27)[1]	7
4 Celerio euphorbiae	Pupa	Lipids, total	(830-1975)	4, 5
5 Hyalophora cecropia	Larva, 5th instar	Phosphorylcholine	6.8	10
6	Pupa[2]	Phosphorylcholine	28(14-43)	
7 Prodenia eridania	Larva, 6th instar	Lipids, total	321	1
8		Cholesterol	12.8	
9		Phospholipid	99[3]	
Coleoptera				
10 Hydrous piceus	Larva	Fatty acids	550	3
11		Unsaponifiable matter	220	
12 Popillia japonica	Larva	Lipids, total	420(360-520)	9
Hymenoptera				
13 Apis mellifera	Larva	Lipids, total	453(370-587)	2
14		Cholesterol	35(25-40)	
15		Phospholipid	84[1]	
16	Prepupa, pupa	Phospholipid	33[1]	
Diptera				
17 Calliphora erythrocephala	Larva, 3rd instar	Phospholipid	10[1]	6
18 Gasterophilus intestinalis	Larva, 3rd instar	Lipids, total	137	8
19 Phormia terra-novae	Larva, 3rd instar	Phospholipid	6[1]	6

/1/ Expressed as mg P/100 ml. /2/ Includes pupa in diapause and developing adult. /3/ Determined by Bloor's method and expressed as weight of phospholipid.

Contributor: Wyatt, Gerard R.

References: [1] Babers, F. H. 1938. J. Agr. Res. 57:697. [2] Bishop, G. H., A. P. Briggs, and E. Ronzoni. 1925. J. Biol. Chem. 66:77. [3] Drilhon, A., and R. G. Busnel. 1946. Bull. Soc. zool. France 71:185. [4] Heller, J. 1932. Biochem. Zschr. 255:205. [5] Heller, J., and A. Moklowska. 1930. Ibid. 219:473. [6] Hopf, H. S. 1940. Biochem. J., Lond. 34:1396. [7] Ito, T., H. Shigematsu, and Y. Horie. 1958. Nippon Sanshigaku Zasshi 27:217. [8] Levenbook, L. 1950. Biochem. J., Lond. 47:336. [9] Ludwig, D., and M. Wugmeister. 1953. Physiol. Zool. 26:254. [10] Wyatt, G. R. In O. Hoffmann-Ostenhof, ed. 1959. Proc. 4th Internat. Congr. Biochem., Vienna, 1958. Pergamon Press, New York. v. 12, p. 161. [11] Wyatt, G. R. Unpublished.

Part II: CARBOHYDRATES

Values in parentheses are ranges, estimate "c" (cf. Introduction).

	Species	Stage	Constituent	Value mg/100 ml	Reference
	(A)	(B)	(C)	(D)	(E)
	Orthoptera				
1	Leucophaea maderae	Adult	Reducing substances, total (as glucose)	(136-340)	23
2	Locusta migratoria	Adult	Fructose	35	13
3	Periplaneta americana	Adult	Reducing substances, total (as glucose)	221(110-288)	22
4			Glucose	30[1]	
5	Schistocerca gregaria	Larva, 5th instar	Reducing substances, total (as glucose)	400	11
6			Glycogen	(30-50)	
7			Glucose	(50-100)	
8			Trehalose	(800-1500)	
9		Adult, ♀	Glucose	24(6-40)[2]	24
10			Trehalose	695(546-848)	
	Lepidoptera				
11	Antheraea mylitta	Pupa	Glycerol	5	30
12	A. polyphemus	Larva	Trehalose	1036	28
13		Pupa	Glycerol	430	28,30
14			Trehalose	1324	
15	Bombyx mori	Larva, 5th instar	Reducing substances, total (as glucose)	51	5,8
16			Fructose	1.6(1.0-1.9)	29
17			Glucose	9[1]	5,8
18				(1-40)[2]	29
19			Glucose-6-phosphate	10(5-14)[3]	28
20			Glycogen	14[4]	28
21			Sorbitol-6-phosphate	85(60-106)[3]	26,27
22			Trehalose	(256-636)	5,8
23				414(306-523)	28
24		Prepupa	Reducing substances, total (as glucose)	70(51-95)	8
25			Glucose	18(10-28)[1]	
26		Pupa	Reducing substances, total (as glucose)	108(95-117)	8
27			Fructose	1.9	29
28			Glucose	30(18-49)[1]	8
29				2.5[2]	29
30			Glycogen	38[4]	28
31			Sorbitol-6-phosphate	5[3]	27
32			Trehalose	202	28
33		Adult	Reducing substances, total (as glucose)	155	8
34			Glucose	16	
35	Celerio euphorbiae	Larva	Reducing substances, total (as glucose)	127(119-136)	10,20
36			Trehalose	(0-1645)	
37		Pupa	Reducing substances, total (as glucose)	(1600-4300)	9,20
38			Glucose	(68-2077)[1]	
39			Trehalose	(131-1348)	
40	Deilephila elpenor	Pupa In diapause	Trehalose	1530(942-1933)	4
41		Developing to adult	Glycogen	(0-8)	
42			Trehalose	(195-1178)	
43	Galleria mellonella	Larva	Glucose	21[?]	28
44			Glucose-6-phosphate	0	
45			Glycogen	41[4]	
46			Trehalose	1508	
47	Hyalophora cecropia	Larva	Glycerol	18	28,30
48			Trehalose	1194	
49		Pupa In diapause	Glucose	6(2-11)[5]	27,30
50			Glycerol	(920-3000)	
51			Trehalose	237(154-465)[5]	

/1/ Estimated as reducing substances fermentable by yeast. /2/ Determined by paper chromatography. /3/ Expressed as mg P/100 ml. /4/ May include polysaccharides other than glycogen. /5/ Determined by enzymic assay.

Part II: CARBOHYDRATES (Continued)

	Species	Stage	Constituent	Value mg/100 ml	Refer- ence
	(A)	(B)	(C)	(D)	(E)
	Lepidoptera (concluded)				
52	Hyalophora cecropia (concluded)	Pupa (concluded) Developing to adult	Glucose	$(0-8)^2$	30
53			Glycerol	(18-1300)	30
54			Glycogen	43	28
55			Trehalose	(539-1159)	28
56		Chilled	Glycogen	28	28
57			Trehalose	580	
58	Prodenia eridania	Larva, 6th instar	Reducing substances, total (as glucose)	65.9	1
59			Glucose	11^1	
60			Glycogen	3.3	
61	Rothschildia orizaba	Pupa	Glycerol	23	30
62	Samia cynthia	Pupa, in diapause	Glucose	0^5	27
63			Glycerol	37(4-116)	
64			Trehalose	$238(128-311)^5$	
65	Sphinx ligustri	Pupa, in diapause	Glycogen	0	4
66			Trehalose	2388	
	Coleoptera				
67	Chalcophora mariana	Larva	Glycogen	0	4
68			Trehalose	5254	
	Dytiscus marginalis	Adult			4
69		♂	Glycogen	11	
70			Trehalose	519	
71		♀	Glycogen	0	
72			Trehalose	711	
73	Ergaster faber	Larva	Glycogen	0	4
74			Trehalose	3331	
75	Hydrous piceus	Adult	Reducing substances, total (as glucose)	61(20-104)	4,7
76			Glucose	$17(5-31)^1$	
77			Glycogen	0	
78			Trehalose	400	
79	Popillia japonica	Larva	Reducing substances, total (as glucose)	248(227-283)	17
80			Glucose	69^1	
81	Tenebrio molitor	Larva	Reducing substances, total (as glucose)	$(10-400)^6$	18,19
82				(71.4-136.2)	14
83			Glucose	122^2	18,19
	Hymenoptera				
84	Anthophora sp	Larva	Trehalose	6554	4
85	Apis mellifera	Larva	Reducing substances, total (as glucose)	685(630-740)	3,21
86			Glycogen	2.8	
87		Adult	Reducing substances, total (as glucose)	2300(1000-4000)	2,4,25
88			Fructose	(800-1000)	
89			Glucose	$(1100-1400)^2$	
90			Trehalose	928(593-1204)	
91	Diprion hercyniae	Larva	Glucose	28^2	28
92			Glycogen	32	
93			Trehalose	795	
	Diptera				
94	Gasterophilus intestinalis	Larva, 3rd instar	Reducing substances, total (as glucose)	356	16
95			Fructose	(200-280)	
96			Glucose	10^5	
97			Glycogen	$(10-20)^4$	
98		Pupa	Fructose	(22-100)	15

/1/ Estimated as reducing substances fermentable by yeast. /2/ Determined by paper chromatography. /4/ May include polysaccharides other than glycogen. /5/ Determined by enzymic assay. /6/ Varies with ambient relative humidity.

Part II: CARBOHYDRATES (Concluded)

	Species	Stage	Constituent	Value mg/100 ml	Reference
	(A)	(B)	(C)	(D)	(E)
	Diptera (concluded)				
99	Phormia regina	Larva	Glucose	(70-125)[2]	6,12
100			Trehalose	0	
101		Adult	Glucose	(33-600)[2,7]	
102			Trehalose	(125-3000)[7]	

/2/ Determined by paper chromatography. /7/ Varies with food intake and with exercise.

Contributor: Wyatt, Gerard R.

References: [1] Babers, F. H. 1938. J. Agr. Res. 57:697. [2] Beutler, R. 1936. Zschr. vergl. Physiol. 24:71. [3] Bishop, G. H., A. P. Briggs, and E. Ronzoni. 1925. J. Biol. Chem. 66:77. [4] Duchateau, G., and M. Florkin. 1959. Arch. internat. physiol. biochim. 67:306. [5] Duchateau, G., M. Florkin, and M. Gromadska. 1958. Ibid. 66:434. [6] Evans, D. R., and V. G. Dethier. 1957-58. J. Insect Physiol. 1:3. [7] Florkin, M. 1936. Bull. Soc. chim. biol., Par. 19:990. [8] Florkin, M. 1937. Arch. internat. physiol., Liége 45:17. [9] Heller, J., and I. Mochnacka. 1951. C. rend. Soc. sc. lett. Varsovie, Cl. 4, 6:56. [10] Heller, J., and A. Moklowska. 1930. Biochem. Zschr. 219:473. [11] Howden, G. F., and B. A. Kilby. 1956. Chem. & Indust. 2:1453. [12] Hudson, A. 1957-58. J. Insect Physiol. 1:293. [13] Humphrey, G. F., and M. Robertson. 1949. Austral. J. Sc. 12:29. [14] Joseph, M. T. 1958. Ann. Entom. Soc. America 51:554. [15] Levenbook, L. 1947. Nature, Lond. 160:465. [16] Levenbook, L. 1950. Biochem. J., Lond. 47:336. [17] Ludwig, D. 1951. Physiol. Zool. 24:329. [18] Marcuzzi, G. 1955. Rendic. Accad. Lincei 18:654. [19] Marcuzzie, M. 1956. Ibid. 20:492. [20] Mochnacka, I., and C. Petryszyn. 1959. Acta biochim. polon. 6:307. [21] Ronzoni, E., and G. H. Bishop. 1929. Tr. 4th Internat. Congr. Entom. 2:361. [22] Todd, M. E. 1957. J. N. York Entom. Soc. 65:85. [23] Todd, M. E. 1958. Ibid. 66:135. [24] Treherne, J. E. 1958. J. Exp. Biol., Lond. 35:611. [25] Von Czarnovsky, C. 1954. Naturwissenschaften 41:577. [26] Wyatt, G. R. In O. Hoffmann-Ostenhof, ed. 1959. Proc. 4th Internat. Congr. Biochem., Vienna, 1958. Pergamon Press, New York. v. 12, p. 161. [27] Wyatt, G. R. Unpublished. [28] Wyatt, G. R., and G. F. Kalf. 1957. J. Gen. Physiol. 40:833. [29] Wyatt, G. R., T. C. Loughheed, and S. S. Wyatt. 1956. Ibid. 39:853. [30] Wyatt, G. R., and W. L. Meyer. 1959. Ibid. 42:1005.

Part III: MISCELLANEOUS ORGANIC ACIDS AND SALTS

Values in parentheses are ranges, estimate "c" (cf. Introduction).

	Species	Stage	Constituent	Value mg/100 ml	Reference
	(A)	(B)	(C)	(D)	(E)
	Orthoptera				
1	Periplaneta americana	Adult	Citric acid	14	5
	Hemiptera				
2	Leptocoris trivittatus	Adult	Citric acid	31	5
3	Rhodnius prolixus	Larva, 5th instar	Citric acid	44	9

Part III: MISCELLANEOUS ORGANIC ACIDS AND SALTS (Concluded)

Species	Stage	Constituent	Value mg/100 ml	Reference
(A)	(B)	(C)	(D)	(E)
Lepidoptera				
4 Antheraea pernyi	Larva, 5th instar	Pyruvic acid	(20.5-27.5)	1
5 A. polyphemus	Pupa	Citric acid	229	5
6 Bombyx mori	Larva, 5th instar	Citric acid	613	3, 5
7		Glyoxylic acid	(30-50)	
8		α-Ketoglutaric acid	(6-7)	
9	Pupa	Citric acid	530	5
10 Galleria mellonella	Larva	Citric acid	9.4	5
11 Hyalophora cecropia	Larva, 5th instar	Citric acid	152	5
12		α-Glycerophosphate	54[1]	10
13		Uridine diphosphate compounds	0.03[1]	2
14	Pupa	Citric acid	229	5
15	Pupa in diapause, and developing adult	α-Glycerophosphate	27(19-36)[1]	10
16		Uridine diphosphate compounds	(0.6-4.6)[1]	2
17 Prodenia eridania	Larva, 6th instar	Citric acid	394	5
18	Adult	Citric acid	90	
19 Protoparce sexta	Larva	Citric acid	421	5
Coleoptera				
20 Dermestes sp	Larva	Citric acid	125	5
21 Photuras sp	Adult	Citric acid	35	5
22 Tenebrio molitor	Larva	Citric acid	72	5
23	Adult	Citric acid	97	9
Hymenoptera				
24 Apis mellifera	Larva, 3rd instar	Citric acid	110	5
25	Adult	Citric acid	46	
26 Vespula maculata	Adult	Citric acid	71	5
Diptera				
27 Gasterophilus intestinalis	Larva, 3rd instar	Citric acid	45	4
28		Fumaric acid	(35-70)	8
29		α-Ketoglutaric acid	93	6
30		Lactic acid	12.3	4
31		Malic acid	(280-430)	8
32		Succinic acid	(203-242)	7
33 Phormia regina	Larva, 3rd instar	Citric acid	240	5
34	Adult	Citric acid	(6.3-8.5)	
35 Sarcophaga bullata	Larva, 3rd instar	Citric acid	198	5
36	Adult	Citric acid	50	

/1/ Expressed as mg P/100 ml.

Contributor: Wyatt, Gerard R.

References: [1] Burova, A. A. 1953. Uchen. zapiski Moskov. gosud. pedag. Inst. 77:33. [2] Carey, F. G., and G. R. Wyatt. 1960. Biochim. biophys. acta, Amst. 41:178. [3] Fukuda, T., T. Hayashi, and M. Matsuda. 1955. Seikagaku 27:147. [4] Levenbook, L. 1950. Biochem. J., Lond. 47:336. [5] Levenbook, L. 1961. J. Insect. Physiol. v. 5. [6] Levenbook, L. Unpublished. [7] Levenbook, L., and Y. L. Wang. 1948. Nature, Lond. 162:7. [8] Nossal, P. M. 1952. Biochem. J., Lond. 50:349. [9] Patterson, D. S. P. 1956. Arch. internat. physiol. biochim. 64:681. [10] Wyatt, G. R. In O. Hoffmann-Ostenhof, ed. 1959. Proc. 4th Internat. Congr. Biochem., Vienna, 1958. Pergamon Press, New York. v. 12, p. 161.

Stage (column B): Intermolt = the stage of the molting cycle when the exoskeleton is fully thickened and hardened (the membranous layer of the exoskeleton is fully formed and can be stripped, with the epidermis, from the remainder of the exoskeleton). Premolt = the stage shortly before molting, characterized by a breakdown of the old skeleton through resorption of mineral and organic constituents, and by a synthesis of the pre-exuvial layers of the new exoskeleton (epicuticle and exocuticle) under the old; period precedes molt by 1-4 days. Molt = the act of shedding the old exoskeleton. Postmolt = 1-3 days following molt, when the new exoskeleton is very soft and flexible.

Part I: FREEZING POINT DEPRESSION

Values in parentheses are ranges, estimate "c" (cf. Introduction).

| | Species | Stage | Freezing Point Depression, °C | | Reference |
			Plasma or Serum	Environmental Fluid	
	(A)	(B)	(C)	(D)	(E)
	Branchiopoda				
1	Artemia salina		0.70	2.75	9
2			0.76	4.85	
3			(0.70-0.82)	3.39	8
4			(1.28-1.52)	10.16	
	Copepoda[1]				
5	Lernaeocera branchialis		1.17	1.97	12
6			1.63	2.04	
	Isopoda				
7	Mesidotea entomon		1.07	0.41	2
	Decapoda				
	Crab				
8	Callinectes hastatus		1.93	Sea water	3
9	Cancer borealis		1.83	Sea water	3
10		Intermolt	1.82	1.64	16, 17
11			1.60	1.23	
12			1.55	0.86	
13	C. pagurus	Intermolt	2.09	2.01	5
14	Carcinus maenas	Intermolt	2.08	2.01	5
15	Cardisoma guanhumi		1.66	2.04	11
16	Eriocheir sinensis		2.05	2.28	4
17		Intermolt	2.21	2.32	14
18	Gecarcinus lateralis		1.65	2.04	11
19	Grapsus grapsus		1.92	2.04	11
20	Heloecius cordiformis		1.95	2.17	6
21	Hemigrapsus nudus		2.00[2]	1.97	7
22	H. oregonensis		2.01[2]	1.97	7
23	Leptograpsus variegatus		1.95	2.13	6
24	Maja squinado	Intermolt	2.02	2.01	5
25	Ocypode albicans		1.70	2.04	11
26	Pachygrapsus crassipes		1.82[2]	1.97	7
27		Intermolt	1.33	Sea water	1
28		Premolt	1.89	Sea water	
29		Molt	2.60	Sea water	
30		Postmolt	2.14	Sea water	
31	P. marmoratus		2.01	2.20	15
32	Rhithropanopeus harisii		2.00[2]	1.97	7
33	Uca crenulata		1.68[2]	1.97	7
	Crayfish				
34	Astacus fluviatilis		0.82	0.02	14
35		Intermolt	0.60	Fresh water	5
36		Premolt	0.70	Fresh water	5
37	A. trowbridgii		0.83	Fresh water	18
38	Cambarus clarkii		0.76	Fresh water	18
39			0.68	Fresh water	13
	Lobster				
40	Homarus americanus		1.81	Sea water	3
41	H. vulgaris	Intermolt	2.25	2.01	5

/1/ Parasitic. /2/ Value read from graph.

Part I: FREEZING POINT DEPRESSION (Concluded)

Species	Stage	Freezing Point Depression, °C		Reference
		Plasma or Serum	Environmental Fluid	
(A)	(B)	(C)	(D)	(E)
Decapoda (concluded)				
Lobster (concluded)				
42 Palinurus vulgaris	Intermolt	2.29	2.01	5
43 Panulirus interruptus		2.19	Sea water	5
Shrimp				10
44 Leander serratus		1.52	1.93	
45		1.70	2.04	
46 L. squilla		1.46	1.93	
47		1.52	2.04	
48 Palaemonetes varians		1.28	1.93	
49		1.40	2.04	

Contributors: (a) Redmond, James R., (b) Travis, Dorothy F.

References: [1] Baumberger, J. P., and J. M. D. Olmsted. 1928. Physiol. Zool. 1:531. [2] Bogucki, M. 1932. Arch. internat. physiol., Liége 35:197. [3] Cole, W. H. 1940. J. Gen. Physiol. 23:575. [4] Conklin, R. E., and A. Krogh. 1938. Zschr. vergl. Physiol. 26:239. [5] Damboviceanu, A. 1932. Arch. roumain. path., Par. 5:239. [6] Edmonds, E. 1935. Proc. Linn. Soc., N. S. Wales 60:233. [7] Jones, L. L. 1941. J. Cellul. Physiol. 18:79. [8] Kuenen, D. J. 1939. Arch. néerl. zool. 3:365. [9] Medwedewa, N. B. 1927. Zschr. vergl. Physiol. 5:547. [10] Panikkar, N. K. 1941. J. Marine Biol. Ass. U. K. 25:317. [11] Pearse, A. S. 1934. Papers from Tortugas Laboratory, Carnegie Institution, Washington, D. C. v. 28, pp. 93-102. [12] Robertson, J. D. 1939. J. Exp. Biol., Lond. 16:387. [13] Schlatter, M. L. 1941. J. Cellul. Physiol. 17:259. [14] Scholles, W. 1933. Zschr. vergl. Physiol. 19:522. [15] Schwabe, E. 1933. Ibid. 19:183. [16] Trevisani, G. A. 1956. M. S. Thesis. University of New Hampshire. [17] Trevisani, G. A. 1958. Ph. D. Thesis. University of New Hampshire. [18] Van Harreveld, A. 1936. Proc. Soc. Exp. Biol., N. Y. 34:428.

Part II: pH

Values in parentheses are ranges, estimate "c" (cf. Introduction).

Species	Stage	Hemolymph pH	Reference
(A)	(B)	(C)	(D)
Isopoda			
1 Ligia exotica	Intermolt	7.80	5, 6
2	Premolt	7.55	
3	Postmolt	7.65	
Decapoda			
Crab			
4 Callinectes hastatus		7.55	2
5 Cancer borealis		7.81	2
6 C. pagurus	Intermolt	(7.6-7.7)	4
7 Carcinus maenas	Intermolt	(7.6-7.7)	4
8 Maja squinado	Intermolt	(7.8-7.9)	4
9 Pachygrapsus crassipes		7.49	8
10	Intermolt + premolt	(8.1-8.4)	1
11	Postmolt	(7.8-8.5)	1

Part II: pH (Concluded)

Species	Stage	Hemolymph pH	Reference
(A)	(B)	(C)	(D)
Decapoda (concluded)			
Crayfish			
12 Astacus fluviatilis	Intermolt	(7.7-7.8)	3, 4
13	Premolt	(7.7-7.8)	
14	Postmolt	(8.1-8.2)	
15 A. trowbridgii		7.55	9
16 Cambarus clarkii		7.55	9
Lobster			
17 Homarus americanus		(7.45-7.61)	2
18 H. vulgaris	Intermolt	(7.6-7.7)	4
19 Palinurus vulgaris	Intermolt	7.4	4
20 Panulirus interruptus		(7.51-7.53)	7

Contributors: (a) Redmond, James R., (b) Travis, Dorothy F.

References: [1] Baumberger, J. P., and J. M. D. Olmsted. 1928. Physiol. Zool. 1:531. [2] Cole, W. H. 1940. J. Gen. Physiol. 23:575. [3] Damboviceanu, A. 1930. C. rend. Soc. biol. 105:913. [4] Damboviceanu, A. 1932. Arch. roumain. path., Par. 5:239. [5] Numanoi, H. 1934. J. Fac. Sc. Univ. Tokyo 3:351. [6] Numanoi, H. 1937. Jap. J. Zool. 7:241. [7] Redmond, J. R. 1955. J. Cellul. Physiol. 46:209. [8] Schlatter, M. L. 1941. Ibid. 17:259. [9] Van Harreveld, A. 1936. Proc. Soc. Exp. Biol., N. Y. 34:428.

Part III: DENSITY, OSMOTIC PRESSURE, SURFACE TENSION

Values in parentheses are ranges, estimate "c" (cf. Introduction).

Species	Property	Plasma or Serum	Reference
(A)	(B)	(C)	(D)
Crab			
1 Callinectes sapidus	Density	1.030	2
2 Carcinus maenas	Colloid osmotic pressure	(3.2-4.0) cm H_2O	1
3 Dromia vulgaris	Colloid osmotic pressure	(3.1-3.6) cm H_2O	1
4 Eriphia spinifrons	Colloid osmotic pressure	(3.1-4.3) cm H_2O	1
5 Libinia dubia	Density	1.027	2
6 Maja squinado	Colloid osmotic pressure	(3.4-3.8) cm H_2O	1
7	Density	(1.034-1.048)	3
8	Surface tension	(67.37-69.50) dynes/cm	3
9 Ocypode albicans	Density	1.036	2
10 Portunus corrugatus	Colloid osmotic pressure	(3.3-4.3) cm H_2O	1
11 Uca pugnax	Density	1.034	2
12 Xantho rivulosus	Colloid osmotic pressure	4.3	1
13 Lobster (Palinurus vulgaris)	Density	(1.041-1.052)	3
14	Surface tension	(72.58-72.87) dynes/cm	

Contributors: (a) Redmond, James R., (b) Travis, Dorothy F.

References: [1] Florkin, M. 1949. Biochemical evolution. Academic Press, New York. p. 157. [2] George, W. C., and J. Nichols. 1948. J. Morph. 83:425. [3] Zunz, E. 1933. Bull. Acad. Belgique 19:1107.

Part IV: ELECTROLYTES

Values in parentheses are ranges, estimate "c" (cf. Introduction).

Species	Stage	Constituent	Plasma or Serum	Reference
(A)	(B)	(C)	(D)	(E)
Cirripedia				
1 Balanus aquilla		Carbon dioxide	12.2 vol %	11
Isopoda				
2 Ligia exotica	Intermolt	Calcium	(0.97-1.10) mg/ml	18, 19
3	Anterior premolt	Calcium	(1.3-1.6) mg/ml	
4	Postmolt	Calcium	(1.3-1.7) mg/ml	
5 Mesidotea entomon		Calcium	0.50 mg/ml	7
6		Chloride	7.30 mg/ml	
7		Magnesium	0.28 mg/ml	
8		Phosphorus, total	0.04 mg/ml	
9		Potassium	0.24 mg/ml	
10		Sodium	4.64 mg/ml	
11		Sulfur, total	0.23 mg/ml	
Decapoda				
Crab				
12 Arenaeus cribarius		Calcium	0.42 mg/ml	27
13		Magnesium	0.14 mg/ml	
14		Potassium	0.45 mg/ml	
15		Sodium	9.80 mg/ml	
16 Callinectes danae		Calcium	0.27 mg/ml	27
17		Magnesium	0.21 mg/ml	27
18		Phosphorus, total	(0.065-0.075) mg/ml	22
19		Potassium	0.55 mg/ml	27
20		Sodium	13.01 mg/ml	27
21 C. hastatus		Calcium	0.79 mg/ml	9
22		Chloride	17.02 mg/ml	
23		Magnesium	0.23 mg/ml	
24		Potassium	0.53 mg/ml	
25		Sodium	10.58 mg/ml	
26		Sulfate	0.91 mg/ml	
27 C. sapidus		Oxygen	0.84 vol % at 21-24°C[1]	23
28 Cancer borealis		Calcium	0.46 mg/ml	9
29		Chloride	16.99 mg/ml	9
30		Copper	(0.027-0.054) mg/ml	1
31		Magnesium	0.53 mg/ml	9
32		Potassium	1.80 mg/ml	9
33		Sodium	10.58 mg/ml	9
34		Sulfate	1.50 mg/ml	9
35	Intermolt	Calcium	1.52 mEq/100 ml (in 100% sea water)	32, 33
36			1.54 mEq/100 ml (in 87% sea water)	
37			1.55 mEq/100 ml (in 75% sea water)	
38			0.99 mEq/100 ml (in 50% sea water)	
39			0.88 mEq/100 ml (in 40% sea water)	
40		Chloride	67.0 mEq/100 ml (in 100% sea water)	32, 33
41			46.0 mEq/100 ml (in 87% sea water)	
42			35.6 mEq/100 ml (in 75% sea water)	
43			33.0 mEq/100 ml (in 50% sea water)	
44			23.0 mEq/100 ml (in 40% sea water)	
45		Magnesium	2.5 mEq/100 ml (in 100% sea water)	32, 33
46			2.0 mEq/100 ml (in 87% sea water)	
47			2.1 mEq/100 ml (in 75% sea water)	
48			1.5 mEq/100 ml (in 50% sea water)	
49			1.0 mEq/100 ml (in 40% sea water)	
50		Potassium	2.00 mEq/100 ml (in 100% sea water)	32, 33
51			1.61 mEq/100 ml (in 87% sea water)	
52			1.57 mEq/100 ml (in 75% sea water)	

/1/ Air equilibrated.

	Species	Stage	Constituent	Plasma or Serum	Reference
	(A)	(B)	(C)	(D)	(E)
	Decapoda (continued)				
	Crab (continued)				
53	Cancer borealis (concluded)	Intermolt (con-cluded)	Potassium (con-cluded)	1.36 mEq/100 ml (in 50% sea water)	32, 33
54				1.06 mEq/100 ml (in 40% sea water)	
55			Sodium	54.62 mEq/100 ml (in 100% sea water)	32, 33
56				41.74 mEq/100 ml (in 87% sea water)	
57				41.74 mEq/100 ml (in 75% sea water)	
58				31.31 mEq/100 ml (in 50% sea water)	
59				22.96 mEq/100 ml (in 40% sea water)	
60	C. irroratus		Oxygen	(0.78-1.24) vol % at 21-24°C[1]	23
61	C. magister		Carbon dioxide	(18.0-27.9) vol %	11
62	C. pagurus[2]	Intermolt	Calcium	0.55 mg/g H_2O	26
63			Chloride	18.08 mg/g H_2O	26
64			Copper	(0.06-0.08) mg/ml	16, 26
65			Magnesium	0.66 mg/g H_2O	26
66			Potassium	0.47 mg/g H_2O	26
67			Sodium	11.55 mg/g H_2O	26
68			Sulfate	2.31 mg/g H_2O	26
69	C. productus		Carbon dioxide	(20.3-24.2) vol %	11
70	Carcinus maenas		Copper	0.09 mg/ml	16
71		Intermolt	Calcium	0.50 mg/ml	5
72				0.49 mg/ml	35
73				0.67 mg/ml	14
74				(0.43-0.65) mg/ml	33
75			Magnesium	0.65 mg/ml	5
76				0.43 mg/ml	35
77			Potassium	0.29 mg/ml	5
78				0.44 mg/ml	35
79				0.66 mg/ml	14
80			Sodium	13.50 mg/ml	14
81				13.27 mg/ml	5
82				11.20 mg/ml	35
83		Postmolt	Calcium	(0.21-0.35) mg/ml	33
84	Echidnocerus formatus		Carbon dioxide	(20.0-22.5) vol %	11
85	Epialtus productus		Carbon dioxide	10.2 vol %	11
86	Eriocheir sinensis	Intermolt	Calcium	0.35 mg/ml	30
87				0.57 mg/ml	5
88			Chloride	19.12 mg/ml	30
89			Magnesium	0.49 mg/ml	30
90			Potassium	0.45 mg/ml	30
91				0.39 mg/ml	5
92			Sodium	11.30 mg/ml	5
93	Hemigrapsus nudus		Carbon dioxide	24.2 vol %	11
94	Lithodes maia[3]	Intermolt	Calcium	0.50 mg/g H_2O	26
95			Chloride	19.03 mg/g H_2O	
96			Magnesium	1.27 mg/g H_2O	
97			Potassium	0.49 mg/g H_2O	
98			Sodium	10.96 mg/g H_2O	
99			Sulfate	2.41 mg/g H_2O	
100	Loxorhynchus grandis		Carbon dioxide	(16.2-20.6) vol % at 15°C	24
101			Oxygen	(0.15-0.53) vol % at 14°C[4]	
102				(0.90-1.44) vol % at 24-25°C[1]	
103	Maja squinado[3]		Carbon dioxide	(4.9-12.3) vol % at 15°C	21
104				(10.83-27.20) vol % at 16-17°C	36
105			Copper	0.035 mg/ml	16
106			Oxygen	(0.84-1.13) vol % at 16-19°C[1]	36
107				0.44 vol % at 21°C[4]	
108		Intermolt	Calcium	0.56 mg/g H_2O	26
109				0.62 mg/ml	15

/1/ Air equilibrated. /2/ Water content of plasma or serum = 963 mg/ml. /3/ Water content of plasma or serum = 954 mg/ml. /4/ Sampled directly from body.

Part IV: ELECTROLYTES (Continued)

Species	Stage	Constituent	Plasma or Serum	Reference
(A)	(B)	(C)	(D)	(E)
Decapoda (continued)				
Crab (concluded)				
110 Maja squinado[3] (concluded)	Intermolt (concluded)	Chloride	20.19 mg/g H_2O	26
111		Magnesium	1.10 mg/g H_2O	26
112		Phosphorus		15
112		Total P	0.008 mg/ml	
113		Inorganic P	0.007 mg/ml	
114		Potassium	0.50 mg/g H_2O	26
115			0.50 mg/ml	15
116		Sodium	11.49 mg/g H_2O	26
117			11.53 mg/ml	15
118		Sulfate	1.43 mg/g H_2O	26
119		Sulfur, total	0.916 mg/ml	6
120	Premolt	Calcium	0.43 mg/ml	15
121		Chloride	31.17 mg/ml	
122		Phosphorus		
122		Total P	0.024 mg/ml	
123		Inorganic P	0.009 mg/ml	
124		Potassium	0.52 mg/ml	
125		Sodium	11.32 mg/ml	
126	Molt	Calcium	0.60 mg/ml	15
127		Chloride	28.85 mg/ml	
128		Potassium	0.47 mg/ml	
129		Sodium	7.62 mg/ml	
130	Postmolt	Calcium	0.40 mg/ml	15
131		Chloride	31.85 mg/ml	
132		Phosphorus		
132		Total P	0.020 mg/ml	
133		Inorganic P	0.010 mg/ml	
134		Potassium	0.53 mg/ml	
135		Sodium	11.13 mg/ml	
136 Pachygrapsus crassipes		Calcium	0.54 mg/ml	28
137		Chloride	6.91 mg/ml	
138		Magnesium	0.24 mg/ml	
139		Potassium	0.36 mg/ml	
140		Sodium	10.60 mg/ml	
141	Intermolt + premolt	Carbon dioxide	31.9 vol %	2
142	Postmolt	Carbon dioxide	40.4 vol %	2
143 Portunus spinimanus		Calcium	0.58 mg/ml	27
144		Magnesium	0.23 mg/ml	
145		Potassium	0.40 mg/ml	
146		Sodium	13.23 mg/ml	
147 Sesarma dehaani	Intermolt	Calcium	0.75 mg/ml	20
148	Premolt	Calcium	1.04 mg/ml	
149	Postmolt	Calcium	0.66 mg/ml	
150 S. haematocheir	Intermolt	Calcium	0.88 mg/ml	20
151	Premolt	Calcium	1.63 mg/ml	
152	Postmolt	Calcium	0.70 mg/ml	
153 Telphusa fluviatilis	Intermolt	Calcium	0.72 mg/ml	14
154		Potassium	0.33 mg/ml	
155		Sodium	7.75 mg/ml	
Crayfish				
156 Astacus fluviatilis		Copper	0.07 mg/ml	16
157		Phosphorus, inorganic	0.009 mg/ml	4
158		Potassium	0.20 mg/ml	29
159	Intermolt	Calcium	0.48 mg/ml	8
160			0.42 mg/ml	29
161			(0.36-0.43) mg/ml	12, 13

/3/ Water content of plasma or serum = 954 mg/ml.

Part IV: ELECTROLYTES (Continued)

	Species	Stage	Constituent	Plasma or Serum	Reference
	(A)	(B)	(C)	(D)	(E)
	Decapoda (continued)				
162	Crayfish (concluded) Astacus fluviatilis (concluded)	Intermolt (con-cluded)	Carbon dioxide	(36.4-37.2) vol %	12, 13
163			Chloride	6.21 mg/ml	8
164				6.91 mg/ml	29
165				(60-70) mg/ml	13
166			Magnesium	0.06 mg/ml	8, 29
167				(0.14-0.17) mg/ml	13
168			Phosphorus, total	(0.15-0.17) mg/ml	13
169			Potassium	0.11 mg/ml	8
170				(0.02-0.03) mg/ml	13
171			Sodium	3.49 mg/ml	8
172				(1.6-1.7) mg/ml	13
173			Sulfur, non-protein	0.201 mg/ml	29
174		Premolt	Calcium	(0.52-0.60) mg/ml	12, 13
175			Carbon dioxide	(64.9-67.2) vol %	12, 13
176			Chloride	60 mg/ml	13
177			Magnesium	0.13 mg/ml	13
178			Phosphorus, total	(0.10-0.21) mg/ml	13
179			Potassium	0.02 mg/ml	13
180			Sodium	1.4 mg/ml	13
181		Postmolt	Calcium	(0.48-0.56) mg/ml	12, 13
182			Carbon dioxide	(44.3-48.1) vol %	12, 13
183			Chloride	(40-50) mg/ml	13
184			Magnesium	(0.15-0.17) mg/ml	13
185			Phosphorus, total	(0.10-0.12) mg/ml	13
186			Potassium	Trace	13
187			Sodium	1.3 mg/ml	13
188	A. trowbridgii		Calcium	0.47 mg/ml	34
189		Intermolt	Magnesium	0.07 mg/ml	
190			Potassium	0.19 mg/ml	
191	Cambarus clarkii		Calcium	0.49 mg/ml	28, 34
192			Magnesium	0.06 mg/ml	28, 34
193			Phosphorus, inorganic	0.005 mg/ml	17
194			Potassium	0.18 mg/ml	34
195				0.23 mg/ml	28
196			Sodium	4.20 mg/ml	34
197				3.69 mg/ml	28
198	Potamobius astacus	Intermolt	Calcium	0.56 mg/ml	14
199			Potassium	0.19 mg/ml	
200			Sodium	4.9 mg/ml	
201	Lobster Homarus americanus		Calcium	0.97 mg/ml	10
202				0.76 mg/ml	9
203			Carbon dioxide	(5.19-6.04) vol % at 15°C	24
204			Chloride	15.75 mg/ml	10
205				17.55 mg/ml	9
206			Copper	(0.029-0.052) mg/ml	1
207			Magnesium	0.20 mg/ml	10
208				0.22 mg/ml	9
209			Oxygen	(0.17-0.46) vol % at 14°C[4]	24
210				(1.23-1.39) vol % at 23-25°C[1]	
211			Potassium	0.54 mg/ml	10
212				0.35 mg/ml	9
213			Sodium	9.87 mg/ml	10
214				10.67 mg/ml	9
215			Sulfate	0.85 mg/ml	9
216			Sulfur, non-protein	0.134 mg/ml	10

/1/ Air equilibrated.   /4/ Sampled directly from body.

Part IV: ELECTROLYTES (Continued)

	Species	Stage	Constituent	Plasma or Serum	Reference
	(A)	(B)	(C)	(D)	(E)
	Decapoda (concluded)				
	Lobster (concluded)				
217	Homarus vulgaris[5]	Intermolt	Calcium	0.59 mg/g H_2O	26
218			Chloride	18.26 mg/g H_2O	26
219			Copper	0.04 mg/ml	25
220			Magnesium	0.17 mg/g H_2O	26
221			Potassium	0.55 mg/g H_2O	26
222			Sodium	11.71 mg/g H_2O	26
223			Sulfate	0.76 mg/g H_2O	26
224	Nephrops norvegicus[6]	Intermolt	Calcium	0.56 mg/g H_2O	26
225			Chloride	18.40 mg/g H_2O	
226			Magnesium	0.22 mg/g H_2O	
227			Potassium	0.30 mg/g H_2O	
228			Sodium	11.90 mg/g H_2O	
229			Sulfate	1.78 mg/g H_2O	
230	Palinurus vulgaris[7]		Carbon dioxide	5.4 vol % at 15°C	21
231				6.35 vol % at 16°C	36
232			Copper	0.10 mg/ml	16
233			Oxygen	1.48 vol % at 16°C	36
234		Intermolt	Calcium	0.54 mg/g H_2O	26
235			Chloride	19.74 mg/g H_2O	
236			Magnesium	0.40 mg/g H_2O	
237			Potassium	0.40 mg/g H_2O	
238			Sodium	12.52 mg/g H_2O	
239			Sulfate	2.05 mg/g H_2O	
240	Panulirus argus	Intermolt	Calcium	0.46 mg/ml	31
241			Phosphorus Total P	0.061 mg/ml	
242			Inorganic P	0.007 mg/ml	
243		Premolt	Calcium	0.82 mg/ml	
			Phosphorus		
244			Total P	0.092 mg/ml	
245			Inorganic P	0.006 mg/ml	
246		Postmolt	Calcium	0.46 mg/ml	
			Phosphorus		
247			Total P	0.045 mg/ml	
248			Inorganic P	0.006 mg/ml	
249	P. interruptus		Calcium	0.78 mg/ml	28
250			Carbon dioxide	(7.8-12.5) vol % at 15°C	24
251			Magnesium	0.25 mg/ml	28
252			Oxygen	(0.12-1.37) vol % at 10-11°C[4]	24
253				(1.30-2.80) vol % at 24-26°C[1]	
254			Potassium	0.47 mg/ml	28
255			Sodium	12.21 mg/ml	28
256	P. longipes		Copper	(0.043-0.208) mg/ml	3
257			Nickel	(Trace-0.00005) mg/ml	
258	Shrimp (Upogebia pugettensis)		Carbon dioxide	10.2 vol %	11
	Stomatopoda				
259	Squilla mantis		Copper	0.061 mg/ml	16

/1/ Air equilibrated. /4/ Sampled directly from body. /5/ Water content of plasma or serum = 971 mg/ml.
/6/ Water content of plasma or serum = 961 mg/ml. /7/ Water content of plasma or serum = 945 mg/ml.

Contributors: (a) Redmond, James R., (b) Fingerman, Milton, (c) Travis, Dorothy F.

References: [1] Allison, J. B., and W. H. Cole. 1940. J. Biol. Chem. 135:259. [2] Baumberger, J. P., and J. M. D. Olmsted. 1928. Physiol. Zool. 1:531. [3] Beck, A. B., and K. Sheard. 1949. Austral J. Exp. Biol. 27:307.

[4] Bernard, A. 1933. C. rend. Soc. biol. 112:880. [5] Bethe, A., and E. Berger. 1931. Pflügers Arch. 227:571. [6] Bialaszewicz, K. 1932. Arch. internat. physiol., Liége 35:98. [7] Bogucki, M. 1932. Ibid. 35:197. [8] Bogucki, M. 1934. Ibid. 38:172. [9] Cole, W. H. 1940. J. Gen. Physiol. 23:575. [10] Cole, W. H., and L. A. Kazalski. 1939. Bull. Mount Desert Island Biol. Lab. 41:40. [11] Collip, J. B. 1920. J. Biol. Chem. 44:329. [12] Damboviceanu, A. 1930. C. rend. Soc. biol. 105:913. [13] Damboviceanu, A. 1932. Arch. roumain. path., Par. 5:239. [14] Drilhon, A. 1934. Bull. Inst. Oceanogr. Monaco 644:1. [15] Drilhon, A. 1935. Ann. physiol., Par. 11:301. [16] Elvehjem, C. A. 1935. Physiol. Rev. 15:471. [17] Lienemann, L. J. 1938. J. Cellul. Physiol. 11:149. [18] Numanoi, H. 1934. J. Fac. Sc. Univ. Tokyo 3:351. [19] Numanoi, H. 1937. Jap. J. Zool. 7:241. [20] Numanoi, H. 1939. Ibid. 8:357. [21] Parsons, T. R., and W. Parsons. 1923. J. Gen. Physiol. 6:153. [22] Pereira, R. S. 1944. Bol. fac. filosof. ciênc. let., Univ. São Paulo, Zool. 8:147. [23] Redfield, A. C., T. Coolidge, and A. L. Hurd. 1926. J. Biol. Chem. 69:475. [24] Redmond, J. R. 1955. J. Cellul. Physiol. 46:209. [25] Robertson, J. D. 1939. J. Exp. Biol., Lond. 16:387. [26] Robertson, J. D. 1949. Ibid. 26:182. [27] Sawaya, P., and R. S. Pereira. 1946. Bol. fac. filosof. ciênc. let., Univ. São Paulo, Zool. 11:383. [28] Schlatter, M. L. 1941. J. Cellul. Physiol. 17:259. [29] Schleiper, C. 1935. Biol. Rev. Cambridge Philos. Soc. 10:334. [30] Scholles, W. 1933. Zschr. vergl. Physiol. 19:522. [31] Travis, D. F. 1955. Biol. Bull. 109:484. [32] Trevisani, G. A. 1956. M. S. Thesis. University of New Hampshire. [33] Trevisani, G. A. 1958. Ph. D. Thesis. University of New Hampshire. [34] Van Harreveld, A. 1936. Proc. Soc. Exp. Biol., N. Y. 34:428. [35] Webb, D. A. 1940. Proc. R. Soc., Lond., Ser. B, 129:107. [36] Winterstein, H. 1909. Biochem. Zschr. 19:384.

Part V: NITROGENOUS SUBSTANCES

Values in parentheses are ranges, estimate "c" (cf. Introduction).

Species	Stage	Constituent	Plasma or Serum mg/ml	Reference
(A)	(B)	(C)	(D)	(E)
Cirripedia				
1 Pollicipes cornucopia		Protein	2	8
Decapoda				
Crab				
2 Callinectes sp		Uric acid	$(0-0.034)^1$	14
3		Nitrogen, non-protein	$0.237(0.227-0.247)^2$	
4 C. sapidus		Protein	43.9(18.3-120.0)	12
5 Cancer borealis		Hemocyanin	(15.1-29.8)	1
		Nitrogen		
6		Total N	(3.29-6.72)	
7		Protein N	4.43(3.01-6.38)	
8		Non-protein N	0.302(0.201 0.337)	
9 C. irroratus		Protein	53.9(17.5-114.5)	12
10 C. magister		Protein	44.5(11.6-137.5)	12
11 C. pagurus		Protein	(34.94-56.69)	8, 16, 19
12 Carcinus maenas	Intermolt	Protein	37.50	5
13			(43-72)	23
14			(40.8-83.2)	18
15	Postmolt	Protein	(8.2-17.1)	18
16 Dromia vulgaris	Intermolt	Protein	37	21
17 Eriphia spinifrons		Protein	(60.37-88.58)	13
18		Nitrogen, total	11.49(9.66-13.21)	

/1/ Values declined very rapidly with starvation. /2/ Fresh from sea.

Part V: NITROGENOUS SUBSTANCES (Continued)

	Species	Stage	Constituent	Plasma or Serum mg/ml	Reference
	(A)	(B)	(C)	(D)	(E)
	Decapoda (continued)				
	Crab (concluded)				
19	Eupagurus bernhardus		Protein	69	21
20	E. prideauxi		Protein	80	21
21	Hyas araneus		Protein	29	21
22	Libinia sp		Uric acid	(0.010-0.023)	14
23			Nitrogen, non-protein	0.266(0.195-0.330)[2]	
24	L. emarginata		Protein	41.4(7.3-72.5)	12
25	Lithodes maia	Intermolt	Protein	38	20
26	Maja squinado	Intermolt	Protein	(41-53)	21
27				45.0	6
28		Premolt	Protein	36.5	6
29		Postmolt	Protein	12.1	6
30			Protein	(6.81-51.56)	4, 16
31	Pachygrapsus marmoratus	Intermolt	Protein	35	21
32	Portunus depurator	Intermolt	Protein	37	21
33	P. puber	Intermolt	Protein	54	21
34	Telphusa fluviatilis	Intermolt	Protein	45.0	5
	Crayfish				
35	Astacus sp		Ammonia	0.19	9
36	A. fluviatilis		Protein	(33.8-63.2)	4, 13, 15
37			Nitrogen, total	7.51(4.97-11.09)	13
38		Intermolt	Protein	45.0	3
39			Hemocyanin	30.7	
40			Uric acid	(0.20-0.24)	
			Nitrogen		
41			Non-protein N	(0.6-0.8)	
42			Urea N	(0.68-0.70)	
43		Premolt	Protein	65.0	3
44			Hemocyanin	25.0	
45			Uric acid	0.31	
			Nitrogen		
46			Non-protein N	1.6	
47			Urea N	0.79	
48		Postmolt	Protein	60.0	3
49			Hemocyanin	12.6	
50	Cherax albidus		Protein	54.0	17
51	C. destructor		Protein	52.5	17
52	Euastacus armatus		Protein	30.5	17
53	E. elongatus		Protein	69.5	17
54	E. nobilis		Protein	39	17
55	Orconectes immunis		Protein	87	17
56	O. nais		Protein	80	17
57	O. neglectus		Protein	30	17
58	O. virilis		Protein	56.5	17
59	Potamobius astacus	Intermolt	Protein	47.3	5
60	Procambarus simulans		Protein	25	17
	Lobster				
61	Homarus sp		Ammonia	(0.16-0.18)	10
62			Uric acid	(0.020-0.025)	14
63			Nitrogen, non-protein	0.130	14
64	H. americanus		Protein	42.8(22-102)	12, 17
			Nitrogen		1
65			Total N	(3.00-5.73)	
66			Protein N	3.82(2.74-5.31)	
67			Non-protein N	0.221(0.107-0.309)	
68			Hemocyanin	(17.1-31.2)	1
69	H. vulgaris		Protein	22.6	19

/2/ Fresh from sea.

Part V: NITROGENOUS SUBSTANCES (Concluded)

	Species	Stage	Constituent	Plasma or Serum mg/ml	Reference
	(A)	(B)	(C)	(D)	(E)
	Decapoda (concluded)				
	Lobster (concluded) Homarus vulgaris (concluded)		Amino acids		
70			Total	<0.1	11
71			Alanine	0.087	2
72			Arginine	0.016	2
73			Aspartic acid	0.07	2
74			Glutamic acid	0.035	2
75			Glycine	0.24	2
76			Histidine	0.035	2
77			Leucine	0.042	2
78			Lysine	0.021	2
79			Methionine	0	2
80			Phenylalanine	0.002	2
81			Proline	0.06	2
82			Threonine	0	2
83			Tyrosine	0.033	2
84			Valine	0	2
85	Nephrops norvegicus	Intermolt	Protein	33	20
86	Palinurus vulgaris		Amino acids, total	<0.1	7
87			Uric acid	0.01	
			Nitrogen		
88			Non-protein N	0.265	
89			Purine N	0.21	
90			Urea N	0.055	
91		Intermolt	Protein	38	20
92	Panulirus argus	Intermolt	Protein	45.0	22
93		Premolt	Protein	63.0	
94		Postmolt	Protein	31.0	
	Stomatopoda				
95	Squilla mantis	Intermolt	Protein	65	21

Contributors: (a) Redmond, James R., (b) Travis, Dorothy F.

References: [1] Allison, J. B., and W. H. Cole. 1940. J. Biol. Chem. 135:259. [2] Camien, M. N., H. Sarlet, G. Duchâteau, and M. Florkin. 1951. Ibid. 193:881. [3] Dambolviceanu, A. 1932. Arch. roumain. path., Par. 5:239. [4] Delaunay, H. 1913. C. rend. Soc. biol. 73:492. [5] Drilhon, A. 1934. Bull. Inst. Oceanogr. Monaco 644:1. [6] Drilhon, A. 1935. Ann. physiol., Par. 11:301. [7] Florkin, M. 1949. Biochemical evolution. Academic Press, New York. p. 157. [8] Florkin, M., and H. F. Blum. 1934. Arch. internat. physiol., Liége 38:353. [9] Florkin, M., and G. Frappez. 1940. Ibid. 50:197. [10] Florkin, M., and H. Renwort. 1939. Ibid. 49:127. [11] Kermack, W. O., H. Lees, and J. D. Wood. 1955. Biochem. J., Lond. 60:424. [12] Leone, C. A. 1953. Science 118:295. [13] Lustig, B., and T. Ernst. 1937. Biochem. Zschr. 289:365. [14] Morgulis, S. 1922. J. Biol. Chem. 50:Lii. [15] Pinhey, K. G. 1930. J. Exp. Biol., Lond. 7:19. [16] Pora, E. A. 1936. Bull. Inst. Oceanogr. Monaco 689:1. [17] Pryor, C. W., and C. A. Leone. 1952. Biol. Bull. 103:433. [18] Robertson, J. D. 1937. Proc. R. Soc., Lond., Ser. B, 124:162. [19] Robertson, J. D. 1939. J. Exp. Biol., Lond. 16:387. [20] Robertson, J. D. 1949. Ibid. 26:182. [21] Robertson, J. D. 1953. Ibid. 30:277. [22] Travis, D. F. 1955. Biol. Bull. 109:484. [23] Webb, D. A. 1940. Proc. R. Soc., Lond., Ser. B, 129:107.

Part VI: LIPIDS, CARBOHYDRATES, HORMONES

Values in parentheses are ranges, estimate "c" (cf. Introduction).

	Species	Stage	Constituent	Plasma or Serum mg/ml	Reference
	(A)	(B)	(C)	(D)	(E)
	Crab				
1	Callinectes sp		Sugar (as glucose)	(6.45-18.2)[1]	6
2				(1.25-1.38)[2]	
3	C. sapidus	Intermolt	Sugar	0.092	4
4	Cancer pagurus		Sugar (as glucose)	2.2	7
5	Carcinus maenas		Sugar (as glucose)	(0.75-2.60)	2
6	Libinia sp		Sugar (as glucose)	(2.5-4.5)	6
7	L. emarginata	Intermolt	Sugar	0.020	5
8	Maja squinado		Sugar (as glucose)	(0.7-0.9)	2
	Crayfish				
9	Astacus fluviatilis	Intermolt	Lipids, total	5.3	1
10			Fatty acids	0.23	
11			Sterols	0.52	
12			Sugar	(1.6-2.0)	
13		Premolt	Lipids, total	8.4	1
14			Fatty acids	0.90	
15			Sterols	1.84	
16		Postmolt	Lipids, total	2.9	1
17			Fatty acids	0.43	
18			Sterols	1.21	
19	A. trowbridgii	Intermolt	Sugar	(0.16-0.20)	4
	Lobster				
20	Homarus sp		Sugar (as glucose)	(1.9-2.6)	6
21	H. vulgaris		Sugar (as glucose)	(1.0-2.0)	2, 3
22	Palinurus vulgaris		Sugar (as glucose)	(0.75-1.17)	2
23	Panulirus japonicus	Intermolt	Sugar	0.24	8
24	P. penicillatus	Intermolt	Sugar	0.23	8

/1/ Fresh from sea. /2/ Starved for 2 days.

Contributors: (a) Travis, Dorothy F., (b) Redmond, James R.

References: [1] Damboviceanu, A. 1932. Arch. roumain. path., Par. 5:239. [2] Florkin, M. 1937. Bull. Soc. chim. biol., Par. 19:990. [3] Kermack, W. O., H. Lees, and J. D. Wood. 1955. Biochem. J., Lond. 60:424. [4] Kleinholz, L. H., V. J. Havel, and R. Reichert. 1950. Biol. Bull. 99:454. [5] Kleinholz, L. H., and B. C. Little. 1949. Ibid. 96:218. [6] Morgulis, S. 1922. J. Biol. Chem. 50:Lii. [7] Roche, J., and C. Dumazert. 1935. C. rend. Soc. biol. 120:1225. [8] Scheer, B. T., and M. A. R. Scheer. 1951. Physiol. comp. oecol., Gravenh. 2:198.

101. PHYSICAL PROPERTIES AND CHEMICAL COMPOSITION OF HEMOLYMPH: MOLLUSKS

Part I: VOLUME

Volume is percent wet weight without shell, unless otherwise specified. Hemolymph samples from heart, aorta, or hemocoele; values read directly from diluted hemolymph.

	Species	No. of Subjects	Method	Volume	Reference
	(A)	(B)	(C)	(D)	(E)
	Plactophora				
1	Cryptochiton stelleri	15	Inulin	43.8	1
	Gastropoda				
2	Achatina fulica	8	Inulin	40.3	1
3	Aplysia californicus	8	Inulin	79.3	1
4	Archidoris sp	6	Inulin	65.5	1
5	Arion ater	12	Inulin	36.6	1
	Pelecypoda				
6	Lampsilis ventricosa and Amblema costata	25	T-1824	8.0[1]	2
7	Margaritana margaritifera	13	T-1824 or inulin	49.0	1
8	Mytilus californicus	10	Inulin	50.8	1
	Cephalopoda				
9	Octopus honkongensis	13	T-1824 or HgS	5.8	1

/1/ ml/100 g body weight.

Contributor: Reynolds, Monica

References: [1] Martin, A. W., F. M. Harrison, M. J. Huston, and D. M. Stewart. 1958. J. Exp. Biol., Lond. 35:260. [2] Prosser, C. L., and S. J. F. Weinstein. 1950. Physiol. Zool. 23:113.

Part II: FREEZING POINT DEPRESSION AND CHEMICAL CONSTITUENTS

The absolute concentration of inorganic ions in hemolymph varies according to the composition of the aquatic medium. It is therefore desirable to express ionic concentration as relative to osmotic pressure, freezing point depression, or molarity of the aquatic medium. Values for columns F-J are given as weight units relative to chloride designated as 100. Where the absolute value for chloride is given in column E, absolute values for the other ions can be calculated.

	Species or Water	Protein mg/ml	Water Content mg/ml	Freezing Point Depression, °C	Chloride	Ca	Mg	K	Na	SO$_4$	Reference
	(A)	(B)	(C)	(D)	(E)	(F)	(G)	(H)	(I)	(J)	(K)
	Land Pulmonate Gastropoda										
1	Helix pomatia Active, during summer	24.4			1.99 mg/ml	8.60	0.96	9.25	68.9		7
2	Hibernating	33.5			2.80 mg/ml	9.35	1.75	6.50	56.4		
	Fresh-water Pulmonate Gastropoda										
3	Lymnaea stagnalis				1.51 mg/ml	8.11	7.72	7.22	72.6		5

303

Part II: FREEZING POINT DEPRESSION AND CHEMICAL CONSTITUENTS (Continued)

	Species or Water	Protein mg/ml	Water Content mg/ml	Freezing Point Depression, °C	Chloride	Ca	Mg	K	Na	SO$_4$	Reference
			Representative Absolute Values			Relative Weight Unit Cl = 100					
	(A)	(B)	(C)	(D)	(E)	(F)	(G)	(H)	(I)	(J)	(K)
	Marine Prosobranch Gastropoda										
	Sea water[1]		964 at a "chlorinity" of 20^0/00	Approximately 2°C at a "chlorinity" of 20^0/00	20.49 mg/ml at a "chlorinity" of 20^0/00 at temp. of 20°C	2.12	6.69	2.01	55.5	14.0	9, 10
4	Buccinum undatum		966		Cl close to that of surrounding sea water	2.31	7.0	2.88	0.54	12.6	9
5	Neptunea antiqua	24.1	968			2.25	6.8	2.30	55	13.1	9
	Marine Opisthobranch Gastropoda										
6	Aplysia sp			Close to value for Mediterranean (high salinity)	Cl close to that of surrounding sea water	2.25	5.9	2.12	60.7		1
	Sea water[1]		964 at a "chlorinity" of 20^0/00	Approximately 2°C at a "chlorinity" of 20^0/00	20.49 mg/ml at a "chlorinity" of 20^0/00 at temp. of 20°C	2.12	6.69	2.01	55.5	14.0	9, 10
7	Aplysia punctata				Cl close to that of surrounding sea water	2.81	6.2	1.98	58.8	14.7	4
8	Archidoris britannica	0.4	982			2.70	7.2	2.57	55	13.4	10
9	Doris tuberculata					2.64	6.9	3.01	62.5		1
10	Pleurobranchus membranaceus	0.3	980			2.38	6.7	2.36	56	14.3	9
	Fresh-water Pelecypoda										
11	Anodonta cygnea		998		0.37 mg/g H$_2$O	73.3	1.43	3.57			3
12						56.7	2.43	4.32	97.4	40.5	4
13				0.078 ± 0.009	0.415 mg/g H$_2$O	74.2	1.12	4.58	86.3	17.6	8
	Marine Pelecypoda										
14	Mytilus edulis			Variable	Cl close to that of surrounding sea water	2.41	6.15	1.82	53.9		1
15	Ostrea circumpicta		959			2.02	7.28	1.71	56.6	13.4	6
16	Pecten maximus		964			2.82	5.47	2.66	56.9	14.7	4
	Sea water[1]		964 at a "chlorinity" of 20^0/00	Approximately 2°C at a "chlorinity" of 20^0/00	20.49 mg/ml at a "chlorinity" of 20^0/00 at temp. of 20°C	2.12	6.69	2.01	55.5	14.0	9, 10
17	Ensis ensis	4.4	981	Close to value for environmental sea water	Cl close to equilibrium with surrounding sea water	2.30	6.6	3.14	55	12.2	9
18	Mya arenaria	1.3	982			2.26	6.6	2.15	56	14.1	9
19	Mytilus edulis	0.3	984			2.10	6.6	2.70	55	13.6	10
20	M. galloprovincialis	0.8	984			2.29	6.5	2.46	57	17.0	10
21	Ostrea edulis	θ.2	982			2.14	6.9	2.59	55	13.9	10
22	Pecten maximus	2.6	983			2.18	6.5	2.61	55	13.5	9
	Sea water					2.12	6.70	2.00	55.4	14.0	8
23	Mytilus edulis[2]			Isotonic with sea water from freezing point depression 2.09-0.58	When sea water Cl = 21.0 mg/g H$_2$O, hemolymph Cl = 20.78 mg/g H$_2$O	2.43	5.93	2.39	55.5	14.2	8
	Delaware Bay water			1.336	11.31 mg/ml	1.95	6.7	2.56	56.8	13.9	2
24	Venus mercenaria			1.386	13.28 mg/ml	3.24	5.1	1.88	51.2	13.1	2

/1/ The proportions of ions are quite constant, but the absolute concentrations vary. Values in columns C-E are for the arbitrary "chlorinity" of 20 parts per thousand (20^0/00). /2/ Values recalculated.

Part II: FREEZING POINT DEPRESSION AND CHEMICAL CONSTITUENTS (Concluded)

Species or Water	Representative Absolute Values				Relative Weight Unit Cl = 100					Reference
	Protein mg/ml	Water Content mg/ml	Freezing Point Depression, °C	Chloride	Ca	Mg	K	Na	SO$_4$	
(A)	(B)	(C)	(D)	(E)	(F)	(G)	(H)	(I)	(J)	(K)
Marine Pelecypoda (concluded)										
25 Maine sea water			1.759	17.37 mg/ml	2.25	4.7	1.90	60.9	14.1	2
Venus mercenaria			1.760	18.25 mg/ml	2.08	3.35	1.59	55.5	13.4	2
Marine Cephalopoda										
Sea water[1]		964 at a "chlorinity" of 20^0/00	Approximately 2°C at a "chlorinity" of 20^0/00	20.49 mg/ml at a "chlorinity" of 20^0/00 at temp. of 20°C	2.12	6.69	2.01	55.5	14.0	9, 10
26 Eledone cirrosa	105.0	896			2.46	7.0	3.07	54	10.5	9
27				16.8 mg/ml	2.80	8.3	2.80	58.2	24.6	4
28 Loligo forbesi	149.7	866			2.44	6.8	4.35	52	3.9	9
29 Sepia officinalis	67.6	925			2.24		3.54	54	10.9	9
30	109.0	892			2.22	6.7	4.10	51	2.9	10
31		955		18.5 mg/ml	2.95	6.75	2.43	56.6	15.0	4

/1/ The proportions of ions are quite constant, but the absolute concentrations vary. Values in columns C-E are for the arbitrary "chlorinity" of 20 parts per thousand (20^0/00).

Contributor: Smith, Ralph I.

References: [1] Bethe, A., and E. Berger. 1931. Pflügers Arch. 227:571. [2] Cole, W. H. 1940. J. Gen. Physiol. 23:575. [3] Florkin, M., and G. Duchâteau. 1948. Physiol. comp. oecol., Gravenh. 1:29. [4] Hayes, F. R., and D. Pelluet. 1947. J. Marine Biol. Ass. U. K. 26:580. [5] Huf, E. 1934. Pflügers Arch. 235:655. [6] Kumano, M. 1929. Sc. Rep. Tôhoku Univ., Ser. 4, 4:281. [7] Lustig, B., T. Ernst, and E. Reuss. 1937. Biochem. Zschr. 290:95. [8] Potts, W. T. W. 1954. J. Exp. Biol., Lond. 31:376. [9] Robertson, J. D. 1949. Ibid. 26:182. [10] Robertson, J. D. 1953. Ibid. 30:277.

XIV. Lymph

102. PHYSICAL PROPERTIES AND CHEMICAL COMPOSITION OF LYMPH: MAMMALS

Lymph forms part of the extracellular fluid system of the body. Since its basic chemical structure closely resembles that of blood plasma (or serum) and comparisons of the two are so often necessary, data, where available, are given for both lymph and plasma (or serum). For additional information on lymph, consult reference 4, Part I.

Part I: MAN

Values in parentheses are ranges, estimate "c" (cf. Introduction).

	Constituent	No. of Subjects	Thoracic Duct Lymph	Blood Plasma or Serum	Reference
	(A)	(B)	(C)	(D)	(E)
	Electrolytes				
1	Calcium	5	4.2(3.4-5.6) mEq/L	5.0(4.3-5.9) mEq/L	1
2		1	4.4 mEq/L	4.8 mEq/L	3
3	Chloride	5	98(87-103) mEq/L	96(94-98) mEq/L	1
4		1	97 mEq/L	98 mEq/L	3
5	Phosphorus	5	2.4(2.0-3.6) mEq/L	2.5(2.1-3.5) mEq/L	1
6	Inorganic P	1	2.7 mg/100 ml	2.9 mg/100 ml	3
7	Potassium	5	4.7(3.9-5.6) mEq/L	5.0(4.1-5.9) mEq/L	1
8		1	3.3 mEq/L	4.7 mEq/L	3
9	Sodium	5	127(118-132) mEq/L	127(113-135) mEq/L	1
10		1	138 mEq/L	142 mEq/L	3
	Nitrogenous Substances				
11	Protein, total	5	4.89(2.91-7.33) g/100 ml	7.08(5.38-9.40) g/100 ml	1
12		1	(2.80-3.60) g/100 ml	6.0 g/100 ml	2
13		1	5.1 g/100 ml	7.6 g/100 ml	3
14	Albumin	5	2.34(1.50-2.67) g/100 ml	2.86(2.00-3.50) g/100 ml	1
15		1	(1.64-2.45) g/100 ml	3.50 g/100 ml	2
16		1	3.42 g/100 ml	4.30 g/100 ml	3
17	Globulin	5	2.56(1.50-4.80) g/100 ml	4.16(3.10-6.92) g/100 ml	1
18		1	(1.15-1.16) g/100 ml	2.50 g/100 ml	2
19	α_1-	1	0.26 g/100 ml	0.34 g/100 ml	3
20	α_2-	1	0.25 g/100 ml	0.62 g/100 ml	3
21	β_1-	1	0.25 g/100 ml	0.39 g/100 ml	3
22	β_2-	1	0.15 g/100 ml	0.29 g/100 ml	3
23	γ-	1	0.78 g/100 ml	1.46 g/100 ml	3
24	Bilirubin	1	0.8 mg/100 ml	1.0 mg/100 ml	3
25	Creatinine	4	3.0(0.8-8.9) mg/100 ml	3.05(0.8-9.0) mg/100 ml	1
26	Uric acid	5	4.98(1.7-10.8) mg/100 ml	5.12(1.6-10.9) mg/100 ml	1
27		1	4.1 mg/100 ml	4.2 mg/100 ml	3
28	Nitrogen, non-protein	5	46.52(13.4-139.0) mg/100 ml	48.78(15.8-141.0) mg/100 ml	1
29		1	23 mg/100 ml	29 mg/100 ml	3
	Lipids, Carbohydrates				
30	Cholesterol Total	5	71.65(34-106) mg/100 ml	118.6(83-167) mg/100 ml	1
31		1	60 mg/100 ml	207 mg/100 ml	3
32	Free	5	33.76(15-51) mg/100 ml	38.48(27.9-56.0) mg/100 ml	1
33		1	36 mg/100 ml	57 mg/100 ml	3
34	Fat, total	1	1.1 g/100 ml		3
35	Glucose	1	136 mg/100 ml	117 mg/100 ml	1
36		1	140 mg/100 ml	110 mg/100 ml	3
	Enzymes				
37	Aldolase	1	10 units/ml	6 units/ml	3
38	Phosphatase Acid prostatic-	1	0.7 unit/ml	0.3 unit/ml	3
39	Alkaline	1	1.9 units/ml	2.3 units/ml	
40	Transaminase GOT	1	12 units/ml	13 units/ml	3

Part I: MAN (Concluded)

Contributors: (a) Mayerson, H. S., and Wasserman, Karl, (b) Reinhardt, William O., (c) Courtice, F. C.

References: [1] Bierman, H. R., et al. 1953. J. Clin Invest. 32:637. [2] Courtice, F. C., W. J. Simmonds, and A. W. Steinbeck. 1951. Austral. J. Exp. Biol. 29:201. [3] Linder, E., and R. Blomstrand. 1958. Proc. Soc. Exp. Biol., N. Y. 97:653. [4] Yoffey, J. M., and F. C. Courtice. 1956. Lymphatics, lymph and lymphoid tissue. Edward Arnold, London.

Part II: DOG

Values in parentheses are ranges, estimate "b" unless otherwise indicated (cf. Introduction).

	Source of Lymph	Property or Constituent	No. of Sub-jects	Lymph	Blood Plasma or Serum	Refer-ence
	(A)	(B)	(C)	(D)	(E)	(F)
1	Cardiac	Chloride		129 mEq/L	119 mEq/L	7
2	lymphatics	Protein, total	6	3.83(2.94-4.70)^c g/100 ml	5.94(4.67-8.31)^c g/100 ml	6
3		Albumin	6	2.20(1.60-2.60)^c g/100 ml	2.98(2.37-3.56)^c g/100 ml	6
4		Globulin	6	1.63(1.31-2.40)^c g/100 ml	2.96(1.86-5.25)^c g/100 ml	6
5	Cervical	CO_2 pressure	10	40.3(31.3-49.3) mm Hg	46.4(29.4-63.4) mm Hg	11
6	lymphatics	pH	10	7.41(7.33-7.49)	7.34(7.25-7.43)	11
7		Calcium	11	4.9(4.46-5.42)^c mEq/L	5.8(5.42-6.47)^c mEq/L	10
8		Carbon dioxide	10	58.8(46.4-67.2) ml/100 ml	56.8(46.2-67.0) ml/100 ml	11
		Phosphorus				
9		Total P	6	11.8(10.2-13.7)^c mg/100 ml	22.0(18.3-26.1)^c mg/100 ml	10
10		Inorganic P	3	3.3(2.6-4.0)^c mEq/L	3.1(2.4-3.8)^c mEq/L	10
11		Phospholipid P	4	4.1 mg/100 ml	16.0 mg/100 ml	4
12		Potassium		4.2 mEq/L		14
13		Sodium		157 mEq/L	163 mEq/L	7
14				150 mEq/L		14
15		Protein, total	13	3.63(2.09-5.17) g/100 ml	6.25(5.29-7.21) g/100 ml	8
16			16	3.22(1.38-4.57)^c g/100 ml	6.18(5.54-7.23)^c g/100 ml	10
17			4	2.57 g/100 ml	5.65 g/100 ml	4
18		Albumin	13	2.36(1.51-3.21) g/100 ml	3.61(2.71-4.50) g/100 ml	8
19			4	1.72 g/100 ml	3.67 g/100 ml	4
20		Globulin	13	1.26(0.51-2.01) g/100 ml	2.63(1.33-3.96) g/100 ml	8
21			4	0.85 g/100 ml	1.97 g/100 ml	4
22		Amino acids	1	4.84 mg/100 ml	4.90 mg/100 ml	10
23		Creatinine	7	1.40(1.28-1.49)^c mg/100 ml	1.37(1.22-1.54)^c mg/100 ml	10
24		Urea	7	23.5(19.8-33.0)^c mg/100 ml	21.7(17.9-28.0)^c mg/100 ml	10
25		Nitrogen, non-protein	8	37.4(24.2-50.6) mg/100 ml	37.5(26-49) mg/100 ml	8
26			10	34.8(19.8-45.4)^c mg/100 ml	32.6(21.1-46.0)^c mg/100 ml	10
27		Lipids, total	11	305(105-505) mg/100 ml	589(359-819) mg/100 ml	15
28		Cholesterol, total	11	56(26-86) mg/100 ml	137(73-201) mg/100 ml	15
29			4	67 mg/100 ml	258 mg/100 ml	4
30		Fatty acids	4	5.3 mEq/L	14.0 mEq/L	4
31			11	239(69-409) mg/100 ml	438(258-618) mg/100 ml	15
32		Glucose	16	132(107-144)^c mg/100 ml	123(112-143)^c mg/100 ml	10
33			9	101.9(84-125)^c mg/100 ml	103.5(70-135)^c mg/100 ml	13
34		Reducing substances, non-fermentable	10	5.8(3.3-8.3) mg/100 ml	5.5(1.4-9.6) mg/100 ml	12
35	Intestinal	Protein, total	10	2.79(1.17-4.42) g/100 ml	5.67(4.27-7.07) g/100 ml	17
36	lymphatics		10	2.97 g/100 ml	5.98 g/100 ml	21
37			2	3.98 g/100 ml	6.24 g/100 ml	8
38		Albumin	10	1.90(1.50-2.30) g/100 ml	3.47(3.09-3.85) g/100 ml	17
39			10	1.72 g/100 ml	3.18 g/100 ml	21
40			2	2.42 g/100 ml	3.67 g/100 ml	8

Part II: DOG (Continued)

	Source of Lymph	Property or Constituent	No. of Subjects	Lymph	Blood Plasma or Serum	Reference
	(A)	(B)	(C)	(D)	(E)	(F)
41	Intestinal lymphatics (concluded)	Globulin	10	0.64(0.48-0.80) g/100 ml	1.62(1.34-1.90) g/100 ml	17
42			10	1.25 g/100 ml	2.80 g/100 ml	21
43			2	1.56 g/100 ml	2.57 g/100 ml	8
44	Leg lymphatics	Protein, total	8	1.91 g/100 ml	6.46 g/100 ml	8
45			4	1.41 g/100 ml	7.38 g/100 ml	5
46			11	1.70(1.0-2.4) g/100 ml	5.50(4.0-7.0) g/100 ml	3
47		Albumin	8	1.20 g/100 ml	3.62 g/100 ml	8
48		Globulin	8	0.71 g/100 ml	2.84 g/100 ml	8
49		Nitrogen, non-protein		26.7(20-34) mg/100 ml	27.2(19-35) mg/100 ml	3
50			1	37.3 mg/100 ml	36.0 mg/100 ml	8
51		Glucose	10	115(100-130)[c] mg/100 ml	111(100-122)[c] mg/100 ml	12
52	Liver lymphatics	Protein, total	13	4.39(4.07-4.71) mg/100 ml	5.67(5.25-6.09) mg/100 ml	17
53			3	5.32 g/100 ml	6.34 g/100 ml	8
54		Albumin	13	2.74(2.46-3.02) g/100 ml	3.41(3.17-3.65) g/100 ml	17
55			3	2.89 g/100 ml	3.38 g/100 ml	8
56		Globulin	13	1.28(1.10-1.46) g/100 ml	1.8(1.62-1.98) g/100 ml	17
57			3	2.51 g/100 ml	2.96 g/100 ml	8
58	Lung lymphatics	Protein, total	18	3.66(2.81-4.65)[c] g/100 ml		20
59	Renal lymphatics	Protein, total	11	1.84(0.44-4.21)[c] g/100 ml	5.81(5.18-6.88)[c] g/100 ml	19
60		Urea	10	69.7(38.7-164.0)[c] mg/100 ml	53.1(22.8-154.6)[c] mg/100 ml	19
61		Glucose	9	92.7(70-115)[c] mg/100 ml	103.5(70-135)[c] mg/100 ml	13
62	Renal capsular lymphatics	Chloride	14	140.2(114.4-164.1)[c] mEq/L	110.5(80.6-132.0)[c] mEq/L[1]	16
63		Potassium	12	4.03(3.5-5.3)[c] mEq/L	3.95(3.2-4.8)[c] mEq/L	
64		Sodium	27	162.1(126.3-206.2)[c] mEq/L	145.7(137.7-159.7)[c] mEq/L[2]	
65		Protein, total	11	2.91(1.5-4.0)[c] g/100 ml	5.83(4.6-6.8)[c] g/100 ml	
66		Albumin	10	20.2% of total protein	21.2% of total protein	
		Globulin				
67		α_1-	10	10.4% of total protein	8.7% of total protein	
68		α_2-	10	12.8% of total protein	12.1% of total protein	
69		β-	10	38.5% of total protein	3.8% of total protein	
70		γ-	10	17.8% of total protein	21.7% of total protein	
71	Right lymphatic duct	Potassium	5	5.4(3.1-7.7) mEq/L		3
72		Protein, total	21	3.69(3.05-4.35) g/100 ml	5.50(4.24-6.76) g/100 ml	
73		Nitrogen, non-protein	20	31.0(20.0-42.0) mg/100 ml	30.0(18.5-41.5) mg/100 ml	
74	Thoracic duct	CO_2 pressure	6	81(63-102)[c] mm Hg	50(33-64)[c] mm Hg	2
75		pH	6	7.09(6.91-7.21)[c]	7.26(7.17-7.35)[c]	2
76		Calcium	1	4.6 mEq/L	5.2 mEq/L	1
77		Chloride	1	116 mEq/L	110 mEq/L	1
		Phosphorus				
78		Inorganic P	1	2.0 mEq/L	2.4 mEq/L	1
79		Phospholipid P	4	8.9 mg/100 ml	16.0 mg/100 ml	4
80		Potassium		4.7 mEq/L		7
81				4.8 mEq/L		14
82		Sodium		144 mEq/L		14
83		Protein, total	11	4.00(1.88-6.12) g/100 ml	6.19(4.75-7.65) g/100 ml	8
84			6	3.23(2.61-3.85) g/100 ml	5.91(4.93-6.89) g/100 ml	17
85			4	3.44 g/100 ml	5.65 g/100 ml	4
86			6	3.67 g/100 ml	6.11 g/100 ml	9
87		Albumin	11	2.45(1.32-3.58) g/100 ml	3.56(2.42-4.70) g/100 ml	8
88			6	2.04(1.66-2.42) g/100 ml	3.33(2.61-4.05) g/100 ml	17
89			4	2.38(1.31-2.40) g/100 ml	3.67(1.86-5.25) g/100 ml	4
90		Globulin	11	1.54(0.53-2.65) g/100 ml	2.62(1.25-4.15) g/100 ml	8
91			6	0.88(0.64-1.12) g/100 ml	2.08(1.70-2.46) g/100 ml	17
92			4	1.08 g/100 ml	1.97 g/100 ml	4
93		Amino acids	1	2.4 mg/100 ml		18
94		Nitrogen, non-protein	10	39.0(28-50) mg/100 ml	40.0(26-56) mg/100 ml	8
95			4	33.0 mg/100 ml	33.0 mg/100 ml	3
96			1	27.0 mg/100 ml	27.2 mg/100 ml	1

/1/ 15 subjects. /2/ 28 subjects.

Part II: DOG (Concluded)

	Source of Lymph	Property or Constituent	No. of Sub-jects	Lymph	Blood Plasma or Serum	Refer-ence
	(A)	(B)	(C)	(D)	(E)	(F)
97	Thoracic	Lipids, total		(235-583) mg/100 ml	(319-642) mg/100 ml	9
98	duct	Cholesterol, total	4	124 mg/100 ml	258 mg/100 ml	4
99	(concluded)	Fatty acids	4	13.1 mEq/L	14.0 mEq/L	4
100		Glucose	1	124 mg/100 ml	123 mg/100 ml	1

Contributors: (a) Courtice, F. C., (b) Reinhardt, William O., (c) Manery, J. F., (d) Flock, Eunice V., (e) Conklin, Ruth E., (f) Hardenbergh, Esther, (g) Mayerson, H. S., and LeBrie, Stephen J.

References: [1] Arnold, R. M., and L. B. Mendel. 1927. J. Biol. Chem. 72:189. [2] Carlsten, A., and B. Söderholm. 1960. Acta physiol. scand. 48:29. [3] Courtice, F. C. Unpublished. [4] Courtice, F. C., and B. Morris. 1955. Q. J. Exp. Physiol., Lond. 40:138. [5] Drinker, C. K., and M. E. Field. 1931. Am. J. Physiol. 97:32. [6] Drinker, C. K., M. F. Warren, F. W. Maurer, and J. D. McCarrell. 1940. Ibid. 130:43. [7] Drinker, C. K., and J. M. Yoffey. 1941. Lymphatics, lymph, and lymphoid tissue. Harvard University Press, Cambridge. [8] Field, M. E., O. C. Leigh, J. W. Heim, and C. K. Drinker. 1934. Am. J. Physiol. 110:174. [9] Glenn, W. W. L., S. L. Cresson, F. X. Bauer, F. Goldstein, O. Hoffman, and J. E. Healey. 1949. Surg. Gyn. Obst. 89:200. [10] Heim, J. W. 1933. Am. J. Physiol. 103:553. [11] Heim, J. W., and O. C. Leigh. 1935. Ibid. 112:699. [12] Heim, J. W., R. S. Thomson, and F. C. Bartter. 1935. Ibid. 113:548. [13] Kaplan, A., M. Friedman, and H. E. Kruger. 1942. Ibid. 138:553. [14] Manery, J. F. 1954. Physiol. Rev. 34:352. [15] Marble, A., M. E. Field, C. K. Drinker, and R. M. Smith. 1934. Am. J. Physiol. 109:467. [16] Mayerson, H. S., and S. J. LeBrie. Unpublished. [17] Nix, J. T., F. C. Mann, J. L. Bollman, J. H. Grindlay, and E. V. Flock. 1951. Am. J. Physiol. 164:119. [18] Petersen, W. H., and T. P. Hughes. 1925. J. Biol. Chem. 66:229. [19] Sugarman, J., M. Friedman, E. Barrett, and T. Addis. 1942. Am. J. Physiol. 138:108. [20] Warren, M. F., and C. K. Drinker. 1942. Ibid. 136:207. [21] Wells, H. S. 1932. Ibid. 101:421.

Part III: MAMMALS OTHER THAN MAN, DOG

Values in parentheses are ranges, estimate "c" unless otherwise indicated (cf. Introduction).

	Animal	Source of Lymph	Constituent	No. of Sub-jects	Lymph	Blood Plasma or Serum	Refer-ence
	(A)	(B)	(C)	(D)	(E)	(F)	(G)
1	Cat	Cervical lymphatics	Phosphorus, phospholipid	6	3.9 mg/100 ml	7.4 mg/100 ml	4
2			Protein, total	6	3.71 g/100 ml	7.09 g/100 ml	11
3				12	3.50 g/100 ml		6
4				2	4.09 g/100 ml		6
5			Albumin	6	2.44 g/100 ml	3.65 g/100 ml	11
6			Globulin	6	1.05 g/100 ml	3.44 g/100 ml	11
7			Cholesterol, total	6	35.0 mg/100 ml	98.4 mg/100 ml	4
8			Fatty acids	6	5.2 mEq/L	10.8 mEq/L	4
9		Gallbladder lymphatics	Protein, total	2	5.01 g/100 ml	5.43 g/100 ml	10
10			Albumin	2	3.18 g/100 ml	3.38 g/100 ml	
11			Globulin	2	1.83 g/100 ml	2.06 g/100 ml	

Part III: MAMMALS OTHER THAN MAN, DOG (Continued)

	Animal	Source of Lymph	Constituent	No. of Subjects	Lymph	Blood Plasma or Serum	Reference
	(A)	(B)	(C)	(D)	(E)	(F)	(G)
12	Cat (concluded)	Intestinal lymphatics	Protein, total	5	5.26 g/100 ml	6.60 g/100 ml	11
13			Albumin	5	2.62 g/100 ml	3.11 g/100 ml	11
14			Globulin	5	2.64 g/100 ml	3.49 g/100 ml	11
15			Glucose	1	219 mg/100 ml	219 mg/100 ml	8
16		Leg lymphatics	Protein, total		3.31 g/100 ml		6
17		Liver lymphatics	Phosphorus, phospholipid	9	7.1 mg/100 ml	8.1 mg/100 ml	11
18			Protein, total	2	5.17 g/100 ml	5.43 g/100 ml	10
19				5	6.12 g/100 ml	6.60 g/100 ml	11
20			Albumin	2	3.15 g/100 ml	3.38 g/100 ml	10
21				5	2.92 g/100 ml	3.11 g/100 ml	11
22			Globulin	2	2.02 g/100 ml	2.06 g/100 ml	10
23				5	3.20 g/100 ml	3.49 g/100 ml	11
24			Cholesterol, total	9	110 mg/100 ml	131 mg/100 ml	11
25			Fatty acids	9	7.01 mEq/L	7.06 mEq/L	11
26		Right lymphatic duct	Protein, total	1	4.90 g/100 ml	7.40 g/100 ml	3
27		Thoracic duct	Phosphorus, phospholipid	20	4.0 mg/100 ml	7.4 mg/100 ml	4
28			Protein, total		4.80(4.00-5.60)[b] g/100 ml	7.60(6.20-9.00)[b] g/100 ml	9
29				20	4.63 g/100 ml	7.09 g/100 ml	4
30				1	5.68 g/100 ml		6
31			Albumin	20	2.74 g/100 ml	3.65 g/100 ml	4
32			Globulin	20	1.88 g/100 ml	3.44 g/100 ml	4
33			Nitrogen, non-protein	3	44.0 mg/100 ml	45.0 mg/100 ml	16
34			Cholesterol, total	20	43.6 mg/100 ml	98.4 mg/100 ml	4
35			Fatty acids	20	9.1 mEq/L	10.8 mEq/L	4
36	Cow	Cervical lymphatics	Protein, total	8	2.64(2.20-3.34) g/100 ml	6.28(5.39-7.04) g/100 ml	7
37		Leg lymphatics	Albumin	5	1.7 g/100 ml	3.4 g/100 ml	14
38			Globulin	5	1.0 g/100 ml	2.8 g/100 ml	14
39			Nitrogen Amino N	7	6.1 mg/100 ml	5.6 mg/100 ml	7
40			Non-protein N	8	20.3(13.7-27.6) mg/100 ml	20.4(14.3-28.6) mg/100 ml	
41		Foreleg lymphatics	Creatine	8	3.0(2.2-3.9) mg/100 ml	2.8(1.8-4.1) mg/100 ml	7
42			Creatinine	8	1.1(0.9-1.5) mg/100 ml	1.1(0.9-1.3) mg/100 ml	
43			Urea	5	23.0(10.3-36.0) mg/100 ml	23.6(10.2-36.9) mg/100 ml	
44	Goat	Thoracic duct	Protein, total		4.10 g/100 ml	5.30 g/100 ml	3
45			Albumin		1.30 g/100 ml	1.60 g/100 ml	
46			Globulin		2.80 g/100 ml	3.70 g/100 ml	
47	Guinea pig	Cervical lymphatics	Protein, total	1	3.37 g/100 ml	4.64 g/100 ml	6
48		Thoracic duct	Protein, total	1	4.16 g/100 ml	4.72 g/100 ml	
49	Horse	Cervical lymphatics	Protein, total		3.8 g/100 ml		5
50	Monkey, rhesus	Cervical lymphatics	Protein, total	4	3.48 g/100 ml	5.12 g/100 ml	6
51		Thoracic duct	Protein, total	2	3.66 g/100 ml	5.87 g/100 ml	
52	Rabbit	Cervical lymphatics	Protein, total	8	3.18 g/100 ml		6
53		Leg lymphatics	Protein, total	2	1.26 g/100 ml		6

Part III: MAMMALS OTHER THAN MAN, DOG (Concluded)

	Animal	Source of Lymph	Constituent	No. of Subjects	Lymph	Blood Plasma or Serum	Reference
	(A)	(B)	(C)	(D)	(E)	(F)	(G)
54	Rabbit (concluded)	Thoracic duct	Phosphorus, phospholipid	10	4.3 mg/100 ml	4.2 mg/100 ml	12
55			Protein, total	15	3.53 g/100 ml		6
56			Cholesterol, total	10	43 mg/100 ml	46 mg/100 ml	12
57			Fatty acids	10	13.8 mEq/L	11.4 mEq/L	12
58	Rat	Cervical lymphatics	Protein, total	9	3.07 g/100 ml		15
59		Intestinal lymphatics	Cholesterol, total		55.2 mg/100 ml	48 mg/100 ml	2
60					(62.1-69.2) mg/100 ml		1
61			Fatty acids	3	(1000-1572) mg/100 ml		1
62		Liver lymphatics	Cholesterol, total		36.0 mg/100 ml	47.7 mg/100 ml	2
63		Thoracic duct	Phosphorus, phospholipid	5	8.1 mg/100 ml	5.5 mg/100 ml	11
64			Protein, total	10	3.06(1.64-4.48)[b] g/100 ml	5.82(4.40-7.24)[b] g/100 ml	13
65				5	1.94 g/100 ml	5.68 g/100 ml	11
66				19	4.18 g/100 ml		15
67			Albumin	5	1.29 g/100 ml	3.20 g/100 ml	11
68			Globulin	5	0.65 g/100 ml	2.47 g/100 ml	11
69			Cholesterol, total	5	72 mg/100 ml	51 mg/100 ml	11
70				4	(23.3-62.4) mg/100 ml		1
71			Fatty acids	5	9.6 mEq/L	10.4 mEq/L	11
72				4	(742-1460) mg/100 ml		1

Contributors: (a) Courtice, F. C., (b) Reinhardt, William O., (c) Muus, Jytte, (d) Hardenbergh, Esther, (e) Flock, Eunice V.

References: [1] Bloom, B., I. L. Chaikoff, W. O. Reinhardt, and W. G. Dauben. 1951. J. Biol. Chem. 189:261. [2] Bollman, J. L., and E. V. Flock. 1951. Am. J. Physiol. 164:480. [3] Courtice, F. C. Unpublished. [4] Courtice, F. C., and B. Morris. 1955. Q. J. Exp. Physiol., Lond. 40:138. [5] Drinker, C. K., and M. E. Field. 1933. Lymphatics, lymph, and tissue fluid. Williams and Wilkins, Baltimore. [6] Drinker, C. K., and J. M. Yoffey. 1941. Lymphatics, lymph, and lymphoid tissue. Harvard University Press, Cambridge. [7] Glenn, W. W. L., J. Muus, and C. K. Drinker. 1943. J. Clin. Invest. 22:451. [8] Heim, J. W., R. S. Thomson, and F. C. Bartter. 1935. Am. J. Physiol. 113:548. [9] Korner, P. I., and W. J. Simmonds. Unpublished. [10] McCarrell, J. D., S. Thayer, and C. K. Drinker. 1941. Am. J. Physiol. 133:79. [11] Morris, B. Unpublished. [12] Morris, B., and F. C. Courtice. 1955. Q. J. Exp. Physiol., Lond. 40:149. [13] Nix, J. T., E. V. Flock, and J. L. Bollman. 1951. Am. J. Physiol. 164:117. [14] Perlmann, G. E., W. W. L. Glenn, and D. Kaufman. 1943. J. Clin. Invest. 22:627. [15] Reinhardt, W. O., and C. H. Li. 1945. Proc. Soc. Exp. Biol., N. Y. 58:321. [16] Simmonds, W. J. Unpublished.

For a comprehensive review of the subject, consult reference 20. All subjects were non-fasting, unless otherwise specified. Values in parentheses are ranges, estimate "c" (cf. Introduction).

	Subjects				Source of Lymph	Lymphocytes cells/cu mm x 10^3	Ref-er-ence
	Animal	No.	Weight kg	Condition and Anesthetic			
	(A)	(B)	(C)	(D)	(E)	(F)	(G)
1	Man	5	60.6 (48.5-78.5)	Far advanced in neoplastic disease; 3-10 days continuous lymph drainage by cannulation	Thoracic duct	11.4 (2.1-25.5)	3
2	Cat	8	(1.0-2.7)	Fasted 36-72 hours, then fed whipping cream and mutton fat; lymph collected 10-12 hours later	Intestinal lacteals Draining no Peyer's patch	6.99	2
3					Draining a Peyer's patch	67.98	
4		21	1.9	Fed cream 4 hours before cannulation; barbiturate-urethane	Thoracic duct	14.15 (4.3-29.6)	1
5	Cattle, young	4	34.4 (29-38)		Thoracic duct	26.1 (21.5-30.6)	19
6	Dog	10	10.9 (5.4-20.8)	Fasted 24-36 hours; morphine	Thoracic duct	7.2 (3.0-20.0)	4
7	Goat	4	32 (25-35)	Barbiturate-inhalation anesthetic	Thoracic duct	6.9 (2.7-9.0)	19
8	Guinea pig Dunklin-Hart-ley strain	15	0.416 (0.372-0.470)		Thoracic duct	13.40	21
9	Mill-Hill strain	50♂	0.235	Barbiturate	Cervical lymphatics	6.52	13
10		40♂	0.303	Barbiturate	Thoracic duct	14.82	
11	Monkey	5			Cervical lymphatics	22.06 (9.35-57.50)	20
12		1	3.8	Barbiturate	Right lymphatic duct	10.2	11
13		5	2.49	Barbiturate	Right lymphatic duct-functional thoracic duct	40.4 (32.0-56.4)	11
14		4	2.6	Barbiturate	Subclavian lymphatic duct	4.2 (2.5-7.0)	11
15		26	3.5	Barbiturate	Thoracic duct	29.9 (2.9-100.3)	11
16		4			Thoracic duct	20.4 (11.8-38.0)	20
17	Mouse	5	0.03	Barbiturate	Intestinal lacteal lymphatics	47.1	17
18	NIH Web-ster strain	200♂	0.02	40 days old; barbiturate	Thoracic duct, abdominal	11.7 (9.5-13.9)	16
19	Rabbit	1	2.05	Barbiturate	Cervical lymphatics	37.2	11
20		3		Barbiturate	Right lymphatic duct	40.9 (39.5-43.6)	6
21		7	2.3	Prone; barbiturate; post-anesthetic collection	Subclavian lymphatic duct	38.9 (13.8-50.8)	6
22		5	2.3	Sitting; barbiturate; post-anesthetic collection	Subclavian lymphatic duct	22.5 (19.3-26.4)	6
23		9	2.5 (2.1-3.2)	Barbiturate-ether	Thoracic duct	36.1	14
24		7	2.5	Barbiturate	Thoracic duct	32.3	6
25	Rat	8	(0.18-0.24)	Oral saline	Intestinal lymphatics	34.6 (18.3-60.5)	10
26		4	(0.18-0.24)	Oral saline	Liver lymphatics	12.3 (6.2-19.9)	10
27		47	0.27 (0.08-0.50)		Thoracic duct	42.7 (13.7-81.2)	9
28		6	(0.18-0.24)	Oral saline	Thoracic duct	26.52 (10.9-56.1)	10
29		15	(0.18-0.24)	Oral water	Thoracic duct	48.7 (26.3-88.1)	10

	Subjects				Source of lymph	Lymphocytes cells/cu mm x 10³	Ref-er-ence
	Animal	No.	Weight kg	Condition and Anesthetic			
	(A)	(B)	(C)	(D)	(E)	(F)	(G)
30	Rat (con-cluded)	27	0.172 (0.145-0.200)	Oral saline; post-anesthetic collection	Thoracic duct, abdominal	20.0	5
31		8	0.199 (0.16-0.29)	Oral saline; barbiturate-ether; post-anesthetic collection	Thoracic duct, abdominal	3.3 (2.2-6.2)	18
32		6	0.235 (0.20-0.26)	Oral water; barbiturate-ether; post-anesthetic collection	Thoracic duct, abdominal	11.8 (7.2-13.1)	18
33	Long-Evans strain	10♂	(0.25-0.30)	Barbiturate	Cervical lymphatics	7.065 (1.525-17.500)	12
34		10♀	0.30 (0.280-0.334)	Approximately 100 days old; barbiturate	Right lymphatic duct	17.3 (13.0-23.7)	15
35		28♂	0.252 (0.20-0.29)	60 days old; barbiturate	Thoracic duct	31.5	8
36		9♂	0.155 (0.135-0.170)	40 days old; ether; post-anesthetic collection	Thoracic duct, abdominal	32.5 (13.2-61.1)	7
37		9♂	0.274 (0.21-0.31)	60 days old; ether; post-anesthetic collection	Thoracic duct, abdominal	32.15 (15.45-55.90)	7

Contributors: (a) Reinhardt, William O., (b) Yoffey, J. M., (c) Feldman, Joseph, D.

References: [1] Adams, W. S., R. H. Saunders, and J. S. Lawrence. 1945. Am. J. Physiol. 144:297. [2] Baker, R. D. 1932. Anat. Rec. 55:207. [3] Bierman, H. R., et al. 1953. J. Clin. Invest. 32:637. [4] Chistoni, A. 1909. Arch. fisiol., Fir. 6:74. [5] Gowans, J. L. 1957. Brit. J. Exp. Path. 38:67. [6] Hughes, R., A. J. May, and J. G. Widdicombe. 1956. J. Physiol., Lond. 132:384. [7] Hungerford, G. F., and W. O. Reinhardt. 1950. Am. J. Physiol. 160:9. [8] Hungerford, G. F., W. O. Reinhardt, and C. H. Li. 1952. Blood, N. Y. 7:193. [9] Keohane, K. W., and W. K. Metcalf. 1958. Q. J. Exp. Physiol., Lond. 43:408. [10] Mann, J. D., and G. M. Higgins. 1950. Blood, N. Y. 5:177. [11] Reinhardt, W. O. Unpublished. [12] Reinhardt, W. O., and C. H. Li. 1945. Proc. Soc. Exp. Biol., N. Y. 58:321. [13] Reinhardt, W. O., and J. M. Yoffey. 1956. Am. J. Physiol. 187:493. [14] Sanders, A. G., H. W. Florey, and J. M. Barnes. 1940. Brit. J. Exp. Path. 21:254. [15] Schooley, J. 1958. Proc. Soc. Exp. Biol., N. Y. 99:511. [16] Shrewsbury, M. M. 1958. Ibid. 99:53. [17] Shrewsbury, M. M. Unpublished. [18] Shrewsbury, M. M., and W. O. Reinhardt. 1952. Am. J. Physiol. 168:366. [19] Wingvist, G. 1954. Acta anat., Basel, v. 22, suppl. 21. [20] Yoffey, J. M., and F. C. Courtice. 1956. Lymphatics, lymph and lymphoid tissue. Edward Arnold, London. [21] Yoffey, J. M., G. A. Hanks, and L. Kelly. 1958. Ann. N. York Acad. Sc. 73:47.

XV. Cerebrospinal Fluid

104. PHYSICAL PROPERTIES AND CHEMICAL COMPOSITION OF CEREBROSPINAL FLUID: MAMMALS

Part I: MAN

Values in parentheses are ranges, estimate "c" (cf. Introduction).

	Property or Constituent	Value	Reference
	(A)	(B)	(C)
	Physical Properties		
1	Freezing point depression	0.569(0.540-0.603) °C	12
2	pH	7.48(7.35-7.70)	8
3	Pressure	150(70-180) mm H_2O	24
4	Refractive index	1.3351	29
5	Specific gravity	1.0069(1.0062-1.0082)	34
6	Volume	(90-150) ml	24
	General Chemical Components		
7	Lymphocytes	(0-10) cells/cu mm	24
8	Solids, total	1.08(0.85-1.70) %	12
9	Water	99%	25
	Electrolytes		
10	Aluminum	Trace	30
11	Barium	Trace	30
12	Bicarbonate	48.3 mg/100 ml	25
13	Boron	Trace	30
14	Bromide	0.23(0.14-0.38) mg/100 ml	19
15	Calcium	4.56(3.9-5.1) mg/100 ml	20
16	Carbon dioxide	59(57-62) vol %	28
17	Chloride	438(418-452) mg/100 ml	9
18	Copper	0.013(0.006-0.020) mg/100 ml	26
19	Iodine	<0.001 mg/100 ml	13
20	Iron	0.035 mg/100 ml	22
21	Magnesium	2.71(2.40-2.95) mg/100 ml	20
22	Phosphorus	1.53(1.25-2.10) mg/100 ml	23
23	Potassium	9.8(8.5-11.5) mg/100 ml	16
24	Sodium	524(501-543) mg/100 ml	22
25	Strontium	Trace	30
26	Sulfur	0.6 mg/100 ml	33
	Nitrogenous Substances		
	Protein		
27	Total	28(12-43) mg/100 ml	12
28	Lumbar	25(20-40) mg/100 ml	25
29	Cisternal	15 mg/100 ml	25
30	Ventricular	10 mg/100 ml	25
31	Albumin	55(40-70) % of total protein	5, 17
	Globulin		5, 17
32	α-	10(5-20) % of total protein	
33	β-	12(5-20) % of total protein	
34	γ-	11(5-20) % of total protein	
35	γ-Component[1]	5(0-10) % of total protein	5, 17
36	X-Proteins[2]	7(2-15) % of total protein	5, 17
37	Fibrinogen	0	5, 17, 21
	Amino acids		
38	Alanine	1.33 mg/100 ml	6
39	Arginine	0.60 mg/100 ml	31
40	Cystine	0.18 mg/100 ml	31
41	Glutamine	8.95 mg/100 ml	15
42	Glycine	0.17 mg/100 ml	6

/1/ Component migrating between β- and γ- globulins on electrophoresis.   /2/ Two proteins, not lipoproteins, that migrate faster than albumin on electrophoresis at approximately pH 8.

Part I: MAN (Continued)

Property or Constituent	Value	Reference
(A)	(B)	(C)
Nitrogenous Substances (concluded)		
Amino acids (concluded)		
43 Histidine	0.17 mg/100 ml	31
44 Isoleucine	0.10 mg/100 ml	31
45 Leucine	0.14 mg/100 ml	31
46 Lysine	0.28 mg/100 ml	31
47 Methionine	0.04 mg/100 ml	31
48 Phenylalanine	0.19 mg/100 ml	31
49 Threonine	0.28 mg/100 ml	31
50 Tyrosine	0.20 mg/100 ml	31
51 Valine	0.21 mg/100 ml	31
52 Ammonia	(0.096-0.097) mg/100 ml	29
53 Creatinine	1.11(0.54-1.91) mg/100 ml	7
54 Urea	11.7(7.4-16.0) mg/100 ml	22
55 Uric acid	(0.5-2.8) mg/100 ml	11
Nitrogen		
56 Non-protein N	19(12-28) mg/100 ml	12
57 Amino acid N	1.23 mg/100 ml	6
58 Urea N	14 mg/100 ml	25
Lipids, Carbohydrates, Miscellaneous Organic Acids		
59 Cholesterol	(0.24-0.50) mg/100 ml	4
60 Fatty acids	(1-3) mg/100 ml	4
61 Reducing substances, total	65(45-93) mg/100 ml	12
62 Fructose	3.4(2.0-7.5) mg/100 ml	10, 18
63 Hexosamine	9(5-18) mg/100 ml	10
64 Polysaccharides	3.4(2.3-6.8) mg/100 ml	10
65 Acetic acid	13.6(0.28-26.97) mg/100 ml	22
66 Citric acid	0.04 mg/100 ml	3
67 Lactic acid	19(11-27) mg/100 ml	14
68 Pyruvic acid	1.02 mg/100 ml	1
Vitamins, Hormones		
69 Vitamin C (ascorbic acid)	1.8 mg/100 ml	32
70 Inositol	2.7 mg/100 ml	27
71 Cortisone	(0.1-0.2) µg/100 ml	2
72 Hydrocortisone	(0.2-0.4) µg/100 ml	2
73 17-Hydroxycorticosteroids	<2 µg/100 ml	22

Contributors: (a) Fisk, Albert A., (b) Larson, Daniel L., (c) Skaug, Odvar, (d) Klingman, Walter O., (e) Hunter, George, (f) Hoch, Hans, (g) Eastham, M. D.

References: [1] Amatuzio, D. S., and S. Nesbitt. 1950. J. Clin. Invest. 29:1486. [2] Baron, D. N., and D. Abelson. 1954. Nature, Lond. 173:174. [3] Benni, B. 1932. Acta med. scand. Suppl. 50, p. 167. [4] Brown, W. T., E. F. Gildea, and E. B. Man. 1939. Arch. Neur. Psychiat., Chic. 42:260. [5] Bücher, T., D. Matzelt, and D. Pette. 1952. Klin. Wschr. 30:325. [6] Christensen, H. N., P. F. Cooper, Jr., R. D. Johnson, and E. L. Lynch. 1947. J. Biol. Chem. 168:191. [7] Cockrill, J. R. 1931. Arch. Neur. Psychiat., Chic. 25:1297. [8] Cohen, E. N., and R. T. Knight. 1947. Anesthesiology 8:594. [9] Dailey, M. E. 1931. J. Biol. Chem. 93:5. [10] Eastham, M. D., and K. R. Keay. 1952. J. Clin. Path., Lond. 5:319. [11] Flexner, L. B. 1934. Physiol. Rev. 14:161. [12] Fremont-Smith, F., M. E. Dailey, H. H. Merritt, M. P. Carroll, and G. W. Thomas. 1931. Arch. Neur. Psychiat., Chic. 25:1271. [13] Gildea, E. F., and E. B. Man. 1942. Tr. Am. Neur. Ass. 68:80. [14] Glaser, J. 1926. J. Biol. Chem. 69:539. [15] Harris, M. M. 1943. J. Clin. Invest. 22:569. [16] Helmsworth, J. A. 1947. J. Laborat. Clin. M. 32:1486. [17] Hoch, H., and A. Chanutin. 1952. Proc. Soc. Exp. Biol., N. Y. 81:628. [18] Hubbard, R. S., and N. M. Russell. 1937. J. Biol. Chem. 119:647. [19] Hunter, G. Unpublished.

Part I: MAN (Concluded)

[20] Hunter, G., and H. V. Smith. 1960. Nature, Lond. 186:161. [21] Kabat, E. A., D. H. Moore, and H. Landow. 1942. J. Clin. Invest. 21:571. [22] Klingman, W. O. Unpublished. [23] Merritt, H. H., and W. Bauer. 1931. J. Biol. Chem. 90:215. [24] Merritt, H. H., and F. Fremont-Smith. 1937. The cerebrospinal fluid. W. B. Saunders, Philadelphia. [25] Merritt, H. H., F. A. Mettler, and T. J. Putnam. 1947. Fundamentals of clinical neurology. Blakiston, New York. [26] Munch-Petersen, S. 1950. Acta psychiat. neur. scand. 25:251. [27] Nixon, D. A. 1953. J. Physiol., Lond. 119:18. [28] Pincers, J. B., and B. Kramer. 1923. J. Biol. Chem. 57:463. [29] Roeder, F., and O. Rehn. 1942. Die Cerebrospinalflüssigkeit: Untersuchungsmethoden und Klinik für Artze und Tierätze. Springer Verlag, Berlin. [30] Scott, G. H., and J. H. McMillen. 1936. Proc. Soc. Exp. Biol., N. Y. 32:287. [31] Soloman, J. D., S. W. Hier, and O. Bergeim. 1947. J. Biol. Chem. 171:695. [32] Spiegel-Adolph, M., H. T. Wyers, and E. A. Spiegel. 1951. J. Nerv. Ment. Dis. 113:529. [33] Watchorn, E., and R. A. McCance. 1935. Biochem. J., Lond. 29:2291. [34] Wohnan, I. J., B. Evans, and S. Lasker. 1946. Am. J. Clin. Path. (Techn. Sect.) 10:33.

Part II: MAMMALS OTHER THAN MAN

Values in parentheses are ranges, estimate "c" (cf. Introduction).

	Animal	Property or Constituent	Value	Reference
	(A)	(B)	(C)	(D)
1	Cat	Osmotic pressure	1.017 g NaCl/100 g H_2O	1
2		pH	7.45	17
3		Refractive index	1.33435	16
4		Lymphocytes	(0-3) cells/ml	8
5		Calcium	6 mg/100 ml	19
6		Chloride	899 mg/100 ml	8
7			150 mEq/L	6
8		Potassium	5.9 mEq/L	6
9		Sodium	162 mEq/L	6
10		Protein	25 mg/100 ml	6
11		Nitrogen, non-protein	20 mg/100 ml	6
12		Sugar	85 mg/100 ml	8
13		Vitamin C (ascorbic acid)	3.8 mg/100 ml	15
14	Cattle	Freezing point depression	(0.54-0.55) °C	8
15		pH	7.5(7.4-7.6)	10, 11
16		Pressure	(50-180) mm H_2O	22
17		Specific gravity	1.0065(1.006-1.007)	10, 11
18		Lymphocytes	(0-10) cells/ml	8
19		Calcium	(5.1-6.3) mg/100 ml	8
20		Chloride	(650-725) mg/100 ml	8
21		Potassium	(11.2-13.8) mg/100 ml	8
22		Protein	(16-33) mg/100 ml	8
23		Creatinine	1.4 mg/100 ml	4
		Nitrogen		4
24		Non-protein N	16 mg/100 ml	
25		Urea N	11 mg/100 ml	
26		Sugar	(35-70) mg/100 ml	8
27	Dog	pH	7.37(7.35-7.39)	18
28		Pressure	86.5(24-172) mm H_2O	23
29		Refractive index	1.3342	16
30		Specific gravity	1.0056(1.0033-1.0125)	23
31		Volume	(6.7-7.0) ml	23
32		Lymphocytes	3.4(1-8) cells/cu mm	20
33		Chloride	808(761-883) mg/100 ml	23
34		Protein	27.5(11-55) mg/100 ml	23
35		Albumin	27 mg/100 ml	23
36		Globulin	9 mg/100 ml	23
37		Allantoin	0.3(0.25-0.47) mg/100 ml	3

Part II: MAMMALS OTHER THAN MAN (Continued)

	Animal	Property or Constituent	Value	Reference
	(A)	(B)	(C)	(D)
38	Dog (con-	Uric acid	0.23(0.13-0.35) mg/100 ml	3
39	cluded)	Sugar	74(61-116) mg/100 ml	23
40		Vitamin C (ascorbic acid)	6.6 mg/100 ml	15
41	Goat	Specific gravity	1.0049	13
42		Lymphocytes	3 cells/ml	8
43		Chloride	681 mg/100 ml	13
44		Protein	12 mg/100 ml	8, 13
45		Sugar	71 mg/100 ml	8
46	Guinea pig	Calcium	3 mEq/L	5
47		Chloride	122 mEq/L	6
48		Magnesium	2 mEq/L	5
49		Potassium	4 mEq/L	6
50		Sodium	150 mEq/L	6
51		Protein	20 mg/100 ml	6
52		Nitrogen, non-protein	21 mg/100 ml	6
53	Horse	pH	7.25(7.13-7.36)	2
54		Pressure	379(272-490) mm H_2O	2
55		Specific gravity	1.006(1.004-1.008)	2
56		Volume	(170-300) ml	12
57		Lymphocytes	11(4-23) cells/ml	2
58		Calcium	6.26(5.55-6.98) mg/100 ml	2
59		Chloride	737(691-792) mg/100 ml	2
60		Magnesium	1.98(1.06-2.95) mg/100 ml	2
61		Phosphorus, inorganic	1.44(0.87-2.20) mg/100 ml	2
62		Potassium	12.66(10.65-14.20) mg/100 ml	2
63		Protein, total	47.58(28.75-71.75) mg/100 ml	2
64		Albumin	38.64(22.62-67.94) mg/100 ml	2
65		Globulin	9.34(3.37-18.37) mg/100 ml	2
66		Nitrogen, non-protein	26.88(13.72-39.20) mg/100 ml	2
67		Urea	(23-31) mg/100 ml	9
68		Sugar	57.2(40-78) mg/100 ml	2
69		Vitamin C (ascorbic acid)	1.7 mg/100 ml	7
	Monkey	Lymphocytes		8
70		Lumbar	(4-10) cells/ml	
71		Cisternal	(1-3) cells/ml	
72		Chloride	(420-500) mg/100 ml	8
		Protein		8, 21
73		Lumbar	(20-30) mg/100 ml	
74		Cisternal	(8-15) mg/100 ml	
75		Globulin	(0.4-6.3) mg/100 ml	14
76		Sugar	60 mg/100 ml	8
77		Vitamin C (ascorbic acid)	2.3 mg/100 ml	15
78	Rabbit	pH	(7.40-7.85)	21
79		Specific gravity	1.005	8, 21
80		Carbon dioxide	(41.2-48.5) vol %	21
81		Chloride	(600-730) mg/100 ml	8, 21
82		Protein, total	(15-19) mg/100 ml	8
83		Albumin	(15-19) mg/100 ml	21
84		Globulin	0	21
85		Nitrogen, non-protein	(5.6-16.8) mg/100 ml	8
86		Sugar	(50-57) mg/100 ml	8
87		Lactic acid	(1.4-4.0) mg/100 ml	21
88	Sheep	Lymphocytes	(0-15) cells/ml	8
89		Calcium	5.77 mg/100 ml	8
90		Chloride	832(750-868) mg/100 ml	8
91		Magnesium	2.86 mg/100 ml	8
92		Protein, total	(8-70) mg/100 ml	8
93		Nitrogen, non-protein	29(9.6-42.0) mg/100 ml	8
94		Sugar	(48-109) mg/100 ml	8
95	Swine	Lymphocytes	(1-20) cells/ml	8
96		Protein, total	(24-29) mg/100 ml	8
97		Albumin	(17-24) mg/100 ml	8
98		Globulin	(5-10) mg/100 ml	8
99		Sugar	(45-87) mg/100 ml	8

104. PHYSICAL PROPERTIES AND CHEMICAL COMPOSITION OF CEREBROSPINAL FLUID: MAMMALS (Concluded)

Part II: MAMMALS OTHER THAN MAN (Concluded)

Contributors: (a) Cumings, J. N., (b) Fisk, Albert A., (c) Larson, Daniel L., (d) Skaug, Odvar, (e) Smith, Catherine A., (f) Kabat, Elvin A.

References: [1] Aldred, P., C. Hallpike, and A. Ledoux. 1940. J. Physiol., Lond. 98:446. [2] Behrens, H. 1953. Proc. 15th Internat. Vet. Congr. 2(1):1031. [3] Byers, S. O., and M. Friedman. 1949. Am. J. Physiol. 157:394. [4] Carmichael, J., and E. R. Jones. 1939. J. Comp. Path., Lond. 52:222. [5] Citron, L., and D. Exley. 1957. Proc. R. Soc. M., Lond. 50:697. [6] Citron, L., D. Exley, and C. Hallpike. 1956. Brit. M. Bull. 12:101. [7] Errington, B. J., W. S. Hodgkiss, and E. P. Jayne. 1942. Am. J. Vet. Res. 3:242. [8] Fankhauser, R. 1953. Zbl. Veterinärmed. 1(2):156. [9] Fedotov, A. I. 1937. Sborn. Rab. Leningrad Vet. Inst., p. 263. [10] Fedotov, A. I. 1937. Sovet. vet. 10:31. [11] Fedotov, A. I. 1939. Vet. Bull., Lond. 9:49. [12] Fedotov, A. I. 1939. Ibid. 9:583. [13] Fujisawa, Y. 1927. Osaka Igakkai Zasshi, v. 26. [14] Kabat, E. A., A. Wolf, A. E. Bezer, and N. P. Murray. 1951. J. Exp. M. 93:615. [15] Kasahara, M., and Y. Fujisawa. 1930. Zschr. ges. exp. Med. 73:11. [16] Ledoux, A. 1941. Acta biol. belg. 4:506. [17] Ledoux, A. 1943. Bull. Soc. R. Sc. Liége 4:254. [18] McQuarrie, I., and A. T. Shohl. 1925. J. Biol. Chem. 66:307. [19] Merritt, H. H., and W. Bauer. 1931. Ibid. 90:215. [20] Perlstein, M. H., and A. Levinson. 1931-32. Am. J. Physiol. 99:626. [21] Roeder, F., and O. Rehm. 1942. Die Cerebrospinalflüssigkeit: Untersuchungsmethoden und Klinik für Artze und Tierätze. Springer Verlag, Berlin. [22] Sykes, J. F., and L. A. Moore. 1942. Am. J. Vet. Res. 3:364. [23] Teunissen, G. H. B., and M. A. J. Verwer. 1953. Proc. 15th Internat. Vet. Congr. 2(1):1022.

105. CEREBROSPINAL FLUID, POSTMORTEM VS ANTEMORTEM: MAN

pH postmortem values for 26 males, and electrolyte postmortem values for 131 males. Values in parentheses are ranges, estimate "c" (cf. Introduction).

Property or Constituent	Postmortem		Antemortem Value
	Method	Value	
(A)	(B)	(C)	(D)
1 pH	Beckman pH meter and blood electrode assembly provided with rubber cap, at 37.5°C	6.38(6.03-6.95)	(7.35-7.44)
2 Bicarbonate		9.4(4.5-26.0) mEq/L	26(25-28) mEq/L
3 Calcium	Clark-Collip	2.4(1.9-3.4) mEq/L	2.5(2.3-2.6) mEq/L
4 Carbon dioxide	Van Slyke gas volumetric	21(10-58) vol %	59(57-62) vol %
5 Chloride	Van Slyke-Hiller modification of Sendroy method	113(89-142) mEq/L	125(119-128) mEq/L
6 Magnesium	Denis-Brigg	2.9(1.9-3.7) mEq/L	2.0(1.7-2.2) mEq/L
7 Phosphorus, inorganic	Fiske-Subbarow	5.2(0.7-10.5) mEq/L	0.8(0.5-1.2) mEq/L
8 Potassium	Flame photometry	21(5.6-40.0) mEq/L	2.9(2.5-3.7) mEq/L
9 Sodium	Flame photometry	127(107-150) mEq/L	143(134-152) mEq/L

Contributor: Naumann, Hans N.

Reference: Naumann, H. N. 1958. Proc. Soc. Exp. Biol., N. Y. 98:16.

Values in parentheses are ranges, estimate "c" (cf. Introduction).

Condition	Method	No. of Subjects	Carbohydrate		CSF: Blood %	Reference
			Substance	Value mg/100 ml CSF		
(A)	(B)	(C)	(D)	(E)	(F)	(G)
1 Normal	Folin-Peck modification of Folin-Wu	73	Reducing substances	69(46-140)	67	B,1;C-F, 2-6
2	Hagedorn-Jensen	54	Reducing substances	84(46-117)		B,7;C,E,8
3	Somogyi	26	Reducing substances	67(35-90)		B,9;C,E,8
4	Roe, using an E.E.L. colorimeter; confirmed by chromatography	30	Fructose	3.4(2.0-7.5)	680	B,10;C-F, 3,8
5	Morgan-Elson; confirmed by chromatography	10	Hexosamine	9(5-18)		B,11;C,E,8
6	Dische carbazole colorimetric	10	Polysaccharide	3.4(2.3-6.8)		B,9;C,E,8
7 Tubercular meningitis	Folin-Peck modification of Folin-Wu	69	Reducing substances	28(5-86)	21	B,1;C-F, 2-6
8	Hagedorn-Jensen	60	Reducing substances	31(8-73)	28	B,7;C-F, 12-14
9	Somogyi	23	Reducing substances	28(0.8-40)		B,9;C,E,8, 15
10	Roe, using an E.E.L. colorimeter; confirmed by chromatography	32	Fructose	0.8(0-1.5)	100	B,10;C-F,3 8,12,13
11	Morgan-Elson; confirmed by chromatography	23	Hexosamine	9(0-20)		B,11;C,E,8
12 Meningococcal meningitis[1]	Folin-Peck modification of Folin-Wu	28	Reducing substances	8(0-52)	16	B,1;C-F,2, 4,5,16
13	Hagedorn-Jensen	3	Reducing substances	21(7-50)		B,7;C,E,8
14	Roe, using an E.E.L. colorimeter; confirmed by chromatography	7	Fructose	1(0-3.8)	320	B,10;C-F, 3,8,16
15 Lymphocytic exudates[2],	Folin-Peck modification of Folin-Wu	37	Reducing substances	71(46-137)	66	B,1;C-F,2, 4-6
16 other than tubercular meningitis	Hagedorn-Jensen	51	Reducing substances	62(40-86)	56	B,7;C-F, 12,13
17	Somogyi	8	Reducing substances	(38-53)		B,9;C,E,8, 15
18	Roe, using an E.E.L. colorimeter; confirmed by chromatography	40	Fructose	2.8(1.2-6.0)		B,10;C,E, 12,13

/1/ Includes streptococcal and pneumococcal meningitis. /2/ Anterior poliomyelitis, encephalitis, and benign lymphocytic meningitis.

Contributor: Eastham, M. D.

References: [1] Cacioppo, F., and V. B. Bevlotti. 1945. Boll. Soc. ital. biol. sper. 20:244. [2] Eastham, M. D., and K. R. Keay. 1952. J. Clin. Path., Lond. 5:319. [3] Folin, O., and E. A. Peck. 1919. J. Biol. Chem. 38:81. [4] Harrison, G. A. 1947. Chemical methods in clinical medicine. Ed. 3. J. and A. Churchill, London. [5] Hendry, E. 1939. Arch. Dis. Childh., Lond. 14:159. [6] Hubbard, R. S., and N. M. Russell. 1937. J. Biol. Chem. 119:647. [7] Hubbard, R. S., N. G. Russell, and N. M. Russell. 1936. J. Clin. Invest. 15:519. [8] Jamieson, W. M., and J. H. Prain. 1952. Unpublished. [9] Jamieson, W. M., J. H. Prain, and M. D. Eastham. 1951. Paper before Scot. Tuberc. Soc. [10] Levinson, A. 1925. Am. J. Dis. Child. 30:774. [11] Levinson, A., and D. J. Cohn. 1936. Ibid. 51:17. [12] Morgan, W. T. J., and L. A. Elson. 1934. Biochem. Zschr. 28:988. [13] Roe, J. H. 1934. J. Biol. Chem. 107:15. [14] Seibert, F. B., and A. J. Atno. 1946. Ibid. 163:511. [15] Weichzel, M., and G. Herzger. 1936. J. Pediat., S. Louis 9:763. [16] Wilcox, H. B., and J. D. Lyttle. 1923. Arch. Pediat., N. Y. 40:215.

XVI. Nerve Electrolytes and Water Content

107. NERVE ELECTROLYTES: VERTEBRATES AND INVERTEBRATES

Where multiple references appear in column E, the mean value has been calculated from the means reported in the literature.

Part I: MAN

Values in parentheses are ranges, estimate "c" (cf. Introduction).

	Age	Nervous Tissue	Electrolyte	Value mg/100 g fresh tissue	Reference
	(A)	(B)	(C)	(D)	(E)
1	Fetus	Whole brain	Silicon	0.51	5
2		Cerebral hemispheres	Calcium	(8-11)	4
3			Chloride	(125-142)	
4			Iron	(0.49-0.57)	
5			Magnesium	(8-11)	
6			Phosphorus, total	(170-173)	
7			Potassium	(134-186)	
8			Sodium	(168-237)	
9			Sulfur, total	(61-74)	
10	Infant 6 wk	Whole brain	Phosphorus, total	193	6
11			Sulfur, total	58	
12	2 yr	White matter	Phosphorus, total	343	
13			Sulfur, total	148	
14		Gray matter	Phosphorus, total	233	
15			Sulfur, total	82	
16	Adult	Whole brain	Calcium	11	12
17			Copper	0.238	11
18			Magnesium	14	12
19			Phosphorus, total	328	12
20			Potassium	(256-293)	9, 12
21			Sodium	148	9
22			Sulfur, total	207	12
23		White matter	Calcium	11(8-14)	14, 15
24			Chloride	146(128-160)	2, 13, 15
25			Iron	2.59	14
26			Magnesium	26	15
27			Phosphorus, total	424(366-468)	3, 6, 13, 15
28			Potassium	316(232-379)	7, 13, 15
29			Sodium	192(158-225)	13, 15
30			Sulfur, total	122(92-152)	6, 15
31		Gray matter	Calcium	9(7-10)	14, 15
32			Chloride	173(113-215)	2, 13, 15
33			Iron	2.99	14
34			Magnesium	20	15
35			Phosphorus, total	229(203-245)	3, 6, 13, 15
36			Potassium	300(228-345)	7, 13, 15
37				370	8
38				380(350-400)	10
39			Sodium	198(193-203)	13, 15
40				143(130-153)	10
41			Sulfur, total	67(56-77)	6, 15
42		Cerebellum	Zinc	0.70	1
43		Caudate nucleus	Phosphorus, total	294	3
44		Spinal cord	Calcium	18	15
45			Chloride	152	
46			Magnesium	38	
47			Phosphorus, total	548	
48			Potassium	361	
49			Sodium	201	
50			Sulfur	85	
51		Peripheral nerve	Calcium	20	15
52			Chloride	170	2
53			Phosphorus, total	371	15
54			Potassium	295(194-395)	7, 15

Part I: MAN (Concluded)

Contributors: (a) Logan, J. E., (b) Himwich, Williamina A., (c) Elliott, K. A. C., (d) Abood, L. G.

References: [1] Cholak, J., D. M. Hubbard, and R. E. Burkey. 1943. Indust. Engin. Chem., Analyt. Ed. 15:754. [2] Close, H. G. 1933. Biochem. J., Lond. 27:967. [3] Cohen, M. M. 1955. J. Neuropath. 14:70. [4] Kimitsuki, M. 1955. Fukuoka acta med. 46:998. [5] King, E. J., H. Stantial, and M. Dolan. 1933. Biochem. J., Lond. 27:1002. [6] Koch, W., and S. A. Mann. 1907. J. Physiol., Lond. 36:36. [7] Leulier, A., B. Pommé, and A. Bernard. 1935. C. rend. Soc. biol. 119:1228. [8] McLennan, H., and E. J. Harris. 1954. Biochem. J., Lond. 57:329. [9] Ohtsu, T. 1956. Jap. J. M. Sc. Biol. 9:117. [10] Pappius, H. M., and K. A. C. Elliott. 1954. Canad. J. Biochem. Physiol. 32:484. [11] Porter, H., and S. Ainsworth. 1959. J. Neurochem. 5:91. [12] Shohl, A. T. 1939. Mineral metabolism. Reinhold, New York. [13] Stewart-Wallace, A. M. 1939. Brain, Lond. 62:426. [14] Tingey, A. H. 1956. J. Ment. Sc., Lond. 102:178. [15] Weil, A. 1914. Zschr. physiol. Chem. 89:349.

Part II: VERTEBRATES OTHER THAN MAN

Values in parentheses are ranges, estimate "c" (cf. Introduction).

Animal	Age	Nervous Tissue	Electrolyte	Value mg/100 g fresh tissue	Reference
(A)	(B)	(C)	(D)	(E)	(F)
1 Cat	Young	Whole brain	Chloride	153	56
2			Phosphorus, total	238	
3			Potassium	339	
4			Sodium	127	
5	Adult	Whole brain	Calcium	(4-17)	31
6			Chloride	138	56
7				(212-217)	2, 5
8			Phosphorus, total	298	56
9				320	47
10			Potassium	343	56
11				360	55
12			Sodium	121	56
13				130	55
14		Gray matter	Potassium	390(360-410)	42
15			Sodium	145(129-157)	
16		Peripheral nerve	Chloride	216	2
17			Phosphorus, total	406(381-433)	33, 35, 41
18			Potassium	162	26
19			Sodium	199	26
20		Sciatic nerve	Calcium	(15.5-43.6)	32
21			Chloride	220	25
22			Potassium	180	25
23				(148-280)	32
24			Sodium	221	25
25 Cattle	Young	White matter	Calcium	16	53
26			Chloride	176	
27			Magnesium	41	
28			Phosphorus, total	433	
29			Potassium	250	
30			Sodium	144	
31			Sulfur, total	98	
32		Gray matter	Calcium	13	53
33			Chloride	123	
34			Magnesium	23	
35			Phosphorus, total	254	
36			Potassium	340	
37			Sodium	105	
38			Sulfur, total	59	

Part II: VERTEBRATES OTHER THAN MAN (Continued)

	Animal	Age	Nervous Tissue	Electrolyte	Value mg/100 g fresh tissue	Reference
	(A)	(B)	(C)	(D)	(E)	(F)
39	Cattle	Young	Spinal cord	Calcium	32	53
40	(con-	(con-		Chloride	130	
41	cluded)	cluded)		Magnesium	48	
42				Phosphorus, total	517	
43				Potassium	261	
44				Sodium	134	
45				Sulfur, total	104	
46		Adult	Spinal cord	Potassium	(277-351)	11
47				Sodium	(177-223)	
48			Obturator nerve	Potassium	156	11
49				Sodium	214	
50			Optic nerve	Copper	0.18	9
51	Dog	Adult	Brain parts	Chloride	(138-180)	52
52				Potassium	(300-499)	
53				Sodium	(142-161)	
54			White matter	Chloride	153	52
55				Phosphorus, total	409(376-441)	34, 52
56				Potassium	420	52
57				Sodium	134	52
58			Gray matter	Chloride	169	52
59				Phosphorus, total	251(240-261)	34, 52
60				Potassium	401	52
61				Sodium	161	12, 52
62			Spinal cord	Chloride	170	52
63				Phosphorus, total	546	
64				Potassium	370	
65				Sodium	182	
66			Peripheral nerve	Phosphorus, total	236	52
67			Sciatic nerve	Chloride	280	52
68				Potassium	(160-187)	
69				Sodium	(393-448)	
70	Guinea pig	3-5 da	Whole brain	Chloride	133	40
71				Potassium	380	
72				Sodium	121	
73		Adult	Whole brain	Calcium	(4-11)	31
74				Phosphorus, total	297	44
75				Potassium	384(374-393)	24, 48
76			Gray matter	Chloride	161	49
77			Spinal cord	Phosphorus, total	500	44
78			Peripheral nerve	Phosphorus, total	409	44
79	Horse	Adult	Peripheral nerve	Chloride	232(230-234)	2
80				Phosphorus, total	250	3, 17
81				Potassium	156(132-180)	4, 17
82				Sodium	450	17
83				Sulfur, total	40	17
84	Monkey	Adult	White matter	Phosphorus, total	467	7
85			Gray matter	Phosphorus, total	298	7
86			Peripheral nerve	Phosphorus, total	388	7
87			Sciatic nerve	Potassium	(101-209)	25
88				Sodium	(173-279)	
89	Mouse	Newborn	Whole brain	Phosphorus, total	247	23
90				Sulfur, total	139	38
91		Adult	Whole brain	Chloride	103(102-104)	50, 54
92				Phosphorus, total	318	38
93					381(315-447)	1, 51
94				Potassium	404(394-413)	50, 54
95					370	19
96				Sodium	101(98-104)	50, 54
97				Sulfur, total	163	38

Part II: VERTEBRATES OTHER THAN MAN (Continued)

	Animal	Age	Nervous Tissue	Electrolyte	Value mg/100 g fresh tissue	Reference
	(A)	(B)	(C)	(D)	(E)	(F)
98	Rabbit	Adult	Whole brain	Chloride	176	36
99				Manganese	0.036	15
100				Potassium	386	48
101				Sodium	179	36
102			Brain parts	Chloride	(128-163)	36
103				Sodium	(92-145)	
104			Cerebral hemispheres	Potassium	(350-354)	21
105			White matter	Chloride	148(129-166)	28, 36
106				Potassium	369	29
107			Gray matter	Chloride	157(141-173)	28, 36
108				Potassium	399	29
109				Sodium	120	36
110			Spinal cord	Chloride	(142-148)	36
111				Potassium	337	29
112				Sodium	(143-144)	36
113			Peripheral nerve	Chloride	178	36
114				Phosphorus, total	393	37
115				Potassium	185(151-218)	29, 39
116				Sodium	158(136-179)	36, 39
117			Sciatic nerve	Calcium	(28.3-40.0)	32
118				Potassium	(173-410)	
119	Rat	2 da	Whole brain	Chloride	156	27
120		4-7 da	Whole brain	Chloride	152	27, 40
121				Potassium	322	40
122				Sodium	141	40
123		10 and 20 da	Whole brain	Chloride	151(149-152)	27
124		28-32 da	Whole brain	Chloride	117(109-124)	27, 40
125				Potassium	388	40
126				Sodium	110	40
127		70 da	Whole brain	Chloride	113	27
128		Adult	Whole brain	Calcium	11	46
129				Chloride	113(106-120)	36
130				Magnesium	14	30
131				Phosphorus, total	(195-304)	13, 20, 30
132				Potassium	379(344-409)	14, 16, 36, 40
133					314	22
134				Sodium	(118-156)	16, 22
135					114(110-118)	16, 40
136			Gray matter	Potassium	426	43
137				Sodium	104	
138	Sheep	Adult	Whole brain	Phosphorus, total	369	10
139			Gray matter	Potassium	271	45
140			Optic nerve	Copper	0.26	9
141				Zinc	0.26	
142	Swine	Adult	Whole brain	Chloride	(140-180)	8
143	Chicken	1 da	Whole brain	Chloride	117	27
144		3 da	Whole brain	Chloride	110	
145		7 da	Whole brain	Chloride	121	
146		26 da	Whole brain	Chloride	99	
147		42 da	Whole brain	Chloride	106	
148	Frog		Peripheral nerve	Phosphorus, total	330(220-410)	17
149	Bull-		Nerve	Phosphorus, total	290	18
150	Grass-		Nerve	Phosphorus, total	425	18
151	Perch		Whole brain	Chloride	(142-181)	6

Contributors: (a) Logan, J. E., (b) Himwich, Williamina A., (c) Schafer, David E., and Visscher, Maurice B., (d) Elliott, K. A. C.

107. NERVE ELECTROLYTES: VERTEBRATES AND INVERTEBRATES (Continued)

Part II: VERTEBRATES OTHER THAN MAN (Concluded)

References: [1] Albrecht, W. 1956. Zschr. Naturforsch., Ser. B, 11:248. [2] Alcock, N. H., and G. R. Lynch. 1907. J. Physiol., Lond. 36:93. [3] Alcock, N. H., and G. R. Lynch. 1910. Ibid. 39:402. [4] Alcock, N. H., and G. R. Lynch. 1911. Ibid. 42:107. [5] Amberson, W. 1938. Am. J. Physiol. 122:224. [6] Black, V. S. 1946. Rev. canad. biol. 5:311. [7] Bodian, D., and D. Dziewiatkowski. 1950. J. Cellul. Physiol. 35:155. [8] Bohosiewicz, M. 1945. Med. wet., Warsz. 10:148. [9] Bowness, J. M., R. A. Morton, M. H. Shakir, and A. L. Stublis. 1952. Biochem. J., Lond. 51:521. [10] Davidson, J. N., and C. Waymouth. 1944. Ibid. 38:39. [11] Davies, F., R. F. Davies, E. T. B. Francis, and R. Whittam. 1952. J. Physiol., Lond. 118:276. [12] Davies, R. E., and H. A. Krebs. 1952. Biochem. Soc. Symp. 8:77. [13] Donaldson, H. H. 1924. The rat: data and reference tables. Ed. 2. Wistar Institute of Anatomy and Biology, Philadelphia. [14] Ellison, R. J., W. P. Wilson, and E. B. Weiss. 1958. Proc. Soc. Exp. Biol., N. Y. 98:128. [15] Fore, H., and R. A. Morton. 1952. Biochem. J., Lond. 51:600. [16] Gell, C. F., B. D. Polis, and O. Bailey. 1955. Am. J. Physiol. 183:23. [17] Gerard, R. W. 1932. Physiol. Rev. 12:469. [18] Gerard, R. W., and N. Tupikova. 1939. J. Cellul. Physiol. 13:1. [19] Gollan, F., and M. B. Visscher. 1951. Proc. Soc. Exp. Biol., N. Y. 76:746. [20] Hess, A. F., J. Gross, M. Weinstock, and F. S. Berliner. 1932. J. Biol. Chem. 98:625. [21] Himwich, W. A., and W. T. Sullivan. 1956. J. Nerv. Ment. Dis. 124:21. [22] Hoagland, H., and D. Stone. 1948. Am. J. Physiol. 152:423. [23] King, E. J., H. Stantial, and M. Dolan. 1933. Biochem. J., Lond. 27:1002. [24] Krebs, H. A., L. V. Eggleston, and C. Terner. 1951. Ibid. 48:530. [25] Krnjević, K. 1955. J. Physiol., Lond. 128:473. [26] Krnjević, K. 1957. Ibid. 135:281. [27] Lajtha, A. 1957. J. Neurochem., Lond. 1:216. [28] Leovey, F., and E. Kerpel-Fronius. 1928. Arch. exp. Path., Lpz. 138:372. [29] Leulier, A., B. Pommé, and A. Bernard. 1935. C. rend. Soc. biol. 119:1228. [30] Leut'skii, K. H. 1946. Ukrain. Biokhim. Z. 18:87. [31] Linder, G. C. 1940. Biochem. J., Lond. 34:1574. [32] Lissak, K., T. Kovaks. 1942. Pflügers Arch. 245:790. [33] Logan, J. E. 1952. Canad. J. M. Sc. 30:457. [34] Logan, J. E., W. A. Mannell, and R. J. Rossiter. 1952. Biochem. J., Lond. 51:470. [35] Logan, J. E., W. A. Mannell, and R. J. Rossiter. 1952. Ibid. 51:482. [36] Manery, J. F., and A. B. Hastings. 1939. J. Biol. Chem. 127:657. [37] May, R. M. 1930. Bull. Soc. chim. biol., Par. 12:934. [38] May, R. M. 1948. Rev. canad. biol. 7:642. [39] McLennan, H., and E. J. Harris. 1954. Biochem. J., Lond. 57:329. [40] Millichop, J. G., M. Balter, and P. Hernandez. 1958. Proc. Soc. Exp. Biol., N. Y. 99:6. [41] Mott, F. W., and W. D. Halliburton. 1901. Philos. Tr. R. Soc. London, Ser. B, 194:437. [42] Pappius, H. M., and K. A. C. Elliott. 1954. Canad. J. Biochem. Physiol. 32:484. [43] Pappius, H. M., and K. A. C. Elliott. 1956. Ibid. 34:1053. [44] Samuels, A. J., L. L. Boyarsky, R. W. Gerard, B. Libet, and M. Brust. 1951. Am. J. Physiol. 164:1. [45] Setchell, B. P., and G. L. McClymont. 1955. Nature, Lond. 175:998. [46] Streicher, E. 1958. Am. J. Physiol. 194:390. [47] Strickland, K. P. 1952. Canad. J. M. Sc. 30:484. [48] Terner, C., L. V. Eggleston, and H. A. Krebs. 1950. Biochem. J., Lond. 47:139. [49] Thomas, J., and H. McIlwain. 1956. J. Neurochem., Lond. 1:1. [50] Timuras, P. S., D. M. Woodbury, and L. S. Goodman. 1954. J. Pharm. Exp. Ther. 112:80. [51] Torda, C., and H. G. Wolff. 1954. Endocrinology 54:649. [52] Tupikova, N., and R. W. Gerard. 1937. Am. J. Physiol. 119:414. [53] Weil, A. 1914. Zschr. physiol. Chem. 89:349. [54] Woodbury, D. M., and A. Koch. 1957. Proc. Soc. Exp. Biol., N. Y. 94:720. [55] Yannet, H. 1939. Arch. Neur. Psychiat., Chic. 42:237. [56] Yannet, H., and D. C. Darrow. 1938. J. Biol. Chem. 123:295.

Part III: INVERTEBRATES

Animal	Nervous Tissue	Electrolyte	Value mg/100 g fresh tissue	Reference
(A)	(B)	(C)	(D)	(E)
1 Periplaneta americana	Nerve	Magnesium	7	3
2		Potassium	420	
3		Sodium	140	
4 Carcinus sp	Leg nerve	Calcium	52	2
5		Chloride	513	
6		Magnesium	56	
7		Potassium	1014	
8		Sodium	350	
9 Sepia officinalis	Axoplasm	Chloride	255	1
10		Phosphorus	78	
11		Potassium	1260	
12		Sodium	106	

Contributors: (a) Himwich, Williamina A., (b) Schafer, David E., and Visscher, Maurice B.

References: [1] Keynes, R. D., and P. R. Lewis. 1951. J. Physiol., Lond. 114:151. [2] Lewis, P. R. 1952. Biochem. J., Lond. 52:330. [3] Tobias, J. M. 1948. J. Cellul. Physiol. 31:125.

108. WATER CONTENT OF NERVOUS TISSUE: VERTEBRATES

Where multiple references appear in column E, the mean value has been calculated from the means reported in the literature. Values in parentheses are ranges, estimate "c" (cf. Introduction).

Animal	Age	Tissue	Water g/100 g fresh tissue	Reference
(A)	(B)	(C)	(D)	(E)
1 Man	Fetus	Cerebral hemispheres	(91-92)	19
2	Infant	Whole brain	90	5,6
3		Brain parts	(86-91)	4,18
4		White matter	91	18
5		Gray matter	91	18
6		Spinal cord	82	5
7		Peripheral nerve	77	5
8	6 wk	Whole brain	89	20
9	6 mo	Whole brain	80	11
10	2 yr	White matter	77	20
11		Gray matter	85	
12	Other immature	Whole brain	(78-87)	6
13			76	5
14		Spinal cord	73	5
15		Peripheral nerve	64	5
16	Adult	Whole brain	77(76-78)	2,5,11
17			(77-79)	6,41
18		Brain parts	(71-85)	4,17,18,42
19		White matter	70(68-73)	2,4,9,11,15,18,20,33,36,45
20		Gray matter	84(82-85)	2,4,9,11,15,18,20,33,36,45
21		Spinal cord	71(63-75)	5,15,33,40,45
22		Peripheral nerve	66(62-68)	5,38,45
23 Cat	Young	Whole brain	85	47
24	Adult	Whole brain	81	47
25			78	11
26			72	29
27		White matter	69	15
28		Gray matter	82	15

	Animal	Age	Tissue	Water g/100 g fresh tissue	Reference
	(A)	(B)	(C)	(D)	(E)
29	Cat (con-	Adult (con-	Spinal cord	71	15
30	cluded)	cluded)		68	30
31			Peripheral nerve	65(61-67)	3,15,23,32
32			Sciatic nerve	(66-69)	22
33	Cattle	Young	Whole brain	81	11
34			White matter	71(70-73)	45
35			Gray matter	82(82-83)	45
36			Spinal cord	63(63-64)	45
37		Adult[1]	Whole brain	77	11
38			White matter	70(68-71)	2,33,37
39			Gray matter	82(81-82)	2,37
40			Spinal cord	64(64-65)	1,33
41			Peripheral nerve	66	1
42	Dog	Adult	Whole brain	84	11
43			White matter	69(64-71)	2,15,25,33,35,44
44			Gray matter	81(79-82)	2,15,25,35,44
45			Spinal cord	69(67-70)	15,44
46			Peripheral nerve	66(57-71)	3,13,28,44
47	Goat	Adult	Pheripheral nerve	75	3
48	Guinea pig	3-5 da	Whole brain	81	31
49		Adult	Whole brain	79	29
50			Spinal cord	71	30
51	Horse	Adult	Whole brain	71	11
52			Peripheral nerve	69(68-69)	3,33
53	Monkey	Adult	Whole brain	78	11
54			White matter	70	15
55			Gray matter	82	15
56			Spinal cord	70	15
57	Mouse	Newborn	Whole brain	87	27
58		Adult	Whole brain	77	27
59				79(77-80)	27,43,46
60	Rabbit	Adult	Whole brain	79(78-80)	9
61				(81-85)	14,29
62			Brain parts	(77-83)	16,26
63			White matter	70(65-76)	26,34
64			Gray matter	82(81-82)	26,34,39
65			Spinal cord	69	26
66				(67-71)	26,30
67			Peripheral nerve	62(59-66)	26,39
68	Rat	4-7 da	Whole brain	88(87-88)	24,31
69		28-32 da	Whole brain	81	31
70		Adult	Whole brain	(77-88)	8,26
71				78(77-78)	10,12,24,26,31
72			Gray matter	(81-82)	36
73				78	39
74	Sheep	Adult	White matter	75(74-76)	2,7
75			Gray matter	84	
76	Swine	Adult	Whole brain	77	11
77	Chicken	3 da	Whole brain	84	24
78		5 da	Whole brain	84	
79		7 da	Whole brain	82	
80		12 da	Whole brain	81	
81		Adult	Whole brain	78	
82	Goose	Adult	Whole brain	83	2
83	Pigeon	106 da-9 yr	Whole brain	(78-80)	21
84	Frog	Adult	Whole brain	84	2
85			Peripheral nerve	85	13
86	Carp	Adult	Whole brain	74	2

/1/ Ox or cow.

Contributors: (a) Logan, J. E., (b) Himwich, Williamina A.

References: [1] Abderhalden, E., and A. Weil. 1912. Zschr. physiol. Chem. 81:207. [2] Abderhalden, E., and A. Weil. 1913. Ibid. 83:425. [3] Alcock, N. H., and G. R. Lynch. 1907. J. Physiol., Lond. 36:93. [4] Brante, G. 1949. Acta physiol. scand., Suppl. 63, p. 1. [5] Bürger, M. 1956. Medizinische 15:561. [6] Bürger, M. 1957. Abh. sächs. Akad. Wiss. 45:1. [7] Davidson, J. N., and C. Waymouth. 1944. Biochem. J., Lond. 38:39. [8] Donaldson, H. H., and S. Haitai. 1931. J. Comp. Neur. 53:263. [9] Elliott, K. A. C., and H. Jasper. 1949. Am. J. Physiol. 157:122. [10] Ellison, R. J., W. P. Wilson, and E. B. Weiss. 1958. Proc. Soc. Exp. Biol., N. Y. 98:128. [11] Frankel, S., and K. Linnert. 1910. Biochem. Zschr. 26:44. [12] Gell, C. F., B. D. Polis, and O. Bailey. 1955. Am. J. Physiol. 183:23. [13] Gerard, R. W. 1932. Physiol. Rev. 12:469. [14] Graves, J., and H. E. Himwich. 1955. Am. J. Physiol. 180:205. [15] Halliburton, W. D. 1894. J. Physiol., Lond. 15:90. [16] Himwich, W. A., and H. E. Himwich. In J. S. Birren, ed. 1959. Aging and the individual. University of. Chicago Press, Chicago. p. 206. [17] Himwich, W. A., W. T. Sullivan, B. Kelley, H. B. W. Benaron, and B. E. Tucker. In press. J. Nerv. Ment. Dis. [18] Johnson, A. C., A. R. McNabb, and R. J. Rossiter. 1949. Biochem. J., Lond. 44:494. [19] Kimitsuki, M. 1955. Fukuoka acta med. 46:998. [20] Koch, W., and S. A. Mann. 1907. J. Physiol., Lond. 36:36. [21] Koch, M. L., and O. Riddle. 1919. J. Comp. Neur. 31:83. [22] Krnjević, K. 1955. J. Physiol., Lond. 128:473. [23] Krnjević, K. 1957. Ibid. 135:281. [24] Lajtha, A. 1956. J. Neurochem., Lond. 1:216. [25] Logan, J. E. Unpublished. [26] Manery, J. F., and A. B. Hastings. 1939. J. Biol. Chem. 127:657. [27] May, R. M. 1948. Rev. canad. biol. 7:642. [28] May, R. M., and J. Arnoux. 1940. Bull. Soc. chim. biol., Par. 22:286. [29] McColl, J. D., and R. J. Rossiter. 1952. J. Exp. Biol., Lond. 29:196. [30] McColl, J. D., and R. J. Rossiter. 1952. Ibid. 29:203. [31] Millichop, J. G., M. Balter, and P. Hernandez. 1958. Proc. Soc. Exp. Biol., N. Y. 99:6. [32] Mott, F. W., and H. D. Halliburton. 1901. Philos. Tr. R. Soc., Lond., Ser. B, 194:437. [33] Noll, A. 1899. Zschr. physiol. chem. 27:370. [34] Palladin, A., and W. Bjeljaewa. 1924. Hoppe Seyler Zschr. 141:33. [35] Palladin, A., and D. Zuwerkalow. 1924. Ibid. 139:57. [36] Pappius, H. M., and K. A. C. Elliott. 1956. Canad. J. Biochem. Physiol. 34:1007. [37] Petrowsky, D. 1873. Arch. ges. Physiol. 7:367. [38] Randall, L. O. 1938. J. Biol. Chem. 125:723. [39] Rosenthal, O., and D. L. Drabkin. 1943. Ibid. 150:131. [40] Schuwirth, K. 1943. Hoppe Seyler Zschr. 278:1. [41] Shohl, A. T. 1939. Mineral metabolism. Reinhold, New York. [42] Tilney, F., and J. Rosett. 1931. Bull. Neur. Inst. N. York 1:28. [43] Timuras, P. S., D. M. Woodbury, and L. S. Goodman. 1954. J. Pharm. Exp. Ther. 112:80. [44] Tupikova, N., and R. W. Gerard. 1937. Am. J. Physiol. 119:414. [45] Weil, A. 1914. Zschr. physiol. Chem. 89:349. [46] Woodbury, D. M., and A. Koch. 1957. Proc. Soc. Exp. Biol., N. Y. 94:720. [47] Yannet, H., and D. C. Darrow. 1938. J. Biol. Chem. 123:295.

XVII. Fluids of Body Cavities

109. PHYSICAL PROPERTIES AND CHEMICAL COMPOSITION OF SYNOVIAL FLUID: MAMMALS

Part I: MAN

All values are for synovial fluid from the knee joint. Values in parentheses are ranges, estimate "c" unless otherwise indicated (cf. Introduction).

	Property or Constituent	No. of Observations	Value	Reference
	(A)	(B)	(C)	(D)
	Physical Properties			
1	pH		7.39(7.29-7.45)	11
2	Specific gravity		(1.008-1.015)	4
3	Viscosity, intrinsic	26	46.3	15
4	Volume	46+	1.1(0.13-4.00) ml	9, 11, 15
	General Chemical Components			
	Leukocytes			2
5	Total	16	63(13-180) cells/cu mm	
6	Polymorphonuclear	16	6.5(0-25) %	
7	Clasmatocytes	16	10.1(0-26) %	
8	Lymphocytes	16	24.6(6-78) %	
9	Monocytes	16	47.9(0-77) %	
10	Synovial cells	16	4.3(0-12) %	
11	Unclassified phagocytes	16	4.9(0-21) %	
12	Unidentified cells	16	2.2(0-10) %	
13	Solids, total	8+	3.41(1.20-4.83) g/100 g	3, 4, 11
	Electrolytes			
14	Calcium	3	9.7(8.3-10.7) mg/100 ml	1
15	Carbon dioxide	17	57.1(43.1-68.1) vol %	1
16	Potassium	10	4.0(3.5-4.5)[b] mEq/L	16
17	Sodium	10	136.1(132.8-139.4)[b] mEq/L	16
	Nitrogenous Substances			
18	Protein, total	40+	1.72(0.45-3.15) g/100 ml	3, 4, 6, 8, 11-15
19		8	2.80 g/100 ml	8
20	Albumin	1	1.02 g/100 ml	11
21		8	1.89 g/100 ml[1]	8
22	Globulin	1	0.05 g/100 ml	11
23		8	0.91 g/100 ml[1]	8
24	Uric acid	8	3.9(3.3-4.7) mg/100 ml	1
	Nitrogen			
25	Total N	11	0.88(0.71-1.16) g/100 ml	1
26	Non-protein N	9	32.4(22-43) mg/100 ml	1
27	Mucin N	5	104(68-135) mg/100 ml	11
	Carbohydrates, Miscellaneous Organic Acids			
28	Glucosamine, mucin	5	87(50-132) mg/100 ml	11
29	Sugar	14	94.6(68-120) mg/100 ml	1
30	Hyaluronic acid	2+	157(4-297) mg/100 ml	5, 10, 14, 15
31	Lactic acid	2	20.5(13-28) mg/100 ml	1
32	Sialic acid	10	28(16-42) mg/100 ml	7

/1/ Calculated from electrophoretic pattern.

Contributors: (a) Ropes, Marian W., and Bauer, Walter, (b) Sokoloff, Leon, (c) Hunter, John, (d) Platt, David

References: [1] Cajori, F. A., C. Y. Crouter, and R. Pemberton. 1926. Arch. Int. M. 37:92. [2] Coggeshall, H. C., C. F. Warren, and W. Bauer. 1940. Anat. Rec. 77:129. [3] Fisher, A. G. T. 1929. Chronic

Part I: MAN (Concluded)

(non-tuberculous) arthritis. Macmillan, New York. [4] Horiye, K. 1924. Virchows Arch. 251:649. [5] Meyer, K. 1947. Physiol. Rev. 27:335. [6] Olhagen, B. 1950. Acta orthop. scand. 20:114. [7] Pigman, W., W. L. Hawkins, M. G. Blair, and H. L. Holley. 1958. Arthritis Rheum. 1:151. [8] Platt, D., W. Pigman, H. L. Holley, and F. M. Patton. 1956. Arch. Biochem., N. Y. 64:152. [9] Ragan, C. 1946. Proc. Soc. Exp. Biol., N. Y. 63:572. [10] Ragan, C., and K. Meyer. 1949. J. Clin. Invest. 28:56. [11] Ropes, M. W., and W. Bauer. 1953. Synovial fluid changes in joint disease. Harvard University Press, Cambridge. [12] Sandson, J., and D. Hamerman. 1958. Proc. Soc. Exp. Biol., N. Y. 98:564. [13] Schmid, K., and M. B. MacNair. 1958. J. Clin. Invest. 37:708. [14] Sundblad, L. 1950. Acta orthop. scand. 20:105. [15] Sundblad, L. 1953. Acta Soc. med. upsal. 58:113. [16] Yielding, K. L., D. Platt, and H. L. Holley. 1954. Proc. Soc. Exp. Biol., N. Y. 85:665.

Part II: CATTLE

Values in parentheses are ranges, estimate "c" (cf. Introduction).

	Joint	Property or Constituent	No. of Observations	Value	Reference
	(A)	(B)	(C)	(D)	(E)
1	Astragalotibial	Freezing point depression	6	0.535(0.509-0.556) °C	9
2		Osmotic pressure	10	150(127-170) mm H_2O	9
3		pH	23	7.31(7.17-7.43)	9
4		Specific gravity	15	1.010(1.009-1.012)	9
		Viscosity, relative			
5		At 25°C	7+	3.72(2.84-4.15)	9
6		At 20°C	89	5(2-12)	3
7		Volume	124	25(5-65) ml	3
8		Base, total	18	163.2(152.5-180.8) mEq/L	9
		Leukocytes			10
9		Total	25	181.8(55-575) cells/cu mm	
10		Polymorphonuclear	25	2.2(0-8) %	
11		Clasmatocytes	25	15(0-36) %	
12		Lymphocytes	25	40.1(5-62) %	
13		Monocytes	25	36.4(12-54) %	
14		Synovial cells	25	1.2(0-6) %	
15		Unclassified phagocytes	25	3.9(0-16) %	
16		Unidentified cells	25	1.2(0-6) %	
17		Solids, total	15	2.084(1.672-3.886) g/100 g	9
18		Bicarbonate	15	28.5(25.3-31.8) mEq/L	9
19		Calcium	15	3.8(2.7-4.3) mEq/L	9
20		Chloride	31	110.5(104.9-116.3) mEq/L	9
21		Magnesium	8	1.44(1.33-1.72) mEq/L	9
22		Phosphorus	15	2.2(1.5-3.0) mEq/L	9
23		Potassium	6	4.04(3.6-4.4) mEq/L	9
24		Sodium	6	145(140.1-147.8) mEq/L	9
25		Sulfate	6	4.96(4.53-5.42) mEq/L	9
26		Protein, total	36	0.89(0.44-1.41) g/100 ml	5, 9
27				0.80 g/100 ml[1]	8
28		Albumin	7	0.62(0.44-0.86) g/100 ml	9
29				0.44 g/100 ml[1]	8
30		Globulin	7	0.26(0.12-0.34) g/100 ml	9
31				0.36 g/100 ml[1]	8
32		Uric acid	7	1.55(1.20-2.08) mg/100 ml	9
		Nitrogen			
33		Non-protein N	30	21(15-28) mg/100 ml	9
34		Mucin N	12	22(5-40) mg/100 ml	5, 9
35		Hyaluronic acid		(20-25) mg/100 ml	6

/1/ Calculated from electrophoretic pattern.

Part II: CATTLE (Concluded)

	Joint	Property or Constituent	No. of Observations	Value	Reference
	(A)	(B)	(C)	(D)	(E)
36	Atlanto-epistrophial	Leukocytes, total	21	888.4(549-1604) cells/cu mm	4
37	Atlanto-occipital	Leukocytes, total	22	783.9(542-1208) cells/cu mm	4
38	Carpometacarpal	Viscosity, relative, at 25°C	4+	64(29-129)	2
39		Volume	15+	(3.5-15.0) ml	1, 3
		Leukocytes			10
40		Total	12	213.3(100-555) cells/cu mm	
41		Polymorphonuclear	12	1.2(0-4) %	
42		Clasmatocytes	12	7.2(0-14) %	
43		Lymphocytes	12	23(8-44) %	
44		Monocytes	12	63(42-80) %	
45		Synovial cells	12	1.7(0-6) %	
46		Unclassified phagocytes	12	3(0-8) %	
47		Unidentified cells	12	1(0-2) %	
48		Nitrogen, mucin	2	96(63-202) mg/100 ml	2
49	Elbow	Leukocytes, total	15	197.3(53-500) cells/cu mm	4
50	Hip	Volume		(3-27) ml	3
51	Knee	Viscosity, relative, at 20°C	126	51(3.5-575.0)	3
52		Volume	116	10(0-42) ml	3
53		Leukocytes, total	41	246.6(86-483) cells/cu mm	4
54	Temporomandibular	Leukocytes, total	22	1337.5(800-1756) cells/cu mm	4
55	Unspecified	Glucosamine, mucin	3	(22-47) mg/100 ml	7

Contributors: (a) Ropes, Marian W., and Bauer, Walter, (b) Sokoloff, Leon, (c) Hunter, John, (d) Platt, David, (e) Manery, J. F.

References: [1] Bauer, W., G. A. Bennett, A. Marble, and D. Claflin. 1930. J. Exp. M. 52:835. [2] Bauer, W., M. W. Ropes, and H. Waine. 1940. Physiol. Rev. 20:272. [3] Davies, D. V. 1944. J. Anat., Lond. 78:68. [4] Davies, D. V. 1945. Ibid. 79:66. [5] Fisher, A. G. T. 1929. Chronic (non-tuberculous) arthritis. Macmillan, New York. [6] Meyer, K. 1947. Physiol. Rev. 27:335. [7] Ogston, A. G., and J. E. Stanier. 1950. Biochem. J., Lond. 46:364. [8] Platt, D., W. Pigman, H. L. Holley, and F. M. Patton. 1956. Arch. Biochem., N. Y. 64:152. [9] Ropes, M. W., G. A. Bennett, and W. Bauer. 1939. J. Clin. Invest. 18:351. [10] Warren, C. F., G. A. Bennett, and W. Bauer. 1935. Am. J. Path. 11:953.

Part III: MAMMALS OTHER THAN MAN, CATTLE

Values in parentheses are ranges, estimate "c" (cf. Introduction).

	Animal	Joint	Property or Constituent	No. of Observations	Value	Reference
	(A)	(B)	(C)	(D)	(E)	(F)
1	Dog	Knee	pH		(7.29-7.37)	5
2			Volume		(0-0.3) ml	6
			Leukocytes			9
3			Total	14	963.8(327-1450) cells/cu mm	
4			Polymorphonuclear	14	1.7(0-7) %	
5			Clasmatocytes	14	6.5(0-20) %	
6			Lymphocytes	14	15.7(2-36) %	
7			Monocytes	14	68.5(56-90) %	
8			Synovial cells	14	4.8(1-9) %	
9			Unclassified phagocytes	14	3.4(0-14) %	
10		Carpal	Nitrogen, mucin		(43-58) g/100 ml	1,6

	Animal	Joint	Property or Constituent	No. of Observations	Value	Reference
	(A)	(B)	(C)	(D)	(E)	(F)
11	Horse	Astragalotibial	Leukocytes, total	18	192(72-368) cells/cu mm	2
12			Calcium	5	2.6(2.15-3.12) mEq/L	3
13			Chloride	5	90(88.6-91.6) mEq/L	3
14			Phosphorus	5	2.61(1.80-3.57) mg/100 ml	3
15			Albumin		1.17 g/100 ml[1]	4
16			Globulin			4
			α-		0.37 g/100 ml[1]	
17			β-		0.32 g/100 ml[1]	
18			Uric acid	5	5.3(5.0-5.6) mg/100 ml	3
19			Nitrogen, non-protein	5	31.6(27.6-38.4) mg/100 ml	3
20			Reducing sugar	5	83(76.9-88.2) mg/100 ml	3
21		Atlanto-epistrophial	Leukocytes, total	10	534(346-678) cells/cu mm	2
22		Atlanto-occipital	Leukocytes, total	5	594(358-1162) cells/cu mm	2
23		Carpal	Protein, total	4	1.4(0.88-1.95) g/100 ml	1
24			Mucin	4	0.47(0.35-0.69) g/100 ml	
25		Elbow	Leukocytes, total	12	207(107-336) cells/cu mm	2
26		Knee	Leukocytes, total	16	671(390-1638) cells/cu mm	2
27		Radiocarpal	Leukocytes, total	17	234(50-453) cells/cu mm	2
28		Temporomandibular	Leukocytes, total	14	983(412-2350) cells/cu mm	2
29			Viscosity			7
			Intrinsic		51.5	
30			Relative, at 25°C	10	(3-29)	
31			Volume	12	(5-40) ml	6,7
32			Protein, total	5	1.9 g/100 ml	7
33			Hyaluronic acid	10	56 mg/100 ml	7
34	Rabbit		Viscosity			7
			Intrinsic	2	37.4	
35			Relative	2	>300	
36		Knee	Volume		(0.1-0.3) ml	6,7
37			Leukocytes			9
			Total	9	242.5(140-330) cells/cu mm	
38			Polymorphonuclear	9	2.2(0-15) %	
39			Clasmatocytes	9	12.7(2-26) %	
40			Lymphocytes	9	1.5(0-6) %	
41			Monocytes	9	65.5(48-77) %	
42			Synovial cells	9	4.2(0-6) %	
43			Unclassified phagocytes	9	13(8-22) %	
44			Unidentified cells	9	0.7(0-4) %	
45			Protein, total	2	3.6 g/100 ml	7
46			Hyaluronic acid	2	389 mg/100 ml	7
47	Sheep 4 mo	Atlanto-occipital	Leukocytes, total	31	1110(602-1974) cells/cu mm	2
48	1 yr	Astragalotibial	Leukocytes, total	24	207.3(81-405) cells/cu mm	
49		Atlanto-epistrophial	Leukocytes, total	14	1060.7(728-1960) cells/cu mm	
50		Elbow	Leukocytes, total	19	200.1(73-411) cells/cu mm	
51		Knee	Leukocytes, total	16	254.7(113-519) cells/cu mm	
52		Radiocarpal	Leukocytes, total	15	157.5(73-298) cells/cu mm	
53		Temporomandibular	Leukocytes, total	13	993.5(347-1478) cells/cu mm	
54	7 yr[2]	Atlanto-occipital	Leukocytes, total	18	611.7(228-1292) cells/cu mm	
55	Whale	Shoulder-head	Freezing point depression		0.671°C	8
56	(Balaenoptera		Calcium		62.5 mg/100 g	
57	borealis)		Chloride		371.3 mg/100 g	
58			Potassium		3.8 mg/100 g	
59			Sodium		201.2 mg/100 g	
60			Nitrogen			
			Non-protein N		(89-104) mg/100 g	
61			Mucin N		0.19 g/100 ml	
62			Reducing sugar		(8-13) mg/100 g	

/1/ Calculated from electrophoretic pattern. /2/ Pregnant.

Contributors: (a) Sokoloff, Leon, (b) Ropes, Marian W., and Bauer, Walter, (c) Hunter, John

References: [1] Bywaters, E. G. L. 1937. J. Path. Bact., Lond. 44:247. [2] Davies, D. V. 1945. J. Anat., Lond. 79:66. [3] Hare, T., and H. Cohen. 1929. Proc. R. Soc. M., Lond. 22:1121. [4] Hesselvik, L. 1940. Acta med. scand. 105:153. [5] Joseph, N. R., C. I. Reed, and E. Homburger. 1946. Am. J. Physiol. 146:1. [6] Ropes, M. W., W. von B. Robertson, E. C. Rossmeisl, R. B. Peabody, and W. Bauer. 1947. Acta med. scand., Suppl. 196, p. 700. [7] Sundblad, L. 1953. Acta Soc. med. upsal. 58:113. [8] Takemura, N. 1927. Jap. J. M. Sc., Ser. 2, 1:153. [9] Warren, C. F., G. A. Bennett, and W. Bauer. 1935. Am. J. Path. 11:953.

110. EFFECT OF JOINT DISEASES ON SYNOVIAL FLUID: MAN

Part I: CELLULAR CONTENT

Clots (column C) are graded: 1 (small) to 4 (large). Values in parentheses are ranges, estimate "c" (cf. Introduction).

	Condition	Synovial Fluid						
						Leukocytes		
		Gross Appearance	Clot	Erythrocytes per cu mm	Total per cu mm	Poly-morpho-nuclear %	Lympho-cytes %	Mono-cytes %
	(A)	(B)	(C)	(D)	(E)	(F)	(G)	(H)
1	Normal	Clear	0	160 (0-2000)	63 (13-180)	7 (0-25)	25 (6-78)	63 (0-71)
2	Arthritis Gouty	Turbid	1.6(0-4)	54,000 (0-616,000)	13,300 (1,000-70,000)	71 (0-99)	8 (0-43)	21 (1-79)
3	Rheumatoid	Clear to turbid	0.5(0-3)	4,000 (0-75,000)	14,000 (450-75,000)	65 (0-96)	20 (0-92)	15 (0-97)
4	Specific infectious	Very turbid	1.4(0-3)	34,000 (0-148,000)	73,370 (7,800-266,000)	90 (46-100)	3 (0-19)	7 (0-44)
5	Traumatic	Clear to slight-ly turbid	0.3(0-1)	2,190 (0-15,650)	1,320 (50-10,400)	5 (0-36)	36 (0-88)	59 (8-83)
6	Traumatic with hemorrhage	Red	0.6(0-2)	1,305,000 (20,000-6,500,000)	1,540 (100-7,500)	17 (0-77)	28 (0-88)	50 (6-95)
7	Tuberculous	Turbid	0.6(0-3)	28,300 (50-229,000)	73,400 (2,500-105,000)	60 (18-96)	20 (3-49)	19 (0-62)
8	Degenerative joint disease	Clear to slight-ly turbid	0.6(0-2)	11,930 (0-169,000)	720 (70-3,600)	7 (0-58)	37 (4-86)	56 (7-100)
9	Lupus erythemato-sus disseminatus	Clear to turbid	0.1(0-2)	38,490 (0-336,000)	2,860 (100-18,200)	5 (0-32)	30 (0-84)	61 (0-100)
10	Pigmented villinodu-lar synovitis	Turbid	0.8(0-3)	682,000 (29,000-2,724,000)	3,100 (400-11,000)	26 (2-61)	33 (12-64)	40 (12-65)
11	Rheumatic fever	Slightly turbid to turbid	1.1(0-3)	65,000 (0-740,000)	17,800 (300-98,200)	50 (2-98)	11 (0-38)	36 (0-88)

Contributor: Ropes, Marian W.

Reference: Ropes, M. W., and W. Bauer. 1953. Synovial fluid changes in joint disease. Harvard University Press, Cambridge.

Part II: CHEMICAL COMPOSITION

Mucin precipitation (column F) is graded: 1 = few or no flecks in a turbid solution; 2 = small, friable masses in a turbid solution; 3 = soft mass in a clear or slightly turbid solution; 4 = tight, rope-like clump in a clear solution. Values in parentheses are ranges, estimate "c" (cf. Introduction).

		Synovial Fluid				
	Condition	Protein, Total g/100 ml	Albumin g/100 ml	Globulin g/100 ml	Sugar Difference[1] mg/100 ml	Mucin Precipitation
	(A)	(B)	(C)	(D)	(E)	(F)
1	Normal	1.72(1.07-2.13)	1.02	0.05	0(0-10)	4
	Arthritis					
2	Gouty	4.2(2.8-5.0)	2.7(1.4-3.4)	1.5(0.9-2.1)	10(0-50)	2(1-4)
3	Rheumatoid	5.0(3.8-8.9)	2.8(2.1-3.7)	2.2(1.2-3.3)	26(14-87)	2(1-4)
4	Specific infectious	4.8(2.9-6.9)	2.7(2.9-6.9)	1.6(1.5-3.8)	71(40-122)	1(1-4)
5	Traumatic	3.90(2.96-5.05)	3.22(2.65-4.04)	0.93(0.66-1.39)	5(0-10)	4(3-4)
6	Traumatic with hemorrhage	3.88(2.85-5.45)	2.81(2.31-3.48)	1.16(0.59-2.02)	12(8-44)	3(2-4)
7	Tuberculous	5.3(4.0-6.0)	3.3(2.8-4.3)	2.0(1.2-2.8)	60(8-108)	2(1-4)
8	Degenerative joint disease	3.08(1.29-4.87)	2.51(1.66-4.87)	0.75(0.33-1.36)	0(0-10)	4(2-4)
9	Lupus erythematosus disseminatus	2.51(1.52-3.78)	1.41(1.11-2.10)	1.15(0.62-1.68)	22(7-24)	4
10	Pigmented villinodular synovitis	4.2(3.7-4.6)	2.9(2.7-3.2)	1.3(1.0-1.5)	22(0-50)	3(1-4)
11	Rheumatic fever	3.7(1.6-4.9)	2.4(1.2-3.0)	1.1(0.3-1.90)	10(5-50)	4(3-4)

/1/ Blood sugar concentration minus synovial fluid glucose concentration.

Contributor: Ropes, Marian W.

Reference: Ropes, M. W., and W. Bauer. 1953. Synovial fluid changes in joint disease. Harvard University Press, Cambridge.

111. PHYSICAL PROPERTIES AND CHEMICAL COMPOSITION OF SEROUS FLUIDS: VERTEBRATES

In transudates the concentration of blood constituents depends on the plasma concentration of the constituent, the membrane permeability of the constituent, the charge of the ion (electrolytes), and the concentrations of non-diffusible ions (proteins) in the plasma and in the transudate. For non-electrolytes readily passing through the membrane, the concentration in transudate water will equal that in plasma water, provided a steady state is present. In the case of electrolytes, the concentrations in the transudate will differ from those in plasma according to the Gibbs-Donnan law for heterogeneous solutions.

Part I: MAN

Values in parentheses are ranges, estimate "c" unless otherwise indicated (cf. Introduction).

	Property or Constituent	Plasma	Transudates	Pleural Fluid	Pericardial Fluid	Peritoneal Fluid	Reference
	(A)	(B)	(C)	(D)	(E)	(F)	(G)
				Physical Properties			
1	Conductivity, mho x 1000	(10.5-12.4)	14.2(11.3-15.5)			13.4(13.2-13.5)	B,C,30;F,21
2	pH	7.39(7.33-7.45)[b]	(7.45-7.68)	7.64(7.60-7.68)		7.4(6.8-9.8)	B,6,9,19;C,F, 13;D,32
3	Specific gravity	1.027(1.025-1.029)[b]	(1.005-1.015)	1.013		1.012	B,24;C,4;D, F,8
				General Chemical Components			
4	Ash, %	(0.6-1.0)		0.76	0.67	0.98	B,12;D,F,18; E,31

Part I: MAN (Continued)

	Property or Constituent	Plasma	Transudates	Pleural Fluid	Pericardial Fluid	Peritoneal Fluid	Reference
	(A)	(B)	(C)	(D)	(E)	(F)	(G)
	General Chemical Components (concluded)						
5	Solids, %	8.6(7.9-9.1)	18(3.7-59.3)			2.5(2.0-3.0)	B,23;C,F,12
6	Water, %	93(91-95)	94(90.4-99.1)	98(96.4-99.0)		(95-99)	B,30;C,12,13; D,10,13;F, 10
	Electrolytes						
7	Calcium, mEq/L	5.0(4.5-5.5)	4.0(2.6-4.9)	4.3(2.8-5.4)		4.0(2.0-4.9)	B,4;C,10;D,8, 26;F,8,13,21
8	Carbon dioxide, mEq/L	27.0(22.6-30.0)	28.7(22.2-37.3)	23.8(21.3-30.9)		26.7(23.8-29.3)	B,10;C,10,13; D,26;F,13,21
9	Chloride, mEq/L	102.4(98-108)	(120-130)	100(92.3-136.0)	124.5	109(91-121)	B,10;C,4;D,8, 26;E,12;F, 8,13,21
10	Magnesium, mEq/L	(1.4-2.4)	2.0(1.6-2.4)	1.71(0.72-2.41)		0.5	B,4;C,10;D, 26;F,13
11	Phosphorus, mg/100 ml Total	23(18.6-29.0)		11.4(6.2-30.7)			B,14;D,26
12	Inorganic	(3.5-4.5)	3.0(1.2-4.4)	3.8(2.07-5.07)		4.0(1.2-5.3)	B,4;C,2,13;D, 8,26;F,8,13
13	Potassium, mEq/L	4.7(3.6-5.5)	3.4(2.8-6.0)	4.8(2.5-6.6)		4.1(2.0-5.6)	B,10;C,7,10; D,7,10,26; F,7,21
14	Sodium, mEq/L	138(133-148)	140(122-156)	140(136-148)		138(127-155)	B,7;C,7,10,13; D,10,21,26; F,10,13,21
	Nitrogenous Substances						
15	Protein, total[1], g/100 ml	7.2(6.2-7.9)	0.85(0.4-1.3)	1.77(0.3-4.1)	3.3(0.8-4.9)	2.1(0.02-4.50)	B,11;C,13,29; D,16,21,32; E,12,22;F, 12,13,16,21
16	Albumin, g/100 ml	4.8(4.0-5.8)	2.23	0.97(0.80-1.22)	2.23	0.88(0.32-1.64)	B,11;C,15;D, F,0,E,12
17	Globulin, g/100 ml	2.3(1.5-3.3)	0.59	0.79(0.33-1.23)	0.6	0.81(0.21-1.69)	B,11;C,15;D, F,8;E,12
18	Fibrinogen, g/100 ml	0.28(0.20-0.39)	0.03(0-0.8)	0.1(0-0.3)	0.03	0.1(0-0.2)	B,30;C,E,12; D,8,12;F,8
19	Bilirubin, mg/100 ml	0.4(0.1-0.8)[d]	(0-0.2)	(0.1-0.7)		0.5	B,5;C,D,F,20
20	Creatine, mg/100 ml	1.25(1.0-1.6)	3.20	3.02(2.1-4.9)[2]			B,17;C,15;D, 26
21	Creatinine, mg/100 ml	0.92(0.5-1.5)	2.43	1.2(0.7-2.1)		1.25(1.0-2.0)	B,17;C,15;D, 8,26;F,8
22	Histamine, μg/100 ml			(0.5-2400)		(0.5-2.5)	D,F,15
23	Uric acid, mg/100 ml	5.04(2.6-7.5)[3]		4.0(1.9-8.0)		4.2(1.0-5.3)	D,17,27,D,0, 26;F,8
24		3.84(2.0-5.7)[4]					
25	Nitrogen, mg/100 ml Total N	1140(1050-1230)	(318-837)	287(260-339)		150(45-554)	B,2;C,15;D,F, 8
26	Non-protein N	27(15-42)	(27.5-30.0)	31(20.3-42.5)		30.2(20.0-42.8)	B,2;C,15;D,8, 21,26;F,8
27	Amino acid N	4.0(3.5-6.0)	6.38	5.6(4.21-8.86)			B,4;C,15;D,26
28	Ammonia N	(0-0.18)	1.2				B,25;C,15
29	Urea N	14(7-18)	14.39	13(9.8-22.0)		16(11.9-21.0)	B,2;C,15;D,8, 26;F,8

/1/ Some higher than normal values probably included.   /2/ Includes creatinine.   /3/ Males.   /4/ Females.

Part I: MAN (Continued)

Property or Constituent	Plasma	Transudates	Pleural Fluid	Pericardial Fluid	Peritoneal Fluid	Reference
(A)	(B)	(C)	(D)	(E)	(F)	(G)
Lipids						
30 Lipids, total, mg/100 ml	530(385-675)[b]	1500(700-2500)				B,3;C,12
31 Cholesterol, mg/100 ml	(140-250)	40(13-60)	147(20-329)		60(5-148)	B,3;C,12;D,8, 26;F,8
32 Fatty acids, mg/100 ml	316(149-483)[b]		268(129-429)			B,3;D,26
33 Lecithin, mg/100 ml	110(80-200)	(20-100)	50(0-125)		40(0-140)	B,C,4;D,F,8
34 Phosphatide, mg/100 ml	165(110-220)[b]		142		164	B,3;D,F,15
Carbohydrates, Miscellaneous Organic Acids, Hormones						
35 Sugar, mg/100 ml	81(60-95)		92(70-122)		114(86-131)	B,2;D,F,8
36 Lactic acid, mg/100 ml	(5-20)	(17-32)	17.8(10.7-47.3)			B,4;C,15;D, 26
37 17-Hydroxy-cortico-steroids, μg/100 ml	13(2-34)	3(0-11)	8(0-16)	(5-16)	4.2(0-9)	B,1;C-F,28

Contributors: (a) Bowman, Russel O., (b) Davidsohn, Israel, and Tietz, Norbert W.

References: [1] Bliss, E. L., A. A. Sandberg, D. H. Nelson, and K. Eik-Nes. 1953. J. Clin. Invest. 32:818. [2] Bowman, R. O. Unpublished. [3] Boyd, E. M. 1942. J. Biol. Chem. 143:131. [4] Cantarow, A., and M. Trumper. 1955. Clinical biochemistry. W. B. Saunders, Philadelphia. [5] Cantarow, A., C. W. Wirts, Jr., and G. Hollander. 1942. Arch. Int. M. 69:986. [6] Cournand, A., R. L. Riley, E. S. Breed, E. de F. Baldwin, and D. W. Richards, Jr. 1945. J. Clin. Invest. 24:106. [7] Folk, B. P., K. L. Zierler, and J. L. Lilienthal, Jr. 1948. Am. J. Physiol. 153:381. [8] Foord, A. G., G. E. Youngberg, and V. Wetmore. 1929. J. Laborat. Clin. M. 14:417. [9] Gibbs, E. L., W. G. Lennox, L. F. Nims, and F. A. Gibbs. 1942. J. Biol. Chem. 144:325. [10] Greene, C. H., J. L. Bollman, N. M. Keith, and E. G. Wakefield. 1931. Ibid. 91:203. [11] Gutman, A. B., D. H. Moore, E. B. Gutman, V. McClellan, and E. A. Kabat. 1941. J. Clin. Invest. 20:765. [12] Hammarsten, O. 1893. A textbook of physiological chemistry. Ed. 1. J. Wiley and Sons, New York. [13] Hastings, A. B., H. A. Salvesan, J. Sendroy, Jr., and D. D. Van Slyke. 1927. J. Gen. Physiol. 8:701. [14] Helve, O. 1946. Acta med. scand. 125:505. [15] Hoppe-Seyler, F., and H. Thierfelder. 1953. Handbuch der physiologisch- und pathologisch-chemischen Analyse für Arzte, Biologen und Chemiker. Ed. 10. Springer Verlag, Berlin. v. 5. [16] Iverson, P., and A. H. Johansen. 1929. Klin. Wschr. 8:1311. [17] Jellinek, M., and J. M. Looney. 1939. J. Biol. Chem. 128:621. [18] Junk, W., C. Oppenheimer, and L. Pincussen. 1925. Tabulae biol., Berl. 2:527.
[19] Lambertsen, C. J., G. L. Emmell, D. Y. Cooper, H. H. Loeschke, and R. H. Kough. 1950. Fed. Proc., Balt. 9:73. [20] Layne, J. A., F. R. Schemm, and W. W. Hurst. 1950. Gastroenterology 16:91. [21] Loeb, R. F., D. W. Atchley, and W. W. Palmer. 1922. J. Gen. Physiol. 4:591. [22] Maurer, F. W., M. F. Warren, and C. K. Drinker. 1940. Am. J. Physiol. 129:635. [23] Miller, A. T., Jr. 1942. J. Biol. Chem. 143:65. [24] Moore, N. S., and D. D. Van Slyke. 1930. J. Clin. Invest. 8:337. [25] Morgulis, S., and H. M. Jahr. 1919. J. Biol. Chem. 38:435. [26] Pinner, M., and G. Moerke. 1930. Am. Rev. Tuberc. 22:121.
[27] Praetorius, E., and H. Poulsen. 1953. Scand. J. Clin. Lab. Invest. 5:273. [28] Sandberg, A. A., K. Eik-Nes, D. H. Nelson, and F. H. Tyler. 1954. J. Laborat. Clin. M. 43:874. [29] Stead, E. A., and J. V. Warren. 1944. J. Clin. Invest. 23:283. [30] Sunderman, F. W., and F. Boerner. 1949. Normal values in clinical medicine. W. B.

Part I: MAN (Concluded)

Saunders, Philadelphia. [31] Von Gorup-Besanez, E. F. 1878. Lehrbuch der physiologischen Chemie. Ed. 4. F. Vieweg und Sohn, Braunschweig. [32] Yamada, S., et al. 1933. Zschr. ges. exp. Med. 90:342.

Part II: VERTEBRATES OTHER THAN MAN

Values in parentheses are ranges, estimate "c" unless otherwise indicated (cf. Introduction).

	Animal	Property or Constituent	Plasma	Transudates	Pericardial Fluid	Peritoneal Fluid	Reference
	(A)	(B)	(C)	(D)	(E)	(F)	(G)
1	Cat	Chloride, mEq/L				80	19
2		Protein, total[1], g/100 ml	7.58(6.1-9.0)[b]		2.4(2.17-2.67)	(0.6-2.5)	C,14;E,16;F,16, 19
3		Urea nitrogen, mg/100 ml				(7-32)	19
4		Sugar, mg/100 ml	74(64-84)[b]			48	C,3;F,19
5	Dog	Osmotic pressure, mm H_2O			66(48-90)		16
6		pH				7.26(7.13-7.40)	20
7		Water, %	93(91-95)	98.9(98.3-99.3)			7
8		Calcium, mEq/L	4.9(4.5-5.7)	3.5(3.2-4.1)		4.0(2.0-4.9)	C,7;D,1,7,10,17, 18;F,4,9,15
9		Carbon dioxide, mEq/L	24(17.3-27.4)	26.1(21.0-30.8)		21.4(9.8-30.2)	C,7;D,7,8;F,20
10		Chloride, mEq/L	122.5(115.0-136.4)	126(118.8-127.5)		124(111-143)	C,1,7,9,10,17, 18;D,7;F,20
11		Magnesium, mEq/L	2.2(1.4-2.9)	1.7(1.4-2.2)			7
		Phosphorus, mg/100 ml					
12		Total	26	12(11.8-18.4)			C,13;D,1,10
13		Inorganic	4.4(3.2-6.0)	5.6(3.6-7.3)			C,5;D,10,17
14		Potassium, mEq/L	5.3(4.7-6.2)	5.0(4.2-6.1)			7
15		Sodium, mEq/L	159(152-169)	150(144-156)			7
16		Protein, total[1], g/100 ml	(6.1-7.8)	3.0(0.17-4.8)	1.75(0.8-2.9)	2.6(1.63-3.71)	C,10;D,1,7,10, 17,18;E,F,16
17		Albumin, g/100 ml	3.57		1.03(0.75-1.52)		C,11;E,16
18		Globulin, g/100 ml	2.63		0.75(0.45-1.54)		C,11;E,16
19		Creatinine, mg/100 ml		1.4(1.28-1.49)			10
20		Uric acid, mg/100 ml	0.33	Trace			C,6;D,10
		Nitrogen, mg/100 ml					
21		Total N	1100			149(26-295)	C,2;F,20
22		Non-protein N	27(15-40)	34(19.8-45.4)			C,2;D,10
23		Amino acid N		(2.4-4.8)			10,18
24		Urea N		11(9.9-16.5)			10
25		Sugar, mg/100 ml	130(107-144)			180(160-200)	C,1,10,18;F,20
26	Guinea pig	Chloride, mEq/L				109(104-113)	20
27		Sugar, mg/100 ml	95(60-125)			130	C,12;F,20

/1/ Some higher than normal values probably included.

Part II: VERTEBRATES OTHER THAN MAN (Continued)

	Animal	Property or Constituent	Plasma	Transudates	Pericardial Fluid	Peritoneal Fluid	Reference
	(A)	(B)	(C)	(D)	(E)	(F)	(G)
28	Horse	Water, %		(93.5-95.8)			8
29		Chloride, mEq/L		99			8
30		Protein, total[1], g/100 ml		(3.5-4.2)			8
31		Fibrinogen, g/100 ml	0.34	(0.04-2.20)			C,11;D,8
32		Lipid, total, %		(0.3-3.4)			8
33	Monkey	Protein, total[1], g/100 ml			1.71(1.35-2.22)		16
34	Rabbit	Protein, total[1], g/100 ml			2.16(1.48-3.65)	1.53	16
35	Rat	Protein, total[1], g/100 ml			2.07		16
36	Duck	Protein, total[1], g/100 ml			2.51(2.42-2.59)	2.51	16
37	Hen	Protein, total[1], g/100 ml			3.53		16
38	Turtle	pH	7.72(7.46-7.80)		8.25(7.9-8.5)	8.12(7.85-8.42)	22
39		Calcium, mEq/L	4.6(3.1-6.5)	2.4	2.1(0.6-4.5)	3.4(2.4-5.2)	
40		Carbon dioxide, mEq/L	40.4(23.2-52.5)	44	88.5(29-131)	68.9(24-128)	
41		Chloride, mEq/L	86.4(54.5-109.8)	75.6	55.1(15-129)	70.8(33-124)	
42		Magnesium, mEq/L	3.0(0.5-7.9)	0.8	1.1(0.3-3.5)	2.1(0.3-5.0)	
43		Phosphate, mEq/L	1.7(0.9-3.5)		1.4(0.7-2.0)	1.3(0.7-2.4)	
44		Potassium, mEq/L	4.0(2.4-6.7)	2.0	3.15(1.1-6.1)	3.2(2.4-4.3)	
45		Sodium, mEq/L	138(120-163)	123	140(128-152)	137(120-152)	
46		Sulfate, mEq/L	0.5(0.1-1.3)		0.35	0.5(0.1-1.2)	
47	Elasmo-branchs[2]	pH	7.36(7.20-7.63)	7.45(7.15-7.64)	6.12(5.30-6.86)	5.80(5.40-6.35)	21
48		Calcium, mEq/L	4.9(2.9-6.0)	4.6(3.0-6.9)	1.4(0.5-3.5)	3.4(1.7-6.6)	
49		Carbon dioxide, mEq/L	8.2(5.6-11.6)	7.3(4.6-10.5)	0.4(trace-0.5)	0.3(trace-0.4)	
50		Chloride, mEq/L	236(227-266)	262(244-282)	370(366-373)	274(188-332)	
51		Magnesium, mEq/L	2.8(1.7-3.5)	1.0(0.9-1.0)	2.6(1.0-5.0)	17.8(8.0-25.0)	
52		Phosphate, mEq/L	2.0(0.7-3.5)	1.2(0.9-1.7)	0.4(0-0.7)	0.7(0-0.9)	
53		Potassium, mEq/L	5.3(4.5-6.8)	4.8(3.8-6.0)	16.6(8.5-22.0)	6.6(5.2-8.9)	
54		Sodium, mEq/L	259(236-275)	266(262-270)	314(290-321)	246(145-304)	
55		Sulfate, mEq/L	1.0(trace-3.1)	0.4(trace-1.0)	Trace	5.0(trace-14.0)	
56		Creatine, mg/100 ml	2.88(1.8-4.2)	2.4		3.9(3.6-4.2)	
57		Creatinine, mg/100 ml	(0-0.5)		0	(0-0.7)	
		Nitrogen, mg/100 ml					
58		Non-protein N	1090(1070-1125)	681		870(758-1015)	
59		Amino acid N	7.5(5.6-9.4)			(0-2.6)	
60		Ammonia N		(0-1)	3.3	23(8.6-60.4)	
61		Urea N	1179(1045-1300)	971(555-1240)	1067(692-1346)	1013(900-1100)	

/1/ Some higher than normal values probably included. /2/ Head fluid considered a transudate.

Contributors: (a) Bowman, Russel O., (b) Davidsohn, Israel

References: [1] Arnold, R. M., and L. B. Mendel. 1927. J. Biol. Chem. 72:189. [2] Bowman, R. O. Unpublished. [3] De Bodo, R. C., F. W. Co Tui, and A. E. Benaglia. 1937. J. Pharm. Exp. Ther. 61:48. [4] Foord, A. G., G. E. Youngberg, and V. Wetmore. 1929. J. Laborat. Clin. M. 14:417. [5] Freeman, S., and C. J. Farmer. 1935. Am. J. Physiol. 113:200. [6] Friedman, M., and S. O. Byers. 1948. J. Biol. Chem. 175:727. [7] Greene, C. H., J. L. Bollman, N. M. Keith, and E. G. Wakefield. 1931. Ibid. 91:203. [8] Hammarsten, O. 1893. A textbook of physiological chemistry. Ed. 1. J. Wiley and Sons, New York. [9] Hastings, A. B., H. A. Salvesan, J. Sendroy, Jr., and D. D. Van Slyke. 1927. J. Gen. Physiol. 8:701. [10] Heim, J. W. 1933. Am. J. Physiol. 103:553. [11] Howe, P. E. 1925. Physiol. Rev. 5:439. [12] Johnson, D. D. 1950. Endocrinology 46:135. [13] Kerr, S. E., and L. Daoud. 1935. J. Biol. Chem. 109:301. [14] Levin, L., J. H. Leathem, and R. C. Crafts. 1942. Am. J. Physiol. 136:776. [15] Loeb, R. F., D. W. Atchley, and W. W. Palmer. 1922. J. Gen. Physiol. 4:591. [16] Maurer, F. W., M. F. Warren, and C. K. Drinker. 1940. Am. J. Physiol. 129:635. [17] Meyer-Bisch, R., and F. Günther. 1925. Pflügers Arch. 109:81. [18] Petersen, W. H., and T. P. Hughes. 1927. J. Biol. Chem. 66:229. [19] Putnam, T. J. 1923. Am. J. Physiol. 63:548. [20] Schechter, A. J. 1931. Yale J. Biol. 4:167. [21] Smith, H. W. 1929. J. Biol. Chem. 81:407. [22] Smith, H. W. 1929. Ibid. 82:651.

112. PHYSICAL PROPERTIES AND CHEMICAL COMPOSITION OF PERIVISCERAL FLUID: ECHINODERMS

Part I: pH AND SPECIFIC GRAVITY

Property (column B): SP = specific gravity. Values in parentheses are ranges, estimate "c" (cf. Introduction).

	Species	Property	Value	Reference		Species	Property	Value	Reference
	(A)	(B)	(C)	(D)		(A)	(B)	(C)	(D)
	Crinoidea (Sea Lily)					Echinoidea (Sea Urchins) (concluded)			
1	Heliometra glacialis	pH	7.1	1	19	Diadema savingi	pH	7.5	1
	Asteroidea (Sea Stars)				20	Echinarachnius parma	pH	6.90	2
					21	Echinometra mathaei	pH	7.2	1
2	Asterias rubens	pH	(6.65-7.44)	5	22	Echinostrephus aciculatus	pH	7.2	1
3			(7.66-7.77)	6	23	Echinothrix calamaris	pH	7.1	1
4	A. vulgaris	pH	(7.20-7.54)	2	24	E. diadema	pH	6.9	1
5	Astrometis sertulifera	pH	7.3	1	25	Echinus sphaera	SP	1.026	3
6	Ctenodiscus crispatus	pH	(6.49-6.93)	5	26	Heterocentrotus trigonarius	pH	6.8	1
7	Mediaster aequalis	pH	7.6	1	27	Rhinobrissus hemiasteroides	pH	7.6	1
8	Patiria miniata	pH	(7.25-7.40)	1	28	Strongylocentrotus droebachiensis	pH	(7.17-7.78)	5
9	Pisaster brevispinus	pH	(7.0-7.3)	1	29			(7.20-7.84)	2
10	P. giganteus	pH	7.4	1	30			(7.35-8.15)	7
11	P. ochraceus	pH	(7.2-7.4)	1	31	S. franciscanus	pH	(7.38-7.55)	1
12	Poraniopsis inflata	pH	7.3	1	32			7.65	7
13	Pycnopodia helianthoides	pH	(7.2-7.6)	1	33	S. purpuratus	pH	(7.30-7.40)	1
14	Solaster endeca	pH	6.90	2	34	Toxopneustes lividus	SP	1.026	3
15			(6.32-7.25)	5		Holothuroidea (Sea Cucumbers)			
16	S. papposus	pH	(6.58-7.46)	5					
	Echinoidea (Sea Urchins)				35	Actinopyga mauritiana	pH	7.5	1
17	Allocentrotus fragilis	pH	(7.11-7.43)	1	36	Caudina chilensis	SP[1]	(1.0248-1.0252)	4
18	Dendraster execentricus	pH	7.4	1					

/1/ Specific gravity of sea water = 1.0241 [4].

Part I: pH AND SPECIFIC GRAVITY (Concluded)

	Species	Prop-erty	Value	Ref-er-ence		Species	Prop-erty	Value	Ref-er-ence
	(A)	(B)	(C)	(D)		(A)	(B)	(C)	(D)
	Holothuroidea (Sea Cucumbers) (continued)					Holothuroidea (Sea Cucumbers) (concluded)			
37	Chirodota laevis	pH	7.00	2	41	Stichopus californicus	pH	(7.1-7.3)	1
38	Cucumaria frondosa	pH	(6.72-7.36)	5	42	Synapta maculata	pH	7.7	1
39			(7.30-7.80)	2	43	Thelonotus ananus	pH	7.8	1
40	Holothuria leucopsilota	pH	7.2	1					

Contributor: Boolootian, Richard A.

References: [1] Boolootian, R. A. Unpublished. [2] Cole, W. H. 1940. J. Gen. Physiol. 23:575. [3] Geddes, P. 1880. Arch. zool. exp., Par. 8:481. [4] Koizumi, T. 1932. Sc. Rep. Tôhoku Univ., Ser. 4, 7:259. [5] Sarch, M. N. 1931. Zschr. vergl. Physiol. 14:525. [6] Verchowskaja, I. 1931. Ibid. 14:405. [7] Weese, A. 1926. Puget Sound Biol. Sta. Pub. 5:165.

Part II: INORGANIC CONSTITUENTS

	Locale or Species	Inorganic Ions, mM/L						Reference
		Calcium	Chloride	Magnesium	Potassium	Sodium	Sulfate	
	(A)	(B)	(C)	(D)	(E)	(F)	(G)	(H)
	Sea Water							
1	Canada (St. Andrews, New Brunswick)	9.4	494	47.0	9.04	429	26.4	6
2	England (Plymouth)	10.2	542	53.0	9.9	465	35.0	13
3	Japan	9.5	500	50.2	9.0	420	25.0	5
4	U. S. A. (Woods Hole, Massachusetts)	9.7	492	33.8	8.5	457	25.6	9
	Asteroidea (Sea Stars)							
5	Asterias vulgaris	8.99	505	30.7	8.28	460	25.4	3
6		9.37	488	50.8	9.56	413	30.0	
7	Astropecten aurantiacus	14.2	662	53.9	14.3		32.4	2
8	Marthasterias glacialis	10.2	541	51.2	10.9	459	27.6	12
9	Pisaster ochraceus	9.5	552					7
10	Pycnopodia helianthoides	10.0	552					7
11	Solaster endeca	9.56	488	49.8	9.66	420	30.0	3
	Echinoidea (Sea Urchins)							
12	Echinarachnius parma	9.37	488	49.3	9.22	418	29.8	3
13	Echinus esculentus	12.8	547	50.6	14.1	530		1
14		10.0	524	50.3	9.6	444	27.1	11
15	Paracentrotus lividus	13.0	620	52.1	12.7		32.2	2
16			578		12.5			10
17	Sphaerechinus granularis	12.8	619	53.4	12.7		30.5	2
18	Strongylocentrotus	9.56	488	48.6	9.71	420	29.0	3
19	droebachiensis	8.82	510	31.0	9.59	461	25.3	
20	S. franciscanus	11.2	537					7
	Holothuroidea (Sea Cucumbers)							
21	Caudina chilensis	9.0	516	42.5	9.2	454	26.7	8
22		9.7	529	52.8	11.3	439	27.7	4
23	Chirodota laevis	10.20	488	55.1	9.66	420	30.2	3

Part II: INORGANIC CONSTITUENTS (Concluded)

Locale or Species	Inorganic Ions, mM/L						Reference
	Calcium	Chloride	Magnesium	Potassium	Sodium	Sulfate	
(A)	(B)	(C)	(D)	(E)	(F)	(G)	(H)
Holothuroidea (Sea Cucumbers) (concluded)							
24 Cucumaria frondosa	9.35	487	50.1	9.69	420	29.8	3
25 Holothuria stellata	13.5	649	56.4	12.9			1
26 H. tubulosa	13.9	650	59.9	13.7		31.8	2

Contributors: (a) Boolootian, Richard A., (b) Robertson, James D.

References: [1] Bethe, A., and E. Berger. 1931. Arch. ges. Physiol. 227:571. [2] Bialaszewicz, K. 1933. Arch. internat. physiol., Liége 36:41. [3] Cole, W. H. 1940. J. Gen. Physiol. 23:575. [4] Koizumi, T. 1932. Sc. Rep. Tôhoku Univ., Ser. 4, 7:259. [5] Koizumi, T., and K. Hosoi. 1936. Ibid. 10:709. [6] Macallum, A. B. 1903. J. Physiol., Lond. 29:213. [7] Myers, R. 1920. J. Biol. Chem. 41:119. [8] Okazaki, K., and T. Koizumi. 1926. Sc. Rep. Tôhoku Univ., Ser. 4, 2:139. [9] Page, I. H. 1927. Biol. Bull. 52:168. [10] Pora, E. A. 1936. Bull. Inst. Oceanogr. Monaco 689:1. [11] Robertson, J. D. 1939. J. Exp. Biol., Lond. 16:387. [12] Robertson, J. D. 1949. Ibid. 26:182. [13] Webb, D. A. 1940. Proc. R. Soc. Lond., Ser. B, 129:107.

Part III: ORGANIC CONSTITUENTS

Values are mg/100 ml, unless otherwise indicated. Values in parentheses are ranges, estimate "c" (cf. Introduction).

Species	Constituent	Value	Reference
(A)	(B)	(C)	(D)
Asteroidea (Sea Stars)			
1 Asterias rubens	Phosphorus[1]	Trace	12
	Nitrogen		
2	Total N	2.12	12
3	Non-protein N	1.95	4
4	Amino N	0.80	4
5	Ammonia N	0.40	4
6	Urea N	0.09	4
7 Crossaster papposus	Phosphatase activity[2]	0.11 at pH 4.4	9
8		0.58 at pH 9.2	
9 Ctenodiscus crispatus	Nitrogen, total	(2.44-2.72)	12
10 Marthasterias glacialis	Nitrogen, protein	0.6	10
Pisaster brevispinus	Amino acids		5
11	Arginine	1.5	
12	Glycine	6.6	
13	Phenylalanine	1.0	
14	Serine	1.5	
15	Tryptophan	0.01	
	Nitrogen		
16	Arginine N	0.120	
17	Glycine N	1.124	
18	Phenylalanine N	0.085	
19	Serine N	0.200	
20	Tryptophan N	0.001	

/1/ Organic and inorganic. /2/ Expressed as milligrams of inorganic phosphorus liberated per gram of tissue from sodium β-glycerophosphate (after 48-hour hydrolysis at 25°C ± 0.05 and at the optimum pH).

Part III: ORGANIC CONSTITUENTS (Continued)

	Species	Constituent	Value	Reference
	(A)	(B)	(C)	(D)
	Asteroidea (Sea Stars) (concluded)			
	Pisaster giganteus	Nitrogen		6
21		Protein N	Trace	
22		Non-protein N	1.5	
23		Reducing sugar	Trace	
24	P. ochraceus	Creatine	0.12	8
25		Creatinine	0.13	8
		Nitrogen		
26		Total N	(1.70-2.54)	6
27			5.0	8
28		Protein N	Trace	6
29		Non-protein N	2.0	6
30			4.4	8
31		Lipids, total	16.85	6
32		Cholesterol	0.9	8
33		Reducing sugar	(1.0-5.0)	6
	Pycnopodia helianthoides	Nitrogen		
34		Total N		8
35			(1.5-6.0)	
36			4.05	2
37		Non-protein N	(0.8-4.0)	8
38			3.15	2
39		Cholesterol	1.0	8
40		Reducing sugar	1.25	2
41	Solaster endeca		29.0	8
42		Phosphorus[1]	(0.15-1.11)	12
43	S. papposus	Nitrogen, total	1.97	
		Nitrogen, total	(1.36-2.74)	12
	Echinoidea (Sea Urchins)			
	Allocentrotus fragilis	Nitrogen		3
44		Total N	(3.78-4.98)	
45		Non-protein N	(1.28-1.34)	
46	Arbacia pustulosa	Nitrogen, urea	(3.10-4.28)	11
47	Echinarachnius parma	Phosphatase activity[2]	0.67 at pH 5.0	9
48	Echinus esculentus	Phosphorus[1]	1.29	12
49		Nitrogen, total	(1.73-3.48)	
50	E. microtuberculatus	Nitrogen, urea	(1.98-2.51)	11
	Paracentrotus lividus	Nitrogen		4
51		Non-protein N	3.74	
52		Amino N	2.40	
53		Ammonia N	0.24	
54		Purine N	0.23	
55		Urea N	0.12	
56		Uric acid N	0.07	
57	Sphaerechinus granularis	Nitrogen, urea	(3.27-3.61)	11
58	Strongylocentrotus	Phosphorus[1]	(0.35-3.83)	12
59	droebachiensis	Nitrogen, total	(5.11-8.02)	12
60		Phosphatase activity[2]	0.13 at pH 4.0-4.2	9
61			0.12 at pH 9.4	
62	S. franciscanus	Creatine	0.16	8
63		Creatinine	0.27	8
		Nitrogen		
64		Total N	(2.46-6.71)	1
65			12.0	8
66		Protein N	(0.36-0.86)	1
67		Non-protein N	(2.04-6.31)	1
68			8.6	8
69		Ammonia N	0.08	8

/1/ Organic and inorganic. /2/ Expressed as milligrams of inorganic phosphorus liberated per gram of tissue from sodium β-glycerophosphate (after 48-hour hydrolysis at 25°C ± 0.05 and at the optimum pH).

Part III: ORGANIC CONSTITUENTS (Continued)

	Species	Constituent	Value	Reference
	(A)	(B)	(C)	(D)
	Echinoidea (Sea Urchins) (concluded)			
70	Strongylocentrotus franciscanus (concluded)	Nitrogen (concluded) Urea N	0.92	8
71		Uric acid N	Trace	8
72		Cholesterol	4.0	8
73		Reducing sugar	(0.8-5.3)	1
74			61.0	8
				5
75	S. purpuratus	Amino acids Alanine	0.6	
76		Arginine	4.0	
77		Aspartic acid	0.25	
78		Cystine	0.2	
79		Glutamic acid	0.25	
80		Glycine	1.3	
81		Histidine	0.3	
82		Isoleucine	0.4	
83		Leucine	1.0	
84		Methionine	0.3	
85		Serine	6.4	
86		Tyrosine	Trace	
87		Valine	2.2	
88		Nitrogen Total N	5.20	1
89		Protein N	0.47	1
90		Non-protein N	5.43	1
91		Alanine N	0.094	5
92		Arginine N	0.322	5
93		Aspartic acid N	0.263	5
94		Cystine N	0.232	5
95		Glutamic acid N	0.238	5
96		Glycine N	0.243	5
97		Histidine N	0.027	5
98		Isoleucine N	0.043	5
99		Leucine N	0.107	5
100		Methionine N	0.028	5
101		Serine N	0.849	5
102		Valine N	0.262	5
103		Lipids, total	11.60	6
104		Reducing sugar	(1.0-4.7)	1
105		Lactic acid	Trace	7
106		Phosphatase activity[2]	0.13 at pH 6.0	9
107			0.11 at pH 9.4	
	Holothuroidea (Sea Cucumbers)			
108	Cucumaria frondosa	Phosphorus[1]	0.13	12
109		Nitrogen, total	1.13	
110	Holothuria tubulosa	Nitrogen Non-protein N	1.10	4
111		Amino N	0.40	4
112		Ammonia N	0.14	4
113		Purine N	0.04	4
114		Urea N	0.07	4
115			(0.78-1.05)	11
				2
116	Stichopus californicus	Nitrogen Total N	(0.87-2.55)	
117		Non-protein N	2.10	
118		Phosphatase activity[2]	0.22 at pH 5.4	9
119			0.70 at pH 9.2	

/1/ Organic and inorganic. /2/ Expressed as milligrams of inorganic phosphorus liberated per gram of tissue from sodium β-glycerophosphate (after 48-hour hydrolysis at 25°C ± 0.05 and at the optimum pH).

112. PHYSICAL PROPERTIES AND CHEMICAL COMPOSITION OF PERIVISCERAL FLUID: ECHINODERMS (Concluded)

Part III: ORGANIC CONSTITUENTS (Concluded)

Contributors: (a) Boolootian, Richard A., (b) Robertson, James D., (c) Lasker, Reuben

References: [1] Bennett, J., and A. C. Giese. 1955. Biol. Bull. 109:226. [2] Boolootian, R. A. Unpublished. [3] Boolootian, R. A., A. C. Giese, J. S. Tucker, and A. Farmanfarmaian. 1959. Biol. Bull. 116:362. [4] Delaunay, H. 1931. Biol. Rev. Cambridge Philos. Soc. 6:265. [5] Giordana, M. F., H. Harper, and F. Filice. 1950. Wasmann J. Biol. 8:129. [6] Greenfield, L., A. C. Giese, A. Farmanfarmaian, and R. A. Boolootian. 1958. J. Exp. Zool. 139:507. [7] Lasker, R., and A. C. Giese. 1954. Biol. Bull. 106:328. [8] Myers, R. G. 1920. J. Biol. Chem. 41:119. [9] Norris, E. R., and D. A. R. Rama Rao. 1935. Ibid. 108:783. [10] Robertson, J. D. 1949. J. Exp. Biol., Lond. 26:182. [11] Sanzo, L. 1907. Biol. Zbl. 27:479. [12] Sarch, M. N. 1931. Zschr. vergl. Physiol. 14:525.

113. PHYSICAL PROPERTIES AND CHEMICAL COMPOSITION OF PERIVISCERAL FLUID: PARASITIC NEMATODES

Part I: ASCARIS LUMBRICOIDES, LARGE ROUNDWORM OF SWINE

Values in parentheses are ranges, estimate "c" (cf. Introduction).

	Property or Constituent	No. of Observations	Value	Reference
	(A)	(B)	(C)	(D)
	Physical Properties			
1	Conductivity	7	143(137-148) mM NaCl	7
2	Freezing point depression	6	0.655(0.625-0.682) °C	6
3	Osmotic pressure	7	198(187-206) mM NaCl	7
4	pH	13	6.8(6.5-7.0)	6
5	Specific gravity at 20°C	7	1.017(1.015-1.019)	7
	General Chemical Components			
6	Ash (sulfate)	7	0.91(0.85-1.00) g/100 ml	7
7	Solids, total	7	6.8(6.3-7.6) g/100 ml	
	Electrolytes			
8	Calcium	7	5.9(4.7-9.0) mM/L	7
9	Chloride	7	52.7(46.2-56.9) mM/L	7
10	Copper		<0.02 mM/L	9
11	Iron	10	0.13(0.08-0.21) mM/L	9
12	Magnesium	7	4.9(4.5-5.8) mM/L	7
	Phosphorus			
13	Total P	7	17.0(14.6-19.0) mM/L	7
14	Acid-soluble P		74% of total	10
15	Phospholipid P		21% of total	10
16	Potassium	7	24.7(16.4-36.6) mM/L	7
17	Sodium	7	129(118-138) mM/L	7
18	Zinc	10	0.14(0.13-0.19) mM/L	9
	Nitrogenous Substances			
19	Protein, total		4.89 g/100 ml	2
20	Albumin		2.83 g/100 ml	2
21	Globulin		2.06 g/100 ml	2
22	Amino acids, free		19 mg/100 ml	3
23	Alanine		246.9 mM/L	
24	Arginine		110.2 mM/L	
25	Aspartic acid		84.1 mM/L	

Part I: ASCARIS LUMBRICOIDES, LARGE ROUNDWORM OF SWINE (Continued)

Property or Constituent	No. of Observations	Value	Reference
(A)	(B)	(C)	(D)
Nitrogenous Substances (concluded)			
Amino acids, free (concluded)			3
26 Cysteine		13.9 mM/L	
27 Glutamic acid		286.8 mM/L	
28 Glycine		67.9 mM/L	
29 Histidine		36.7 mM/L	
30 Lysine		166.2 mM/L	
31 Methionine		2.8 mM/L	
32 Phenylalanine		10.3 mM/L	
33 Proline		289.3 mM/L	
34 Tryptophan		8.8 mM/L	
35 Tyrosine		177.2 mM/L	
36 Ammonia		0.75 mM/L	12
37 Glutathione		21 mg/100 ml	12
38 Hematin	10	0.03(0.01-0.04) mM/L	9
39 Polypeptides		13.5 mM/L	3
40 Urea		0.17 mM/L	12
Nitrogen			
41 Protein N		700 mg/100 ml	4
42 Non-protein N		53 mg/100 ml	4
43 Amino N		18 mg/100 ml	11
44 Ammonia N		1 mg/100 ml	11
45 Polypeptide N		19 mg/100 ml	11
46 Urea N		10 mg/100 ml	11
Lipids			
47 Cephalin	2	52(43-59) mg/100 ml	10
48 Fatty acids, steam-volatile		40 mM/L	8
49 C_8 acid		1%	
50 C_6 acid		35%	
51 C_5 (methylethylacetic) acid		46%	
52 C_4 (n-butyric) acid		1.9%	
53 C_3 (propionic) acid		4.4%	
54 C_2 (acetic) acid		11.1%	
55 Lecithin	2	129(122-137) mg/100 ml	10
Phospholipids			10
56 Total	2	195(191-200) mg/100 ml	
57 Choline-containing	2	144(141-148) mg/100 ml	
58 Ethanolamine-containing	2	123(119-128) mg/100 ml	
59 Serine-containing	2	21(18-24) mg/100 ml	
60 Sphingomyelin	2	15(11-19) mg/100 ml	10
Carbohydrates, Miscellaneous Organic Acids, Vitamins			
61 Glucose	5	1.22(1.12-1.38) mM/L	9
62 Glycogen		0.9 g/100 ml[1]	5
63		0.4 g/100 ml[2]	
64 Trehalose		0.5 g/100 ml[1]	5
65		0.8 g/100 ml[2]	
66 Succinic acid		8.4 mM/L	1
67 Uronic acid		0.2 mM/L	9
68 Vitamin C (ascorbic acid)	10	0.05(0.04-0.07) mM/L	3

/1/ Males. /2/ Females.

Contributors: (a) Rogers, W. P., (b) Doran, David J., and Tromba, Francis G., (c) Savel, Jean, (d) Smyth, J. D.

References: [1] Beuding, E., and G. W. Farrow. 1956. Exp. Parasit., N. Y. 5:345. [2] Cavier, R., and J. Savel.

Part I: ASCARIS LUMBRICOIDES, LARGE ROUNDWORM OF SWINE (Concluded)

1951. Bull. Soc. chim. biol., Par. 33:455. [3] Cavier, R., and J. Savel. 1954. Ibid. 36:1433. [4] Cavier, R., and J. Savel. 1954. C. rend. Acad. sc. 238:2035. [5] Fairbairn, D., and R. F. Passey. 1957. Exp. Parasit., N. Y. 6:566. [6] Hobson, A. D., W. Stephenson, and L. C. Beadle. 1952. J. Exp. Biol., Lond. 29:1. [7] Hobson, A. D., W. Stephenson, and A. Eden. 1952. Ibid. 29:22. [8] Moyle, V., and E. Baldwin. 1952. Biochem. J., Lond. 51:504. [9] Rogers, W. P. 1945. Parasitology, Lond. 36:211. [10] Rogers, W. P., and M. Lazerus. 1949. Ibid. 39:302. [11] Savel, J. 1954. Ph. D. Thesis. Université de Paris. [12] Savel, J. 1955. Rev. path. comp., Par. 55:52.

Part II: PARASCARIS EQUORUM, LARGE ROUNDWORM OF HORSE

Value in parentheses is range, estimate "c" (cf. Introduction).

	Property or Constituent	Value	Reference		Property or Constituent	Value	Reference
	(A)	(B)	(C)		(A)	(B)	(C)
1	Osmotic pressure[1]	185(163-199) mM NaCl	4	6	Protein, total	4.08 g/100 ml	3
2	Ash (sulfate)	0.92 g/100 ml	3	7	Albumin	3.51 g/100 ml	3
3	Bases, purine	33 mg/100 ml	3	8	Globulin	0.57 g/100 ml	3
4	Solids, total	5.2 g/100 ml	3	9	Nitrogen, amino	42.5 mM/L	1
5	Chloride	58.2 mM/L	1	10	Reducing sugars (as glucose)	150 mg/100 ml	2

/1/ 10 observations.

Contributors: (a) Rogers, W. P., (b) Savel, Jean, (c) Doran, David J., and Tromba, Francis G.

References: [1] Duval, M., and A. Courtois. 1928. C. rend. Soc. biol. 99:1952. [2] Faure-Fremiet, E. 1913. Arch. anat. micr., Par. 15:435. [3] Flury, F. 1912. Naumyn-Schmiedeberg's Arch. exp. Path. 67:275. [4] Schopfer, W. H. 1926. Parasitology, Lond. 18:277.

114. PHYSICAL PROPERTIES AND CHEMICAL COMPOSITION OF CYSTIC FLUID: PARASITIC CESTODES

Values in parentheses are ranges, estimate "c" (cf. Introduction).

	Cestode	Property or Constituent	No. of Observations	Value	Reference
	(A)	(B)	(C)	(D)	(E)
1	Echinococcus granulosus (parasitic flatworm of man)	pH		7.4	4
2		Specific gravity	7	1.008(1.0057-1.0088)	4
3		Ash		(790-830) mg/100 g	1
4		Solids, total		(1260-1300) mg/100 g	1
5		Calcium		4 mg/100 g	1
6		Chloride		425 mg/100 g	1
7		Magnesium		4 mg/100 g	1
8		Phosphorus		12 mg/100 g	1
9		Potassium		(33-41) mg/100 g	1
10		Sodium		393 mg/100 g	1
11		Sulfur		(140-170) mg/100 g[1]	1

/1/ According to Von Brand, high value may be due to error [3].

	Cestode	Property or Constituent	No. of Obser-vations	Value	Refer-ence
	(A)	(B)	(C)	(D)	(E)
12	Echinococcus granulosus	Protein		(90-150) mg/100 g	1
13	(parasitic flatworm of	Nitrogen, non-protein		(34-40) mg/100 g	1
14	man) (concluded)	Lipids		(36-41) mg/100 g	1
15		Reducing substances, total (as glucose)		(30-40) mg/100 g	1
16	Cysticercus tenuicollis	Freezing point depression	12	0.64(0.55-0.68) °C	2
17	(parasitic flatworm of	pH	32	6.5(6.3-6.8)	
18	rabbit)	Specific gravity	10	1.0097(1.004-1.015)	
19		Ash		830 mg/100 g	
20		Solids, total	6	1590(1420-1760) mg/100 g	
21		Calcium		9 mg/100 g	
22		Chloride		422 mg/100 g	
23		Magnesium		4 mg/100 g	
24		Phosphorus		5 mg/100 g	
25		Sulfur		6 mg/100 g	
26		Protein		(300-500) mg/100 g	
27		Reducing substances, total (as glucose)	4	138(120-166) mg/100 g	

Contributor: Smyth, J. D.

References: [1] Mazzocco, P. 1923. C. rend. Soc. biol. 88:342. [2] Schopfer, W. H. 1932. Rev. suisse Zool. 39:64. [3] Von Brand, T. 1952. Chemical physiology of endoparasitic animals. Academic Press, New York. [4] Wernicke, R., and E. Savino. 1923. C. rend. Soc. biol. 88:343.

XVIII. Body Water

115. TOTAL BODY WATER: MAN

Total body water, i.e., water in the extracellular and intracellular compartments, is usually measured as the volume of distribution in the body of an appropriate indicator after a single intravenous injection. The most reliable, commonly-used indicators are antipyrine and the heavy isotopes, deuterium oxide, or tritium oxide. During fetal life and early childhood there is a rapid decrease in total body water, after which the water content remains nearly constant at 72% ± 2 of the fat-free weight. From birth to puberty there is no apparent difference between male and female in body water content; following puberty, however, the proportion of body water increases in the male and decreases in the female.

Part I: ANTIPYRINE DETERMINATION

In the presence of edema, equilibration may be slowed. In some instances, the concentration of antipyrine in pleural and ascitic fluid may be greater than the concentration of plasma water, necessitating direct, continued analysis of each compartment to prevent error. [4, 8, 10, 15] Values in parentheses are ranges, estimate "b" unless otherwise indicated (cf. Introduction).

	Subjects Specification	No.	Total Body Water ml/kg body weight	Reference		Subjects Specification	No.	Total Body Water ml/kg body weight	Reference
	(A)	(B)	(C)	(D)		(A)	(B)	(C)	(D)
1	Newborn	5	754(647-861)	8	13	60-79 yr	5♀	422	14, 16
2	Newborn-6 mo		(720-830)[c]	7	14	>80 yr	4♀	488	14, 16
3	6 mo-11 yr		(530-630)[c]	7	15	Adult		(393-579)[c]	15
4	1-12 mo	8	627(504-750)	8	16			557[3]	10
5	1-10 yr	8	569(491-647)	8	17		20[2]	497(487-507)	11
6	18-46 yr	81♂[1]	611(430-729)[c]	12	18		10[2]	549	9
7	17-39 yr	23♂	548	1-3, 5, 13-16	19		16[2]	506(470-542)[4]	17
8	20-39 yr	18♀	444	14, 16	20		16[2]	506(480-532)[5]	17
9	26-65 yr	16[2]	497(463-531)	17	21		33♂	585	6
10	40-59 yr	31♂	545	1-3, 5, 13-16	22		51♂	527(403-682)[c]	8, 16
11	40-59 yr	4♀	446	14, 16	23		31♀	446(292-528)[c]	8, 16
12	>60 yr	18♂	516	1-3, 5, 13-16	24	<70 kg	26♂	559(450-668)	1, 16
					25	>70 kg	22♂	549(435-663)	1, 16

/1/ Navy personnel. /2/ Number of observations. /3/ Edematous subjects. /4/ 4-Iodo-antipyrine. /5/ N-Acetyl-4-amino-antipyrine.

Contributors: (a) Chesley, Leon C., (b) Gaudino, Mario, (c) Rubin, Mitchell I., and Calcagno, Philip L., (d) Krupp, Marcus A.

References: [1] Berger, E. Y., M. F. Dunning, J. M. Steele, R. Jackenthal, and B. B. Brodie. 1950. Am. J. Physiol. 162:318. [2] Brodie, B. B., E. Y. Berger, J. Axelrod, M. F. Dunning, Y. Porosowska, and J. M. Steele. 1951. Proc. Soc. Exp. Biol., N. Y. 77:794. [3] Deane, N. 1951. J. Clin. Invest. 30:1469. [4] Deane, N. 1952. Meth. M. Res. 5:159. [5] Deane, N., and H. W. Smith. 1952. J. Clin. Invest. 31:197. [6] Faller, I. L., D. Petty, J. H. Last, L. R. Pascale, and E. E. Bond. 1955. J. Laborat. Clin. M. 45:748. [7] Friis-Hansen, B. J., M. Holiday, and T. Stapleton. 1950. Am. J. Dis. Child. 80:516. [8] Friis Hansen, D. J., M. Holiday, T. Stapleton, and W. M. Wallace. 1951. Pediatrics 7:321. [9] Grunner, O. 1957. Klin. Wschr. 35:347. [10] Hurst, W. W., and F. R. Sherum. 1951. Am. J. Med. 10:516. [11] Ikkos, D., R. Luft, and B. Sjorgren. 1954. Metabolism 3:400. [12] Osserman, E. F., G. C. Pitts, W. C. Welham, and A. R. Behnke. 1950. J. Appl. Physiol. 2:633. [13] Prentice, T. C., et al. 1952. J. Clin. Invest. 31:412. [14] Scribante, P., P. Maurice, and P. Favarger. 1952. Helvet. physiol. pharm. acta 10:224. [15] Soberman, R. J., B. B. Brodie, B. B. Levy, J. Axelrod, V. Hollander, and J. M. Steele. 1949. J. Biol. Chem. 179:31. [16] Steele, J. M., E. Y. Berger, M. F. Dunning, B. B. Brodie, and E. Klein. 1950. Am. J. Physiol. 162:313. [17] Talso, P. J., T. N. Lahr, N. Spafford, G. Ferenzi, and H. R. Jackson. 1955. J. Laborat. Clin. M. 46:619.

Part II: DEUTERIUM OXIDE AND TRITIUM OXIDE DETERMINATIONS

Deuterium oxide and tritium oxide are useful indicators in measuring total body water because of their rapid equilibration time. Since there is a change in the molecular weight of these substances as compared to water, there is a possibility that their rate of exchange in the body may not be the same as that of non-isotopic water. The error introduced through exchange of the isotope deuterium oxide with hydrogen atoms of organic molecules has been estimated to give results as high as 1.0-1.5% of the body weight. [2,12,14,17,21,23] Values in parentheses are ranges, estimate "b" unless otherwise indicated (cf. Introduction).

	Subjects Specification	No.	Total Body Water ml/kg body weight	Reference
	(A)	(B)	(C)	(D)
	Deuterium Oxide			
1	Premature birth	13[1]	(702-830)[C2]	9
2	Newborn	9	757(703-811)	4,7
3	0-1 da	6[1]	790(638-842)	8
4	1-10 da	9[1]	740(700-780)	8
5	1-3 mo	7[1]	723(679-767)	8
6	1 mo-1 yr	9	626(509-745)	4
7	3-6 mo	5[1]	701(651-751)	8
8	6 mo-1 yr	8[1]	604(570-638)	8
9	6 mo-11 yr	11[1]	(532-628)[C2]	9
10	1-2 yr	5[1]	587(545-629)	8
11	1-9 yr	11	589(548-630)	4
12	2-3 yr	9[1]	635(601-669)	8
13	3-5 yr	5[1]	622(578-666)	8
14	5-10 yr	4[1]	615(565-665)	8
15	10-16 yr	15[1]	580(556-604)	8
16		9♂	590(516-664)	4
17		6♀	562(489-633)	4
18	17-39 yr	45♂	602(502-702)	4,11,13,16,22,23
19	18-32 yr	17♂	618(559-702)[C]	21
20	20-31 yr	11♀	519(456-599)[C]	21
21		18♀	512(456-599)[C]	4
22	35-54 yr	10♂	554(447-641)[C]	4
23		6♀	482(405-543)[C]	4
24	<40 yr	19♀	511(430-592)	4,23
25	>40 yr	10♀	468(389-547)	4,23
26	40-59 yr	14♂	572(471-673)	4,11,13,16,22,23

	Subjects Specification	No.	Total Body Water ml/kg body weight	Reference
	(A)	(B)	(C)	(D)
	Deuterium Oxide (concluded)			
27	>60 yr	3♂	541(478-628)[C]	4,11,13,16,22,23
28	Adult		630	12
29			624[3]	14
30		47♂	598(420-720)[C]	3,5,9,11,17,18,21-23
31		13♀	510(420-599)[C]	3,5,9,11,17,18,21-23
32		33♂	612	6
33	<60 kg	16♀	505(415-595)	4,23
34	>60 kg	15♀	486(395-577)	4,23
35	<70 kg	37♂	626(517-735)	4,11,13,16,22,23
36	>70 kg	42♂	560(470-650)	4,11,13,16,22,23
	Pregnant			
37	2nd trimester	6	547(485-600)[C]	15
38	3rd trimester	6	544(487-592)[C]	15
39	3rd trimester	3	527(503-557)[C]	10
40	Postpartum	6	520(437-581)[C]	15
	Tritium Oxide			
41	20-25 yr	4♂	603(575-630)	20
42	23-49 yr	13♂	607(511-703)	1
43	34-56 yr	15♂	521(479-567)	20
44	Adult		647	19

/1/ Number of observations. /2/ Deuterium oxide and antipyrine. /3/ Edematous subjects.

Contributors: (a) Chesley, Leon C., (b) Gaudino, Mario, (c) Rubin, Mitchell I., and Calcagno, Philip L., (d) Krupp, Marcus A., (e) Schwartz, Irving L., (f) Weil, William B., Jr.

References: [1] Cooper, J. A., N. S. Radin, and C. Borden. 1958. J. Laborat. Clin. M. 52:129. [2] Deane, N. 1952. Meth. M. Res. 5:159. [3] Edelman, I. S. 1952. Am. J. Physiol. 171:279. [4] Edelman, I. S., et al. 1952. Surg. Gyn. Obst. 95:1. [5] Edelman, I. S., J. M. Olney, A. H. James, L. Brooks, and F. D. Moore. 1952. Science 115:447. [6] Faller, I. L., D. Petty, J. H. Last, L. R. Pascale, and E. E. Bond. 1955. J. Laborat. Clin. M. 45:748. [7] Flexner, L. B., W. S. Wilde, N. K. Proctor, D. B. Cowie, G. J. Vosburgh, and L. M. Hellman. 1947. J. Pediat., S. Louis 30:413. [8] Friis-Hansen, B. J. 1957. Acta paediat., Upps., v. 46, suppl. 110. [9] Friis-Hansen, B. J., M. Holiday, T. Stapleton, and W. Wallace. 1951. Pediatrics 7:321. [10] Haley, H. B., and J. W. Woodbury. 1952. J. Clin. Invest. 31:635. [11] Hardy, J. D., P. K. Sen, and D. L. Drabkin. 1951. Surg. Gyn. Obst. 93:103. [12] Hevesy, G., and E. Hofer. 1934. Nature, Lond. 134:879. [13] Holander, V., P. Chang, and F. W. Co Tui. 1949. J. Laborat. Clin. M. 34:680. [14] Hurst, W. W., and F. R. Sherum. 1951. Am. J. Med. 10:516. [15] Hutchinson, D. L., A. A. Plentl, and H. C. Taylor. 1953. J. Clin. Invest. 33:235. [16] London, I. M.,

Part II: DEUTERIUM OXIDE AND TRITIUM OXIDE DETERMINATIONS (Concluded)

and D. Rittenberg. 1950. J. Biol. Chem. 184:687. [17] Moore, F. G. 1946. Science 104:157. [18] Moore, F. G. 1947. J. Am. M. Ass. 141:646. [19] Pace, N., L. Kline, H. K. Schachman, and M. Hareferist. 1947. J. Biol. Chem. 168:459. [20] Prentice, T. C., et al. 1952. J. Clin. Invest. 31:412. [21] Schloerb, P. R., B. J. Friis-Hansen, I. S. Edelman, A. K. Solomon, and F. D. Moore. 1950. Ibid. 29:1296. [22] Schwartz, I. L., A. Nelson, P. Weisz, M. H. Maxwell, E. Breed, and L. Silver. 1952. Fed. Proc., Balt. 11:142. [23] Soberman, R., B. B. Brodie, B. B. Levy, J. Axelrod, V. Hollander, and J. M. Steele. 1949. J. Biol. Chem. 179:31.

Part III: DESICCATION AND SPECIFIC GRAVITY DETERMINATIONS

Desiccation determination: Intact subject weighed before and after drying to constant weight, usually at a temperature of 105°C ± 5. Specific gravity determination: Body water calculated from an empirical relationship between percent of body water, percent of body fat, and body specific gravity. Values in parentheses are ranges, estimate "b" unless otherwise indicated (cf. Introduction).

	Subjects Specification (A)	No. (B)	Total Body Water ml/kg body weight (C)	Reference (D)		Subjects Specification (A)	No. (B)	Total Body Water ml/kg body weight (C)	Reference (D)
	Desiccation					Desiccation (concluded)			
	Fetus				8	Newborn		796	7
1	<100 g	33	914(871–957)	6,8,9,13,15	9	(concluded)		664	7
2	100–499 g	36	882(837–927)	6,8,9,13,15,20	10	Adult		679	14
3	500–999 g	14	852(792–912)	6,9,11,13,15, 18,20	11			676	2
					12		4♂	635	3,14,17,19
4	1000–1499 g	10	832(798–866)	6,8,9,11,13,18	13		1♀	560	19
5	1500–2499 g	10	783(710–856)	4,5,6,9,20	14		5	648(580–678)c	1,14,16
6	Fetus or newborn, >2500 g	17	708(598–818)	3,5,6,9,10,13, 20		Specific Gravity			
7	Newborn		740	7	15	Adult	9	543(444–596)c	12

Contributors: (a) Chesley, Leon C., (b) Schwartz, Irving L., (c) Rubin, Mitchell I., and Calcagno, Philip L., (d) Krupp, Marcus A.

References: [1] Aron, H. In S. Hatai. 1917. Am. J. Anat. 21:23. [2] Aron, H. In C. Oppenheimer, ed. 1927. Handbuch der Biochemie des Menschen und der Tiere. Ed. 2. Gustav Fischer, Jena. v. 7. [3] Bischoff, E. 1863. Zschr. rat. Med., Ser. 3, 20:75. [4] Brubacher, H. 1890. Zschr. Biol. 27:517. [5] Camerer, W., Jr. 1902. Ibid. 43:1. [6] Fehling, H. 1877. Arch. Gyn., Berl. 11:523. [7] Friis-Hansen, B. J., M. Holiday, T. Stapleton, and W. Wallace. 1951. Pediatrics 7:321. [8] Givens, M. H., and I. G. Macy. 1933. J. Biol. Chem. 102:7. [9] Iob, V., and W. W. Swanson. 1934. Am. J. Dis. Child. 47:302. [10] Klose, E. 1914. Jahrb. Kinderh. 80:154. [11] Langstein, L., and F. Edelstein. 1917. Zschr. Kinderh. 15:49. [12] Messinger, W. J., and J. M. Steele. 1949. Proc. Soc. Exp. Biol., N. Y. 70:316. [13] Michel, C. 1900. Obstétrique 5:252. [14] Mitchell, H. H., T. S. Hamilton, F. R. Steggerda, and H. W. Bean. 1945. J. Biol. Chem. 158:625. [15] Schmitz, E. 1924. Arch. Gyn., Berl. 121:1. [16] Skelton, H. 1927. Arch. Int. M. 40:140. [17] Volkmann, A. W. 1874. Ber. sächs. Ges. Wiss. 26:202. [18] Von Bezold, A. 1857. Zschr. wiss. Zool. 8:487. [19] Widdowson, E. M., R. A. McCance, and C. M. Spray. 1951. Clin. Sc., Lond. 10:113. [20] Widdowson, E. M., and C. M. Spray. 1951. Arch. Dis. Childh., Lond. 26:205.

For information on methods, see Table 115. Values in parentheses are ranges, estimate "b," "c," or "d" as indicated (cf. Introduction).

Subjects			Method	Total Body Water ml/kg body weight	Reference
Animal	Specification	No.			
(A)	(B)	(C)	(D)	(E)	(F)
1 Cat	Newborn	7	Desiccation	807	44,49
2	2 wk	1	Desiccation	738	44
3	12 wk	1	Desiccation	666	44
4	Adult	1	Desiccation	580	46
5		3	Desiccation	677(642-724)[c]	3,32,47
6		1	Deuterium oxide	615	9
7		8[1]	Sodium chloride	500(420-560)[c]	10
8		11	Urea	630(565-715)[c]	10
9 Cattle	Adult	19	Desiccation	710(680-730)[c2]	32
10		30	Specific gravity	537(431-633)[c]	27
11		5	Urea	625(580-686)[c]	35
12	Fattened	30	Antipyrine	539(431-647)[b]	27
13 Dog	Newborn	5	Desiccation	812(806-820)[c2]	3,32
14		7	Desiccation	779(737-803)[c]	18,44
15	42 da		Desiccation	705	4
16	100 da		Desiccation	689	4
17	Young	11	Desiccation	700(670-730)[b]	35,41,44
18	Adult	8[1]	Antipyrine	599(539-679)[c]	24
19		14	Antipyrine	583(532-679)[c]	24,42
20		6	Desiccation	628(550-662)[c]	11,12,22,35
21		33	Deuterium oxide	619(525-713)[d]	16,36
22		40	Deuterium oxide	589(350-900)[c]	9,15,16,39
23	Lean	7	Antipyrine	734(639-795)[c]	24,41
24		4	Desiccation	700(619-756)[c]	36,48
25	Obese	14	Desiccation	596(503-690)[b]	35,36,48
Guinea pig	Fetus				17
26	<12 g	4	Desiccation	894(863-966)[c]	
27	27-52 g	5	Desiccation	822(808-839)[c]	
28	71-112 g	4	Desiccation	716(684-754)[c]	
29	Newborn	11	Desiccation	710	26,49
30	15 da	5	Desiccation	779	43
31	Adult	50	Desiccation	635(464-708)[c]	33,37
32		6♂	Desiccation	727(711-743)[b]	6
33		6♀	Desiccation	718(686-750)[b]	6
34		5[1]	Deuterium oxide	650(600-670)[c]	14
35 Hamster	Adult	1♂	Desiccation	674	6
36 Monkey	Adult	5	Antipyrine	695(628-721)[c]	41
37		7	Desiccation	691(650-720)[c]	22,41
38 Mouse	Fetus, ½ term	5	Desiccation	871	45
39	Newborn	69	Desiccation	833	43,45
40	15 da	31	Desiccation	757	43
41	30 da	39	Desiccation	766	43
42	Adult	4	Desiccation	747(700-783)[c2]	3,32
43		6♂	Desiccation	727(687-767)[b]	6
44		6♀	Desiccation	685(600-765)[b]	6
45		16♀	Desiccation	740(712-768)[b2]	2
Rabbit	Fetus				13
46	<1 g	2	Desiccation	915(914-915)[c]	
47	10-50 g	14	Desiccation	840(784-896)[b]	
48	>50 g	2	Desiccation	816(815-818)[c]	
49	Newborn	16	Desiccation	830(772-888)[d]	4,13,49
50	Young	6	Desiccation	720(651-767)[c]	4,13
51	Adult	4	Antipyrine	743(688-778)[c]	40,41
52		8♂	Desiccation	704(646-762)[b]	6
53		8♀	Desiccation	668(622-714)[b]	6
54		10	Desiccation	729(692-770)[c2]	3,22,32,40
55		20	Desiccation	708(590-830)[b]	22,31,34,36,41
56		9	Deuterium oxide	728(676-774)[c]	31
57		2	Deuterium oxide	741(702-779)[c]	25
58		2	Tritium oxide	559(545-573)[c]	34

/1/ Number of observations.   /2/ ml/kg fat-free body weight.

	Subjects			Method	Total Body Water ml/kg body weight	Reference
	Animal	Specification	No.			
	(A)	(B)	(C)	(D)	(E)	(F)
	Rat	Fetus				
59		<0.2 g	165	Desiccation	922(918-926)[b]	1,20
60		0.2-0.5 g	147	Desiccation	912(903-921)[d]	1,20
61		0.5-1.0 g	96	Desiccation	900(892-908)[b]	1,20
62		1.0-2.5 g	150	Desiccation	885(876-894)[d]	1,20
63		2.5-5.0 g	12	Desiccation	874(867-881)[b]	1
64		Newborn	177	Desiccation	868(851-885)[d]	1,20,23,26,29,49
65		2 da	43	Desiccation	832(809-855)[b]	20
66		4 da	38	Desiccation	822(807-837)[b]	20
67		6 da	36	Desiccation	814(773-855)[b]	20
68		7-9 da	47	Desiccation	797(757-837)[d]	20,23,29
69		10-15 da	25	Desiccation	757(719-795)[d]	20,23
70		20-30 da	25	Desiccation	712(676-748)[d]	20,23,29
71		Weanling	3	Desiccation	747(742-753)[b2]	2
72		1-2 mo	28	Desiccation	697(662-732)[d]	20,23,28,29
73		2-3 mo	13	Desiccation	684(643-725)[d]	20,29
74		Adult	313	Desiccation	638(536-740)[d]	5,7,19,20,23,28,29,38
75			9	Desiccation	670(653-697)[c]	8,23,28,32
76			7♂	Desiccation	730(715-744)[b2]	2
77			12♂	Desiccation	666(622-710)[b]	6
78			12♀	Desiccation	683(653-713)[b]	6
79			2	Deuterium oxide	655(635-675)[c]	30
80		Lean, <5.5% fat	25♂	Desiccation	690(676-704)[d]	38
81			24♀	Desiccation	684(670-698)[d]	
82		Average, 8-14% fat	48♂	Desiccation	660(620-700)[d]	
83			34♀	Desiccation	650(610-690)[d]	
84		Obese, 15-26% fat	40♂	Desiccation	558(508-608)[d]	
85			38♀	Desiccation	586(516-656)[d]	
86	Sheep	Young	34[1]	Antipyrine	618(450-720)[c]	21
87			44[1]	I[131]-antipyrine	623(480-740)[c]	
88		Adult	16[1]	Antipyrine	553(370-630)[c]	
89			18[1]	I[131]-antipyrine	562(350-650)[c]	
90	Swine	Newborn	19	Desiccation	834	49,50
91		17 da	3	Desiccation	799(796-802)[c]	50

/1/ Number of observations. /2/ ml/kg fat-free body weight.

Contributors: (a) Chesley, Leon C., (b) Schwartz, Irving L., (c) Rubin, Mitchell I., and Calcagno, Philip L.

References: [1] Angulo y Gonzalez, A. W. 1932. Anat. Rec. 52:117. [2] Annegers, J. 1954. Proc. Soc. Exp. Biol., N. Y. 87:454. [3] Aron, H. In S. Hatai. 1917. Am. J. Anat. 21:23. [4] Aron, H. In C. Oppenheimer, ed. 1927. Handbuch der Biochemie des Menschen und der Tiere. Ed. 2. Gustav Fischer, Jena. v. 7, pp. 152-234. [5] Ashworth, U. S., and G. R. Cowgill. 1938. J. Nutrit. 15:73. [6] Cizek, L. J. 1954. Am. J. Physiol. 179:104. [7] Da Costa, E., and R. Clayton. 1950. J. Nutrit. 41:597. [8] Drake, T. G. H., C. F. McKhann, and J. F. Gamble. 1930. J. Exp. M. 51:867. [9] Edelman, I. S. 1952. Am. J. Physiol. 171:279. [10] Eggleton, M. G. 1951. J. Physiol., Lond. 115:482. [11] Engels, W. 1904. Naunyn-Schmiedeberg's Arch. Exp. Path., 51:346. [12] Falck, C. P., and T. Scheffer. 1854. Arch. physiol. Heilk. 13:508. [13] Fehling, H. 1877. Arch. Gyn., Berl. 11:523. [14] Flexner, L. B., A. Gellhorn, and M. Merrell. 1942. J. Biol. Chem. 144:35. [15] Fogelman, M. J., P. O'B. Montgomery, and C. A. Moyer. 1952. Am. J. Physiol. 169:94. [16] Gaudino, M., and M. F. Levitt. 1949. J. Clin. Invest. 28:1487. [17] Gellhorn, A., and L. B. Flexner. 1942. Am. J. Physiol. 136:750. [18] Gerhartz, H. 1910. Pflügers Arch. 135:104. [19] Haldi, J., G. Giddings, and W. Wynn. 1944. Am. J. Physiol. 141:83. [20] Hamilton, B., and M. M. Dewar. 1938. Growth, Montreal 2:13. [21] Hansard, S. L., and W. A. Lyke. 1956. Proc. Soc. Exp. Biol., N. Y. 93:263. [22] Harrison, H. E., D. C. Darrow, and H. Yannet. 1936. J. Biol. Chem. 113:515. [23] Hatai, S. 1917. Am. J. Anat. 21:23. [24] Harrold, M., and L. Sapirstein. 1952. Proc. Soc. Exp.

Biol., N. Y. 79:419. [25] Hevesy, G., and C. F. Jacobsen. 1940. Acta physiol. scand. 1:11. [26] Inaba, R. 1911. Arch. Anat. Physiol., Lpz. Physiol. Abt., p. 1. [27] Kraybill, H. F., O. G. Hankins, and H. L. Bitter. 1951. J. Appl. Physiol. 3:681. [28] Light, A. E., P. K. Smith, A. H. Smith, and W. E. Anderson. 1934. J. Biol. Chem. 107:689. [29] Lowrey, L. G. 1913. Anat. Rec. 7:143. [30] McDougall, E. J., F. Verzár, H. Erlenmeyer, and H. Gaertner. 1934. Nature, Lond. 134:1006. [31] Moore, F. D. 1946. Science 104:157. [32] Moulton, C. R. 1923. J. Biol. Chem. 57:79. [33] Pace, N., and E. N. Rathbun. 1945. Ibid. 158:685. [34] Pace, N., L. Kline, H. K. Schachman, and M. Harfenist. 1947. Ibid. 168:459. [35] Painter, E. 1940. Am. J. Physiol. 129:744. [36] Pfeiffer, L. 1887. Zschr. Biol., n. F. 5, 23:340. [37] Rathbun, E. N., and N. Pace. 1945. J. Biol. Chem. 158:667. [38] Scheer, B. T., E. Straub, M. Fields, E. R. Meserve, C. Hendrick, and H. J. Deuel, Jr. 1947. J. Nutrit. 34:581. [39] Schwartz, I. L., A. Nelson, P. Weisz, M. H. Maxwell, E. Breed, and L. Silver. 1952. Fed. Proc., Balt. 11:142. [40] Soberman, R. J. 1949. Proc. Soc. Exp. Biol., N. Y. 70:172. [41] Soberman, R. J. 1950. Ibid. 74:789. [42] Soberman, R. J., R. P. Keating, and R. D. Maxwell. 1951. Am. J. Physiol. 164:450. [43] Spray, C. M., and E. M. Widdowson. 1950. Brit. J. Nutrit. 4:332. [44] Thomas, K. 1911. Arch. Anat. Physiol., Lpz., Physiol. Abt., p. 9. [45] Von Bezold, A. 1857. Zschr. wiss. Zool. 8:487. [46] Von Voit, C. 1866. Zschr. Biol. 2:307. [47] Von Voit, C. In H. Skelton. 1927. Arch. Int. M. 40:140. [48] Weigert, R. 1905. Jahrb. Kinderh. 61:178. [49] Widdowson, E. M. 1950. Nature, Lond. 166:626. [50] Wilson, M. B. 1902-03. Am. J. Physiol. 8:197.

117. TOTAL BODY WATER: FISHES

Total body water determined by desiccation. Values in parentheses are ranges, estimate "c" (cf. Introduction).

	Animal	No. of Speci- mens	Body Weight kg	Total Body Water ml/kg body weight	Reference
	(A)	(B)	(C)	(D)	(E)
	Fresh-water Osteichthyes				
1	Bowfin (Amia calva)	6	1.963(1.020-3.265)	745(726-764)	3
2	Buffalo, bigmouth (Ictiobus cyprinellus)	8	3.395(1.980-5.440)	706(641-760)	3
3	Carp (Cyprinus carpio)	7	2.412(1.585-3.190)	714(701-731)	3
4	Gar, shortnosed (Lepisosteus platostomum)	7	1.185(0.855-1.730)	667(645-707)	3
5	Paddlefish (Polyodon spathula)	5	4.679(3.740-5.910)	740(713-774)	3
6	Sturgeon, lake (Acipenser fulvescens)	8	3.058(2.275-4.530)	727(715-740)	3
7	Sucker, white (Catostomus commersonii)	2	0.617(0.580-0.655)	744(741-748)	3
	Marine Osteichthyes				
8	Barracuda (Sphyraena barracuda)	9	2.336(1.430-4.575)	706(681-733)	3
	Grouper				3
9	Epinephelus striatus	2	1.270(0.930-1.610)	717(704-731)	
10	Mycteroperca tigris	1	5.885	711	
11	Moray, green (Gymnothorax funebris)	6	4.062(3.050-4.815)	637(561-718)	3
12	Parrot fish, rainbow (Pseudoscarus guacamaia)	14	4.396(1.650-6.370)	731(712-750)	3
	Snapper				3
13	Lutianus aya	2	3.765(3.130-4.400)	713(712-715)	
14	L. griseus	6	3.711(1.900-4.680)	723(705-740)	
	Chondrichthyes				
15	Dogfish, Pacific spiny (Squalus suckleyi)	16	2.301(1.122-4.480)	717.8(684-754)	1
16	Ratfish (Hydrolagus colliei)	13	1.056(0.520-1.573)	714.5(687-748)	1
	Skate				1
17	Raja binoculata	3	4.878(2.646-8.470)	826(817-834)	
18	R. rhina	10	3.908(1.400-5.760)	800.3(800-836)	
	Agnatha				
19	Lamprey, sea (Petromyzon marinus)	12	0.190(0.154-0.261)	756(737-798)	2

Contributor: Thorson, Thomas B.

References: [1] Thorson, T. B. 1958. Physiol. Zool. 31:16. [2] Thorson, T. B. 1959. Science 130:99. [3] Thorson, T. B. 1959. Unpublished.

118. EXTRACELLULAR BODY WATER: MAN

Part I: CONSTANT INFUSION TECHNIQUE

Extracellular fluid spaces were measured by means of an equilibrating infusion to compensate for renal excretion. Spaces were calculated by dividing total amount of test substance in the body at any instant after equilibration was established (difference between amounts infused and excreted, or total recovery after infusion, or both) by plasma concentration at that instant. Inulin is not metabolized to any appreciable degree, shows no evidence of storage in any tissue, does not penetrate erythrocytes or escape through normal renal tubules, and is physiologically inert when properly prepared; however, disadvantageously, it diffuses slowly. Inulin is rapidly excreted by glomerular filtration. [1, 4, 12, 13, 16, 22] Ferrocyanide has the advantage of achieving equilibration sooner than does inulin, and is rapidly excreted by the kidneys [14]. Mannitol is rapidly excreted by the kidneys, but recovery from the urine is incomplete, indicating some degree of utilization for which no simple correction can be made [9, 10, 20]. Sucrose does not enter erythrocytes or cerebrospinal fluid in more than trace amounts; rapid equilibration occurs, with rapid excretion by the kidneys. [7, 15, 17, 18] Values in parentheses are ranges, estimate "c" unless otherwise indicated (cf. Introduction).

	Subjects		Method	Extracellular Water ml/kg body weight	Reference
	Specification	No.			
	(A)	(B)	(C)	(D)	(E)
1	Newborn	4	Ferrocyanide	353(297-414)	3
2		6	Inulin	346(275-419)	
3	2-9 mo	4♂, 13♀	Inulin	267(240-290)	14
4	18-35 yr	10♂	Inulin	150(115-173)	5, 11, 13
5	20-32 yr	11♀	Inulin	192(189-249)	5, 11
6	38-55 yr	11♂	Inulin	175(144-222)	5, 11, 13
7	38-49 yr	5♀	Inulin	238(190-236)	5, 11, 19
8	56-71 yr	8♂	Inulin	190(133-245)	5, 11, 13
9	Adult	36	Inulin	158(131-185)[b]	2, 7, 13, 22-24
10			Mannitol	177[1]	20
11			Mannitol	161	9
12			Mannitol	(187-230)	10
13		6	Mannitol	159(141-189)	22
14		25	Sucrose	178(143-213)[b]	6-8
15			Sucrose	206	17, 18
16			Sucrose	(177-264)	15
17			Sucrose	177.6	21
18			Sucrose	(162-191)	7

/1/ Approximately.

Contributors: (a) Chesley, Leon C., (b) Gaudino, Mario, (c) Rubin, Mitchell I., and Calcagno, Philip L., (d) Krupp, Marcus A.

References: [1] Berger, E. Y., M. F. Dunning, B. B. Brodie, and J. M. Steele. 1949. Fed. Proc., Balt. 8:10. [2] Berger, E. Y., M. F. Dunning, J. M. Steele, R. Jackenthal, and B. B. Brodie. 1950. Am. J. Physiol. 162:318. [3] Calcagno, P. L., G. S. Husson, and M. I. Rubin. 1951. Proc. Soc. Exp. Biol., N. Y. 77:309. [4] Cotlove, E. 1952. Fed. Proc., Balt. 2:28. [5] Crawford, E. J., and M. Gaudino. 1952. Anesthesiology 13:374. [6] Deane, N. 1951. J. Clin. Invest. 30:1469. [7] Deane, N., G. E. Schreiner, and J. S. Robertson. 1951. Ibid. 30:1463. [8] Deane, N., and H. W. Smith. 1952. Ibid. 31:197. [9] Dominguez, R., A. C. Corcoran, and I. H. Page. 1947. J. Laborat. Clin. M. 32:1192. [10] Elkinton, J. R. 1947. J. Clin. Invest. 26:1088. [11] Gaudino, M. Unpublished.

Part I: CONSTANT INFUSION TECHNIQUE (Concluded)

[12] Gaudino, M., and M. F. Levitt. 1949. Am. J. Physiol. 157:387. [13] Gaudino, M., I. L. Schwartz, and M. F. Levitt. 1948. Proc. Soc. Exp. Biol., N. Y. 68:507. [14] Katcher, A. L., M. F. Levitt, A. Y. Sweet, and H. L. Hodes. 1953. J. Clin. Invest. 32:1013. [15] Keith, N. M., and M. H. Power. 1938. Am. J. Physiol. 120:203. [16] Kruhffer, P. 1946. Acta physiol. scand. 11:16. [17] Lavietes, P. H., J. Bourdillon, and K. A. Klinghoffer. 1936. J. Clin. Invest. 15:261. [18] Lavietes, P. H., J. Bourdillon, and J. P. Peters. 1935. Ibid. 14:705. [19] Levitt, M. F., and M. E. Bader. 1951. Am. J. Med. 11:715. [20] Newman, E. V., J. Bordley, III, and J. Winternitz. 1944. Bull. Johns Hopkins Hosp. 75:253. [21] Raisz, C. G., M. K. Young, Jr., and C. T. Stenson. 1953. Am. J. Physiol. 174:72. [22] Schwartz, I. L., E. S. Breed, and M. H. Maxwell. 1950. J. Clin. Invest. 29:517. [23] Schwartz, I. L., A. Nelson, P. Weisz, M. H. Maxwell, E. Breed, and L. Silver. 1952. Fed. Proc., Balt. 11:142. [24] Schwartz, I. L., D. Schachter, and N. Freinkel. 1949. J. Clin. Invest. 28:1117.

Part II: THIOCYANATE SPACE

Thiocyanate was given by single injection. Spaces were calculated, without corrections, by dividing the plasma concentration into the total amount of thiocyanate in the body. In adults, the proportion of thiocyanate-available water decreases with increasing body weight, suggesting that thiocyanate space correlates better with surface area than with body weight. In growing children, the space decreases in proportion to body weight, but increases in proportion to surface area. Thiocyanate is distributed rapidly, but it also penetrates erythrocytes, is present in partly bound form in serum, enters glandular cells, and may become intracellular in pathological states [5, 6, 11, 14-16, 22-24]. Values in parentheses are ranges, estimate "b" unless otherwise indicated (cf. Introduction).

Subjects		Extracellular Water ml/kg body weight	Reference
Specification	No.		
(A)	(B)	(C)	(D)
1	<1 mo	10	412(354-470)	7, 8
2	1-12 mo	36	364(268-460)	7, 8
3	1-6 yr	65	309(236-382)	6-8, 19
4	6-10 yr	22	296(236-356)	6-8, 19
5	10-18 yr	71♂	286(228-344)	6, 7, 19, 21
6	Adult	134♂	248(188-308)	4, 5, 9, 12-15, 17, 20, 22, 23
7		3[1]	(192-240)[c]	12
8			226	16
9			271	18
10		37♀	208(144-272)[2]	5, 10, 20, 23
11	<50 kg	14♀	220(160-280)	5, 10, 20, 23
12	50-69 kg	17♀	198(138-258)	5, 10, 20, 23
13	<60 kg	11♂	248(154-342)	4, 5, 9, 12-15, 17, 20, 22, 23
14	60-69 kg	42♂	249(196-302)	4, 5, 9, 12-15, 17, 20, 22, 23
15	>70 kg	3♀	183	5, 10, 20, 23
16	70-79 kg	37♂	241(176-306)	4, 5, 9, 12-15, 17, 20, 22, 23
17	>80 kg	28♂	221(182-260)	4, 5, 9, 12-15, 17, 20, 22, 23
	Pregnant,			
18	1st trimester	16	281(196-366)	1-3
19	2nd trimester	68	284(221-347)	1-3
20	3rd trimester	2457	303(233-373)	1-3, 10
21	<60 kg	507	325(281-369)	
22	60-69 kg	974	310(250-370)	
23	70-79 kg	581	297(246-348)	
24	80-89 kg	252	278(227-329)	
25	90-99 kg	112	260(202-318)	
26	>100 kg	31	241(191-291)	

/1/ Number of observations. /2/ Very atypical distribution.

Contributors: (a) Chesley, Leon C., (b) Gaudino, Mario, (c) Rubin, Mitchell I., and Calcagno, Philip L., (d) Krupp, Marcus A.

Part II: THIOCYANATE SPACE (Concluded)

References: [1] Caton, W. L., C. C. Roby, D. E. Reid, and J. G. Gibson, II. 1949. Am. J. Obst. 57:471. [2] Chesley, L. C. 1943. Surg. Gyn. Obst. 76:589. [3] Chesley, L. C., and E. R. Chesley. 1943. Am. J. Obst. 45:748. [4] Corse, L., Jr., J. M. Olney, Jr., R. W. Steenburg, M. R. Ball, and F. D. Moore. 1950. J. Clin. Invest. 29:1280. [5] Crandall, L. A., and M. X. Anderson. 1934. Am. J. Digest. Dis. 1:126. [6] Doxiadis, S. A., and D. Gairdner. 1948. Clin. Sc., Lond. 6:257. [7] Ely, R. S., and W. W. Sutow. 1952. Pediatrics 10:115. [8] Fellers, F. X., H. L. Barnett, K. Hare, and H. McNamara. 1949. Ibid. 3:622. [9] Forbes, W. H., D. B. Dill, and F. G. Hall. 1940. Am. J. Physiol. 130:739. [10] Freis, E. D., and J. F. Kenny. 1948. J. Clin. Invest. 27:283. [11] Gaudino, M., and M. F. Levitt. 1949. Am. J. Physiol. 157:387. [12] Gaudino, M., I. L. Schwartz, and M. F. Levitt. 1948. Proc. Soc. Exp. Biol., N. Y. 68:507. [13] Henschel, A., O. Mickelsen, H. L. Taylor, and A. Keys. 1947. Am. J. Physiol. 150:170. [14] Kaltreider, N. L., G. R. Meneely, J. R. Allen, and W. F. Bale. 1941. J. Exp. M. 74:569. [15] Lavietes, P. H., J. Bourdillon, and K. A. Klinghoffer. 1936. J. Clin. Invest. 15:261. [16] Lavietes, P. H., J. Bourdillon, and J. P. Peters. 1935. Ibid. 14:705. [17] Ling, W. S. M., and H. Sprinz. 1948. Am. J. M. Sc. 215:555. [18] Moore, F. D. 1946. Science 104:157. [19] Morse, M., D. E. Cassels, and F. W. Schlutz. 1947. Am. J. Physiol. 151:438. [20] Schloerb, P. R., B. J. Friis-Hansen, I. S. Edelman, A. K. Solomon, and F. D. Moore. 1950. J. Clin. Invest. 29:1296. [21] Schlutz, F. W., M. Morse, D. E. Cassels, and L. V. Iob. 1940. J. Pediat., S. Louis. 17:466. [22] Schwartz, I. L., D. Schachter, and N. Freinkel. 1949. J. Clin. Invest. 28:1117. [23] Stewart, J. D., and G. M. Rourke. 1941. J. Laborat. Clin. M. 26:1383. [24] Winkler, A. W., J. R. Elkinton, and A. J. Eisenman. 1943. Am. J. Physiol. 139:239.

Part III: SODIUM SPACE

Subjects injected with radioactive sodium (Na^{24}). Sodium space is, at best, a mathematical ratio and not a measurement of a liquid volume of distribution, since radioactive sodium does not completely exchange with body sodium for at least 24 hours and since a certain proportion of that exchange occurs with solid phase sodium. Values in parentheses are ranges, estimate "b" unless otherwise indicated (cf. Introduction).

	Subjects Specification	No.	Extracellular Water ml/kg body weight	Reference		Subjects Specification	No.	Extracellular Water ml/kg body weight	Reference
	(A)	(B)	(C)	(D)		(A)	(B)	(C)	(D)
1	<1 mo	36	403(280-525)	2, 3, 6	7	Adult (con-		(217-297)[c]	4
2	1-12 mo	21	358(244-472)	2, 6	8	cluded)		(264-270)[c]	8
3	1-6 yr	9	317(225-409)	2, 6	9	<60 kg	14	314(195-433)	1, 2, 4, 6-9
4	6-10 yr	4	335(245-425)	2, 6	10	60-70 kg	13	288(232-344)	1, 2, 4, 6-9
5	>10 yr	66	275(189-361)	1, 2, 4, 6-9	11	70-80 kg	25	267(190-344)	1, 2, 4, 6-9
6	Adult		265	5	12	>80 kg	14	236(183-289)	1, 2, 4, 6-9

Contributors: (a) Chesley, Leon C., (b) Weil, William B., Jr., (c) Rubin, Mitchell, I., and Calcagno, Philip L., (d) Gaudino, Mario, (e) Krupp, Marcus A.

References: [1] Deane, N., G. E. Schreiner, and J. S. Robertson. 1951. J. Clin. Invest. 30:1463. [2] Fellers, F. X., H. L. Barnett, K. Hare, and H. McNamara. 1949. Pediatrics 3:622. [3] Flexner, L. B., W. S. Wilde, N. K. Proctor, D. B. Cowie, G. J. Vosburgh, and L. M. Hellman. 1947. J. Pediat., S. Louis 30:413. [4] Kaltreider, N. L., G. R. Meneely, J. R. Allen, and W. F. Bale. 1941. J. Exp. M. 74:569. [5] Moore, F. D. 1946. Science 104:157. [6] Perley, A., G. B. Forbes, and M. M. Pennoyer. 1951. J. Pediat., S. Louis 38:299. [7] Schwartz, I. L., A. Nelson, P. Weisz, M. H. Maxwell, E. Breed, and L. Silver. 1952. Fed. Proc., Balt. 11:142. [8] Schwartz, I. L., D. Schachter, and N. Freinkel. 1949. J. Clin. Invest. 28:1117. [9] Warner, G. F., E. L. Dobson, C. E. Rodgers, M. E. Johnston, and N. Pace. 1952. Circulation, N. Y. 5:915.

118. EXTRACELLULAR BODY WATER: MAN (Concluded)

Part IV: BROMIDE, CHLORIDE, AND SULFATE SPACES

Bromide is distributed throughout the body similarly to chloride. Bromide and chloride enter blood cells and gastrointestinal secretions; bromide does not enter the cerebral spinal fluid compartment freely. [2, 11] Chloride is not entirely extracellular; blood, connective tissue, gastric mucosa, testis, and probably lung, all have a large proportion of chloride-containing cells. [8] Sulfate has the advantage of not permeating erythrocytes; however, rapid excretion may prevent its use in edema. Correction is necessary for serum endogenous sulfate [2]. Radiosulfate requires approximately five hours to equilibrate between plasma and ascitic fluid. Radiosulfate space should be regarded not as a measure of anatomical extracellular space, but rather as an index of physiological extracellular water (plasma and those fluid compartments with which radiosulfate rapidly exchanges ions and small molecules). Values in parentheses are ranges, estimate "b" unless otherwise indicated (cf. Introduction).

Subjects		No. and Sex	Method[1]	Extracellular Water ml/kg body weight	Reference
Specification					
(A)		(B)	(C)	(D)	(E)
	Fetus				12
1	20 wk		Chloride	625	
2	24 wk		Chloride	580	
3	32 wk		Chloride	510	
4	At birth		Chloride	430	12
5	18.6(17-22) yr	$11\sigma^2$	$S^{35}O_4$	191(157-225)	10
6	20-60+ yr	σ	Bromide	276(186-366)	1
7		$\female$	Bromide	251(158-344)	
8	26.3(22-31) yr	9σ	$S^{35}O_4$	167(123-211)	10
9	62.6(61-65) yr	5σ	$S^{35}O_4$	149(85-213)	10
10	65.3(56-76) yr	$8\female$	$S^{35}O_4$	155(113-197)	10
11	Adult	65σ	Bromide	273(208-327)	1, 2, 11
12		3σ	Cl^{38}	243(189-320)[c]	9, 13
13		$\sigma, \female$	Cl^{38}	260(222-288)[c]	5
14		σ	Sulfate	240(208-289)[c]	6
15			Sulfate	200	6, 7
16		10σ	$S^{35}O_4$	163(132-194)	14
17		$\sigma, \female$	$S^{35}O_4$	151(100-208)	14, 15
18	40-70+ kg	σ	Bromide	274(206-342)	3
19		$\female$	Bromide	245(187-303)	
20	Pregnant, 3rd trimester	25	Bromide	288(223-343)	4

/1/ Cl^{38} = radioactive chlorine; $S^{35}O_4$ = sulfate with radioactive sulfur. /2/ Young soldiers.

Contributors: (a) Chesley, Leon C., (b) Weil, William B., Jr., (c) Rubin, Mitchell I., and Calcagno, Philip L., (d) Krupp, Marcus A.

References: [1] Berger, E. Y., M. F. Dunning, J. M. Steele, R. Jackenthal, and B. B. Brodie. 1950. Am. J. Physiol. 162:318. [2] Brodie, B. B., E. Brand, and S. Leshin. 1939. J. Biol. Chem. 130:555. [3] Dunning, M. F., J. M. Steele, and E. Y. Berger. 1951. Proc. Soc. Exp. Biol., N. Y. 77:854. [4] Friedman, M. M., M. J. Goodfriend, P. F. Berlin, and T. Goldstein. 1951. Am. J. Obst. 61:609. [5] Gamble, J. L., Jr., J. S. Robertson, C. A. Hannigan, C. G. Foster, and L. Farr. 1953. J. Clin. Invest. 32:483. [6] Lavietes, P. H., J. Bourdillon, and K. A. Klinghoffer. 1936. Ibid. 15:261. [7] Lavietes, P. H., J. Bourdillon, and J. P. Peters. 1935. Ibid. 14:705. [8] Manery, J. F., and A. B. Hastings. 1939. J. Biol. Chem. 127:657. [9] Moore, F. D. 1946. Science 104:157. [10] Ryan, R. J., L. R. Pascal, T. S. Inouye, and L. Bernstein. 1956. J. Clin. Invest. 35:1119. [11] Schwartz, I. L., D. Schachter, and N. Freinkel. 1949. Ibid. 28:1117. [12] Stearns, G. 1939. Physiol. Rev. 19:415. [13] Threefoot, S. A., G. E. Burch, and C. T. Ray. 1952. J. Clin. Invest. 31:666. [14] Walser, M. 1952. Proc. Soc. Exp. Biol., N. Y. 79:372. [15] Walser, M., D. W. Seldin, and A. Grollman. 1953. J. Clin. Invest. 32:299.

119. EXTRACELLULAR BODY WATER: VERTEBRATES OTHER THAN MAN

For information on methods, see table 118. Values in parentheses are ranges, estimate "b" unless otherwise indicated (cf. Introduction).

Subjects		Method[1]	Extracellular Water ml/kg body weight	Reference
Animal	No.			
(A)	(B)	(C)	(D)	(E)
1 Cat	2	Chloride	318(316-320)	24
2	2	Thiocyanate	288	
3 Dog	13	Bromide	325(240-410)	4, 7, 15
4	9	Chloride	305(207-403)	8, 19, 43
5		Cl^{38}	247	43
6		Galactose	250	39
7	50	Inulin	198(145-251)	13-16, 34, 37
8	9	Mannitol	216(166-241)c	33
9	9[2]	Mannitol	241(198-319)c	21
10		Magnesium sulfate	(190-260)c	36
11	35	Na^{24}	284(208-360)	13, 15, 22, 34, 37, 43
12		Sulfate	(210-320)c	36
13		$S^{35}O_4$	201(156-246)	41
14		Thiocyanate	346	43
15		Thiocyanate	275	23
16		Thiocyanate	380	40
17	176	Thiocyanate	320(239-408)	3, 5, 6, 10, 11, 13-15, 17, 21, 22, 28, 29, 38
18 12.5-18.1 kg	25[3]	Inulin	161.5	31
19 Horse	4	Thiocyanate	275	10
20 Monkey	16	Thiocyanate	208(121-295)	30
21 Rabbit		Bromide	309	18
22	3	Chloride	270(250-280)c	19
23	11	Inulin	158(140-190)c	23
24	6	Inulin	266(254-275)c	32
25	39	Na^{24}	263(219-307)	1
26	28	Thiocyanate	235(135-335)[4]	1, 2, 23, 32
27 Rat		Chloride	290	19, 27
28	6	Inulin	249(187-330)c	42
29	14	Na^{24}	281(238-324)	26, 27, 35
30	21	$S^{35}O_4$	340(158-522)	35
31	33	Thiocyanate	300(260-340)	12, 25
32 220 g	40[3]	Chloride	320	9
Chicken				20
33 13 da	7[3]	Thiocyanate	407	
34 30 da	6[3]	Thiocyanate	399	
35 27 da	7[3]	Thiocyanate	438	
36 35 da	12[3]	Thiocyanate	462	

/1/ Cl^{38} = radioactive chlorine; Na^{24} = radioactive sodium; $S^{35}O_4$ = sulfate with radioactive sulfur. /2/ Nephrectomized animals. /3/ Number of observations. /4/ Very atypical distribution.

Contributors: (a) Chesley, Leon C., (b) Weil, William B., Jr., (c) Rubin, Mitchell I., and Calcagno, Philip L.

References: [1] Aikawa, J. K. 1950. Am. J. Physiol. 162:695. [2] Aikawa, J. K., G. T. Harrell, and T. B. Miller. 1951. J. Clin. Invest. 30:575. [3] Ashworth, C. T., and A. J. Gill. 1944. Am. J. Physiol. 142:435. [4] Berger, E. Y., M. F. Dunning, J. M. Steele, R. Jackenthal, and B. B. Brodie. 1950. Ibid. 162:318. [5] Bloodworth, J. M. B., Jr. 1952. Endocrinology 50:174. [6] Bonnycastle, D. D. 1947. Am. J. Physiol. 151:504. [7] Brodie, B. B., E. Brand, and S. Leshin. 1939. J. Biol. Chem. 130:555. [8] Burch, G. E., S. A. Threefoot, and C. T. Ray. 1950. J. Laborat. Clin. M. 35:331. [9] Cheek, D. B., C. D. West, and C. C. Golden. 1957. J. Clin. Invest. 36:340. [10] Crandall, L. A., Jr., and M. X. Anderson. 1934. Am. J. Digest. Dis. 1:126. [11] Elkinton, J. R., and M. Taffel. 1942. Am. J. Physiol. 138:126. [12] Ferguson, F. C., Jr. 1951. Proc. Soc. Exp. Biol., N. Y. 77:259. [13] Gaudino, M., and M. F. Levitt. 1949. Am. J. Physiol. 157:387. [14] Gaudino, M., and M. F. Levitt. 1949. J. Clin. Invest. 28:1487. [15] Gaudino, M., I. L. Schwartz, and M. F. Levitt. 1948. Proc. Soc. Exp. Biol., N. Y. 68:507. [16] Greenberg, J., I. L. Schwartz, M. Spinner, L. Silver, and N. Starr. 1952.

Am. J. Physiol. 168:86. [17] Gregersen, M. I., and J. D. Stewart. 1939. Ibid. 125:142. [18] Hahn, L. A., and G. C. Hevesey. 1941. Acta physiol. scand. 1:347. [19] Harrison, H. E., D. C. Darrow, and H. Yannet. 1936. J. Biol. Chem. 113:515. [20] Hegsted, D. M., D. Wilson, J. P. Melner, and P. H. Girra. 1951. Proc. Soc. Exp. Biol., N. Y. 78:114. [21] Houck, C. R. 1951. Am. J. Physiol. 165:102. [22] Kaltreider, N. L., G. R. Meneely, J. R. Allen, and W. F. Bale. 1941. J. Exp. M. 74:569. [23] Kruhoffer, P. 1946. Acta physiol. scand. 11:16. [24] Lands, A. M., R. A. Cutting, and P. S. Larson. 1940. Am. J. Physiol. 130:421. [25] Lolli, G., M. Rubin, and L. A. Greenberg. 1944. Q. J. Alcohol 5:1. [26] Manery, J. F., and W. F. Bale. 1941. Am. J. Physiol. 132:215. [27] Manery, J. F., and L. F. Haege. 1941. Ibid. 134:83. [28] McAllister, F. F. 1938. Ibid. 124:391. [29] Mellors, R. C., E. Muntwyler, F. R. Mautz, and W. E. Abbott. 1942. J. Biol. Chem. 144:785. [30] Overman, R. R., and H. A. Feldman. 1947. Am. J. Physiol. 148:455. [31] Raisz, C. G., M. K. Young, Jr., and C. T. Stenson. 1953. Ibid. 174:72. [32] Rodbard, S., H. Saiki, A. Malin, and C. Young. 1951. Ibid. 167:485. [33] Schwartz, I. L. 1950. Ibid. 160:526. [34] Schwartz, I. L., A. Nelson, P. Weisz, M. H. Maxwell, E. Breed, and L. Silver. 1952. Fed. Proc., Balt. 11:142. [35] Sheatz, G. C., and W. S. Wilde. 1950. Am. J. Physiol. 162:687. [36] Smith, P. K., A. W. Winkler, and B. M. Schwartz. 1939. J. Biol. Chem. 129:51. [37] Soberman, R. J., R. P. Keating, and R. D. Maxwell. 1951. Am. J. Physiol. 164:450. [38] Sunderman, F. W., and F. C. Dohan. 1941. Ibid. 132:418. [39] Sveinson, S. L. 1940. Skand. Arch. Physiol. 83:188. [40] Wallace, G. B., and B. B. Brodie. 1937. J. Pharm. Exp. Ther. 61:397. [41] Walser, M., D. W. Seldin, and A. Grollman. 1953. J. Clin. Invest. 32:299. [42] Wilde, W. S. 1945. Am. J. Physiol. 143:666. [43] Winkler, A. W., J. R. Elkinton, and A. J. Eisenman. 1943. Ibid. 139:239.

120. EXTRACELLULAR BODY WATER: FISHES

Values in parentheses are ranges, estimate "c" (cf. Introduction).

	Animal	No. of Speci- mens	Body Weight kg	Method	Extracellular Fluid Volume ml/kg body weight	Ref- er ence
	(A)	(B)	(C)	(D)	(E)	(F)
	Fresh-water Osteichthyes					
1	Bowfin (Amia calva)	6	1.963(1.020-3.265)	Sucrose	189(146-256)	3
2	Buffalo, bigmouth (Ictiobus cyprinellus)	8	3.395(1.980-5.440)	Sucrose	132(109-156)	3
3	Carp (Cyprinus carpio)	7	2.412(1.585-3.190)	Sucrose	155(120-221)	3
4	Gar, shortnosed (Lepisosteus platostomum)	7	1.185(0.855-1.730)	Sucrose	136(125-148)	3
5	Paddlefish (Polyodon spathula)	5	4.679(3.740-5.910)	Sucrose	156(141-169)	3
6	Sturgeon, lake (Acipenser fulvescens)	8	3.058(2.275-4.530)	Sucrose	201(154-275)	3
7	Sucker, white (Catostomus commersonii)	2	0.617(0.580-0.655)	Sucrose	122(118-127)	3
	Marine Osteichthyes					
8	Barracuda (Sphyraena barracuda)	8	2.151(1.430-4.575)	Sucrose	159(116-191)	3
	Grouper					3
9	Epinephelus striatus	2	1.270(0.930-1.610)	Sucrose	145(131-160)	
10	Mycteroperca tigris	1	5.885	Sucrose	125	
11	Moray, green (Gymnothorax funebris)	6	4.062(3.050-4.815)	Sucrose	158(122-194)	3
12	Parrot fish, rainbow (Pseudoscarus guacamaia)	8	5.451(1.700-12.550)	Inulin	114(92-145)	3
13		4	4.096(2.000-5.820)	Raffinose	144(127-164)	
14		8	4.696(1.650-6.830)	Sucrose	166(143-189)	
	Snapper					3
15	Lutianus aya	2	3.765(3.130-4.400)	Sucrose	140	
16	L. griseus	6	3.711(1.900-4.680)	Sucrose	140(122-153)	
	Chondrichthyes					
17	Dogfish, Pacific spiny (Squalus suckleyi)	13	2.818(1.122-4.700)	Inulin	127(114-144)	1
18		2	2.605(2.380-2.830)	Raffinose	152(151-154)	
19		3	2.183(1.562-3.150)	Sucrose	212(185-243)	

Animal	No. of Specimens	Body Weight kg	Method	Extracellular Fluid Volume ml/kg body weight	Reference
(A)	(B)	(C)	(D)	(E)	(F)
Chondrichthyes (concluded)					
20 Ratfish (Hydrolagus colliei)	8	1.202(0.790-1.461)	Inulin	106(97-116)	1
Skate					1
21 Raja binoculata	2	5.995(3.520-8.470)	Inulin	132(109-155)	
22 R. rhina	8	5.701(1.400-16.550)	Inulin	118(91-160)	
Agnatha					
23 Lamprey, sea (Petromyzon marinus)	12	0.190(0.154-0.261)	Sucrose	239(200-287)	2

Contributor: Thorson, Thomas B.

References: [1] Thorson, T. B. 1958. Physiol. Zool. 31:16. [2] Thorson, T. B. 1959. Science 130:99. [3] Thorson, T. B. 1959. Unpublished.

121. INTRACELLULAR BODY WATER: MAN, DOG

Intracellular water is calculated as the difference between total body water (deuterium oxide or antipyrine space) and extracellular water (inulin or sucrose space). Values in parentheses are ranges, estimate "b" or "c" as indicated (cf. Introduction).

Subjects			Volume of Distribution ml/kg body weight	Reference
Animal	Specification	No.		
(A)	(B)	(C)	(D)	(E)
1 Man	<20 yr	4♂	412(368-441)c	1-3, 5
2	20-35 yr	9♂	422(388-475)c	1-3, 5
3	36-49 yr	11♂	427(286-525)c	1-3, 5
4	>50 yr	8♂	385(309-468)c	1-3, 5
5	Adult	32♂	413(308-518)b	1-3, 5
6		2♀	289(285-293)b	1, 3
7	<70 kg	17♂	424(318-530)b	1-3, 5
8	>70 kg	15♂	404(303-505)b	1-3, 5
9 Dog		18	396(315-477)b	5, 6
10		8♀	430	4

Contributor: Chesley, Leon C.

References: [1] Berger, E. Y., M. F. Dunning, J. M. Steele, R. Jackenthal, and B. B. Brodie. 1950. Am. J. Physiol. 162:318. [2] Deane, N. 1951. J. Clin. Invest. 30:1469. [3] Deane, N., and H. W. Smith. 1952. Ibid. 31:197. [4] Guadino, M., and M. F. Levitt. 1949. Ibid. 28:1487. [5] Schwartz, I. L., A. Nelson, P. Weisz, M. H. Maxwell, E. Breed, and L. Silver. 1952. Fed. Proc., Ball. 11.142. [6] Soberman, R. J., R. P. Keating, and R. D. Maxwell. 1951. Am. J. Physiol. 164:450.

XIX. Urine

122. PHYSICAL PROPERTIES AND CHEMICAL COMPOSITION OF URINE: MAMMALS

Part I: MAN

Values are mg/kg body wt/da, unless otherwise specified. In reducing values to mg/kg, a body weight of 70 kg was assumed, unless specific weight was reported in the reference. Values in parentheses are ranges, estimate "c" (cf. Introduction).

	Property or Constituent (A)	Method (B)	Value (C)	Reference (D)
	Physical Properties			
1	Freezing point depression		(0.87-2.71) °C	33
2	pH		(4.8-7.8)	10
3	Specific gravity		(1.002-1.040)	10
4	Volume		(8.6-28.6) ml/kg body wt/da	62
	General Chemical Components			
5	Solids		(55-70) g/da	10
6	Water		20(7-42) ml/kg body wt/da	2,62,66,70
	Electrolytes			
7	Aluminum	Brown colorimetric (phosphotungstic acid)	0.0011(0.0007-0.0016)	60
8	Arsenic		0.00033(0-0.0013)	135
9	Bicarbonate		2.0(0.5-12.0)	39
10	Bromine	Conway thiosulfate titration	(0.012-0.110)	18
11	Calcium	Michaels, et al, phosphate precipitation	3.3(0.6-8.3)	46,81
12	Chlorine	Volhard titration	100(40-180)	4,46
13	Copper	Delphine carbamate	0.0005(0.0003-0.0007)	126
14	Fluorine	Icken, et al, alizarin	0.022(0.007-0.100)[1]	46,79
15	Iodine	Phillips-Curtis; Trevarrow	(0.0001-0.0070)	13,19,78,83
16	Iron	Hummel-Willard orthophenanthroline	0.007	35
17	Lead	Cholak spectrographic	0.0004(0.00016-0.00110)	60
18	Magnesium	McCrudden	1.35(0.42-2.40)	44
19	Manganese	Cholak spectrographic	(0.0001-0.0014)	60,61
20	Nickel	Kent-McCance spectrographic	(0.002-0.004)	61
	Phosphorus			
21	Inorganic P	Fiske-Subbarow colorimetric	12(10-15)	129
22	Organic P	Bell-Doisy magnesia precipitation; colorimetric	0.131(0.089-0.187)	46,92,144
23	Potassium	Chloroplatinate	34(16-56)	17,46
24	Selenium	Mathews, et al, electro-titrimetric modification of iodine-thiosulfate	0.0005(0-0.002)	115
25	Silicon	King-Dolan	0.13(0.06-0.20)	8,42
26	Sodium	Chloroplatinate	60(25-94)	4,46
	Sulfur			36
27	Total S	Folin barium chloride	16.0(5.1-20.6)	
28	Inorganic S	Folin barium chloride	11.1(3.5-17.5)	
29	Ethereal S	Folin barium chloride; hydrolysis	0.95(0.56-1.40)	
30	Neutral S	Folin barium chloride	1.9(1.05-2.60)	
31	Tin	Cholak spectrographic	(0.00013-0.00025)	60,61
32	Zinc		0.0052(0.0016-0.0064)	61
	Nitrogenous Substances			
33	Protein	Dean-Webb immunological method; Gunton-Burton technique; electrophoresis	(0.03-1.00)	5,74,80,96, 116,122, 139
34	Adenine	Krüger-Schmid copper oxide precipitation	0.02(0.016-0.024)	136
35	Allantoin	Wiechouski mercury precipitation	0.17(0.14-0.21)	138
	Amino acids			
36	Total		(20-40)	124
37	Free		(13-20)	124
38	Alanine, total	Carsten-Cannon ion-exchange chromatography	0.55	15

/1/ Upper limit of range was obtained in an area of Texas where dental fluorosis is endemic.

	Property or Constituent	Method	Value	Reference
	(A)	(B)	(C)	(D)
	\multicolumn{4}{c}{Nitrogenous Substances (continued)}			
	Amino acids (continued)			
	Arginine			15,27-29, 107,125, 131,140
39	Total	Carsten-Cannon ion-exchange chromatography; Van Pilsum colorimetric (Sakaguchi); microbiological assay	0.45(0.34-0.50)	
40	Free	Carsten-Cannon ion-exchange chromatography; Van Pilsum colorimetric (Sakaguchi); microbiological assay	0.16(0.07-0.30)	
	Aspartic acid			26,27,131, 140
41	Total	Carsten-Cannon ion-exchange chromatography; microbiological assay	1.7(1.2-2.7)	
42	Free	Carsten-Cannon ion-exchange chromatography; microbiological assay	0.04(0.01-0.07)	
43	Citrulline	Young, et al, filter paper chromatography	0.9(0-2.8)	143
	Cystine			
44	Total	Microbiological assay	1.7(1.0-2.6)	113,123
45	Free	Microbiological assay	1.3(0.6-1.9)	107
	Glutamic acid			15,27,48, 131
46	Total	Carsten-Cannon ion-exchange chromatography; microbiological assay	(3.7-5.0)	
47	Free	Carsten-Cannon ion-exchange chromatography; microbiological assay	0.8(0-1.5)	
	Glycine			
48	Total	Microbiological assay	6.5	27
49	Free	Carsten-Cannon ion-exchange chromatography	2.2	15
	Histidine			
50	Total	Carsten-Cannon ion-exchange chromatography; microbiological assay	2.7(1.0-5.0)	15,27,28, 123,140
51	Free	Carsten-Cannon ion-exchange chromatography; microbiological assay	2.0(1.2-2.7)	15,27,28, 140
52	Hydroxyproline, total	Carsten-Cannon ion-exchange chromatography	0.02	15
	Isoleucine			27-29,107, 131,140
53	Total	Microbiological assay	0.20(0.1-0.3)	
54	Free	Microbiological assay	0.08(0.04-0.20)	
	Leucine			27-29,107, 131,140
55	Total	Microbiological assay	0.30(0.22-0.45)	
56	Free	Microbiological assay	0.13(0.05-0.17)	
	Lysine			15,27-29, 107,131, 140
57	Total	Carsten-Cannon ion-exchange chromatography; microbiological assay	0.8(0.48-1.70)	
58	Free	Carsten-Cannon ion-exchange chromatography; microbiological assay	0.4(0.17-0.67)	
	Methionine			15,27-29, 107,131, 140
59	Total	Carsten-Cannon ion-exchange chromatography; microbiological assay	0.14(0.10-0.17)	
60	Free	Carsten-Cannon ion-exchange chromatography; microbiological assay	0.05(0.03-0.10)	
61	Ornithine	Carsten-Cannon ion-exchange chromatography	0.15	15
	Phenylalanine			15,27-29, 131,140
62	Total	Carsten-Cannon ion-exchange chromatography; microbiological assay	0.30(0.21-0.54)	
63	Free	Carsten-Cannon ion-exchange chromatography; microbiological assay	0.17(0.09-0.23)	
	Proline			140
64	Total	Microbiological assay	0.61(0.3-0.9)	
65	Free	Microbiological assay	0.12(0.03-0.20)	
	Serine			15,131
66	Total	Carsten-Cannon ion-exchange chromatography; microbiological assay	0.6(0.5-0.7)	

	Property or Constituent	Method	Value	Reference
	(A)	(B)	(C)	(D)
	Nitrogenous Substances (continued)			
	Amino acids (concluded) Serine (concluded)			
67	Free	Carsten-Cannon ion-exchange chromatography; microbiological assay	0.3(0.2-0.5)	15,131
68	Taurine	Young, et al, filter paper chromatography	(0.11-0.20)	143
	Threonine			15,27-29, 107,131, 140
69	Total	Carsten-Cannon ion-exchange chromatography; microbiological assay	0.50(0.36-2.60)	
70	Free	Carsten-Cannon ion-exchange chromatography; microbiological assay	0.25(0.11-0.35)	
	Tryptophan			28,29,131, 140
71	Total	Microbiological assay	0.40(0.23-0.70)	
72	Free	Microbiological assay	0.20(0.11-0.36)	
	Tyrosine			123,131,140
73	Total	Microbiological assay	0.7(0.44-0.82)	
74	Free	Microbiological assay	0.2(0.15-0.30)	
	Valine			27-29,107, 131,140
75	Total	Microbiological assay	0.3(0.25-0.42)	
76	Free	Microbiological assay	0.09(0.04-0.18)	
77	Bilirubin	Naumann talc absorption	0.70	85
78	Coproporphyrin I and III	Schwarz, et al, ultraviolet fluorescence	(0.00024-0.00400)	32,103,133
79	Creatine	Van Pilsum colorimetric (Sakaguchi); Folin picric acid; Peters picric acid; Ennor, et al, diacetyl	0.8(0-2.0)	31,49,52, 76,125
80	Creatinine	Folin picric acid	23(15-30)	49,76,125, 128
81	Guanidinoacetic acid	Dubnoff-Borsook ion-exchange; Van Pilsum, et al, barium hydroxide, zinc sulfate precipitation	(0.2-0.5)	69,125
82	Guanine	Weissmann, et al, ion-exchange chromatography	0.006(0.003-0.009)	136
83	8-Hydroxy-7-methyl-	Weissmann, et al, ion-exchange chromatography	0.02(0.016-0.030)	
84	7-Methyl-	Weissmann, et al, ion-exchange chromatography	0.09(0.08-0.11)	
85	N^2-Methyl	Weissmann, et al, ion-exchange chromatography	0.007(0.006-0.009)	
86	Hippuric acid		(1-10)	118
87	Histamine	Barsoum-Gaddum guinea pig ileum	(0.0002-0.0010)	89,98
88	Hypoxanthine	Weissmann, et al, ion-exchange chromatography	0.14(0.08-0.19)	136
89	1-Methyl-	Weissmann, et al, ion-exchange chromatography	0.006(0.003-0.010)	
90	Imidazole derivatives	Koessler-Hanke p-phenyldiazonium sulfonate	(2-3)	65
91	Indoxylsulfuric acid (indican)	Sharlit alcoholic thymol	1.0(0.5-2.0)	105,106
92	Methionine sulfoxide	Carsten-Cannon ion-exchange chromatography; Young, et al, filter paper chromatography	(0-0.31)	15,143
93	Purine bases	Krüger-Schmid copper oxide precipitation	(0.2-1.0)	46
94	6-Succinopurine	Weissmann, et al, ion-exchange chromatography	0.014	137
95	Theophylline	Dikstein, et al, ion-exchange chromatography	Trace	23
96	Urea	Urease	(200-500)	46,50,130
97	Uric acid	Brown colorimetric (phosphotungstic acid)	2.0(0.8-3.0)	3
98	1-3-Dimethyl-	Dikstein, et al, ion-exchange chromatography	Trace	23
99	Urobilin	Sparkman p-dimethylaminobenzaldehyde	(0.143-1.857)	68,110,134
100	Urobilinogen	Sparkman p-dimethylaminobenzaldehyde	(0.043-0.357)	68,110,134
101	Xanthine	Weissmann, et al, ion-exchange chromatography	0.09(0.07-0.12)	136

	Property or Constituent	Method	Value	Reference
	(A)	(B)	(C)	(D)
	Nitrogenous Substances (concluded)			
	Nitrogen			
102	Total N	Kjeldahl digestion and distillation	(130-300)	46,52,132
103	Amino acid N		(3-6)	45
104	Ammonia N	Folin aeration of alkaline solution	(3-13)	36,108,109, 132
	Lipids, Carbohydrates, Miscellaneous Organic Acids			
105	Cholesterol		(0-0.0714)	75
106	Reducing substances		(7-21)	10
107	Acetone bodies, total	Weichselbaum-Somogyi acetone precipitation; Nessler-Abels; Messinger iodine titration; Behre-Benedict salicylic aldehyde	0.2(0.03-0.30)	1,6,51,112
108	Acetoacetic acid	Weichselbaum-Somogyi acetone precipitation	0.04(0.03-0.06)	112
	Carbolic acid (phenol)			21,37,102
109	Total	Schmidt ether extraction; Deichmann-Schafer spectrophotometric	(0.2-0.6)	
110	Free	Schmidt ether extraction; Deichmann-Schafer spectrophotometric	(0-0.05)	
111	Carbonic acid		2.7(2.1-3.3)	39
112	Citric acid	Taussky-Shorr pentabromoacetone; Pucker, et al, pentabromoacetone; Thumberg enzymatic	(3-20)	9,84,120, 121
113	Formic acid	Dakin, et al, ether extraction, mercuric chloride; Benedict distillation, mercuric chloride	0.8(0.4-2.0)	7,20
114	Lactic acid	Friedmann-Graeser titration	3.0(2-5)	40
115	Oxalic acid	Powers-Levatin	0.5(0.3-0.7)	46,67,82,86
	Vitamins, Metabolites			
116	B_1 (thiamine)	Hennessy-Cerecedo; Meckelsen, et al, Schultz, et al; Jowett fluorometric	0.003(0.0006-0.0060)	14,22,41, 43,58,59, 87
117	B_2 (riboflavin)	Microbiological assay; Ferrebee fluorometric; Conner-Straub absorption	0.0124(0.002-0.024)	11,22,34, 64,87,117
118	B_6 (pyridoxine)	Microbiological assay	(0.00008-0.00270)	54,71,104
119	B_{12} (cyanocobalamine)	Microbiological assay	$0.44 \times 10^{-6}(0.23 \times 10^{-6}$ to $0.79 \times 10^{-6})$	95
120	B_c (folic acid)	Microbiological assay	0.000058(0.00003-0.00030)	22,95,141
121	B_x (p-aminobenzoic acid)	Microbiological assay	(0.002-0.003)	22
122	C (ascorbic acid)	Roe, et al, dinitrophenylhydrazine	(0.1-0.4)	16
123	H (biotin)	Microbiological assay	0.0005(0.0002-0.0010)	22,53,119
124	Choline	Microbiological assay	0.079(0.068-0.130)	55,72
125	Citrovorum factor	Microbiological assay	0.000037(0.000023-0.000069)	95
126	Inositol	Microbiological assay	0.2	57
127	Niacin (nicotinic acid)	Microbiological assay; Ellinger-Kader; Harris, et al	0.0034(0.002-0.020)	22,30,47, 56,64,90
128	Niacinamide (nicotinamide)	Microbiological assay; Ellinger-Kader	0.02(0.01-0.05)	30,56
129	Pantothenic acid	Microbiological assay	0.045(0.016-0.100)	22,88,111, 142
130	Dehydroascorbic acid	Roe, et al, dinitrophenylhydrazine	(0.19-0.29)	16
131	Dehydroascorbic plus diketogulonic acids	Roe-Kuether, for dehydroascorbic and diketogulonic acids together	0.23(0-1.28)	38
132	Diketogulonic acid	Roe, et al, dinitrophenylhydrazine	(0.14-0.19)	16
133	N'-Methylnicotinamide	Najjar, and Huff-Perlzweig acetone	(0.04-0.60)	22,30,56
134	Pyridoxal	Microbiological assay	0.001(0.0007-0.0053)	54,91
135	Pyridoxamine	Microbiological assay	0.0016(0.0004-0.0030)	91
136	4-Pyridoxic acid	Microbiological assay; Huff-Perlzweig fluorometric	(0.009-0.160)	54,71,91, 101
137	Trigonelline	Perlzweig; Kodicek-Wang; Sarett modification of Kodicek	(0.030-0.300)	64,90,100

Part I: MAN (Continued)

	Property or Constituent	Method	Value	Reference
	(A)	(B)	(C)	(D)
	Hormones			
	Aldosterone			127
138	♂	Paper chromatography	0.00005(0.00001-0.00013)	
139	♀	Paper chromatography	0.00006(0.00003-0.00010)	
	Androgens			25
140	♂, 3-5 yr	Zimmermann reaction	0.21	
141	♂, 20-40 yr	Zimmermann reaction	0.26(0.20-0.33)	
142	♂, 60+ yr	Zimmermann reaction	0.07(0.03-0.13)	
143	♀, 3-5 yr	Zimmermann reaction	0.05	
144	♀, 20-40 yr	Zimmermann reaction	0.20(0.18-0.21)	
145	♀, 60+ yr	Zimmermann reaction	0.04(0.015-0.130)	
	Androsterone			99
146	♂	Paper chromatography; Zimmermann reaction	0.05(0.035-0.060)	
147	♀	Paper chromatography; Zimmermann reaction	0.06(0.05-0.08)	
	Etiocholanolone			99
148	♂	Paper chromatography; Zimmermann reaction	0.06(0.04-0.07)	
149	♀	Paper chromatography; Zimmermann reaction	0.05(0.03-0.06)	
	Estradiol			
150	♀, follicular phase	Brown	0.00003(0-0.00005)	12
151	♀, luteal phase	Brown	0.0001(0.00007-0.00017)	12
152	♀, post-menopause	Brown	0.00001(0-0.00009)	77
	Estriol			
153	♀, follicular phase	Brown	0.0001(0-0.0003)	12
154	♀, luteal phase	Brown	0.0004(0.00013-0.00130)	12
155	♀, post-menopause	Brown	0.00005(0-0.00018)	77
	Estrone			
156	♀, follicular phase	Brown	0.00008(0.00006-0.00012)	12
157	♀, luteal phase	Brown	0.0002(0.00017-0.00040)	12
158	♀, post-menopause	Brown	0.00003(0-0.00012)	77
	17-Hydroxysteroids			93,94
159	♂	Porter-Silber reaction	0.08(0.04-0.17)	
160	♀	Porter-Silber reaction	0.06(0.02-0.14)	
	17-Ketogenic adreno-corticoids			24
161	♂	Norymberski reaction	0.21(0.15-0.31)	
162	♀	Norymberski reaction	0.18(0.12-0.30)	
163	α-Ketol steroids	Madar-Buck B. T. reaction	0.26(0.13-0.47)	73
	Pregnanediol			63
164	♂	Klopper	0.013(0.005-0.020)	
165	♀, follicular phase	Klopper	0.018(0.013-0.025)	
166	♀, luteal phase	Klopper	0.055(0.03-0.07)	
167	♀, post-menopause	Klopper	0.01(0.005-0.014)	
	Pregnanetriol			114
168	♀, follicular phase	Paper chromatography; Klopper procedure	0.025	
169	♀, luteal phase	Paper chromatography; Klopper procedure	0.032	
170	♀, post-menopause	Paper chromatography; Klopper procedure	0.011	
171	Tetrahydrocortisol	Paper chromatography	0.024(0.008-0.050)	97
172	Tetrahydrocortisone	Paper chromatography	0.054(0.02-0.12)	97

Contributors: (a) Van Pilsum, John F., (b) Pearson, William N., (c) Hinman, Frank, Jr., (d) Kanter, Gerald S.

References: [1] Abels, J. C. 1937. J. Biol. Chem. 119:663. [2] Addis, T., and J. Oliver. 1931. The renal lesion in Bright's disease. P. B. Hoeber, New York. [3] Aldersberg, D., and M. Ellenberg. 1939. J. Biol. Chem. 128:379. [4] Ashe, B. I., and H. O. J. Mosenthal. 1937. J. Am. M. Ass. 108:1161. [5] Bashford, H. H. 1926. Lancet, Lond. 211:1305. [6] Behre, J. A. 1931. J. Biol. Chem. 92:679. [7] Benedict, E. M., and G. A. Harrop.

1922. Ibid. 54:443. [8] Bloomfield, I. J., R. R. Sayers, and F. H. Goldman. 1932. Pub. Health Rep., Wash. 50:421. [9] Boothby, W. M., and M. Adams. 1934. Am. J. Physiol. 107:471. [10] Bradley, S. E. 1945. Med. Clin. N. America 29:1314. [11] Brewer, W., T. Porter, R. Ingalls, and M. A. Ohlson. 1946. J. Nutrit. 32:583. [12] Brown, J. B. 1955. Lancet, Lond. 268:320. [13] Bruger, M., J. W. Hinton, and W. G. Lough. 1941. J. Laborat. Clin. M. 26:1942. [14] Carden, G. A., W. D. Province, and J. W. Ferrebee. 1940. Proc. Soc. Exp. Biol., N. Y. 45:1. [15] Carsten, M. E. 1952. J. Am. Chem. Soc. 74:5954. [16] Chen, S. D., and C. Shuck. 1951. J. Nutrit. 23:111. [17] Clark, G. W. 1926. Univ. Calif. Pub. Physiol. 5(17):195. [18] Conway, E. J., and J. C. Flood. 1936. Biochem. J., Lond. 30:716. [19] Curtis, G. M., I. D. Puppel, V. V. Cole, and N. L. Matthews. 1937. J. Laborat. Clin. M. 22:1014. [20] Daken, H. D., N. W. Janney, and A. J. Wakeman. 1913. J. Biol. Chem. 14:341. [21] Deichmann, W., and L. J. Schafer. 1942. Am. J. Clin. Path. 12:129. [22] Denko, C. W., W. E. Grundy, J. W. Porter, G. W. Berryman, T. E. Friedmann, and J. B. Youmans. 1946. Arch. Biochem., N. Y. 10:33. [23] Dikstein, S., F. Bergman, and M. Chaimovitz. 1958. J. Biol. Chem. 230:203. [24] Diszfalusy, E., L. O. Plantin, G. Binke, and A. Westman. 1955. Acta endocr., Kbh. 18:356. [25] Dorfman, R. I., and R. A. Shipley. 1956. The androgens. J. Wiley, New York. [26] Dozzi, D. L. 1940. Am. J. Digest. Dis. 7:123. [27] Dunn, M. S., M. N. Camien, S. Shankman, and H. Block. 1947. Arch. Biochem., N. Y. 13:207. [28] Eckhardt, R. D., and C. S. Davidson. 1948. J. Clin. Invest. 27:727. [29] Eckhardt, R. D., and C. S. Davidson. 1949. J. Biol. Chem. 177:687. [30] Ellinger, P., and M. M. A. Kader. 1949. Biochem. J., Lond. 44:27. [31] Ennor, A. H., and L. A. Stocken. 1953. Ibid. 55:310. [32] Ericksen, L. 1950. Nature, Lond. 167:691. [33] Evans, C. L. 1952. Principles of human physiology. Ed. 11. Lea and Febiger, Philadelphia. [34] Ferrebee, J. W. 1940. J. Clin. Invest. 19:251. [35] Figueroa, W. G., W. S. Adams, F. W. Davies, and S. H. Bassett. 1955. J. Laborat. Clin. M. 46:534. [36] Folin, O. 1905. Am. J. Physiol. 13:45. [37] Folin, O., and W. Dennis. 1915. J. Biol. Chem. 22:309. [38] Freeman, J. T., R. Hafkesbring, and E. K. Caldwell. 1951. Gastroenterology 18:224. [39] Gamble, J. L. 1954. Chemical anatomy, physiology and pathology of extracellular fluid. Harvard University Press, Cambridge. [40] Gambigliani-Zoccoli, A., R. Giacchero, E. Zambelli, and C. Reschia. 1939. Zschr. klin. Med. 135:457. [41] Gifft, H. H., and H. M. Hauck. 1946. J. Nutrit. 31:635. [42] Goldwater, L. J. 1936. J. Indust. Hyg. 18:163. [43] Gorham, A. T., J. C. Abels, A. L. Robins, and C. P. Rhoads. 1942. J. Clin. Invest. 21:161. [44] Gwens, M. H. 1918. J. Biol. Chem. 34:119. [45] Harrow, B. 1946. Textbook of biochemistry. Ed. 4. W. B. Saunders, Philadelphia. [46] Hawk, P. B., B. L. Oser, and W. H. Summerson. 1947. Practical physiological chemistry. Ed. 12. Blakiston, Philadelphia. [47] Henderson, L. M., G. B. Ramasama, and B. C. Johnson. 1949. J. Biol. Chem. 181:731. [48] Hier, S. W. 1948. N. York Acad. Sc. 10:280. [49] Hobson, W. 1939. Biochem. J., Lond. 33:1425. [50] Howe, P. E., and P. B. Hawk. 1908. J. Biol. Chem. 5:477. [51] Hubbard, R. S., and C. J. Noback. 1925. Ibid. 63:391. [52] Hyde, E. 1940. Ibid. 134:95. [53] Jenson, T. 1948. Acta derm. vener., Stockh. 28:468. [54] Johnson, B. C., T. S. Hamilton, and H. H. Mitchell. 1945. J. Biol. Chem. 158:619. [55] Johnson, B. C., T. S. Hamilton, and H. H. Mitchell. 1945. Ibid. 159:5. [56] Johnson, B. C., T. S. Hamilton, and H. H. Mitchell. 1945. Ibid. 159:231. [57] Johnson, B. C., H. H. Mitchell, and T. S. Hamilton. 1945. Ibid. 161:357. [58] Jowett, M. 1940. Biochem. J., Lond. 34:1348. [59] Karrer, W. 1937. Helvet. chim. acta. 20:1147. [60] Kehoe, R. A., J. Cholak, and R. V. Story. 1940. J. Nutrit. 19:579. [61] Kent, N. L., and R. A. McCance. 1941. Biochem. J., Lond. 35:877. [62] Kilduffe, R. A. 1937. Clinical urinalysis and its interpretation. F. A. Davis, Philadelphia. [63] Klopper, A., E. A. Mitchie, and J. B. Brown. 1955. J. Endocr., Lond. 12:209. [64] Kodicek, E., and Y. L. Wang. 1941. Nature, Lond. 148:23. [65] Koessler, K. K., and M. T. Hanke. 1924. J. Biol. Chem. 59:803. [66] Kolmer, J. A., and F. Boerner. 1945. Approved laboratory technique. Ed. 4. D. Appleton-Century, New York. [67] Lamden, M. P., and G. A. Chrystowski. 1954. Proc. Soc. Exp. Biol., N. Y. 85:190. [68] Lemberg, R., and J. W. Legge. 1949. Hematin compounds and bile pigments.

Interscience, New York. [69] Levedahl, B. H., and L. T. Samuels. 1948. J. Biol. Chem. 176:327. [70] Levinston, S. A., and R. P. MacFate. 1943. Clinical laboratory diagnosis. Ed. 2. Lea and Febiger, Philadelphia. [71] Linkswiler, H., and M. E. Reynolds. 1950. J. Nutrit. 41:523. [72] Luecke, R. W., and P. B. Peterson. 1944. J. Biol. Chem. 153:259. [73] Marks, L. J., J. H. Leftin, and P. Leonard. 1957. J. Clin. Endocr. Metab. 17:407. [74] Marrack, J. R., and R. G. S. Johns. 1950. Biochem. J., Lond. 47:xxxi. [75] Mattice, M. R. 1936. Chemical procedures for clinical laboratories. Lea and Febiger, Philadelphia. [76] Maw, G. A. 1947. Biochem. J., Lond. 41:482. [77] McBride, J. M. 1957. J. Clin. Endocr. Metab. 17:1440. [78] McClendon, J. F., and J. C. Hathaway. 1923. Proc. Soc. Exp. Biol., N. Y. 21:129. [79] McClure, F. J. 1944. Pub. Health Rep., Wash. 59:1575. [80] McGarry, E., A. H. Sehon, and B. Rose. 1955. J. Clin. Invest. 34:832. [81] Michaels, G. D., C. T. Anderson, S. Margen, and L. W. Kinsell. 1949. J. Biol. Chem. 180:175. [82] Müller, P. 1937. Verh. Verein. Schweiz. Physiol. 1:8. [83] Nakar, I. 1938. J. Orient. M., Dairen 28:557. [84] Natelson, S., J. K. Lugovoy, and J. B. Pincus. 1947. J. Biol. Chem. 170:597. [85] Naumann, H. N. 1936. Biochem. J., Lond. 36:692. [86] Oikawa, S. 1937. Jap. J. M. Sc., Ser. 2, 3:217. [87] Oldham, H., B. B. Sheft, and T. Porter. 1950. J. Nutrit. 41:231. [88] Pelczar, M. J., Jr., and J. W. Porter. 1941. Proc. Soc. Exp. Biol., N. Y. 47:3. [89] Pellerat, J., and M. Murat. 1945. C. rend. Soc. biol. 39:1139. [90] Perlzweig, W. A., H. P. Sarett, and L. H. Margoles. 1942. J. Am. M. Ass. 118:28. [91] Rabinowitz, J. C., and E. E. Snell. 1949. Proc. Soc. Exp. Biol., N. Y. 70:235. [92] Rae, J. J. 1937. Biochem. J., Lond. 31:1622. [93] Reddy, W. J., N. A. Hyder, J. C. Laidlow, A. E. Renold, and G. W. Thorn. 1956. J. Clin. Endocr. Metab. 16:380. [94] Reddy, W. J., D. Jenkins, and G. W. Thorn. 1952. Metabolism 1:511. [95] Register, V. D., and H. P. Sarett. 1951. Proc. Soc. Exp. Biol., N. Y. 77:837. [96] Rigas, D. A., and C. G. Heller. 1951. J. Clin. Invest. 30:853. [97] Romanoff, L. P., K. Rodriquez, J. Seelye, and G. Pincus. 1957. J. Clin. Endocr. Metab. 17:777. [98] Rose, B., J. A. P. Pare, K. K. Pump, R. L. Stanford, K. R. Mackenzie, and E. H. Venning. 1951. Proc. 2nd Clin. ACTH Conf. 1:519. [99] Rubin, B. L., R. I. Dorfman, and G. Pincus. 1954. Recent Progr. Hormone Res. 9:213. [100] Sarett, H. P. 1943. J. Biol. Chem. 150:159. [101] Sarett, H. P. 1951. Ibid. 189:769. [102] Schmidt, E. G. 1942. Ibid. 145:533. [103] Schwarz, S., S. Cohen, and C. J. Watson. MDDC-304. Office of Technical Services, Department of Commerce, Washington, D. C. [104] Scudi, J. V., K. Unna, and W. Antopol. 1940. J. Biol. Chem. 135:371. [105] Sharlit, H. 1933. Ibid. 99:537. [106] Sharlit, H. 1938. Arch. Pediat., N. Y. 55:377. [107] Sheffner, A. L., J. B. Kirsner, and W. L. Palmer. 1948. J. Biol. Chem. 175:107. [108] Sherman, H. C., and A. O. Gettler. 1912. Ibid. 11:323. [109] Smith, M. 1926. Ibid. 68:15. [110] Sparkman, R. 1939. Arch. Int. M. 63:858. [111] Spector, H., T. S. Hamilton, and H. H. Mitchell. 1945. J. Biol. Chem. 161:145. [112] Stark, I. E., and M. Somogyi. 1943. Ibid. 147:319. [113] Steele, B. F., H. E. Suberlich, M. S. Reynolds, and C. A. Baumann. 1947. J. Nutrit. 33:209. [114] Stern, M. I. 1957. J. Endocr., Lond. 16:180. [115] Sterner, J. H., and V. Lidfeldt. 1941. J. Pharm. Exp. Ther. 73:205. [116] Stewart, V. P. 1918. J. Am. M. Ass. 71:1050. [117] Strong, F. M., R. E. Feeney, B. Moore, and H. T. Parsons. 1941. J. Biol. Chem. 137:363. [118] Sunderman, F. W., and F. Boerner. 1949. Normal values in clinical medicine. W. B. Saunders, Philadelphia. [119] Sydenstricker, V. P., S. A. Singal, A. P. Briggs, N. M. de Vaughn, and H. Isbell. 1942. Science 95:176. [120] Taussky, H. H. 1949. J. Biol. Chem. 181:195. [121] Taussky, H. H., and E. Shorr. 1947. Ibid. 169:103. [122] Theobald, G. W. 1932. Lancet, Lond. 223:1380. [123] Tompsett, S. L., and J. Fitzpatrick. 1950. Brit. J. Exp. Path. 31:70. [124] Van Pilsum, J. F. Unpublished. [125] Van Pilsum, J. F., R. P. Martin, E. Kito, and J. Hess. 1956. J. Biol. Chem. 222:225. [126] Van Ravesteyn, A. H. 1944. Acta med. scand. 118:163. [127] Venning, E.H., I. Dyrenfurth, and C. J. P. Giroud. 1956. J. Clin. Endocr. Metab. 16:1326. [128] Vestergaard, P., and R. Leverett. 1958. J. Laborat. Clin. M. 51:211. [129] Walker, B. S. 1931. Ibid. 17:347. [130] Walker, B. S., and A. W. Rowe. 1927. Am. J. Physiol. 81:738. [131] Wallraff, E. B., E. C. Brodie, and A. L. Borden. 1950. J. Clin. Invest. 29:1542. [132] Wang, C. C., J. E.

122. PHYSICAL PROPERTIES AND CHEMICAL COMPOSITION OF URINE: MAMMALS (Continued)

Part I: MAN (Concluded)

Hawks, B. Huddleston, A. A. Wood, and E. A. Smith. 1930. J. Nutrit. 3:79. [133] Watson, C. J., V. Hawkinson, S. Schwarz, and D. Sunderland. 1949. J. Clin. Invest. 28:447. [134] Watson, C. J., S. Schwarz, V. Sborov, and E. Bertie. 1944. Am. J. Clin. Path. 14:605. [135] Webster, S. H. 1941. Pub. Health Rep., Wash. 56:1953. [136] Weissmann, B., P. A. Bromberg, and A. B. Gutman. 1957. J. Biol. Chem. 224:423. [137] Weissmann, B., and A. B. Gutman. 1957. Ibid. 229:239. [138] Wiechouski, W. 1909. Biochem. J., Lond. 19:368. [139] Williams, J. B. 1908. N. York M. J. 66:927. [140] Woodson, H. W., S. W. Hier, J. D. Solomon, and O. Bergeim. 1948. J. Biol. Chem. 172:613. [141] Wright, L. D., and A. D. Welch. 1943. Science 98:179. [142] Wright, L. D., and E. Q. Wright. 1942. Proc. Soc. Exp. Biol., N. Y. 49:80. [143] Young, M. K., H. K. Berry, E. Beerstecher, Jr., and J. S. Berry. 1951. Univ. Texas Pub. 5109. p. 189. [144] Youngburg, G. E., and G. W. Pucher. 1924. J. Biol. Chem. 62:31.

Part II: MAMMALS OTHER THAN MAN

Values are mg/kg body wt/da, unless otherwise specified. In reducing values to mg/kg, the following body weights (in kilograms) were assumed unless a specific weight was recorded in the reference: cat, 2.5; cattle, 500; dog, 12; goat, 50; guinea pig, 0.5; horse, 630; monkey, 12; pig, 200; rabbit, 2.0; rat, 0.33. Values in parentheses are ranges, estimate "c" (cf. Introduction).

	Animal (A)	Property or Constituent (B)	Value (C)	Reference (D)
1	Cat	Freezing point depression	5.0°C	30
2		Specific gravity	1.030(1.020-1.040)	30
3		Volume	(10-20) ml/kg body wt/da	47
4		Calcium	(0.20-0.45)	34
5		Allantoin	80	62
6		Creatinine	(12-20)	47
7		Histamine	(0.006-0.300)	2
8		Imidazole derivatives	(3-4)	55
9		Urea	(800-4000)	47
10		Uric acid	(0.2-13.0)	47
		Nitrogen		
11		Total N	(500-1100)	47
12		Ammonia N	60	35, 47
13		Carbolic acid (phenol)	(8-25)	36
14		N'-Methylnicotinamide	(0.030-0.200)	31
15	Cattle	Volume	(17-45) ml/kg body wt/da	29
16		Calcium	(0.10-1.40)	39, 48, 49
17		Chlorine	140	59
18		Magnesium	(3-7)	12, 39
19		Phosphorus	(5-13)[1]	12, 39
20			(0.06-0.14)[2]	
21		Sulfate, total	(3-15)[3]	17
		Sulfur		17
22		Inorganic S	(0.2-5.0)[3]	
23		Ethereal S	(1.6-7.0)[3]	
24		Neutral S	(0.8-3.0)[3]	
25		Allantoin	(20-60)	56, 62, 82
26		Creatine	(1-2)	82
27		Creatinine	(15-20)	16, 17, 82
28		Hippuric acid	(50-200)	16, 17, 109
29		Purine bases	(0.2-3.0)	56, 82
30		Urea	(50-60)	82
31		Uric acid	(1-4)	56, 82

/1/ **Males.** /2/ Females. /3/ After 24-hour fast.

370

Part II: MAMMALS OTHER THAN MAN (Continued)

	Animal	Property or Constituent	Value	Reference
	(A)	(B)	(C)	(D)
32	Cattle (concluded)	Nitrogen Total N	(40-450)	17, 56, 82
33		Ammonia N	(1-17)	56, 82
34		Acetone bodies	(0.5-5.0)	17, 60
35		Citric acid	(1-3)	12
36		Vitamin B$_1$ (thiamine)	0.010	103
37		Vitamin B$_2$ (riboflavin)	0.020	103
38		Vitamin C (ascorbic acid)	(0.040-0.140)	105
39		Niacin (nicotinic acid)	(0.040-0.050)	103
40		Pantothenic acid	0.170	103
41		Androgens	0.0070[1]	53, 61
42	Dog	Freezing point depression	(1.573-3.638) °C	30
43		Specific gravity	1.025(1.016-1.060)	30
44		Volume	(20-100) ml/kg body wt/da	29
45		Calcium	(1-3)	101, 111
46		Magnesium	(1.7-3.0)	43, 45, 101, 111
47		Phosphorus	(20-30)	43, 45
48		Potassium	(40-100)	101, 111
49		Sulfate, total	(30-50)	108
		Sulfur		108
50		Total S	(25-40)	
51		Ethereal S	(1.3-3.5)	
52		Neutral S	(5-10)	
53		Allantoin	(35-45)	1, 10, 41, 64
54		Creatine	(10-50)	50, 82, 108
55		Creatinine	(30-80)	16, 50, 108
56		Hippuric acid	34	25
57		Histamine	(0.010-0.300)	2, 78
58		Urea	(300-500)	65, 91
59		Uric acid	4.5	77
		Nitrogen		
60		Total N	(250-800)	6, 43, 45, 50, 65
61		Ammonia N	(30-60)	6, 50
62		Acetone bodies	(5-6)	69
63		Carbolic acid (phenol)	5	36
64		Citric acid	(2-20)	13, 80
65		Vitamin B$_2$ (riboflavin)	(0.010-0.020)	94
66		Choline	(0.200-0.500)	67
67		Niacinamide	(0.300-0.400)	31
68		Pantothenic acid	0.130	97
69		N'-Methylnicotinamide	(0.090-0.800)	31
70		Androgens	(0.010-0.030)	85
71		Formaldehydogenic steroids	0.010	20
72		17-Ketosteroids	(0.040-0.100)	85
73	Goat	Specific gravity	1.030(1.015-1.045)	30
74		Volume	(10-40) ml/kg body wt/da	29
75		Calcium	1	82
76		Phosphorus	1	82
77		Allantoin	(30-70)	56, 82
78		Creatine	(3-4)	82
79		Creatinine	10	82
80		Hippuric acid	(200-300)	82
81		Purine bases	(2-8)	56, 82
82		Urea	230	82
83		Uric acid	(2-5)	56, 82
		Nitrogen		
84		Total N	(120-400)	56, 82
85		Ammonia N	(3-5)	82
86		Carbolic acid (phenol)	15	36
87		Vitamin B$_1$ (thiamine)	0.006	70
88		Vitamin B$_2$ (riboflavin)	0.020	70

/1/ Males.

Animal	Property or Constituent	Value	Reference
(A)	(B)	(C)	(D)
89 Goat (con-	Niacin (nicotinic acid)	(0.050-0.200)	87
90 cluded)	Pantothenic acid	0.160	70
91	N'-Methylnicotinamide	(0.060-0.090)	87
92 Guinea pig	Sulfur, neutral	(5-8)	16
93	Allantoin	50	79
94	Creatinine	30	16, 99
95	Nitrogen, total	180	99
96	Carbolic acid (phenol)	24	2
97 Horse	Freezing point depression	(1.77-2.00) °C	30
98	Specific gravity	1.040(1.025-1.060)	30
99	Volume	(3-18) ml/kg body wt/da	29
100	Allantoin	(5-15)	56
101	Hippuric acid	100	51
102	Histamine	(0.0001-0.0030)	2
103	Purine bases	0.04	56
104	Uric acid	(1-2)	56
105	Nitrogen, total	(100-160)	56, 84
106	Vitamin B_2 (riboflavin)	0.002	92
107	Vitamin C (ascorbic acid)	0.090	105
108	Niacin (nicotinic acid)	(0.002-0.007)	96, 103
109	N'-Methylnicotinamide	(0.003-0.020)	100
110	Estrogens	(0.020-1.000)[1]	28, 66
111		(0.200-0.400)[2]	
112 Monkey	Volume	(70-80) ml/kg body wt/da	8
113	Calcium	15	8
114	Chlorine	100	8
115	Magnesium	5.2	8
116	Phosphorus	15	8
117	Potassium	200	8
118	Sulfate, total	(20-30)	8
	Sulfur		8
119	Inorganic S	12	
120	Ethereal S	(3-4)	
121	Neutral S	(4-5)	
122	Allantoin	(5-10)	26, 64
123	Creatine	(0-14)	58, 90
124	Creatinine	(20-60)	26, 58, 90
125	Hippuric acid	(4-5)	57
126	Purine bases	(5-6)	57, 90
127	Urea	(200-700)	57, 90
128	Uric acid	(1-2)	26, 90
	Nitrogen		8, 57, 90
129	Total N	(140-400)	
130	Ammonia N	(2-10)	
131	Androgens	0.010	107
132 Rabbit	Volume	(50-75) ml/kg body wt/da	81
133	Calcium	(3-7)	106
134	Chlorine	(190-300)	81
135	Phosphorus	(10-60)	15, 74, 106
136	Sulfur, neutral	(4-10)	16
137	Allantoin	(60-80)	26, 62, 64, 79
138	Coproporphyrin I and III	(0.003-0.012)	95
139	Creatine	(13-20)	81
140	Creatinine	(20-50)	11, 16, 18, 81, 99
141	Hippuric acid	100	32
142	Histamine	(0.020-0.200)	2
143	Indoxylsulfuric acid (indican)	(0-trace)	3
144	Urea	(1200-1500)	52
145	Uric acid	(4-6)	42
	Nitrogen		
146	Total N	(120-300)	74, 99, 106
147	Ammonia N	(3-5)	11, 106

/1/ Males. /2/ Females

	Animal	Property or Constituent	Value	Reference
	(A)	(B)	(C)	(D)
148	Rabbit (con-	Acetone bodies	(0.4-1.0)	5
149	cluded)	Carbolic acid (phenol)	30	36
150		Niacin (nicotinic acid)	(0.250-0.700)	31
151		Androgens	(0.003-0.020)	22
152		17-Ketosteroids	(0.030-1.000)	21, 22, 24
153	Rat	Volume	(150-300) ml/kg body wt/da	46
154		Calcium	(3-9)	33, 76
155		Chlorine	(50-75)	68
156		Phosphorus	30	91
157		Potassium	(50-60)	76
158		Sulfur, neutral	(7-20)	16
159		Allantoin	(100-600)	7, 40, 64
		Arginine		4
160		Total	2.7	
161		Free	1.3	
162		Aspartic acid, free	0.29	4
163		Citrulline	(0.54-2.5)	89
164		Cystine, total	0.5	4
165		Glutamic acid, total	7.1	4
166		Glycine, total	6.9	4
		Histidine		4
167		Total	1.5	
168		Free	0.43	
		Isoleucine		4
169		Total	2.2	
170		Free	0.43	
171		Leucine, free	2.4	4
		Lysine		4
172		Total	4.6	
173		Free	1.0	
174		Methionine, free	0.4	4
175		Phenylalanine, free	0.8	4
176		Taurine	(0.54-2.50)	89
		Threonine		4
177		Total	2.9	
178		Free	0.63	
179		Tryptophan, free	0.47	4
180		Tyrosine, free	0.47	4
181		Valine, free	0.93	4
182		Trigonelline	(0.300-0.700)	54
183		Creatine	(0-13)	19, 104
184		Creatinine	(24-40)	7, 16, 38, 104
185		Histamine	(0.020-0.200)	2
186		Urea	(1000-1600)	38, 88
187		Uric acid	(8-12)	7, 37, 40
		Nitrogen		
188		Total N	(200-1000)	14, 44, 99
189		Ammonia N	(10-30)	38, 46
190		Carbolic acid (phenol)	(6-60)	23
191		Citric acid	53	98
192		Vitamin B$_1$ (thiamine)	(0.003-0.013)	93, 110
193		Vitamin B$_2$ (riboflavin)	(0.040-0.080)	92, 94
194		Vitamin C (ascorbic acid)	(1.0-6.0)	63, 83
195		Niacin (nicotinic acid)	(0.090-0.120)	54
196		Niacinamide (nicotinamide)	(0.200-0.700)	31
197		Pantothenic acid	(0.300-0.600)	73
198		N'-Methylnicotinamide	(0.900-5.000)	31
199		Androgens	0.018	27
200	Sheep	Specific gravity	1.030(1.015-1.045)	30
201		Volume	(10-40) ml/kg body wt/da	29
202		Calcium	2	82
203		Phosphorus	0.2	82
204		Allantoin	(20-50)	56, 79, 82

Part II: MAMMALS OTHER THAN MAN (Continued)

	Animal	Property or Constituent	Value	Reference
	(A)	(B)	(C)	(D)
205	Sheep (con-	Creatine	(0-6)	82
206	cluded)	Creatinine	10	82
207		Hippuric acid	(20-40)	82, 86
208		Purine bases	(2-5)	56, 82
209		Urea	210	82
210		Uric acid	(2-4)	56, 82
		Nitrogen		
211		Total N	(120-350)	51, 56, 82
212		Ammonia N	(0-8)	51, 82
213		Choline	0.060	67
214		Niacin (nicotinic acid)	(0.080-0.130)	87
215		N'-Methylnicotinamide	(0.018-0.060)	87
216		Estrogens	(0.00005-0.00300)[2]	9
217	Swine	Specific gravity	1.012(1.010-1.050)	30
218		Volume	(5-30) ml/kg body wt/da	29
219		Sulfur, neutral	(1-3)	16
220		Allantoin	(20-80)	56, 62, 79
221		Creatine	(15-25)	72
222		Creatinine	(20-90)	16, 72, 99
223		Purine bases	(3-4)	56
224		Urea	430	102
225		Uric acid	(1-2)	56
226		Nitrogen, total	(40-240)	71, 75, 99
227		Carbolic acid (phenol)	(1-3)	36
228		Vitamin C (ascorbic acid)	0.160	105

/2/ Females.

Contributors: (a) Van Pilsum, John F., (b) Hinman, Frank, Jr.

References: [1] Allan, F. W., and L. R. Cerecedo. 1931. J. Biol. Chem. 93:293. [2] Anrep, G. V., M. S. Ayadi, G. S. Barsoum, J. R. Smith, and M. M. Talaat. 1944. J. Physiol., Lond. 103:155. [3] Asayama, C. 1916. J. Am. M. Ass. 67:475. [4] Bakerman, H. A., M. Silverman, and F. S. Daft. 1951. J. Biol. Chem. 188:117. [5] Banerjee, S., and G. Bhattacharya. 1949. Ibid. 178:145. [6] Bartlett, P. D., O. H. Gaebler, and A. Harmon. 1949. Ibid. 180:1021. [7] Bass, A. D., J. Tepperman, D. A. Richert, and W. W. Westerfeld. 1950. Proc. Soc. Exp. Biol., N. Y. 73:687. [8] Baumann, L., and E. Oviatt. 1915. J. Biol. Chem. 22:43. [9] Beck, A. B. 1950. Austral. J. Agr. Res. 1:322. [10] Běher, W. T., and O. H. Gaebler. 1950. J. Nutrit. 41:447. [11] Bernheim, F., M. L. C. Bernheim, and H. R. Higgens. 1945. Am. J. Physiol. 145:115. [12] Blosser, T. H., and V. R. Smith. 1950. J. Dairy Sc. 33:329. [13] Boothby, W. M., and M. Adams. 1934. Am. J. Physiol. 107:471. [14] Bothwell, J. W., and J. N. Williams, Jr. 1951. J. Nutrit. 45:245. [15] Brain, R. T., H. D. Kay, and P. G. Marshall. 1928. Biochem. J., Lond. 22:628. [16] Brody, S., R. C. Procter, and U. S. Ashworth. 1934. Res. Bull. Univ. Missouri Agr. Exp. Sta. 214:34. [17] Carpenter, T. A. 1927. Am. J. Physiol. 81:519. [18] Cheetham, R. W. S., and H. Zwarenstein. 1938. Biochem. J., Lond. 32:871. [19] Coffman, J. R., and F. C. Kock. 1939. Proc. Soc. Exp. Biol., N. Y. 42:779. [20] Corcoran, A. C., and I. H. Page. 1948. J. Laborat. Clin. M. 33:1326. [21] Danford, P. A., and H. G. Danford. 1950. Endocrinology 47:139. [22] Davis, C. T., C. R. Slater, and B. Krichesky. 1949. Ibid. 44:83. [23] Deichmann, W., and L. J. Schafer. 1942. Am. J. Clin. Path. 12:129. [24] DeKoning, K. B., and S. J. Glass. 1948. Proc. Soc. Exp. Biol., N.Y. 68:320. [25] Delprat, G. D., and G. H. Whipple. 1921. J. Biol. Chem. 49:229. [26] Dinning, J. S., and P. L. Day. 1949. Ibid. 181:897. [27] Dorfman, R. I. 1938. Ibid. 123:xxx. [28] Dow, D. S., and C. E. Allen. 1949. Sc. Agr. 29:330. [29] Dukes, H. H. 1947. The physiology of domestic animals. Ed. 6. Comstock, Ithaca. [30] Ellenberger, W., and A. Scheunert. 1925. Lehrbuch der vergleichenden Physiologie der Haussäugetiere. Ed. 3. Parey, Berlin. [31] Ellinger, P., and M. M. Abdel Kader. 1949.

Biochem. J., Lond. 44:77. [32] Epstein, A. A., and S. Bookman. 1912. J. Biol. Chem. 13:117. [33] Fairhall, L. T. 1926. Ibid. 70:495. [34] Fiske, C. H., and M. A. Logan. 1931. Ibid. 93:211. [35] Folin, O., and R. D. Bell. 1917. Ibid. 29:329. [36] Folin, O., and W. Denis. 1915. Ibid. 22:309. [37] Folin, O., and W. Denis. 1916. Ibid. 26:497. [38] Folin, O., and J. L. Morris. 1913. Ibid. 14:509. [39] Forbes, E. B., R. B. French, and T. V. Letonoff. 1928. J. Nutrit. 1:201. [40] Friedman, M. 1948. Am. J. Physiol. 152:302. [41] Friedman, M., and S. O. Byers. 1948. J. Biol. Chem. 175:727. [42] Friedman, M., and S. O. Byers. 1950. Am. J. Physiol. 163:684. [43] Givens, M. H., and L. B. Mendel. 1917. J. Biol. Chem. 31:421. [44] Gordon, G. S., H. M. Evans, and M. E. Simpson. 1947. Endocrinology 40:375. [45] Greenwald, I., and J. Gross. 1925. J. Biol. Chem. 66:201. [46] Griffith, J. Q. 1949. The rat in laboratory investigation. Ed. 2. J. B. Lippincott, Philadelphia. [47] Hammett, F. S. 1915. J. Biol. Chem. 22:551. [48] Hansard, S. L., C. L. Comar, and M. P. Plumlee. 1952. J. Animal Sc. 11:524. [49] Hart, E. B., H. Steenbock, O. L. Kline, and G. C. Humphrey. 1931. J. Dairy Sc. 14:307. [50] Hawk, P. B. 1910. J. Biol. Chem. 8:465. [51] Healy, D. J., J. F. Bullard, and H. D. Spears. 1928. J. Am. Vet. M. Ass. 73:87. [52] Herrin, R. C. 1947. Am. J. Physiol. 149:492. [53] Hooker, C. W. 1937. Endocrinology 21:655. [54] Huff, J. W., and W. A. Perlzweig. 1942. J. Biol. Chem. 142:401. [55] Hunter, G. 1925. Biochem. J., Lond. 19:34. [56] Hunter, A., and M. H. Givens. 1914. J. Biol. Chem. 18:403. [57] Hunter, A., and M. H. Givens. 1914. Ibid. 17:55. [58] Jailer, J. W. 1940. Am. J. Physiol. 130:503. [59] Keitt, T. E. 1916. In 29th Ann. Rep. S. Carolina Exp. Sta. Clemson College, South Carolina. p. 24. [60] Knodt, C. B., J. C. Shaw, and G. C. White. 1942. J. Dairy Sc. 25:851. [61] Kock, F. C. 1937. Physiol. Rev. 17:153. [62] Kostyak, J. 1941. Közl. összehas. élet & kórt. 29:178. [63] Langwill, K. E., C. G. King, and G. MacLeod. 1945. J. Nutrit. 30:99. [64] Larson, H. W. 1931. J. Biol. Chem. 94:727. [65] Larson, P. S., and I. L. Chaikoff. 1937. J. Nutrit. 13:287. [66] Levin, L. 1949. J. Biol. Chem. 178:229. [67] Luecke, R. W., and P. B. Pearson. 1945. Ibid. 158:561. [68] Machle, W., E. W. Scott, and E. J. Largent. 1942. J. Indust. Hyg. 24:199. [69] Maignon, F., and E. Kinthakis. 1928. C. rend. Acad. sc. 186:463. [70] Marsh, D. C., P. B. Pearson, and I. W. Rupel. 1947. J. Dairy Sc. 30:867. [71] McCollum, E. V., and D. R. Hoagland. 1913. J. Biol. Chem. 16:299. [72] McCollum, E. V., and H. Steenbock. 1912. Ibid. 13:209. [73] McIlwain, H., and F. Hawking. 1943. Lancet, Lond. 1:449. [74] Mendel, L. B., and J. F. Lyman. 1910. J. Biol. Chem. 8:115. [75] Miller, E. R. 1929. J. Am. Vet. M. Ass. 74:376. [76] Miller, H. G. 1926. J. Biol. Chem. 70:593. [77] Miller, G. E., L. S. Danzey, and J. H. Talbott. 1951. Am. J. Physiol. 164:155. [78] Misrahy, G., and S. Salams. 1947. Ibid. 150:420. [79] Miyahara, T. 1934. Sei i kwai v. 53(8-9). [80] Morendo, G. C., and L. Flore. 1949. Minerva med., Tor. 39(2):149. [81] Morgulis, S., and H. C. Spencer. 1936. J. Nutrit. 12:191. [82] Morris, S., and S. C. Ray. 1939. Biochem. J., Lond. 33:1217. [83] Musulin, R. R., R. H. Tully, III, H. E. Longenecker, and C. G. King. 1939. J. Biol. Chem. 129:437. [84] Nietsche, H. 1937. Biochem. Zschr. 294:174. [85] Paschkis, K. E., A. Cantarow, A. E. Rakoff, L. P. Hansen, and A. A. Walking. 1943. Proc. Soc. Exp. Biol., N. Y. 53:213. [86] Pazur, J. H., and W. A. DeLong. 1948. Sc. Agr. 28:39. [87] Pearson, P. B., W. A. Perlzweig, and F. Rosen. 1949. Arch. Biochem., N. Y. 22:191. [88] Persike, E. C. 1948. Endocrinology 42:356. [89] Reed, J. G. 1951. Univ. Texas Pub. 5109. p. 139. [90] Rheinberger, M. B. 1936. J. Biol. Chem. 115:343. [91] Richet, C., Jr. 1929. J. Laborat. Clin. M. 15:9. [92] Robinson, F. A. 1951. The vitamin B complex. J. Wiley and Sons, New York. [93] Salcedo, J., Jr., V. A. Najjar, L. E. Holt, Jr., and E. W. Hutzler. 1948. J. Nutrit. 36:307. [94] Sarett, H. P., J. R. Klein, and N. A. Perlzweig. 1942. Ibid. 24:295. [95] Schwarz, S., and R. Zagaria. MDDC-504. Technical Information Service, USAEC, Oak Ridge, Tenn. [96] Schweigert, B. S., P. B. Pearson, and M. C. Wilkening. 1947. Arch. Biochem., N. Y. 12:139. [97] Silber, R. H. 1944. J. Nutrit. 27:425. [98] Simola, P. E., and T. Kosunen. 1938. Suom. Kem. 11B:22. [99] Smuts, D. B. 1935. J. Nutrit. 9:403. [100] Spector, H., T. S. Hamilton, and H. H. Mitchell. 1945. J. Biol. Chem. 161:145. [101] Stehle, R. L. 1917. Ibid. 31:461. [102] Stekol, J. A. 1936. Ibid. 113:675.

Part II: MAMMALS OTHER THAN MAN (Concluded)

[103] Terri, A. E., M. Leavitt, D. Josselyn, N. F. Colovos, and H. A. Keener. 1950. Ibid. 182:509.

[104] Tidwell, H. C. 1946. Proc. Soc. Exp. Biol., N. Y. 63:13. [105] Ugolini, M. 1942. Biochim. ter. sper. 29:187. [106] Underhill, F. P., and L. J. Bogert. 1916. J. Biol. Chem. 27:161. [107] Valle, J. R., S. B. Henriques, and O. B. Henriques. 1947. Endocrinology 41:335. [108] Vassel, B., R. Partridge, and M. L. Crossley. 1944. Arch. Biochem., N. Y. 4:59. [109] Warth, F. J., and N. C. Das Gupta. 1928. Biochem. J., Lond. 22:621. [110] Wertz, A. W., P. S. van Horn, and L. E. Lloyd. 1951. J. Nutrit. 43:181. [111] Whelan, M. 1925. J. Biol. Chem. 63:585.

123. URINE ELECTROLYTE EXCRETION RATE: VERTEBRATES

Part I: TERRESTRIAL MAMMALS

Values in parentheses are ranges, estimate "c" (cf. Introduction).

	Animal	Electrolyte	Concentration mEq/L	Excretion Rate		Reference
				mEq/da	mEq/kg/da	
	(A)	(B)	(C)	(D)	(E)	(F)
1	Man[1]	Ammonia[2]	27(20-50)	38(30-70)	0.7(0.4-1.5)	C,D,4,14,25,40;E,10,40
2		Bicarbonate[3]	1.1(0-26)	1.5(0-36)	0.02(0-0.5)	14
3		Calcium	7.5(1.4-13.0)	8(2-18)	0.14(0.08-0.23)	C,4,5,14,26,27,40;D,5,14,26,27,40;E,5,40
4		Chloride	110(49-210)	118(58-250)	1.6(1.0-2.2)	C,4,14;D,3,14,18,40;E,3,40
5		Magnesium	8.2(5.8-11.6)	9(6-16)	0.15(0.11-0.21)	C,34;D,14,26,40,47;E,40,47
6		Phosphate	28(22-41)	36(22-54)[4]	0.6(0.5-0.9)	C,14,34;D,3,14,34,40;E,3,34,40
7		Potassium	50(27-119)	64(53-91)	1.1(0.8-1.2)	C,14,31;D,14,27,40;E,3,40
8		Sodium	114(35-167)	120(40-186)	1.9(1.3-2.4)	C,4,14,31;D,E,14,27,40
9		Sulfate	26(13-56)	37(11-56)	0.6(0.2-0.9)	C,14,19;D,E,14,19,40
10	Cat[5]	Calcium	2.95	0.11	0.04	28
11		Magnesium	11.9	0.4	0.13	28
12		Phosphate		22	3.6	9
13	Cow	Calcium		18.0(4.5-74.3)	0.04(0.01-0.14)	11
14		Chloride		282(127-606)	0.6(0.1-1.1)	11
15		Magnesium		339(154-578)	0.66(0.26-1.02)	11
16		Potassium		2370(1650-2980)	5(3-6)	11
17		Sodium		360(89-475)	0.7(0.2-1.1)	11
18	Dog[6]	Ammonia[2]	69(4-190)	25(2.9-82)	1.2(0.2-3.7)	C,51;D,E,17,51
19		Bicarbonate	39	18(0.01-71)	1.3(0.05-3.2)	C,51,52;D,51-53;E,51
20		Calcium	2.12(0.18-7.70)	1.3(0.1-7.0)	0.11(0.08-0.14)	C,52;D,E,1,52
21		Chloride	76(0-289)	40(0-222)	2.0(0-10.3)	C,8,22,35,41,51,52;D,8,22,28,41,51-53; E,22,28,41,51
22		Magnesium	8.3(2.8-26.9)	3.9(0.7-20.7)	0.21(0.05-0.53)	C,D,41,52;E,28,41
23		Phosphate	(0-120)	7(0-38)[4]	0.25(0-1.04)	C,51,52;D,28,33,51-53;E,28,33,51
24		Potassium	84(18-234)	31(3-128)	1.0(0.1-2.4)	C,8,51,52;D,8,13,17,51,52;E,13,17,51
25		Sodium	74(2-189)	32(1-209)	1.9(0.04-13)	C,8,22,41,52;E,8,16,22,41,52
26		Sulfate	48(6-233)	26(1-48)	1.7(0.05-3.1)	C,41,52;D,15,17,41,52;E,15,17,41
27	Rabbit[7]	Calcium	5.2(1.6-11.4)	1.7(0.46-3.4)	0.86(0.29-1.7)	28
28		Chloride	41(3.4-94)	3.6(0.8-9.8)	0.5(0.1-1.4)	32
29		Magnesium	8.5	2.7	1.47	28
30		Phosphate	4.6(1.5-6.9)	1.4(0.6-2.1)	0.75(0.3-1.3)	28
31		Sodium	60			32

/1/ Water excretion = 1400(500-3000) ml/da; 20(7-42) ml/kg/da [2,18,45]. /2/ Excretion rate is directly proportional to urinary pH. /3/ Excretion rate dependent upon urinary pH. No appreciable amount excreted at pH 5.2; 1.5 mEq/da at pH 6.0; 6 mEq/da at pH 6.6; 14 mEq/da at pH 7.0; 36 mEq/da at pH 7.4. [14] /4/ Base equivalence assumed as 1.0. /5/ Water excretion = 36 ml/da; 12 ml/kg/da [28]. /6/ Water excretion = 420(122-2000) ml/da [13,16,22,30,51,52]; 20(5-55) ml/kg/da [13,22,30,41,51]. /7/ Water excretion = 258(34-935) ml/da; 90(19-295) ml/kg/da [12,28,32,49,50].

Part I: TERRESTRIAL MAMMALS (Continued)

Animal	Electrolyte	Concentration mEq/L	Excretion Rate		Reference
			mEq/da	mEq/kg/da	
(A)	(B)	(C)	(D)	(E)	(F)
32 Rat[8]	Ammonia[2]		0.7	3.0	39
33	Calcium		0.09(0.02-0.16)	0.26(0.08-0.46)	20,29,38
34	Chloride	96	1.3(0.4-1.9)	3.4(0.9-8.2)	C,6,42;D,29,37,46;E,24,29,37,44
35	Magnesium		0.17(0.04-0.3)	0.86	D,20,37,38;E,20
36	Phosphate		0.5(0.27-0.55)	3.3(0.8-3.6)	21,29
37	Potassium	230(190-260)	0.9(0.4-1.9)	4.0(2.7-5.4)	C,37,D,20,37,38,46,48;E,20,37,38
38	Sodium	90.4	1.4(0.2-1.9)	4.5(1.7-7.3)	C,42;D,20,37,38,46,48;E,20,38
39	Sulfate	5.5	0.17(0.13-0.21)	0.8	C,E,37;D,36,37

/2/ Excretion rate is directly proportional to urinary pH. /8/ Water excretion = 12(4.3-24.0) ml/da [7,39,43]; 50(38-100) ml/kg/da [7,23,39,43].

Contributors: (a) Peschel, Ernst, (b) Booker, Walter M.

References: [1] Barbour, H. G., and J. E. Winter. 1931. J. Pharm. Exp. Ther. 43:607. [2] Barclay, J. A., W. T. Cooke, R. A. Kenney, and M. E. Nutt. 1947. Am. J. Physiol. 148:327. [3] Bassett, S. H., C. A. Elden, and W. S. McCann. 1932. J. Nutrit. 5:1. [4] Cantarow, A., and M. Trumper. 1945. Clinical biochemistry. W. B. Saunders, Philadelphia. [5] Carswell, H. E., and J. E. Winter. 1931. J. Biol. Chem. 93:411. [6] Corey, E. L., and S. W. Britton. 1941. Am. J. Physiol. 133:511. [7] Danford, P. A., and H. G. Danford. 1951. Ibid. 164:690. [8] Davis, A. K., A. C. Bass, and R. R. Overman. 1951. Ibid. 166:493. [9] Eggleton, M. G., and Y. A. Habib. 1949. J. Physiol., Lond. 110:98. [10] Farquharson, R. F., W. T. Salter, D. M. Tibbetts, and J. C. Aub. 1931. J. Clin. Invest. 10:221. [11] Forbes, E. B., J. A. Schulz, C. H. Hunt, A. R. Winter, and R. F. Remler. 1922. J. Biol. Chem. 52:281. [12] Forster, R. P. 1952. Am. J. Physiol. 168:666. [13] Foulks, J., G. H. Mudge, and A. Gilman. 1952. Ibid. 168:642. [14] Gamble, J. L. 1947. Chemical anatomy, physiology and pathology of extracellular fluid. Harvard University Press, Cambridge. [15] Goudsmit, A., Jr., M. H. Power, and J. L. Bollman. 1939. Am. J. Physiol. 125:506. [16] Green, D. M., and A. Farah. 1949. Ibid. 158:444. [17] Harris, F. D., A. F. Hartmann, Jr., D. Rolf, and H. L. White. 1952. Ibid. 168:20. [18] Hawk, P. B., B. L. Oser, and W. H. Summerson. 1947. Practical physiological chemistry. Blakiston, Philadelphia. [19] Hayman, J. M., Jr., and S. M. Johnston. 1932. J. Clin. Invest. 11:607. [20] Hegstedt, D. M., D. Wilson, G. McPhee, and F. J. Stare. 1951. Am. J. Physiol. 164:695. [21] Kochakian, C. D., and A. R. Terepka. 1951. Ibid. 165:142. [22] Kuschinsky, G., and H. Langecker. 1947. Arch. exp. Path., Lpz. 204:699. [23] Kuschinsky, G., H. Langecker, and R. Hotovy. 1947. Ibid. 204:752. [24] Langecker, H., and G. Kuschinsky. 1947. Ibid. 204:738. [25] Lotspeich, W. D., and R. F. Pitts. 1947. J. Biol. Chem. 168:611. [26] McCance, R. A., and E. M. Widdowson. 1939. Biochem. J., Lond. 33:523. [27] McKay, E. M., and A. M. Butler. 1935. J. Clin. Invest. 14:923. [28] Mendel, L. B., and S. R. Benedict. 1904. Am. J. Physiol. 16:118. [29] Miller, H. G. 1926. J. Biol. Chem. 70:593. [30] Mulinos, M. G., C. L. Spingarn, and M. E. Lojkin. 1941. Am. J. Physiol. 135:102. [31] Overman, R. R., and A. K. Davis. 1947. J. Biol. Chem. 168:641. [32] Pickering, G. W., and M. Prinzmetal. 1940. J. Physiol., Lond. 98:314. [33] Pitts, R. F., and R. S. Alexander. 1944. Am. J. Physiol. 142:648. [34] Renvall, G. 1904. Skand. Arch. Physiol., Berl. 15:94. [35] Roemmelt, J. C., O. W. Sartorius, and R. F. Pitts. 1949. Am. J. Physiol. 159:124. [36] Sandberg, M., and D. Perla. 1936. J. Biol. Chem. 113:35. [37] Sandberg, M., D. Perla, and O. M. Holly. 1937. Endocrinology 21:346. [38] Sandberg, M., D. Perla, and O. M. Holly. 1937. Ibid. 21:352. [39] Sartorius, O. W., D. Calhoon, and R. F. Pitts. 1952. Ibid. 51:444. [40] Sartorius, O. W., J. C. Roemmelt, and R. F. Pitts. 1949. J. Clin. Invest. 28:423. [41] Schwartz, B. M., P. K. Smith, and A. W. Winkler. 1942. Am. J. Physiol. 137:658. [42] Sellers, A. L., S. Smith, III, H. C. Goodman, and J. Marmorston. 1951. Ibid. 166:619. Semple, R. E. 1952. Ibid. 168:55. [44] Silvette, H. 1940. Ibid. 128:747. [45] Smith, H. W. 1951. The kidney.

Part I: TERRESTRIAL MAMMALS (Concluded)

Structure and function in health and disease. Oxford University Press, New York. [46] Stein, J. D., L. L. Bennett, A. A. Batts, and C. H. Li. 1952. Am. J. Physiol. 171:587. [47] Tibbetts, D. M., and J. C. Aub. 1937. J. Clin. Invest. 16:491. [48] Whitney, J. E., and L. L. Bennett. 1952. Endocrinology 50:657. [49] Wilkinson, D. M., and R. A. McCance. 1940. Q. J. Exp. Physiol., Lond. 30:249. [50] Wills, J. H., and E. Main. 1948. Am. J. Physiol. 154:220. [51] Winkler, A. W., and P. K. Smith. 1942. Ibid. 138:94. [52] Wolf, A. V., and S. M. Ball. 1949. Ibid. 158:205. [53] Wolf, A. V., and S. M. Ball. 1950. Ibid. 160:353.

Part II: AQUATIC AND SEMIAQUATIC VERTEBRATES

Values in parentheses are ranges, estimate "c" (cf. Introduction).

Animal	Electrolyte	Excretion Rate	Reference		Animal	Electrolyte	Excretion Rate	Reference
(A)	(B)	(C)	(D)		(A)	(B)	(C)	(D)
Mammals					**Fishes (concluded)**			
1 Seal (Phoca	Calcium	4.01 mM/L	12	26	Goosefish	Chloride	(2-98) mM/L	7, 8
2 vitulina)[1]	Chloride	289 mM/L		27	(Lophius	Magnesium	(38-151) mM/L	1, 8
3	Magnesium	195 mM/L		28	piscatorius)	Phosphate	(1-17) mM/L	8
4	Phosphate	(Trace-26.7) mM/L		29		Sulfate	(40-110) mM/L	8
5	Sulfate	766 mM/L		30	Hake, silver	Chloride	0	8
6 Whale	Calcium	2.7 mM/L/da	6	31	(Merluccius	Magnesium	(19-127) mM/L	
7	Chloride	362 mM/L/da		32	bilinearis)	Phosphate	(65-92) mM/L	
8	Potassium	74 mM/L/da		33		Sulfate	(20-86) mM/L	
9	Sodium	266 mM/L/da		34	Lamprey Lampetra fluviatilis	Chloride	0.7 mM/L	15
Amphibians				35	Petromyzon marinus	Chloride	4.7 mM/L	9
10 Frog	Chloride	1.89 mM/L/da	6	36	Sawfish (Pristis microdon)	Chloride	5.5 mM/L	14
11	Phosphate	2.35 mM/L/da			Sculpin			
12	Potassium	0.95 mM/L/da		37	Common (My-	Chloride	(0-29) mM/L	2-4
13	Sodium	2.44 mM/L/da		38	oxocephalus	Magnesium	(36-161) mM/L	8
Fishes				39	octodecim-	Phosphate	(50-155) mM/L	8
14 Dab, rusty	Chloride	70 mM/L	8	40	spinosus)	Sulfate	(6-85) mM/L	8
15 (Limanda	Magnesium	125 mM/L		41	Daddy- (M.	Chloride	(0-124) mM/L	3, 8
16 ferruginea)	Phosphate	75 mM/L		42	scorpius)	Magnesium	(72-167) mM/L	8
17	Sulfate	44 mM/L		43		Phosphate	(64-158) mM/L	8
18 Dogfish, Atlantic Smooth (Mustelus canis)	Chloride	262 mM/L	10	44		Sulfate	(30-102) mM/L	8
				45	Sole, gray	Chloride	(0-48) mM/L	8
19 Spiny (Squalus	Chloride	150 mM/L/da	6	46	(Glyptoceph-	Magnesium	(44-47) mM/L	
20 acanthias)	Phosphate	79 mM/L/da	13	47	alus sp)	Phosphate	(5-46) mM/L	
21 Eel (Anguilla sp)	Calcium	7.5 mM/L/da	6	48		Sulfate	(28-49) mM/L	
22	Chloride	>76 mM/L	11	49	Toadfish (Opsanus tau)	Chloride	>86 mM/L	4
23	Potassium	5.7 mM/L/da	6	50	Trout, rainbow (Salmo irideus)	Chloride	(1.9-11.8) mM/L	5
24	Sodium	2.44 mM/L/da	6					
25 Goldfish (Carassius auratus)	Chloride	(2.5-4.1) mM/L	5					

/1/ 40-lb female; values obtained 3-10 hours after feeding.

Contributors: (a) Booker, Walter M., (b) Wirtschafter, Z. T.

References: [1] Brull, L., and Y. Cuypers. 1954. Arch. internat. physiol., Liége 62:70. [2] Clarke, R. W. 1934. J. Cellul. Physiol. 5:73. [3] Forster, R. P. 1953. Ibid. 42:487. [4] Grafflin, A. L. 1931. Am. J. Physiol. 97:602.

[5] Krogh, A. 1937. Zschr. vergl. Physiol. 24:656. [6] Krogh, A. 1939. Osmotic regulations in aquatic animals. Cambridge University Press, London. [7] Marshall, E. K., Jr. 1930. Am. J. Physiol. 94:1. [8] Pitts, R. F. 1934. J. Cellul. Physiol. 4:389. [9] Sawyer, W. 1955. Unpublished. [10] Scott, G. G. 1913. Ann. N. York Acad. Sc. 23:1. [11] Smith, H. W. 1930. Am. J. Physiol. 93:480. [12] Smith, H. W. 1935-36. J. Cellul. Physiol. 7:465. [13] Smith, H. W. 1939. Ibid. 14:95. [14] Smith, H. W., and C. G. Smith. 1931. Am. J. Physiol. 98:279. [15] Wikgren, B. 1953. Acta zool. fenn. 71:1.

124. URINE ELECTROLYTE REABSORPTION RATE: MAN, DOG

Values in parentheses are ranges, estimate "c" (cf. Introduction).

	Animal	Electrolyte	Plasma Concentration mM/L	Reabsorption Rate		Remarks	Reference
				mM/min	mM/min/100 ml glomerular filtrate		
	(A)	(B)	(C)	(D)	(E)	(F)	(G)
1	Man	Bicarbonate	(28.0-38.4)[1]		2.80(2.6-3.0)		C,11;E,13
2		Chloride	107.8 (105.0-110.9)	12.35 (10.37-15.60)	10.50 (10.3-10.97)		13,15
3		Phosphate	(3.5-5.5)	0.130 (0.100-0.150)[2]			16
4		Sodium	134(122-142)	13.66(11.1-16.7)	13.20(11.1-16.7)	Normal subjects and patients without congestive heart failure; some on low-sodium diet	8
5	Dog	Bicarbonate	(25-70)[1]	1.88(1.26-2.54)	2.50(2.08-3.00)		14
6		Calcium	1.83(1.73-1.93)[3]	0.073 (0.072-0.074)	0.110(0.10-0.12)		5
7		Chloride	112.3 (110.0-118.6)	7.85(5.08-6.00)	11.23(11.0-11.8)		3
8			127.0(126-128)	7.70(6.2-10.2)	11.50 (10.24-13.0)	Under conditions of acidosis and with NaCl loading	7
9		Phosphate	(3.0-17.3)[1]	0.10(0.05-0.14)	0.146 (0.135-0.155)		C,12;D,E, 1,4,5,12
10		Potassium	4.23(3.90-5.29)	0.195 (0.122-0.276)[4]	0.369 (0.308-0.512)[4]	10 experiments on 10 subjects under pentobarbital anesthesia	2,9,10
11		Sodium	145(131-155)	8.15(6.03-10.1)	13.80(12.4-14.4)	16 experiments on 3 trained, unanesthetized subjects given orally 50 ml 0.9% saline/kg body wt	17
12			143(132-149)	6.07(4.38-9.00)	13.53(12.7-14.1)	9 experiments on subjects anesthetized with 125 mg chloralose/kg body wt	17
13			180(169-196)	7.29(4.42-10.20)	12.80(11.2-14.2)	Values obtained on same subjects used in collecting data for line 12; given intravenous infusion of 5% NaCl	17
14		Sulfate	(2.2-20.0)[1]	0.075(0.05-0.10)[2]	0.135 (0.080-0.205)		6

/1/ Lower limit of range considered to be plasma concentration at which urinary excretion occurs. /2/ Tubular maximum rate of reabsorption (Tm) characterized by a fixed, reproducible reabsorptive capacity when load (plasma concentration x glomerular filtration rate) exceeds Tm by 1.5 times or more. /3/ Serum concentration; glomerular filtration concentration = 1.10(1.03-1.20) mM/L [5]. /4/ Considered to be net reabsorption; probable that both reabsorption of filtered potassium and tubular secretion occur.

Contributor: Selkurt, Ewald E.

References: [1] Ayer, J. L., W. A. Schiess, and R. F. Pitts. 1947. Am. J. Physiol. 151:168. [2] Berliner, R. W., T. J. Kennedy, Jr., and J. G. Hilton. 1950. Ibid. 162:348. [3] Hare, R. S., K. Hare, and D. M. Phillips. 1943. Ibid. 140:334. [4] Hogben, C. A. M., and J. L. Bollman. 1951. Ibid. 164:670. [5] Jahan, I., and R. F. Pitts. 1948. Ibid. 155:42. [6] Lotspeich, W. D. 1947. Ibid. 151:311. [7] Lotspeich, W. D., R. C. Swan, and R. F. Pitts. 1947. Ibid. 148:445. [8] Mokotoff, R., G. Ross, and L. Leiter. 1948. J. Clin. Invest. 27:1. [9] Mudge, G. H., A. Ames, J. Foulks, and A. Gilman. 1950. Am. J. Physiol. 161:151. [10] Mudge, G. H., J. Foulks, and A. Gilman. 1950. Ibid. 161:159. [11] Pitts, R. F. 1934. J. Cellul. Physiol. 4:389. [12] Pitts, R. F., and R. S. Alexander. 1944. Am. J. Physiol. 142:648. [13] Pitts, R. F., J. L. Ayer, and W. A. Schiess. 1949. J. Clin. Invest. 28:35. [14] Pitts, R. F., and W. D. Lotspeich. 1946. Am. J. Physiol. 147:138. [15] Sartorius, O. W., J. C. Roemmelt, and R. F. Pitts. 1949. J. Clin. Invest. 28:423. [16] Schiess, W. A., J. L. Ayer, W. D. Lotspeich, and R. F. Pitts. 1948. Ibid. 27:57. [17] Selkurt, E. E. Unpublished.

125. EFFECT OF VARIOUS PROTEIN DIETS ON NITROGENOUS CONSTITUENTS OF URINE: MAN

Part I: AVERAGE-PROTEIN DIET

Approximate nitrogen content of diet = 10 g N/da. Values are mg/kg body wt/da, unless otherwise specified. Values in parentheses are ranges, estimate "c" unless otherwise indicated (cf. Introduction).

	Property or Constituent	No. of Subjects	Value	Remarks	Reference
	(A)	(B)	(C)	(D)	(E)
1	Urine volume, ml/kg body wt/da	400♂	19.5(10-30)[d]	70 kg body weight assumed	1
2	Water content, ml/kg body wt/da	400♂	18.4(8.0-24.5)[d]	Estimated, using Long's coefficient; 70 kg body weight assumed	1
	Amino acids				
	Arginine			Diluted urine; determinations obtained microbiologically after hydrolysis with H_2SO_4; 66.8 kg mean body weight	11
3	Total	13♂, 5♀	0.36(0.18-0.68)		
4	Free	13♂, 5♀	0.32(0.16-0.54)		
	Aspartic acid				
5	Total	13♂, 5♀	2.48(1.31-3.89)		
6	Free	13♂, 5♀	0.017(0-0.35)		
7	Citrulline, free	12♂	0.58(0.26-0.70)	Estimated from paper chromatography determinations of creatinine for 8 controls and 4 alcoholics; 70 kg body weight assumed	2
8	Cystine, free	13♂, 5♀	1.31(0.68-2.06)	Diluted urine; determinations obtained microbiologically after hydrolysis with H_2SO_4; 66.8 kg mean body weight	11
	Glutamic acid				
9	Total	13♂, 5♀	5.27(1.58-11.55)		
10	Free	13♂, 5♀	0.54(0-0.96)		
	Glycine			Probably occurs in conjugation as hippuric acid; determinations obtained microbiologically after hydrolysis with HCl, using Lactobacillus mesenteroides P-60 which also responds to hippuric acid; 70 kg body weight assumed	5
11	Total	4♂, 2♀	7.25		
12	Free	4♂, 2♀	10.0		
	Histidine			Diluted urine; determinations obtained microbiologically after hydrolysis with H_2SO_4; 66.8 kg mean body weight	11
13	Total	13♂, 5♀	3.04(0.98-6.59)		
14	Free	13♂, 5♀	2.82(0.91-5.70)		
	Isoleucine				
15	Total	13♂, 5♀	0.34(0.18-0.50)		
16	Free	13♂, 5♀	0.089(0-0.32)		

Part I: AVERAGE-PROTEIN DIET (Continued)

	Property or Constituent	No. of Subjects	Value	Remarks	Reference
	(A)	(B)	(C)	(D)	(E)
	Amino acids (concluded)				
	Leucine			Diluted urine; determinations obtained microbiologically after hydrolysis with H_2SO_4; 66.8 kg mean body weight	11
17	Total	13♂, 5♀	0.32(0.18-0.60)		
18	Free	13♂, 5♀	0.14(0.057-0.280)		
	Lysine				
19	Total	13♂, 5♀	1.10(0.53-2.49)		
20	Free	13♂, 5♀	0.50(0.27-1.32)		
	Methionine				
21	Total	13♂, 5♀	0.13(0.06-0.23)		
22	Free	13♂, 5♀	0.12(0.062-0.230)		
	Phenylalanine				
23	Total	13♂, 5♀	0.35(0.15-0.68)		
24	Free	13♂, 5♀	0.25(0.11-0.51)		
	Proline				
25	Total	13♂, 5♀	0.64(0.35-0.93)		
26	Free	13♂, 5♀	0.13(0.056-0.220)		
27	Serine, free	4	0.44(0.21-0.52)	Determinations obtained microbiologically; 61.5 kg mean body weight	9
	Threonine			Diluted urine; determinations obtained microbiologically after hydrolysis with H_2SO_4; 66.8 kg mean body weight	11
28	Total	13♂, 5♀	0.81(0.22-1.27)		
29	Free	13♂, 5♀	0.37(0.19-0.74)		
	Tryptophan			Determinations obtained microbiologically from alkali-hydrolyzed urine; basic hydrolysis causes racemization of unknown extent, so that values are probably too low; 66.8 kg mean body weight	11
30	Total	13♂, 5♀	0.62(0.17-1.29)		
31	Free	13♂, 5♀	0.37(0.19-0.74)		
	Tyrosine			Diluted urine; determinations obtained microbiologically after hydrolysis with H_2SO_4; 66.8 kg mean body weight	11
32	Total	13♂, 5♀	0.79(0.35-1.55)		
33	Free	13♂, 5♀	0.31(0.16-0.67)		
	Valine				
34	Total	13♂, 5♀	0.30(0.17-0.45)		
35	Free	13♂, 5♀	0.68(0-0.11)		
	Nitrogen				
36	Total N	52-54♂	164(98.5-230.0)[b]	70 kg body weight assumed	7
37	Allantoin N	7	0.16(0.12-0.24)	70 kg body weight assumed	6
38	α-Amino N		2.0(1.5-3.2)[d]	Estimated; 70 kg body weight assumed	8
39	Ammonia N	52-54♂	6.0(1.7-10.3)[b]	70 kg body weight assumed	7
40	Creatine N	6♀	0.93(0.35-2.03)	(46.5-72.2) kg body weight	10
41	Creatinine N	52-54♂	8.1(5.3-11.0)[b]	70 kg body weight assumed	7
42		6♀	7.9(7.3-8.9)	(46.5-72.2) kg body weight	10
43	Hippuric acid N	2♀	1.2(0.9-1.4)[d]	Values greatly influenced by specific fruits in diet (i.e., prunes, cranberries); not appreciably affected by dietary protein level; 56 kg body weight assumed	3
44	Purine N		0.6(0.3-0.9)[d]	Values influenced by intake of dietary purines which may or may not be associated with protein intake	4
45	Urea N	52-54♂	137(110-163.5)[b]	70 kg body weight assumed	7
46	Uric acid N	52-54♂	2.1(1.0-3.6)[b]	Values influenced by intake of dietary purines which may or may not be associated with protein intake; 70 kg body weight assumed	7

Contributor: Pearson, William N.

References: [1] Beard, H. H. 1935. Human Biol. 7:419. [2] Beerstecher, E., et al. 1950. Arch. Biochem., N. Y. 29:27. [3] Blatherwick, N. R., and M. L. Lond. 1923. J. Biol. Chem. 57:815. [4] Burian, R., and H. Schur.

Part I: AVERAGE-PROTEIN DIET (Concluded)

1900. Arch. ges. Physiol. 80:241. [5] Dunn, M. S., M. N. Camien, S. Shankman, and H. Block. 1947. Arch. Biochem., N. Y. 13:207. [6] Fosse, R., A. Brunel, and P.-E. Thomas. 1931. C. rend. Acad. sc. 192:1615. [7] Jellinek, E. M., and J. M. Looney. 1939. J. Biol. Chem. 128:621. [8] Pearson, W. N. Unpublished. [9] Steele, B. F., H. E. Sauberlich, M. S. Reynolds, and C. A. Baumann. 1947. J. Nutrit. 33:209. [10] Wang, C. C., J. E. Hawks, B. Huddlestun, A. A. Wood, and E. A. Smith. 1930. Ibid. 3:79. [11] Woodson, H. W., S. W. Hier, J. D. Solomon, and O. Bergeim. 1948. J. Biol. Chem. 172:613.

Part II: HIGH- AND LOW-PROTEIN DIETS

Approximate nitrogen content: high-protein diet = 19 g N/da, low-protein diet = 6 g N/da. Values are mg/kg body wt/da, unless otherwise specified, and were calculated on the basis of an actual or assumed body weight of 70 kg, unless otherwise specified. Values for total amino acids were obtained from acid-hydrolyzed urine, and those for free amino acids from non-hydrolyzed urine.

	Property or Constituent	No. of Subjects	High-Protein Diet	Low-Protein Diet	Reference		Property or Constituent	No. of Subjects	High-Protein Diet	Low-Protein Diet	Reference
	(A)	(B)	(C)	(D)	(E)		(A)	(B)	(C)	(D)	(E)
1	Urine volume, ml/kg body wt/da	400♂	24.5	20.6	1		Amino acids (concluded)				3
2	Water content, ml/kg body wt/da	400♂	19.8	19.1	1		Lysine				
	Amino acids				3	15	Total	9♂	0.73	0.60	
	Arginine					16	Free	9♂	0.39	0.30	
3	Total	9♂	0.30	0.29		17	Methionine, total	9♂	0.17	0.16	
4	Free	9♂	0.29	0.23			Phenylalanine				
5	Aspartic acid, total	9♂	1.93	1.63		18	Total	9♂	0.29	0.23	
6	Cystine, free	9♂	3.38	0.94		19	Free	9♂	0.16	0.16	
	Glutamic acid					20	Threonine, total	9♂	0.64	0.54	
7	Total	9♂	4.57	4.25		21	Tryptophan, free	9♂	0.29	0.20	
8	Free	9♂	0.27	0.34		22	Tyrosine, free	9♂	0.31	0.25	
	Glycine[1]					23	Valine, total	9♂	0.39	0.33	
9	Total	9♂	9.85	9.25			Nitrogen				
10	Free	9♂	14.0	10.70		24	Total N	400♂	218	114	1
	Histidine					25	Ammonia N	400♂	9.7	6.2	1
11	Total	9♂	2.32	1.77		26	Creatine N	6♀[2]	1.9	0.45	5
12	Free	9♂	2.1	1.3		27	Creatinine N	400♂	9.0	7.7	1
13	Isoleucine, total	9♂	0.20	0.19		28		6♀[2]	8.0	7.8	5
14	Leucine, total	9♂	0.30	0.27		29	Purine N[3]		0.7		2
						30	Urea N	400♂	189	88	1
						31	Uric acid N		3.4[4]		4

/1/ Probably occurs in conjugation as hippuric acid. /2/ Body weight = 46.5-72.2 kg. /3/ Values influenced by intake of dietary purines which may or may not be associated with protein intake. /4/ Subjects on high purine diet.

Contributor: Pearson, William N.

References: [1] Beard, H. H. 1935. Human Biol. 7:419. [2] Burian, R., and H. Schur. 1900. Arch. ges. Physiol. 80:241. [3] Dunn, M. S., et al. 1949. Am. Rev. Tuberc. 60:439. [4] Taylor, C. M., and M. S. Rose. In P. B. Hawk, B. L. Oser, and W. H. Summerson. 1947. Practical physiological chemistry. Ed. 12. Blakiston, Philadelphia. p. 964. [5] Wang, C. C., J. E. Hawks, B. Huddlestun, A. A. Wood, and E. A. Smith. 1930. J. Nutrit. 3:79.

Part III: PROTEIN-FREE DIET

Diet contained little or no nitrogen. With the exception of tryptophan, values for amino acids were obtained from acid-hydrolyzed urine.

	Constituent	Subjects No. and Sex	Weight[1] kg	Value mg/kg body wt/da	Reference		Constituent	Subjects No. and Sex	Weight[1] kg	Value mg/kg body wt/da	Reference
	(A)	(B)	(C)	(D)	(E)		(A)	(B)	(C)	(D)	(E)
	Amino acids				2		Amino acids (concluded)				2
1	Arginine	♀	56	0.27		12	Tyrosine	♀	56	0.75	
2	Aspartic acid	♀	56	1.46		13	Valine	♀	56	0.19	
3	Glutamic acid	♀	56	3.00			Nitrogen				
4	Histidine	♀	56	1.73		14	Total N	1♂	64.75[3]	25	3
5	Isoleucine	♀	56	0.16		15	Ammonia N	1♂	64.75[3]	3.5	3
6	Leucine	♀	56	0.24		16	Creatinine N	1♂	64.75[3]	8.6	3
7	Lysine	♀	56	0.52		17		25♀		6.3	1
8	Methionine	♀	56	0.07		18	Purine N	1♂	65[3]	0.23[4]	5
9	Phenylalanine	♀	56	0.39		19	Urea N	1♂	64.75[3]	5.4	3
10	Threonine	♀	56	0.58		20	Uric acid N		70	1.0[4]	4
11	Tryptophan[2]	♀	56	0.11							

/1/ Assumed weight, unless otherwise specified. /2/ Obtained from alkali-hydrolyzed urine; basic hydrolysis causes racemization of unknown extent, so that value is probably too low. /3/ Actual weight. /4/ Endogenous value; subjects on purine-free diet.

Contributor: Pearson, William N.

References: [1] Bricker, M. L., and J. M. Smith. 1951. J. Nutrit. 44:553. [2] Hier, S. W. 1948. Tr. N. York Acad. Sc., Ser. 2, 10:280. [3] Smith, M. 1926. J. Biol. Chem. 68:15. [4] Taylor, C. M., and M. S. Rose. In P. B. Hawk, B. L. Oser, and W. H. Summerson. 1947. Practical physiological chemistry. Ed. 12. Blakiston, Philadelphia. p. 964. [5] Umeda, N. 1915. Biochem. J., Lond. 9:421.

126. NON-PROTEIN NITROGEN IN URINE: VERTEBRATES AND INVERTEBRATES

Part I. MAMMALS

Values are percent of non-protein nitrogen in urine, unless otherwise specified. Other non-protein N (column I): U = undetermined N; A = allantoin N; P = purine N. Values in parentheses are ranges, estimate "c" (cf. Introduction).

	Animal	No. of Subjects	No. of Observations	Amino N	Ammonia N	Creatinine N	Urea N	Uric Acid N	Other Non-protein N	Reference
	(A)	(B)	(C)	(D)	(E)	(F)	(G)	(H)	(I)	(J)
1	Man	6	30		4.3 (2.7-5.7)	3.6 (3.1-4.9)	87.5 (84.5-90.1)	0.8 (0.5-1.5)	U 3.8 (2.0-6.4)	1
2	Dog			0.90	6.0	0.5[1]	63.4	0.07	U 20.3	2
	Camel									6
3	Camelus bactrianus, pregnant	2	6	(1.2-2.1)	(1.7-3.8)	(11.1-13.1)[1]	(65.2-69.0)	(0.8-1.8)	U (14.0-16.1)	
4	C. dromedarius	1	2	(0.2-1.7)	(12.3-19.1)	(17.6-18.1)[1]	(32.5-55.5)	0.3	U (12.7-19.8)	
	Cat									3
5	Purine-rich diet	1	3		(4.0-4.9)	(0.6-0.7)	(68.0-89.5)	0.1		
6	Purine-free diet	1	3		(3.9-7.9)	(2.5-3.9)	(79.5-85.5)	0.01		
7	Protein-rich diet	1	25		(3.5-5.5)	(0.49-1.07)	(77.6-89.4)	(0.10-0.35)		
8	Low-protein diet	1	25		(5.7-11.1)	(1.40-2.46)	(57.9-80.1)	(0-0.09)		

/1/ Creatinine N plus creatine N.

Part I: MAMMALS (Concluded)

	Animal	No. of Subjects	No. of Observations	Amino N	Ammonia N	Creatinine N	Urea N	Uric Acid N	Other Non-protein N	Reference
	(A)	(B)	(C)	(D)	(E)	(F)	(G)	(H)	(I)	(J)
9	Dog	2	26		(3.5-28.0)	(0.9-10.0)[1]	(71.0-96.5)		U (1.4-21.9)	4
10	Hyena			0.95	4.0	0.88[2]	89.3	0.06	A 1.75 P 0.23 U 2.8	2
11	Leopard			0.86	3.2	1.32[2]	87.1	0.06	A 0.52 P 0.25 U 6.7	2
	Llama									6
12	Auchenia huanacos	1	2	(1.3-1.4)	(1.8-2.2)	(9.1-11.7)[1]	(60.5-67.7)	(0.7-0.8)	U (19.0-23.9)	
13	A. vicunna		1		4.5	7.3[1]	59.6	0.3	U 28.3	
	Seal (Phoca vitulina)									7
14	Fasting	1	5		(9.9-16.8)[3]	(12.9-30.8)[1,3]	(52.4-72.8)[3]			
15	Non-fasting	1	20		(2.0-7.5)[3]	(7.1-31.1)[1,3]	(61.4-89.8)[3]			
16	Tiger			0.95	3.3	1.72[2]	89.1	0.06	P 0.18 U 3.4	2
17	Weasel			0.89	2.6	1.67[2]	91.0	0.16	A 0.48 P 0.58 U 2.6	2
	Whale[4]									5
18	Balaenoptera borealis				5.7 (3.2-9.4)	0.8 (0.5-1.2)[2]	87.6 (83.2-93.4)	1.8 (0.6-4.25)	U 3.9 (2.3-6.1)	
19	B. physalus				(1.9-3.6)	(0.3-3.8)[2]	(85.5-93.0)	(1.6-4.4)	U (2.7-3.1)	

/1/ Creatinine N plus creatine N.   /2/ Creatinine N and/or creatine N.   /3/ Percent of nitrogen listed; total nitrogen not determined.   /4/ Urine obtained postmortem.

Contributors: Scheer, Bradley T., and Neiland, Kenneth A.

References: [1] Folin, O. 1905. Am. J. Physiol. 13:45. [2] Fuse, N. 1925. Jap. J. M. Sc., Ser. 2, 1:103. [3] Hammett, F. S. 1915. J. Biol. Chem. 22:551. [4] Osterberg, E., and C. G. L. Wolf. 1907. Biochem. Zschr. 5:304. [5] Schmidt-Nielsen, S., and J. Holmsen. 1921. Arch. internat. physiol., Liége 18:128. [6] Smith, H. W. 1928. J. Biol. Chem. 78:409. [7] Smith, H. W. 1936. J. Cellul. Physiol. 7:465.

Part II: BIRDS, REPTILES, AMPHIBIANS

Values are percent of non-protein nitrogen in urine. Other non-protein nitrogen (column J): C = creatine N; c = creatinine N; Cc = creatine N plus creatinine N; P = purine N; H = hippuric acid N; GX = guanidine N plus xanthine N. Values in parentheses are ranges, estimate "c" (cf. Introduction).

	Animal	No. of Subjects	No. of Observations	Allantoin N	Amino N	Ammonia N	Urea N	Uric Acid N	Undetermined Non-protein N	Other Non-protein N	Reference
	(A)	(B)	(C)	(D)	(E)	(F)	(G)	(H)	(I)	(J)	(K)
						Birds					
1	Chicken (Gallus domesticus)	5	10-15			17.3 (14.9-19.5)	10.4 (9.2-11.5)	62.9 (59.4-69.5)	1.4 (0.3-2.9)	Cc 8.0 (7.4-9.1)	2
2						1.5	0.9	70.0	27.6		10
3	Duck					3.2	4.2	71.9	20.7		10
4	Goose					13.5		80.0	6.5		10
5	Swan					15.8	2.6	68.7	13.9		10

	Animal	No. of Subjects	No. of Observations	Allantoin N	Amino N	Ammonia N	Urea N	Uric Acid N	Undetermined Nonprotein N	Other Nonprotein N	Reference
	(A)	(B)	(C)	(D)	(E)	(F)	(G)	(H)	(I)	(J)	(K)
	Reptiles										
6	Alligator, American	3	18			(66-81)	(0-17.0)	(7.0-19.8)	(0.2-23.0)		3
	Lizard										
7	Chalcides ocellatus		1	2.7	2.5	0	0	92.5		C 1.17 c 0.11 P 0.33	7
8	Phrynosoma cornutum					0.4	0	99.5			13
9	Scincus officinalis			1.6	0.7	3.0		93.6		C 0.30 c 0.07 P 0.6	7
10	Python	1[1]				8.7		89.0			1
	Snake										
11	Eryx thebaicus	9[2]	1		1.1	5.7	0	62.8	29.1	C 0.20 c 0.03 H 0.95 P 0.3	6
12	Zamenis diadema	15[2]	1		4.5	4.3	2.0	67.0	17.2	C 0.06 c 0.03 H 2.7 P 2.0	5
	Tortoise										
13	Chelone mydas	3[3]		13.6	7.5	43.0	0	2.2	12.2	C 6.0 c 1.5 H 13.8	4
14		4[3,4]		(4.4-25.0)	(5.4-18.4)	(29-51)	(0-12)	(1.4-6.3)	(2.4-22)	Cc (5.2-11.5)[5] H (8.0-23.0)	
15	Chrysemys pinta	4[3]			3.8	11.1 (9.8-21.7)	24.1	13.9 (7.4-27.7)	40.6	Cc 5.5	14
16	Emys orbicularis		3	(0.3-0.9)	19.7 (15.8-21.9)	14.4 (10.6-18.8)	47.1 (26.4-69.0)	2.5 (1.4-4.0)	14.8	GX (0.5-1.2)	9
17	Kinixys erosa		2	0.4	13.7 (12.7-14.7)	6.1 (5.7-6.5)	61.0 (50-72)	4.2 (3.5-5.0)	15.2	GX 0.4	9
18	K. youngii		5	(0.3-1.3)	15.2 (7.7-22.0)	6.0 (2.9-12.5)	44.0 (30.3-72.7)	5.5 (3.4-8.7)	26.4	GX (0.3-3.8)	9
19	Kinosternum subrubrum		1	1.1	10.0	24.0	22.9	0.7	40.3	GX 1.0	9
20	Pelusios derbianus		1	1.0	20.6	18.5	24.4	4.5	27.2		9
21	Testudo denticulata		3	(6.7-8.6)	15.6 (9.4-22.2)	6.0 (3.9-8.7)	29.1 (26.8-31.2)	6.7 (4.9-7.7)	32.1	GX (1.7-5.0)	9
22	T. elegans		2	(1.0-1.2)	13.1 (10.6-15.5)	6.2 (5.9-6.5)	8.5 (7.8-9.1)	56.1 (54.3-57.8)	12.0	GX (0.9-5.1)	9
23	T. graeco		2	(1.4-1.9)	6.6 (4.5 8.6)	4.1	22.3 (15.3-29.3)	51.9 (48.7-55.0)	4.0	GX (8.7-10.1)	9
24	Turtle	2[3]				(14.5-17.7)	(31.1-45.1)	(14.0-19.1)		Cc (3.5-11.3)[5]	8
	Amphibians										
	Frog Rana sp										11
25	At 11°C					20.9	68.2		10.2		
26	At 22°C					12.2	77.6		10.2		
27	R. virescens, hibernating	4				5.1 (1.2-7.4)	87.4 (81.9-90.5)	0.3 (0.2-0.4)	(1.9-13.7)		12

/1/ Only solid portion of urine analyzed. /2/ Pooled samples. /3/ Bladder urine obtained postmortem. /4/ One animal pregnant. /5/ Creatine N, or creatine N plus creatinine N.

Part II: BIRDS, REPTILES, AMPHIBIANS (Concluded)

Contributors: Scheer, Bradley T., and Neiland, Kenneth A.

References: [1] Bacon, R. F. 1909. Philippine J. Sc. 4:165. [2] Davis, R. E. 1927. J. Biol. Chem. 74:509. [3] Hopping, A. 1923. Am. J. Physiol. 66:145. [4] Khalil, F. 1947. J. Biol. Chem. 171:611. [5] Khalil, F. 1948. Ibid. 172:101. [6] Khalil, F. 1948. Ibid. 172:105. [7] Khalil, F. 1951. Ibid. 189:443. [8] Lewis, H. B. 1918. Science 48:376. [9] Moyle, V. 1949. Biochem. J., Lond. 44:581. [10] Needham, J. 1931. Chemical embryology. Macmillan, New York. v. 2, pp. 1055-1145. [11] Przylecki, S. J., J. Opienska, and H. Giedroyc. 1922. Arch. internat. physiol., Liége 20:207. [12] Van Heyde, H. C. 1921. J. Biol. Chem. 46:421. [13] Weese, A. O. 1917. Science 46:517. [14] Wiley, F. H., and H. B. Lewis. 1927. Am. J. Physiol. 81:692.

Part III: FISHES

Values are percent non-protein nitrogen in urine. Type or Method (column C): BU = bladder urine, RC = retention catheter. Values in parentheses are ranges, estimate "c" (cf. Introduction).

	Fish	No. of Speci- mens	Type or Method	Amino N	Ammonia N	Creatine N	Creati- nine N	Urea N	Uric Acid N	Undeter- mined Non- protein N	Ref- er- ence
	(A)	(B)	(C)	(D)	(E)	(F)	(G)	(H)	(I)	(J)	(K)
1	Angler fish Lophius sp	1[1]	BU	5.0	2.0			28.0		65.0	1
2	L. piscatorius	4[1]	BU	(5.3-14.3)	(0.3-1.3)	(23.0-61.7)	(1.5-4.1)	(0.1-2.7)	(0.2-0.4)	(28.2-63.4)	3
3	Non-fasting	7[1]	BU[2]	(14.9-34.0)	(2.0-5.4)	(21.0-46.5)		(1.5-3.6)	(0.7-1.8)	(20.0-51.0)	4
4	Fasting	1	BU[2]	(2.9-10.0)	(0.8-2.3)	(35.4-55.5)		(0.8-2.9)	(0.8-3.5)	(33.0-51.9)	4
5	Bowfin (Amia calva), fasting	1	RC	0.9	32.2	17.4		15.6	22.6		4
6	Carp (Cyprinus carpio), fast- ing	4	RC		(3.3-21.6)	(18.2-65.1)	(0-2.9)	3.7	0.6	(32.0-78.5)	4
7	Catfish, blue (Ictalurus furcatus)	1	RC	20.0	27.4	5.1	2.8	24.6		16.9	4
8	Cod (Gadus callarias), fasting	2	BU[2]	(14.8-21.4)		(51.1-52.6)	(2.2-3.1)	(6.5-11.2)	(1.7-2.4)	(15.2-19.0)	4
9	Eel (Anguilla chrysypa), fasting	2	RC		(11.7-23.4)	(20.9-28.0)	(0.9-2.6)	(10.7-23.4)	(1.3-5.4)	(17.1-55.9)	4
10	Flounder (Pseu- dopleuro- nectes ameri- canus)	2	BU[3]	(8.2-9.7)	(1.8-2.6)	(15.0-26.1)		(13.5-21.2)	(1.2-1.3)	(48.3-51.1)	2
11	Gar pike (Lepi- sosteus osseus), fast- ing	1	RC	4.1	33.9	3.3	0.8	5.0		53.0	4
12	Goldfish (Caras- sius auratus), fasting	2	RC		(6.2-15.7)	(11.9-19.2)	0	Trace	1.1	(71.3-74.5)	4
13	Grouper (Epi- nephelus morio)	1	RC	6.4		14.7	2.4	30.8		45.7	4

/1/ Number of subjects. /2/ Obtained postmortem. /3/ Obtained with urinary papilla ligated at least 24 hours.

Part III: FISHES (Concluded)

Fish	No. of Speci- mens	Type or Method	Amino N	Ammonia N	Creatine N	Creati- nine N	Urea N	Uric Acid N	Undeter- mined Non- protein N	Ref- er- ence
(A)	(B)	(C)	(D)	(E)	(F)	(G)	(H)	(I)	(J)	(K)
14 Lungfish (Protopterus aethiopicus)				61.0	10.2		27.6	1.2		5
15 Numbfish (Torpedo sp)			1.7	1.7			85.3		11.3	1
16 Sculpin (Myoxo- cephalus octodecim- spinosus)	2	BU[3]	(4.0-4.4)	(1.3-2.0)	(22.4-25.0)		(14.1-15.3)	0.7	(54.2-55.9)	2
17 Sheepshead (Archosargus probatoceph- alus)	2	RC	(15.0-19.9)	(8.4-9.6)	(6.5-9.2)	(5.9-9.0)	(22.9-23.0)	(6.4-8.4)	(25.1-26.4)	4
18 Swellfish, northern (Spheroides maculatus)	3	BU[2]	20.6	(5.1-6.2)	(12.4-53.7)	(0-5.0)	(1.8-19.1)	(0.8-1.2)	(9.1-84.6)	4

/2/ Obtained postmortem. /3/ Obtained with urinary papilla ligated at least 24 hours.

Contributors: Scheer, Bradley T., and Neiland, Kenneth A.

References: [1] Delaunay, H. 1926. C. rend. Soc. biol. 101:371. [2] Grafflin, A. L., and R. G. Gould. 1936. Biol. Bull. 70:16. [3] Grollman, A. 1929. J. Biol. Chem. 81:267. [4] Smith, H. W. 1929. Ibid. 81:727. [5] Smith, H. W. 1930. Ibid. 88:97.

Part IV: INVERTEBRATES

Values are percent of non protein nitrogen in urine, unless otherwise specified. Values in parentheses are ranges, estimate "c" (cf. Introduction).

Animal	Amino N	Ammonia N	Purine N	Urea N	Uric Acid N	Undetermined Non-protein N	Refer- ence
(A)	(B)	(C)	(D)	(E)	(F)	(G)	(H)
Insects							
1 Rhodnius prolixus[1]					(90-92)	(8-10)	4
Crustaceans							
2 Cancer pagurus	20.0	42.9	10.0	12.8	2.8	11.5	2,3
3 Maja squinado	(16.4-27.9)	(4.0-12.0)	(0-7.4)	(2.1-8.5)	(0-4.7)	(51.4-71.1)	2,3
Mollusks							
4 Octopus vulgaris	12.5	(12.5-33.3)	25.0	5.2	1.4	29.2	2,3
5 Sepia officinalis	(7.2-8.4)	(64.4-69.6)	(3.2-4.9)	(1.4-2.1)	(2.1-2.2)	(18.6-20.2)	2,3
Annelids							
6 Pheretima posthuma		45.0[2]		55.0[2]			1

/1/ Pooled samples. /2/ Percent of combined ammonia N plus urea N.

126. NON-PROTEIN NITROGEN IN URINE: VERTEBRATES AND INVERTEBRATES (Concluded)

Part IV: INVERTEBRATES (Concluded)

Contributors: Scheer, Bradley T., and Neiland, Kenneth A.

References: [1] Bahl, K. N. 1945. Q. J. Micr. Sc., Lond. 85:343. [2] Delaunay, H. 1927. Bull. Sta. biol. Arcachon 24:95. [3] Delaunay, H. 1931. Biol. Rev. Cambridge Philos. Soc. 6:265. [4] Wigglesworth, V. B. 1931. J. Exp. Biol., Lond. 8:411.

127. WATER TURNOVER: VERTEBRATES AND INVERTEBRATES

Water turnover is modified by particular factors of energy exchange and of excretion (work, solute excretion, fecal residues, temperature, air humidity). Values are for animals in resting state.

Part I: TERRESTRIAL VERTEBRATES

Turnover (column D) estimated by measuring free water consumed, by ascertaining water content of food voluntarily ingested, and by computing water of oxidation of food (0.13 g/kg-cal) under circumstances where body weight remained constant.

	Animal	No. of Observations	Body Weight g	Water Turnover ml/kg/da	Water Consumption[1] ml/kg/da	Urine Output ml/kg/da	Reference
	(A)	(B)	(C)	(D)	(E)	(F)	(G)
1	Man	166	65,000	40	35	19	15
2	Camel		300,000	10[2]		2.5[3]	21
3	Cat	42	2900	84	72	41	11
4		50	4490	72			17
	Cattle						
5	Steer	28	584,000	48	40	9	18
6	Brahman, dry	44	409,000	61	55		16
7	Holstein, dry	21	745,000	67	60		4
8	Holstein, milking	44	529,000	159	148		16
9	Jersey, milking	44	403,000	128	118		16
10	Dog	120	18,600	60	46	19	1
11		240	10,700	56			17
12	Elephant	9	3,670,000	46	42	13	7
13	Guinea pig (Cavia sp)	37	450	170	145		3
14	Hamster (Mesocricetus sp)	54	70	216	184		3
15	Horse	34	420,000	62	55	12	22
16	Monkey (Macacus rhesus)	30	4900	82	70	53	14
	Mouse						
17	Mus musculus	34	21	204	101	43	6
18	Peromyscus leucopus	58	20	154	90		9
19	P. maniculatus	79	15	192	124		9, 19
20	Rabbit	105	3670	130	113	74	12
21		59	2400		137		8
	Rat						
22	Dipodomys spectabilis	32	106	82	55[4]		5
23	Rattus norvegicus	210	225	163	139	58	2
24					154	43	10
25	Sigmodon sp		130		177		8
26	Vole (Microtus sp)	71	29	273	211		9
27	Fowl (Gallus sp)	43	1550	161	130		13

/1/ In drink and food. /2/ In winter; increases to 40-50 ml/kg/da in summer as result of water used for heat regulation [21]. /3/ When laboratory fed and watered; 1.7 ml/kg/da when deprived of water; more than 23 ml/kg/da when grazing in winter [21]. /4/ In food only [20].

Contributor: Adolph, E. F.

Part I: TERRESTRIAL VERTEBRATES (Concluded)

References: [1] Adolph, E. F. 1938. Am. J. Physiol. 123:486. [2] Adolph, E. F. 1943. Physiological regulations. Jaques Cattell Press, Lancaster, Pennsylvania. tab. 21. [3] Adolph, E. F. Unpublished. [4] Atkeson, F. W., and T. R. Warren. 1934. J. Dairy Sc. 17:265. [5] Bailey, V. 1923. Sc. Month. 17:66. [6] Barbour, H. G., and J. Trace. 1937. Am. J. Physiol. 118:77. [7] Benedict, F. G. 1936. Carnegie Institution, Washington, D. C. Pub. 474. [8] Bruce, H. M. 1950. J. Anim. Techn. 1:2. [9] Dice, L. R. 1922. Ecology 3:29. [10] Eversole, W. J. Unpublished. [11] Gasnier, A., and A. Mayer. 1937. Ann. physiol., Par. 13:175. [12] Gompel, M., F. Hamon, and A. Mayer. 1936. Ibid. 12:471. [13] Hart, W. M., and H. E. Essex. 1942. Am. J. Physiol. 136:657. [14] Krohn, P. L., and S. Zuckerman. 1937. J. Physiol., Lond. 88:369. [15] Magee, H. E. 1937. J. Hyg., Lond. 37:30. [16] Ragsdale, A. C., H. J. Thompson, D. M. Worstell, and S. Brody. 1950. Res. Bull. Univ. Missouri Agr. Exp. Sta. 460. [17] Richter, C. P. 1938. Am. J. Physiol. 122:668. [18] Ritzman, E. G., and F. G. Benedict. 1938. Carnegie Institution, Washington, D. C. Pub. 494. [19] Ross, L. G. 1930. Biol. Bull. 59:326. [20] Schmidt-Nielsen, B., K. Schmidt-Nielsen, A. Brokaw, and H. Schneiderman. 1948. J. Cellul. Physiol. 32:331. [21] Schmidt-Nielsen, K. Unpublished. [22] Zuntz, N., and O. Hagemann. 1898. Untersuchungen über den Stoffwechsel des Pferdes bei Ruhe und Arbeit. P. Parey, Berlin.

Part II: AQUATIC ANIMALS

Turnover (column F) estimated by measuring excretory volumes in steady states of water exchange, usually when no food was available to animal.

	Animal	No. of Obser-vations	Environment	Tempera-ture °C	Body Volume ml	Water Turnover % body volume/da	Refer-ence
	(A)	(B)	(C)	(D)	(E)	(F)	(G)
	Amphibians						
	Frog						
1	Rana esculenta	25	Fresh water		65	22	16
2	R. pipiens	19	Fresh water	20	32	40	2
3	R. temporaria	5	Fresh water		9	100	16
4	Newt (Triton marmoratus)	4	Fresh water		5	43	16
5	Salamander	4	Fresh water		20	53	16
6	Toad (Bufo vulgaris)	5	Fresh water		22	117	16
	Fishes						
7	Eel (Anguilla sp)	5	Sea water		250	6.5	20
8	Sculpin (Myoxocephalus sp)	5	Sea water		180	11.5	20
	Arthropods						
	Insect						
9	Chironomus sp, larva	10	Fresh water		0.1	22	5
10	Corethra sp, larva	3	Fresh water	20	6.2	19	18
	Crustacean						
11	Cambarus sp	10	Fresh water		13	5.3	10
12	Cancer sp	2	Sea water		300	6.5	17
13	Carcinus sp	6	Sea water		40	10.0	15
14	Eriocheir sp		Fresh water	13	60	3.6	19
15	Maja sp	3	Sea water		2200	2.7	3
16	Potamobius sp	6	Fresh water		46	4.1	6
	Annelids						
17	Earthworm (Lumbricus sp)	68	Fresh water	19	4	60	21

Part II: AQUATIC ANIMALS (Concluded)

	Animal	No. of Observations	Environment	Temperature °C	Body Volume ml	Water Turnover % body volume/da	Reference
	(A)	(B)	(C)	(D)	(E)	(F)	(G)
	Protozoans						
18	Amoeba mira	3	Sea water		0.6×10^{-12}	4300	11
19	A. proteus	8	Fresh water	23	300×10^{-8}	360	1
20	Cothurnia sp	8	Sea water	15	1.2×10^{-8}	700	7,8
21	Cyclidium sp		Fresh water		0.2×10^{-8}	22,000	14
22	Euplotes sp		Fresh water	25	30×10^{-8}	10,000	12
23	Lembus sp		Fresh water	26	0.2×10^{-8}	60,000	12
24	Leucophrys sp		Fresh water	21	47×10^{-8}	3300	13
25	Paramecium sp		Fresh water	22	19×10^{-8}	6200	4
26	Rhabdostyla sp	1	Fresh water	15	0.8×10^{-8}	11,000	9
27	Spirostomum sp		Fresh water		220×10^{-8}	550	14
28	Zoothamnium sp	9	Fresh water	15	1.4×10^{-8}	5500	9
29	Z. marinum	1	Sea water	15	12×10^{-8}	750	7

Contributor: Adolph, E. F.

References: [1] Adolph, E. F. 1926. J. Exp. Zool. 44:355. [2] Adolph, E. F. 1939. Ann. physiol., Par. 15:353. [3] Bialaszewicz, K. 1932. Arch. internat. physiol., Liége 35:98. [4] Hance, R. T. 1917. J. Exp. Zool. 23:287. [5] Harnisch, O. 1934. Zschr. vergl. Physiol. 21:281. [6] Herrmann, F. 1931. Ibid. 14:479. [7] Kitching, J. A. 1934. J. Exp. Biol., Lond. 11:364. [8] Kitching, J. A. 1936. Ibid. 13:11. [9] Kitching, J. A. 1938. Ibid. 15:143. [10] Lienemann, L. J. 1938. J. Cellul. Physiol. 11:149. [11] Mast, S. O., and D. L. Hopkins. 1941. Ibid. 17:31. [12] Maupas, E. 1883. Arch. zool. exp., Par., Ser. 2, 1:427. [13] Maupas, E. 1888. Ibid. 6:165. [14] Metzner, P. 1927. Tabulae biol., Berl. 4:490. [15] Nagel, H. 1934. Zschr. vergl. Physiol. 21:468. [16] Rey, P. 1937. Ann. physiol., Par. 13:1081. [17] Robertson, J. D. 1939. J. Exp. Biol., Lond. 16:387. [18] Schaller, F. 1949. Zschr. vergl. Physiol. 31:684. [19] Scholles, W. 1933. Ibid. 19:522. [20] Smith, H. W. 1930. Am. J. Physiol. 93:480. [21] Wolf, A. V. 1940. J. Cellul. Physiol. 15:355.

128. WATER EXCRETION: AQUATIC ANIMALS

Part I: MAMMALS, REPTILES, AMPHIBIANS

Values in parentheses are ranges, estimate "c" (cf. Introduction).

	Animal	Excretion	Remarks	Reference
	(A)	(B)	(C)	(D)
	Mammals			
1	Dolphin (Tursiops truncatus)	<50 ml/kg/da	Determined by catheterization; 2 females, 1½ years old, 1 observation each	4
2	Seal (Phoca vitulina)	800 ml/da	Determined by cannulation; 20 young animals, anesthetized	6,10
3		(0.06-0.1) ml/min	1 female, 18 kg, fasting	5
4		1.0 ml/min	1 female, 18 kg, 4-7 hours after meal of herring	
	Reptiles			
5	Alligator (Alligator mississipiensis)	(10.2-28.8) ml/kg/da	Determined by catheterization; body weight = 12.5 kg; hydrated	2

Part I: MAMMALS, REPTILES, AMPHIBIANS (Concluded)

Animal	Excretion	Remarks	Reference
(A)	(B)	(C)	(D)
Amphibians			
Frog			
6 Rana catesbeiana	(36-49) ml/kg/da		7
7	54.8 ml/kg/da	4 animals, fasting	9
8 R. pipiens	<17 ml/kg/hr	Determined from weight change; 27 observations on adult animals; temperature = 18-23°C; water consumption = 13 ml/kg/hr, through skin	1, 8
9 Toad (Bufo regularis)	3 ml/hr	Temperature = 26°C	3

Contributors: (a) Giere, Frederic A., (b) Fregly, Melvin J.

References: [1] Adolph, E. F. 1927. J. Exp. Zool. 47:31. [2] Burgess, W. W., A. M. Harvey, and M. K. Marshall. 1933. J. Pharm. Exp. Ther. 49:237. [3] Ewer, R. F. 1951. J. Exp. Biol., Lond. 28:374. [4] Fetcher, E. S., and G. W. Fetcher. 1942. J. Cellul. Physiol. 19:123. [5] Hiatt, E. P., and R. B. Hiatt. 1942. Ibid. 19:221. [6] Irving, L., K. C. Fisher, and F. C. McIntosh. 1935. Ibid. 6:387. [7] Marshall, E. K. 1932. Ibid. 2:349. [8] Rubenstein, B. B. 1935. Ibid. 6:85. [9] Smith, H. W. 1929. J. Biol. Chem. 81:727. [10] Smith, H. W. 1935. J. Cellul. Physiol. 7:465.

Part II: FISHES

Values in parentheses are ranges, estimate "c" (cf. Introduction).

Animal	Excretion ml/kg/da	Remarks	Reference
(A)	(B)	(C)	(D)
Fresh-water Teleosts			
1 Bowfin (Amia calva)	14.4	Determined by catheterization, 1 animal, fasting	21
2 Carp (Cyprinus carpio)	51	Determined by catheterization; 6 animals, fasting	21
3	(60-150)		22
Catfish			
4 Ameiurus sp	300(150-330)		14
5 A. nebulosus	(51-79)	Determined by catheterization; 5 animals, fasting	9
Eel			
6 Anguilla chrysypa	(15-35)	Determined by catheterization; 2 animals, fasting	21
7 A. rostrata	(0.4-5.0)	Water consumption = 50-200 ml/kg/da	22
8 A. vulgaris	(0.4-5.0)	Starved	22
9 Flounder (Platichthys flesus)	24	In 4% saline	10
10 Gar pike (Lepisosteus osseus)	19.2	Determined by catheterization; 1 animal, fasting	21
11 Goldfish (Carassius auratus)	(60-150)		22
12	(40-110)		12
13	52	Determined by catheterization; 4 animals, fasting	21
14 Sucker (Catostomus commersonii)	(7-26)	Determined by catheterization; 8 animals, fasting	9
15 Trout (Salmo irideus)	(60-106)		12

Part II: FISHES (Continued)

Animal	Excretion ml/kg/da	Remarks	Reference
(A)	(B)	(C)	(D)
Fresh-water Elasmobranchs			
16 Sawfish (Pristis microdon)	250(150-460)	Body weight = 1.05-8.62 kg	23,24
Marine Teleosts			
Eel			
17 Conger sp	(3-5)		3
18 Muraena sp	5(1.1-15)	3 observations; body weight = 2-3 kg	6
19 Goosefish (Lophius piscatorius)	(20-30)	Body weight = 2-3 kg	3,22
20	(12.9-54.4)	11 animals	13
21	29.4	1 animal	7
22	18		6
23 Pipefish (Syngnathus sp)	80	10 observations; body weight = 6-8 g	6
24 Scorpion fish (Scorpaena sp)	(10-12)		3
Sculpin			
25 Myoxocephalus octodecimspinosus	<40	Determined by catheterization; 76 observations on 16 animals; water consumption = 50-200 ml/kg/da	13
26	(1.0-28.9)		8,17
27	(2.6-23.5)		15
28	(11-40)	Starved	22
29 M. scorpius	26.2(9.8-42.0)	4 observations on 1 animal	17
30	35.6	Determined by catheterization; 24 animals	7
31 Sea horse (Hippocampus sp)	(80-120)	12 observations; body weight = 2-5 g	6
32 Toadfish (Opsanus tau)	(0.6-9.4)	15 animals	13
33	2.5(0.6-9.4)	In brackish water	8
34 Wrymouth (Cryptacanthodes maculatus)	(1.5-11.0)	8 animals	13
Marine Elasmobranchs			
Dogfish			
35 Mustelus canis	21.8		18,24
36	15.8	Determined by catheterization	11
37	15.4	Determined by catheterization; 8 animals	5
38	11.4	Determined by catheterization; 8 animals; cord severed at level of dorsal fin	5
39 Scyliorhinus caniculus	1.5	Determined by catheterization; 2 females, fasting	16
40 Scyllium catulus	(4-5)		1
41 Squalus acanthias	(9.2-43.7)	Determined by catheterization; males	4
42	26.8(23.0-35.7)	Determined by catheterization; 12 observations on males, fasting	19,20
43	(4.7-12.2)	Determined by cannulation; 75 adult males	13
44 S. suckleyi	1.4		23
45	33.6		25
Cyclostomes			
Lamprey			
46 River (Lampetra fluviatilis)	362		26
47 Sea (Petromyzon marinus)	159		2

Contributors: (a) Giere, Frederic A., (b) Fregly, Melvin J.

References: [1] Baglioni, S. 1907. Beitr. chem. Phys. Path. 9:50. [2] Black, V. S. In M. E. Brown, ed. 1957. The physiology of fishes. Academic Press, New York. ch. 4. [3] Burian, R. 1909. Zschr. biol. Tech. Meth. 1:383. [4] Clarke, R. W., and H. W. Smith. 1932. J. Cellul. Physiol. 1:131. [5] Denis, W. 1912-13. J. Biol. Chem. 13:225. [6] Edwards, J. S., and L. Condorelli. 1928. Zschr. biol. Techn. Meth. 86:383. [7] Foster, R. P. 1953. J. Cellul. Physiol. 42:487. [8] Grafflin, A. L. 1931. Zschr. biol. Techn. Meth. 97:602. [9] Haywood, C., and M. J. Clapp. 1942. Biol. Bull. 83:363. [10] Henschel, J. 1936. Wiss. Meeres-Untersuch., Abt. Kiel 22:89. [11] Kempton, R. T. 1953. Biol. Bull. 104:45. [12] Krogh, A. 1937. Zschr. vergl. Physiol. 24:656. [13] Marshall, E. K. 1930. Am. J. Physiol. 94:1. [14] Marshall, E. K. 1934. Physiol. Rev. 14:133. [15] Marshall, E. K., and A. L. Grafflin. 1932. J. Cellul. Physiol. 1:161. [16] Perks, A. M. 1959. Ph. D. Thesis. St. Andrews University, Scotland. [17] Pitts, R. F. 1934. J. Cellul. Physiol. 4:389. [18] Scott, G. G. 1913. Ann. N. York Acad. Sc. 23:1. [19] Shannon, J. A. 1934. J. Cellul. Physiol. 4:211. [20] Shannon, J. A. 1940. Ibid. 16:285. [21] Smith, H. W. 1929. J. Biol. Chem. 81:727. [22] Smith, H. W. 1930. Am. J. Physiol. 93:480. [23] Smith, H. W. 1931. Ibid. 98:279. [24] Smith, H. W. 1936. Biol. Rev. Cambridge Philos. Soc. 11:49. [25] White, F. D. 1931. Contr. Canad. Biol. Fish. 6:343. [26] Wikgren, B. 1953. Acta zool. fenn. 71:1.

Part III: ARTHROPODS, MOLLUSKS

Values in parentheses are ranges, estimate "c" (cf. Introduction).

Animal (A)	Excretion (B)	Remarks (C)	Reference (D)
Arthropods			
1 Insect Sialis lutaria	<3% body wt/da	Determined from weight change	4
2 Crustacean Palaemonetes varians	(0.46-0.55) % body wt/hr	Determined by cannulation; 12 observations	1
3	0.40% body wt/hr	Determined from weight change; 4 observations	
4 Potamon nilotius	(0.05-0.6) % body wt/da	Determined from weight change	5
Mollusks			
5 Clam Anodonta sp	2.37 ml/da	Determined from filtration rate into pericardium; 10 animals; body weight = 50 g; temperature = 17°C	2
6 A. cygnea	1.9 ml/hr	Temperature = 15°C	3
7	1.9 ml/hr	Inferred from weight loss; 4 animals; temperature = 15°C	3

Contributor: Giere, Frederic A.

References: [1] Parry, G. 1955. J. Exp. Biol., Lond. 32:408. [2] Picken, L. E. R. 1937. Ibid. 14:20. [3] Potts, W. T. W. 1954. Ibid. 31:614. [4] Shaw, J. 1955. Ibid. 32:353. [5] Shaw, J. 1959. Ibid. 36:157.

Part I: MAN

Values in parentheses are ranges, estimate "b" unless otherwise indicated (cf. Introduction).

	Specification	Method	Subjects		Value	Reference
			Age	No.		
	(A)	(B)	(C)	(D)	(E)	(F)
1	Renal blood flow, ml/min/	Calculated from renal plasma flow	16-60 yr	61♂	1209(697-1721)	27,29
2	1.73 sq m body surface	divided by 1 minus hematocrit	<20-45 yr	27♂	1076(660-1492)	7
3	area		20-29 yr	9♂	1077(777-1377)	11
4			30-39 yr	9♂	1181(727-1635)	11
5			40-49 yr	10♂	1008(596-1420)	11
6			50-59 yr	11♂	849(603-1095)	11
7			60-69 yr	10♂	775(497-1053)	11
8			70-79 yr	9♂	589(323-855)	11
9			80-89 yr	12♂	475(193-757)	11
10			16-55 yr	17♀	982(614-1350)	27,29
11			<20-45 yr	23♀	973(503-1443)	7
12				19♀[1]	1359(881-1837)	7
13			<20-40 yr	13♀[2]	919(451-1387)	7
14			Adult	31♀[3]	962(602-1322)	9
15	Renal plasma flow, ml/min/	Determined by diodrast clearance	2-8 da	5	72.7	12
	1.73 sq m body surface	without correction for extraction				
	area	ratio				
16		Determined by p-aminohippurate	4-28 da	7[4]	148.6	1
17		clearance without correction for	10-22 da	4	228.5	25
18		extraction ratio	37-95 da	8[4]	203.2	2
19			1-5.9 mo	8	326.1	25
20			6-11.7 mo	10	480.3	25
21			12-19 mo	11	518.9(319.9-717.9)	25
22			2-12 yr	19	654(413-895)	25
23		Determined by diodrast clearance;	16-60 yr	61♂	697(425-969)	27,29
24		constant infusion technique	20-29 yr	9♂	613.5(464.3-762.7)	11
25			21-25 yr	10♂	600(388-812)	5
26			30-39 yr	9♂	649.3(414.5-884.1)	11
27			40-49 yr	10♂	573.8(350.6-797.0)	11
28			50-59 yr	11♂	500.4(326.4-674.4)	11
29			60-69 yr	10♂	442.1(281.7-602.5)	11
30			70-79 yr	9♂	354.0(187.2-520.8)	11
31			80-89 yr	12♂	288.8(111.6-466.0)	11
32			16-55 yr	17♀	594(390-798)	27,29
33			19-27 yr	10♀	628(428-828)	5
34			<20-45 yr	19♀[1]	800(498-1102)	7
35			<20-40 yr	13♀[2]	571(393-749)	7
36			Adult	34♀[3]	617(397-837)	9
37		Determined by p-aminohippurate	16-49 yr	30♂	654(328-980)	28
38		clearance; constant infusion	21-32 yr	9♂	613(399-827)	8
39		technique	Adult	8♂	628(538-718)	6
40				8♂	603(435-771)	14
41				11♀	592(286-898)	28
42		Determined by p-aminohippurate	<20-45 yr	27♂	557(251-863)	7
43		clearance; subcutaneous injec-		23♀	557(271-843)	7
		tion technique				
44	Glomerular filtration rate,	Determined by inulin or mannitol	2-8 da	14	38.5(16.7-60.3)	12,20,24,25
45	ml/min/1.73 sq m body	clearance	4-28 da	20[4]	45.1(26.1-64.1)	1,2,31
46	surface area		10-22 da	18	50.4(32.2-68.6)	20,25
47			37-95 da	11[4]	58.2(30.2-86.2)	2,31
48			1-5.9 mo	14	76.6(39.4-113.8)	24,25
49			6-11.7 mo	10	103.2(49.4-157.0)	25
50			12-19 mo	11	126.7(62.1-191.3)	25
51			2-12 yr	37	127.0(89.4-164.6)	3,24,25
52		Determined by inulin clearance;	16-49 yr	34♂	124.0(72.4-175.6)	28
53		constant infusion technique	16-60 yr	67♂	131(88-174)	27,29
54			18-45 yr	25♂	140(76-204)	16

/1/ Pregnant, 2-8 lunar months. /2/ Pregnant, 9 and 10 lunar months. /3/ Pregnant, near term. /4/ Premature
infants.

	Specification	Method	Subjects Age	No.	Value	Reference
	(A)	(B)	(C)	(D)	(E)	(F)
55	Glomerular filtration rate,	Determined by inulin clearance;	20-29 yr	9♂	122.8(90.0-155.6)	11
56	ml/min/1.73 sq m body	constant infusion technique	21-25 yr	10♂	125(116.2-133.8)	5
57	surface area (concluded)		28-60 yr	24♂	136(97.4-174.6)	27,29
58			30-39 yr	9♂	115.0(93.4-136.6)	11
59			40-49 yr	10♂	121.2(74.6-167.8)	11
60			50-59 yr	11♂	99.3(70.1-128.5)	11
61			60-69 yr	10♂	96(45-147)	11
62			70-79 yr	9♂	89.0(49.4-128.6)	11
63			80-89 yr	12♂	65.3(24.5-106.1)	11
64			Adult	8♂	130(99.2-160.8)	6
65				26♂	126(91.8-160.2)	4
66			16-55 yr	10♀	115(89.4-140.6)	27,29
67				21♀	117(85.8-148.2)	27,29
68			19-27 yr	10♀	118(90.2-145.8)	5
69			<20-40 yr	10♀[2]	156(95-217)	7
70			Adult	8♀	119(111-127)	17
71				16♀	109(82-136)	28
72				19♀[5]	183(139-227)	17
73				12♀[6]	129(43-215)	17
74				57♀[3]	126(68.6-183.4)	9
75				10♀[3]	131(67-195)	10
76				8♀[7,8]	126(94-158)	10
77		Determined by inulin clearance;	<20-45 yr	27♂	118(79-157)	7
78		single intravenous injection	20-50 yr	36♂	124.0(97.4-150.6)	15
79		technique	<20-45 yr	23♀	122(73.4-170.6)	7
80				17♀[1]	170(123.6-216.4)	7
81			20-50 yr	20♀	119(93.4-144.6)	15
82	Filtration fraction, %	Calculated from glomerular filtra-	2-8 da	5	0.49	12
83		tion rate divided by renal plasma	4-28 da	7[4]	0.34	1
84		flow	10-22 da	3	0.24	25
85			37-95 da	8[4]	0.33	2
86			1-5.9 mo	6	0.24	25
87			6-11.7 mo	10	0.22(0.08-0.36)	25
88			12-19 mo	11	0.25(0.15-0.35)	25
89			2-12 yr	19	0.20(0.12-0.28)	25
90			16-49 yr	31♂	0.192(0.122-0.262)	28
91			16-60 yr	61♂	0.19(0.142-0.238)	27,29
92			<20-45 yr	27♂	0.216(0.152-0.28)	7
93			20-29 yr	9♂	0.201(0.175-0.227)	11
94			21-25 yr	10♂	0.214(0.144-0.284)	5
95			30-39 yr	9♂	0.184(0.112-0.256)	11
96			40-49 yr	10♂	0.213(0.149-0.277)	11
97			50-59 yr	11♂	0.205(0.145-0.265)	11
98			60-69 yr	10♂	0.215(0.147-0.283)	11
99			70-79 yr	9♂	0.262(0.104-0.420)	11
100			80-89 yr	12♂	0.229(0.153-0.305)	11
101			16-55 yr	17♀	0.202(0.140-0.264)	27,29
102			19-27 yr	10♀	0.189(0.155-0.223)	5
103			<20-45 yr	23♀	0.227(0.131-0.323)	7
104				17♀[1]	0.221(0.117-0.325)	7
105			<20-40 yr	10♀[2]	0.289(0.211-0.367)	7
106			Adult	26♀[3]	19.5	9
107				11	0.194(0.116-0.272)	28
108	Diodrast Tm (tubular	Calculated as rate of diodrast	16-60 yr	40♂	51.8(34.4-69.2)	27,29
109	excretory mass), mg I/	excretion in urine minus rate of	20-29 yr	9♂	54.6(35.6-73.6)	11
110	min/1.73 sq m body	diodrast filtration	21-25 yr	10♂	50.6(37.6-63.6)	5
111	surface area		30-39 yr	9♂	51.0(33.8-68.2)	11
112			40-49 yr	10♂	49.9(30.3-69.5)	11

/1/ Pregnant, 2-8 lunar months. /2/ Pregnant, 9 and 10 lunar months. /3/ Pregnant, near term. /4/ Premature infants. /5/ Pregnant less than 38 weeks. /6/ Pregnant more than 37 weeks. /7/ From group of 10 subjects in preceding line of data. /8/ Second week postpartum.

	Specification	Method	Subjects Age	No.	Value	Reference
	(A)	(B)	(C)	(D)	(E)	(F)
113	Diodrast Tm (tubular excretory mass), mg I/ min/1.73 sq m body surface area (concluded)	Calculated as rate of diodrast excretion in urine minus rate of diodrast filtration	50-59 yr	11♂	45.3(32.7-57.9)	11
114			60-69 yr	10♂	44.5(26.3-62.7)	11
115			70-79 yr	9♂	39.0(24.4-53.6)	11
116			80-89 yr	12♂	30.8(11.2-50.4)	11
117			Adult	82♂	50	28
118			16-55 yr	14♀	42.6(23.6-61.6)	27,29
119			19-27 yr	10♀	44.2(34.6-53.8)	5
120	p-Aminohippurate Tm (tubular excretory mass), mg/ min/1.73 sq m body surface area	Calculated as rate of p-amino-hippurate excretion in urine minus rate of p-aminohippurate filtration	4-28 da	7⁴	12.9	1
121			10-22 da	6	21.4	25
122			37-95 da	8	17.2	2
123			1-5.9 mo	9	51.4	25
124			6-11.7 mo	8	50.5	25
125			12-19 mo	9	61.2(18.8-103.6)	25
126			2-12 yr	18	73.7(35.9-111.5)	25
127			16-49 yr	35♂	79.8(46.4-113.2)	28
128			20-29 yr	1♂	108.7	30
129			30-39 yr	6♂	87.7(61.9-113.5)	30
130			40-49 yr	11♂	79.4(60.4-98.4)	30
131			50-59 yr	8♂	72.2(40.6-103.8)	30
132			60-69 yr	17♂	66.2(39.6-92.8)	30
133			70-79 yr	17♂	59.4(34.2-84.6)	30
134			80-89 yr	10♂	38.6(11.4-65.8)	30
135			Adult	8♂	65.6(48.2-83.0)	6
136				43♂	77.2	28
137				16♀	77.2(55.6-98.8)	28
138	Glucose Tm (tubular absorptive mass), mg/ min/1.73 sq m body sur-face area	Calculated as rate of glucose filtration minus rate of glucose excretion in urine	4-28 da	3⁴	77	31
139			37-95 da	3⁴	104	31
140			2-12 yr	6	543(285-801)	13
141			20-29 yr	3♂	358.7(324-395)ᶜ	22
142			28-60 yr	24♂	375(215-535)	27,29
143			30-39 yr	9♂	333.6(112.6-221.0)	22
144			40-49 yr	12♂	315.1(224.7-405.5)	22
145			50-59 yr	14♂	308.2(178.2-438.2)	22
146			60-69 yr	14♂	260.2(131.0-389.4)	22
147			70-79 yr	15♂	239.3(146.5-332.1)	22
148			80-89 yr	9♂	219.2(118.8-319.6)	22
149			16-55 yr	11♀	303(193-413)	27,29
	Urea clearance, ml/min/ 1.73 sq m body surface area					
150	Whole blood	Calculated from urea concentration in urine times urine flow, divid-ed by urea concentration in blood	2-28 da	26	(17-34)ᶜ	19
151			54-356 da	21	(35-55)ᶜ	
152			2-13 yr	69	(72-78)ᶜ	
153		Calculated from urea concentration in urine times urine flow (2 ml/ min/1.73 sq m body surface area), divided by urea concen-tration in blood	2-8 da	4	23.2	12
154			4-28 da	21⁴	31.5(20.5-42.5)	1
155			10-22 da	6	36.0	25
156			37-95 da	8⁴	40.0	2
157			1-5.9 mo	10	55.4(23.2-87.6)	25,26
158			6-11.7 mo	8	67.9	25,26
159			12-19 mo	8	71.1	25
160			2-12 yr	24	75.0(38.0-112.0)	21,25
161		Calculated as maximal or standard clearance according to Møller, McIntosh, and Van Slyke [23]	40-49 yr	20♂	95(66.2-123.8)	18
162			50-59 yr	20♂	86(44.8-127.2)	
163			60-69 yr	20♂	82(47.2-116.8)	
164			70-79 yr	20♂	65(30-100)	
165			80-89 yr	20♂	61(11-111)	
166	Plasma	Determined simultaneously with inulin clearance; urine flow greater than 2 ml/min		10♀³	79(21-137)	10
167				8♀⁷,⁸	77(45-109)	

/3/ Pregnant, near term. /4/ Premature infants. /7/ From group of 10 subjects in preceding line of data.
/8/ Second week postpartum.

Part I: MAN (Concluded)

Contributors: (a) Lauson, Henry D., (b) Barnett, Henry L., (c) Hiatt, Edwin P., (d) Miller, John H., (e) Kanter, Gerald S., (f) Brodsky, William A.

References: [1] Barnett, H. L., K. Hare, H. McNamara, and R. Hare. 1948. J. Clin. Invest. 27:691. [2] Barnett, H. L., K. Hare, H. McNamara, and R. Hare. 1948. Proc. Soc. Exp. Biol., N. Y. 69:55. [3] Barnett, H. L., H. McNamara, S. Shultz, and R. Tompsett. 1949. Pediatrics 3:418. [4] Berger, E. Y., S. J. Farber, and D. P. Earle, Jr. 1947. Proc. Soc. Exp. Biol., N. Y. 66:62. [5] Brun, C., T. Hilden, and F. Raaschou. 1947. Acta med. scand. 127:464. [6] Brun, C., T. Hilden, and F. Raaschou. 1947. Ibid. 127:471. [7] Bucht, H. 1951. Scand. J. Clin. Invest., Oslo, v. 3, suppl. 3. [8] Chapman, C. B., A. Henschel, J. Minckler, A. Forsgren, and A. Keys. 1948. J. Clin. Invest. 27:639. [9] Chesley, L. C. 1951. Med. Clin. N. America 35:699. [10] Chesley, L. C., and L. O. Williams. 1945. Am. J. Obst. 50:367. [11] Davies, D. F., and N. W. Shock. 1950. J. Clin. Invest. 29:496. [12] Dean, R. F. A., and R. A. McCance. 1947. J. Physiol., Lond. 106:431. [13] Galan, E., M. Perez-Stable, J. M. Martin, and O. G. Faez. 1947. Arch. méd. enf. 26:102. [14] Heller, B., and H. Jacobson. In C. B. Chapman, A. Henschel, J. Minckler, A. Forsgren, and A. Keys. 1948. J. Clin. Invest. 27:639. [15] Hogeman, O. 1948. Acta med. scand., Suppl. 216a. [16] Josephson, B., and O. Lindahl. 1943-44. Ibid. 116:20. [17] Lange, W. A., D. G. Johnson, and R. W. Bonsnes. Unpublished. [18] Lewis, W. H., Jr., and A. S. Alving. 1938. Am. J. Physiol. 123:500. [19] McCance, R. A., and E. M. Widdowson. 1952. Lancet, Lond. 263:860. [20] McCrory, W. W., C. W. Forman, H. McNamara, and H. L. Barnett. 1952. J. Clin. Invest. 31:357. [21] McIntosh, J. F., E. Møller, and D. D. Van Slyke. 1929. Ibid. 6:467. [22] Miller, J. H., R. K. McDonald, and N. W. Shock. 1952. J. Geront. 7:196. [23] Møller, E., J. F. McIntosh, and D. D. Van Slyke. 1929. J. Clin. Invest. 6:427. [24] Richmond, J. B., H. Kravitz, W. Segar, and H. A. Waisman. 1951. Proc. Soc. Exp. Biol., N. Y. 77:83. [25] Rubin, M. I., E. Bruck, and M. Rapoport. 1949. J. Clin. Invest. 28:1144. [26] Schoenthal, L., D. Lurie, and M. Kelly. 1933. Am. J. Dis. Child. 45:41. [27] Smith, H. W. 1943. Lectures on the kidney. University of Kansas, Lawrence. [28] Smith, H. W. 1951. The kidney. Oxford University Press, New York. [29] Smith, H. W., W. Goldring, H. Chasis, H. A. Ranges, and S. E. Bradley. 1943. J. Mount Sinai Hosp. N. York 10:59. [30] Watkin, D. M. Unpublished. [31] Weintraub, D. H., P. L. Calcagno, N. K. Kelleher, and M. I. Rubin. 1952. Proc. Soc. Exp. Biol., N. Y. 81:542.

Part II: DOG, RABBIT, RAT

Values in parentheses are ranges, estimate "b" (cf. Introduction).

Animal	Specification	No. of Subjects	Value	Reference
(A)	(B)	(C)	(D)	(E)
1 Dog	Renal plasma flow, ml/min/sq m body surface area		250(28-372)	4
2		75	266(134-398)	13
3			295(179-411)	23
4			246	22
5	Glomerular filtration rate, ml/min/sq m body surface area		69(39.4-98.6)	4
6		75	84(45.8-122.2)	13
7			104(74-134)	23
8			76	22
9	Filtration fraction, %	75	0.317(0.213-0.421)	13
10			(0.297-0.353)	4,22,23
11	p-Aminohippurate Tm, mg/min/sq m body surface area		19.1(15.5-22.7)	22

Part II: DOG, RABBIT, RAT (Concluded)

	Animal	Specification	No. of Subjects	Value	Reference
	(A)	(B)	(C)	(D)	(E)
12	Dog (concluded)	Glucose Tm, mg/min/sq m body surface area	9	302.6	20,21
13		Urea clearance, ml/min/sq m body surface area	10	55.6(28.2-83.0)	14
14				34.9(22.7-47.1)	17
15				53.1(31.1-75.1)	24
16				(49.8-57.7)	18,19,27
17	Rabbit	Renal plasma flow, ml/min/sq m body surface area	21	296(178-414)	22
18				194(190-198)	15
19		Glomerular filtration rate, ml/min/sq m body surface area	21	50(31.6-68.4)	2
20				24	15
21		Filtration fraction, %	21	0.170	2
22		Diodrast Tm, mg I/min/sq m body surface area		33.4(29.14-37.66)	15
23		Glucose Tm, mg/min/sq m body surface area		78.7(51.9-105.5)	15
24		Urea clearance, ml/min/sq m body surface area	25	25.5	25
25	Rat	Renal plasma flow, ml/min/kg body wt	134	22.2(16.6-27.8)	7
26				(13.3-26.6)	1,6,9,10,16,26
27				41.4	11
28		Glomerular filtration rate, ml/min/kg body wt		2.7(1.5-3.9)	10
29			134	3.47(2.61-4.33)	7
30				6.0(5.38-6.62)	1
31				6.6(6.04-7.16)	9
32				6.5(6.12-6.88)	11
33				6.10(5.78-6.42)	3
34				(3.5-9.2)	5,6,16,26
35		Filtration fraction, %	134	0.170(0.096-0.244)	6
36				(0.16-0.31)	1,9-11,26
37		Diodrast Tm, mg I/min/kg body wt	134	1.32(0.96-1.68)	7
38				1.83(1.57-2.09)	1
39				(1.17-1.42)	6,10,26
40		p-Aminohippurate Tm, mg/min/kg body wt		1.8(1.7-1.9)	11
41				3.5(2.98-3.62)	5
42				2.9(2.78-3.02)	3
43		Urea clearance, ml/min/sq m body surface area	8	10.9(4.7-17.1)	8
44				19.3	12

Contributors: (a) Lauson, Henry D., (b) Miller, John H.

References: [1] Braun-Menendez, E., and H. Chiodi. 1946. Rev. Soc. argent. biol. 22:314. [2] Brod, J., and J. H. Sirota. 1949. Am. J. Physiol. 157:31. [3] Corcoran, A. C., G. Masson, R. Reuting, and I. H. Page. 1948. Ibid. 154:170. [4] Corcoran, A. C., and I. H. Page. 1939. Ibid. 126:354. [5] Corcoran, A. C., and I. H. Page. 1947. Fed. Proc., Balt. 6:91. [6] Dicker, S. E., and H. Heller. 1945. J. Physiol., Lond. 103:449. [7] Dicker, S. E., and H. Heller. 1946. Ibid. 104:353. [8] Farr, L. E., and J. E. Smadel. 1936. Am. J. Physiol. 116:349. [9] Friedeman, S. M. 1947. Ibid. 148:387. [10] Friedeman, S. M., and C. A. Livingstone. 1942. Ibid. 137:564. [11] Friedeman, S. M., J. R. Polley, and C. L. Friedeman. 1947. Ibid. 150:340. [12] Herrin, R. C. 1939. Proc. Soc. Exp. Biol., N. Y. 42:695. [13] Houck, C. R. 1948. Am. J. Physiol. 153:169. [14] Jolliffe, N., and H. W. Smith. 1931. Ibid. 98:572. [15] Laake, H. 1945. Acta med. scand., Suppl. 168. [16] Lippman, R. W. 1948. Am. J. Physiol. 152:27. [17] Orth, O. S., and J. W. Stutzman. 1938. Proc. Soc. Exp. Biol., N. Y. 39:403. [18] Ralli, E. P., M. Brown, and A. Pariente. 1931. Am. J. Physiol. 97:432. [19] Rhoads, C. P., A. S. Alving, A. Hiller, and D. D. Van Slyke. 1934. Ibid. 109:329. [20] Shannon, J. A., S. Farber, and L. Troast. 1941. Ibid. 133:752. [21] Shannon, J. A., and S. Fisher. 1938. Ibid. 122:765. [22] Smith, H. W. 1951. The kidney: structure and function in health and disease. Oxford University Press, New York. p. 541. [23] Stamler, J., L. N. Katz, and S. Rodbard. 1949. J. Exp. M. 90:511. [24] Summerville, W. W., R. F. Hanzal, and H. Goldblatt. 1932. Am. J. Physiol. 102:1. [25] Taylor, F. B., D. R. Drury, and T. Addis. 1923. Ibid. 65:55. [26] Watschinger, B., and G. Werner. 1949. Zschr. ges. inn. Med. 11:435. [27] White, H. L., and P. Heinbecker. 1938. Am. J. Physiol. 123:566.

XX. Digestive Secretions

130. PHYSICAL PROPERTIES AND CHEMICAL COMPOSITION OF SALIVA: MAMMALS

Part I: MAN

With the exception of lines 86-91, values are for mixed secretions of the salivary glands. Values in parentheses are ranges, estimate "c" (cf. Introduction).

	Property or Constituent	No. of Observations	Saliva Stimulant	Value	Reference
	(A)	(B)	(C)	(D)	(E)
	**Physical Properties and General Chemical Components**				
1	Freezing point depression		None	(0.07-0.34) ^{o}C	12
2	pH	3405	None	6.75(5.6-7.6)	3
3		39	Paraffin	7.45(7.2-7.6)	22
4	Rate of flow	148	None	0.57(0.1-1.8) ml/min	32
5		148	Paraffin	1.9(0.4-4.8) ml/min	
6	Specific gravity		None	(1.010-1.020)	7, 12, 20
7	Solids, total	69	Paraffin	581(386-860) mg/100 ml	37
	**Electrolytes**				
8	Bicarbonate	25	None	6.44(3.48-10.70) mEq/L	8
9		25	Paraffin	15.74(8.12-19.47) mEq/L	
10	Calcium	650	None	5.8(5.2-9.7) mg/100 ml	1
11		39	Paraffin	5.5(3.5-9.2) mg/100 ml	22
12	Carbon dioxide		None	12(5-25) vol %	19
13			Paraffin	25(8-44) vol %	
14	Chloride		None	15.5(8.4-17.7) mEq/L	19
15			Paraffin	11.8(8.7-17.7) mEq/L	
16	Cobalt	37	Paraffin	2.44(0-12.53) µg/100 ml	10
17	Copper	20	None	6.3(2-22) µg/100 ml	31
18		48	Paraffin	25.9(10.0-47.5) µg/100 ml	10
19	Fluoride		None	(0-0.005) mEq/L	19
20	Iodine		None	(0-350) µg/100 ml	4
21	Magnesium		None	0.58(0.16-1.06) mEq/L	19
22	Phosphorus Total P	50	None	20.4 mg/100 ml	29
23	Inorganic P	180	None	14.9(7.4-21.1) mg/100 ml	29
24	Organic P	50	None	5.5 mg/100 ml	29
25	Lipid P	207	None	0.119(0.02-0.24) mg/100 ml	27
26	Potassium	148	None	80.3(56-148) mg/100 ml	32
27		148	Paraffin	78.0(50-95) mg/100 ml	
28	Sodium	147	None	23.2(8-56) mg/100 ml	32
29		148	Paraffin	57.3(19-133) mg/100 ml	
	**Nitrogenous Substances**				
30	Protein, total	25	None	386(156-630) mg/100 ml	8
31		25	Paraffin	242(140-527) mg/100 ml	
32	Mucin	30	None	250 mg/100 ml	21
33		30	Paraffin	270(80-600) mg/100 ml	
34	Amino acids Alanine	9	None	1.2(0.5-2.9) mg/100 ml	2
35	Arginine	18	Paraffin	(3.3-10.0) mg/100 ml	25
36	Aspartic acid	9	None	0.15(0.13-0.33) mg/100 ml	2
37	Cystine	18	Paraffin	(0.16-0.45) mg/100 ml	25
38	Glutamic acid	9	None	1.2(0.5-1.3) mg/100 ml	25
39			Paraffin	(3.0-12.6) mg/100 ml	30
40	Glycine	9	None	1.4(0.5-3.6) mg/100 ml	2
41		18	Paraffin	(1.9-15.5) mg/100 ml	25
42	Histidine	18	Paraffin	(0.35-2.00) mg/100 ml	25
43	Isoleucine	18	Paraffin	(0.2-0.9) mg/100 ml	25
44	Leucine	18	Paraffin	(0.025-0.300) mg/100 ml	25
45	Lysine	9	None	0.77(0.15-1.50) mg/100 ml	2
46		18	Paraffin	(0.4-1.5) mg/100 ml	23

Part I: MAN (Continued)

	Property or Constituent	No. of Observations	Saliva Stimulant	Value	Reference
	(A)	(B)	(C)	(D)	(E)
	Nitrogenous Substances (concluded)				
	Amino acids (concluded)				
47	Methionine	2	Paraffin	(0.005-0.010) mg/100 ml	25
48	Phenylalanine	18	Paraffin	(0.6-2.5) mg/100 ml	25
49	Proline	18	Paraffin	(0.35-1.50) mg/100 ml	25
50	Serine	9	None	0.66(0.33-1.20) mg/100 ml	2
51		18	Paraffin	(1.0-1.8) mg/100 ml	23
52	Threonine	18	Paraffin	(0.4-5.6) mg/100 ml	23
53	Tryptophan	18	Paraffin	(0.2-0.9) mg/100 ml	23
54	Tyrosine	18	Paraffin	(0.2-1.0) mg/100 ml	23
55	Valine	18	Paraffin	(0.7-2.2) mg/100 ml	23
56	Ammonia	81[1]	None	2.6 mM/L	33
57			Paraffin	3.5(0.8-7.1) mM/L	12
58	Creatinine	3	Paraffin	0.35(0.275-0.455) mg/100 ml	28
59	Urea	9	None	12.7(8.2-18.1) mg/100 ml	39
60		15	Paraffin	8.8(0-14.3) mg/100 ml	38
61	Uric acid		None	1.5(0.5-2.9) mg/100 ml	19, 34
62		72	Paraffin	4.8(1.5-8.7) mg/100 ml	38
63	Thiocyanate	35	None	13.4(3.1-27.5) mg/100 ml	13
	Nitrogen				
64	Total N	20	Paraffin	90.0(36.1-125.3) mg/100 ml	6
65	Protein N	20	Paraffin	63.6(22.9-88.2) mg/100 ml	6
66	Non-protein N	20	Paraffin	36.4(8.2-62.4) mg/100 ml	6
67	Ammonia N	94[2]	None	3.8(0.5-9.9) mg/100 ml	33
	Lipids, Carbohydrates, Miscellaneous Organic Acids				
68	Cholesterol		None	7.5(3-15) mg/100 ml	19
69	Glucose	16	None	19.6(11.28-28.08) mg/100 ml	40
70		10	Paraffin	20.7(14.04-30.00) mg/100 ml	
71	Citric acid	121	Paraffin	1.05(0.20-3.15) mg/100 ml	41
72	Lactic acid		None	0.17 mEq/L	19
	Vitamins				
73	B$_1$ (thiamine)	8	None	0.7 μg/100 ml	16
74		23	Paraffin	(0.2-1.4) μg/100 ml	15
75	B$_2$ (riboflavin)	8	None	5.0 μg/100 ml	16
76	B$_6$ (pyridoxine)	17	Paraffin	0.6(0.1-1.7) μg/100 ml	24
77	B$_{12}$ (cyanocobalamine)	2	Paraffin	0.33(0.15-0.50) μg/100 ml	17
78	B$_c$ (folic acid)	20	Paraffin	2.4(0.3-7.5) μg/100 ml	24
79	C (ascorbic acid)	110	Paraffin	0.07(0-0.372) mg/100 ml	18
80	H (biotin)	8	None	0.08 μg/100 ml	16
81	K	8	None	1.5 μg/100 ml	16
82	Choline	7	None	0.65(0.47-0.99) mg/100 ml	11
83		87	Paraffin	1.62(0.62-3.64) mg/100 ml	
84	Niacin (nicotinic acid)	90	Paraffin	11.5(2.34-40.90) μg/100 ml	9
85	Pantothenic acid	41	Paraffin	8.8(1.2-19.0) μg/100 ml	26
	Enzymes[3]				
86	Cholinesterase		Paraffin	0.33(0.23-0.43) units/L[4]	35
87	Esterase, total		Paraffin	0.34(0.12-0.65) units/L[5]	37
88	β-Glucuronidase		Paraffin	(170-1750) units/L[6]	14
89	Lipase		Paraffin	1.42(0.25-2.58) units/L[7]	37
90	Lysozyme		Paraffin	670(250-1360) units/L	5
91	Phosphatase, acid		Paraffin	4.23(2.5-7.7) units/L[8]	36

/1/ 12-year-old children.   /2/ 7-year-old children.   /3/ Parotid gland secretion.   /4/ β-Carbonaphthoxycholine iodide substrate.   /5/ β-Naphthyl acetate substrate.   /6/ Sodium-8-benzoyl amino-2-naphthyl glucuronide substrate. /7/ β-Naphthyl laurate substrate.   /8/ Monosodium-β-naphthyl phosphate substrate.

Contributors: (a) Niedermeier, William, (b) Frazer, A. C.; Sammons, H. G.; and Okunzua, G.; (c) Grad, Bernard

Part I: MAN (Concluded)

References: [1] Becks, H., and W. W. Wainwright. 1946. J. Dent. Res. 25:267. [2] Berry, H. K. 1951. Univ. Texas Pub. 5109. p. 157. [3] Browley, R. E. 1935. J. Dent. Res. 15:79. [4] Cantarow, A., and M. Trumper. 1955. Clinical biochemistry. Ed. 5. W. B. Saunders, Philadelphia. p. 165. [5] Chauncey, H. H., F. Lionetti, R. A. Winer, and V. F. Lisanti. 1954. J. Dent. Res. 33:321. [6] Deakins, M., V. D. Cheyne, B. G. Bibby, and M. van Kesteren. 1941. Ibid. 20:161. [7] Dewar, M. R., and G. J. Parfitt. 1954. Ibid. 33:596. [8] Dreizen, S., A. I. Reed, W. Niedermeier, and T. D. Spies. 1953. Ibid. 32:497. [9] Dreizen, S., A. I. Reed, and T. D. Spies. 1951. Internat. Zschr. Vitaminforsch., Bern 22:396. [10] Dreizen, S., H. A. Spies, and T. D. Spies. 1952. J. Dent. Res. 31:137. [11] Eagle, E. 1941. J. Laborat. Clin. M. 27:103. [12] Evans, C. L., and H. Hartridge. 1952. Principles of human physiology. Ed. 11. Lea and Febiger, Philadelphia. p. 853. [13] Fishman, E. J., and A. Fishman. 1948. J. Laborat. Clin. M. 33:772. [14] Fishman, W. H., B. Springer, and R. Brunetti. 1948. J. Biol. Chem. 173:449. [15] Fujishiro, I. 1951. Igaku to Seibutsugaku 23:59. [16] Glavind, J. 1948. Internat. Zschr. Vitaminforsch., Bern 20:234. [17] Granados, H., J. Glavind, B. Noer, and H. Dam. 1950. Acta path. microb. scand. 27:501. [18] Hafkesbring, R., and J. T. Freeman. 1952. Am. J. M. Sc. 224:324. [19] Harrow, B., and A. Mazur. 1954. Textbook of biochemistry. Ed. 6. W. B. Saunders, Philadelphia. p. 116. [20] Hawk, P. B., B. L. Oser, and W. H. Summerson. 1954. Practical physiological chemistry. Ed. 13. Blakiston, New York. p. 351. [21] Inouye, J. M. 1930. J. Dent. Res. 10:7. [22] Karshan, M., F. Krasnow, and L. E. Krejci. 1931. Ibid. 11:573. [23] Kesel, R. G., J. F. O'Donnell, E. R. Kirch, and E. C. Wach. 1947. Am. J. Orthodont. 33:68. [24] Kauffman, S. L., G. J. Kasai, and S. A. Koser. 1953. J. Dent. Res. 32:840. [25] Kirch, E. R., R. G. Kesel, J. F. O'Donnell, and E. C. Wach. 1947. Ibid. 26:297. [26] Kniesner, A. H., A. W. Mann, and T. D. Spies. 1942. Ibid. 21:259. [27] Krasnow, F. 1945. Ibid. 24:319. [28] Ladell, W. S. S. 1947. J. Physiol., Lond. 106:237. [29] Lura, H. E. 1947. J. Dent. Res. 26:203. [30] Morris, J. L., and V. Jersey. 1923. J. Biol. Chem. 56:31. [31] Munch-Petersen, S. 1951. Scand. J. Clin. Lab. Invest. 2:335. [32] Niedermeier, W. 1953. Fed. Proc., Balt. 12:251. [33] Nikifonk, G., S. H. Jackson, M. H. Cox, and R. M. Grainger. 1956. J. Pediat., S. Louis 49:425. [34] Pigman, W., and A. J. Reid. 1952. J. Am. Dent. Ass. 45:325. [35] Ravin, H. A., K. C. Tsou, and A. M. Seligman. 1951. J. Biol. Chem. 191:843. [36] Seligman, A. M., H. H. Chauncey, M. M. Nachlas, L. H. Manheimer, and H. A. Ravin. 1951. Ibid. 190:7. [37] Seligman, A. M., and M. M. Nachlas. 1950. J. Clin. Invest. 29:31. [38] Updegraff, H., and H. B. Lewis. 1924. J. Biol. Chem. 61:633. [39] Wu, H., and D. Y. Wu. 1951. Proc. Soc. Exp. Biol., N. Y. 76:130. [40] Young, D. 1941. J. Dent. Res. 20:597. [41] Zipkin, I., and F. J. McClure. 1949. Ibid. 28:613.

Part II: MAMMALS OTHER THAN MAN

Values in parentheses are ranges, estimate "c" (cf. Introduction).

Animal	Property or Constituent	Saliva Source	Value	Reference
(A)	(B)	(C)	(D)	(E)
1 Buffalo	pH	Parotid gland	8.8	5
2	Ash	Mixed	680 mg/100 ml	
3	Solids, total	Parotid gland	850 mg/100 ml	
4	Chloride	Mixed	4.2 mEq/L	
5	Magnesium	Mixed	4.9 mEq/L	
6	Phosphorus	Mixed	115.8 mM/L	
7	Potassium	Parotid gland	15 mg/100 ml	
8	Sodium	Mixed	120.4 mEq/L	

Part II: MAMMALS OTHER THAN MAN (Continued)

	Animal	Property or Constituent	Saliva Source	Value	Reference
	(A)	(B)	(C)	(D)	(E)
9	Cat	pH	Mixed	7.5	3
10		Bicarbonate	Submaxillary gland	12.8(11.6-13.6) mEq/L	7
11		Chloride	Submaxillary gland	(16.8-36.0) mEq/L	7
12		Potassium	Submaxillary gland	8.6(7.7-9.2) mEq/L	7
13		Sodium	Submaxillary gland	31.0(24.0-46.0) mEq/L	7
14	Cattle	pH	Mixed	(8.1-8.8)	5
15		Specific gravity	Mixed	(1.002-1.009)	4
16		Ash	Mixed	(830-860) mg/100 ml	5
17		Solids, total	Submaxillary gland	886 mg/100 ml	3
18		Water	Mixed	99.1 %	3
19		Bicarbonate	Mixed	91.5 mEq/L	5
20		Chloride	Mixed	4.3 mEq/L	6
21		Magnesium	Mixed	5.0 mEq/L	6
22		Phosphate	Mixed	359 mg/100 ml	6
23		Sodium	Mixed	120 mEq/L	6
24		Sulfate	Mixed	14.5 mg/100 ml	6
25	Dog	pH	Mixed	(7.50-7.56)	3
26		Ash	Mixed	(290-610) mg/100 ml	1
27		Solids, total	Mixed	(440-1610) mg/100 ml	1
28		Bicarbonate	Parotid gland	55(34.7-69.1) mEq/L	2
29		Calcium	Mixed	(2.9-6.6) mEq/L	1
30			Parotid gland	8.6(5.0-10.3) mEq/L	2
31		Chloride	Mixed	(16.3-69.3) mEq/L	1
32			Parotid gland	81.9(37.5-103.7) mEq/L	2
33		Phosphorus, total	Mixed	(1.2-3.0) mg/100 ml	1
34		Potassium	Mixed	(12.3-23.7) mEq/L	1
35			Parotid gland	11.4(4.3-12.6) mEq/L	2
36		Sodium	Parotid gland	108(48.8-132.9) mEq/L	2
37	Goat	pH	Parotid gland	(8.12-8.32)	5
38		Specific gravity	Parotid gland	(1.002-1.063)	
39		Ash	Mixed	(20-1020) mg/100 ml	
40		Solids, total	Mixed	(710-1960) mg/100 ml	
41		Chloride	Parotid gland	(2.8-3.4) mEq/L	
42		Nitrogen, total	Mixed	(10-46) mg/100 ml	
43	Horse	pH	Mixed	(7.31-8.62)	5
44		Specific gravity	Mixed	(1.001-1.008)	4
45			Parotid gland	(1.005-1.007)	
46		Ash	Mixed	(113-549) mg/100 ml	4
47		Solids, total	Mixed	1000 mg/100 ml	3
48		Water	Parotid gland	99.0 %	3
49		Chloride	Mixed	(0.0056-0.0611) mEq/L	3
50		Nitrogen	Mixed	(0.01-0.05) mM/L	4
51	Sheep	pH	Mixed	(8.4-8.7)	5
52		Specific gravity	Parotid gland	(1.009-1.011)	
53		Ash	Mixed	(700-900) mg/100 ml	
54		Solids, total	Mixed	1100 mg/100 ml	
55		Bicarbonate	Mixed	(52.2-126.4) mEq/L	
56			Parotid gland	104 mEq/L	
57		Calcium	Mixed	(0.8-1.5) mEq/L	
58			Parotid gland	0.4 mEq/L	
59		Chloride	Mixed	(7.0-12.1) mEq/L	
60			Parotid gland	17 mEq/L	
61		Magnesium	Mixed	(0.5-0.8) mEq/L	
62			Parotid gland	0.6 mEq/L	
63		Phosphorus Total P	Mixed	(37-72) mM/L	
64		Inorganic P	Parotid gland	52 mEq/L	
65		Potassium	Mixed	(4.1-11.8) mEq/L	
66			Parotid gland	8 mEq/L	
67		Sodium	Mixed	(160.9-200.8) mEq/L	
68			Parotid gland	177 mEq/L	
69		Nitrogen	Mixed	(3.2-7.1) mM/L	

Part II: MAMMALS OTHER THAN MAN (Concluded)

	Animal	Property or Constituent	Saliva Source	Value	Reference
	(A)	(B)	(C)	(D)	(E)
70	Swine	pH	Mixed	(7.15-7.44)	4
71		Specific gravity	Parotid gland	(1.002-1.009)	
72			Submaxillary gland	(0.9996-0.0010)	
73			Sublingual gland	(1.002-1.009)	
74		Ash	Parotid gland	(120-360) mg/100 ml	
75			Submaxillary gland	164 mg/100 ml	
76			Sublingual gland	320 mg/100 ml	
77		Nitrogen	Parotid gland	(0.004-0.099) mM/L	
78			Submaxillary gland	(0.006-0.025) mM/L	
79			Sublingual gland	(0.006-0.025) mM/L	

Contributors: (a) Frazer, A. C.; Sammons, H. G.; and Okunzua, G.; (b) Liebowitz, Daniel, (c) Grad, Bernard, (d) Webster, Donald R., and Skoryna, Stanley C., (e) De Beer, Edwin J., (f) Wilson, D. Wright

References: [1] Baxter, H. 1933. J. Biol. Chem. 102:203. [2] De Beer, E. J., and D. W. Wilson. 1932. Ibid. 95:671. [3] Dukes, H. H. 1947. The physiology of domestic animals. Ed. 6. Comstock, Ithaca. pp. 260-278. [4] Lenkeit, W. 1933. Erg. Physiol. 35:573. [5] McDougall, E. I. 1948. Biochem. J., Lond. 43:99. [6] Sharma, G. K. 1936. Ind. J. Vet. Sc. 6:266. [7] Stavraky, G. W. 1940. Am. J. Physiol. 129:539.

131. PHYSICAL PROPERTIES AND CHEMICAL COMPOSITION OF ESOPHAGEAL SECRETIONS: DOG

Values in parentheses are ranges, estimate "c" (cf. Introduction).

	Property or Constituent	Value		Property or Constituent	Value
	(A)	(B)		(A)	(B)
1	Acid-combining power	(11.5-15.0) mEq/L	7	Solids	(1.25-1.47) g/100 g
2	pH	(7.5-8.3)	8	Calcium	(6.2-6.9) mg/100 g
3	Rate of secretion	(0.013-0.140) ml/min	9	Chloride	(501-618) mg/100 g
4	Specific gravity	1.007	10	Phosphorus, total	(0.9-1.2) mg/100 g
5	Ash	(0.96-1.05) g/100 g	11	Potassium	(51.0-58.2) mg/100 g
6	Organic material	(0.26-0.52) g/100 g	12	Nitrogen, total	(52.5-142.4) mg/100 g

Contributor: Liebowitz, Daniel

Reference: Babkin, B. P. 1950. Secretory mechanism of the digestive glands. Ed. 2. P. B. Hoeber, New York.

132. PHYSICAL PROPERTIES AND CHEMICAL COMPOSITION OF GASTRIC JUICE: VERTEBRATES

Part I: MAN

Values in parentheses are ranges, estimate "c" (cf. Introduction).

	Property or Constituent	Value	Remarks	Reference
	(A)	(B)	(C)	(D)
	Physical Properties and General Chemical Components			
1	Freezing point depression	(0.55-0.62) °C		10
2		(0.298-0.816) °C	Fasting	1
3	pH	(1.49-8.38)		6
4	Rate of secretion	1.0(0.7-9.5) ml/min	Dilution technique	11, 15, 16
5	Specific gravity	1.006(1.004-1.010)		1
6	Water	118(11-233) ml	Deuterium oxide method	9
7		0.4(0.1-1.2) % of total body water		
	Electrolytes			
8	Bicarbonate	(0-130) mg/100 ml		3
9	Calcium	(1.04-7.00) mg/100 ml		3
10		3.6(2.0-4.8) mEq/L	Fasting	2
11	Chloride	(77.6-159.0) mEq/L	Fasting	12
12		(131.4-170.0) mEq/L	Histamine stimulation	
13	Magnesium	(2.2-9.4) mg/100 ml		3
14	Phosphate	(1.17-4.20) mg/100 ml		3
15	Potassium	10(0.5-32.5) mEq/L		18
16		11.6(6.4-16.6) mEq/L	Fasting	2
17	Sodium	60(0-116) mEq/L		18
18		49(18.7-69.5) mEq/L	Fasting	2
	Hydrochloric acid			12
19	Total	(46.0-118.3) mEq/L	Fasting	
20		(85.6-137.3) mEq/L	Histamine stimulation	
21	Free	(0-115.0) mEq/L	Fasting	
22		(78.1-135.0) mEq/L	Histamine stimulation	
	Nitrogenous Substances			
23	Protein	330 mg/100 ml		20
24	Mucoprotein	100(0-460) mg/100 ml		8
25	Mucin	0.36(0.15-1.50) g/100 g		5
	Amino acids			19
26	Alanine	(1.8-2.7) mg/100 ml	Fasting	
27		(2.0-2.6) mg/100 ml	Caffeine stimulation	
28	Arginine	(3.3-3.6) mg/100 ml	Fasting	
29		(3.5-5.0) mg/100 ml	Caffeine stimulation	
30	Aspartic acid	(1.7-2.3) mg/100 ml	Fasting	
31		(1.6-2.5) mg/100 ml	Caffeine stimulation	
32	Cystine	(1.8-3.7) mg/100 ml	Fasting	
33		(1.6-4.4) mg/100 ml	Caffeine stimulation	
34	Glycine	(1.3-1.6) mg/100 ml	Fasting	
35		(1.2-2.1) mg/100 ml	Caffeine stimulation	
36	Glutamic acid	(2.0-3.2) mg/100 ml	Fasting	
37		(2.6-4.7) mg/100 ml	Caffeine stimulation	
38	Histidine	(1.3-2.0) mg/100 ml	Fasting	
39		(1.3-1.8) mg/100 ml	Caffeine stimulation	
40	Isoleucine	(0.7-1.4) mg/100 ml	Fasting	
41		(2.3-2.5) mg/100 ml	Caffeine stimulation	
42	Leucine	(1.2-2.2) mg/100 ml	Fasting	
43		(1.2-3.3) mg/100 ml	Caffeine stimulation	
44	Lysine	(1.4-1.8) mg/100 ml	Fasting	
45		(1.3-1.6) mg/100 ml	Caffeine stimulation	
46	Methionine	(0.8-1.5) mg/100 ml	Fasting	
47		(0.9-1.9) mg/100 ml	Caffeine stimulation	
48	Phenylalanine	(0.8-1.8) mg/100 ml	Fasting	
49		(0.7-1.6) mg/100 ml	Caffeine stimulation	
50	Proline	(1.7-3.2) mg/100 ml	Fasting	
51		(2.2-3.3) mg/100 ml	Caffeine stimulation	
52	Serine	(1.6-2.3) mg/100 ml	Fasting	
53		(1.9-2.1) mg/100 ml	Caffeine stimulation	

Part I: MAN (Concluded)

	Property or Constituent	Value	Remarks	Reference
	(A)	(B)	(C)	(D)
	Nitrogenous Substances (concluded)			
	Amino acids (concluded)			19
54	Threonine	(1.5-2.5) mg/100 ml	Fasting	
55		2.0 mg/100 ml	Caffeine stimulation	
56	Tryptophan	(1.4-1.9) mg/100 ml	Fasting	
57		(1.2-1.9) mg/100 ml	Caffeine stimulation	
58	Tyrosine	(1.0-1.1) mg/100 ml	Fasting	
59		(0.9-1.3) mg/100 ml	Caffeine stimulation	
60	Histamine	(0.0013-0.0535) mg/100 ml		4
61	Urea	2.0 mg/100 ml		3
	Nitrogen			
62	Total N	(0.91-2.18) mg/ml	Fasting	12
63		(0.73-1.34) mg/ml	Histamine stimulation	
64	a-Amino N	(5.6-8.4) mg/100 ml	Fasting	19
65		(7.2-14.4) mg/100 ml	Caffeine stimulation	
	Carbohydrates, Miscellaneous Organic Acids, Vitamins			
66	Fucose	13.8 mg/100 ml		20
67	Glucose	(0.35-1.19) mg/ml	Fasting	12
68		(0.33-1.12) mg/ml	Histamine stimulation	
69	Hexosamine	32.7 mg/100 ml	Fasting	20
70	Hexose, total	32.1 mg/100 ml		20
71	Glucuronic acid	2.0 mg/100 ml		20
72	Sialic acid	7.31 mg/100 ml		20
73	Vitamin C (ascorbic acid)	0.95(0.91-1.05) mg/100 ml		7
	Enzymes			
74	Lipase	(7.0-8.4) units/ml		14
75	Lysozyme	7.57(2.6-19.2) μg/ml		17
76	Pepsin	4119(0-8335) Hb units/hr	Basal conditions; lyophilized bovine hemoglobin powder substrate	13
77		(9.7-62.8) units/ml	After test meal; plasma protein substrate	11, 16

Contributors: (a) Frazer, A. C.; Sammons, H. G.; and Okunzua, G.; (b) Leibowitz, Daniel

References: [1] Babkin, B. P. 1950. Secretory mechanism of the digestive glands. Ed. 2. P. B. Hoeber, New York. [2] Bernstein, R. E. 1952. J. Laborat. Clin. M. 40:707. [3] Bodansky, O. 1952. Biochemistry of disease. Macmillan, New York. [4] Brown, C. L., and R. G. Smith. 1935. Am. J. Physiol. 113:450. [5] Brunner, P. 1946-47. Acta med. scand. 126:384. [6] Dunham, L. J., and A. Brunschwig. 1946. Cancer Res. 6:54.
[7] Freeman, J. T., R. Hafkesbring, and E.K. Caldwell. 1951. Gastroenterology 18:224. [8] Glass, G. B. J., and L. G. Boyd. 1949. Ibid. 12:821. [9] Gotch, F., J. Nadell, and I. E. Edelman. 1957. J. Clin. Invest. 36:289. [10] Houssay, B. A., J. T. Lewis, O. Orias, E. Braun Mendendez, E. Hug, V. G. Foglia, and L. F. Leloir. 1951. Human physiology. McGraw-Hill, New York. [11] Hunt, J. N. 1951. J. Physiol., Lond. 113:169. [12] Ihre, B. 1938. Acta med. scand., Suppl. 95. [13] Janowitz, H. D., and F. Hollander. 1952. J. Clin. Invest. 31:338.
[14] Koningsberger, V. J., E. J. Slijper, and H. J. Vonk, ed. 1946. Tabulae biol., Amst. 21(1):1.
[15] Liebowitz, D. Unpublished. [16] Liebowitz, D., H. H. Stone, D. LeVine, K. G. Scott, and T. L. Althausen. 1957. Gastroenterology 32:268. [17] Lobstein, O. E., and S. J. Fogelson. 1951. Am. J. Digest. Dis. 18:282. [18] Lockwood, J. S., and H. T. Randall. 1949. Bull. N. York Acad. M. 25:228. [19] Muting, D. 1954. Naturwissenschaften 41:580. [20] Richmond, V., R. Caputo, and S. Wolf. 1955. Gastroenterology 29:1017.

Part II: DOG

Values in parentheses are ranges, estimate "c" (cf. Introduction).

	Property or Constituent	Value	Remarks	Reference
	(A)	(B)	(C)	(D)
	Physical Properties			
1	Freezing point depression	0.59(0.49-0.64) °C		6
2	pH	(1.0-4.5)		2
3	Rate of secretion	(0.30-1.45) ml/min	Dilution technique	7
4	Specific gravity	(1.002-1.004)		5
	General Chemical Components			
5	Ash	132.5 mg/100 ml		5
6	Organic matter	294.4 mg/100 ml		5
7	Solids, total	(430-650) mg/100 ml		6
	Electrolytes			
8	Calcium	(0.95-3.30) mEq/L		1
9	Chloride	172.9 mEq/L		5
10		123(98-143) mEq/L	Sham feeding	13
11	Magnesium	0.5 mg/100 ml		3
12	Phosphate	0.25 mg/100 ml		3
13	Potassium	7.2 mEq/L		5
14		15.2(10.3-22.0) mEq/L	Sham feeding	13
15	Sodium	22 mEq/L		6
16		64.0(46.3-79.0) mEq/L	Sham feeding	13
	Hydrochloric acid			
17	Total	32(0-50) mEq/L	Sham feeding	13
18	Free	151(0-168.2) mEq/L	Food stimulation	5
	Nitrogenous Substances			
19	Mucin	1.0(0.1-77.0) g/100 g		3
	Amino acids		Values are M free amino acid/M threonine; sham feeding	11
20	Arginine	(0.08-0.26)		
21	Aspartic acid	(0.30-0.68)		
22	Glutamic acid	(0.81-2.36)		
23	Histidine	(0.04-0.08)		
24	Isoleucine	(1.11-1.93)		
25	Leucine	(1.30-3.58)		
26	Lysine	(0.15-0.26)		
27	Methionine	(0.13-0.22)		
28	Phenylalanine	(0.06-0.44)		
29	Proline	(0.05-0.21)		
30	Serine	(0.43-0.76)		
31	Threonine	1.00		
32	Tryptophan	(0.03-0.04)		
33	Tyrosine	(0.30-0.36)		
34	Valine	(1.07-1.30)		
35	Ammonia	(1.2-4.6) mM/L		1
36	Histamine	(4-22) μg/L	Sham feeding	10
	Nitrogen			
37	Total N	(50-80) mg/100 ml		6
38	Protein N	(18.0-19.9) mg/100 ml	Sham feeding	8
39	Non-protein N	(9.8-10.9) mg/100 ml		8
40	Total base N	(5.37-6.59) mg/100 ml		8
41	Volatile base N	(1.78-2.55) mg/100 ml		8
42	Non-volatile base N	(3.59-4.04) mg/100 ml		8
43	Creatine N + creatinine N	(0.09-0.11) mg/100 ml		8
44	Histidine N + arginine N	(1.56-1.77) mg/100 ml		8
45	Humin bodies N	(3.29-3.73) mg/100 ml		8
46	Lysine fraction N	(1.88-2.17) mg/100 ml		8
47	Mono-amino fraction N	(0.70-1.02) mg/100 ml	Phosphotungstic acid filtrate	8
48	Purine fraction N	(0.10-0.11) mg/100 ml		8
49	Urea N	(0.11-0.16) mg/100 ml		8

Part II: DOG (Concluded)

	Property or Constituent	Value	Remarks	Reference
	(A)	(B)	(C)	(D)
	Vitamins, Enzymes			
50	Vitamin C (ascorbic acid)	0.692(0.33-1.51) mg/100 ml		12
51	Lipase	(0.9-3900) units/ml		9
52	Pepsin	81(41-164) units/ml	Sham feeding	13
53	Urease	3160	μg ammonia nitrogen released/g wet stomach tissue/hr at 37°C	4

Contributors: (a) Frazer, A. C.; Sammons, H. G.; and Okunzua, G.; (b) Liebowitz, Daniel

References: [1] Babkin, B. P. 1950. Secretory mechanism of the digestive glands. Ed. 2. P. B. Hoeber, New York. [2] Bishop, D. W., F. A. Brown, T. L. Jahn, C. L. Prosser, and V. J. Wulff. 1950. Comparative animal physiology. W. B. Saunders, Philadelphia. [3] Bodansky, O. 1952. Biochemistry of disease. Macmillan, New York. [4] Conway, E. J. 1953. The biochemistry of gastric acid secretion. C. C. Thomas, Springfield, Ill. [5] Dukes, H. H. 1955. The physiology of domestic animals. Ed. 7. Comstock, Ithaca. [6] Evans, C. L., and H. Hartridge. 1952. Principles of human physiology. Ed. 11. Lea and Febiger, Philadelphia. [7] Gray, J. S., and G. R. Bucher. 1941. Am. J. Physiol. 133:542. [8] Komarov, S. A. 1937-38. J. Laborat. Clin. M. 23:828. [9] Koningsberger, V. J., E. J. Slijper, and H. J. Vonk, ed. 1946. Tabulae biol., Amst. 21(1):1. [10] Macintosh, F. C. 1938. Q. J. Exp. Physiol., Lond. 28:95. [11] Nasset, E. S., and A. Davenport. 1954-55. J. Appl. Physiol. 7:447. [12] Peters, G. A., and H. E. Martin. 1937. Proc. Soc. Exp. Biol., N. Y. 36:76. [13] Villareal, R., W. F. Ganong, and S. J. Gray. 1955. Am. J. Physiol. 183:485.

Part III: VERTEBRATES OTHER THAN MAN, DOG

Values in parentheses are ranges, estimate "c" unless otherwise indicated (cf. Introduction).

	Animal	Property or Constituent	Value	Remarks	Reference
	(A)	(B)	(C)	(D)	(E)
1	Cat	Ash	(121-384) mg/100 ml	Food stimulation	1
2		Organic matter	(48-265) mg/100 ml	Food stimulation	1
3		Solids, total	(169-649) mg/100 ml	Food stimulation	1
4		Calcium	(1.7-5.3) mEq/L	Food stimulation	1
5		Chloride	(155.5-165.7) mEq/L	Food stimulation	1
6		Phosphorus	(0.16-0.55) mg/100 ml	Food stimulation	1
7		Potassium	(11.5-13.6) mEq/L	Food stimulation	1
8		Sodium	(12.17-55.65) mEq/L	Food stimulation	1
9		Hydrochloric acid Total	(127.5-154.7) mEq/L		1
10		Free	(97.25-122.20) mEq/L	Histamine and sham feeding stimulation	
11		Histamine	(2.5-4.5) μg/100 ml		1
12		Nitrogen	(10-41) mg/100 ml	Food stimulation	1
13		Reducing sugar (as glucose)	(4.0-35.6) mg/100 ml		1
14		Lipase	(47-3000) units/ml		13
15		Pepsin	(0-400) Mett units		1
16		Urease	1210	μg ammonia nitrogen released/g wet stomach tissue/hr at 37°C	3

	Animal	Property or Constituent	Value	Remarks	Reference
	(A)	(B)	(C)	(D)	(E)
17	Cattle	pH	(6.0-7.8)		2
18			(2.0-4.1)	Contents of abomasum	4
19		Rate of secretion	(0.5-2.0) ml/min	Dilution technique	4
20		Specific gravity	(1.002-1.003)		4
21		Acid	(36-98) mEq/L		16
22		Nitrogen	2404 mg/100 g dry matter	Contents of abomasum	17
23	Goat	Specific gravity	1.006		4
24		Acid	(4-84) mEq/L		16
25	Horse	pH	4.46(1.13-6.80)		4
26		Rate of secretion	(6.9-20.7) ml/min	Dilution technique	4
27		Hydrochloric acid, free	(39-58) mEq/L		4
28		Lipase	(5.5-400) units/ml		13
29	Rabbit	Water	65(35-95)[b] ml	Deuterium oxide method	8
30			4.1(2.3-5.9)[b] % of body water		
31		Chloride	8.7(1.9-15.5)[b] mEq/L		15
32		Potassium	0.7(0.1-1.3)[b] mEq/L		15
33		Sodium	0.8(0-1.6)[b] mEq/L		15
34		Lipase	(40-88) units/ml		13
35	Rat	pH	(2.0-4.0)		19
36		Lipase	130 units/ml		13
37		Urease	296	μg ammonia nitrogen released/g wet stomach tissue/hr at 37°C	3
38	Sheep	Freezing point depression	(0.56-0.61) °C	Contents of abomasum	4
39		pH	(7.6-8.2)		6
40			(1.05-3.60)	Contents of fistulated abomasum	7, 16
41		Dry matter	(3700-8200) mg/100 ml	Contents of abomasum	7
42		Calcium, soluble	(190-335) mEq/L	Contents of abomasum	7
43		Chloride	(141-177) mEq/L	Contents of abomasum	16
44		Magnesium, soluble	(9.9-18.9) mEq/L	Contents of abomasum	7
45		Phosphorus, inorganic	(34-100) mg/100 ml	Contents of abomasum	7
46		Acid	86 mEq/L	Contents of abomasum	16
47		Lipase	(0.45-12.00) units/ml		13
48	Swine	pH	(3.75-4.00)	Fasting; gastric fistula	14
49		Rate of secretion	1.05(0.73-1.40) ml/min	Fasting; gastric fistula	14
50		Ash	(400-800) mg/100 ml		12
51		Dry matter	(900-2400) mg/100 ml		12
52		Chloride	112(109-115) mEq/L	Fasting; gastric fistula	14
53		Potassium	10 mEq/L	Fasting; gastric fistula	14
54		Sodium	96(82-111) mEq/L	Fasting; gastric fistula	14
55		Acid	100 mEq/L		12
56		Lipase	(13-7500) units/ml		13
57		Pepsin	33.5(4.0-37.5) pepsin units	Amount of pepsin that digests 1 ml of 1% edestin solution in 30 minutes	12
58	Woodchuck	pH	3.8		1
59		Rate of secretion	(0.0013-0.0070) ml/min	Dilution technique	1
		Hydrochloric acid			1
60		Total	(30-56) mEq/L		
61		Free	(18.0-48.8) mEq/L		
62	Chicken	pH	2.60		5
		Acid		Histamine stimulation	18
63		Total	(120-180) mEq/L		
64		Free	(80-150) mEq/L		
65		Lipase	(0.8-75.0) units/ml		13
66	Pigeon	pH	2.00		5
		Acid			18
67		Total	(60-148) mEq/L		
68			(120-195) mEq/L	Histamine stimulation	
69		Free	(40-136) mEq/L		
70			(70-160) mEq/L	Histamine stimulation	
71		Pepsin	(0-36) Mett units	Histamine stimulation	18

Part III: VERTEBRATES OTHER THAN MAN, DOG (Concluded)

	Animal	Property or Constituent	Value	Remarks	Reference
	(A)	(B)	(C)	(D)	(E)
72	Frog	pH	(1.6-2.5)		9
73		Rate of secretion	(10-40) μL/1.4 sq cm mucosa	In vitro mucosal chamber technique	10, 11
74		Chloride	(2.5-3.5) mEq/1.4 sq cm mucosa	In vitro mucosal chamber technique	10, 11
75		Potassium	0.6(0.3-0.7) μEq/1.4 sq cm mucosa	In vitro mucosal chamber technique	10, 11
76		Hydrochloric acid	1.2(1-3) μEq/1.4 sq cm mucosa	In vitro mucosal chamber technique	10, 11

Contributors: (a) Frazer, A. C.; Sammons, H. G.; and Okunzua, G.; (b) Liebowitz, Daniel

References: [1] Babkin, B. P. 1950. Secretory mechanism of the digestive glands. Ed. 2. P. B. Hoeber, New York. [2] Bishop, D. W., G. A. Brown, T. L. Jahn, C. L. Prosser, and V. J. Wulff. 1950. Comparative animal physiology. W. B. Saunders, Philadelphia. [3] Conway, E. J. 1953. The biochemistry of gastric acid secretion. C. C. Thomas, Springfield, Ill. [4] Dukes, H. H. 1955. The physiology of domestic animals. Ed. 7. Comstock, Ithaca. [5] Farner, D. S. 1942. Poult. Sc. 21:445. [6] Fulton, J. F. 1950. A textbook of physiology. W. B. Saunders, Philadelphia. [7] Garton, G. A. 1951. J. Exp. Biol., Lond. 28:358. [8] Gotch, F., J. Nadell, and I. E. Edelman. 1957. J. Clin. Invest. 36:289. [9] Harris, J. D. 1958. Am. J. Physiol. 195:499. [10] Harris, J. D. 1959. Ibid. 196:1266. [11] Harris, J. D. Unpublished. [12] Heyenga, H. 1939. Jahrber. Vet. Med. 65:299. [13] Koningsberger, V. J., E. J. Slijper, and H. J. Vonk, ed. 1946. Tabulae biol., Amst. 21(1):1. [14] Liebowitz, D., and E. E. Ellis. In press. Gastric secretory studies in the pig. [15] Lockwood, J. S., and H. T. Randall. 1949. Bull. N. York Acad. M. 25:228. [16] Masson, M. J., and A. T. Phillipson. 1952. J. Physiol., Lond. 116:98. [17] Raynaud, P. 1955. Arch. sc. physiol., Par. 9:35. [18] Schmidt, C. R., and A. C. Ivy. 1939. J. Cellul. Physiol. 13:219. [19] Van den Broeck, C. J. H., and A. P. de Groot. 1948. Physiol. comp. oecol., Gravenh. 1:148.

133. PHYSICAL PROPERTIES AND CHEMICAL COMPOSITION OF BILE: VERTEBRATES

Part I: MAN

Values in parentheses are ranges, estimate "c" (cf. Introduction).

	Property or Constituent	Bile		Reference
		Gallbladder	Liver	
	(A)	(B)	(C)	(D)
	Physical Properties			
1	Freezing point depression	0.56°C[1]		6
2	pH	6.0(5.6-8.0)	7.5(6.2-8.5)	13
3	Rate of secretion	(0.13-0.20) ml/min	(2.6-15.0) ml/kg body wt/24 hr	13
4	Specific conductivity	(99-137)/ohm cm at 30°C[1]		1
5	Specific gravity	1.026(1.010-1.032)	(1.008-1.015)	B,13;C,14
6	Surface tension	(38.95-41.31) dynes/cm[1]		1
7	Viscosity	(0.843-2.342) centipoises[1]		1
	General Chemical Components			
8	Acids	5180(1400-9200) mg/100 ml	1090(420-1830) mg/100 ml	15
9	Base, total		(150-180) mEq/L	4

/1/ Source of bile uncertain.

Part I: MAN (Continued)

	Property or Constituent	Bile		Reference
		Gallbladder	Liver	
	(A)	(B)	(C)	(D)
		General Chemical Components (concluded)		
10	Dry matter	18,000 mg/100 ml	(2300-3300) mg/100 ml	12
11	Inorganic matter	(500-1100) mg/100 ml	(200-900) mg/100 ml	4
12	Salts	11,500 mg/100 ml	(650-1400) mg/100 ml	12
13	Solids, total	11,140(4,700-16,500) mg/100 ml	2600(1000-4000) mg/100 ml	15
14	Water	85.92%	97.48%	B,2;C,8
		Electrolytes		
15	Bicarbonate	(8-12) mEq/L	40 mEq/L	B,14;C,2
16	Calcium	(5.0-7.0) mEq/L	(2.0-4.5) mEq/L	4
17	Chloride	(15-30) mEq/L	(75-110) mEq/L	4
18	Copper	(0.063-1.070) mg/100 ml[1]		9
19	Iodine Fasting subjects	(4-14) µg/100 ml[1]		5
20	Fed subjects	50 µg/100 ml[1]		
21	Iron	(0.031-1.680) mg/100 ml	6.8(4.8-7.8) mg/100 ml	7
22	Magnesium		1.5 mEq/L	13
23	Phosphorus	140 mg/100 ml	(9.0-22.3) mg/100 ml	12
24	Potassium		(2.6-12.0) mEq/L	10
25	Sodium		(131-164) mEq/L	10
		Nitrogenous Substances		
26	Protein, total	(315-539) mg/100 ml	273 mg/100 ml	11
27	Mucin + pigment	3420(1800-4300) mg/100 ml	610(430-930) mg/100 ml	15
28	Pigment	(200-1500) mg/100 ml	(50-170) mg/100 ml	4
29	Bilirubin	1000 mg/100 ml	(20-200) mg/100 ml	16
30	Coproporphyrin	10.07 µg/100 ml		3
31	Urobilinogen		0.6 mg/24 hr	8
32	Urea	(20-45) mg/100 ml	23.6 mg/100 ml	11
33	Nitrogen Total N	490 mg/100 ml	(67-92) mg/100 ml	12
34	Amino acid N	(6.0-21.6) mg/100 ml	5.4 mg/100 ml	11
35	Peptide N	(3.9-27.0) mg/100 ml	14.0 mg/100 ml	11
		Lipids, Carbohydrates, Vitamins		
36	Cholesterol	630(350-930) mg/100 ml	120(80-170) mg/100 ml	15
37	Fat, neutral	370(150-560) mg/100 ml	110(40-300) mg/100 ml	15
38	Fatty acids	970(900-1090) mg/100 ml	110(80-140) mg/100 ml	15
39	Lecithin	3500 mg/100 ml	(100-575) mg/100 ml	12
40	Phosphatide	(200-500) mg/100 ml	(50-80) mg/100 ml	4
41	Phospholipid	200(180-220) mg/100 ml	(50-60) mg/100 ml	15
42	Glucides, total	240 mg/100 ml	(35-91) mg/100 ml	12
43	Reducing sugars	80 mg/100 ml	(17-52) mg/100 ml	12
44	Choline, total	550 mg/100 ml	(35-89) mg/100 ml	12

/1/ Source of bile uncertain.

Contributors: (a) Frazer, A. C.; Sammons, H. G.; and Okunzua, G.; (b) Liebowitz, Daniel

References: [1] Aenile, E. O., and S. Garcia Fernandez. 1952. An. Fac. farm. Porto 12:107. [2] Bodansky, O. 1952. Biochemistry of disease. Macmillan, New York. [3] Brugsch, J. 1952. Zschr. ges. inn. Med. 7:321. [4] Cantarow, A., and B. Schepartz. 1954. Biochemistry. Ed. 1. W. B. Saunders, Philadelphia. p. 267. [5] Cantarow, A., and M. Trumper. 1955. Clinical biochemistry. Ed. 5. W. B. Saunders, Philadelphia. p. 165. [6] Hawk, P. B., B. L. Oser, and W. H. Summerson. 1954. Practical physiological chemistry. Ed. 13. Blakiston, New York. [7] Horrall, A. H. 1938. Bile, its toxicity and relation to disease. University of Chicago Press, Chicago. [8] Houssay, B. A., et al. 1951. Human physiology. McGraw-Hill, New York. [9] Judd, E. S., and

Part I: MAN (Concluded)

T. J. Dry. 1935. J. Laborat. Clin. M. 20:609. [10] Lockwood, J. S., and H. T. Randall. 1949. Bull. N. York Acad. M. 25:228. [11] Nagl, F. 1953-54. Zschr. klin. Med. 151:429. [12] Polonovski, M., and R. Bourrillon. 1952. Bull. Soc. chim. biol., Par. 34:703. [13] Sobotka, H. 1937. Physiological chemistry of the bile. Williams and Wilkins, Baltimore. [14] Sunderman, F. W., and F. Boerner. 1949. Normal values in clinical medicine. W. B. Saunders, Philadelphia. [15] West, E. S., and W. R. Todd. 1955. Textbook of biochemistry. Ed. 2. Macmillan, New York. [16] With, T. K. 1954. Biology of bile pigments. A. Frost-Hansen, Bogforlag. Copenhagen.

Part II: VERTEBRATES OTHER THAN MAN

Values in parentheses are ranges, estimate "c" (cf. Introduction).

| Animal | Property or Constituent | Bile | | Reference |
		Gallbladder	Liver	
(A)	(B)	(C)	(D)	(E)
1 Cat	pH	(5.0-6.0)		2
2	Rate of secretion		14.0 ml/kg body wt/24 hr	16
3	Base, fixed	27.4(26.1-31.8) mEq/L	17.2(15.7-19.4) mEq/L	10
4	Chloride	5(0-20) mEq/L	12(10-13) mEq/L	10
5	Pigment	(238-1190) mg/100 ml	119(52-218) mg/100 ml	16
6	Coproporphyrin	95.8 μg/100 ml		4
7	Phosphatase, alkaline	(190-416) units[1]/100 ml		7
8 Cattle	pH	(6.74-7.47)		18
9	Rate of secretion		15.4 ml/kg body wt/24 hr	16
10	Specific gravity		(1.022-1.025)	17
11	Acids	(1550-1700) mg/100 ml		18
12	Ash + alkali	(1250-1300) mg/100 ml		18
13	Water	90(83-91) %		18
14	Iron		(3-6) mg/100 ml	11
15	Mucin	500 mg/100 ml		18
16	Mucin + pigment	76(24-102) mg/100 ml	95 mg/100 ml	16
17	Lipids, total	(100-160) mg/100 ml		18
18	Cholesterol	60 mg/100 ml		18
19	Fat, neutral	(100-600) mg/100 ml		18
20 Dog	pH	(5.18-6.97)	(7.1-8.5)	C,2;D,8,15
21	Rate of secretion		12.0(5.2-52.5) mg/kg body wt/24 hr	16
22	Specific gravity		(1.008-1.015)	8
23	Acids	4.5(0.3-19.7) g/ml		18
24	Dry matter	(11,400-24,600) mg/100 ml	(2300-4500) mg/100 ml	14
25	Salts	(7,900-15,000) mg/100 ml	(500-2400) mg/100 ml	14
26	Water	91(76.0-97.1) %	95.9%	18
27	Bicarbonate		(14-68) mEq/L	3,15
28	Calcium	26.1 mEq/L	(3.7-7.2) mEq/L	15,18
29	Chloride		70(59-105) mEq/L	15
30	Iodine	(13-113) μg/100 ml[2]		18
31	Iron	(0.09-0.18) mg/100 ml	(1.8-16.0) mg/100 ml	4
32	Magnesium		3.6(2.2-5.0) mEq/L	15
33	Phosphorus, total	(87-280) mg/100 ml	(10-15) mg/100 ml	14
34	Potassium		(5.1-6.0) mEq/L	15
35	Sodium		168(150-203) mEq/L	15
36	Protein, total	(190-520) mg/100 ml	(130-210) mg/100 ml	14
37	Mucin + pigment	(96-387) mg/100 ml	107(16-387) mg/100 ml	16
38	Allantoin	18.9 mg/100 ml[2]		18
39	Ammonia	(0.4-0.6) mg/100 ml[2]		18

/1/ King-Armstrong unit; phenylphosphate substrate, modified Bodansky method. /2/ Source of bile uncertain.

	Animal	Property or Constituent	Bile		Reference
			Gallbladder	Liver	
	(A)	(B)	(C)	(D)	(E)
40	Dog (con-cluded)	Bilirubin	(92-170) mg/100 ml[3]	(42-55) mg/100 ml[3]	14
41		Coproporphyrin	146.7 µg/100 ml		4
42		Uric acid		(0.37-0.50) mg/100 ml[4]	18
43		Nitrogen, total	(255-635) mg/100 ml	(65-105) mg/100 ml	14
44		Cholesterol	(80-100) mg/100 ml	(4-15) mg/100 ml	14
45		Fatty acids, total	(1600-5000) mg/100 ml	(175-270) mg/100 ml	14
46		Lecithin	(2250-7000) mg/100 ml	(250-400) mg/100 ml	14
47		Glucides	(736-938) mg/100 ml		14
48		Reducing sugars	(64-72) mg/100 ml		14
49		Choline, total	(340-1110) mg/100 ml	(39-58) mg/100 ml	14
50		Phosphatase, alkaline	(0-900) units[1]/ml		1,12,13
51	Goat	Rate of secretion		11.8 ml/kg body wt/24 hr	16
52		Specific gravity		(1.004-1.010)	8
53		Ash		(480-760) mg/100 ml	8
54		Dry matter		(2880-4720) mg/100 ml	8
55		Pigment		126 mg/100 ml	16
56	Guinea pig	pH	(7.2-9.1)		18
57		Rate of secretion		228 ml/kg body wt/24 hr	16
58		Acids	780 mg/100 ml		18
59		Ash + alkali	100 mg/100 ml		18
60		Solids, total	2160 mg/100 ml		18
61		Water	97.8%		18
62		Iron	(0.09-0.18) mg/100 ml		11
63		Mucin	510 mg/100 ml		18
64		Mucin + pigment	(10-19) mg/100 ml	10 mg/100 ml	16
65		Lipids, total	140 mg/100 ml		18
66	Horse[5]	Rate of secretion		20.8 ml/kg body wt/24 hr	16
67		Specific gravity		1.010	6
68		Pigment		33(12.0-37.8) mg/100 ml	16
69	Rabbit	pH	(6.4-6.7)[4]		18
70		Rate of secretion		118 ml/kg body wt/24 hr	16
71		Specific gravity	1.048		18
72		Acids	(1100-2600) mg/100 ml		18
73		Bicarbonate		46 mEq/L	18
74		Calcium		4.8(4.0-9.5) mEq/L[4]	18
75		Chloride		82 mEq/L	18
76		Iodine Fasting		(4-14) µg/100 ml	18
77		Fed		(26-69) µg/100 ml	
78		Iron		0.13 mg/100 ml	11
79		Magnesium		0.5 mEq/L	18
80		Phosphate		2.5 mEq/L	18
81		Potassium		5.7 mEq/L	18
82		Sodium		151 mEq/L	18
83		Sulfate		4.4 mEq/L	18
84		Ammonia		(0.022-0.070) mg/100 ml	18
85		Pigment	(87.2-131.4) mg/100 ml	21.8 mg/100 ml	16
86		Cholesterol	(10-120) mg/100 ml		18
87		Reducing sugars		20 mg/100 ml	18
88		Phosphatase, alkaline	(56-302) units[1]/ml		12
89	Rat[5]	pH		8.3(7.9-8.5)	5
90		Rate of secretion		(28.6-47.1) ml/kg body wt/24 hr	16
91		Specific gravity		1.011	5,9
92		Mucin + pigment		(11-19) mg/100 ml	16
93		Bilirubin		8.3 mg/100 ml/24 hr	9
94		Cholesterol		12.7 mg/100 ml/24 hr	9
95	Sheep	pH	(5.98-6.72)		18
96		Rate of secretion		12.1 ml/kg body wt/24 hr	16

/1/ King-Armstrong unit; phenylphosphate substrate, modified Bodansky method. /3/ Van den Bergh method [19].
/4/ Fistula bile. /5/ Gallbladder absent.

Part II: VERTEBRATES OTHER THAN MAN (Concluded)

	Animal	Property or Constituent	Bile		Reference
			Gallbladder	Liver	
	(A)	(B)	(C)	(D)	(E)
97	Sheep	Specific gravity		(1.025-1.031)	17
98	(con-	Water	92%	95%	18
99	cluded)	Pigment	(50-110) mg/100 ml	107.5 mg/100 ml	16
100		Coproporphyrin	77.4 μg/100 ml		4
101	Swine	Rate of secretion		25.2 ml/kg body wt/24 hr	16
102		Acids	(7,900-12,000) mg/100 ml		18
103		Salts	7200 mg/100 ml	(8,500-12,000) mg/100 ml	14
104		Solids, total	10,600 mg/100 ml	(11,500-18,900) mg/100 ml	14
105		Phosphorus, total	20.5 mg/100 ml	(48-116) mg/100 ml	14
106		Protein	420 mg/100 ml	(280-410) mg/100 ml	14
107		Mucin + pigment	24(20-60) mg/100 ml	33 mg/100 ml	16
108		Bilirubin		(32.0-61.5) mg/100 ml	14
109		Coproporphyrin	77.4 μg/100 ml		4
110		Nitrogen, total	266 mg/100 ml	(370-480) mg/100 ml	14
111		Lipids, total	1800 mg/100 ml		18
112		Cholesterol	37 mg/100 ml	(130-180) mg/100 ml	14
113		Fat, neutral	(200-450) mg/100 ml		18
114		Fatty acids, total	370 mg/100 ml	(820-2000) mg/100 ml	14
115		Lecithin	520 mg/100 ml	(1200-2900) mg/100 ml	14
116		Glucides, total		(120-300) mg/100 ml	14
117		Reducing sugars		(37-150) mg/100 ml	14
118		Choline, total	80 mg/100 ml	(180-450) mg/100 ml	14
119	Chicken	pH		(6.0-6.2)	8
120		Rate of secretion		14.2 ml/kg body wt/24 hr	16
121		Mucin + pigment	413 mg/100 ml	147 mg/100 ml	16
122	Goose	Acids	19,000 mg/100 ml		18
123		Ash + alkali	2100 mg/100 ml		
124		Solids, total	21,950 mg/100 ml		
125		Water	77.3%		
126		Mucin + pigment	3100 mg/100 ml		

Contributors: (a) Frazer, A. C.; Sammons, H. G.; and Okunzua, G.; (b) Liebowitz, Daniel, (c) Wilson, D. Wright

References: [1] Armstrong, A. R., and E. J. King. 1934. Canad. M. Ass. J. 31:14. [2] Best, C. H., and N. B. Taylor. 1955. The physiological basis of medical practice. Ed. 6. Williams and Wilkins, Baltimore. [3] Bodansky, O. 1952. Biochemistry of disease. Macmillan, New York. [4] Brugsch, J. 1952. Zschr. ges. inn. Med. 7:321. [5] Byers, S. O., M. Friedman, and F. Michaelis. 1950. Fed. Proc., Balt. 9:20. [6] Carr, J. G. 1944. Vet. Bull., Lond. 14:66. [7] Dalgaard, J. B. 1949. Acta physiol. scand. 15:298. [8] Dukes, H. H. 1955. The physiology of domestic animals. Ed. 7. Comstock, Ithaca. [9] Friedman, M., S. O. Byers, and F. Michaelis. 1950. Am. J. Physiol. 162:577. [10] Gamble, J. L., and M. A. McIver. 1928. J. Exp. M. 48:852. [11] Horrall, A. H. 1938. Bile, its toxicity and relation to disease. University of Chicago Press, Chicago. [12] Jacoby, F., and B. F. Martin. 1951. J. Anat., Lond. 85:391. [13] King, E. J. 1951. Micro-analysis in medical biochemistry. Ed. 2. J. and A. Churchill, London. [14] Polonovski, M., and R. Bourrillon. 1952. Bull. Soc. chim. biol., Par. 34:703. [15] Reinhold, J. G., and D. W. Wilson. 1934. Am. J. Physiol. 107:378. [16] Schmidt, C. R., and A. C. Ivy. 1937. J. Cellul. Physiol. 10:365. [17] Smith, F. 1917. A manual of veterinary physiology. Ed. 4. Eger, Chicago. [18] Sobotka, H. 1937. Physiological chemistry of the bile. Williams and Wilkins, Baltimore. [19] Van den Bergh, A. A. H., and W. Grotepass. 1934. Brit. M. J. 1:1157.

Part I: MAN

Secretion collected by external pancreatic fistula. Values in parentheses are ranges, estimate "c" (cf. Introduction).

Property or Constituent	Value	Reference	Property or Constituent	Value	Reference
(A)	(B)	(C)	(A)	(B)	(C)
Physical Properties			**Nitrogenous Substances**		
1 Freezing point depression	0.625°C	7	17 Protein, total	(190-340) mg/100 ml	9
			18 Albumin	60 mg/100 ml	9
2 pH	(8.6-8.8)	5	19 Globulin	40 mg/100 ml	9
3 Rate of secretion	1.0(0.02-5.20) ml/min	11	20 Creatinine	Trace	5
4 Specific gravity	(1.005-1.014)	11	21 Urea	(0.5-4.0) mg/100 ml	5
General Chemical Components			22 Uric acid	Trace	5
			Nitrogen		9
5 Ash	(570-860) mg/100 ml	4,10	23 Total N	(190-340) mg/100 ml	
Solids			24 Non-protein N	14.3 mg/100 ml	
6 Total	(1240-1540) mg/100 ml	4,10,14	25 Urea N	5.0 mg/100 ml	
7 Organic	(380-690) mg/100 ml	10	26 Uric acid N	0.2 mg/100 ml	
8 Water	98.7%	8	**Carbohydrates, Enzymes**		
Electrolytes[1]			27 Glucose	(8.5-18.0) mg/100 ml	5
9 Bicarbonate	70(66-127) mEq/L	3	28 Amylase	(6.4-31.1) units/100 ml	1
10 Calcium	(2.2-3.2) mEq/L	9	29 Lipase	(300-2728) units/100 ml	1
11 Chloride	76.6(54.1-95.2) mEq/L	6	30 Phosphatase	(0.8-12.7) Bodansky units/100 ml	5
12 Magnesium	0.3 mEq/L	12	Proteolytic enzymes		13
13 Phosphate	(0.026-1.220) mEq/L	5,12	31 Total	(9.4-139.0) mg trypsin/100 ml[2]	
14 Potassium	4.6(2.6-7.4) mEq/L	3	32 Active	(0.04-16.50) mg trypsin/100 ml[2]	
15 Sodium	141(113-153) mEq/L	3	33 Trypsin	(7.1-42.8) units/100 ml	2
16 Sulfate	8.4 mEq/L	12			

/1/ Traces of copper and zinc present; cobalt, iron, and nickel absent.   /2/ Casein substrate.

Contributors: (a) Hollander, Franklin, (b) Frazer, A. C.; Sammons, H. G.; and Okunzua, G.; (c) Liebowitz, Daniel

References: [1] Baxter, S. G. 1935-36. Am. J. Digest. Dis. 2:109. [2] Bodansky, O. 1933. J. Biol. Chem. 100:561. [3] Bodansky, O. 1952. Biochemistry of disease. Macmillan, New York. [4] Glaessner, K. 1903-04. Zschr. physiol. Chem. 40:465. [5] Kogut, B., M. J. Matzner, and A. E. Sobel. 1936. J. Clin. Invest. 15:393. [6] Lockwood, J. S., and H. T. Randall. 1949. Bull. N. York Acad. M. 25:228. [7] Luckhardt, A. B., F. Stangl, and F. C. Koch. 1923. Am. J. Physiol. 63:397. [8] Mattice, M. R. 1936. Chemical procedures for clinical laboratories. Lea and Febiger, Philadelphia. [9] Miller, J. M., and T. B. Wiper. 1944. Ann. Surg. 120:852. [10] Schumm, O. 1902. Zschr. physiol. Chem. 36:292. [11] Sunderman, F. W., and F. Boerner. 1949. Normal values in clinical medicine. W. B. Saunders, Philadelphia. [12] Tria, E., and G. Fabriani. 1941. Atti Accad. Italia 2:381. [13] Troll, W., H. Doubilet, and T. Cancro. 1951. Gastroenterology 19:326. [14] Wohlgemuth, J. 1912. Biochem. Zschr. 39:302.

Part II: MAMMALS OTHER THAN MAN

Values in parentheses are ranges, estimate "c" (cf. Introduction).

	Animal	Property or Constituent	Value	Reference
	(A)	(B)	(C)	(D)
1	Cat	Calcium	(4.6-5.1) mEq/L	1
2		Chloride	(67-93) mEq/L	8
3	Cattle	Rate of secretion	4.2 ml/min	6
4		Calcium	(0.4-2.8) mEq/L	7
5		Chloride	(93-124) mEq/L	7
6		Magnesium	(Trace-0.7) mEq/L	7
7		Potassium	(8-9) mEq/L	7
8		Sodium	(148-156) mEq/L	7
9	Dog	Acid combining power[1]	(58.8-80.4) mEq/L	15
10		Freezing point depression	(0.56-0.66) °C	2,17
11		pH	(7.1-8.2)	2,5
12		Rate of secretion	(0.2-1.1) ml/min	2,6
13		Specific gravity	(1.004-1.031)	14,20
14		Ash	(840-970) mg/100 ml	14,15
		Solids		
15		Total	(1400-6390) mg/100 ml	2,14,15
16		Organic	(480-2200) mg/100 ml	15
17		Water	98.04%	6
18		Bicarbonate	(93-143) mEq/L	2,19
19		Calcium	(1.8-2.0) mEq/L	2
20		Chloride	(71-106) mEq/L	2
21		Magnesium	(0.2-1.4) mEq/L	7,14
22		Phosphate	(0.7-3.6) mM/L	2,8,12,14
23		Potassium	(2.5-7.0) mEq/L	2,8,14,15
24		Sodium	(149-162) mEq/L	2
25		Protein	(500-4800) mg/100 ml	5
26		Urea	(24.0-58.5) mg/100 ml	12
		Nitrogen		
27		Total N	(100-936) mg/100 ml	2,11,14,15,20
28		Protein N	(74.8-84.3) mg/100 ml	15
29		Non-protein N	(18-84) mg/100 ml	12,15
30		Glucose	25 mg/100 ml	13
31		Lactate	(0.1-0.7) mEq/L	12,13
32		Amylase[1]	(23,900-47,500) mg maltose/ml[2]	10
33		Lipase[1]	(9,750-33,250) ml 0.05 NaOH/ml[3]	9
34		Pseudocholinesterase[1]	(420-1080) units[4]/ml	16
35		Trypsin[1]	(407.5-2440.0) mg tyrosine/ml[5]	9
36	Rabbit	Rate of secretion	0.006 ml/min	19
37		Amylase	(1.6-8.3) units/min	4
38		Lipase	(0-0.4) units/min	4
39			(4.2-6.8) ml 0.01 normal NaOH/ml[6]	3
40		Trypsin	(7.50-24.15) units[7]/min	4
41			(686-5140) units/ml	19
42	Swine	Rate of secretion	1.0 ml/min	6
43		Ash	(500-1900) mg/100 ml	18
		Solids		18
44		Total	(1200-2500) mg/100 ml	
45		Organic	(500-700) mg/100 ml	

/1/ Secretin stimulated. /2/ Starch substrate. /3/ Olive oil emulsion substrate. /4/ Unit = amount of enzyme that liberates 1 μL CO_2/min; 0.06 M acetylcholine perchlorate substrate. /5/ Casein substrate. /6/ Vagus nerve cut. /7/ Unit = 0.1 ml juice capable of flocculating 2 ml milk.

Contributors: (a) Hollander, Franklin, (b) Frazer, A. C.; Sammons, H. G.; and Okunzua, G.; (c) Liebowitz, Daniel

References: [1] Agren, G. 1935. Biochem. Zschr. 281:358. [2] Ball, E. G. 1930. J. Biol. Chem. 86:449. [3] Baxter, S. G. 1931. Am. J. Physiol. 96:343. [4] Baxter, S. G. 1935-36. Am. J. Digest. Dis. 2:109. [5] Best, C. H., and N. B. Taylor. 1955. The physiological basis of medical practice. Ed. 6. Williams and Wilkins, Baltimore. [6] Dukes, H. H. 1955. The physiology of domestic animals. Ed. 7. Comstock, Ithaca.

[7] Frouin, A., and P. Gérard. 1912. C. rend. Soc. biol. 72:98. [8] Gamble, J. L., and M. A. McIver. 1928. J. Exp. M. 48:849. [9] Grossman, M. I., H. Greengard, and A. C. Ivy. 1942-43. Am. J. Physiol. 138:676. [10] Hallenbeck, G. A., M. Dworetzky, and C. F. Code. 1950. Ibid. 162:117. [11] Hart, W. H., and J. E. Thomas. 1945. Gastroenterology 4:409. [12] Hartmann, A. F., and R. Elman. 1929. J. Exp. M. 50:387. [13] Hata, M. 1940. Mitt. Med. Akad. Kioto 30:279. [14] Johnston, C. G., and E. G. Ball. 1930. J. Biol. Chem. 86:643. [15] Komarov, S. A., G. O. Langstroth, and D. R. McRae. 1939. Canad. J. Res. 17(D):113. [16] McCance, R. A., L. M. Brown, R. S. Comline, and D. A. Titchen. 1951. Nature, Lond. 168:788. [17] Pincussohn, L. 1907. Biochem. Zschr. 4:484. [18] Sineschekov, A. D. 1939. Fiziol. Z. SSSR 27:70. [19] Thomas, J. E. 1950. The external secretions of the pancreas. C. C. Thomas, Springfield, Ill. [20] Thomas, J. E., and J. O. Crider. 1944. Am. J. Physiol. 140:574.

135. PHYSICAL PROPERTIES AND CHEMICAL COMPOSITION OF DUODENAL SECRETION: MAMMALS

Part I: MAN

Values in parentheses are ranges, estimate "c" (cf. Introduction).

Property or Constituent	Value	Reference	Property or Constituent	Value	Reference
(A)	(B)	(C)	(A)	(B)	(C)
Physical Properties			**Nitrogenous Substances (concluded)**		
1 Icteric index	59(17-299)	4	Amino acids (concluded)		3
2 Osmotic pressure	199.8(138-276) mOsm/L	6	26 Threonine	1.8 mg/100 ml	
3 pH	(5.8-7.6)	10	27 Tryptophan	1.1 mg/100 ml	
4 Rate of secretion	1.07(0.37-2.50) ml/min	6	28 Tyrosine	0.5 mg/100 ml	
5 Specific gravity	1.0078(1.0040-1.0107)	14	29 Valine	1.9 mg/100 ml	
Electrolytes			30 Bilirubin	5.56(0.9-18.0) mg/100 ml	5
6 Bicarbonate	7.8(4.0-21.1) mEq/L	6	31 Urobilinogen	0.85(0-3.65) mg/100 g	5
7 Calcium	12.4 mg/100 ml	6	Nitrogen		
8 Chloride	86.1(50.8-132.6) mEq/L	6	32 Total N	47(33-61) mg/100 ml	6
9 Phosphorus, total	5.1(4.7-5.5) mg/100 ml	6	33 α-Amino N	9.2 mg/100 ml	3
10 Potassium	(1.0-11.0) mEq/L	12	**Lipids, Miscellaneous Organic Acids**		
11 Sodium	(84.8-143.4) mEq/L	10	34 Cholesterol	36.1(0-315) mg/100 ml	14
Nitrogenous Substances			35 Cholic acid	(130-460) mg/100 ml	9
Amino acids		3	**Enzymes**		
12 Alanine	3.1 mg/100 ml		36 Amylase	(2-8) units/ml[1]	2
13 Arginine	2.9 mg/100 ml		37	637 glucose units/hr[2]	8
14 Aspartic acid	3.0 mg/100 ml		38 Lipase	(20-60) units/ml[3]	2
15 Cystine	4.5 mg/100 ml		39 Fatty acid-	179 units/hr[4]	8
16 Glutamic acid	2.2 mg/100 ml		40 Phosphatase, alkaline	(10-30) Bodansky units/100 ml[5]	11
17 Glycine	1.7 mg/100 ml		Proteolytic enzymes		13
18 Histidine	1.2 mg/100 ml		41 Total	(35.4-78.4) mg trypsin/100 ml[6]	
19 Isoleucine	1.1 mg/100 ml				
20 Leucine	1.2 mg/100 ml		42 Active	(16.4-47.5) mg trypsin/100 ml[6]	
21 Lysine	2.2 mg/100 ml				
22 Methionine	2.0 mg/100 ml		43 Trypsin	(8-30) units/ml[7]	2
23 Phenylalanine	1.7 mg/100 ml		44	87.7 units/hr[8]	8
24 Proline	3.0 mg/100 ml				
25 Serine	2.0 mg/100 ml				

/1/ Starch solution substrate, Agren and Lagerlöf method [1]. /2/ Starch solution substrate, Lagerlöf method [8]. /3/ Olive oil substrate, Frazer method [2]. /4/ Tributyrin substrate, Lagerlöf method [8]. /5/ Disodium phenylphosphate substrate, King method [7]; value rises to 200 after fatty meal. /6/ Casein substrate. /7/ Azo-albumin substrate, Tomarelli method [12]. /8/ Lagerlöf method [8].

Part I: MAN (Concluded)

Contributors: (a) Frazer, A. C.; Sammons, H. G.; and Okunzua, G.; (b) Cummins, Alvin J., (c) Forrest, Andrew P. M.

References: [1] Agren, G., and H. O. Lagerlöf. 1936. Acta med. scand. 90:1. [2] Anderson, C. M., J. M. French, H. G. Sammons, A. C. Frazer, J. W. Gerrard, and J. M. Smellie. 1952. Lancet, Lond. 262:837. [3] Austin, J. H., and D. D. Gammon. 1931. J. Clin. Invest. 10:287. [4] Free, A. H., A. J. Beams, and V. C. Myers. 1943. Gastroenterology 1:88. [5] Hollan, O. R. 1950. Ibid. 16:418. [6] Karr, W. G., and W. O. Abbott. 1935. J. Clin. Invest. 14:893. [7] King, E. J. 1951. Micro-analysis in medical biochemistry. Ed. 2. J. and A. Churchill, London. p. 70. [8] Lagerlöf, H. O. 1942. Acta med. scand., Suppl. 128. [9] Ross, C. A. C., A. C. Frazer, J. M. French, J. W. Gerrard, H. G. Sammons, and J. M. Smellie. 1955. Lancet, Lond. 268:1087. [10] Ross, C. A. C., and H. G. Sammons. Unpublished. [11] Sammons, H. G., and M. D. Thompson. Unpublished. [12] Tomarelli, R. M., J. Charney, and M. L. Harding. 1949. J. Laborat. Clin. M. 34:428. [13] Troll, W., H. Doubilet, and T. Cancro. 1951. Gastroenterology 19:326. [14] Voegtlin, W. L., H. Greengard, and A. C. Ivy. 1934. Am. J. Physiol. 110:198.

Part II: MAMMALS OTHER THAN MAN

With the exception of horse and sheep, values are for secretions of the Brunner's glands and duodenal mucosa. Values in parentheses are ranges, estimate "c" (cf. Introduction).

Animal	Property or Constituent	Value	Reference	Animal	Property or Constituent	Value	Reference
(A)	(B)	(C)	(D)	(A)	(B)	(C)	(D)
1 Cat	pH	(8.7-8.9)	3	20 Rabbit	pH	(8.6-9.0)	3
2	Specific gravity	1.009		21	Specific gravity	1.009	
3	Inorganic matter	8.42 mg/g		22	Inorganic matter	10.23 mg/g	
4	Organic matter	4.88 mg/g		23	Organic matter	4.98 mg/g	
5	Solids, total	13.30 mg/g		24	Solids, total	15.21 mg/g	
6 Dog	pH	8.4	3	25 Sheep[2]	pH	(2.3-4.7)	4
7	Specific gravity	1.009		26	Specific gravity	1.007	
8	Inorganic matter	9.26 mg/g		27	Ash	(3.9-6.5) mg/g	
9	Organic matter	6.15 mg/g		28	Dry matter	(30-66) mg/g	
10	Solids, total	15.41 mg/g		29	Acidity, total	(39-62) mEq/L	
11 Goat	pH	(8.2-8.4)	3	30	Acid, volatile	(5-19) mEq/L	
12	Specific gravity	(1.007-1.008)		31	Chloride	(109-135) mEq/L	
13	Inorganic matter	7.73 mg/g		32 Swine	pH	(8.4-8.9)	3
14	Organic matter	6.83 mg/g		33	Specific gravity	(1.007-1.008)	
15	Solids, total	14.56 mg/g		34	Inorganic matter	6.81 mg/g	
16 Horse[1]	pH	7.13	2	35	Organic matter	4.99 mg/g	
17	Specific gravity	1.008	1	36	Solids, total	11.80 mg/g	
18	Water	98.47%	1				
19	Mucus	0.95%	1				

/1/ Duodenal juice. /2/ Duodenal content.

Contributors: (a) Frazer, A. C.; Sammons, H. G.; and Okunzua, G.; (b) Forrest, Andrew P. M.

References: [1] Colin, G. 1872. Traité de physiologie comparée des animaux, considérée dans ses rapports avec les sciences naturelles, la médecine, la zootechnie et l'economie rurale. Ed. 2. J. B. Baillière & fils. v. 1, p. 818. [2] Dukes, H. H. 1955. The physiology of domestic animals. Ed. 7. Comstock, Ithaca. [3] Florey, H. W., and H. E. Harding. 1934. J. Path. Bact., Lond. 39:255. [4] Masson, M. J., and A. T. Phillipson. 1952. J. Physiol., Lond. 116:98.

136. PHYSICAL PROPERTIES AND CHEMICAL COMPOSITION OF JEJUNAL SECRETION: MAN, DOG

Values in parentheses are ranges, estimate "c" (cf. Introduction).

	Animal (A)	Property or Constituent (B)	Value (C)	Reference (D)
1	Man	Freezing point depression	0.507(0.400-0.577) °C	5
2		Osmolar concentration	268(212-305) mM/L	5
3		pH	6.51(5.07-7.07)	2
4		Rate of secretion	0.43(0.17-0.70) ml/min	7
5		Base, total	139(114-162) mEq/L	5
6		Bicarbonate	13(2-32) mEq/L	5
7		Calcium	10.1(5.2-11.6) mg/100 ml[1]	4
8			8.0(5.4-12.8) mg/100 ml[2]	
9		Chloride	117(80-139) mEq/L	5
10		Phosphorus, total	10.1(7.1-13.2) mg/100 ml[1]	4
11			7.2(7.1-7.3) mg/100 ml[2]	
12		Bilirubin	5.99(0.80-18.50) mg/100 ml	3
13		Urobilinogen	0.62(0-2.96) mg/100 g	3
14		Nitrogen, total	55(45-63) mg/100 ml	4
15			56(45-73) mg/100 ml	
16		Lipase	6(3-10) units/ml	6
17	Dog	pH	6.83(6.46-7.28)	1
18		Ash	0.88(0.76-0.94) g/100 ml	
19		Solids	1.65(1.22-2.34) g/100 ml	
20		Bicarbonate	21.7(5.2-30.0) mEq/L	
21		Calcium	2.7(1.6-5.4) mEq/L	
22		Chloride	147(141-153) mEq/L	
23		Magnesium	0.9(0.2-1.9) mEq/L	
24		Phosphate	3.1(1.2-7.9) mEq/L	
25		Potassium	6.3(4.2-10.2) mEq/L	
26		Sodium	141(126-152) mEq/L	

/1/ Upper jejunum. /2/ Lower jejunum.

Contributors: (a) Cummins, Alvin J., (b) De Beer, Edwin J., (c) Wilson, D. Wright

References: [1] De Beer, E. J., C. G. Johnston, and D. W. Wilson. 1935. J. Biol. Chem. 108:113. [2] Gotschlick, E. 1928. Deut. Arch. klin. Med. 159:288. [3] Hollan, O. R. 1950. Gastroenterology 16:418. [4] Karr, W. G., and W. O. Abbott. 1935. J. Clin. Invest. 14:893. [5] McGee, L. C., and A. B. Hastings. 1945. Gastroenterology 4:243. [6] Owles, W. H. 1937. Clin. Sc., Lond. 3:11. [7] Owles, W. H. 1937. Ibid. 3:21.

137. PHYSICAL PROPERTIES AND CHEMICAL COMPOSITION OF ILEAL SECRETION: MAN, DOG

Part I: MAN

Portion of ileum beyond pylorus: upper = 90 cm; middle = 120 cm; lower = 160 cm. Values in parentheses are ranges, estimate "c" (cf. Introduction).

	Property or Constituent (A)	Portion of Ileum (B)	Value (C)	Reference (D)		Property or Constituent (A)	Portion of Ileum (B)	Value (C)	Reference (D)
	Physical Properties					General Chemical Components			
1	Osmotic pressure		277(238-299) mOs/L	3	7	Ash		0.866%	1
					8	Dry matter		9.3(6.0-13.6) %	9
2	pH	Upper	6.10[1]	3	9	Solids		1.16%	1
3		Middle	7.05(6.77-7.21)		10	Water		90.5(86.4-93.9) %	9
4		Lower	7.23(7.16-7.31)			Electrolytes			
5	Rate of secretion	Middle	0.56(0.18-1.05) ml/min	3					
6		Lower	0.37(0.28-0.47) ml/min		11	Bicarbonate	Upper	2.3 mEq/L	3

/1/ Sammons method [7].

137. PHYSICAL PROPERTIES AND CHEMICAL COMPOSITION OF ILEAL SECRETION: MAN, DOG (Continued)

Part I: MAN (Concluded)

	Property or Constituent	Portion of Ileum	Value	Reference		Property or Constituent	Portion of Ileum	Value	Reference
	(A)	(B)	(C)	(D)		(A)	(B)	(C)	(D)
	Electrolytes (continued)					Electrolytes (concluded)			
12	Bicarbonate	Middle	19.8(3.9-39.8) mEq/L	3	26	Sodium		129.4(105.4-143.7) mEq/L	4
13	(concluded)	Lower	14.6(10.4-17.0) mEq/L			Nitrogenous Substances			
14	Calcium	Upper	5.3(5.2-5.4) mg/100 ml	3	27	Bilirubin		8.45(1.2-32.5) mg/100 ml	2
15		Middle	7.9(5.0-12.8) mg/100 ml		28	Urobilinogen		0.30(0-0.97) mg/100 g	2
16		Lower	7.4(5.0-9.8) mg/100 ml		29	Nitrogen,	Upper	47(40-54) mg/100 ml	3
17	Chloride	Upper	128.6 mEq/L	3	30	total	Middle	69(53-86) mg/100 ml	
18		Middle	118.7(101.0-132.6) mEq/L		31		Lower	44(34-53) mg/100 ml	
19		Lower	126.6(123.9-128.2) mEq/L			Enzymes			
20	Iron		17.0(2.2-17.7) mg/100 ml	9					
21	Magnesium		22.8(18.4-27.9) mg/100 ml	9	32	Lipase		2.5(1.4-4.3) units/ml[1]	6
22	Phosphorus,	Upper	5.8(4.5-7.1) mg/100 ml	3	33			325(80-780) ml/24 hr[1]	
23	total	Middle	5.7(4.5-7.3) mg/100 ml		34	Mucinase		(150-1000) units/24 hr[2]	5
24		Lower	6.3 mg/100 ml		35	Proteolytic activity		242(40-685) units[3]	8
25	Potassium		11.2(5.9-29.3) mEq/L	4					

/1/ Sammons method [7]. /2/ Sammons method [5]. /3/ Tomarelli method [7].

Contributors: (a) Cummins, Alvin J., (b) Senior, John, and Fitts, William T., Jr., (c) Frazer, A. C.; Sammons, H. G.; and Okunzua, G.

References: [1] Bickel, A., and H. R. Kanitz. 1934. Biochem. Zschr. 270:378. [2] Hollan, O. R. 1950. Gastroenterology 16:418. [3] Karr, W. G., and W. O. Abbott. 1935. J. Clin. Invest. 14:893. [4] Lockwood, J. S., and H. T. Randall. 1949. Bull. N. York Acad. M. 25:228. [5] Sammons, H. G. 1951. Lancet, Lond. 261:239. [6] Sammons, H. G. Unpublished. [7] Sammons, H. G., A. C. Frazer, and M. Thompson. 1956. J. Clin. Path. 9:379. [8] Sammons, H. G., C. A. C. Ross, and W. A. Wood. 1955. Clin. Sc., Lond. 14:157. [9] Welch, C. S., E. G. Wakefield, and M. Adams. 1936. Arch. Int. M. 58:1095.

Part II: DOG

Values in parentheses are ranges, estimate "c" (cf. Introduction).

	Property or Constituent	Value	Reference		Property or Constituent	Value	Reference
	(A)	(B)	(C)		(A)	(B)	(C)
	Physical Properties & General Chemical Components				Electrolytes (concluded)		
1	pH	(7.61-8.66)	2	9	Sodium	151(146-156) mEq/L	2
2	Ash	(0.89-0.98) g/100 ml	2		Enzymes		
3	Solids	(1.31-1.78) g/100 ml	2	10	Amylase	(530-1242) mg/hr	4
	Electrolytes			11	Invertase	(686-1415) mg/hr	4
4	Bicarbonate	91.9(69.8-114.0) mEq/L	2	12	Lipase	(51.5-119.0) mg/hr	4
5	Calcium	(5.0-5.5) mEq/L		13	Peptidase	(28.1-65.2) mg/hr	4
6	Chloride	78.4(68.1-87.9) mEq/L	2	14	Phosphatase, alkaline	(51.68-239.89) Bodansky units[1]	3
7	Phosphate	(0.5-0.7) mEq/L	2	15	Sucrase	(113-1415) mg/hr[2]	4
8	Potassium	(4.7-6.8) mEq/L	2				

/1/ Sodium glycerophosphate substrate, Bodansky method [1]. /2/ Sucrose substrate, Shaffer-Somogyi method.

419

Contributors: (a) Senior, John, and Fitts, William T., Jr., (b) De Beer, Edwin J., (c) Wilson, D. Wright, (d) Frazer, A. C.; Sammons, H. G.; and Okunzua, G.

References: [1] Bodansky, A. J. 1933. J. Biol. Chem. 101:93. [2] De Beer, E. J., C. G. Johnston, and D. W. Wilson. 1935. Ibid. 108:113. [3] Kosman, A. J., J. W. Kaulbersz, and S. Freeman. 1943. Am. J. Physiol. 138:236. [4] Schiffrin, M. J., and E. S. Nasset. 1939. Ibid. 128:70.

138. DIGESTIVE ENZYMES: VERTEBRATES

Symbols: (+) = present, (-) = absent, (±) = doubtful.

Animal	Organ	Tissue (T) or Secretion (S)	Amylase (Diastase)	Carbonic Anhydrase	Elastase	Enterokinase	Erepsin, Peptidase	Invertase (Saccharase)	Lipase, Esterases	Maltase	Pepsin	Phosphatase	Ribonuclease	Rennin (Chymosin)	Trypsin, Other Non-acid Proteases	Urease	Reference
(A)	(B)	(C)	(D)	(E)	(F)	(G)	(H)	(I)	(J)	(K)	(L)	(M)	(N)	(O)	(P)	(Q)	(R)
1 Man	Salivary gland	T							+								20
2		S	+				+		+			+					10
3	Esophagus	T							+								20
4	Stomach	T							+		+	+				+	J,20;L,M,10;Q,7
5		S							+		+			-[1]			J,15;L,10;O,21
6	Pancreas	T					+		+								15
7		S	+				+		+	+					+		D,K,P,4;H,J,15
8	Small intestine	T	+				+					+					D,10;H,15;M,17
9		S	±			+	+	+	±								D,15;G-J,24
10	Cecum and colon	T										+					17
11 Cat	Salivary gland	T										+					17
12		S	-														10
13	Stomach	T		+					+			+				+	E,4;J,10;M,17;Q,7
14		S								+							4
15	Pancreas	T		+			+			+		±					E,K,4;H,10;M,17
16		S	+						+								4
17	Small intestine	T		+		+	±					+			+		E,4;G,H,P,10;M, 17
18		S	+			+	±	±	-						-		D,H,I,P,24;G,10; J,17
19	Cecum and colon	T							+			+					J,13;M,17
20	Colon	S							-								13
21 Cow	Salivary gland	S	±						+								10
22	Esophagus	T									-						15
23	Stomach	T	+						+					+[2]		+	D,P,17;J,10;O,20
24		S								+				±[2]			L,4;O,10
25	Pancreas	T	+						+				+		+		D,15;J,10;N,P,20
26		S	+												+		15
27	Small intestine	T								-		+					L,15;M,9
28		S				+											10
29 Dog	Salivary gland	S	-						+								10
30	Esophagus	T									-						15

/1/ In adult. /2/ Only in young.

	Animal	Organ	Tissue (T) or Secretion (S)	Amylase (Diastase)	Carbonic Anhydrase	Elastase	Enterokinase	Erepsin, Peptidase	Invertase (Saccharase)	Lipase, Esterases	Maltase	Pepsin	Phosphatase	Ribonuclease	Rennin (Chymosin)	Trypsin, Other Non-acid Proteases	Urease	Reference
	(A)	(B)	(C)	(D)	(E)	(F)	(G)	(H)	(I)	(J)	(K)	(L)	(M)	(N)	(O)	(P)	(Q)	(R)
31	Dog	Stomach	T		+					+							+	E,4;J,15;Q,7
32	(con-cluded)		S	±						+		+			±²			D,J,15;L,O,3
33		Pancreas	T	+		+		+		+				+		+		D,H,J,P,4;F,5;N,16
34			S	+				+		+	+					+		4
35		Small intestine	T				+	+		+			+					G,4;H,J,15;M,17
36			S	+			+	+	±	±						±		D,I,J,P,24;G,H,4
37		Cecum and colon	S	±			-	±		+								D,J,15;G,H,11
38	Goat	Salivary gland	S	-														15
39		Stomach	T														-	17
40			S												+²			
41		Small intestine	S	±			+	-	±	±						-		D,H-J,P,24;G,10
42	Guinea pig	Salivary gland	S	+														10
43		Stomach	T							+								10
44		Pancreas	T			+		+										F,6;H,10
45			S							+								15
46		Small intestine	T					+										10
47	Horse	Salivary gland	S	±						+								D,15;J,17
48		Stomach	T							+								10
49		Small intestine	T									-						15
50			S³	+			+		+	-	+					+		D,I-K,P,1;G,10
51		Cecum and colon	T	+														22
52	Monkey	Salivary gland	S	+				+										D,10;H,3
53		Stomach	S									+						19
54		Small intestine	S				+											10
55	Rabbit	Salivary gland	S	±														3
56		Stomach	T		+					+		+	+				+	E,4;J,10;L,15;M,17;Q,7
57			S							+								15
58		Pancreas	T		+			+										E,4;H,10
59			S	+						+						+		4
60		Small intestine	T		+			+				-	+					E,4;H,L,15;M,17
61			S	+			+	-		±						-		D,H,J,P,24;G,10
62		Cecum and colon	T											+				17
63	Rat	Salivary gland	S	+														18
64		Stomach	T	+	+					+		+					+	D,14;E,4;J,10;L,17;Q,7
65		Pancreas	T	+	+	+				+						+		D,E,J,P,4;F,6
66			S	+														4
67		Small intestine	T	+	+		+	+			+		+					D,H,K,23;E,4;G,M,17
68		Colon	T	+														14
69	Sheep	Salivary gland	S	-						+								10
70		Esophagus	T									-						15
71		Stomach	T							+		+			+²		+	J,10;L,Q,17;O,21
72		Pancreas	T	+						+				+		+		D,J,10;N,2;P,17
73			S	+												+		D,10;P,17
74		Small intestine	S					+										10
75		Cecum and colon	T						-									15
76	Swine	Salivary gland	S	+														10
77		Esophagus	T									-						15
78		Stomach	T					+		+		+					+	H,J,L,10;Q,7
79			S	-								+			+²			D,L,8;O,10

/2/ Only in young.   /3/ Lactase also present [1].

Animal	Organ	Tissue (T) or Secre- tion (S)	Enzyme														Reference
			Amylase (Diastase)	Carbonic Anhydrase	Elastase	Enterokinase	Erepsin, Peptidase	Invertase (Saccharase)	Lipase, Esterases	Maltase	Pepsin	Phosphatase	Ribonuclease	Rennin (Chymosin)	Trypsin, Other Non-acid Proteases	Urease	
(A)	(B)	(C)	(D)	(E)	(F)	(G)	(H)	(I)	(J)	(K)	(L)	(M)	(N)	(O)	(P)	(Q)	(R)
80 Swine (con- clud- ed)	Pancreas	T	+		+		+		+				+		+		D,H,J,P,10;F,12; N,16
81		S	+		+										+		D,P,15;F,12
82	Small intestine	T				+	-		+		±	+					G,16;H,24;J,10;L, 15;M,17
83		S	+			+		±	±						-		D,I,J,P,24;G,10
84 Chicken	Salivary gland	S	+														10
85	Stomach	T							+		+						J,10;L,20
86	Pancreas	T	+														10
87	Small intestine	T	+														10
88 Frog	Salivary gland	S	+														10
89	Esophagus	T									+						15
90	Stomach	T									+					+	L,10;Q,7
91		S									+						10
92	Pancreas	T					+		+						+		H,10;K,P,17
93	Small intestine	T					+		-								H,10;K,17
94 Fish	Salivary gland	S	±														15
95	Esophagus	T									+						15
96	Stomach	T							+		+			−[1]			J,10;L,O,15
97	Pancreas	T	+						+	+					+		D,10;J,K,P,17
98	Small intestine	T	±						+	-							D,10;J,15;K,17

/1/ In adult.

Contributors: Hollander, Franklin, and Lauber, Frances U.

References: [1] Alexander, F., and A. K. Chowdhury. 1958. Nature, Lond. 181:190. [2] Aqvist, S. E. G., and C. B. Anfinsen. 1959. J. Biol. Chem. 234:1112. [3] Babkin, B. P. 1929. Die äussere Sekretion der Verdauungs- drüsen. Ed. 2. Springer Verlag, Berlin. [4] Babkin, B. P. 1950. Secretory mechanism of the digestive glands. Ed. 2. P. B. Hoeber, New York. [5] Carter, A. E. 1956. Science 123:669. [6] Cohen, H., H. Megel, and W. Kleinberg. 1958. Proc. Soc. Exp. Biol., N. Y. 97:8. [7] Conway, E. J. 1953. The biochemistry of gastric acid secretion. C. C. Thomas, Springfield, Ill. [8] Dukes, H. H. 1955. The physiology of domestic animals. Ed. 7. Comstock, Ithaca. [9] Harris, E. S., W. R. Bergren, L. A. Bavetta, and J. W. Mehl. 1952. Proc. Soc. Exp. Biol., N. Y. 81:593. [10] Koningsberger, V. J., E. J. Slijper, and H. J. Vonk, ed. 1946. Tabulae biol., Amst. v. 21, pt. 1. [11] Kuvaeva, I. B. 1957. Fiziol. Z. SSSR 43:311. [12] Lewis, U. J., D. E. Williams, and N. G. Brink. 1956. J. Biol. Chem. 222:705. [13] Martin, B. F. 1959. Nature, Lond. 183:1464. [14] McGeachin, R. L., and K. F. Norwood, Jr. 1959. Am. J. Physiol. 196:972. [15] Oppenheimer, C. 1925-26. Die Fermente und ihre Wirkungen. Ed. 5. Georg Thieme, Leipzig. v. 1 and 2. [16] Oppenheimer, C., and L. Pincussen, ed. 1929. Ibid. Georg Thieme, Leipzig. v. 3. [17] Oppenheimer, C. 1935-39. Ibid. Suppl. (2v.) W. Junk, Verlag, Den Haag. [18] Schneyer, L. H., and C. A. Schneyer. 1956. Fed. Proc., Balt. 15:164. [19] Smith, G. P., and F. P. Brooks. 1959. Ibid. 18:147. [20] Sumner, J. B., and K. Myrbäck. 1951. The enzymes: chemistry and mechanism of action. Academic Press, New York. v. 1. [21] Sumner, J. B., and K. Myrbäck. 1951. Ibid. Academic Press, New York. v. 2. [22] Sym, E. A., W. Stankiewicz, and F. Zielinski. 1939. Enzymologia, Den Haag 6:113. [23] Van Genderen, H., and C. Engel. 1938. Ibid. 5:71. [24] Wright, R. D., M. A. Jennings, H. W. Florey, and R. Lium. 1940. Q. J. Exp. Physiol., Lond. 30:73.

139. GASTRIC SECRETION TESTS: MAN

Part I: BASAL SECRETION AND HISTAMINE RESPONSE

Method of determining <u>basal secretion</u>: Levin tube introduced through nose into stomach after overnight fast; tip of tube approximately at level of the angulus (fluoroscopically checked); stomach emptied completely, residue discarded, and continuous aspiration initiated; 15-minute samples analyzed throughout a 1-hour period. Method of determining <u>histamine response</u>: Immediately following completion of procedure for measuring basal secretion, histamine dihydrochloride (0.01 mg histamine base/kg body weight) administered subcutaneously, and gastric content collected every 15 minutes for 1 hour. Values in parentheses are ranges, estimate "b" (cf. Introduction).

	Test	Subjects			Volume ml/hr	Free HCl Concentration mEq/L[1]	Free HCl Output mEq/hr
		Sex	No.	Age, yr			
	(A)	(B)	(C)	(D)	(E)	(F)	(G)
1	Basal	♂	49	20-29	77.6(0-120.6)	33.9(0-94.9)	2.6(0-8.8)
2	secretion		80	30-39	77.2(0-159.0)	31.4(0-65.2)	2.7(0-8.4)
3			80	40-49	90.6(5.3-175.9)	31.5(0-86.6)	3.1(0-9.5)
4			80	50-59	77.2(0-155.4)	28.9(0-82.2)	2.4(0-7.9)
5			30	60+	65.1(0-148.0)	16.1(0-69.1)	1.2(0-4.0)
6		♀	34	20-29	69.0(0-158.5)	26.3(0-73.4)	2.0(0-6.9)
7			58	30-39	71.2(0-155.8)	23.3(0-73.1)	1.9(0-7.5)
8			64	40-49	71.8(0-154.4)	21.4(0-73.8)	2.1(0-7.8)
9			56	50-59	60.2(0-132.9)	13.3(0-54.9)	0.9(0-3.6)
10			29	60+	47.6(0-101.6)	10.1(0-31.3)	1.1(0-7.1)
11	Histamine	♂	49	20-29	124.8(7.0-242.6)	76.7(8.8-144.6)	9.8(0-20.4)
12	response		80	30-39	137.8(20.5-255.1)	76.1(15.6-136.6)	11.2(0-24.7)
13			80	40-49	147.4(12.3-282.5)	72.2(0-155.8)	11.7(1.7-21.7)
14			80	50-59	127.2(0-264.1)	66.9(0-141.6)	9.5(0-34.0)
15			30	60+	108.3(0-254.6)	44.3(0-128.2)	6.3(0-18.7)
16		♀	34	20-29	93.9(3.2-184.6)	64.8(5.1-124.5)	6.1(0-14.4)
17			58	30-39	104.0(5.8-202.2)	60.4(0-125.3)	6.7(0-15.4)
18			64	40-49	104.7(0-228.6)	59.1(0-124.2)	6.7(0-17.0)
19			56	50-59	97.0(0-196.4)	47.8(0-116.1)	5.5(0-15.2)
20			29	60+	84.3(0-193.3)	45.3(0-112.0)	5.1(0-15.1)

/1/ 1 mEq/L = 1 "clinical unit" or 1 "degree of acidity" (ml of 0.1 normal NaOH required to neutralize 100 ml of gastric secretion).

<u>Contributors</u>: (a) Notkin, Louis J., (b) Roth, James L. A., (c) Livermore, George R., Jr.

<u>Reference</u>: Levin, E., J. B. Kirsner, and W. L. Palmer. 1951. Gastroenterology 19:88.

Part II: NOCTURNAL SECRETION AND INSULIN RESPONSE

Method of determining <u>nocturnal secretion</u>: At 5:30 p. m., all subjects given identical meal containing 37 g carbohydrate, 3 g protein, and no fat (no food or water permitted thereafter). At 8:00 p. m., Levin tube introduced through nose into stomach (fluoroscopically checked), and stomach completely emptied. At 8:30 p. m., continuous suction initiated and maintained until 8:30 a. m. the following morning; hourly samples analyzed throughout 12-hour period. Method of determining <u>insulin response</u>: Lagerlöf-Ågren double tube introduced into duodenum and stomach, and one or more fasting specimens obtained, followed by elicitation of histamine response. 16 international units of insulin administered intravenously 1 hour after histamine injection (secretory impulse seems to coincide with, or to follow immediately the lowest point of hypoglycemia, 35-40 minutes after intravenous injection of insulin). Values in parentheses are ranges, estimate "c" (cf. Introduction).

	Test	Subjects			Volume ml/hr	Free HCl Concentration mEq/L[1]	Free HCl Output mEq/hr	Reference
		Sex	No.	Age, hr				
	(A)	(B)	(C)	(D)	(E)	(F)	(G)	(H)
1	Nocturnal	♂	10[2]	20-29	49.3(14.4-77.4)	32(1-64)	1.6(0.03-4.8)	2
2	secretion		10[3]	30-38	60.0(27.7-99.0)	29(5-90)	1.9(0.2-7.8)	
3			1	60	30.4	9	0.3	
4		♀	12[2]	19-32	38.3(12.3-75.3)	27(3-72)	1.2(0.05-5.7)	
5	Insulin	♂	18	16-35	140.3(84.5-204.0)	122.9(103.0-139.9)[4]	17.2(8.8-26.9)[5]	1
6	response	♀	6	16-26	108.6(70.0-176.0)	122.6(105.3-132.6)[6]	13.3(7.4-23.3)[7]	

/1/ 1 mEq/L = 1 "clinical unit" or 1 "degree of acidity" (ml of 0.1 normal NaOH required to neutralize 100 ml of gastric secretion). /2/ 17 determinations. /3/ 15 determinations. /4/ Total = 128.5(111.5-144.3) mEq/L. /5/ Total = 18.0(9.4-28.5) mEq/hr. /6/ Total = 128.5(111.9-137.8) mEq/L. /7/ Total = 14.0(7.8-24.3) mEq/hr.

Part II: NOCTURNAL SECRETION AND INSULIN RESPONSE (Concluded)

Contributors: (a) Livermore, George R., Jr., (b) Roth, James L. A., (c) Notkin, Louis J.

References: [1] Ihre, B. J. E. 1938. Acta med. scand., Suppl. 95, p. 1. [2] Levin, E., J. B. Kirsner, W. L. Palmer, and C. Butler. 1948. Arch. Surg. 56:345.

Part III: TEST MEAL RESPONSE

3746 normal subjects observed 1 hour after test meal of 8 arrowroot cookies and 400 ml water. Values in parentheses are ranges, estimate "b" (cf. Introduction).

	Subjects		Volume ml/hr	Free HCl mEq/L[1]	Total HCl mEq/L[1]	Achlorhydria, %	
	Sex	Age, yr				True	Apparent
	(A)	(B)	(C)	(D)	(E)	(F)	(G)
1	♂	20-24	118.0(19.0-217.0)	46.7(13.7-79.7)	63.5(30.5-96.5)		
2		25-29	116.5(15.5-217.5)	47.0(13.0-81.0)	63.0(30.6-95.4)		2.0
3		30-34	113.5(13.5-213.5)	47.0(14.0-80.0)	62.5(30.1-94.9)	3.0	5.2
4		35-39	109.5(12.5-206.5)	47.0(14.0-80.0)	61.7(28.9-94.5)	6.3	8.5
5		40-44	105.0(13.0-197.0)	46.5(13.5-79.5)	60.7(26.3-95.1)	9.5	11.7
6		45-49	101.0(15.0-187.0)	45.5(12.1-78.9)	59.5(22.7-96.3)	12.7	15.0
7		50-54	97.5(15.5-179.5)	43.7(8.5-88.9)	58.3(10.1-96.5)	16.0	18.5
8		55-59	95.0(11.0-179.0)	41.5(4.1-78.9)	57.0(18.6-95.4)	19.3	21.5
9		60-64	93.5(3.5-183.5)	39.3(0.5-78.1)	55.5(17.9-93.1)	22.0	25.0
10		65-69	92.0(0-186.0)	37.3(0.3-74.3)	53.7(18.7-98.7)	22.5	26.0
11		70-79	91.0(0-192.0)	33.5(0-67.5)	50.5(17.1-83.9)	17.0	21.0
12	♀	20-24	100.5(22.5-178.5)	32.0(3.0-61.0)	49.7(20.7-78.7)	2.0	3.0
13		25-29	100.0(22.0-178.0)	33.0(5.0-61.0)	50.0(21.6-78.4)	4.5	6.5
14		30-34	99.0(21.0-177.0)	33.0(5.6-60.4)	50.5(21.1-79.9)	7.3	10.0
15		35-39	97.7(19.7-175.7)	33.0(5.0-61.0)	50.5(20.3-80.7)	10.0	13.5
16		40-44	96.0(16.0-174.0)	33.0(5.4-60.6)	50.5(20.1-80.9)	12.7	17.0
17		45-49	94.0(17.0-171.0)	33.0(6.0-60.0)	50.5(22.1-78.9)	14.5	20.5
18		50-54	92.0(17.0-167.0)	33.0(5.0-61.0)	50.5(21.1-79.9)	18.2	24.0
19		55-59	89.5(15.5-163.5)	33.5(3.5-63.5)	50.5(19.9-81.1)	21.0	27.5
20		60-64	87.0(15.0-159.0)	33.5(1.5-65.5)	50.5(18.5-82.5)	23.5	31.0
21		65-69	84.0(14.0-154.0)	33.5(1.5-65.5)	50.5(17.1-83.9)	26.3	31.5
22		70-79	79.0(13.0-145.0)	33.5(3.1-63.9)	50.5(16.1-84.9)	24.0	28.7

/1/ 1 mEq/L = 1 "clinical unit" or 1 "degree of acidity" (ml of 0.1 normal NaOH required to neutralize 100 ml of gastric secretion).

Contributors: (a) Roth, James, L. A., (b) Notkin, Louis J., (c) Livermore, George R., Jr.

Reference: Vanzant, F. R., W. C. Alvarez, J. Berkson, and G. B. Eusterman. 1933. Arch. Int. M. 52:616.

XXI. Reproductive Secretions

140. PHYSICAL PROPERTIES AND CHEMICAL COMPOSITION OF PROSTATIC FLUID: MAN, DOG

Values in parentheses are ranges, estimate "c" unless otherwise indicated (cf. Introduction).

Property or Constituent	Man[1]	Dog[2]	Reference
(A)	(B)	(C)	(D)
Physical Properties			
1 pH	6.5(6.3-6.6)	6.1(5.8-6.5)[b]	7
2 Specific gravity	1.022(1.018-1.027)[3]	(1.006-1.008)	B,3;C,1
3 Volume of ejaculate	(13-32) % of semen[4]	97% of semen	B,7;C,6
General Chemical Components			
4 Water	93.2(92.7-93.6) %	98.1(97.5-98.7)[b]	7
Electrolytes			
5 Calcium	60(57-65) mEq/L	0.6 mEq/L	B,6;C,4
6 Carbon dioxide	4.2(3.1-5.4) mM/L	2.05(1.51-2.59)[b] mM/L	B,6;C,1
7 Chloride	38(35-46) mEq/L	156(144-168)[b] mEq/L	B,6;C,1
Phosphorus			
8 Inorganic P	1(1-2) mg/100 ml[5]	Trace	B,6;C,4
9 Acid-soluble P	1.09(0.65-1.77) mEq/L	Trace	4
10 Lipid P	7(6-9) mg/100 ml[6]	(1-2) mg/100 ml[3,6]	7
11 Potassium	48(29-61) mEq/L	5.1(4.7-5.5)[b] mEq/L	B,6;C,4
12 Sodium	153(149-158) mEq/L	159(154-165)[b] mEq/L	B,6;C,4
Nitrogenous Substances			
13 Protein, total	2550(2460-2640) mg/100 ml	0.8 mg/100 ml	B,6;C,4
14 Spermine	+		7
Nitrogen			
15 Total N	416(295-511) mg/100 ml	210 mg/100 ml[7]	B,6;C,9
16 Non-protein N	54(30-90) mg/100 ml	22 mg/100 ml	B,6;C,4
Lipids			
17 Lipids, total	286(260-310) mg/100 ml	(30-40) mg/100 ml	B,10;C,7
18 Cephalin	107(82-135) mg/100 ml[8]		10
19 Cholesterol	80(62-105) mg/100 ml	166(130-210) mg/100 ml	B,10;C,9
20 Fatty acids, volatile (as CH_3COOH)		10 mg/100 ml	11
21 Glycerylphosphorylcholine		20(2-38)[h] mg/100 ml[9]	11
Phosphatides			
22 Total	179.8(144.2-225.0) mg/100 ml		10
23 Ether-insoluble	72.8(62.6-90.0) mg/100 ml[8]		10
Miscellaneous Organic Acids, Vitamins			
24 Citric acid	(480-2690) mg/100 ml	30 mg/100 ml	B,5;C,7
25 Vitamin C (ascorbic acid)	0.54(0.51-0.57)[b] mg/100 ml	0.8(0.6-0.9) mg/100 ml	1
Enzymes			
26 Amylase	+	+	7
27 Diamine oxidase	+		7
28 Fibrinolysin	+	+	7
29 Fibrogenase	+	+	7
Phosphatase			
30 Acid	(25,500-172,700) units[10]/100 ml	(3-286) units[10]/100 ml[11]	B,2;C,1
31 Alkaline	Low	(0-107) units[10]/100 ml[11]	B,8;C,1

/1/ Values are for resting fluid. /2/ Values are for fluid of animals under pilocarpine stimulation. /3/ 14 observations. /4/ 21 observations. /5/ 16 observations. /6/ Multiply by 25.8 to obtain total phospholipids. /7/ 30 observations. /8/ 10 observations. /9/ 8 observations. /10/ Unit = the amount of phosphatase which, when allowed to act upon monophenylphosphate, liberates 1 mg of phenol in 1 hour at 37°C. /11/ 17 observations.

Contributors: (a) White, I. G., (b) Bitman, Joel, (c) McKenzie, Fred F.; Wu, S. H.; and Das, Jogananda

References: [1] Berg, O. C., C. Huggins, and C. V. Hodges. 1941. Am. J. Physiol. 133:82. [2] Huggins, C. 1945. Physiol. Rev. 25:281. [3] Huggins, C. 1947. Harvey Lect., Balt. 42:148. [4] Huggins, C., M. H. Masina, L. Eichelberger, and J. D. Wharton. 1939. J. Exp. M. 70:543. [5] Huggins, C., and W. Neal. 1942. Ibid. 76:527. [6] Huggins, C., W. W. Scott, and J. H. Heinen. 1942. Am. J. Physiol. 136:467. [7] Mann, T. 1954. Biochemistry of semen. Methuen, London. [8] Mann, T., and C. Lutwak-Mann. 1951. Physiol. Rev. 31:27. [9] Moore, R. A., M. L. Miller, and A. McLellan. 1941. J. Urol., Balt. 46:132. [10] Scott, W. W. 1945. Ibid. 53:712. [11] White, I. G. 1959. Unpublished.

141. PHYSICAL PROPERTIES AND CHEMICAL COMPOSITION OF SEMEN: MAN

Values in parentheses are ranges, estimate "c" unless otherwise indicated (cf. Introduction).

Property or Constituent	No. of Observations	Value	Reference
(A)	(B)	(C)	(D)
Physical Properties			
1 Conductivity		(88-107) mho x 10^{-4}	15
2 Freezing point depression		(0.55-0.58) °C	15
3 pH		7.4(7.1-7.5)	15
4 Specific gravity		1.035(1.031-1.039)	7
5 Spermatozoa		100(50-150) million/ml	17
6 Volume of ejaculate		3.5(2.0-6.0) ml	15
General Chemical Components			
7 Water		91.8(89.1-94.4) %	15
Electrolytes			
8 Calcium	32	15(7-31) mEq/L[1]	11
9 Carbon dioxide		54(43-74) ml/100 ml	17
10 Chloride		43(28-57) mEq/L[1]	9
11 Magnesium		12 mEq/L	15
Phosphorus			
12 Total P	1	112(90-120) mg/100 ml	15
13 Inorganic P		11 mg/100 ml	15
14 Acid-soluble P	10	95(67-140) mg/100 ml	10
15 Lipid P		6 mg/100 ml[2]	15
16 Potassium		23(17-27) mEq/L[1]	9
17 Sodium		117(100-133) mEq/L[1]	9
18 Zinc	3[3]	14.0(5.0-22.0) mg/100 ml	15
Nitrogenous Substances			
19 Protein		4.5(3.30-6.85) g/100 ml	9
20 Amino acids, free		+	15
21 Ammonia		2 mg/100 ml	15
22 Creatine	20[3]	20 mg/100 ml	19
23 Ergothioneine		(0-trace)	15
24 Spermine		(20-250) mg/100 ml	15
25 Urea		72 mg/100 ml[1]	15
26 Uric acid		6 mg/100 ml	15
Nitrogen[4]			
27 Total N	34	913(560-1225) mg/100 ml	15
28 Non-protein N	22	90(53-130) mg/100 ml	9, 15

/1/ For seminal plasma. /2/ Multiply by 25.8 to obtain total phospholipids [15]. /3/ Number of subjects.
/4/ Total protein = 6.25 x (total nitrogen minus non-protein nitrogen).

	Property or Constituent	No. of Observations	Value	Reference
	(A)	(B)	(C)	(D)

Lipids, Carbohydrates

	Property or Constituent	No. of Observations	Value	Reference
29	Cholesterol		80 mg/100 ml	9
30	Fatty acids, volatile (as CH_3COOH)		4	18
31	Glycerylphosphorylcholine	4	70(50-100) mg/100 ml	2
32	Phosphorylcholine		(70-2000) mg/100 ml	15
33	Plasmalogen	1	0[1]	5
34	Fructose	150	290(50-600) mg/100 ml	6

Miscellaneous Organic Acids, Vitamins, Hormones

	Property or Constituent	No. of Observations	Value	Reference
35	Citric acid	371	480(0-2340) mg/100 ml	15
36	Lactic acid		35(20-50) mg/100 ml	15
37	Vitamin C (ascorbic acid)	9	12.8(11.2-14.4)[b] mg/100 ml	15
38	Choline		(256-380) mg/100 ml	2
39	Inositol, total	10^3	(50-70) mg/100 ml	4
40	Male hormones		+	15
41	Female hormones		+	15

Enzymes

	Property or Constituent	No. of Observations	Value	Reference
	β-N-Acetylglucosaminidase			1
42	As phenol		11,200 μg/ml[5]	
43	As o- or p-nitrophenol		19,600 μg/ml[5]	
44	Aminopeptidase		++	13
45	Amylase		+	15
46	Cholinesterase		+	15
47	Diamine oxidase		+	15
48	Fibrinolysin		++	8
	Galactosidase			1
49	α- (as phenol)		0	
50	β- (as o- or p-nitrophenol)		125 μg/ml[5]	
	Glucosidase			1
51	α- (as o- or p-nitrophenol)		160 μg/ml[5]	
52	β- (as o- or p-nitrophenol)		0	
53	β-Glucuronidase (as phenolphthalein)		350 μg/ml[5]	1
54	Hyaluronidase		++	15
	Mannosidase			1
	α-			
55	As phenol		105 μg/ml[5]	
56	As o- or p-nitrophenol		355 μg/ml[5]	
57	β- (as phenol)		200 μg/ml[5]	
58	5-Nucleotidase		+	14
59	Pepsinogen		++	12, 16
	Phosphatase			
60	Acid	173	370,000(50,000-800,000) units[6]/100 ml	3
61	Alkaline		Low	15

/1/ For seminal plasma. /3/ Number of subjects. /5/ Liberated in 1 hour at 37°C. /6/ Units = the amount of phosphatase which, when allowed to act upon monophenylphosphate, liberates 1 mg of phenol in 1 hour at 37°C.

Contributors: (a) White, I. G., (b) McKenzie, Fred F.; Wu, S. H.; and Das, Jogananda, (c) Lundquist, Frank

References: [1] Conchie, J., and T. Mann. 1957. Nature, Lond. 179:1190. [2] Dawson, R. M. C., T. Mann, and I. G. White. 1957. Biochem. J., Lond. 65:627. [3] Engberg, H., E. Andersson, B. Sury, and J. Raft. 1947. J. Endocr., Oxf. 5:42. [4] Hartree, E. F. 1957. Biochem. J., Lond. 66:131. [5] Hartree, E. F., and T. Mann. 1959. Ibid. 71:423. [6] Harvey, C. 1948. Nature, Lond. 162:812. [7] Huggins, C. 1947. Harvey Lect., Balt. 42:148. [8] Huggins, C. B., and W. Neal. 1942. J. Exp. M. 76:527. [9] Huggins, C., W. W. Scott, and J. H. Heinen. 1942. Am. J. Physiol. 136:467. [10] Lundquist, F. 1947. Acta physiol. scand. 13:322. [11] Lundquist, F. 1949. Ibid., Suppl. 66. [12] Lundquist, F., and H. H. Seedorff. 1952. Nature, Lond. 170:1115. [13] Lundquist, F.,

141. PHYSICAL PROPERTIES AND CHEMICAL COMPOSITION OF SEMEN: MAN (Concluded)

T. Thorsteinsson, and O. Buus. 1955. Biochem. J., Lond. 59:69. [14] Mann, T. 1945. Ibid. 39:451. [15] Mann, T. 1954. Biochemistry of semen. Methuen, London. [16] Seedorff, H. H. 1956. Spermapepsin-undersøgelser. G. E. C. Gad, Copenhagen. [17] White, I. G. 1958. Anim. Breed. Abstr. 26(2):109. [18] White, I. G. 1959. Unpublished. [19] White, I. G., and D. E. Griffith. 1958. Austral. J. Exp. Biol. 36:97.

142. PHYSICAL PROPERTIES AND CHEMICAL COMPOSITION OF SEMEN: MAMMALS OTHER THAN MAN

Part I: DOG

Values in parentheses are ranges, estimate "c" unless otherwise indicated (cf. Introduction).

	Property or Constituent	No. of Subjects	Value	Reference
	(A)	(B)	(C)	(D)
	Physical Properties			
1	Conductivity		$(129-138)$ mho x 10^{-4}	5
2	Freezing point depression		$(0.58-0.60)^{\circ}$C	5
3	pH	100^1	6.8(5.8-6.9)	3
4	Specific gravity		1.011	5
5	Spermatozoa	100^1	125(4-540) million/ml	3
6	Volume of ejaculate	100^1	10.0(1.0-25.0) ml	3
	General Chemical Components			
7	Water		97.6%	5
	Electrolytes			
8	Calcium	3	0.5 mEq/L	1
9	Chloride	3	150 mEq/L	1
10	Copper	3	0.5 mg/100 ml	1
11	Iron	3	0.05 mg/100 ml	1
12	Magnesium	3	0.5 mEq/L	1
13	Phosphorus, acid-soluble	3	7.4 mg/100 ml	1
14	Potassium	3	8 mEq/L	1
15	Sodium	3	156 mEq/L	1
16	Zinc	3	8.0 mg/100 ml	1
	Nitrogenous Substances			
17	Creatine	3	0	7
18	Nitrogen, total	3	480 mg/100 ml	1
	Lipids, Carbohydrates, Acids			
19	Lipids, total		182 mg/100 ml	5
20	Fatty acids, volatile (as CH_3COOH)		10 mg/100 ml	6
21	Glycerylphosphorylcholine	4	$180(110-240)^b$ mg/100 ml	6
22	Fructose	3	0.6 mg/100 ml	1
23	Sorbitol		<0.1 mg/100 ml	4
24	Citric acid		Trace	5
	Enzymes			
	β-N-Acetylglucosaminidase			2
25	As phenol		3250 µg/ml^2	
26	As o- or p-nitrophenol		6900 µg/ml^2	
27	Amylase		+	5
28	Fibrinogenase		+	5
29	Fibrinolysin		+	5
	Galactosidase			2
30	α- (as phenol)		0	
31	β- (as o- or p-nitrophenol)		70 µg/ml^2	

/1/ Number of observations. /2/ Liberated in 1 hour at 37°C.

Part I: DOG (Concluded)

Property or Constituent	No. of Subjects	Value	Reference
(A)	(B)	(C)	(D)
Enzymes (concluded)			
			2
32 Glucosidase α- (as o- or p-nitrophenol)		20 μg/ml^2	
33 β- (as o- or p-nitrophenol)		0	
34 β-Glucuronidase (as phenolphthalein)		10 μg/ml^2	2
35 Hyaluronidase		+	5
Mannosidase α-			2
36 As phenol		180 μg/ml^2	
37 As o- or p-nitrophenol		410 μg/ml^2	
38 β- (as phenol)		15 μg/ml^2	

/2/ Liberated in 1 hour at 37°C.

Contributors: (a) White, I. G., (b) McKenzie, Fred F.; Wu, S. H.; and Das, Jogananda

References: [1] Bartlett, D. J. 1958. Nature, Lond. 182:1605. [2] Conchie, J., and T. Mann. 1957. Ibid. 179:1190. [3] Harrop, A. E. 1956. 3rd Internat. Congr. Anim. Reprod. p. 95. [4] King, T. E., F. A. Isherwood and T. Mann. In O. Hoffmann-Ostenhof, ed. 1959. Proc. 4th Internat. Congr. Biochem., Vienna, 1958. v. 15, p. 77. [5] Mann, T. 1954. Biochemistry of semen. Methuen, London. [6] White, I. G. 1959. Unpublished. [7] White, I. G., and D. E. Griffith. 1958. Austral. J. Exp. Biol. 36:97.

Part II: CATTLE

Values in parentheses are ranges, estimate "c" unless otherwise indicated (cf. Introduction).

Property or Constituent	No. of Subjects	No. of Observations	Value	Reference
(A)	(B)	(C)	(D)	(E)
Physical Properties				
1 Conductivity			105(90-116) mho x 10^{-4}	13
2 Freezing point depression			0.61(0.54-0.73) °C	13
3 pH			6.9(6.4-7.8)	13
4 Specific gravity		125	1.034(1.015-1.053)	1
5 Spermatozoa			1000(300-2000) million/ml	13
6 Volume of ejaculate			4.0(2.0-10.0) ml	13
General Chemical Components				
7 Water	10	1	90.5%	13
Electrolytes				
8 Calcium	5	10	23(10-40)^b mEq/L	4
9 Carbon dioxide			16 ml/100 ml	13
10 Chloride		107	50 mEq/L^1	15
11 Copper	5	10	0.6(0.2-1.0)^b mg/100 ml	4
12 Iron	5	10	0.6(0.3-0.9)^b mg/100 ml	4
13 Magnesium	5	10	10(8-12)^b mEq/L	4
Phosphorus				
14 Total P	5	10	80(20-100)^b mg/100 ml	4
15 Inorganic P	10	1	9 mg/100 ml	13
16 Acid-soluble P	10	1	33 mg/100 ml	13
17 Lipid P	10	1	9 mg/100 ml^2	13

/1/ For seminal plasma. /2/ Multiply by 25.8 to obtain total phospholipids [13].

Part II: CATTLE (Continued)

	Property or Constituent	No. of Subjects	No. of Observations	Value	Reference
	(A)	(B)	(C)	(D)	(E)
	Electrolytes (concluded)				
18	Potassium	4	16	45(20-70) mEq/L	5
19	Sodium	5	10	115(65-165)[b] mEq/L	4
	Nitrogenous Substances				
20	Proteose			+	13
	Amino acids				11
21	Alanine			0.25 mg/100 ml[1]	
22	Aspartic acid			0.09 mg/100 ml[1]	
23	Glutamic acid			0.35 mg/100 ml[1]	
24	Glycine			0.09 mg/100 ml[1]	
25	Histidine			0.16 mg/100 ml[1]	
26	Phenylalanine			0.16 mg/100 ml[1]	
27	Serine			0.13 mg/100 ml[1]	
28	Ammonia	10	1	2 mg/100 ml	13
29	Creatine			3 mg/100 ml	13
30	Creatinine			12 mg/100 ml	13
31	Ergothioneine			(0-trace)	13
32	Spermine			0	17
33	Urea	10	1	4 mg/100 ml	13
34	Uric acid	10	1	6 mg/100 ml	13
	Nitrogen[3]				13
35	Total N	10	1	756 mg/100 ml	
36	Non-protein N	10	1	48 mg/100 ml	
	Lipids, Carbohydrates				
37	Fatty acids, volatile (as CH_3COOH)			5 mg/100 ml	18
38	Glycerylphosphorylcholine	6	7	350(100-500) mg/100 ml	6
39	Phosphorylcholine			Trace	17
40	Plasmalogen			(30-90) mg/100 ml	2
41	Fructose	26	660	550(200-900)[b] mg/100 ml	7
42	Sorbitol			(10-140) mg/100 ml	10
	Miscellaneous Organic Acids, Salts				
43	Citric acid		660	700(300-1100) mg/100 ml	7
44	Lactic acid		10	29(15-43) mg/100 ml	13
45	Sulfite		14	8.1 mg/100 ml	11
	Vitamins, Hormones				
46	Vitamin B_1 (thiamine)		10	0.09(0.03-0.15) mg/100 ml	13
47	Vitamin B_2 (riboflavin)		10	0.21(0.15-0.31) mg/100 ml	13
48	Vitamin C (ascorbic acid)		14	6.1(3.0-9.0) mg/100 ml	11, 13
49	Inositol, total	4	6	60(40-90) mg/100 ml	8
50	Niacin (nicotinic acid)		10	0.36(0.25-0.55) mg/100 ml	13
51	Pantothenic acid		10	0.37(0.23-0.47) mg/100 ml	13
52	Male hormones			+	13
	Enzymes				
53	β-N-Acetylglucosaminidase (as phenol)			16,700 μg/ml[4]	3
54	ʟ-Amino acid oxidase			+	13
55	Amylase			+	12
	Galactosidase				3
56	α- (as phenol)			0	
57	β- (as o- or p-nitrophenol)			420 μg/ml[4]	
	Glucosidase				3
58	α- (as o- or p-nitrophenol)			60 μg/ml[4]	
59	β- (as o- or p-nitrophenol)			0	

/1/ For seminal plasma. /3/ Total protein = 6.25 x (total nitrogen minus non-protein nitrogen). /4/ Liberated in 1 hour at 37°C.

Part II: CATTLE (Concluded)

	Property or Constituent	No. of Subjects	No. of Observations	Value	Reference
	(A)	(B)	(C)	(D)	(E)
	Enzymes (concluded)				
60	β-Glucuronidase (as phenolphthalein)			1030 μg/ml[4]	3
61	Hyaluronidase			+++	13
	Mannosidase				3
62	α- (as o- or p-nitrophenol)			620 μg/ml[4]	
63	β- (as phenol)			265 μg/ml[4]	
64	5-Nucleotidase			+++	9
65	Peptidases			+	16
	Phosphatase				14
66	Acid		56	170(50-340) units[5]/100 ml	
67	Alkaline		56	390(100-3460) units[5]/100 ml	
68	Proteinases			0	16
69	Xanthine oxidase			+	13

/4/ Liberated in 1 hour at 37°C. /5/ Unit = the amount of phosphatase which, when allowed to act upon mono-phenylphosphate, liberates 1 mg of phenol in 1 hour at 37°C.

Contributors: (a) White, I. G., (b) McKenzie, Fred F.; Wu, S. H.; and Das, Jogananda

References: [1] Anderson, J. 1946. J. Agr. Sc. 36:258. [2] Boguth, W. 1952. Naturwissenschaften 39:432. [3] Conchie, J., and T. Mann. 1957. Nature, Lond. 179:1190. [4] Cragle, R. G., G. W. Salisbury, and J. H. Muntz. 1958. J. Dairy Sc. 41:1273. [5] Cragle, R. G., G. W. Salisbury, and N. L. van Demark. 1958. Ibid. 41:1267. [6] Dawson, R. M. C., T. Mann, and I. G. White. 1957. Biochem. J., Lond. 65:627. [7] Ehlers, M. H., F. H. Flerchinger, and R. E. Erb. 1953. J. Dairy Sc. 36:1020. [8] Hartree, E. F. 1957. Biochem. J., Lond. 66:131. [9] Heppel, L. A., and R. J. Hilmoe. 1951. J. Biol. Chem. 188:665. [10] King, T. E., F. A. Isherwood, and T. Mann. In O. Hoffmann-Ostenhof, ed. 1959. Proc. 4th Internat. Congr. Biochem., Vienna, 1958. v. 15, p. 77. [11] Larson, B. L., and G. W. Salisbury. 1953. J. Biol. Chem. 201:601. [12] Lundblad, G., and E. Hultin. 1952. Exp. Cell Res. 3:506. [13] Mann, T. 1954. Biochemistry of semen. Methuen, London. [14] Reid, J. T., G. M. Ward, and R. L. Salsbury. 1948. Am. J. Physiol. 153:235. [15] Rothschild, L., and H. Barnes. 1954. J. Exp. Biol., Lond. 31:561. [16] Thorsteinsson, T. 1958. Am. J. Physiol. 194:341. [17] White, I. G. 1958. Anim. Breed. Abstr. 26(2):109. [18] White, I. G. 1959. Unpublished.

Part III: HORSE

Values in parentheses are ranges, estimate "c" unless otherwise indicated (cf. Introduction).

	Property or Constituent	No. of Observations	Value	Reference
	(A)	(B)	(C)	(D)
	Physical Properties			
1	Conductivity		$123(111-130)$ mho x 10^{-4}	7
2	Freezing point depression		$0.56°C$	8
3	pH	9	$7.4(7.2-7.8)$	7
4	Specific gravity		$(1.012-1.015)$	8
5	Spermatozoa		$120(30-800)$ million/ml	7
6	Volume of ejaculate		$70(30-300)$ ml	7
	General Chemical Components			
7	Water		95.7%	8
	Electrolytes			
8	Calcium		10 mEq/L	7
9	Carbon dioxide		24 ml/100 ml	7
10	Chloride		$74(24-124)$ mEq/L	7
11	Magnesium		2 mEq/L	7
	Phosphorus			
12	Total P	3	$17(10-30)$ mg/100 ml	8
13	Inorganic P		17 mg/100 ml	7
14	Acid-soluble P	3	$14(10-30)$ mg/100 ml	8
15	Potassium		17 mEq/L	7
16	Sodium		30 mEq/L	8
	Nitrogenous Substances			
17	Ammonia		1 mg/100 ml	7
18	Creatine		6 mg/100 ml	7
19	Creatinine		4 mg/100 ml	7
20	Ergothioneine	15	$8(3-15)$ mg/100 ml	8
21	Spermine		0	1
22	Urea		3 mg/100 ml	7
	Nitrogen[1]			7
23	Total N		167 mg/100 ml	
24	Non-protein N		55 mg/100 ml	
	Lipids, Carbohydrates			
25	Lipids, total		172 mg/100 ml	8
26	Cholesterol		4 mg/100 ml	8
27	Fatty acids, volatile (as CH_3COOH)		5 mg/100 ml	10
28	Glycerylphosphorylcholine	2	$(40-120)$ mg/100 ml	3
29	Phosphorylcholine		0	9
30	Plasmalogen	2	0^2	5
31	Fructose	8	$2(0-6)$ mg/100 ml	8
32	Sorbitol		$(20-60)$ mg/100 ml	6
	Miscellaneous Organic Acids, Vitamins, Hormones			
33	Citric acid	15	$25(8-60)$ mg/100 ml	8
34	Lactic acid		15 mg/100 ml	7
35	Inositol, total	6	$40(20-50)$ mg/100 ml	4
36	Male hormones		+	7
	Enzymes			
	β-N-Acetylglucosaminidase			2
37	As phenol		470 µg/ml[3]	
38	As o- or p- nitrophenol		630 µg/ml[3]	

/1/ Total protein = 6.25 x (total nitrogen minus non-protein nitrogen). /2/ For seminal plasma. /3/ Liberated in 1 hour at 37°C.

Part III: HORSE (Concluded)

	Property or Constituent	No. of Observations	Value	Reference
	(A)	(B)	(C)	(D)
	Enzymes (concluded)			
	Galactosidase			2
39	α- (as phenol)		0	
40	β- (as o- or p-nitrophenol)		40 μg/ml^3	
	Glucosidase			2
41	α- (as o- or p-nitrophenol)		0	
42	β- (as o- or p-nitrophenol)		0	
43	β-Glucuronidase (as phenolphthalein)		30 μg/ml^3	2
	Mannosidase			2
	α-			
44	As phenol		140 μg/ml^3	
45	As o- or p-nitrophenol		300 μg/ml^3	
46	β- (as phenol)		0	

/3/ Liberated in 1 hour at 37°C.

Contributors: (a) White, I. G., (b) McKenzie, Fred F.; Wu, S. H.; and Das, Jogananda

References: [1] Bollinger, A. 1935. Austral. M. J. 2:794. [2] Conchie, J., and T. Mann. 1957. Nature, Lond. 179:1190. [3] Dawson, R. M. C., T. Mann, and I. G. White. 1957. Biochem. J., Lond. 65:627. [4] Hartree, E. F. 1957. Ibid. 66:131. [5] Hartree, E. F., and T. Mann. 1959. Ibid. 71:423. [6] King, T. E., F. A. Isherwood, and T. Mann. In O. Hoffmann-Ostenhof, ed. 1959. Proc. 4th Internat. Congr. Biochem., Vienna, 1958. v. 15, p. 77. [7] Mann, T. 1954. Biochemistry of semen. Methuen, London. [8] Mann, T., E. Leone, and C. Polge. 1956. J. Endocr., Oxf. 13:279. [9] White, I. G. 1958. Anim. Breed. Abstr. 26(2):109. [10] White, I. G. 1959. Unpublished.

Part IV: SHEEP

Values in parentheses are ranges, estimate "c" unless otherwise indicated (cf. Introduction).

	Property or Constituent	No. of Subjects	No. of Observations	Value	Reference
	(A)	(B)	(C)	(D)	(E)
	Physical Properties				
1	Conductivity			63(49-81) mho x 10^{-4}	6
2	Freezing point depression			0.64(0.55-0.70)°C	6
3	pH			6.9(5.9-7.3)	6
4	Spermatozoa			3000(2000-5000) million/ml	6
5	Volume of ejaculate			1.0(0.7-2.0) ml	6
	General Chemical Components				
6	Water	10	1	85.2%	6
	Electrolytes				
7	Calcium	10	1	5 mEq/L	6
8	Carbon dioxide			16 ml/100 ml	6
9	Chloride	10	1	24 mEq/L	6
10	Copper			0.2 mg/100 ml	6
11	Iron			0.8 mg/100 ml	6
12	Magnesium	10	1	2 mEq/L	6

433

Part IV: SHEEP (Concluded)

	Property or Constituent	No. of Subjects	No. of Observations	Value	Reference
	(A)	(B)	(C)	(D)	(E)
	Electrolytes (concluded)				
	Phosphorus				6
13	Total P	10	1	357 mg/100 ml	
14	Inorganic P	10	1	12 mg/100 ml	
15	Acid-soluble P	10	1	171 mg/100 ml	
16	Lipid P	10	1	29 mg/100 ml[1]	
17	Potassium	10	1	19 mEq/L	6
18	Sodium	10	1	45 mEq/L	6
19	Zinc			1.0 mg/100 ml	6
	Nitrogenous Substances				
20	Proteose			+	6
21	Ammonia	10	1	2 mg/100 ml	6
22	Creatine	20	1	2 mg/100 ml	11
23	Ergothioneine			(0-trace)	6
24	Urea	10	1	44 mg/100 ml	6
25	Uric acid	10	1	6 mg/100 ml	6
	Nitrogen[2]				6
26	Total N	10	1	875 mg/100 ml	
27	Non-protein N	10	1	57 mg/100 ml	
	Lipids, Carbohydrates				
28	Fatty acids, volatile (as CH_3COOH)			10 mg/100 ml	10
29	Glycerylphosphorylcholine	6	6	1650(1100-2100) mg/100 ml	1
30	Phosphorylcholine			0	9
31	Plasmalogen			380 mg/100 ml	4
32	Fructose	6	18	550(200-900)[b] mg/100 ml	2
33	Sorbitol			(20-120) mg/100 ml	5
	Miscellaneous Organic Acids, Vitamins				
34	Citric acid		10	137(110-260) mg/100 ml	6
35	Lactic acid		10	36 mg/100 ml	6
36	Vitamin C (ascorbic acid)			5.1(1.6-8.1) mg/100 ml	8
37	Inositol, total	10	5	40(35-45) mg/100 ml	3
	Enzymes				
38	Cholinesterase			++	6
39	5-Nucleotidase			+	7
	Phosphatase				
40	Acid			+	7
41	Alkaline			High	6

/1/ Multiply by 25.8 to obtain total phospholipids. /2/ Total protein = 6.25 x (total nitrogen minus non-protein nitrogen).

Contributors: (a) White, I. G., (b) McKenzie, Fred F.; Wu, S. H.; and Das, Jogananda

References: [1] Dawson, R. M. C., T. Mann, and I. G. White. 1957. Biochem. J., Lond. 65:627. [2] Glover, T. O. 1956. J. Endocr., Oxf 13:235. [3] Hartree, E. F. 1957. Biochem. J., Lond. 66:131. [4] Hartree, E. F., and T. Mann. 1959. Ibid. 71:423. [5] King, T. E., F. A. Isherwood, and T. Mann. In O. Hoffmann-Ostenhof, ed. 1959. Proc. 4th Internat. Congr. Biochem., Vienna, 1958. v. 15, p. 77. [6] Mann, T. 1954. Biochemistry of semen. Methuen, London. [7] Mann, T. 1945. Biochem. J., Lond. 39:451. [8] Roy, A., Y. R. Karnik, S. N. Lukutke, S. Bhattacharya, and P. Bhattacharya. 1950. Ind. J. Dairy Sc. 3:42. [9] White, I. G. 1958. Anim. Breed. Abstr. 26(2):109. [10] White, I. G. 1959. Unpublished. [11] White, I. G., and D. E. Griffith. 1958. Austral J. Exp. Biol. 36:97.

Part V: SWINE

Values in parentheses are ranges, estimate "c" (cf. Introduction).

Property or Constituent	No. of Observations	Value	Reference
(A)	(B)	(C)	(D)
Physical Properties			
1 Conductivity		129(123-135) mho x 10^{-4}	8
2 Freezing point depression		0.62(0.59-0.63) °C	8
3 pH		7.5(7.3-7.9)	8
4 Spermatozoa		100(25-300) million/ml	8
5 Volume of ejaculate		250(150-500) ml	8
General Chemical Components			
6 Water	19	95.4(93.8-97.8) %	8
Electrolytes			
7 Calcium	19	3(1-3) mEq/L	8
8 Carbon dioxide		50 ml/100 ml	8
9 Chloride	19	92(42-120) mEq/L	8
10 Magnesium	19	9(4-12) mEq/L	8
Phosphorus			8
11 Total P		66 mg/100 ml	
12 Inorganic P		2 mg/100 ml	
13 Acid-soluble P		24 mg/100 ml	
14 Lipid P		6 mg/100 ml[1]	
15 Potassium	19	66(22-103) mEq/L	8
16 Sodium	19	284(123-368) mEq/L	8
Nitrogenous Substances			
17 Proteose		+	8
18 Ammonia		1 mg/100 ml	8
19 Creatinine		0.3 mg/100 ml	8
20 Ergothioneine	20	15(10-20) mg/100 ml	3
21 Spermine		0	9
22 Urea		5 mg/100 ml	8
23 Uric acid		3 mg/100 ml	8
Nitrogen[2]			8
24 Total N	19	613(334-765) mg/100 ml	
25 Non-protein N		22 mg/100 ml	
Lipids, Carbohydrates			
26 Glycerylphosphorylcholine	4	(110-240) mg/100 ml	2
27 Phosphorylcholine		0	9
28 Plasmalogen	1	0[3]	5
29 Fructose	20	5(4-6) mg/100 ml	3
30 Sorbitol		(5-20) mg/100 ml	6
Miscellaneous Organic Acids, Vitamins			
31 Citric acid	20	80(60-100) mg/100 ml	3
32 Lactic acid		27 mg/100 ml	8
33 Inositol, total	3	(600-750) mg/100 ml	4
Enzymes			
β-N-Acetylglucosaminidase			1
34 As phenol		104,750 μg/ml[4]	
35 As o- or p-nitrophenol		220,000 μg/ml[4]	
36 Cholinesterase		++	8
Galactosidase			1
37 α- (as phenol)		0	
38 β- (as o- or p-nitrophenol)		50 μg/ml[4]	

/1/ Multiply by 25.8 to obtain total phospholipids. /2/ Total protein = 6.25 x (total nitrogen minus non-protein nitrogen). /3/ For seminal plasma. /4/ Liberated in 1 hour at 37°C.

Part V: SWINE (Concluded)

Property or Constituent	No. of Observations	Value	Reference
(A)	(B)	(C)	(D)
Enzymes (concluded)			
Glucosidase			1
39 α- (as o- or p-nitrophenol)		0	
40 β- (as o- or p-nitrophenol)		0	
41 β-Glucuronidase (as phenolphthalein)		0	1
42 Hyaluronidase		++	8
Mannosidase			1
α-			
43 As phenol		450 μg/ml^4	
44 As o- or p-nitrophenol		1120 μg/ml^4	
45 β- (as phenol)		0	
46 5-Nucleotidase		Low	7
47 Phosphatase, acid		Low	7

/4/ Liberated in 1 hour at 37°C.

Contributors: (a) White, I. G., (b) McKenzie, Fred F.; Wu, S. H.; and Das, Jogananda

References: [1] Conchie, J., and T. Mann. 1957. Nature, Lond. 179:1190. [2] Dawson, R. M. C., T. Mann, and I. G. White. 1957. Biochem. J., Lond. 65:627. [3] Glover, T. O., and T. Mann. 1954. J. Agr. Sc. 44:355. [4] Hartree, E. F. 1957. Biochem. J., Lond. 66:131. [5] Hartree, E. F., and T. Mann. 1959. Ibid. 71:423. [6] King, T. E., F. A. Isherwood, and T. Mann. In O. Hoffmann-Ostenhof, ed. 1959. Proc. 4th Internat. Congr. Biochem., Vienna, 1958. v. 15, p. 77. [7] Mann, T. 1945. Biochem. J., Lond. 39:451. [8] Mann, T. 1954. Biochemistry of semen. Methuen, London. [9] White, I. G. 1958. Anim. Breed. Abstr. 26(2):109.

Part VI: OTHER MAMMALS

Values in parentheses are ranges, estimate "c" unless otherwise indicated (cf. Introduction).

	Animal	No. of Observations	Property or Constituent	Value	Reference
	(A)	(B)	(C)	(D)	(E)
1	Buffalo	48	pH	6.3(6.0-6.6)^b	8
2		48	Spermatozoa	630(210-770) million/ml	
3		48	Volume of ejaculate	2.5(0.5-4.5) ml	
4	Fox		pH	(6.2-6.4)	7
5			Spermatozoa	70(30-250) million/ml	
6			Volume of ejaculate	1.5(0.2-4.0) ml	
7	Goat	100	pH	6.4(6.0-6.8)^b	8
8		100	Spermatozoa	2600(650-7500) million/ml	8
9		100	Volume of ejaculate	0.7(0.5-0.9)^b ml	8
10			Fructose	+	7
11	Guinea pig		Fructose	+	6
12		31	Vitamin C (ascorbic acid)	8.2(6.8-9.6)^b mg/100 ml	
13			Vesiculase	+	
14	Rabbit		Conductivity	94(86-101) mho x 10^{-4}	7
15			Freezing point depression	(0.55-0.59) °C	7
16			pH	(6.6-7.5)	7
17			Spermatozoa	700(100-2000) million/ml	7
18			Volume of ejaculate	1.0(0.4-6.0) ml	7

Part VI: OTHER MAMMALS (Concluded)

	Animal	No. of Observations	Property or Constituent	Value	Reference
	(A)	(B)	(C)	(D)	(E)
19	Rabbit	1[1]	Creatine	2 mg/100 ml	12
20	(con-		Fatty acids, volatile (as CH$_3$COOH)	8 mg/100 ml	11
21	cluded)	3	Glycerylphosphorylcholine	280(210-370) mg/100 ml	2
22			Phosphorylcholine	0	10
23		72	Fructose	(40-42) mg/100 ml	10
24			Sorbitol	80 mg/100 ml	5
25			Citric acid	(110-550) mg/100 ml	4
26		1	Inositol	30 mg/100 ml	3
			β-N-Acetylglucosaminidase		1
27			As phenol	15,700 μg/ml^2	
28			As o- or p-nitrophenol	36,300 μg/ml^2	
			Galactosidase		1
29	·		α- (as phenol)	260 μg/ml^2	
30			β- (as o- or p-nitrophenol)	840 μg/ml^2	
			Glucosidase		1
31			α- (as o- or p-nitrophenol)	55 μg/ml^2	
32			β- (as o- or p-nitrophenol)	0	
33			β-Glucuronidase (as phenolphthalein)	70 μg/ml^2	1
34			Hyaluronidase	+++	7
			Mannosidase		1
			α-		
35			As phenol	310 μg/ml^2	
36			As o- or p-nitrophenol	1320 μg/ml^2	
37			β- (as phenol)	1020 μg/ml^2	
38			Peptidases	+	9
39			Proteinases	0	9
40	Rat		Phosphorylcholine	+	6, 7
41			Fructose	+	
42			Hyaluronidase	+	
			Phosphatase		
43			Acid	Low	
44			Alkaline	Low	
45			Vesiculase	+	

/1/ 20 subjects. /2/ Liberated in 1 hour at 37ºC; values are for seminal plasma.

Contributors: (a) White, I. G., (b) McKenzie, Fred F.; Wu, S. H.; and Das, Jogananda

References: [1] Conchie, J., and T. Mann. 1957. Nature, Lond. 179:1190. [2] Dawson, R. M. C., T. Mann, and
I. G. White. 1957. Biochem. J., Lond. 65:627. [3] Hartree, E. F. 1957. Ibid. 66:131. [4] Humphrey, G. F., and
T. Mann. 1948. Nature, Lond. 161:352. [5] King, T. E., F. A. Isherwood, and T. Mann. In O. Hoffmann-Ostenhof,
ed. 1959. Proc. 4th Internat. Congr. Biochem., Vienna, 1958. v. 15, p. 77. [6] Mann, T. 1949. Advance.
Enzymol. 9:329. [7] Mann, T. 1954. Biochemistry of semen. Methuen, London. [8] Shukla, D. D., and
P. Bhattacharya. 1949. Ind. J. Vet. Sc. 19:161. [9] Thorsteinsson, T. 1958. Am. J. Physiol. 194:341.
[10] White, I. G. 1958. Anim. Breed. Abstr. 26(2):109. [11] White, I. G. 1959. Unpublished. [12] White, I. G.,
and D. E. Griffith. 1958. Austral. J. Exp. Biol. 36:97.

For additional determinations on seminal fluid of chicken, consult references 12, 16-42; pigeon, references 43, 44; turkey, references 21, 45-51. Values in parentheses are ranges, estimate "c" unless otherwise indicated (cf. Introduction).

	Animal	No. of Observations	Property or Constituent	Value	Reference
	(A)	(B)	(C)	(D)	(E)
1	Chicken		pH	7.6(6.8-8.4)	13, 15
2		11	Spermatozoa	3800(800-6800)[b] million/ml	6
3		11	Volume of ejaculate	0.6(0.4-1.0)[b] ml	6
4		8	Calcium	4 mEq/L	7
5		8	Chloride	59 mEq/L	7
6		8	Potassium	11 mEq/L	7
7		8	Sodium	171 mEq/L	7
8		8	Amino acids, free	1200(850-1550) mg/100 ml	8
9		8	Glutamic acid	1067.5(890-1340) mg/100 ml	8
10		8	Creatine	92.4(72-112) mg/100 ml	8
11		18	Nitrogen, non-protein	160(110-280) mg/100 ml	8
12			Fatty acids, volatile (as CH_3COOH)	3 mg/100 ml	2
13		14	Glycerylphosphorylcholine	15(0-40) mg/100 ml	2, 14
14		30	Glucose	35(25-55) mg/100 ml	3
15			Sorbitol	10 mg/100 ml	5
16			Citric acid	0	7
17	Duck		Volume of ejaculate	0.82(0.1-3.3) ml	11
18	Goose		Volume of ejaculate	0.2(0.05-0.60) ml	4
19	Pigeon		Volume of ejaculate	0.005 ml	12
20	Turkey	48	Freezing point depression	0.653°C	1
21		64	pH	7.7(7.0-8.1)	9
22		60	Spermatozoa	6800(4800-8200) million/ml	10
23		32	Volume of ejaculate	0.21(0.08-0.37) ml	9
24		48	Potassium	29.1(27.1-31.1)[b] mEq/L	1
25		48	Sodium	147(143-151)[b] mEq/L	1

Contributors: (a) White, I. G., (b) McCartney, M. G., (c) Van Drimmelen, G. C., (d) Shaffner, C. S.

References: [1] Brown, K. I. 1959. Poult. Sc. 38(4):804. [2] Dawson, R. M. C., T. Mann, and I. G. White. 1957. Biochem. J., Lond. 65:627. [3] De Muelenaere, H. J. H., and G. V. Quicke. 1958. S. Afr. J. Agr. Sc. 1:67. [4] Johnson, A. S. 1954. Poult. Sc. 33:638. [5] King, T. E., F. A. Isherwood, and T. Mann. In O. Hoffmann-Ostenhof, ed. 1959. Proc. 4th Internat. Congr. Biochem., Vienna, 1958. v. 15, p. 77. [6] Lake, P. E. 1957. J. Agr. Sc. 49:120. [7] Lake, P. E., E. J. Butler, J. W. McCallum, and I. J. MacIntyre. 1958. Q. J. Exp. Physiol., Lond. 43:309. [8] Lake, P. E., and W. M. McIndoe. 1959. Biochem. J., Lond. 71:303. [9] McCartney, M. G. 1956. Poult. Sc. 35:137. [10] McCartney, M. G., and K. I. Brown. 1959. Ibid. 38:390. [11] Onishi, N., and Y. Kato. 1955. Bull. Nat. Inst. Agr. Sc., Ser. G, 11:17. [12] Van Drimmelen, G. C. 1951. Onderstepoort J. Vet. Sc., Res. Suppl. 1, p. 212. [13] Wales, R. G., and I. G. White. 1958. Austral. J. Biol. Sc. 11:177. [14] White, I. G. 1959. Unpublished. [15] Wilcox, F. H., and C. S. Shaffner. 1957. J. Appl. Physiol. 11:429. [16] Allen, C. J., and L. R. Champion. 1955. Poult. Sc. 34:1332. [17] Amantea, G. 1922. Rendic. Accad. Lincei, Ser. 5, 31:207. [18] Bogdonoff, P. D., Jr., and C. S. Shaffner. 1953. Poult. Sc. 33:665. [19] Buckner, G. O., and J. H. Martin. 1928. Am. J. Physiol. 89:164. [20] Burrows, W. H., and J. P. Quinn. 1937. Poult. Sc. 16:19. [21] Burrows, W. H., and J. P. Quinn. 1939. U. S. Dept. Agr. Circ. 525. p. 13. [22] Cooper, D. M., and J. G. Rowell. 1957. Poult. Sc. 36:284. [23] Cooper, D. M., and J. G. Rowell. 1958. Ibid. 37:699. [24] Craft, W. A., C. H. McElroy, and R. Penquite. 1926. Ibid. 5:187. [25] Gowe, R. S., and J. R. Howes. 1956. Ibid. 35:983. [26] Grondzinski, Z., and J. Marchlewski. 1935. Bull. internat. Acad. Cracovie, Cl. sc. math. 11:347. [27] Hunsaker, W. G., J. R. Aitkin, and G. S. Lindblad. 1956. Poult. Sc. 35:649. [28] Hutt, F. B. 1928-29. Proc. R. Soc. Edinburgh 49:102. [29] Ishikawa, H. 1930. 4th World's Poult. Congr. pp. 90-94. [30] Nishiyama, H. 1957. J. Fac. Agr., Kyushu Univ. 11:63. [31] Parker, J. E., F. F. McKenzie, and H. L. Kempster. 1942. Res.

Bull. Univ. Missouri Agr. Exp. Sta. 347:50. [32] Payne, L. F. 1914. Oklahoma Agr. Exp. Sta. Circ. 30. [33] Raimo, H. F. 1943. Bol. indúst. animal, S. Paulo 6:16. [34] Sampson, F. R., and D. C. Warren. 1939. Poult. Sc. 18:301. [35] Shaffner, C. S., and F. N. Andrews. 1948. Ibid. 27:91. [36] Schindler, H., R. Volcani, and S. Weinstein. 1958. Ibid. 37:21. [37] Skaller, F. 1951. 9th World's Poult. Congr. 3:124. [38] Warren, D. C., and C. L. Gish. 1943. Poult. Sc. 22:108. [39] Warren, D. C., and L. Kilpatrick. 1929. Ibid. 8:237. [40] Wheeler, N. C., and F. N. Andrews. 1943. Ibid. 22:361. [41] Williams, C., and W. H. McGibbon. 1956. Ibid. 35:617. [42] Zagami, V. 1937. Rendic. Accad. Lincei, Ser. 6, 26:123. [43] Amantea, G. 1925. Physiol. Abstr., Lond. 10:423. [44] Owen, R. D. 1941. Poult. Sc. 20:428. [45] Burrows, W. H., and S. J. Marsden. 1938. Ibid. 17:408. [46] Carson, J. D., F. W. Lorenz, and V. S. Asmundson. 1955. Ibid. 34:336. [47] Lorenz, F. W., N. E. Wilson, and V. S. Asmundson. 1955. Ibid. 34:634. [48] McCartney, M. G. 1951. Ibid. 30:663. [49] McCartney, M. G., V. D. Chamberlin, R. D. Carter, and J. W. Wyne. 1958. Ibid. 37:363. [50] Pace, D. M., D. F. Moravec, and F. E. Mussehl. 1952. Ibid. 31:577. [51] Parker, J. E. 1946. Ibid. 25:65.

144. EFFECT OF CHEMICALS ON SEMEN: MAN

Spermicidal time = duration of sperm motion after addition of spermicide. SpT = spermicidal time, SLg = sperm longevity (duration of sperm motion, without spermicide), SLc = sperm locomotion; (+) = increased, (-) = decreased, (0) = no significant change, (±) = increased then decreased.

Part I: POTASSIUM ACID PHTHALATE

Ratio of spermicide (2.8% potassium acid phthalate) to semen = 1:1. Repeated ejaculation reduces semen volume and sperm count, but has no effect on spermicidal time or life span [1, 5, 10]. During hot weather, spermicidal time and longevity are decreased [8, 10, 16].

	Specification	No. of Donors	No. of Specimens	No. of Observations	Age of Semen hr	Spermicidal Time, min, at: 37°C	25°C	5°C	Effect on: SpT	SLg[1]	SLc	Reference
	(A)	(B)	(C)	(D)	(E)	(F)	(G)	(H)	(I)	(J)	(K)	(L)
1	Control, with 2.8%	4	8	330	<1/4		37			-	-	12
2	potassium acid	12	244	2440	<1/4		61			-	-	15
3	phthalate	12	12	244	<1/4		60			-	-	1,11,13
4		10	32		<1/4		49			-	-	14
5		28	>1000	>10,000	<1/4		58			-	-	1-15
6		25	500	>5000	<1/4	45	55	60		-	-	9
7	Semen at constant		14	74	<1/4		60		-	-	- or 0	1-15
8	temperature,				12		52					
9	with 2.8%				24		43					
10	potassium acid				36		39					
11	phthalate				48		28					
12					60		18					
13	Semen at decreas-	1	1	30	1/2	78	78	78	+	+	- or 0	1-15
14	ing temperature,				6	62	75	78				
15	with 2.8%				12	40	70	78				
16	potassium acid				18	18	58	77				
17	phthalate				24	11	47	76				
18					36		35	75				
19					48		24	72				
20					60		16	63				
21					72		11	54				
22					84			45				
23					96			37				
24					108			28				
25					120			19				
26					132			15				
27					144			13				

/1/ Sperm longevity = 53 hours at 37°C, 160 hours at 25°C, and 300 hours at 5°C.

Part I: POTASSIUM ACID PHTHALATE (Concluded)

Contributor: Brown, Royal L.

References: [1] Brown, R. L. 1942. Studies in human fertility (Alpha Omega Research Prize Award). Unpublished. [2] Brown, R. L. 1943. Am. J. Obst. 46:873. [3] Brown, R. L. 1943. J. Urol., Balt. 50:786. [4] Brown, R. L. 1943. South. M. J. 36:619. [5] Brown, R. L. 1943. Urol. Cut. Rev. 47:372. [6] Brown, R. L. 1944. Am. J. Obst. 47:407. [7] Brown, R. L. 1944. J. Laborat. Clin. M. 29:211. [8] Brown, R. L. 1944. J. Urol., Balt. 51:443. [9] Brown, R. L. 1946. Ibid. 55:113. [10] Brown, R. L. 1945. Urol. Cut. Rev. 49:336. [11] Brown, R. L., and C. J. Gamble. 1940. Human Fertility 5:97. [12] Brown, R. L., and C. J. Gamble. 1941. Ibid. 6:1. [13] Brown, R. L., and C. J. Gamble. 1943. Ibid. 8:4. [14] Brown, R. L., and C. J. Gamble. 1943. Ibid. 8:9. [15] Brown, R. L., I. Levenstein, and B. Becker. 1943. Ibid. 8:65. [16] McCleod, J., and R. S. Hotchkiss. 1941. Endocrinology 28:780.

Part II: OTHER CHEMICAL SPERMICIDES

Ratio of spermicide to semen = 1:1. Spermatozoa exposed to X ray are unable to cause syngamy or embryogenesis [1, 19, 20]. Information may be found in the literature on the following as spermicides: alkalis [20, 22], metal salts and aldehydes [2, 13, 15, 23], phenols [13, 15], acids [22], tetrazolium salts [3], and antibiotics [21]. Underlined values are for controls, using 2.8% potassium acid phthalate.

	Spermicide	No. of Donors	No. of Speci-mens	No. of Obser-vations	Age of Semen hr	Spermicidal Time, min, at:					Effect on:			Refer-ence
						37ºC		25ºC		5ºC		SpT	SLg	SLc	
	(A)	(B)	(C)	(D)	(E)	(F)		(G)		(H)		(I)	(J)	(K)	(L)
1	Distilled water	6	10		<1/4	<u>65</u>	16	<u>65</u>	15			-	-	+	13
2						<u>42</u>	9	<u>52</u>	12						
3						<u>4</u>		<u>32</u>	8						
4	Histamine di-	5	8	260	<1/3		112		112		112	-	-	±	11,13
5	hydrochloride				1	<u>103</u>	71	<u>108</u>	102	<u>112</u>	108				
6	(1:1000 in				1-1/2	<u>98</u>	5	<u>105</u>	93	<u>111</u>	106				
7	buffered glu-				2	<u>84</u>		<u>100</u>	88	<u>112</u>	90				
8	cose solution)				4	<u>78</u>		<u>100</u>	64	<u>110</u>	77				
9					6	<u>65</u>		<u>97</u>	31	<u>111</u>	63				
10					12	<u>49</u>		<u>65</u>	3	<u>109</u>	21				
11	Lactic acid, 2%	1	1	30	1/2		154		154		154	-	-	-	4-18
12	(proprietary)				6		126		150		156				
13					12		81		138		155				
14					18		37		120		152				
15					24		11		96		148				
16					36				62		144				
17					48				40		140				
18					60				22		132				
19					72				11		123				
20					84						106				
21					96						87				
22					108						65				
23					120						40				
24					132						22				
25					144						13				
26	Ricinoleic acid,	1	1	30	1/2		50		50		50	-	-	-	4-18
27	3% (propri-				6		35		44		50				
28	etary)				12		22		40		51				
29					18		17		35		48				
30					24		11		29		48				
31					36				21		44				
32					48				17		41				

Part II: OTHER CHEMICAL SPERMICIDES (Continued)

Spermicide	No. of Donors	No. of Specimens	No. of Observations	Age of Semen hr	Spermicidal Time, min, at:			Effect on:			Reference
					37°C	25°C	5°C	SpT	SLg	SLc	
(A)	(B)	(C)	(D)	(E)	(F)	(G)	(H)	(I)	(J)	(K)	(L)
33 Ricinoleic acid, 3% (proprietary) (concluded)	1	1	30	60		14	37	-	-	-	4-18
34				72		11	33				
35				84			19				
36				96			17				
37				108			15				
38				120			14				
39				132			12				
40				144			13				
41 Brass shavings	3	3	37	<1/3		48 48		-	-	0 or -	11,16
42				4		42 42					
43				8		40 17					
44				12		36 3					
45				16		32 1					
46 Copper shavings	3	3	37	<1/3		53 53		-	-	-	11,16
47				4		52 48					
48				8		49 15					
49				12		48 6					
50				16		44 4					
51				20		38 3					
52				24		35 1					
Rubber (particles, condom, eye dropper bulb) 5-min exposure[1]											
53	7	7	161	<1/5		61 61		-	-	-	13,16
54				4		59 57					
55				8		57 54					
56				12		53 45					
57				16		48 38					
58				20		45 34					
59				24		39 37					
60				28		32 17					
61				32		29 3					
62 Constant exposure	7	7	154	<1/5		58 58		-	-	-	13,16
63				4		57 27					
64				8		54 9					
65				12		47 1					

/1/ Underlined values in column G are spermicidal times for sperm unexposed to rubber and mixed in 1:1 ratio with 2.8% potassium acid phthalate; values not underlined in column G are spermicidal times for sperm exposed for indicated time to rubber, then tested with 2.8% potassium acid phthalate at indicated ages.

Contributor: Brown, Royal L.

References: [1] Amoroso, E. C., and A. S. Parkes. 1947. Proc. R. Soc., Lond., Ser. B, 134:57. [2] Baker, J. R. 1935. The chemical control of conception. Chapman and Hall, London. [3] Bishop, D. W., and H. P. Mathews. 1952. Science 115.209. [4] Brown, R. L. 1913. Am. J. Obst. 16.073. [5] Brown, R. L. 1943. J. Urol., Balt. 50:786. [6] Brown, R. L. 1943. South. M. J. 36:619. [7] Brown, R. L. 1943. Urol. Cut. Rev. 47:372. [8] Brown, R. L. 1944. Am. J. Obst. 47:407. [9] Brown, R. L. 1944. J. Laborat. Clin. M. 29:211. [10] Brown, R. L. 1944. J. Urol., Balt. 51:443. [11] Brown, R. L. 1945. Urol. Cut. Rev. 49:336. [12] Brown, R. L. 1946. J. Urol., Balt. 55:113. [13] Brown, R. L. 1942. Studies in human fertility (Alpha Omega Research Prize Award). Unpublished. [14] Brown, R. L., and C. J. Gamble. 1940. Human Fertility 5:97. [15] Brown, R. L., and C. J. Gamble. 1941. Ibid. 6:1. [16] Brown, R. L., and C. J. Gamble. 1943. Ibid. 8:4. [17] Brown, R. L., and C. J. Gamble. 1943.

Part II: OTHER CHEMICAL SPERMICIDES (Concluded)

Ibid. 8:9. [18] Brown, R. L., I. Levenstein, and B. Becker. 1943. Ibid. 8:65. [19] Kosin, I. L. 1944. Physiol. Zool. 17:289. [20] Rugh, R. 1939. Proc. Am. Philos. Soc. 81:447. [21] Seneca, H., and D. Ides. 1953. J. Urol., Balt. 70:947. [22] Shedlovsky, L., D. Belcher, and I. Levenstein. 1942. Am. J. Physiol. 136:535. [23] Voge, C. I. B. 1935. The chemistry and physics of contraceptives. Jonathan Cape, London.

Part III: DILUENTS

Ratio of diluent to spermicide to semen = 4:1:5.

	Diluent	Spermicide[1]	No. of Donors	No. of Specimens	Age of Semen hr	Spermicidal Time, min, at 25°C	Effect on:			Reference
							SpT	SLg	SLc	
	(A)	(B)	(C)	(D)	(E)	(F)	(G)	(H)	(I)	(J)
1	Buffered glucose	Lactic acid, 2%	7	7	1/4-1	28	0	0	0	2
2	saline	Ricinoleic acid, 3%	7	7	1/4-1	3	0	0	0	
3	Sodium chloride,	Lactic acid, 2%	7	7	1/4-1	26	-	-	0	2
4	0.85%[2]	Ricinoleic acid, 3%	7	7	1/4-1	3	0	-	0	
5	Dextrose, 5%[2]	Lactic acid, 2%	7	7	1/4-1	19	-	0	0	2
6		Ricinoleic acid, 3%	7	7	1/4-1	9	+	0	0	
7	Protein (egg	Lactic acid, 2%	7	7	1/4-1	133	+	0	0	1, 2
8	white)[2]	Ricinoleic acid, 3%	7	7	1/4-1	19	+	0	0	

/1/ Proprietary. /2/ As compared to effect of buffered glucose saline.

Contributor: Brown Royal L.

Reference: [1] Brown, R. L. 1942. Studies in human fertility (Alpha Omega Research Prize Award). Unpublished. [2] Brown, R. L., C. J. Gamble. 1940. Human Fertility 5:97.

145. EFFECT OF BIOLOGICAL FLUIDS ON SEMEN: MAN

Spermicidal time = duration of sperm motion after addition of spermicide. Sperm longevity = duration of sperm motion without spermicide. SpT = spermicidal time, SLg = sperm longevity, SLc = sperm locomotion; (+) = increased, (-) = decreased, (0) = no significant change.

Part I: MALE SECRETIONS AND URINE

Ratio of diluent to spermicide (2.8% potassium acid phthalate) to semen = 1:2:1. Underlined values are for controls, using 2.8% potassium acid phthalate.

	Diluent[1]	No. of Donors	No. of Specimens	Age of Semen hr	Spermicidal Time, min, at:			Effect on:			Reference
					37°C	25°C	5°C	SpT	SLg	SLc	
	(A)	(B)	(C)	(D)	(E)	(F)	(G)	(H)	(I)	(J)	(K)
1	Epididymal	2	2	<1/3	91	91	91	0	0	0	1-3
2	secretion			8	69 7	90 91	91 90				
3				16	39 43	84 84	89 88				
4				24	2 4	71 73	86 86				
5				48		59 56	77 72				
6				72		2 3	68 68				
7				96			51 52				
8				120			38 37				
9				144			3				

/1/ Added just prior to first test.

Part I: MALE SECRETIONS AND URINE (Concluded)

	Diluent[1]	No. of Donors	No. of Specimens	Age of Semen hr	Spermicidal Time, min, at: 37°C		25°C		5°C		Effect on: SpT	SLg	SLc	Reference
	(A)	(B)	(C)	(D)	(E)		(F)		(G)		(H)	(I)	(J)	(K)
10	Cowper's	2	2	<1/3	91		91		91		0	0	0	1-3
11	gland			8	72	70	90	91	91	92				
12	secretion			16	39	42	84	85	87	88				
13				24	2	3	73	72	85	85				
14				48			58	56	73	72				
15				72			2	2	67	66				
16				96					51	52				
17				120					37	37				
18				144					4					
19	Prostatic	2	2	<1/3	91		91		91		0	0	0	1-3
20	secretion			8	69	73	90	92	91	91				
21				16	40	43	84	83	89	88				
22				24	2	5	73	73	86	86				
23				48			57	55	77	78				
24				72			1	3	68	76				
25				96					52	51				
26				120					39	38				
27				144					3					
28	Urine,	3	3	<1/4	73		73		73		-	-	0	1, 2
29	normal			2	68	60	72	70	72	71				
30				4	62	41	70	62	71	70				
31				6	43	26	68	48	72	67				
32				12	18	6	66	36	71	54				
33				24	4		62	12	70	40				
34				48			39		66	9				
35				72			3		58					
36				96					42					
37				120					21					
38				144					6					
39	Urine,	2	3	<1/4	70		70		70		-	-	0	1, 2
40	diabetic			2	69	68	68	69	70	70				
41	(3+)			4	60	50	67	66	70	69				
42				6	41	32	67	55	69	68				
43				12	18	12	66	48	69	65				
44				24	4		52	33	68	60				
45				48			36	12	65	32				
46				72			7		56	3				
47				96					40					
48				120					18					
49				144					4					
50	Urine,	1	1[3]	<1/4	96	96	96	96	96	96	-	-	0 or	2, 4
51	icteric[2]			2	92	87	95	94	97	95			+	
52	(3+)			4	80	69	93	91	96	94				
53				6	76	23	89	88	95	92				
54				12	61	1	84	70	94	89				
55				24	8		72	22	90	70				
56				48			34		84	41				
57				72			4		76	2				
58				96					67					
59				120					41					
60				144					8					

/1/ Added just prior to first test. /2/ In acute cholecystitis and cholangitis. /3/ 132 observations.

Contributor: Brown, Royal L.

References: [1] Brown, R. L. 1942. Studies in human fertility (Alpha Omega Research Prize Award). Unpublished. [2] Brown, R. L. 1944. J. Urol., Balt. 51:443. [3] Brown, R. L. 1945. Urol. Cut. Rev. 49:336. [4] Brown, R. L., and C. J. Gamble. 1940. Human Fertility 5:97.

Part II: FEMALE SECRETIONS AND PERITONEAL FLUID

Diluent, mixed with semen, kept at 37°C. Dt = diluent, Sn = semen. Values in parentheses are ranges, estimate "c" (cf. Introduction).

	Diluent	No. of Donors	No. of Speci-mens	No. of Obser-vations	Age of Semen[1] hr	Sperm Longevity min	Dt:Sn	Effect on: SpT	SLg	SLc	Refer-ence
	(A)	(B)	(C)	(D)	(E)	(F)	(G)	(H)	(I)	(J)	(K)
1	Control[2]	3	6	>100	<1/2	696(582-786)					1,2
2	Vaginal secretion	3	6	>100	<1/2	402(272-579)	1:1	-	-	0 or -	1,2
3	Cervical secretion	3	6	>100	<1/2	691(596-763)	1:1	0	0	0	1,2
4	Uterine secretion	3	6	>100	<1/2	697(562-754)	1:1	0	0	0	1,2
5	Fallopian tube secretion	3	6	>100	<1/2	666(446-783)	1:1	0	0	0	1,2
6	Control[2]	3	3	>50	<1/4	675(556-776)					1,2
	Ovarian secretion										1,2
7	Follicular	2	2	>50	<1/4	800(793-807)	1:1	0	0	0	
8	Corpus luteum	3	3	>50	<1/4	755(712-793)	1:1	0	0	0	
9	Cyst	3	3	>50	<1/4	744(740-750)	1:1	0	0	0	
10	Control[2]	2	2	5	<1/4	1190(1033-1350)					1
11	Peritoneal fluid[3]	2	2	5	<1/4	1157(1025-1208)	1:2	0	0	0	1
12						1150(1010-1365)	1:1	0	0	0	
13						1137(1042-1185)	2:1	0	0	0	
14						1182(1032-1330)	4:1	0	0	0	
15						1186(1024-1360)	6:1	0	0	0	
16						1186(1030-1330)	8:1	0	0	0	

/1/ Age at which diluent was added. /2/ Without diluent or spermicide. /3/ Donors of peritoneal fluid: 2 with liver cirrhosis, 2 with peritoneal metastases.

Contributor: Brown, Royal L.

References. [1] Brown, R. L. 1943. Am. J. Obst. 46:873. [2] Brown, R. L. 1944. J. Laborat. Clin. M. 29:211.

XXII. Fluids During Pregnancy

146. BLOOD AND URINE CHARACTERISTICS STABLE DURING PREGNANCY: MAN

The physical properties and chemical constituents listed below remain relatively stable throughout pregnancy, though at levels differing from those in non-pregnant subjects. Values in parentheses are ranges, estimate "c" unless otherwise indicated (cf. Introduction).

	Property or Constituent	Value	Reference		Property or Constituent	Value	Reference
	(A)	(B)	(C)		(A)	(B)	(C)
	Whole Blood				Serum (concluded)		
1	Creatinine	0.46 mg/100 ml	8	12	Calcium	9.6 mg/100 ml	1
2	Uric acid	3.0 mg/100 ml	9	13	Chloride	494 mg/100 ml	9
	Nitrogen			14	Phosphorus	3.2 mg/100 ml	1
3	Non-protein N	28.0 mg/100 ml	9	15	Potassium	19.5 mg/100 ml	4
4	Urea N	8.7 mg/100 ml	8	16	Sodium	330 mg/100 ml	7
5	Glucose	80.0 mg/100 ml	9	17	Amino acids, free	19.5(12.25-26.25) mg/100 ml	10
	Plasma			18	Lactic dehydrogenase	103(49-157)[b] units/100 ml	5
6	Iodine	11 μg/100 ml	6	19	Phosphatase	6.6 Bodansky units/100 ml	1
7	Fibrinogen	500 mg/100 ml	6	20	Transaminase	18.5(14.64-22.36)[b] units/100 ml	2
8	Fats, neutral	353(203-503)[b] mg/100 ml	3		Urine		
	Serum				Nitrogen		9
9	CO$_2$ combining power	48 vol/100 ml	9	21	Total N	(8-12) g/24 hr	
10	pH	7.4	9	22	Ammonia N	(3-5) % of total N	
11	Base, total	157 mM	9	23	Urea N	(70-85) % of total N	

Contributors: Escoffier-Lambiotte, C., and Tcherdakoff, Philippe

References: [1] Bodansky, M. 1936. Am. J. Clin. Path. 9:36. [2] Borglin, N. E. 1958. J. Clin. Endocr. 18:872. [3] Boyd, E. M. 1934. J. Clin. Invest. 13:347. [4] Dieckmann, W. J. 1941. The toxemias of pregnancy. Mosby, St. Louis. [5] Hagerman, D. D., and F. M. Wellington. 1959. Am. J. Obst. 77:348. [6] Jayle, M. F. In M. Polonovski, ed. Pathologie chimique. G. Masson, Paris. [7] Lambiotte, C. Unpublished. [8] Sims, E. A. H., and K. E. Krantz. 1958. J. Clin. Invest. 37:1764. [9] Stander, H. S. In J. W. Williams. 1941. Obstetrics. Ed. 8. Appleton-Century-Crofts, New York. [10] Wirtschafter, Z. T. 1958. Am. J. Obst. 76:1219.

147. VARIATIONS IN BLOOD CONSTITUENTS DURING PREGNANCY: MAN

Method: P = photometry, V = Van Slyke, E = paper electrophoresis, S = Sperry and Brand, D = digitonin (Sperry and Webb), H = Hawkes, O = orthophenanthrolene (Shapira, et al), B = biological assay with Lactobacillus leishmannii, U = unspecified.

	Constituent	No. of Subjects	Method	Month of Pregnancy								Reference
				II	III	IV	V	VI	VII	VIII	IX	
	(A)	(B)	(C)	(D)	(E)	(F)	(G)	(H)	(I)	(J)	(K)	(L)
	Whole Blood											
1	Hemoglobin, %	216	P		87.08	84.80	84.29	81.88	77.21	77.49	78.41	5
2	Vitamin E, mg/100 ml	178	U	0.66			0.75			0.88		3
	Serum											
3	Iron, μg/100 ml		O	144.0	155.1	151.4	133.6	104.3	79.9	94.5	96.5	4
4	Protein, total, mg/100 ml	6-14	V	7100	7000	6800	6600	6600	6500	6600	6600	6
5	Albumin, mg/100 ml	6-14	E	4360	4430	4180	3950	3790	3740	3690	3520	6
6	Globulin, mg/100 ml	6-14	E	2740	2570	2620	2650	2810	2760	2910	3080	6
7	Lipids, total, mg/100 ml	25	S	688	653	694	745	737	900	964	1018	2
	Cholesterol, mg/100 ml											2
8	Total	25	D	200	152	189	207	211	239	266	257	
9	Ester	25	D	151	115	151	163	165	180	195	193	
10	Phospholipids, mg/100 ml	25	H	240	263	258	278	282	333	346	357	2
11	Vitamin B$_{12}$, μg/100 ml	318	B	0.0417			0.0377			0.0311		1

Contributor: Tcherdakoff, Philippe

References: [1] Boger, W. P., L. D. Wright, G. D. Beck, and G. M. Bayne. 1956. Proc. Soc. Exp. Biol., N. Y. 92:140. [2] De Alvarez, R. R., D. F. Gaiser, D. M. Simkins, E. K. Smith, and G. E. Bratvold. 1959. Am. J. Obst. 77:743. [3] Gounelle, H., A. Francois, C. Marnay, and M. Robey. 1955. C. rend. Soc. biol. 149:288. [4] Guilhem, P., A. Potonnier, and M. Monrozies. 1956. Gyn. obst., Par. 55:449. [5] Simpson, A. S. 1954. J. Obst. Gyn. Brit. Empire 61:807. [6] Von Studnitz, W. 1955. Scand J. Clin. Lab. Invest. 7:324.

148. ELECTROLYTE AND NITROGEN BALANCE AT TERM: MAN

Values are estimates of the difference between daily intake and daily output of various constituents in normal pregnant women at term.

	Constituent	Balance mg/24 hr	Reference
	(A)	(B)	(C)
1	Calcium	+280	1
2	Chloride	+0.88	2
3	Iron	+(1.0-1.5)	2
4	Phosphorus	+210	1
5	Potassium	+0.51	2
6	Sodium	+1.26	2
7	Nitrogen	+1360	1

Contributors: Escoffier-Lambiotte, C., and Tcherdakoff, Philippe

References: [1] Coons, C. M., and K. J. Blunt. 1930. J. Biol. Chem. 86:1. [2] Jayle, M. F. 1952. In M. Polonovski, ed. Pathologie chimique. G. Masson, Paris.

149. BODY WATER AND BLOOD VOLUMES AT TERM: MAN

Values are averages for normal pregnancies at term.

Fluid Compartment	Method	Value	Reference
(A)	(B)	(C)	(D)
1 Body water, total	Antipyrine	38.8 L[1]	2
2 Extracellular space	Inulin	15.5 L[2]	2
3 Sodium space	Na[22]	11.8 L/sq m	1
4 Exchangeable sodium	Na[22]	2776 mEq	1
5 Water content of blood		82.7%	4
Blood volume			
6 Whole blood		5.4 L	5
7 Erythrocyte		1.9 L	5
8 Plasma	Gregersen's	3.3 L[3]	3
9 Hematocrit		38.2%	2

/1/ 54.8% of body weight. /2/ 21.6% of body weight. /3/ 4.8% of body weight.

Contributors: Escoffier-Lambiotte, C., and Tcherdakoff, Philippe

References: [1] Dieckmann, W. J., and R. Pottinger. 1957. Am. J. Obst. 74:816. [2] Escoffier-Lambiotte, C., D. P. Moore, and H. C. Taylor. 1953. Ibid. 66:18. [3] McLennan, C. E. 1950. Ibid. 59:662. [4] Oberst, F. W., and E. D. Plass. 1936. Ibid. 31:61. [5] Roscoe, M. H., and G. M. M. Donaldson. 1946. J. Obst. Gyn. Brit. Empire 53:430.

150. HORMONE VARIATION IN BLOOD AND URINE DURING PREGNANCY: MAN

Part I: BLOOD

Method: F = fluorimetry, P = Porter and Silber, G = Gardner, C = chromatography, U = unspecified. Values in parentheses are ranges, estimate "c" (cf. Introduction).

Hormone	No. of Subjects	Method	II	III	IV	V	VI	VII	VIII	IX	Reference
(A)	(B)	(C)	(D)	(E)	(F)	(G)	(H)	(I)	(J)	(K)	(L)
Plasma											
1 Estriol, µg/100 ml	10	F								7.8	5
2 Estrone-estradiol, µg/100 ml	10	F								168	5
3 17-Hydroxysteroids, µg/100 ml	17	P	11.0	9.8	13.3	17.6	12.7	17.9	21.5	11.7	1
4 17-Ketosteroids, µg/100 ml	30	G								18.0	3
5 Pregnanediol, µg/100 ml	130	C		(0-15)	(10-25)	(25-30)	(25-30)	(25-30)	(30-60)	(40-60)	2
Serum											
6 Gonadotropins[1], I.U./100 ml		U	100,000	35,000	12,000	8000	5000	5000	8000	5000	4

/1/ Values selected from composite curves of Jones [4].

Contributors: Escoffier-Lambiotte, C., and Tcherdakoff, Philippe

References: [1] Birke, G., C. A. Gemzell, L. O. Plantin, and H. Robbe. 1958. Acta endocr., Kbh. 27:389. [2] Deshpande, G. N., and I. F. Sommerville. 1958. Lancet, Lond. 2:1046. [3] Gardner, L. I., R. L. Walton, W. Ellis, and E. C. Hughes. 1954. Proc. Soc. Exp. Biol., N. Y. 86:804. [4] Jones, G. E. S., E. Delfs, and H. M. Stran. 1944. Bull. Johns Hopkins Hosp. 75:359. [5] Varangot, J., and A. Seeman. 1957. C. rend. Soc. biol. 151:2125.

Part II: URINE

Method: C = chromatography, S = Stimmel, G = Gibson and Norynbenski, Z = chromatography and Zimmerman's reaction, U = unspecified. Values in parentheses are ranges, estimate "c" (cf. Introduction).

	Hormone	No. of Subjects	Method	Month of Pregnancy								Reference
				II	III	IV	V	VI	VII	VIII	IX	
	(A)	(B)	(C)	(D)	(E)	(F)	(G)	(H)	(I)	(J)	(K)	(L)
	Aldosterone, µg/24 hr											6
1	Free	7	C		2.0	1.4				1.8	1.3	
2	Acid hydrolysis	7	C		12.5	19.4				14.4	20.9	
3	Glycuronide	7	C		10.3	4.1				8.4	2.5	
	Estrogens, µg/24 hr											5
4	Estradiol		S	127	134	206	270	520	500	900		
5	Estriol		S	215	266	1480	3390	4300	4400	7000		
6	Estrone		S	209	256	740	800	1024	848	1460		
7	Gonadotropins[1], I.U./L		U	25,000	30,000	18,000	3000	(500–700)				2
8	17-Hydroxysteroids, mg/24 hr	72	G	(5–18)								4
9	17-Ketosteroids, mg/24 hr	17	Z	8.2		6.9	8.6	10.5	9.3	8.9	12.6	1
10	Pregnanediol, mg/24 hr		U	16	15	36	21	62	38	86	50	3

/1/ Values selected from composite curves based on results obtained by Cheymol [2].

Contributors: Escoffier-Lambiotte, C., and Tcherdakoff, Philippe

References: [1] Birke, G., C. A. Gemzell, L. O. Plantin, and H. Robbe. 1958. Acta endocr., Kbh. 27:389. [2] Cheymol, J., and R. Henry. 1947. Rapp. Ier Congr. Internat. Biol. Clin. p.221. [3] Guterman, H. S., and M. S. Schroeder. 1948. J. Laborat. Clin. M. 33:356. [4] Martin, J. D., and I. H. Mills. 1958. Clin. Sc., Lond. 17:137. [5] Stimmel, V. 1946. J. Biol. Chem. 165:73. [6] Venning, E. H., and I. Dyrenfurth. 1956. J. Clin. Endocr. 16:426.

151. PHYSICAL PROPERTIES AND CHEMICAL COMPOSITION OF AMNIOTIC FLUID: MAN

Values in parentheses are ranges, estimate "c" (cf. Introduction).

	Property or Constituent	Value	Reference		Property or Constituent	Value	Reference
	(A)	(B)	(C)		(A)	(B)	(C)
	Physical Properties				**Nitrogenous Substances (concluded)**		
1	CO_2 combining power	37 vol/100 ml	2	16	Glutathione	13 mg/100 ml	2
2	Osmotic pressure	265.5 mOsm	1	17	Uric acid	4.4 mg/100 ml	2
3	Specific gravity	(1.006–1.008)	5		Nitrogen		
4	Volume	700(400–1200) ml	3	18	Non-protein N	(24–25) mg/100 ml	6
				19	Urea N	20 mg/100 ml	2
	General Chemical Components				**Lipids, Carbohydrates**		
5	Water	98.5%	5	20	Lipids, total	48 mg/100 ml	2
	Electrolytes			21	Cholesterol	2 mg/100 ml	2
				22	Fatty acids	23 mg/100 ml	2
6	Calcium	7.2 mg/100 ml	2	23	Fructose	(1–2) mg/100 ml	4
7	Chloride	365 mg/100 ml	2	24	Glucose	4 mg/100 ml	4
8	Iron	0.07 mg/100 ml	2		**Miscellaneous Organic Acids**		
9	Magnesium	2.2 mg/100 ml	2				
10	Phosphorus, inorganic	2.7 mg/100 ml	2	25	Ketoglutaric acid	0.51 mg/100 ml	4
11	Potassium	19 mg/100 ml	2	26	Pyruvic acid	1.35 mg/100 ml	4
12	Sodium	290 mg/100 ml	2		**Hormones**		
13	Sulfur, inorganic	3.7 mg/100 ml	2		17-Ketosteroids		2
	Nitrogenous Substances			27	♂ fetus	0.228 mg/100 ml	
14	Protein, total	260 mg/100 ml	2	28	♀ fetus	0.062 mg/100 ml	
15	Creatinine	2 mg/100 ml	2				

151. PHYSICAL PROPERTIES AND CHEMICAL COMPOSITION OF AMNIOTIC FLUID: MAN (Concluded)

Contributors: Escoffier-Lambiotte, C., and Tcherdakoff, Philippe

References: [1] Battaglia, F., H. Prystowsky, C. Smisson, A. Hellegers, and P. Bruns. 1959. Surg. Gyn. Obst. 109:509. [2] Hanon, F. 1957. Rev. fr. gyn. obst. 52:57. [3] Lambiotte, C., and P. Rosa. 1949. Gyn. obst., Par. 48:161. [4] Palliez, R., G. Biserte, J. Savary, and J. Montreuil. 1957. Bruxelles med. 37:429. [5] Stander, H. J. In J. W. Williams. 1936. Obstetrics. Ed. 7. Appleton-Century-Crofts, New York. [6] Stuckert, H., A. Cantarow, and R. C. Davis. 1933. Surg. Gyn. Obst. 57:1.

152. pH OF MATERNAL AND FETAL BLOOD: MAMMALS

Observations were fetal rather than neonatal, except where pre-respiratory samples were demonstrated to be similar to pre-delivery samples. The pH of umbilical blood of the apneic newborn has not been included, but can be found in references 3 and 10. Values for the fetus should not be superficially compared to those for the adult, especially values for pH and other variables that reflect the state of pulmonary ventilation in the respiring mammal. For example, the excretion of carbon dioxide from the fetus occurs, in the absence of special pumps, when the CO_2 pressure of fetal blood exceeds the CO_2 pressure of the maternal blood; thus, elevation of CO_2 pressure in the fetus is not per se an abnormal condition. [4] Blood: V = antecubital vein, A = artery. Values in parentheses are ranges, estimate "b" (cf. Introduction).

| | Animal | Duration of Pregnancy | | Maternal | | | | Fetal | | | Reference |
		Days	% Term	Condition	No. of Observations	Blood	pH	No. of Observations	Umbilical Vein Blood pH	Umbilical Artery Blood pH	
	(A)	(B)	(C)	(D)	(E)	(F)	(G)	(H)	(I)	(J)	(K)
1	Man	280	100	Normal	28	V	7.28	28	7.32(7.30-7.34)	7.28(7.24-7.32)	2
2		280	100	Induced acidosis[1]	10	V	7.28	10	7.14(7.04-7.24)	7.08(6.92-7.24)	2
3		230-280	82-100	Diabetes	18	V	7.34	18	7.25(7.19-7.31)	7.17(7.09-7.25)	9
4	Goat	68	46	Normal	7	A	7.39	7	7.34(7.30-7.38)	7.25(7.19-7.31)	6
5		102	69	Normal	9	A	7.40	10	7.35(7.31-7.39)	7.31(7.25-7.37)	6
6		139	94	Normal	7	A	7.40	8	7.33(7.29-7.37)	7.32(7.24-7.40)	6
7	Rabbit	23-31	74-100	Normal	12	A	7.40	47	7.37(7.11-7.63)		11
8				Induced acidosis[1]	3	A	7.37	10	7.20(7.04-7.36)[2]		1
9	Sheep	70	47	Normal	15	A	7.44	22	7.39(7.35-7.43)	7.36(7.30-7.42)	5
10		88	60	Normal	14	A	7.46	21	7.41(7.37-7.45)	7.36(7.30-7.42)	5
11		106	72	Normal	16	A	7.44	16	7.36(7.32-7.40)	7.33(7.27-7.39)	5
12		124	84	Normal	11	A	7.47	13	7.37(7.33-7.41)	7.33(7.25-7.41)	5
13		142	96	Normal	9	A	7.45	13	7.36(7.30-7.42)	7.31(7.23-7.39)	5
14		105	72	Induced acidosis[1]	4	A	7.45	4	7.37(7.31-7.43)	7.34(7.26-7.42)	8
15	Swine	106	92	Normal	6	A	7.39	12	7.37(7.33-7.41)	7.34(7.28-7.40)	7

/1/ Ammonium chloride administered to mothers. /2/ Pooled samples obtained by decapitation.

Contributor: Kaiser, Irwin H.

References: [1] Dancis, J., M. Worth, Jr., and P. B. Schneidau. 1957. Am. J. Physiol. 188:535. [2] Goodlin, R. C. and I. Kaiser. 1957. Am. J. M. Sc. 233:662. [3] James, L. S., I. M. Weisbrot, C. E. Prince, D. A. Haladay, and V. Apgar. 1958. J. Pediat., S. Louis 52:379. [4] Kaiser, I. 1959. Am. J. Obst. 77:573. [5] Kaiser, I., and J. N. Cummings. 1958. Am. J. Physiol. 193:627. [6] Kaiser, I., and J. N. Cummings. 1958. Ibid. 195:481. [7] Kaiser, I., and J. N. Cummings. 1959. Am. J. Obst. 77:10. [8] Kaiser, I., J. N. Cummings, S. R. M. Reynolds, and J. P. Marbarger. 1958. J. Appl. Physiol. 13:171. [9] Kaiser, I., and R. C. Goodlin. 1958. Pediatrics 22:1097. [10] Noguchi, M. 1937. Jap. J. Obst. 20:248. [11] Young, I. M. 1952. Am. J. Physiol. 170:434.

Data were determined at time of birth and pertain only to term pregnancies. Values in parentheses are ranges, estimate "c" unless otherwise indicated (cf. Introduction).

	Property or Constituent	No. of Subjects	Vessel	Value	Reference
	(A)	(B)	(C)	(D)	(E)
			Whole Blood		
1	O$_2$ capacity	88	Umbilical vein	20.8(16.0-26.0) vol %	16
2	O$_2$ content	20	Umbilical vein	12.5(1.8-16.2) vol %	17
3			Umbilical artery	6.2(0.9-8.5) vol %	
4	O$_2$ saturation	20	Umbilical vein	65.0(25.0-71.0) %	15
5			Umbilical artery	30.0(6.0-35.0) %	
6	O$_2$ pressure	20	Umbilical vein	30.0(18.0-40.0) mm Hg	15, 18
7			Umbilical artery	18.0(10.0-20.0) mm Hg	
8	Erythrocytes	79	Umbilical vein	4.6(3.1-5.6) million/cu mm	27
9		67	Capillary	4.7(3.5-5.6) million/cu mm	27
10	Hemoglobin, total	50	Umbilical vein	15.5(10.0-24.7) g/100 ml	4
11	Leukocytes	13	Capillary	24.945(15.25-45.00) thousand/cu mm	5
12	Neutrophils	13	Capillary	68.7(53.0-82.5) % of leukocytes	5
13	Eosinophils	13	Capillary	2.1(0-5.5) % of leukocytes	5
14	Monocytes	13	Capillary	6.5(3.0-11.5) % of leukocytes	5
15	Lymphocytes	13	Capillary	18.3(9.0-36.0) % of leukocytes	5
16	Neutrophilic myelocytes	13	Capillary	3.6(0-10.0) % of leukocytes	5
17	Nucleated erythrocytes	200	Umbilical vein	7.3(0-15) per 100 leukocytes	1
18	Platelets	73	Umbilical vein	227(140-290) thousand/cu mm	11
19	Glutathione (red cell)	16	Umbilical vein	279.5(248.7-310.3)[b] μM/100 ml erythrocytes	20
			Plasma		
20	CO$_2$ content	4	Umbilical vein	23.9(23.5-24.4) mM/L	19
21			Umbilical artery	26.2(25.0-27.4) mM/L	
22	CO$_2$, physically dissolved	4	Umbilical vein	1.3(1.1-1.5) mM/L	19
23			Umbilical artery	1.4(1.3-1.6) mM/L	
24	CO$_2$ pressure	4	Umbilical vein	42.1(37.0-49.1) mm Hg	19
25			Umbilical artery	46.4(41.4-52.8) mm Hg	
26	Osmotic pressure	10	Umbilical vein	292.7(287.6-296.6) mOsm/kg H$_2$O	2
27	pH at 38°C	4	Umbilical vein	7.35(7.29-7.41)	19
28			Umbilical artery	7.35(7.27-7.42)	
29	Bicarbonate	4	Umbilical vein	22.6(22.1-22.9) mM/L	19
30			Umbilical artery	24.7(23.5-26.0) mM/L	
31	Calcium	121	Umbilical vein	11.3(7.3-16.9) mg/100 ml	24
32	Chloride	12	Umbilical vein	11.29(10.91-11.67)[b] mEq/100 ml	26
33	Phosphate, inorganic	12	Umbilical vein	5.58(5.33-5.83)[b] mg/100 ml	26
34	Phosphorus	121	Umbilical vein	5.6(4.2-8.0) mg/100 ml	24
35	Total	12	Umbilical vein	6.27(5.69-6.85)[b] mg/100 ml	26
36	Potassium	10	Umbilical vein	4.4(3.1-5.8) mEq/L	2
37	Sodium	10	Umbilical vein	140.2(137.0-145.0) mEq/L	2
38	Protein, total	14	Umbilical vein	5.2(4.5-5.8) g/100 ml	2
39	Albumin	8	Umbilical vein	4.16(4.12-5.59) g/100 ml	21
40	Globulin	8	Umbilical vein	2.37(1.36-3.23) g/100 ml	21
	Nitrogen				
41	Non-protein N	40	Umbilical vein	27.4(25-30) mg/100 ml	14
42	Amino acid N	12	Umbilical vein	5.11(4.67-5.55)[b] mg/100 ml	26
43	Creatinine N	12	Umbilical vein	0.397(0.319-0.475)[b] mg/100 ml	26
44	Urea N	12	Umbilical vein	8.8(3.7-13.6) mg/100 ml	10
45	Lipids, total	29	Umbilical vein	198.0(97-367) mg/100 ml	3
	Cholesterol				3
46	Total	29	Umbilical vein	34.0(17-86) mg/100 ml	
47	Free	29	Umbilical vein	14.0(6-29) mg/100 ml	
48	Ester	29	Umbilical vein	20.0(0-57) mg/100 ml	
49	Fat, neutral	29	Umbilical vein	90.0(0-283) mg/100 ml	3
50	Fatty acids, total	29	Umbilical vein	140.0(59-297) mg/100 ml	3
51	Phospholipid	29	Umbilical vein	61.0(21-166) mg/100 ml	3
52	Fructose	12	Umbilical vein	4.2(3.6-4.8)[b] mg/100 ml	6
53	Glucose	12	Umbilical vein	110.0(100.0-120.0)[b] mg/100 ml	25
54	Lactate	12	Umbilical vein	27.4(24.0-30.8)[b] mg/100 ml	26

	Property or Constituent	No. of Subjects	Vessel	Value	Reference
	(A)	(B)	(C)	(D)	(E)
	Plasma (concluded)				
55	Vitamin A	143	Umbilical vein	49.0(24.0-79.0) I.U./100 ml	7
56	Vitamin B_1 (thiamine)	48	Umbilical vein	11.63(4.90-20.59) μg/100 ml	22
57	Vitamin C (ascorbic acid)	25	Umbilical vein	1.15(0.71-1.73) mg/100 ml	9
58	Vitamin E (tocopherol)	54	Umbilical vein	0.34(0.10-0.58)[b] mg/100 ml	23
59	Androsterone	15	Umbilical vein	12.1(5.0-25.0) μg/100 ml	12
60	Dehydroepiandrosterone	17	Umbilical vein	35.8(15.0-69.0) μg/100 ml	12
61	17-Hydroxycorticosteroid	9[1]	Umbilical vein	23.2(0.2-65.8) μg/100 ml	13
62		7[2]	Umbilical vein	4.2(0.6-0.5) μg/100 ml	
	Serum				
	Vitamin B_2 (riboflavin)				8
63	Total	12	Umbilical vein	3.70(3.12-4.28)[b] μg/100 ml	
64	Free	12	Umbilical vein	2.14(1.78-2.50)[b] μg/100 ml	
65	Vitamin B_{12} (cyanocobalamine)	18	Umbilical vein	378.1(301.5-354.7)[b] μμg/ml	20
66	Vitamin B_{12} binding substance	7	Umbilical vein	2.75(2.59-2.91)[b] μμg/ml	20
67	Transaminase	7	Umbilical vein	37.3(32.06-42.54)[b] μM/ml	20
68	Flavin-adenine dinucleotide	12	Umbilical vein	1.29(0.97-1.61)[b] μg/100 ml	8
69	Riboflavin mononucleotide	12	Umbilical vein	0.28(0-58)[b] μg/100 ml	8

/1/ Vaginal delivery. /2/ Cesarean section.

Contributor: Prystowsky, Harry

References: [1] Anderson, G. W. 1941. Am. J. Obst. 42:1. [2] Battaglia, F., H. Prystowsky, C. Smisson, A. Hellegers, and P. Bruns. 1960. Pediatrics 25:2. [3] Boyd, E. M. 1936. Am. J. Dis. Child. 52:1319. [4] Cotter, J., and H. Prystowsky. Unpublished. [5] Forkner, C. E. 1929. Bull. Johns Hopkins Hosp. 45:75. [6] Hagermann, D. D., and C. A. Villee. 1952. J. Clin. Invest. 31:911. [7] Lund, C. J., and M. S. Kimble. 1943. Am. J. Obst. 46:207. [8] Lust, J. E., D. D. Hagermann, and C. A. Villee. 1954. J. Clin. Invest. 33:38. [9] Manahan, C. P., and N. J. Eastman. 1938. Bull. Johns Hopkins Hosp. 62:478. [10] McCance, R. A., and E. M. Widdowson. 1947. Lancet, Lond. 1:787. [11] Merritt, K. K., and L. T. Davidson. 1933. Am. J. Dis. Child. 46:990. [12] Migeon, C. J., A. R. Keller, and E. G. Holmstrom. 1955. Bull. Johns Hopkins Hosp. 97:415. [13] Migeon, C. J., H. Prystowsky, M. M. Grumbach, and C. M. Byran. 1956. J. Clin. Invest. 35:488. [14] Pommerenke, W. T. 1936. Ibid. 15:485. [15] Prystowsky, H. 1957. Bull. Johns Hopkins Hosp. 101:48. [16] Prystowsky, H. 1958. Obst. Gyn., N. Y. 12:264. [17] Prystowsky, H. 1959. Am. J. Obst. 78:483. [18] Prystowsky, H., A. Hellegers, and P. Bruns. 1960. Surg. Gyn. Obst. 110:495. [19] Prystowsky, H., A. Hellegers, and P. Bruns. Unpublished. [20] Prystowsky, H., A. Hellegers, E. Ranke, B. Ranke, and B. F. Chow. 1959. Am. J. Obst. 77:1. [21] Remington, C., and J. H. Bickford. 1947. Lancet, Lond. 2:781. [22] Slobody, L. B., M. M. Willner, and J. Mestern. 1949. Am. J. Dis. Child. 77:736. [23] Straumfjord, J. V., and M. L. Quaife. 1946. Proc. Soc. Exp. Biol., N. Y. 61:369. [24] Todd, W. R., D. G. Chuinard, and M. T. Wood. 1939. Am. J. Dis. Child. 57:1278. [25] Villee, C. A. 1953. J. Appl. Physiol. 5:437. [26] Villee, C. A. In Tr. 1st Conf. Gestation, 1954. Josiah Macy, Jr., Foundation, N. Y. p. 91. [27] Wegelius, R. 1948. Acta paediat., Upps., Suppl. 4, p. 107.

XXIII. Milk

154. PHYSICAL PROPERTIES AND CHEMICAL COMPOSITION OF MILK: MAN

For additional information on milk, consult reference 17, Part I.

Part I: IMMATURE MILK

Values in parentheses are ranges, estimate "c" (cf. Introduction).

Property or Constituent	No. of Observations	Colostrum[1] Value	No. of Observations	Transitional Milk[2] Value	Reference
(A)	(B)	(C)	(D)	(E)	(F)
Physical Properties					
1 Fat melting point				32°C	3
2 Specific gravity		1.034	2	1.035(1.034-1.036)	C, 4; E, 15
General Chemical Components					
3 Ash	68	0.30(0.24-0.36) g/100 ml	68	0.25(0.18-0.35) g/100 ml	1
4	105	0.35(0.20-0.72) g/100 ml	95	0.26(0.14-0.42) g/100 ml	22
5 Solids, total	29	12.8(10.0-16.7) g/100 ml	46	13.3(10.5-15.6) g/100 ml	15
6 Water		87.2 g/100 ml		86.4 g/100 ml	17
Electrolytes					
7 Calcium	22	23(13-34) mg/100 ml	22	26(21-33) mg/100 ml	24
8	28	48(24-66) mg/100 ml	46	46(23-63) mg/100 ml	15
9	115	28(14-49) mg/100 ml	100	30(18-49) mg/100 ml	22
10 Chlorine	8	59(44-101) mg/100 ml	21	46(30-72) mg/100 ml	15
11	186	78(20-233) mg/100 ml	126	48(17-116) mg/100 ml	22
12 Copper	3	0.04(0.02-0.05) mg/100 ml	12	0.05(0.04-0.07) mg/100 ml	16
13 Iodine	37	12.2 µg/100 ml	8	2.4 µg/100 ml	18
14		(4.5-45) µg/100 ml			6
15 Iron	3	0.04(0.02-0.05) mg/100 ml	12	0.04(0.02-0.05) mg/100 ml	16
16	7	0.10 mg/100 ml			7
17 Magnesium	28	4(3-8) mg/100 ml	44	4(2-5) mg/100 ml	15
18	21	3(1-5) mg/100 ml	22	4(3-5) mg/100 ml	24
19 Manganese		Trace			4
Phosphorus					
20 Total P	28	16(8-25) mg/100 ml	46	20(10-32) mg/100 ml	15
21	65	13(6-21) mg/100 ml	65	17(10-24) mg/100 ml	22
22	21	14(10-18) mg/100 ml	22	15(13-18) mg/100 ml	24
23 Lipid P	1	2 mg/100 ml	5	3(2-4) mg/100 ml	11
24 Potassium	11	74(66-87) mg/100 ml	25	64(53-77) mg/100 ml	15
25 Sodium	28	50(26-136) mg/100 ml	44	29(19-54) mg/100 ml	15
26 Sulfur	8	23(20-26) mg/100 ml	19	20(15-23) mg/100 ml	15
27 Zinc	7	0.559(0.072-0.981) mg/100 ml	25	0.382(0.039-0.588) mg/100 ml	16
Nitrogenous Substances					
Protein					
28 Total	100	3.2(1.2-14.1) g/100 ml	56	1.6(0.8-2.0) g/100 ml	22
29	99	2.0(1.4-2.9) g/100 ml	99	1.7(1.1-2.6) g/100 ml	1
30	167	5.5(1.4-21.5) g/100 ml	160	1.6(1.1-2.7) g/100 ml	21
31 Casein	40	2.058(0.726-5.172) g/100 ml	84	0.917(0.408-1.841) g/100 ml	21
32 Lactalbumin			2	0.8(0.7-0.8) g/100 ml	15
33 Lactoglobulin	39	3.542(0.42-13.25) g/100 ml	83	0.497(0.210-1.363) g/100 ml	21
34 Whey	1	1.7 g/100 ml			12
Amino acids					
35 Arginine	10	75(62-96) mg/100 ml	28	64(48-89) mg/100 ml	19
36 Cystine				55 mg/100 ml	2
37 Histidine	10	41(35-46) mg/100 ml	28	38(29-45) mg/100 ml	19
38 Isoleucine	10	100(88-115) mg/100 ml	28	97(73-121) mg/100 ml	19
39 Leucine	10	169(145-214) mg/100 ml	28	151(113-197) mg/100 ml	19

/1/ 1st-5th day of lactation.   /2/ 6th-10th day of lactation.

Part I: IMMATURE MILK (Continued)

	Property or Constituent	Colostrum[1]		Transitional Milk[2]		Reference
		No. of Observations	Value	No. of Observations	Value	
	(A)	(B)	(C)	(D)	(E)	(F)
	Nitrogenous Substances (concluded)					
	Amino acids (concluded)					
40	Lysine	9	114(95-139) mg/100 ml	28	113(86-148) mg/100 ml	19
41	Methionine	10	26(19-36) mg/100 ml	28	24(16-34) mg/100 ml	19
42	Phenylalanine	10	70(60-84) mg/100 ml	28	63(48-74) mg/100 ml	19
43	Threonine	10	84(75-104) mg/100 ml	28	79(61-96) mg/100 ml	19
44	Tryptophan	10	32(25-42) mg/100 ml	26	28(23-33) mg/100 ml	19
45	Tyrosine				125 mg/100 ml	2
46	Valine	10	118(98-149) mg/100 ml	28	105(77-136) mg/100 ml	19
47	Urea			1	23.3 mg/100 ml	15
	Nitrogen					
48	Protein N		424 mg/100 ml		251 mg/100 ml	17
49	Casein N		188 mg/100 ml		110 mg/100 ml	
50	Lactalbumin N				126 mg/100 ml	
51	Lactoglobulin N				78 mg/100 ml	
52	Whey N		267 mg/100 ml			
53	Non-protein N	7	91(51-127) mg/100 ml	21	84(48-140) mg/100 ml	21
54				2	48(42-53) mg/100 ml	15
55	Amino acid N			2	4(4-5) mg/100 ml	15
	Lipids, Carbohydrates					
56	Cholesterol	7	31(24-45) mg/100 ml	10	29(14-44) mg/100 ml	8
57	Fat	25	2.7(0.7-3.8) g/100 ml	10	3.0(1.5-4.5) g/100 ml	C,10;E, 8
58		16	3.6(1.9-12.7) g/100 ml	9	3.9(1.2-9.6) g/100 ml	C, 9;E, 20
59		88	3.2(0.9-8.2) g/100 ml	88	3.7(1.6-7.1) g/100 ml	1
60	Lactose	88	6.4(4.6-7.4) g/100 ml	88	6.7(4.8-7.6) g/100 ml	1
61		199	5.7(1.1-7.9) g/100 ml	140	6.8(5.7-8.4) g/100 ml	22, 23
	Vitamins					
62	A	24	161(75-305) μg/100 ml	26	88(58-183) μg/100 ml	15
63		21	51(16-125) μg/100 ml			10
64	Carotenoids	24	137(41-385) μg/100 ml	26	38(23-63) μg/100 ml	15
65		21	114(22-559) μg/100 ml			10
	B[1] (thiamine)					
66	Total	47	(0.5-27) μg/100 ml	26	(5-26) μg/100 ml	14
67		25	2(1-3) μg/100 ml	35	6(2-10) μg/100 ml	15
68		19	19(4-82) μg/100 ml			10
69	Free	19	0.4(0.1-0.9) μg/100 ml	35	0.8(0.2-1.9) μg/100 ml	15
	B[2] (riboflavin)					15
70	Total	25	30.2(12.0-45.3) μg/100 ml	35	36.9(27.5-49.0) μg/100 ml	
71	Free	19	19.0(7.7-27.0) μg/100 ml	33	24.0(16.6-40.8) μg/100 ml	
72	B[12] (cyanocobalamine)	12	0.045(0.010-0.15) μg/100 ml	5	0.036(0.003-0.070) μg/100 ml	5
73	B[c] (folic acid)	8	0.05(0.01-0.15) μg/100 ml	2	0.02(0.015-0.025) μg/100 ml	5
74	C (ascorbic acid)	16	4.1(1.7-7.2) mg/100 ml	15	4.6(2.7-6.6) mg/100 ml	13
75		17	7.2(4.7-10.4) mg/100 ml	20	7.1(4.5-9.0) mg/100 ml	15
76		24	1.4(0.4-4.8) mg/100 ml			10
77	E (tocopherol)	6	1.48(0.25-2.9) mg/100 ml	9	1.32(0.48-3.0) mg/100 ml	20
78	H (biotin)	20	0.1(trace-0.3) μg/100 ml	35	0.4(trace-1.8) μg/100 ml	15
79	Niacin (nicotinic acid)	29	75(50-145) μg/100 ml	34	175(60-360) μg/100 ml	15
80			(<10-80) μg/100 ml			10
81	Pantothenic acid	29	183(29-302) μg/100 ml	33	288(135-412) μg/100 ml	15

/1/ 1st-5th day of lactation. /2/ 6th-10th day of lactation.

Contributors: Macy, Icie G., and Kelly, Harriet J.

Part I: IMMATURE MILK (Concluded)

References: [1] Bell, M. 1928. J. Biol. Chem. 80:239. [2] Block, R., and D. Bolling. 1950. Arch. Biochem., N. Y. 25:350. [3] Bosworth, A. W. 1934. J. Biol. Chem. 106:235. [4] Castellanos, A. O., and A. Lizarralde. 1943. Rev. As. argent. diet. 1:199. [5] Collins, R. A., A. E. Harper, M. Schreiber, and C. A. Elvehjem. 1951. J. Nutrit. 43:313. [6] Elmer, A. W., and W. Rychlik. 1934. C. rend. Soc. biol. 117:530. [7] Escudero, P., and E. Pierangeli. 1943. Rev. As. argent. diet. 1:85. [8] Fox, F. W., and J. A. Gardner. 1924. Biochem. J., Lond. 18:127. [9] Hammett, F. S. 1917. J. Biol. Chem. 29:381. [10] Herraiz, M., and H. G. de Alvarez-Herrero. 1943. Rev. As. argent. diet. 1:95. [11] Hess, A. F., and F. D. Helman. 1925. J. Biol. Chem. 64:781. [12] Holt, L. E., A. M. Courtney, and H. L. Fales. 1915. Am. J. Dis. Child. 10:229. [13] Ingalls, T. H., R. Draper, and H. M. Teel. 1938. Ibid. 56:1011. [14] Knott, E. M., S. C. Kleiger, and F. Bracamonte-Torres. 1943. J. Nutrit. 25:49. [15] Macy, I. G. 1949. Am. J. Dis. Child. 78:589. [16] Macy, I. G. Unpublished. [17] Macy, I. G., H. J. Kelly, and R. E. Sloan. 1953. The composition of milks. Nat. Acad. Sc.-Nat. Res. Counc., Washington, D. C. Pub. 254. p. 62. [18] Mauer, E., and S. Diez. 1926. Münch. med. Wschr. 73:17. [19] Miller, S., et al. 1950. J. Nutrit. 40:499. [20] Neuweiler, W. 1948. Internat. Zschr. Vitaminforsch., Bern 20:108. [21] Waller, H., R. Aschaffenburg, and M. W. Grant. 1941. Biochem. J., Lond. 35:272. [22] Widdows, S. T., M. F. Lowenfeld, M. Bond, C. Shishkin, and E. I. Taylor. 1935. Ibid. 29:1145. [23] Widdows, S. T., M. F. Lowenfeld, M. Bond, and E. I. Taylor. 1930. Ibid. 24:327. [24] Winikoff, D. 1944. Med. J. Australia 31:660.

Part II: MATURE MILK

Values in parentheses are ranges, estimate "c" (cf. Introduction).

Property or Constituent	No. of Observations	Value	Reference
(A)	(B)	(C)	(D)
Physical Properties			
1 Fat melting point		(26.0-26.5) $^{\circ}$C	4
2		(33.5-38.9) $^{\circ}$C	36
3 Refractive index at 40°C		(1.4556-1.4583)	36
4 Specific gravity	94	1.031(1.024-1.043)	35
General Chemical Components			
5 Ash	26	0.20(0.16-0.24) g/100 ml	18
6	94	0.20(0.09-0.50) g/100 ml	35
7 Salts		0.313 g/100 ml	3
8 Solids, total	27	12.2(9.8-15.6) g/100 ml	18
9	610	12.9(10.3-17.5) g/100 ml	27
10 Water		87.6 g/100 ml	29
Electrolytes			
11 Aluminum		Trace	10,11
12 Barium		Trace	10,11
13 Boron		Trace	10,11
14 Bromine	17	912(327-1502) μg/100 ml	25
15 Calcium	55	28(15-40) mg/100 ml	5
16	31	40(20-60) mg/100 ml	33
17	628	34(17-61) mg/100 ml	27
18 Chlorine	216	38(9-73) mg/100 ml	27
19	10	34(30-40) mg/100 ml	21
20	44	50(16-158) mg/100 ml	5
21 Chromium	5	Trace	11
22 Copper	67	0.03(0.01-0.07) mg/100 ml	28
23 Iodine		(4.5-9.0) μg/100 ml	12

	Property or Constituent	No. of Observations	Value	Reference
	(A)	(B)	(C)	(D)
			Electrolytes (concluded)	
24	Iron	14	0.36(0.29-0.45) mg/100 ml	34
25		67	0.03(0.02-0.09) mg/100 ml	28
26	Lead	30	Trace	10
27		4	0.016(0.005-0.032) mg/100 ml	40
28		52	(0.001-0.018) mg/100 ml	20
29	Lithium		Trace	10,11
30	Magnesium	302	4(2-6) mg/100 ml	27
31	Manganese	30	Trace	10
32	Molybdenum		Trace	10,11
	Phosphorus			
33	Total P	7	16(12-19) mg/100 ml	17
34		55	17(10-35) mg/100 ml	5
35		628	14(7-27) mg/100 ml	27
36	Inorganic P	51	5.13(1.5-8.77) mg/100 ml	5
37	Lipid P	11	3(2-4) mg/100 ml	17
38	Potassium	26	48(30-66) mg/100 ml	18
39		45	55(42-70) mg/100 ml	26
40		54	52(27-81) mg/100 ml	5
41	Rubidium	30	Trace	10
42	Silver	6	Trace	11
43	Sodium	26	13(2-25) mg/100 ml	18
44		302	17(6-44) mg/100 ml	27
45	Strontium		Trace	10,11
46	Sulfur	116	14(5-30) mg/100 ml	27
47	Titanium	6	Trace	11
48	Vanadium	6	Trace	11
49	Zinc	2	0.26(0.12-0.39) mg/100 ml	37
50		58	0.118(0.017-0.302) mg/100 ml	28
			Nitrogenous Substances	
	Protein			
51	Total	27	0.9(0.8-1.0) g/100 ml	13
52		94	1.5(0.8-5.6) g/100 ml	35
53		583	1.1(0.7-2.0) g/100 ml	27
54	Casein	166	0.37(0.14-0.68) g/100 ml	27
55	Lactalbumin	163	0.36(0.14-0.60) g/100 ml	27
56	Lactoglobulin		0.172 g/100 ml	15
57	Whey	31	0.7(0.4-1.0) g/100 ml	33
	Amino acids			
58	Alanine		35 mg/100 ml	44
59	Arginine	147	45(28-64) mg/100 ml	30
60	Aspartic acid		116 mg/100 ml	44
61	Cystine		20 mg/100 ml	1
62			41 mg/100 ml	44
63	Glutamic acid		230 mg/100 ml	44
64	Glycine		0 mg/100 ml	44
65	Histidine	147	23(16-34) mg/100 ml	30
66	Isoleucine	147	68(46-102) mg/100 ml	30
67	Leucine	147	108(72-159) mg/100 ml	30
68	Lysine	147	76(53-104) mg/100 ml	30
69	Methionine	146	14(9-21) mg/100 ml	30
70	Phenylalanine	147	41(30-58) mg/100 ml	30
71	Proline		80 mg/100 ml	44
72	Serine		69 mg/100 ml	44
73	Threonine	147	54(40-76) mg/100 ml	30
74	Tryptophan	144	18(13-26) mg/100 ml	30
75	Tyrosine		50 mg/100 ml	1
76			78 mg/100 ml	2
77	Valine	147	71(48-114) mg/100 ml	30

	Property or Constituent	No. of Observations	Value	Reference
	(A)	(B)	(C)	(D)
	Nitrogenous Substances (concluded)			
78	Creatine	3	3.5(3.2-3.9) mg/100 ml	9
79		41	3.1(0-12.4) mg/100 ml	27
80	Creatinine	3	1.5(1.1-1.8) mg/100 ml	9
81		44	3.0(2.0-5.1) mg/100 ml	27
82	Urea	3	26.5(25.2-29.0) mg/100 ml	9
83		52	37.8(26.7-49.4) mg/100 ml	27
84	Uric acid	3	2.5(2.2-2.7) mg/100 ml	9
85		56	6.6(3.9-12.3) mg/100 ml	27
86	Nitrogen Protein N		188 mg/100 ml	29
87	Casein N		63 mg/100 ml	
88	Lactalbumin N		47 mg/100 ml	
89	Lactoglobulin N		31 mg/100 ml	
90	Whey N		94 mg/100 ml	
91	Non-protein N	31	47(37-68) mg/100 ml	33
92		151	32(17-60) mg/100 ml	27
93	Amino acid N	3	7.2(4.6-8.6) mg/100 ml	9
94		157	5.0(2.8-11.3) mg/100 ml	27
	Lipids, Carbohydrates, Miscellaneous Organic Acids			
95	Cholesterol	27	13(7-19) mg/100 ml	41
96		7	27(13-47) mg/100 ml	14
97	Fat	37	3.9(0.7-8.0) g/100 ml	8
98		10	3.3(2.1-5.4) g/100 ml	16
99		94	3.3(0.5-9.0) g/100 ml	35
100	Lecithin	1	78 mg/100 ml	22
101	Lactose	55	7.1(5.8-8.4) g/100 ml	42
102	Citric acid		(35-125) mg/100 ml	19
	Vitamins			
103	A	264	61(15-226) µg/100 ml	27
104		1390	49 µg/100 ml	23
105	Carotenoids	265	25(2-77) µg/100 ml	27
106	B₁ (thiamine) Total	277	14(8-23) µg/100 ml	27
107		44	18(6-31) µg/100 ml	39
108	Free	258	5.3(1.2-15.8) µg/100 ml	27
109		61	4.3(1.3-12.4) µg/100 ml	38
110	B₂ (riboflavin) Total	272	37.3(19.8-79.0) µg/100 ml	27
111		43	52.4(12.6-100.0) µg/100 ml	39
112	Free	256	24.2(10.5-61.8) µg/100 ml	27
113	B₆ (pyridoxine)	3	18(10-22) µg/100 ml	27
114		9	4(2-9) µg/100 ml	43
115	B₁₂ (cyanocobalamine)	3	Trace	6
116	Bc (folic acid)	22	0.22(0.14-0.36) µg/100 ml	27
117		3	0.14(0.09-0.18) µg/100 ml	6
118	C (ascorbic acid)	233	5.2(0.9-11.2) mg/100 ml	27
119		261	3.7(0.4-7.7) mg/100 ml	45
120	D		(0.4-10) U.S.P. units/100 ml	24
121	E (tocopherol)	5	0.90(0.78-1.14) mg/100 ml	31
122		10	0.24(0.10-0.48) mg/100 ml	16
123	H (biotin)	10	0.2(0.1-0.3) µg/100 ml	32
124	K		50(0-200) Dam-Glavind units/100 ml	7
125	Choline Total	29	9(5-14) mg/100 ml	27
126	Free	3	2 mg/100 ml	

Part II: MATURE MILK (Concluded)

Property or Constituent	No. of Observations	Value	Reference
(A)	(B)	(C)	(D)
Vitamins (concluded)			
Inositol			27
127 Total	7	45(39-56) mg/100 ml	
128 Free	5	44(39-52) mg/100 ml	
129 Niacin (nicotinic acid)	268	183(66-330) µg/100 ml	27
130	9	160(120-220) µg/100 ml	43
131 Pantothenic acid	269	246(86-584) µg/100 ml	27
132	9	160(80-300) µg/100 ml	43

Contributors: Macy, Icie G., and Kelly, Harriet J.

References: [1] Beach, E. F., S. S. Bernstein, O. D. Hoffman, D. M. Teague, and I. G. Macy. 1941. J. Biol. Chem. 139:57. [2] Block, R., and D. Bolling. 1950. Arch. Biochem., N. Y. 25:350. [3] Bosworth, A. W., and L. L. Van Slyke. 1916. J. Biol. Chem. 24:187. [4] Brown, J. B., and B. M. Orians. 1946. Arch. Biochem., N. Y. 9:201. [5] Burhans, C. W., and D. N. Smith. 1923. Am. J. Dis. Child. 26:304. [6] Collins, R. A., A. E. Harper, M. Schreiber, and C. A. Elvehjem. 1951. J. Nutrit. 43:313. [7] Dam, H., J. Glavind, E. H. Larson, and P. Plum. 1942. Acta med. scand. 112:210. [8] Denis, W., and A. S. Minot. 1918. J. Biol. Chem. 36:59. [9] Denis, W., and A. S. Minot. 1919. Ibid. 37:353. [10] Dingle, H., and J. H. Sheldon. 1938. Biochem. J., Lond. 32:1078. [11] Drea, W. F. 1938. J. Nutrit. 16:325. [12] Elmer, A. W., and W. Rychlik. 1934. C. rend. Soc. biol. 117:530. [13] Escudero, P., and S. G. Waisman. 1946. Bol. Soc. quím. Perú 12:152. [14] Fox, F. W., and J. A. Gardner. 1924. Biochem. J., Lond. 18:127. [15] Gamble, J. A., N. R. Ellis, and A. K. Besley. 1939. Composition and properties of goat's milk as compared with cow's milk. U. S. Dept. Agr. Techn. Bull. 671. [16] Harris, P. L., M. L. Quaife, and P. O'Grady. 1952. J. Nutrit. 46:459. [17] Hess, A. F., and F. D. Helman. 1925. J. Biol. Chem. 64:781. [18] Holt, L. E., A. M. Courtney, and H. L. Fales. 1915. Am. J. Dis. Child. 10:229. [19] Jerlov, E. 1929. Sven. läk. tidn. 1:17. [20] Kasahara, M., and S. Nosu. 1935. Jahrb. Kinderh. 146:78. [21] Keller, A., and H. Mai. 1930. Schweiz. med. Wschr. 60:487. [22] Koch, W., and H. S. Woods. 1905-06. J. Biol. Chem. 1:203. [23] Kon, S. K., and E. H. Mawson. 1950. Human milk. Wartime studies of certain vitamins and other constituents. Med. Res. Counc., London Sp. Rep. Ser. 269. [24] Lawrence, J. M., B. L. Herrington, and L. A. Maynard. 1945. Am. J. Dis. Child. 70:193. [25] Leone, A., and E. Cadeddu. 1940. Riv. clin. pediat. 38:257. [26] Leulier, A., L. Revol, and R. Paccard. 1937. C. rend. Soc. biol. 124:1114. [27] Macy, I. G. 1949. Am. J. Dis. Child. 78:589. [28] Macy, I. G. Unpublished. [29] Macy, I. G., H. J. Kelly, and R. E. Sloan. 1953. The composition of milks. Nat. Acad. Sc.-Nat. Res. Counc., Washington, D. C. Pub. 254. p. 62. [30] Miller, S., and V. Ruttinger. 1951. Proc. Soc. Exp. Biol., N. Y. 77:96. [31] Neuweiler, W. 1948. Internat. Zschr. Vitaminforsch., Bern 20:108. [32] Neuweiler, W., and W. Ritter. 1949. Ibid. 21:239. [33] Plimmer, R. H. A., and J. Lowndes. 1937. Biochem. J., Lond. 31:1751. [34] Reis, F., and H. H. Chakmakjian. 1932. J. Biol. Chem. 98:237. [35] Richmond, H. D. In A. E. Leach. 1920. Food inspection and analysis. Ed. 4. John Wiley and Sons, Philadelphia. [36] Roller, P. E. 1934. J. Pediat., S. Louis 4:238. [37] Sato, M., and K. Murata. 1931. Tr. Tottori Soc. Agr. Sc. 2:206. [38] Slater, E. C., and E. J. Rial. In C. E. Roderuck, H. H. Williams, and I. G. Macy. 1945. Am. J. Dis. Child. 70:162. [39] Sundararajan, A. R. In C. E. Roderuck, M. N. Coryell, H. H. Williams, and I. G. Macy. 1945. Ibid. 70:171. [40] Tracy, A., and J. McPheat. 1944. Biochem. J., Lond. 37:683. [41] Wacker, L., and K. F. Beck. 1921. Zschr. Kinderh. 27:288. [42] Widdows, S. T., M. F. Lowenfeld, M. Bond, and E. I. Taylor. 1930. Biochem. J., Lond. 24:327. [43] Williams, R. J., V. H. Cheldelin, and H. K. Mitchell. 1942. Univ. Texas Pub. 4237:97. [44] Williamson, M. B. 1944. J. Biol. Chem. 156:47. [45] Winikoff, D. 1946. Med. J. Australia 33:205.

For additional information on milk, consult reference 48. Values in parentheses are ranges, estimate "c" (cf. Introduction).

	Property or Constituent	No. of Observations	Value	Reference
	(A)	(B)	(C)	(D)
	Physical Properties			
1	Fat melting point	484	(17.6-52.9) °C	26
2	Freezing point depression	1224	0.544(0.523-0.566) °C	44
3	Osmotic pressure	70	196.4	62
4	pH	151	6.62(6.55-6.68)	16
	Refractive index			
5	At 25°C	304	(1.4531-1.4610)	26
6	At 40°C	14	1.3464(1.3458-1.3472)	53
7	Specific gravity	1448	1.035(1.021-1.036)	63
8	Surface tension	12	52.8(51.7-55.0) dynes/sq cm	42
9	Viscosity at 15°C	12	1.75	42
	General Chemical Components			
10	Ash	800	0.71(0.35-1.21) g/100 ml	41
11		10	0.68(0.64-0.74) g/100 ml	14
12	Salts		0.901 g/100 ml	11
13	Solids, total	1447	13.3(8.5-19.6) g/100 ml	63
14		134	12.3(10.5-14.7) g/100 ml	39
15	Water		87.3 g/100 ml	48
	Electrolytes			
16	Aluminum		Trace	23,24,66
17	Barium		Trace	10,23,24
18	Boron	17	0.016(0.009-0.023) mg/100 ml	36
19	Bromine	7	21.4(18.4-24.1) µg/100 ml	12
20	Calcium	116	137(56-381) mg/100 ml	47
21		56	113(105-126) mg/100 ml	16
22	Chlorine	1006	129(70-290) mg/100 ml	13
23		27	108(93-141) mg/100 ml	47
24	Chromium		Trace	24
25	Cobalt		0.06 µg/100 ml	3
26	Copper	24	0.04(0.02-0.40) mg/100 ml	19,21
27		13	0.008(0.005-0.015) mg/100 ml	47
28		20	0.06(0.03-0.16) mg/100 ml	52
29	Fluorine	3	0.01(0.007-0.014) mg/100 ml	61
30	Iodine	132	54(13-187) µg/100 ml	56
31		43	0.8(0.4-16.2) µg/100 ml	28
32	Iron	220	0.09(0.03-0.14) mg/100 ml	18
33		24	0.20(0.15-0.38) mg/100 ml	19,21
34		25	0.36(0.14-1.00) mg/100 ml	55
35		61	0.03(0.01-0.06) mg/100 ml	37
36	Lead		Trace	23,24
37	Lithium		Trace	10,23,24,66
38	Magnesium	113	13(7-22) mg/100 ml	47
39	Manganese	24	0.002 mg/100 ml	2
40	Molybdenum		0.073(0.018-0.147) mg/L	5
41	Nickel	28	0.0003(0.00-0.02) mg/100 ml	4
	Phosphorus			
42	Total P	89	91(56-112) mg/100 ml	47
43		30	107(84-128) mg/100 ml	60
44	Inorganic P	3	72.4(69.4-74.5) mg/100 ml	8
45	Lipid P	18	6(4-14) mg/100 ml	29
46	Potassium	115	143(38-287) mg/100 ml	47
47	Rubidium		Trace	10,23
48	Ruthenium		Trace	66
49	Silicon		Trace	66
50	Silver		Trace	24
51	Sodium	114	57(31-214) mg/100 ml	47
52		20	77(39-139) mg/100 ml	38

	Property or Constituent	No. of Observations	Value	Reference
	(A)	(B)	(C)	(D)

			Electrolytes (concluded)	
53	Strontium		Trace	10, 23, 24, 66
54	Sulfur	27	30(24-36) mg/100 ml	47
55	Tin	3	0	23
56	Titanium		Trace	10, 24, 66
57	Vanadium		Trace	24, 66
58	Zinc	68	0.39(0.17-0.66) mg/100 ml	47

			Nitrogenous Substances	
	Protein			
59	Total	800	3.6(2.1-6.4) g/100 ml	41
60		62	2.9(2.4-3.7) g/100 ml	20
61	Casein	800	3.0(1.8-6.3) g/100 ml	41
62		62	2.2(1.4-3.1) g/100 ml	20
63	Lactalbumin	28	0.227(0.141-0.322) g/100 ml	58
64		58	0.42(0.27-0.57) g/100 ml	20
65	Lactoglobulin	28	0.172(0.068-0.370) g/100 ml	58
66		58	0.26(0.14-0.42) g/100 ml	20
67	Whey	800	0.5(0.2-1.4) g/100 ml	41
68		62	0.67(0.36-0.94) g/100 ml	20
	Amino acids			
69	Alanine		75 mg/100 ml	65
70	Arginine	15	133(102-173) mg/100 ml	25
71		6	100(90-120) mg/100 ml	33
72	Aspartic acid		166 mg/100 ml	65
73	Cystine		34 mg/100 ml	9
74			23 mg/100 ml	6
75	Glutamic acid		680 mg/100 ml	65
76	Glycine		11 mg/100 ml	65
77	Histidine	15	92(61-118) mg/100 ml	25
78		12	110(70-130) mg/100 ml	57
79	Isoleucine	15	218(166-172) mg/100 ml	25
80		12	240(180-290) mg/100 ml	57
81	Leucine	15	312(242-396) mg/100 ml	25
82	Lysine	15	256(200-330) mg/100 ml	25
83		12	290(248-382) mg/100 ml	43
84	Methionine	15	71(56-98) mg/100 ml	25
85		12	90(72-131) mg/100 ml	43
86	Phenylalanine	15	153(111-207) mg/100 ml	25
87		12	170(140-220) mg/100 ml	57
88	Proline		250 mg/100 ml	65
89	Serine		160 mg/100 ml	65
90	Threonine	15	152(115-201) mg/100 ml	25
91	Tryptophan	15	49(36-64) mg/100 ml	25
92		10	60(40-80) mg/100 ml	57
93	Tyrosine	6	170(160-180) mg/100 ml	33
94	Valine	15	239(189-297) mg/100 ml	25
95	Creatine	28	3.8(2.4-5.6) mg/100 ml	58
96	Creatinine	28	0.68(0.19-1.22) mg/100 ml	58
97	Urea	28	10.7(6.1-20.4) mg/100 ml	58
98	Uric acid	28	2.3(1.1-3.7) mg/100 ml	58
	Nitrogen			
99	Protein N		518 mg/100 ml	48
100	Casein N		440 mg/100 ml	
101	Lactalbumin N		63 mg/100 ml	
102	Lactoglobulin N		31 mg/100 ml	
103	Whey N		94 mg/100 ml	
104	Non-protein N	62	42(20-67) mg/100 ml	20
105		28	26(18-32) mg/100 ml	58
106	Amino acid N	3	4.2(4.0-4.5) mg/100 ml	22
107	Ammonia N	28	0.63(0.17-1.19) mg/100 ml	58
108	Proteose peptone N	28	20.2(9.3-36.2) mg/100 ml	58

	Property or Constituent	No. of Observations	Value	Reference
	(A)	(B)	(C)	(D)

	Lipids, Carbohydrates, Miscellaneous Organic Acids			
	Cholesterol			
109	Total	109	11(7-17) mg/100 ml	51
110		9	22(17-28) mg/100 ml	59
111	Free	7	12(10-15) mg/100 ml	51
112	Fat	1449	4.4(1.9-9.8) g/100 ml	63
113		800	3.6(1.7-6.5) g/100 ml	41
114	Lecithin	15	34(27-44) mg/100 ml	35
115		3	80(72-86) mg/100 ml	40
116	Lactose	800	4.9(2.1-6.1) g/100 ml	41
117	Citric acid	30	197(100-312) mg/100 ml	60
118		17	254(215-290) mg/100 ml	27
119	Lactic acid		3 mg/100 ml	45

	Vitamins			
120	A	58	27(17-38) µg/100 ml	16
121	Carotenoids	58	37(12-79) µg/100 ml	
	B$_1$ (thiamine)			
122	Total	56	43(28-90) µg/100 ml	16
123	Free	28	23 µg/100 ml	30
124	B$_2$ (riboflavin)	400	(60-342) µg/100 ml	31
125		58	156(116-202) µg/100 ml	16
126	B$_6$ (pyridoxine)	23	6(3-11) µg/100 ml	64
127		20	66(47-95) µg/100 ml	48
128	B$_{12}$ (cyanocobalamine)	332	0.36(0.07-1.15) µg/100 ml	15
129	B$_c$ (folic acid)	98	0.17(0.01-0.60) µg/100 ml	15
130	C (ascorbic acid)	704	1.9(1.0-3.1) mg/100 ml	34
131		180	1.4(0.7-2.3) mg/100 ml	54
132	D		(0.3-4.6) U.S.P. units/100 ml	7
133	E (tocopherol)		0.06 mg/100 ml	1
134	H (biotin)	135	2.0(0.2-5.9) µg/100 ml	49
135		30	5.0(1.6-11.0) µg/100 ml	64
136	K		200(0-400) Dam-Glavind units/100 ml	17
	Choline			
137	Total	25	10(4-16) mg/100 ml	47
138	Free	21	4(2-7) mg/100 ml	46
	Inositol			
139	Total	48	8(6-12) mg/100 ml	47
140		30	18(3-39) mg/100 ml	64
141	Free	27	6(4-9) mg/100 ml	47
142	Niacin (nicotinic acid)	144	66(21-125) µg/100 ml	49
143		10	100(80-150) µg/100 ml	50
144	Pantothenic acid	30	290(170-460) µg/100 ml	64
145		72	361(155-568) µg/100 ml	49

Contributors: Macy, Icie G., and Kelly, Harriet J.

References: [1] Abderhalden, R. 1947. Biochem. Zschr. 318:47. [2] Archibald, J. G. 1941. Milk Plant Month. 30:36. [3] Archibald, J. G. 1947. J. Dairy Sc. 30:293. [4] Archibald, J. G. 1949. Ibid. 32:877. [5] Archibald, J. G. 1951. Ibid. 34:102ₑ. [6] Beach, E. F., S. S. Bernstein, O. D. Hoffman, D. M. Teague, and I. G. Macy. 1941. J. Biol. Chem. 139:57. [7] Bechtel, H. E., and C. A. Hoppet. 1936. J. Nutrit. 11:537. [8] Benjamin, H. R., A. F. Hess, and J. Gross. 1933. J. Biol. Chem. 103:383. [9] Block, R., and D. Bolling. 1950. Arch. Biochem. 25:350. [10] Blumberg, H., and O. S. Rask. 1933. J. Nutrit. 6:285. [11] Bosworth, A. W., and L. L. Van Slyke. 1916. J. Biol. Chem. 24:187. [12] Casini, A. 1946. Ann. chim. applicata 36:219. [13] Caulfield, W. J., and W. H. Riddell. 1935. Cornell Vet. 25:334. [14] Cole, L. J., and I. Johansson. 1930. J. Dairy Sc. 16:565.

[15] Collins, R. A., R. E. Boldt, C. A. Elvehjem, and E. B. Hart. 1953. Ibid. 36:29. [16] Dahlberg, A. C., H. S. Adams, and M. E. Held. 1953. Sanitary milk control in relation to sanitary, nutritive, and other qualities of milk. Nat. Acad. Sc.-Nat. Res. Counc., Washington, D. C. Pub. 250. [17] Dam, H., J. Glavind, E. H. Larsen, and P. Plum. 1942. Acta med. scand. 112:210. [18] Davidson, L. S. P., and I. Leitch. 1934. Nutrit. Abstr., Aberdeen 3:901. [19] Davies, W. L. 1931-32. J. Dairy Res. 3:86. [20] Davies, W. L. 1932. Ibid. 4:142. [21] Davies, W. L. 1935. Ibid. 6:363. [22] Denis, W., and A. S. Minot. 1919. J. Biol. Chem. 37:353. [23] Dingle, H., and J. H. Sheldon. 1938. Biochem. J., Lond. 32:1078. [24] Drea, W. F. 1938. J. Nutrit. 16:325. [25] Duncan, C. W., G. I. Watson, K. M. Dunn, and R. E. Ely. 1952. J. Dairy Sc. 35:128. [26] Eckles, C. H., and R. H. Shaw. 1913. The influence of the stage of lactation on the composition and properties of milk. U. S. Dept. Agr. Bull. 155. [27] Fabris, A. 1951. Mondo Latte 10:598. [28] Fishbein, M. 1937. J. Am. M. Ass. 108:729. [29] Graham, W. R., Jr., and H. D. Kay. 1933-34. J. Dairy Res. 5:54. [30] Halliday, N., and H. Deuel, Jr. 1941. J. Biol. Chem. 140:555. [31] Hand, D. B., and P. F. Sharp. 1939. J. Dairy Sc. 22:779. [32] Hodson, A. Z. 1944. J. Nutrit. 27:415. [33] Hodson, A. Z., and G. M. Krueger. 1946. Arch. Biochem., N. Y. 10:55. [34] Holmes, A. D., F. Tripp, E. A. Woelffer, and G. H. Satterfield. 1942. Food Res. 7:111. [35] Horrall, B. E. 1935. Indiana Agr. Exp. Sta. Bull. 401. [36] Hove, E., C. A. Elvehjem, and E. B. Hart. 1939. Am. J. Physiol. 127:689. [37] Johnston, F. A. 1944. Food Res. 9:212. [38] Jones, T. S. G., and W. L. Davies. 1935. Biochem. J., Lond. 29:978. [39] Kahlenberg, O. J., and L. Voris. 1931. J. Agr. Res. 43:749. [40] Koch, W., and H. S. Woods. 1905-06. J. Biol. Chem. 1:203. [41] König, and Karsch. In A. E. Leach. 1920. Food inspection and analysis. Ed. 4. John Wiley and Sons, Philadelphia. [42] Kopaczewski, W. 1936. Lait 16:356. [43] Kuiken, K. A., and P. B. Pearson. 1949. J. Nutrit. 39:167. [44] Lampert, L. M. 1939. J. Ass. Off. Agr. Chem. 22:768. [45] Ling, E. R. 1951. J. Sc. Food Agr. 2:279. [46] Macy, I. G. 1949. Am. J. Dis. Child. 78:589. [47] Macy, I. G. Unpublished. [48] Macy, I. G., H. J. Kelly, and R. E. Sloan. 1953. The composition of milks. Nat. Acad. Sc.-Nat. Res. Counc., Washington, D. C. Pub. 254. p. 62. [49] Maynard, L. A. Unpublished. [50] McDowall, F. H., N. O. Bathurst, and I. L. Campbell. 1947. N. Zealand J. Sc. Techn. 28a:316. [51] Nataf, B., O. Mickelsen, A. Keys, and W. E. Petersen. 1948. J. Nutrit. 36:495. [52] Quam, G. N., and A. Hellwig. 1928. J. Biol. Chem. 78:681. [53] Rangappa, K. S. 1948. Biochim. biophys. acta, Amst. 2:207. [54] Rasmussen, R., N. B. Guerrant, A. O. Shaw, R. C. Welch, and S. I. Bechdel. 1936. J. Nutrit. 11:425. [55] Reis, F., and H. H. Chakmakjian. 1932. J. Biol. Chem. 98:237. [56] Remington, R. E., and G. C. Supplee. 1934. J. Dairy Sc. 17:19. [57] Sarker, B. C. R., R. W. Luecke, C. W. Duncan, and R. E. Ely. 1949. Ibid. 32:671. [58] Shahani, K. M., and H. H. Sommer. 1951. Ibid. 34:1010. [59] Shope, R. E., and J. W. Gowen. 1928. J. Exp. M. 48:21. [60] Sommer, H. H., and E. B. Hart. 1919. J. Biol. Chem. 40:137. [61] Stearns, G. Unpublished. [62] Sundberg, T. 1931. Sven. kem. tdskr. 43:198. [63] Tobey, E. R. 1944. Analyses of dairy products, milk and cream. Maine Agr. Exp. Sta. Off. Insp. Bull. 191. [64] Williams, R. J., V. H. Cheldelin, and H. K. Mitchell. 1942. Univ. Texas Pub. 4237:97. [65] Williamson, M. B. 1944. J. Biol. Chem. 156:47. [66] Wright, N. C., and J. Papish. 1929. Science 69:78.

For additional information on milk, consult reference 17. Values in parentheses are ranges, estimate "c" (cf. Introduction).

	Property or Constituent	No. of Observations	Value	Reference
	(A)	(B)	(C)	(D)
	Physical Properties			
1	Freezing point depression		0.582°C	19
2	pH	19	(6.33-6.52)	21
3	Specific gravity	200	1.030(1.028-1.036)	16
4	Surface tension		52.0 dynes/sq cm	7
	General Chemical Components			
5	Ash	200	0.76(0.39-1.06) g/100 ml	16
6	Salts		0.939 g/100 ml	2
7	Solids, total	50	13.8(9.7-17.4) g/100 ml	22
8		18	15.1(12.5-19.1) g/100 ml	18
9	Water		86.6 g/100 ml	17
	Electrolytes			
10	Aluminum	4	Trace	6
11	Barium	4	Trace	6
12	Boron		0.018 mg/100 ml	13
13	Calcium	27	137(112-164) mg/100 ml	9
14		31	130(103-176) mg/100 ml	15
15	Chlorine	31	115(56-168) mg/100 ml	15
16		4	204(158-260) mg/100 ml	1
17	Chromium	4	Trace	6
18	Copper	6	0.02 mg/100 ml	20
19	Iron	31	0.02(0.01-0.05) mg/100 ml	15
20	Lead	4	Trace	6
21	Lithium	4	Trace	6
22	Magnesium	31	13(10-18) mg/100 ml	15
23		27	17(13-22) mg/100 ml	9
24	Manganese	4	0.008(0.007-0.009) mg/100 ml	14
25	Molybdenum	4	0 mg/L	6
	Phosphorus			
26	Total P	27	112(88-134) mg/100 ml	9
27		13	122(92-161) mg/100 ml	18
28	Inorganic P	11	77.2(57.7-94.5) mg/100 ml	18
29		4	81.0(72.0-105.3) mg/100 ml	1
30	Organic P	4	14.4(12.0-15.9) mg/100 ml	1
31	Lipid P	2	4(3-5) mg/100 ml	8
32	Potassium	31	189(144-217) mg/100 ml	15
33		27	170(106-242) mg/100 ml	9
34	Silver	4	Trace	6
35	Sodium	31	42(19-60) mg/100 ml	15
36	Strontium	4	Trace	6
37	Sulfur	31	3(2-4) mg/100 ml	15
38	Titanium	4	Trace	6
39	Vanadium	4	Trace	6
40	Zinc	4	Trace	6
	Nitrogenous Substances			
	Protein			
41	Total	50	3.6(2.1-4.8) g/100 ml	22
42	Casein	200	3.2(2.4-3.9) g/100 ml	16
43	Lactalbumin	4	0.440(0.376-0.573) g/100 ml	1
44	Lactoglobulin		0.261 g/100 ml	7
45	Whey	200	1.1(0.8-2.0) g/100 ml	16
	Nitrogen			
46	Protein N		518 mg/100 ml	17
47	Casein N		392 mg/100 ml	
48	Lactalbumin N		63 mg/100 ml	
49	Lactoglobulin N		47 mg/100 ml	
50	Whey N		173 mg/100 ml	

	Property or Constituent	No. of Observations	Value	Reference
	(A)	(B)	(C)	(D)
	Nitrogenous Substances (concluded)			
51	Nitrogen (concluded) Non-protein N		40 mg/100 ml	7
	Lipids, Carbohydrates, Miscellaneous Organic Acids			
52	Cholesterol	15	24(17-39) mg/100 ml	5
53	Fat	200	4.8(3.1-7.6) g/100 ml	16
54		50	4.8(1.2-8.4) g/100 ml	22
55	Lactose	200	4.5(3.3-5.8) g/100 ml	16
56		50	4.8(4.0-6.4) g/100 ml	22
57	Citric acid	4	151(131-171) mg/100 ml	1
	Vitamins			
58	B_1 (thiamine) Total	4	39(32-48) μg/100 ml	23
59		10	58(47-68) μg/100 ml	12
60	Free	10	8.6(4.2-22.8) μg/100 ml	12
61	B_2 (riboflavin)	30	117(76-235) μg/100 ml	11
62		4	110(89-120) μg/100 ml	23
63	B_6 (pyridoxine)	4	7(4-13) μg/100 ml	23
64	B_{12} (cyanocobalamine)	44	0.024(0.005-0.140) μg/100 ml	4
65	B_c (folic acid)	9	0.03(0-0.16) μg/100 ml	4
66	C (ascorbic acid)	16	1.8(0.9-3.2) mg/100 ml	10
67		5	0.9(0.7-1.1) mg/100 ml	3
68	H (biotin)	4	6.3(4.7-8.3) μg/100 ml	23
69	Inositol	4	21(14-26) μg/100 ml	23
70	Niacin (nicotinic acid)	4	250(200-320) μg/100 ml	23
71	Pantothenic acid	4	240(130-320) μg/100 ml	23

Contributors: Macy, Icie G., and Kelly, Harriet J.

References: [1] Bosworth, A. W., and L. L. Van Slyke. 1916. J. Biol. Chem. 24:177. [2] Bosworth, A. W., and L. L. Van Slyke. 1916. Ibid. 24:187. [3] Chakraborty, R. K. 1935. Ind. J. M. Res. 23:347. [4] Collins, R. A., R. E. Boldt, C. A. Elvehjem, and E. B. Hart. 1953. J. Dairy Sc. 36:29. [5] Dam, H. 1934. Hoppe Seyler Zschr. 224:127. [6] Drea, W. F. 1938. J. Nutrit. 16:325. [7] Gamble, J. A., N. R. Ellis, and A. K. Besley. 1939. Composition and properties of goat's milk as compared with cow's milk. U. S. Dept. Agr. Techn. Bull. 671. [8] Hess, A. F., and F. D. Helman. 1925. J. Biol. Chem. 64:781. [9] Holmes, A. D., J. W. Kuzmeski, H. G. Lindquist, and H. B Rodman. 1946. Am. J. Dis. Child. 71:647. [10] Holmes, A. D., H. G. Lindquist, and E. J. Finnegan. 1950. J. Am. Diet. Ass. 26:179. [11] Holmes, A. D., H. G. Lindquist, and E. K. Greenwood. 1945. J. Dairy Sc. 28:853. [12] Houston, J., S. K. Kon, and S. Y. Thompson. 1940. J. Dairy Res. 11:155. [13] Hove, E., C. A. Elvehjem, and E. B. Hart. 1939. Am. J. Physiol. 127:689. [14] Kemmerer, A. R., and W. R. Todd. 1931. J. Biol. Chem. 94:317. [15] Kondo, K., and S. Mori. 1932. J. Chem. Soc. Jap. 53:1163. [16] König, and Karsch. In A. E. Leach. 1920. Food inspection and analysis. Ed. 4. John Wiley and Sons, Philadelphia. [17] Macy, I. G., H. J. Kelly, and R. E. Sloan. 1953. The composition of milks. Nat. Acad. Sc.-Nat. Res. Counc., Washington, D. C. Pub. 254. p. 62. [18] Peterson, V. E., and G. W. Turner. 1939. J. Nutrit. 17:293. [19] Princivalle, E. 1948. Ann. chim. appl. Roma 38:617. [20] Quam, G. N., and A. Hellwig. 1928. J. Biol. Chem. 78:681. [21] Trout, G. M. 1941. Michigan Agr. Exp. Sta. Q. Bull. 23:254. [22] Voorhies, E. C. 1921. The milk goat in California. California Agr. Exp. Sta. Bull. 285. [23] Williams, R. J., V. H. Cheldelin, and H. K. Mitchell. 1942. Univ. Texas Pub. 4237:97.

157. GENERAL CHEMICAL COMPONENTS OF MILK: MAMMALS

Values are g/100 g whole milk. Values in parentheses are ranges, estimate "c" (cf. Introduction).

	Animal	Ash	Water	Protein	Fat	Carbohydrates	Reference
	(A)	(B)	(C)	(D)	(E)	(F)	(G)
1	Man		86.5	1.2	4.6	6.9	18
2		0.2	88.6	1.3	3.5	6.5	25
3		0.3	87.4	2.2	3.8	6.3	10
4		0.2	87.5	1.25	3.5	7.5	15
5	Anteater	0.8	63	11	20	0.3	5
6	Ass	0.49	89.9	(1.00-2.04)	(1.4-1.5)	(6.09-6.19)	7
7		0.4	90.4	1.8	1.2	6.2	22
8		0.4	91.2	1.5	1.2	6.0	30
9		0.3	89.7	2.1	1.5	6.4	28
10	Bison	0.9	86.9	4.8	1.7	5.7	19
11	Buffalo	0.76	82.7	5.9	7.9	4.5	30
12		0.8	81.6	5.9	7.87	4.9	13
13	Chinese	0.86	76.8	6.0	12.6	3.7	28
14	Egyptian	0.8	82.8	4.2	8.0	4.9	22
15		0.83	83.1	4.4	7.3	4.47	12
16	Philippine	0.84	78.5	5.9	10.4	4.3	28
17	Camel	0.7	87.6	3.0	5.4	3.3	28
18		0.7	87.1	3.9	2.8	5.4	22
19		0.65	88.3	3.6	2.5	5.0	30
20		0.8	88.4	3.0	4.0	3.4	17
21	Cat		73[1]	11.1	10.9	3.4	10
22		0.5	81.6	9.1	3.3	4.9	30
	Cattle						
23	Ayrshire	0.6	87.1	3.3	4.1	4.8	3
24	Brown Swiss	0.7	87.0	3.5	3.8	4.9	3
25	Guernsey	0.7	85.5	3.9	5.0	4.9	3
26	Holstein	0.7	88.0	3.1	3.5	4.7	3
27	Jersey	0.7	85.6	3.8	5.2	4.6	3
28		0.7	(85.7-88.2)	(3.2-3.8)	(3.4-5.3)	(4.6-4.7)	11
29	Deer	1.4	65.9	10.4	19.7(18.8-23.0)	2.6	22
30	Dog	1.35	75.4	10.1	9.5		13
31		1.2	76.1	10.0	10.0	2.7	19
32			75.8	9.3	10.5	2.7	8
33		0.91	77.0	9.7	9.3	3.1	30
34		1.2	77.4	7.5	8.3	3.7	2
35	Dolphin		(67.4-75.5)	(9.4-11.1)	(11-18)	(0.4-0.8)	9
36		0.6	41.1	11.2	45.8	1.3	13
37		0.46	48.8		43.71		30
38	Elephant	(0.6-0.7)	(67.9-73.7)	(3.0-3.1)	(15.0-19.6)	(3.2-7.7)	7
39		0.7	68.1	3.5	20.6	7.2	30
40		0.76	73.1	4.8	15.1	3.4	24
41		0.4		3.4	6.7	6.4	14
42	Fox	0.9	(80.9-81.9)	(6.5-6.7)	(5.4-5.8)	(4.9-5.1)	19
43		1.0	81.9	6.4	6.3	4.6	32
44	Goat	0.85	86.9	3.8	4.1	4.4	30
45		0.8	85.7	4.3	4.8	4.5	22
46		0.8	87.9	3.2	3.7	4.6	10
47		0.8	88.3	3.1	3.5	4.55	11
48	Guinea pig			8.8	8.3	3.0	10
49		0.8	81.7	7.0	7.9	2.6	19
50		0.8		5.2	7.1	2.2	1
51		0.95	82.1	8.55	5.5	2.93	23
52	Hippopotamus	0.1	90.4		4.5	4.4	13
53	Horse			2.4	1.2	7.9	10
54		0.4	89.9	2.1	1.3	6.3	7
55		0.3	90.1	3.8	1.1	6.7	22
56		0.35	90.2	2.14	0.6	6.73	30
57	Llama	0.8	86.5	3.9	3.2	5.6	30
58	Monkey	0.26	87.7	2.1	3.9	5.9	29
59		0.1	89.1	2.3	1.5	7.0	19
60	Mouse				10.2		19, 20

/1/ Approximately.

	Animal	Ash	Water	Protein	Fat	Carbohydrates	Reference
	(A)	(B)	(C)	(D)	(E)	(F)	(G)
61	Mule	0.5	89.2	2.1	1.9	5.7	22
62		(0.38-0.53)	(89.1-91.6)	(1.6-2.3)	(1.59-1.98)	(4.80-6.04)	13
63	Orangutan	0.24	88.5	1.43	3.5	6.02	26
64	Rabbit	2.6	69.5	15.5	10.5	2.0	13
65		2.0	73.1	10.9	12.1	1.8	4
66				10.4	16.7	2.0	7
67	Rat	1.5	69.3	11.8	14.8	2.83	6
68			77.8	7.0	12.4	3.39	21
69			72.1		13.8		16
70		1.2	71.0	8.7	9.3	3.74	20
71	Reindeer	1.4	63.3	10.3	22.5	2.5	28
72		(1.2-1.5)	(66.3-68.2)	(5.2-11.1)	(17.1-18.7)	(2.1-2.7)	31
73		1.4	62.0	10.4	23.6	2.5	22
74		1.4	64.3	10.9	19.7	2.6	30
75	Seal	0.86(0.80-0.91)	46.0(43.8-50.0)	9.7(6.7-12.0)	42.0(40.4-42.8)		27
76	Sheep	0.9	80.1	6.5	6.9	4.9	22
77		0.9	83.6	5.2	6.2	4.2	13
78				5.0	2.6	5.4	10
79		0.93	83.9	5.2	6.2	4.2	30
80	Mountain-	0.83	81.1	5.7	7.1	5.1	30
81	Swine	(1.0-1.1)	(83.5-84.0)	(7.0-7.9)	(3.7-5.0)	(3.5-4.0)	22
82				7.2	4.6	3.1	7
83		1.07	81.0	6.20	7.06	4.25	30
84	Whale	(1-1.7)		(10-14)	(31-39)		27
85		1.6	62.4	12.0	22.0	2.0	19
86		0	70.2	9.4	19.4	1.0	22
87		1.7	61.7	11.95	22.2	1.8	30
88	Zebra	0.7	86.2	3.0	4.8	5.3	30

Contributor: Luckey, T. D.

References: [1] Abdoholden, E. 1899. Zschr. physiol. Chem. 27:408. [2] Anderson, H. D., B. C. Johnson, and A. Arnold. 1940. Am. J. Physiol. 129:631. [3] Armstrong, T. V. 1959. J. Dairy Sc. 42:1. [4] Bergman, A. J., and C. W. Turner. 1937. J. Biol. Chem. 120:21. [5] Brody, S. 1945. Biogenetics and growth. Reinhold, New York. [6] Cox., W. W., Jr., and A. J. Mueller. 1937. J. Nutrit. 13:429. [7] Davies, W. L. 1939. The chemistry of milk. Van Nostrand, New York. [8] Dengiès, G. 1937. Bull. Soc. Pharm. Bordeaux 73:241. [9] Eichelberger, L., E. S. Fetcher, Jr., E. M. K. Geiling, and B. J. Vos, Jr. 1940. J. Biol. Chem. 134:171. [10] Folin, O., W. Denis, and A. S. Minot. 1919. Ibid. 37:349. [11] Gamble, J. A., N. R. Ellis, and A. K. Beslay. 1939. Composition and properties of goat's milk as compared with cow's milk. U. S. Dept. Agr. Techn. Bull. 671. [12] Ghoneim, A., and M. T. El-Katib. 1947. Nature, Lond. 159:273. [13] Grimmer, W. 1925. Tabulae biol., Berl. 2:536. [14] Hindle, E. M. In Zoo Life. 1950. Zoological Society, London. v. 5, no. 1. [15] Holt, L. E., and R. McIntosh. 1933. Diseases of infancy and childhood. Ed. 10. Appleton-Century, New York. p. 147. [16] Houston, J., and S. K. Kon. 1939. Biochem. J., Lond. 33:1655. [17] Kiselera, N. T. 1957. Chem. Abstr. 51:2198d. [18] Kon, S. K., and E. H. Mawson. 1950. Human milk. Med. Res. Counc. Spec. Rep., Lond. 296. [19] Luckey, T. D. Unpublished. [20] Luckey, T. D., T. J. Mende, and J. Pleasants. 1954. J. Nutrit. 54:345. [21] Mayer, D. T. 1935. Ibid. 10:343. [22] Monjonnier, T., and H. C. Troy. 1926. The technical control of dairy products. Ed. 2. Caspar, Krueger Dory Co., Milwaukee, Wisconsin. [23] Neymork, M. 1937. Skand. Arch. Physiol., Berl. 76:158. [24] Nottbohm, F. E. 1939. Verratspflege Lebensmittelforsch. 2:150. [25] Plimmer, E., and J. Londes. 1937. Biochem. J., Lond. 31:1751. [26] Schumacher, H. M. 1934. Zschr. Kinderh. 56:415. [27] Siveraten, E. Unpublished. [28] U. S. Department of Agriculture. 1939. Yearbook. [29] Van Wagenen, G., H. E. Himwich, and H. R. Catchpole. 1941. Proc. Soc. Exp. Biol., N. Y. 48:133. [30] Winkler, W. 1930. Handbuch der Milch Wirtschaft. 1:21. [31] Yippo, A. 1927. Zschr. Kinderh. 43:225. [32] Young, E. G., and G. A. Grant. 1931. J. Biol. Chem. 93:805.

XXIV. Dermal Secretions

158. PHYSICAL PROPERTIES AND CHEMICAL COMPOSITION OF SWEAT: MAN

Eccrine sweat, a clear aqueous solution, is generally 99.0-99.5% water and 0.5-1.0% solids (the latter are approximately half inorganic and half organic) [25]. Quantitative studies of the dissolved substances in sweat have been made by analysis of sweat samples collected from the skin, but in only a few instances directly from the sweat pore; by analysis of sweat residues washed from the skin; and by estimation of sweat components in material balance studies [23]. Methods and techniques have been carefully evaluated by Robinson [23], who also has thoroughly reviewed the literature on the chemical composition of sweat [24]. For additional information on sweat, consult references 1, 4, 14, 15, 20. Values in parentheses are ranges, estimate "c" (cf. Introduction).

	Property or Constituent	Value	Reference
	(A)	(B)	(C)
	Physical Properties		
1	pH	(3.8-6.5)	25
2	Rate of production, maximum	(17.7-38.2) ml/min	16
3	Specific gravity	(1.001-1.006)	25
	General Chemical Components		
4	Solids, total	(1.174-1.597) %	19
5	Water	(99.0-99.5) %	25
	Electrolytes		
6	Calcium	(1-8) mg/100 ml	24
7	Chloride	(36-468) mg/100 ml	3
8	Copper	0.006 mg/100 ml	18
9	Iodine	0.9(0.5-1.2) µg/100 ml	30
10	Iron	0.027(0.022-0.045) mg/100 ml	13
11	Magnesium	(0.004-0.286) mg/100 ml	18
12	Manganese	0.006(0.003-0.007) mg/100 ml	18
13	Phosphorus	(0.009-0.043) mg/100 ml	18
14	Potassium	(21-126) mg/100 ml	2
15	Sodium	(24-312) mg/100 ml	3
16	Sulfur	(0.7-7.4) mg/100 ml	31
	Nitrogenous Substances		
	Amino acids		6
17	Arginine	13.6(6.05-17.00) mg/100 ml	
18	Histidine	8(4.25-14.00) mg/100 ml	
19	Isoleucine	2.27(1.63-3.73) mg/100 ml	
20	Leucine	2.69(1.98-3.75) mg/100 ml	
21	Lysine	2.26(1.96-3.38) mg/100 ml	
22	Phenylalanine	2.19(1.70-3.47) mg/100 ml	
23	Threonine	5.38(2.13-8.18) mg/100 ml	
24	Tryptophan	1.12(0.75-1.85) mg/100 ml	
25	Tyrosine	3.15(1.32-5.45) mg/100 ml	
26	Valine	2.96(2.40-4.35) mg/100 ml	
27	Creatinine	(0.1-1.3) mg/100 ml	24
28	Urea	(12-57) mg/100 ml	24
29	Uric acid	0.16(0.07-0.25) mg/100 ml	26
	Nitrogen		
30	Total N	33.2 mg/100 ml	5
31	Non-protein N	(27-64) mg/100 ml	22
32	Amino acid N	(1.1-10.2) mg/100 ml	7
33	Ammonia N	(5-9) mg/100 ml	7
34	Urea N	(5-36) mg/100 ml	17
	Carbohydrates, Miscellaneous Organic Acids, Hormones		
35	Sugar (as glucose)	(1-3) mg/100 ml	24
36	Carbolic acid (phenol)	(2-8) mg/100 ml	27
37	Lactic acid	(285-336) mg/100 ml	32
38	Corticoids	(4-8) µg/100 ml	21

Property or Constituent	Value	Reference
(A)	(B)	(C)
	Vitamins	
39	B_1 (thiamine)	0.15(0-0.6) μg/100 ml	17
40	B_2 (riboflavin)	(0-0.5) μg/100 ml	17
41	B_6 (pyridoxine)	(0.04-0.17) μg/100 ml	11
42	B_C (folic acid)	(0.53-0.88) μg/100 ml	9
43	B_X (p-aminobenzoic acid)	0.24(0.08-1.70) μg/100 ml	12
44	C (as dehydroascorbic acid)	70.5 μg/100 ml	28
45	Choline	7.1 μg/100 ml	8
46	Inositol	21(15-36) μg/100 ml	12
47	Niacin (nicotinic acid)	(1.7-8.7) μg/100 ml	10
48	Pantothenic acid	(1.5-7.7) μg/100 ml	29

Contributors: (a) Darling, Robert C., (b) Rothman, Stephen, and Lorincz, Allan L., (c) Kvorning, Sven Ancher, (d) Randall, Walter C., (e) Levey, Stanley, (f) Goodyer, Allan V. N.

References: [1] Adolph, E. F. 1947. Physiology of man in the desert. Interscience, New York. [2] Borchardt, W. 1926. Pflügers Arch. 214:169. [3] Conn, J. W. 1949. Arch. Int. M. 83:416, [4] Dill, D. B. 1938. Life, heat and altitude. Harvard University Press, Cambridge. [5] Dill, D. B., F. G. Hall, and H. T. Edwards. 1938. Am. J. Physiol. 123:412. [6] Hier, S. W., T. Cronbleet, and O. Bergeim. 1946. J. Biol. Chem. 166:327. [7] Itoh, S., and T. Nakayama. 1952. Jap. J. Physiol. 2:248. [8] Johnson, B. C., T. S. Hamilton, and H. H. Mitchell. 1945. J. Biol. Chem. 159:5. [9] Johnson, B. C., T. S. Hamilton, and H. H. Mitchell. 1945. Ibid. 159:425. [10] Johnson, B. C., T. S. Hamilton, and H. H. Mitchell. 1945. Ibid. 159:231. [11] Johnson, B. C., T. S. Hamilton, and H. H. Mitchell. 1945. Ibid. 158:619. [12] Johnson, B. C., H. H. Mitchell, and T. S. Hamilton. 1945. Ibid. 161:357. [13] Johnson, F. A., T. J. McMillan, and E. R. Evans. 1950. J. Nutrit. 42:285. [14] Kuno, Y. 1934. Physiology of human perspiration. J. and A. Churchill, London. [15] Kuno, Y. 1956. Human perspiration. C. C. Thomas, Springfield, Illinois. [16] Ladell, W. S. S. 1949. J. Physiol., Lond. 108:440. [17] Mickelsen, O., and A. Keys. 1943. J. Biol. Chem. 149:479. [18] Mitchell, H. H., and T. S. Hamilton. 1949. Ibid. 178:345. [19] Mosher, H. H. 1932. Ibid. 99:781. [20] Newburgh, L. H. 1949. Physiology of heat regulation. W. B. Saunders, Philadelphia. [21] Nichols, J., and A. T. Miller. 1948. Proc. Soc. Exp. Biol., N. Y. 69:448. [22] Peters, J. P., and D. D. Van Slyke. 1946. Quantitative clinical chemistry. Williams and Wilkins, Baltimore. v. 1. [23] Robinson, S., and A. H. Robinson. In J. M. Steele, ed. 1954. Methods in medical research. Year Book Publishers, Chicago. v. 6. [24] Robinson, S., and A. H. Robinson. 1954. Physiol. Rev. 34:221. [25] Rothman, S. 1954. Physiology and biochemistry of the skin. University of Chicago Press, Chicago. [26] Saiki, A. K., G. Olmanson, and G. A. Talbert. 1932. Am. J. Physiol. 100:328. [27] Schultz, W. 1940. Arch. Derm. Syph., Berl. 181:471. [28] Shields, J. B., B. C. Johnson, T. S. Hamilton, and H. H. Mitchell. 1945. J. Biol. Chem. 161:351. [29] Spector, H., T. S. Hamilton, and H. H. Mitchell. 1945. Ibid. 161:145. [30] Spector, H., H. H. Mitchell, and T. S. Hamilton. 1945. Ibid. 161:137. [31] Talbert, G. A., F. Stinchfield, and H. Staff. 1933. Am. J. Physiol. 106:488. [32] Thurmon, F. M., and B. Ottenstein. 1952. J. Invest. Derm. 18:333.

159. EFFECT OF HEAT, EXERCISE, AND CHEMICAL SUBSTANCES ON COMPOSITION OF SWEAT: MAN

Values in parentheses are ranges, estimate "c" (cf. Introduction).

	Constituent	Condition or Variable	No. of Subjects	Value	Remarks	Reference
	(A)	(B)	(C)	(D)	(E)	(F)
				Electrolytes		
1	Calcium	Normal		(1.12-2.50) mM/L	83 determinations	7
2				1.25(0.1-3.0) mM/L	210 determinations	33
3			4	0.84(0.35-1.13) mM/L	4 collection periods	11
4		Hot, humid environment	4	0.50(0.1-1.1) mM/L	Repeated observations	22
5			1	(0.1-0.8) mM/L	Repeated observations on different days	
6		1st half-hour of exposure	4	1.3 mM/L	Continuous exposure	
7		2nd half-hour of exposure	4	0.8 mM/L		
8		5th half-hour of exposure	4	0.1 mM/L		
9		6th half-hour of exposure	4	0.1 mM/L		
	Chloride	Acclimatization to heat			Sweat collected from:	
10		Before	1	29 mM/L	Arm	21
11			1	99 mM/L	Face	
12			1	57 mM/L	Thigh	
13			1	43 mM/L	Torso	
14		After	1	36 mM/L	Arm	
15			1	57 mM/L	Face	
16			1	18 mM/L	Thigh	
17			1	16 mM/L	Torso	
18		2nd day of exposure, resting	5♂	89.0 mM/L	Healthy soldiers living 24 hr/da in 120°F temperature chamber	6
19		14th day of exposure, resting	5♂	59.4 mM/L		
20		2nd day of exposure, walking 4 mi/hr	5♂	104.7 mM/L		
21		14th day of exposure, walking 4 mi/hr	5♂	66.9 mM/L		
		Skin temperature				
22		Warm	4	34 mM/L	Working in heat	27
23				60 mM/L		10
24			4	70 mM/L		38
25		Cool	4	25 mM/L	Working	27
26				54 mM/L		10
27			4	6 mM/L		38
		Sweat rate				
28		High	10	51.5 mM/L	NaCl intake constant	19
29			7	31.9 mM/L		9
30				62 mM/L		10
31		Low	10	13 mM/L	NaCl intake constant	19
32			7	25.9(10.1-43.8) mM/L		9
33				56 mM/L		10
34		Continuous	9♂, 11♀	108(90-173) mM/L	Collected directly from palmar sweat pores by micropipette	16
35		Intermittent	9♂, 11♀	308(194-463) mM/L		
		Work				
36		Before	31♂	56 mM/L	Competing lumberjacks	2
37		After	31♂	37.6 mM/L		
38		Hot environment		(8-35) mM/L	Cl intake = 52 mEq/da	28
39				20 mM/L	Cl intake = 203 mEq/da	28
40				5.1 mM/L	NaCl intake = 2.9 g/da	8
41		Before acclimatization		51 mM/L	NaCl intake = 14.5 g/da	8
42		After acclimatization		17 mM/L		
43	Copper	Hot, humid environment	4	0.0025(0.0020-0.0034) mM/L		22
44	Iodine	Normal	8	3.0(1.5-6.3) µg/L	Sweat iodine concentration averaged 35% of plasma level; 18 observations	25
45			3	9.5(5.4-12.2) µg/L	Without supplemental diet	32

	Constituent	Condition or Variable	No. of Subjects	Value	Remarks	Reference
	(A)	(B)	(C)	(D)	(E)	(F)
			Electrolytes (continued)			
46	Iodine (concluded)	Elevated iodine intake	3	36.5(26.2-41.7) μg/L	Following 14 daily doses of 2 mg potassium iodide	32
47	Iron	Normal		0.005(0-0.038) mM/L	If epithelial cells completely eliminated from sample, only traces of iron found in sweat	1
48		Hot, humid environment	4	0.0049(0.0040-0.0057) mM/L	4 collections	11
		Climatic variation			No significant difference due to environmental conditions	22
49		Cool, dry environment		0.037 mM/L		
50		Hot, humid environment		0.031 mM/L		
51	Magnesium	Normal	5	(0.058-1.8) mM/L	79 determinations	33
52		Hot, humid environment	4	(0.0018-0.17) mM/L	Repeated observations	22
53	Manganese	Hot, humid environment	4	0.0011(0.0006-0.0014) mM/L		22
54	Phosphorus	After administration of 15 g Na_2HPO_4	6	0.97 mM/L		34
55		Low phosphorus diet	6	0.58 mM/L		34
56		Hot, humid environment	4	0.008(0.003-0.14) mM/L	Repeated observations	22
57	Potassium	Normal	5	12.8(7.25-37.00) mM/L	105 observations	33
		Acclimatization to heat			Healthy soldiers living 24 hr/da in 120°F temperature chamber	6
58		2nd day of exposure, resting	5♂	7.55 mM/L		
59		14th day of exposure, resting	5♂	4.29 mM/L		
60		1st day of exposure, walking 4 mi/hr	5♂	8.22 mM/L		
61		14th day of exposure, walking 4 mi/hr	5♂	4.44 mM/L		
62		After administration of adrenocortical extract	1	6.1 mM/L	Subject thoroughly acclimatized and trained to work in moist heat	23
		Bath, radiant heat			8 successive daily exposures of 2 hours each	20
63		1st day of exposure	1	15.0 mM/L		
64		8th day of exposure	1	26.2 mM/L		
		Sweat rate				
65		High	10	9.2 mM/L		19
66			7	3.1 mM/L		9
67		Low	10	8.0 mM/L		19
68			7	2.7(1.9-4.2) mM/L		9
		Work			Competing lumberjacks	2
69		Before	31♂	10.5 mM/L		
70		After	31♂	9.4 mM/L		
71		Work and rest	1	4.86(3.6-5.6) mM/L	21 observations	30
72	Sodium	Normal	18	34.3(17.0-51.6) mM/L	Hospital patients awaiting hernia repair or biopsies	26
		Acclimatization to heat				
73		Before		51 mM/L	NaCl intake = 14.5 g/da	8
74		After		17 mM/L		
75		After		5.1 mM/L	NaCl intake = 2.9 g/da	
76		2nd day of exposure, resting	5♂	89.3 mM/L	Healthy soldiers living 24 hr/da in 120°F temperature chamber	6
77		14th day of exposure, resting	5♂	63.2 mM/L		
78		2nd day of exposure, walking 4 mi/hr	5♂	105.2 mM/L		
79		14th day of exposure, walking 4 mi/hr	5♂	75.1 mM/L		
		Administration of desoxy-corticosterone acetate			Temperate climate	8
80		Before		90 mM/L		
81		After		55 mM/L		

	Constituent	Condition or Variable	No. of Subjects	Value	Remarks	Reference
	(A)	(B)	(C)	(D)	(E)	(F)
			Electrolytes (concluded)			
82	Sodium (concluded)	Bath, radiant heat 1st day of exposure	1	180 mM/L	8 successive daily exposures of 2 hours each	20
83		8th day of exposure	1	63 mM/L		
84		Sweat rate High	10	63 mM/L	NaCl intake = 15 g/da	19
85			7	31.9 mM/L	124 tests	9
86		Low	10	18 mM/L	NaCl intake = 15 g/da	19
87			7	23.3(7.3-52.7) mM/L	124 tests	9
			Nitrogenous Substances			
88	Ammonia	Normal	3	6.5(4.7-8.8) mM/L	3 daily samples	24
89			19	3.45(1.7-5.6) mM/L	Repeated observations	3
90			14♂	2.8 mM/L		4
91			10♀	3.5 mM/L		4
92			2	4.0 mM/L	Eccrine sweat	35
93			2	29 mM/L	Apocrine sweat	35
94		Sweat rate Profuse	5♂, 5♀	4.5 mM/L	Collected by micropipette from palmar sweat pores; 55 samples	13
95		Intermittent	5♂, 5♀	17.0 mM/L		
96	Creatinine	Normal	2♀	0.08(0.04-0.11) mM/L	Collected by micropipette from palmar sweat pores; fasting subjects	15
97		Acclimatization to heat		(0.055-0.065) mM/L	Collected from 4 skin surfaces	21
98		2nd day of exposure, resting	5♂	0.048 mM/L	Healthy soldiers living 24 hr/da in 120°F temperature chamber	6
99		14th day of exposure, resting	5♂	0.034 mM/L		
100		2nd day of exposure, walking 4 mi/hr	5♂	0.06 mM/L		
101		14th day of exposure, walking 4 mi/hr	5♂	0.029 mM/L		
102		Hot chamber	3	0.05(0.018-0.070) mM/L	3 daily collections	24
103		Work in heat		(0.028-0.069) mM/L[1]	Trained personnel walking 3 mi/hr in hot environment	5
104				(0.009-0.018) mM/L[2]		
105		Alternate work and rest		0.023 mM/L	Experiment conducted at high sweat rates	12
106		After drinking 500 ml of 5% creatinine solution		0.025 mM/L		
107	Urea	Normal	19	8.62(6.20-12.10) mM/L	Repeated observations	3
108			14♂	3.6 mM/L		4
109			10♀	3.2 mM/L		4
110		Acclimatization to heat Before		5 mM/L	Collected from 4 different skin surfaces	21
111		After		5 mM/L		
112		Before	1	15.5 mM/L	Collected from arm in impermeable arm-bag	36
113		After	1	9.2 mM/L		
114		Before	1	5.4 mM/L	Collected from general body surfaces	36
115		After	1	6.0 mM/L		
116		Hot chamber	3	9.7(6.7-13.5) mM/L	3 daily samples	24
117		Sweat rate Profuse		11.3(5.3-32.0) mM/L	Collected by micropipette from palmar sweat pores; 77 samples; urea higher in sweat than in blood	18
118		Intermittent		46.0(11.5-105.0) mM/L		
119		After 3 g urea, orally		(11.5-24.0) mM/L		
120		Rest		4.7 mM/L	Urea in sweat does not reflect moderate changes in blood urea	39
121		Work		4.7 mM/L		
122		Alternate work and rest	1	5.75(3.8-7.0) mM/L	11 observations	30

/1/ "Apparent" creatinine. /2/ "True" creatinine.

	Constituent	Condition or Variable	No. of Subjects	Value	Remarks	Reference
	(A)	(B)	(C)	(D)	(E)	(F)
			Nitrogenous Substances (concluded)			
123	Uric acid	Normal		0.048(0-0.10) mM/L	Pure palmar sweat; 34 samples	14
124		Acclimatization to heat		(0.014-0.018) mM/L	Collected from 3 different skin surfaces	21
125		Hot chamber, 40-50°C	3	0.018(0.012-0.030) mM/L	3 daily samples	24
		Sweat rate			Palmar sweat	29
126		Profuse		0 mM/L		
127		Intermittent		0.048 mM/L		
128	Nitrogen, total	Acclimatization to heat 2nd day of exposure, resting	5♂	66.4 mg/100 ml	Healthy soldiers living 24 hr/da in 120°F temperature chamber	6
129		14th day of exposure, resting	5♂	51.5 mg/100 ml		
130		2nd day of exposure, walking 4 mi/hr	5♂	53.8 mg/100 ml		
131		14th day of exposure, walking 4 mi/hr	5♂	25.8 mg/100 ml		
		Sweat rate				
132		High	7	28 mg/100 ml		9
133		Low	7	33.2(25.6-51.3) mg/100 ml		
134		High	4	23 mg/100 ml	Repeated exposure to different environmental conditions	22
135		Low		18 mg/100 ml		
			Carbohydrates			
136	Reducing sugars (as glucose)	Normal	14♂	1.1 mM/L		4
137			10♀	0.70 mM/L		4
138			23	0.60(0.155-2.2) mM/L	76 determinations	31
139		Hot chamber	3	0.83(0.33-1.2) mM/L	3 daily collections	24
140		After phlorizin, intradermally	1	1.5 mM/L	Average of 2 experiments	39
		Sweat rate			Collected by micropipette from palmar sweat pores; 47 samples	17
141		Profuse		(0-0.61) mM/L		
142		Intermittent		(0-0.89) mM/L		
143		After 20 g glucose, intravenously		(0-1.0) mM/L		
			Salts			
144	Lactate	Normal		(5.0-8.7) mM/L		9
		Acclimatization to heat				
145		Before		22.8 mM/L	Collected from 4 different skin surfaces; 4 samples	21
146		After		13.6 mM/L		
147		Before	1♂	33.3 mM/L	Working in hot, humid environment	37
148		After	1♂	11.0 mM/L		
149		Before	1	24.4 mM/L	Collected from arm in impermeable arm-bag	36
150		After	1	12.3 mM/L		
151		Before	1	9.4 mM/L	Collected from general body surfaces	36
152		After	1	8.1 mM/L		
153		Eccrine sweat	4♂, 1♀	(31.6-37.5) mM/L	Lactic acid in sweat higher in male than female	35
154		Apocrine sweat	4♂, 1♀	(27.5-36.5) mM/L		
155		Elevated blood lactate		7.5(6.8-8.8) mM/L	Sweat lactate not influenced by sweat rate, rectal temperature, or blood lactate levels	39
156		Hot chamber	3	8.2(3.8-11.9) mM/L	3 daily samples	24
157		Alternate work and rest	1	9.7(7.55-13.60) mM/L	11 observations	30

Contributor: Randall, Walter C.

159. EFFECT OF HEAT, EXERCISE, AND CHEMICAL SUBSTANCES ON COMPOSITION OF SWEAT: MAN (Concluded)

References: [1] Adams, W. S., A. Leslie, and M. H. Levin. 1950. Proc. Soc. Exp. Biol., N. Y. 74:46.
[2] Ahlman, K. L., O. Eränko, M. J. Korvonen, and V. Leppänen. 1952. J. Appl. Physiol. 4:911. [3] Amatruda, T. T., Jr., and L. G. Welt. 1953. Ibid. 5:759. [4] "Annotations." 1934. Lancet, Lond. 226:641. [5] Bass, D. E., and I. T. Dobalian. 1953. J. Appl. Physiol. 5:555. [6] Bass, D. E., C. R. Kleeman, M. Quinn, A. Henschel, and A. H. Hegnauer. 1955. Medicine, Balt. 34:323. [7] Bryant, J. E., and G. A. Talbert. 1931. Am. J. Physiol. 97:509. [8] Conn, J. W. 1949. Advance. Int. M., N. Y. 3:373. [9] Dill, D. B., F. G. Hall, and H. T. Edwards. 1938. Am. J. Physiol. 123:412. [10] Johnson, R. E., G. C. Pitts, and F. C. Consolazio. 1944. Ibid. 141:575. [11] Johnston, F. A., T. J. McMillan, and E. R. Evans. 1950. J. Nutrit 42:285. [12] Ladell, W. S. S. 1947. J. Physiol., Lond. 106:237. [13] Lobitz, W. C., Jr., and H. L. Mason. 1948. Arch. Derm. Syph., Chic. 57:69. [14] Lobitz, W. C., Jr., and H. L. Mason. 1948. Ibid. 57:387. [15] Lobitz, W. C., Jr., and H. L. Mason. 1948. Ibid. 57:907. [16] Lobitz, W. C., Jr., and A. E. Osterberg. 1947. Ibid. 56:462. [17] Lobitz, W. C., Jr., and A. E. Osterberg. 1947. Ibid. 56:819. [18] Lobitz, W. C., Jr., and A. E. Osterberg. 1947. Ibid. 56:827. [19] Locke, W., N. B. Talbot, H. S. Jones, and J. Worcester. 1951. J. Clin. Invest. 30:325. [20] McCance, R. A. 1938. Am. J. Physiol. 92:208. [21] Mickelsen, O., and A. Keys. 1943. J. Biol. Chem. 149:479. [22] Mitchell, H. H., and T. S. Hamilton. 1949. Ibid. 178:345. [23] Moreira, M., R. E. Johnson, A. P. Forbes, and F. Consolazio. 1945. Am. J. Physiol. 143:169. [24] Mosher, H. H. 1933. J. Biol. Chem. 99:781. [25] Nelson, N., E. C. Palmer, E. R. Park, P. Weymouth, and W. D. Bean. 1947. J. Clin. Invest. 26:301. [26] Reynolds, T. 1952. Proc. Soc. Exp. Biol., N. Y. 79:118. [27] Robinson, S., S. D. Gerking, E. S. Turrell, and R. K. Kincaid. 1950. J. Appl. Physiol. 2:654. [28] Robinson, S., R. K. Kincaid, and R. K. Rhamy. 1950. Ibid. 3:55. [29] Robinson, S., and A. H. Robinson. 1954. Physiol. Rev. 34:202. [30] Rothman, S. 1954. Physiology and biochemistry of the skin. University of Chicago Press, Chicago. [31] Silvers, S., W. Forster, and G. A. Talbert. 1928. Am. J. Physiol. 84:577. [32] Spector, H., H. H. Mitchell, and T. S. Hamilton. 1945. J. Biol. Chem. 161:137. [33] Talbert, G. A., C. Haugen, R. Carpenter, and J. E. Bryant. 1933. Am. J. Physiol. 104:441. [34] Talbert, G. A., F. Stinchfield, and H. Staff. 1933. Ibid. 106:488. [35] Thurmon, F. M., and B. Ottenstein. 1952. J. Invest. Derm. 18:333. [36] Van Heyningen, R. E., and J. S. Weiner. 1952. J. Physiol., Lond. 116:395. [37] Weiner, J. S., and R. E. van Heyningen. 1949. Nature, Lond. 164:351. [38] Weiner, J. S., and R. E. van Heyningen. 1952. J. Appl. Physiol. 4:725. [39] Weiner, J. S., and R. E. van Heyningen. 1952. Ibid. 4:734.

160. PHYSICAL PROPERTIES AND CHEMICAL COMPOSITION OF SEBUM: MAN

Sebum, a thick, semi-fluid substance, is composed of fat and epithelial debris from the cells of the malpighian layer of the skin. For determinations on hair, consult reference 9. Values in parentheses are ranges, estimate "c" (cf. Introduction).

	Property or Constituent	Body Area	Value	Reference
	(A)	(B)	(C)	(D)
	Physical Properties			
1	Melting point	Forearm	35.8°C	5-7
2	Specific gravity at 20°/4°C	Forehead	0.911	2
3	Surface tension	Forehead	24.89 dynes/cm	2
4	Viscosity at 30°C	Forehead	859.7 millipoises	2
	Chemical Constituents			
	Fatty acids			
5	Combined[1]	Forearm	34.6(27.5-41.0) g/100 g	5-7
6		Scalp	28(21-39) g/100 g	1, 3
7	Triglycerides	Forearm	32.5 g/100 g	5-7
8		Forehead	44 g/100 g	4
9	Waxes (including cholesterol esters)	Scalp	16 g/100 g	9
10	Free	Forearm	28.3(22.0-32.2) g/100 g	5-7, 10
11		Forehead	38 g/100 g	4
12		Scalp	33 g/100 g	1, 3
13	Unsaponifiable matter, total	Forearm	30.1(25.1-35.9) g/100 g	5-7
14		Scalp	34(29-40) g/100 g	1, 3
15	Aliphatic alcohols	Forearm	6.2(4.7-6.9) g/100 g	5-7
16		Scalp	9 g/100 g	1, 3
17	Straight-chain	Forearm	2.4 g/100 g	5-7
18		Scalp	4.5 g/100 g	3
19	Branched-chain	Forearm	3.8 g/100 g	5-7
20		Scalp	0.9 g/100 g	3
21	Cholesterol	Forearm	4.1(2.7-6.9) g/100 g	5-7
22		Forehead	3.5 g/100 g	4
23		Scalp	3.5 g/100 g	1, 3, 8
24	Dihydrocholesterol	Forearm	0.1 g/100 g	5-7
25	Hydrocarbons	Forearm	8.1(5-20) g/100 g	5-7
26		Scalp	9 g/100 g	3
27	Phosphatides	Forehead	0.9 g/100 g	4
28	Squalene	Forearm	5.5(3.3-11.2) g/100 g	5-7
29		Scalp	7(4-10) g/100 g	1, 8

/1/ As triglycerides, waxes, and other esters.

Contributors: (a) Wheatley, Victor R., (b) Truter, E. V., (c) Brun, Robert, (d) Kvorning, Sven Ancher

References: [1] Bloom, R. E., S. Woods, and N. Nicolaides. 1955. J. Invest. Derm. 24:97. [2] Butcher, E. O., and A. Coonin. 1949. Ibid. 12:249. [3] Houghen, F. W. 1955. Biochem. J., Lond. 59:302. [4] Kvorning, S. A. 1949. Acta pharm. tox., Kbh. 5:383. [5] MacKenna, R. M. B., V. R. Wheatley, and A. Wormall. 1950. J. Invest. Derm. 15:33. [6] MacKenna, R. M. B., V. R. Wheatley, and A. Wormall. 1952. Biochem. J., Lond. 52:161. [7] MacKenna, R. M. B., V. R. Wheatley, and A. Wormall. Unpublished. [8] Nicolaides, N., and S. Rothman. 1952. J. Invest. Derm. 19:389. [9] Nicolaides, N., and S. Rothman. 1953. Ibid. 21:9. [10] Weitkamp, A. W., A. M. Smiljanic, and S. Rothman. 1947. J. Am. Chem. Soc. 69:1936.

161. CHEMICAL COMPOSITION OF SEBUM: VERTEBRATES OTHER THAN MAN

Sebum is present in untreated skin, hair, or wool of mammals; in birds, it is present in the preen gland oil.

	Animal (A)	Constituent (B)	Value g/100 g (C)	Reference (D)
1	Camel	Isocholesterol[1]	2.2	2
2	Goat	Isocholesterol[1]	2.5	2
3	Guinea pig	Fatty acids		7
		Combined[2]	49.3	
4		Free	6.0	
5		Unsaponifiable matter, total	44.8	7
6		Aliphatic alcohols	5.0	
7		Straight-chain	0.1	
8		Branched-chain	4.9	
9		Aliphatic diols	11.2	
10		Cholesterol	17.9	
11		Lathosterol[3]	1.8	
12		Hydrocarbons	1.5	
13	Llama	Isocholesterol[1]	1.2	2
14	Mouse	Fatty acids		7
		Combined[2]	36.7	
15		Free	7.5	
16		Unsaponifiable matter, total	54.6	7
17		Aliphatic alcohols	5.9	
18		Straight-chain	0.1	
19		Branched-chain	5.8	
20		Aliphatic diols	27.5	
21		Cholesterol	4.5	
22		Lathosterol[3]	8.1	
23		Hydrocarbons	1.1	
24	Ox	Fatty acids		1
		Combined[2]	53.4	
25		Free	5.1	
26		Unsaponifiable matter, total	42.7	1
27		Cholesterol	14.4	1
28		Isocholesterol[1]	<0.1	2
29	Rabbit	Fatty acids		7
		Combined[2]	43.6	
30		Free	9.0	
31		Unsaponifiable matter, total	45.9	7
32		Aliphatic alcohols	31.5	
33		Straight-chain	20.8	
34		Branched-chain	10.7	
35		Aliphatic diols	2.2	
36	Rabbit (concluded)	Unsaponifiable matter, total (concluded)		7
		Cholesterol	3.5	
37		Lathosterol[3]	0.1	
38		Hydrocarbons	3.4	
39	Rat	Fatty acids		7
		Combined[2]	51.4	
40		Free	7.4	
41		Unsaponifiable matter, total	41.4	7
42		Aliphatic alcohols	17.6	
43		Straight-chain	4.5	
44		Branched-chain	13.1	
45		Aliphatic diols	2.9	
46		Cholesterol	5.8	
47		Lathosterol[3]	4.4	
48		Hydrocarbons	1.5	
49	Sheep	Fatty acids		4
		Combined[2]	44.0	
50		Free	11.0	
51		Unsaponifiable matter, total	46.1	4
52		Aliphatic alcohols	9.0	3
53		Straight-chain	1.5	
54		Branched-chain	7.5	
55		Aliphatic diols	2.5	3
56		Cholesterol	10.0	3
57		Dihydrocholesterol	2.5	3
58		Isocholesterol[1]	12.5	3
59		Lathosterol[3]	2.5	3
60		Hydrocarbons	<1	3
61	Duck	Fatty acids, combined[2]	47.6	5,6
62		Aliphatic alcohols	48.0	5,6
63		Straight-chain	48.0	
64		Branched-chain	0	
65		Cholesterol	1.4	5,6
66	Goose	Fatty acids, combined[2]	47.5	5,6
67		Aliphatic alcohols	48.0	5,6
68		Straight-chain	48.0	
69		Branched-chain	0	
70		Cholesterol	0.25	5,6

/1/ A mixture of lanosterol, dihydrolanosterol, agnosterol, and dihydroagnosterol. /2/ As triglycerides, waxes, and other esters. /3/ Cholest-7-en-3β-ol.

Contributor: Wheatley, Victor R.

References: [1] Koppenhoefer, R. M. 1936. J. Biol. Chem. 116:321. [2] Lederer, E., and P. K. Tchen. 1945. Bull. Soc. chim. biol., Par. 27:419. [3] Truter, E. V. 1951. Q. Rev. Chem. Soc., Lond. 5:390. [4] Weitkamp, A. W. 1945. J. Am. Chem. Soc. 67:447. [5] Weitzel, G., A. M. Fretzdorff, and J. Wojahn. 1952. Hoppe Seyler Zschr. 291:46. [6] Weitzel, G., and K. Lennert. 1951. Ibid. 288:251. [7] Wheatley, V. R., and A. T. James. 1957. Biochem. J., Lond. 65:36.

162. COMPONENT FATTY ACIDS OF SEBUM: MAMMALS

Values are g/100 g.

	Acid	Man	Guinea pig	Mouse	Rabbit	Rat	Sheep	Reference
	(A)	(B)	(C)	(D)	(E)	(F)	(G)	(H)
1	C_{10} and lower	0.2			0.1		0.5	B, 2;E, 4;G, 3
	C_{11}							
2	n-	Trace			0.3			B, 2;E, 4
3	iso-1	Trace					0.6	B, 2;G, 3
	C_{12}							
4	n-	3.6			2.2		0.4	B, 2;E, 4;G, 3
5	iso-1	Trace					0.4	B, 2;G, 3
6	α-hydroxy-						0.6	1
	C_{13}							
7	n-	0.3			6.6			B, 2;E, 4
8	iso-1	0.3			0.6		1.0	B, 2;E, 4;G, 3
	C_{14}							
9	n-	6.4	0.3	0.7	10.8	1.6	2.8	B, 2;C-F, 4;G, 3
10	iso-	0.3		0.2	0.7	2.6	2.8	B, 2;D-F, 4;G, 3
11	mono-en-	0.8		0.4	0	0.5		B, 2;D-F, 4
12	α-hydroxy-						3.6	1
	C_{15}							
13	n-	2.3	1.6	1.1	6.0	0.8		B, 2;C-F, 4
14	iso-1	0.7	0.7	0.3	1.3	1.1	4.8	B, 2;C-F, 4;G, 3
15	mono-en-	0.6	0	0.7	0	0		B, 2;C-F, 4
16	di-en-	0.3						2
	C_{16}							
17	n-	24.2	15.8	5.0	24.0	17.4	2.8	B, 2;C-F, 4;G, 3
18	iso-	0.3	0.5	1.7	0.5	4.7	5.8	B, 2;C-F, 4;G, 3
19	poly-iso-2				1.8			4
20	mono-en-	9.1	1.1	7.3	0	2.1		B, 2;C-F, 4
21	α-hydroxy-						18.3	1
	C_{17}							
22	n-	1.1	5.8	1.7	6.8	3.1		B, 2;C-F, 4
23	iso-1	0.7	2.4	0.9	1.7	5.0	3.6	B, 2;C-F, 4;G, 3
24	poly-iso-2	1.3			11.0			B, 2;E, 4
25	mono-en-	1.6	0.8	0.9	0	0		B, 2;C-F, 4
	C_{18}							
26	n-	8.0	4.0	3.9	8.2	8.9	0.2	B, 2;C-F, 4;G, 3
27	iso-1	1.8		0.7		11.3	4.0	B, 2;D, F, 4;G, 3
28	poly-iso-2		3.1		14.3			4
29	mono-en-	35.6	7.7	10.0	3.7	11.3		B, 2;C-F, 4
30	di-en-					3.1		4
31	poly-en-					1.7		4
32	α-hydroxy-						4.2	1
	C_{19}							
33	n-		2.2	2.2				4
34	iso-1		9.8	1.0		3.1	4.8	C, D, F, 4;G, 3
35	mono-en-		3.1					4
	C_{20}							
36	n-			9.2		6.8	0.6	D, F, 4;G, 3
37	iso-1		4.3	5.1			5.0	C, D, 4;G, 3
38	poly-iso-					4.1		4
39	Over C_{20}	0	37.0	46.0	0	10.0	36.0	B, 2;C-F, 4;G, 3

/1/ Single methyl branch; whether iso- or anteiso- not indicated. /2/ Several methyl branches.

Contributor: Wheatley, Victor R.

References: [1] Horn, D. H. S., F. W. Hougen, E. von Rudloff, and D. A. Sutton. 1954. J. Chem. Soc., Lond. 1:177. [2] James, A. T., and V. R. Wheatley. 1956. Biochem. J., Lond. 63:269. [3] Weitkamp, A. W. 1945. J. Am. Chem. Soc. 67:447. [4] Wheatley, V. R., and A. T. James. 1957. Biochem. J., Lond. 65:36.

XXV. Fluids of Ear and Eye

163. PHYSICAL PROPERTIES AND CHEMICAL COMPOSITION OF LABYRINTHINE FLUIDS: CAT, DOG, GUINEA PIG

Cerebrospinal fluid values given for comparative purposes only. For determinations on fish, consult reference 4.

	Animal	Property or Constituent	No. of Subjects	Method	Fluid	Value	Reference
	(A)	(B)	(C)	(D)	(E)	(F)	(G)
1	Cat	pH	5	Electrometric	Endolymph	7.82	6
2			8	Electrometric	Perilymph	7.87	
3			10	Electrometric	Cerebrospinal	7.45	
4		Osmotic pressure	6	Hill thermoelectric	Endolymph	1.058 g NaCl/100 g H_2O	1
5			6	Hill thermoelectric	Perilymph	1.046 g NaCl/100 g H_2O	
6			6	Hill thermoelectric	Cerebrospinal	1.017 g NaCl/100 g H_2O	
7		Refractive index		Abbé refractometer at 22°C	Endolymph	1.33455	5
8				Abbé refractometer at 22°C	Perilymph	1.33495	
9				Abbé refractometer at 22°C	Cerebrospinal	1.33435	
10		Chloride	6	Microanalysis	Endolymph	158.2 mEq/L	6
11			7	Microanalysis	Perilymph	152.3 mEq/L	6
12			4		Perilymph	150 mEq/L	3
13			7	Microanalysis	Cerebrospinal	150.9 mEq/L	6
14			4		Cerebrospinal	150 mEq/L	3
15		Potassium	12	Flame photometry	Perilymph	6.0 mEq/L	3
16			12	Flame photometry	Cerebrospinal	5.9 mEq/L	
17		Sodium	12	Flame photometry	Perilymph	164 mEq/L	3
18			12	Flame photometry	Cerebrospinal	162 mEq/L	
19		Protein	5	Microanalysis	Perilymph	142 mg/100 ml	3
20			5	Microanalysis	Cerebrospinal	25 mg/100 ml	
21		Nitrogen, non-protein	5	Microanalysis	Perilymph	21 mg/100 ml	3
22			5	Microanalysis	Cerebrospinal	20 mg/100 ml	
23	Dog	Refractive index		Abbé refractometer at 22.5°C	Endolymph	1.3347	5
24				Abbé refractometer at 22.5°C	Perilymph	1.3349	5
25				Pulfrich refractometer at 17.5°C	Perilymph	1.335147	10
26				Abbé refractometer at 22.5°C	Cerebrospinal	1.3342	5
27				Pulfrich refractometer at 17.5°C	Cerebrospinal	1.33527	10
28	Guinea pig[1]	pH	25	Electrochemical microelectrode	Endolymph	7.4	7
29			25	Electrochemical microelectrode	Perilymph	7.9	
30		Calcium		Flame photometry	Endolymph[2]	3 mEq/L	2
31				Flame photometry	Perilymph	3 mEq/L	
32				Flame photometry	Cerebrospinal	3 mEq/L	
33		Chloride	3		Endolymph[2]	110 mEq/L	3
34			14	Microanalysis	Endolymph[2]	107.1 mEq/L	9
35			9		Perilymph	120 mEq/L	3
36			17	Microanalysis	Perilymph	121.5 mEq/L	9
37			9		Cerebrospinal	122 mEq/L	3
38			19	Microanalysis	Cerebrospinal	122.4 mEq/L	9
39		Magnesium		Flame photometry	Endolymph[2]	0.9 mEq/L	2
40				Flame photometry	Perilymph	2 mEq/L	
41				Flame photometry	Cerebrospinal	2 mEq/L	
42		Potassium	9	Flame photometry	Endolymph[2]	142 mEq/L	3
43			10	Microanalysis	Endolymph[2]	144.4 mEq/L	9
44			12	Flame photometry	Perilymph	5 mEq/L	3
45			13	Microanalysis	Perilymph	4.8 mEq/L	9
46			12	Flame photometry	Cerebrospinal	4 mEq/L	3
47			11	Microanalysis	Cerebrospinal	4.2 mEq/L	9
48		Sodium	8	Flame photometry	Endolymph[2]	26 mEq/L	3
49			12	Microanalysis	Endolymph[2]	15.8 mEq/L	9
50			12	Flame photometry	Perilymph	148 mEq/L	3
51			18	Microanalysis	Perilymph	150.3 mEq/L	9
52			12	Flame photometry	Cerebrospinal	150 mEq/L	3
53			17	Microanalysis	Cerebrospinal	152 mEq/L	9

/1/ For additional values, consult reference 8. /2/ Utricular.

	Animal	Property or Constituent	No. of Subjects	Method	Fluid	Value	Reference
	(A)	(B)	(C)	(D)	(E)	(F)	(G)
54	Guinea	Protein	6	Microanalysis	Endolymph[2]	25 mg/100 ml	3
55	pig		4	Microanalysis	Endolymph[2]	15 mg/100 ml	9
56	(con-		6	Microanalysis	Perilymph	75 mg/100 ml	3
57	clud-		10	Microanalysis	Perilymph	50 mg/100 ml	9
58	ed)		6	Microanalysis	Cerebrospinal	20 mg/100 ml	3
59			6	Microanalysis	Cerebrospinal	21 mg/100 ml	9
60		Nitrogen,	6	Microanalysis	Endolymph[2]	21.5 mg/100 ml	3
61		non-protein	6	Microanalysis	Perilymph	20 mg/100 ml	
62			6	Microanalysis	Cerebrospinal	21 mg/100 ml	

/2/ Utricular.

Contributor: Smith, Catherine A.

References: [1] Aldred, P., C. Hallpike, and A. Ledoux. 1940. J. Physiol., Lond. 98:446. [2] Citron, L., and D. Exley. 1957. Proc. R. Soc. M., Lond. 50:697. [3] Citron, L., D. Exley, and C. Hallpike. 1956. Brit. M. Bull. 12:101. [4] Kaieda, J. 1930. Hoppe Seyler Zschr. 188:193. [5] Ledoux, A. 1941. Acta biol. belg. 4:506. [6] Ledoux, A. 1943. Bull. Soc. R. Sc. Liége 12:254. [7] Misrahy, G., K. Hildreth, L. Clark, and E. Shinabarger. 1958. Am. J. Physiol. 194:393. [8] Miyake, H. 1960. J. Otorhinolaryngological Soc. Japan 63:1. [9] Smith, C., O. H. Lowry, and M.-L. Wu. 1954. Laryngoscope 64:141. [10] Szasz, T. 1923. Zschr. Hals &c. Heilk. 6:256.

164. PHYSICAL PROPERTIES AND CHEMICAL COMPOSITION OF AQUEOUS HUMOR: MAMMALS

Part I: MAN

Values in parentheses are ranges, estimate "c" (cf. Introduction).

	Property or Constituent	Value	Reference		Property or Constituent	Value	Reference
	(A)	(B)	(C)		(A)	(B)	(C)
1	pH	7.21	2	8	Sodium	409 mg/100 ml	3
2	Volume	150 µL	9	9	Protein, total	(31-1000) mg/100 g	6
3		350 µL	7	10	Urea	6.0 mM/kg H_2O	1
4	Bicarbonate	21.5 mM/kg H_2O	2	11	Glucose	73(56-111) mg/100 g	10
5	Carbon dioxide	26.3 mM/kg H_2O	11	12	Hexosamine	(14.9-18.3) mg/g	8
6	Chloride	126 mM/kg H_2O	2	13	Citric acid	(2.6-3.2) mg/100 g	4
7		430(411-436) mg/100 ml H_2O	5	14	Ascorbate	0.92 mM/kg H_2O	2

Contributors: (a) Langham, Maurice E., (b) Love, R. Malcolm

References: [1] Adler, F. H. 1953. Physiology of the eye. Ed. 2. Henry Kimpton, London. [2] Becker, B. 1957. A.M.A. Arch. Ophth. 57:793. [3] Cogianut, B. 1948. Schweiz. med. Wschr. 78:200. [4] Grönvall, H. 1937. Acta ophth., Kbh., Suppl. 14, p. 279. [5] Kinsey, V. E. 1949. J. Gen. Physiol. 32:329. [6] Kronfeld, P. C., C. K. Lin, and T. H. Lus. 1941. Am. J. Ophth. 24:401. [7] Mestrezat, W., and A. Magitot. 1921. C. rend. Soc. biol. 84:185. [8] Meyer, K., E. M. Smyth, and E. Gallardo. 1938. Am. J. Ophth. 21:1083. [9] Niesnamoff, E. 1896. Arch. Ophth., Berl. 42:1. [10] Vanzetti, G., and R. Sidenari. 1947. Rass. ital. ottalm. 16:65. [11] Von Sallmann, L., and J. Grandi, Jr. 1946. Arch. Ophth., Chic. 35:643.

Part II: CAT, DOG, MONKEY

Values in parentheses are ranges, estimate "c" unless otherwise indicated (cf. Introduction).

	Animal	Property or Constituent	No. of Specimens	Value	Reference
	(A)	(B)	(C)	(D)	(E)
1	Cat	Bicarbonate	8	30.4 mM/kg H_2O	3
2		Carbon dioxide	8	31.0(26.0-36.0)[b] mM/kg H_2O	19
3		Chloride		131 mM/kg H_2O	3
4				458 mg/100 ml H_2O	6
5		Potassium		23 mg/100 ml H_2O	6
6		Sodium		365 mg/100 ml H_2O	6
7				150 mM/kg H_2O	4
8				157 mM/kg H_2O	2
9		Urea		4.5 mM/kg H_2O	1
10				(41-54) mg/100 g	16
11		Glucose		(67-95) mg/100 g	5
12				80(54-91) mg/100 g	17
13		Hexosamine		(20-47) mg/g	13
14		Ascorbate		0.1 mM/kg H_2O	11
15		Vitamin C (ascorbic acid)		0.16(0.13-0.22) mg/100 g	18
16	Dog	O_2 pressure[1]		(40-50) mm Hg	15
17		Refractive index	34	1.33504(1.33478-1.33532)	10
18		Volume		850 μL	14
19				430 μL	12
20				(400-500) μL	7
21		Carbon dioxide	6	29.5(24.3-34.7)[b] mM/kg H_2O	19
22			10	60.2(58.3-62.5) vol %	10
23		Chloride		442(430-458) mg/100 ml H_2O	9
24		Phosphorus, inorganic	15	1.1(0.83-1.50) mg/100 ml	10
25		Sodium		143 mM/kg H_2O	8
26		Sulfur, inorganic	15	0.35(0.24-0.50) mg/100 ml	10
27		Creatinine	23	1.7(1.0-1.9) mg/100 ml	10
		Nitrogen			10
28		Total N	18	40(27-55) mg/100 ml	
29		Protein N	16	15(5-25) mg/100 ml	
30		Non-protein N	24	24(12-40) mg/100 ml	
31		Amino acid N	14	9(8.0-10.3) mg/100 ml	
32		Urea N	16	12(11-15) mg/100 ml	
33		Glucose		74.5 mg/100 ml	10
34		Hexosamine		(12-20) mg/g	13
35	Monkey	Bicarbonate	1	24.4 mM/kg H_2O	3
36		Carbon dioxide	6	28.9(22.3-35.5)[b] mM/kg H_2O	19
37		Chloride	3	122 mM/kg H_2O	3

/1/ Determined by analysis of a bubble of gas after equilibration in anterior chamber.

Contributors: (a) Langham, Maurice E., (b) Krause, Arlington C., (c) Duke-Elder, W. Stewart, (d) Love, R. Malcolm

References: [1] Benham, G. H. In F. H. Adler. 1953. Physiology of the eye. Ed. 2. Henry Kimpton, London. [2] Davson, H. 1939. J. Physiol., Lond. 96:192. [3] Davson, H., and C. P. Luck. 1957. Ibid. 137:279. [4] Duke-Elder, W. S., G. H. Benham, and H. Davson. 1937. Ibid. 89:61. [5] Duke-Elder, W. S., and H. Davson. 1949. Brit. J. Ophth. 33:21. [6] Duke-Elder, W. S., and A. J. B. Goldsmith. 1951. Recent advances in ophthalmology. Ed. 4. Mosby, St. Louis. [7] Emmert, E. 1886. Zschr. vergl. Augenh., Lpz. 4:40. [8] Gaedertz, A., and A. Wittgenstein. 1927. Arch. Ophth., Berl. 118:738. [9] Kinsey, V. E. 1949. J. Gen. Physiol. 32:329. [10] Krause, A. C., and A. M. Yudkin. 1930. J. Biol. Chem. 88:471. [11] Langham, M. E. 1950. J. Physiol., Lond. 111:388. [12] Mestrezat, W., and A. Magitot. 1921. C. rend. Soc. biol. 84:185. [13] Meyer, K., E. M. Smyth, and E. Gallardo. 1938. Am. J. Ophth. 21:1083. [14] Niesnamoff, E. 1896. Arch. Ophth., Berl. 42:1.

Part II: CAT, DOG, MONKEY (Concluded)

[15] Pierce, H. F., J. S. Friendenwald, and D. Freeman. 1933. Am. J. Physiol. 104:553. [16] Robertson, J. D., and P. C. Williams. 1939. J. Physiol., Lond. 95:139. [17] Vidal, F., and J. Malbran. 1943. Arch. oft. hisp. amer. 18:405. [18] Vidal, F., and J. Malbran. 1943. Ibid. 18:454. [19] Von Sallmann, L., and J. Grandi, Jr. 1946. Arch. Ophth., Chic. 35:643.

Part III: GUINEA PIG, RABBIT, RAT

Values in parentheses are ranges, estimate "c" unless otherwise indicated (cf. Introduction).

	Animal	Property or Constituent	Value	Remarks	Reference
	(A)	(B)	(C)	(D)	(E)
1	Guinea pig	Bicarbonate	34.8(30.1-38.5) mM/kg H_2O		4
2		Carbon dioxide	40.0(35.2-44.8)[b] mM/kg H_2O	14 subjects	26
3		Chloride	107(104.24-109.76)[b] mM/kg H_2O	12 subjects	14
4	Rabbit	O_2 pressure	(40-50) mm Hg	Determined by use of Krogh's micrometer technique	6
5			55.2(50.8-59.6)[b] mm Hg	20 conscious subjects; determined by use of a polarographic apparatus	12
6			48.2(43.0-53.4)[b] mm Hg	35 anesthetized subjects; determined by use of a polarographic apparatus	12
7		pH	7.57		14
8			7.53	28 subjects	26
9			7.60(7.56-7.64)[b]	12 subjects	19
10		Volume	250 μL		25
11			270 μL		23
12			300 μL		10
13		Bicarbonate	31.9 mM/kg H_2O		19
14			30.5(28.1-32.9)[b] mM/kg H_2O	12 subjects	1
15			32 mM/kg H_2O	8 subjects	5
16			30.9(29.5-32.3)[b] mM/kg H_2O		5
17		Calcium	1.4 mM/kg H_2O		14
18		Carbon dioxide	31.4(26.6-36.2)[b] mM/kg H_2O	6 subjects	26
19			31.6(29.2-34.0)[b] mM/kg H_2O	12 subjects	1
20		Chloride	388(368-405) mg/100 ml H_2O		13
21			105 mM/kg H_2O	8 subjects	5
22			108 mM/kg H_2O	8 subjects	15
23		Magnesium	0.5 mM/kg H_2O		14
24		Orthophosphate	0.7 mM/kg H_2O		14
25		Phosphate, inorganic	4 mg/100 ml H_2O		9
26		Potassium	4.7 mM/kg H_2O		14
27			4.7(4.4-5.0)[b] mM/kg H_2O		20
28		Sodium	139 mM/kg H_2O		22
29			143 mM/kg H_2O		15
30			135.6(133.6-137.6)[b] mM/kg H_2O	10 subjects	19
31			153.1(144.3-161.9)[b] mM/kg H_2O		2
32		Sulfate	0.6 mM/kg H_2O		14
33		Protein, total	40 mg/100 g		3
34			(10-40) mg/100 g		21
35		Urea	7.4 mM/kg H_2O		16
36			27(18.7-59.0) mg/100 ml H_2O		16
37		Glucose	164 mg/100 g		7
38			5.6 mM/kg H_2O		15
39			6.8 mM/kg H_2O		28
40			7.2 mM/kg H_2O		8
41		Hexosamine	(21-36) mg/g		24

Part III: GUINEA PIG, RABBIT, RAT (Concluded)

	Animal	Property or Constituent	Value	Remarks	Reference
	(A)	(B)	(C)	(D)	(E)
42	Rabbit	Lactate	8.8 mM/kg H_2O		14
43	(con-		9.4(8.8-10.0)[b] mM/kg H_2O	10 subjects	18
44	cluded)	Lactic acid	24 mg/100 ml H_2O		9
45		Ascorbate	(1.2-2.8) mM/kg H_2O		14
46			(1.4-4.0) mM/kg H_2O		17
47			(1.6-2.3) mM/kg H_2O		27
48		Vitamin C (ascorbic acid)	21.97 mg/100 g		11
49	Rat	Carbon dioxide	33.8(31.4-36.2)[b] mM/kg H_2O	13 subjects	4

Contributors: (a) Langham, Maurice E., (b) Love, R. Malcolm, (c) Duke-Elder, W. Stewart

References: [1] Becker, B. 1957. Am. J. Ophth. 44(2):402. [2] Cole, D. F. 1959. Brit. J. Ophth. 43:268. [3] Davson, H. 1956. Physiology of the ocular and cerebrospinal fluids. Little and Brown, Boston. [4] Davson, H., and C. P. Luck. 1956. J. Physiol., Lond. 132:454. [5] Davson, H., and C. P. Luck. 1957. Ibid. 137:279. [6] De Haan, J. 1922. Arch. néerl. Physiol. 7:245. [7] Duke-Elder, W. S. 1942. Textbook of ophthalmology. Mosby, St. Louis. v. 1. [8] Duke-Elder, W. S., and H. Davson. 1949. Brit. J. Ophth. 33:21. [9] Duke-Elder, W. S., and A. J. B. Goldsmith. 1951. Recent advances in ophthalmology. Ed. 4. Mosby, St. Louis. [10] Emmert, E. 1886. Zschr. vergl. Augenh., Lpz. 4:40. [11] Franta, J. 1937. Arch. Augenh. 110:574. [12] Heald, K., and M. E. Langham. 1956. Brit. J. Ophth. 40:705. [13] Kinsey, V. E. 1949. J. Gen. Physiol. 32:329. [14] Kinsey, V. E. 1950. Arch. Ophth., Chic. 44:215. [15] Kinsey, V. E. 1951. J. Gen. Physiol. 34:389. [16] Kinsey, V. E., and P. Robinson. 1946. J. Biol. Chem. 162:325. [17] Langham, M. E. 1950. J. Physiol., Lond. 111:388. [18] Langham, M. E. 1952. Ibid. 117:461. [19] Langham, M. E., and P. Lee. 1957. Brit. J. Ophth. 41:65. [20] Langham, M. E., and I. S. Taylor. 1956. Ibid. 40:321. [21] Langham, M. E., and C. B. Taylor. In press. J. Physiol., Lond. [22] Lebermann, F. 1925. Arch. Augenh. 96:355. [23] Mestrezat, W., and A. Magitot. 1921. C. rend. Soc. biol. 84:185. [24] Meyer, K., E. M. Smyth, and E. Gallardo. 1938. Am. J. Ophth. 21:1083. [25] Niesnamoff, E. 1896. Arch. Ophth., Berl. 42:1. [26] Von Sallmann, L., and J. Grandi, Jr. 1946. Arch. Ophth., Chic. 35:643. [27] Waters, I. W. 1950. Biochem. J., Lond. 46:575. [28] Weekers, R. 1941. Recherches experimentales et cliniques concernant la pathogenic des cataractes. Thesis, Univ. Liége.

Part IV: CATTLE, GOAT, SHEEP, SWINE

Values in parentheses are ranges, estimate "c" unless otherwise indicated (cf. Introduction).

	Animal	Property or Constituent	Value	Reference
	(A)	(B)	(C)	(D)
1	Cattle	Ash	0.89%	8
2		Water	99.0%	4
3		Chloride	437(359-515)[b] mg/100 g	4
4		Copper	0.01 mg/100 g	2
5		Iron	0.016(0.011-0.022) mg/100 g	14
6		Manganese	1.2(1.0-1.5) µg/100 g	14
7		Potassium	27.3(25.7-28.9)[b] mg/100 g	4
8		Sodium	340(321.6-358.4)[b] mg/100 g	4
9		Zinc	0.0004 mM/kg H_2O	12
10		Hyaluronic acid	4.0 mg/100 ml H_2O	6
11	Calf	Volume	930 µL	9
12			(800-850) µL	7
13		Potassium	20.1(17.4-24.6) mg/100 g	13

Part IV: CATTLE, GOAT, SHEEP, SWINE (Concluded)

	Animal	Property or Constituent	Value	Reference
	(A)	(B)	(C)	(D)
	Cattle (con-cluded)			
14	Ox	Volume	1730 μL	9
15			1000 μL	7
16			3100 μL	11
17		Calcium	7.4 mg/100 ml	3
18		Carbon dioxide	44.0 vol %	3
19		Chloride	406 mg/100 ml	3
20		Phosphorus, total	5.4 mg/100 ml	3
21		Potassium	20 mg/100 ml	3
22		Sodium	316 mg/100 ml	3
23			147 mM/kg H_2O	15
24		Sulfur, total	(5.0-7.4) mg/100 ml	3
25		Protein, total	22.1 mg/100 ml	3
26		Creatinine	1.3 mg/100 ml	3
27		Urea	17.0 mg/100 ml	3
28		Uric acid	(1.7-4.1) mg/100 ml	3
		Nitrogen		3
29		Total N	20.1 mg/100 ml	
30		Protein N	3.5 mg/100 ml	
31		Non-protein N	16.4 mg/100 ml	
32		Amino acid N	5.5 mg/100 ml	
33		Glucose	36.0 mg/100 ml	3
34		Hexosamine	(11.9-15.5) mg/g	10
35		Lactic acid	18.9 mg/100 ml	3
36	Cow	Volume	1600 μL	9
37		Sodium	146 mM/kg H_2O	1
38		Albumin	8 mg/100 g	5
39		Globulin	9 mg/100 g	5
40	Goat	Carbon dioxide	21.8(18.6-25.0)[b] mM/kg H_2O	16
41	Sheep	Volume	800 μL	9
42			400 μL	7
43		Hexosamine	(10.5-15.5) mg/g	10
44	Swine	Volume	335 μL	9
45			(170-200) μL	7
46			450 μL	11
47		Hexosamine	(11-19) mg/g	10

Contributors: (a) Langham, Maurice E., (b) Love, R. Malcolm, (c) Krause, Arlington C., (d) Duke-Elder, W. Stewart

References: [1] Baurmann, M. 1929. Ber. deut. ophth. Ges. 47:156. [2] Bowness, J. M., R. A. Morton, M. H. Shakis, and A. L. Stubbs. 1952. Biochem. J., Lond. 51:521. [3] Cohen, M., J. A. Killian, and N. Metzgar. 1926. Contributions to ophthalmic science. G. Banta, Menasha, Wisconsin. v. 9. [4] Davson, H. 1949. Brit. J. Ophth. 33:175. [5] Davson, H. 1956. Physiology of the ocular and cerebrospinal fluids. Little and Brown, Boston. [6] Duke-Elder, W. S., and A. J. B. Goldsmith. 1951. Recent advances in ophthalmology. Ed. 4. Mosby, St. Louis. [7] Emmert, E. 1886. Zschr. vergl. Augenh., Lpz. 4:40. [8] Fore, H., and R. A. Morton. 1952. Biochem. J., Lond. 51:603. [9] Mestrezat, W., and A. Magitot. 1921. C. rend. Soc. biol. 84:185. [10] Meyer, K., E. M. Smyth, and E. Gallardo. 1938. Am. J. Ophth. 21:1083. [11] Niesnamoff, E. 1896. Arch. Ophth., Berl. 42:1. [12] Nitzescu, J. J., and J. B. Georgescu. 1935. Klin. Wschr. 1:97. [13] Salit, P. W. 1939. Biochem. Zschr. 301:253. [14] Tauber, F. W., and A. C. Krause. 1943. Am. J. Ophth. 26:263. [15] Tron, E. 1926. Arch. Ophth., Berl. 117:677. [16] Von Sallmann, L., and J. Grandi, Jr. 1946. Arch. Ophth., Chic. 35:643.

Part V: HORSE

Values in parentheses are ranges, estimate "c" (cf. Introduction).

Property or Constituent	Value	Reference	Property or Constituent	Value	Reference
(A)	(B)	(C)	(A)	(B)	(C)
Physical Properties			Nitrogenous Substances		
1 Volume	2400 µL	5	25 Protein, total	20.1 mg/100 ml	3, 4
General Chemical Components			26	16.0 mg/100 ml	5
			27	(20.6-23.1) mg/100 ml	1
2 Water	99.69%	4	28 Albumin	7.8 mg/100 ml	3, 4
Electrolytes			29 Globulin	12.3 mg/100 ml	3, 4
			30 Amino acids	29.0 mg/100 ml	3, 4
3 Calcium	6.2 mg/100 ml	3, 4	31 Creatinine	2.0 mg/100 ml	3, 4
4	7.0 mg/100 ml	5	32	1.2 mg/100 ml	1
5	(7.5-8.5) mg/100 ml	1	33 Urea	28.0 mg/100 ml	3, 4
6 Carbon dioxide	48.0 vol %	1	34	46.0 mg/100 ml	5
7	23.9(17.3-30.5) mM/kg H₂O	2	35	(26-30) mg/100 ml	1
8 Chloride	437.1 mg/100 ml	3, 4	36 Uric acid	(Trace-4.5) mg/100 ml	1
9	429 mg/100 ml	5	Nitrogen		
10	401 mg/100 ml	1	37 Total N	26.8 mg/100 ml	3, 4
11 Copper	0.0003 mM/kg H₂O	6	38	23.3 mg/100 ml	5
12 Magnesium	2.6 mg/100 ml	3, 4	39	(22.9-29.8) mg/100 ml	1
13	1.8 mg/100 ml	5	40 Protein N	(3.3-3.7) mg/100 ml	1
Phosphorus			41 Non-protein N	23.6 mg/100 ml	3, 4
14 Total P	1.4 mg/100 ml	1	42	(19.0-25.0) mg/100 ml	1
15 Inorganic P	3.3 mg/100 ml	3, 4	43 Amino acid N	4.7 mg/100 ml	1
16	3.2 mg/100 ml	5	Lipids, Carbohydrates, Miscellaneous Organic Acids		
17 Potassium	18.9 mg/100 ml	3, 4			
18	(20.6-22.4) mg/100 ml	1	44 Fats	4.0 mg/100 ml	3
19 Sodium	278.7 mg/100 ml	3, 4	45 Glucose	98.3 mg/100 ml	3, 4
20	(319-330) mg/100 ml	1	46	94.0 mg/100 ml	5
21	157 mM/kg H₂O	7	47	(77-83) mg/100 ml	1
Sulfur			48 Lactic acid	205.0 mg/100 ml	3
22 Total S	6.5 mg/100 ml	1	49	60.0 mg/100 ml	5
23 Inorganic S	6.1 mg/100 ml	3, 4	50	21.5 mg/100 ml	1
24	1.24 mg/100 ml	5			

Contributors: (a) Langham, Maurice E., (b) Duke-Elder, W. Stewart

References: [1] Cohen, M., J. A. Killian, and N. Metzgar. 1926. Contributions to ophthalmic science. G. Banta, Menasha, Wisconsin. v. 9. [2] Davson, H., and C. P. Luck. 1956. J. Physiol., Lond. 132:454. [3] Duke-Elder, W. S. 1930. Brit. J. Ophth., Monogr. Suppl. 4, p. 25. [4] Duke-Elder, W. S. 1942. Textbook of ophthalmology. Mosby, St. Louis. v. 1. [5] Mestrezat, W., and A. Magitot. 1921. C. rend. Soc. biol. 84:185. [6] Nitzescu, J. J., and J. B. Georgescu. 1935. Klin. Wschr. 1:97. [7] Stavy, Z., and R. Winternitz. 1932. Hoppe Seyler Zschr. 212:215.

165. PHYSICAL PROPERTIES AND CHEMICAL COMPOSITION OF VITREOUS HUMOR: MAMMALS

Part I: MAN

Determinations for lines 2-6 and 8-10 made on 2-5 ml vitreous humor pooled from both eyes of 211 males (average age 58 years), examined approximately nine hours after death. Values in parentheses are ranges, estimate "c" (cf. Introduction).

	Property or Constituent	Method	Value	Reference
	(A)	(B)	(C)	(D)
		Physical Properties		
1	Volume		3.9 ml	1
		Electrolytes		
2	Calcium	Clark-Collip	3.6(2.8-5.2) mEq/L	3
3	Chloride	Van Slyke-Hiller modification of Sendroy method	114(89-145) mEq/L	3
4	Phosphorus	Fiske-Subarow photoelectric	1.2(0.1-3.3) mEq/L	3
5	Potassium	Flame photometry	7.7(3.3-12.0) mEq/L	3
6	Sodium	Flame photometry	144(118-154) mEq/L	3
		Nitrogenous Substances		
7	Bilirubin	Malloy-Evelyn	0	4
8	Creatinine	Folin-Wu photoelectric	1.2(0.3-3.0) mg/100 ml	3
9	Urea	Direct nesslerization	79(24-172) mg/100 ml	3
		Carbohydrates		
10	Glucose[1]	Folin-Wu photoelectric modification	62(17-105) mg/100 ml	3
11	Hexosamine		37 μg/g	2

/1/ "True glucose" as determined by the use of Somogyi's zinc filtrates.

Contributors: (a) Naumann, Hans N., (b) Langham, Maurice E.

References: [1] Mestrezat, W., and A. Magitot. 1921. C. rend. Soc. biol. 84:185. [2] Meyer, K., E. M. Smyth, and E. Gallardo. 1938. Am. J. Ophth. 21:1083. [3] Naumann, H. N. 1959. A.M.A. Arch. Ophth. 62:356. [4] Naumann, H. N., and J. M. Young. 1960. Proc. Soc. Exp. Biol., N. Y. 105:70.

Part II: CAT, DOG, MONKEY, RABBIT

Values in parentheses are ranges, estimate "c" unless otherwise indicated (cf. Introduction).

	Animal	Property or Constituent	Value	Reference
	(A)	(B)	(C)	(D)
1	Cat	Urea	47.0 mg/100 ml H_2O	3
2		Glucose	2.5 mM/kg H_2O	2
3		Hexosamine	(17-40) μg/g	5
4	Dog	Volume	3.2 ml	4
5		Carbon dioxide	25.1(22.3-27.9)[b] mM/kg H_2O[1]	1
6		Hexosamine	(19-44) μg/g	5
7	Monkey	Carbon dioxide	24.1(17.3-30.9)[b] mM/kg H_2O[1]	1
8	Rabbit	pH	(7.0-7.1)	7
9		Volume	2.0 ml	4
10		Carbon dioxide	26.2(19.8-32.6)[b] mM/kg H_2O[2]	1
11		Orthophosphate	(1.1-1.3) mM/kg H_2O	6
12		Glucose	4.8 mM/kg H_2O	2
13		Hexosamine	(28-35) μg/g	5

/1/ 4 subjects. /2/ 8 subjects.

Part II: CAT, DOG, MONKEY, RABBIT (Concluded)

Contributors: (a) Langham, Maurice E., (b) Duke-Elder, W. Stewart

References: [1] Davson, H., and C. P. Luck. 1956. J. Physiol., Lond. 132:454. [2] Duke-Elder, W. S., and H. Davson. 1949. Brit. J. Ophth. 33:21. [3] Duke-Elder, W. S., and A. J. B. Goldsmith. 1951. Recent advances in ophthalmology. Ed. 4. Mosby, St. Louis. [4] Mestrezat, W., and A. Magitot. 1921. C. rend. Soc. biol. 84:185. [5] Meyer, K., E. M. Smyth, and E. Gallardo. 1938. Am. J. Ophth. 21:1083. [6] Palm, E. 1949. Acta ophth., Kbh. 27:36. [7] Von Sallmann, L. 1945. Arch. Ophth., Chic. 33:32.

Part III: CATTLE

Values in parentheses are ranges, estimate "c" (cf. Introduction).

	Animal	Property or Constituent	Value	Reference
	(A)	(B)	(C)	(D)
1	Calf	Volume	11.82 ml	12
2		Calcium	3.2 mM/kg H_2O	5
3		Chloride	109 mM/kg H_2O	5
4		Orthophosphate	0.3 mM/kg H_2O	5
5		Potassium	20.5(18.2-25.9) mg/100 g	15
6			10.0 mM/kg H_2O	5
7		Sodium	333.2 mg/100 g	18
8			139 mM/kg H_2O	5
9	Ox	Volume	20.9 ml	12
10		Calcium	3.5 mM/kg H_2O	5
11			(7.9-8.6) mg/100 ml	3
12		Carbon dioxide	46.6 vol %	3
13		Chloride	113 mM/kg H_2O	5
14			124 mM/kg H_2O	17
15			(407-413) mg/100 ml	3
16		Magnesium	0.4 mM/kg H_2O	17
17		Orthophosphate	0.1 mM/kg H_2O	5
18		Phosphorus, total	2 mg/100 ml	3
19		Potassium	6.4 mM/kg H_2O	3
20			7.7 mM/kg H_2O	5
21			(24.9-25.0) mg/100 ml	3
22		Sodium	131 mM/kg H_2O	3
23			147 mM/kg H_2O	17
24			142 mM/kg H_2O	5
25			(301-307) mg/100 ml	3
26		Sulfur, total	4 mg/100 ml	3
27		Protein, total	(39.3-43.7) mg/100 ml	3
28		Carnosine	0.24(0.16-0.29) mg/100 g	7
29		Creatine	1.6 mg/100 ml	3
30		Creatinine	(1.1-1.3) mg/100 ml	3
31		Urea	(19.8-20.4) mg/100 ml	3
32		Uric acid	(2.8-3.3) mg/100 ml	3
		Nitrogen		3
33		Total N	(22.7-24.6) mg/100 ml	
34		Protein N	(6.9-7.0) mg/100 ml	
35		Non-protein N	(15.7-17.6) mg/100 ml	
36		Amino acid N	1.8 mg/100 ml	
37		Glucose	(39-41) mg/100 ml	3
38		Hexosamine	(125-206) µg/g	13
39		Lactic acid	14.8 mg/100 ml	3
40		Vitamin B_2 (riboflavin)	0.8 µg/100 ml	14
41	Cow	Volume	20.3 ml	12
42		Potassium	3.5 mM/kg H_2O	11
43		Sodium	119 mM/kg H_2O	11

Part III: CATTLE

Animal	Property or Constituent	Value	Reference
(A)	(B)	(C)	(D)
44 Male, female	Ash	0.85%	6
45	Chloride	411 mg/100 g	18
46	Copper	26(18-34) μg/100 g	16
47	Iron	12(6-20) μg/100 g	16
48	Magnesium	2.08 mg/100 g	19
49	Manganese	3.1(1.9-4.2) μg/100 g	16
50		0.8(0.5-1.3) μg/100 g	6
51	Potassium	23.4(16.7-32.0) mg/100 g	15
52	Sodium	301.0 mg/100 g	18
53	Zinc	29(25-42) μg/100 g	16
54		0.35 mg/100 g	2
55	Albumin	14.5 mg/100 ml	1
56	Globulin	31.7 mg/100 ml	1
57	Creatine	4.14(2.15-5.30) mg/100 g	9
58	Creatinine	0.96(0.85-1.10) mg/100 g	9
59	Citric acid	1.1(0.9-1.2) mg/100 g	8
60	Formic acid	1.15(0.78-1.65) mg/100 g	10
61	Hyaluronic acid	62.0 mg/100 ml H_2O	4
62	Malic acid	7.9(7.7-8.1) mg/100 g	8

Contributors: (a) Langham, Maurice E., (b) Krause, Arlington C., (c) Love, R. Malcolm, (d) Hubbard, Ruth

References: [1] Balacz, E. A. 1954. Am. J. Ophth. 38:21. [2] Bowness, J. M., R. A. Morton, M. H. Shakis, and A. L. Stubbs. 1952. Biochem. J., Lond. 51:521. [3] Cohen, M., J. A. Killian, and N. Metzgar. 1926. Contributions to ophthalmic science. G. Banta, Menasha, Wisconsin. v. 9, pp. 216-228. [4] Duke-Elder, W. S., and A. J. B. Goldsmith. 1951. Recent advances in ophthalmology. Ed. 4. Mosby, St. Louis. [5] Fischer, F. P. In H. Davson. 1949. Physiology of the eye. Blakiston, New York. [6] Fore, H., and R. A. Morton. 1952. Biochem. J., Lond. 51:603. [7] Krause, A. C. 1936. Arch. Ophth., Chic. 16:986. [8] Krause, A. C., and A. M. Stack. 1939. Ibid. 22:66. [9] Krause, A. C., and F. W. Tauber. 1939. Ibid. 21:1027. [10] Krause, A. C., and R. Weekers. 1939. Arch. opht., Par. 3:225. [11] Lebermann, F. 1925. Arch. Augenh. 96:355. [12] Mestrezat, W., and A. Magitot. 1921. C. rend. Soc. biol. 84:185. [13] Meyer, K., E. M. Smyth, and E. Gallardo. 1938. Am. J. Ophth. 21:1083. [14] Philpot, F. J., and A. Pirie. 1943. Biochem. J., Lond. 37:250. [15] Salit, P. W. 1939. Biochem. Zschr. 301:253. [16] Tauber, F. W., and A. C. Krause. 1943. Am. J. Ophth. 26:260. [17] Tron, E. 1926. Arch. Ophth., Berl. 117:677. [18] Von Sallmann, L. 1951. Tabulae biol., Berl. 22:1. [19] Wolff, R., and A. Bourquard. 1937. C. rend. Soc. biol. 124:319.

Part IV: SHEEP, SWINE

Values in parentheses are ranges, estimate "c" (cf. Introduction).

Animal	Property or Constituent	Value	Reference
(A)	(B)	(C)	(D)
1 Sheep	Volume	7.0 ml	3
2	Copper	0.03 mg/100 g	1
3	Magnesium	2.93 mg/100 g	5
4	Zinc	0.029 mg/100 g	1
5	Hexosamine	(48-81) μg/g	4
6 Swine	Volume	3.2 ml	3
7	Calcium	(7.8-8.1) mg/100 ml	2
8	Carbon dioxide	(44.3-48.5) vol %	2

Part IV: SHEEP, SWINE (Concluded)

Animal	Property or Constituent	Value	Reference
(A)	(B)	(C)	(D)
9 Swine	Chloride	423 mg/100 ml	2
10 (con-	Phosphorus, total	3.3 mg/100 ml	2
11 cluded)	Potassium	28.4 mg/100 ml	2
12	Sodium	318 mg/100 ml	2
13	Sulfur, total	4.5 mg/100 ml	2
14	Protein, total	(33-45) mg/100 ml	2
15	Urea	(12.6-23.4) mg/100 ml	2
16	Uric acid	0.45 mg/100 ml	2
	Nitrogen		2
17	Total N	(18.3-22.3) mg/100 ml	
18	Protein N	(5.3-7.3) mg/100 ml	
19	Non-protein N	(13.2-15.0) mg/100 ml	
20	Amino acid N	(2.7-3.0) mg/100 ml	
21	Glucose	30 mg/100 ml	2
22	Hexosamine	(41-63) μg/g	4
23	Lactic acid	17.5 mg/100 ml	2

Contributors: (a) Langham, Maurice E., (b) Love, R. Malcolm

References: [1] Bowness, J. M., R. A. Morton, M. H. Shakis, and A. L. Stubbs. 1952. Biochem. J., Lond. 51:521. [2] Cohen, M., J. A. Killian, and N. Metzgar. 1926. Contributions to ophthalmic science. G. Banta, Menasha, Wisconsin. v. 9, pp. 216-228. [3] Mestrezat, W., and A. Magitot. 1921. C. rend Soc. biol. 84:185. [4] Meyer, K., E. M. Smyth, and E. Gallardo. 1938. Am. J. Ophth. 21:1083. [5] Wolff, R., and A. Bourquard. 1937. C. rend. Soc. biol. 124:319.

Part V: HORSE

Values in parentheses are ranges, estimate "c" (cf. Introduction).

Property or Constituent	Value	Reference	Property or Constituent	Value	Reference
(A)	(B)	(C)	(A)	(B)	(C)
Physical Properties			Electrolytes (concluded)		
1 Volume	28.8 ml	5	15 Sodium (con-cluded)	(307-313) mg/100 ml	1
General Chemical Components			Sulfur		
2 Solids	1.1087%	3	16 Total S	2.0 mg/100 ml	1
3 Water	99.68%	3	17 Inorganic S	6.2 mg/100 ml	2,3
Electrolytes			Nitrogenous Substances		
4 Calcium	6.8 mg/100 ml	2,3	Protein		
5	(8.1-8.8) mg/100 ml	1	18 Total	65.2 mg/100 ml	2,3
6 Carbon dioxide	49.0 vol %	1	19	(21.1-22.5) mg/100 ml	1
7 Chloride	416.8 mg/100 ml	2,3	20 Residual	25.0 mg/100 ml	2,3
8	(389-409) mg/100 ml	1	21 Albumin	7.7 mg/100 ml	2,3
9 Magnesium	2.0 mg/100 ml	2,3	22 Globulin	11.5 mg/100 ml	2,3
Phosphorus			23 Mucoprotein	21.1 mg/100 ml	2,3
10 Total P	1.6 mg/100 ml	1	24 Vitrein	25.0 mg/100 ml H_2O	4
11 Inorganic P	3.1 mg/100 ml	2,3	25 Amino acids	30.3 mg/100 ml	2,3
12 Potassium	19.2 mg/100 ml	2,3	26 Creatinine	1.0 mg/100 ml	2,3
13	(23.9-24.6) mg/100 ml	1	27 Urea	29.0 mg/100 ml	2,3
14 Sodium	273.1 mg/100 ml	2,3	28	(16-40) mg/100 ml	1

Part V: HORSE (Concluded)

Property or Constituent	Value	Reference		Property or Constituent	Value	Reference
(A)	(B)	(C)		(A)	(B)	(C)
Nitrogenous Substances (concluded)				Lipids, Carbohydrates, Miscellaneous Organic Acids		
29 Uric acid	(1.0-2.1) mg/100 ml	1	36 Cholesterol	5.0 mg/100 ml	2,3
Nitrogen			37 Fats	7.0 mg/100 ml	3
30 Total N	30.1 mg/100 ml	2,3	38 Glucose	97.3 mg/100 ml	2,3
31	(14.2-35.7) mg/100 ml	1	39	(63-76) mg/100 ml	1
32 Protein N	(3.4-3.6) mg/100 ml	1	40 Lactic acid	17.5 mg/100 ml	1
33 Non-protein N	26.4 mg/100 ml	2,3			
34	(14.2-32.3) mg/100 ml	1			
35 Amino acid N	2.1 mg/100 ml	1			

Contributors: (a) Langham, Maurice E., (b) Duke-Elder, W. Stewart

References: [1] Cohen, M., J. A. Killian, and N. Metzgar. 1926. Contributions to ophthalmic science. G. Banta, Menasha, Wisconsin. v. 9, pp. 216-228. [2] Duke-Elder, W. S. 1930. Brit. J. Ophth., Monogr. Suppl. 4, p. 25. [3] Duke-Elder, W. S. 1942. Textbook of ophthalmology. Mosby, St. Louis. v. 1. [4] Duke-Elder, W. S., and A. J. B. Goldsmith. 1951. Recent advances in ophthalmology. Ed. 4. Mosby, St. Louis. [5] Mestrezat, W., and A. Magitot. 1921. C. rend. Soc. biol. 84:185.

166. PHYSICAL PROPERTIES AND CHEMICAL COMPOSITION OF TEARS: MAN

Tears vary in physical and chemical composition, depending upon whether the fluid is collected from the ducts of the lacrimal gland or from the conjunctival sac. Fluid from the latter is slightly opalescent as it includes all the products of the conjunctival secretions, including mucus and epithelial debris [15]. Electrophoretic analysis of tears demonstrates the presence of four to six components [22], and indicates that tear and serum proteins are different substances with differences in the absolute and relative sizes of their fractions [12]. The presence of certain amino acids [1,22] and mucus polysaccharides [12] has also been observed. Values in parentheses are ranges, estimate "b" or "c" (cf. Introduction).

Property or Constituent	Subjects Age	No. and Sex	No. of Determinations	Method	Value	Remarks	Reference
(A)	(B)	(C)	(D)	(E)	(F)	(G)	(H)
Physical Properties							
1 Conductivity		50			0.90% NaCl		7,17
2 Freezing point depression	Adult	3	3	Bechmann thermometer	0.551°C	Samples collected 3 times daily in Wright capsules and pooled	19
3 pH	Adult	77	77	Beckman pH meter	7.4(7.3-7.7)^c	Lacrimation induced by instilling distilled water	9
4				Brown's colorimetric	7.35	Lacrimation artificially induced	10
5		50			7.4		7,17
6 Refractive index	22-40 yr[1]	16	40	Refractometer	1.3369 (1.3361-1.3379)^c	No artificial lacrimator used	20
7 Vapor pressure	35 yr	5♂, 5♀	10	Krogh modification of A. V. Hill method	0.90(0.87-0.92)^c % NaCl	Lacrimation stimulated by placing capillary tube along inner side of lower lid	13
8		50			0.93		7,17

/1/ Age range for all but 2 subjects.

	Property or Constituent	Subjects		No. of Determinations	Method	Value	Remarks	Reference
		Age	No. and Sex					
	(A)	(B)	(C)	(D)	(E)	(F)	(G)	(H)
					Physical Properties (concluded)			
9	Volume		5			(0.50-0.67)[c] g/16 hr	During waking hours	21
10		12-29 yr	♂			13 mm/5 min	Schirmer test (measures linear distance tears are absorbed on strip of filter paper when one end is placed in conjunctival sac)	8
11		15-29 yr	♀			20 mm/5 min		
					General Chemical Components			
12	Ash	Adult	2	2	Gravimetric	1.05 g/100 ml	Samples collected 3 times daily in Wright capsules and pooled	19
13	Solids, total	Adult	2	2	Gravimetric	1.8 g%	Samples collected 3 times daily in Wright capsules and pooled	19
14	Water	Adult	2	2	Gravimetric	98.2 g%	Samples collected 3 times daily in Wright capsules and pooled	19
					Electrolytes			
15	Bicarbonate					26 mEq/L		7
16	Chloride	Young	2♂	19	Modification of differential potentiometric titrations of MacInnes and Dole	128.0 (117.6-138.4)[b] mEq/L	Lacrimation induced by sliced onions	23
17		8-12 yr (+5 adult ♀)	32	32	Keys titration	135 (101.8-168.2)[c] mEq/L	Lacrimation induced by sliced onions	4
18			20	2	Sendroy technique	135.5 (134.5-136.5)[b] mEq/L	No artificial lacrimator used	5
19	Potassium	Young	2♂	36	Perkin-Elmer photometer	14.9(7.7-22.1)[b] mEq/L	Lacrimation induced by sliced onions	23
20		8-12 yr (+5 adult ♀)	32	32	Flame photometry	29.0(22.8-35.2)[b] mEq/L	Lacrimation induced by sliced onions	4
21	Sodium	Young	2♂	42	Perkin-Elmer photometer	146(126-166)[b] mEq/L	Lacrimation induced by sliced onions	23
22		8-12 yr (+5 adult ♀)	32	32	Flame photometry	142.0 (108.4-175.6)[b] mEq/L	Lacrimation induced by sliced onions	4
					Nitrogenous Substances			
23	Protein, total	5-64 yr	30	30	Nephelometry	0.360 (0.136-0.592)[c] g/100 ml	Varies with rate of tear flow	2,3,11
24		Adult	3	3	Calculated from nitrogen content	0.669 g/100 ml	Varies with rate of tear flow; samples collected 3 times daily in Wright capsules and pooled	2,3,19
25	Albumin	Adult	3	3	Hawk and Bergeim	0.394 g/100 ml	Samples collected 3 times daily in Wright capsules and pooled	19
26	Globulin	Adult	3	3	Calculated by subtracting albumin from total protein	0.275 g/100 ml		19

	Property or Constituent	Subjects		No. of Determinations	Method	Value	Remarks	Reference
		Age	No. and Sex					
	(A)	(B)	(C)	(D)	(E)	(F)	(G)	(H)
	Nitrogenous Substances (concluded)							
27	Ammonia					0.005 g/100 ml	Samples collected 3 times daily in Wright capsules and pooled	19
28	Urea	Adult	2	2	Marshall urease	0.03 g/100 ml	Samples collected 3 times daily in Wright capsules and pooled	19
29			2	36	Micromodification of Archibald colorimetric	1.02(0.88-1.16)[b] g/100 ml x plasma concentration	Lacrimation induced by sliced onions	23
30	Nitrogen Total N	Adult	6	6	Folin micro-Kjeldahl	0.158 g/100 ml	Samples collected 3 times daily in Wright capsules and pooled	19
31	Non-protein N	Adult	4	4	Folin micro-Kjeldahl	0.051 g/100 ml		
	Carbohydrates							
32	Reducing substance (as glucose)		12			6.06(2.8-7.7)[c] mg/100 ml	Greatly reduced by prolonged tearing	5
33	Glucose		12	24	Fermentation	2.5(0-5.0)[c] mg/100 ml	Lacrimation induced by tear gas	5
	Miscellaneous Organic Acids, Vitamins, Enzymes							
34	Citric acid	Adult	1♂, 1♀	6	Enzymatic	(0.5-0.7)[c] mg/100 ml	No artificial lacrimator used	6
35	Vitamin C (ascorbic acid)					0.14 mg/100 ml	Precorneal and preconjunctival film	14
36	Lysozyme		17	35	Viscosimetric	1438(800-2500)[c] units^2/ml		18

/2/ Unit = the amount of enzyme required to reach half viscosity in 10 minutes [16].

Contributors: (a) Harris, John E., (b) Leopold, Irving H., (c) Ballintine, Elmer J., (d) Ridley, Frederick

References: [1] Balik, J. 1952. Česk. ofth. 8:167. [2] Balik, J., and F. Hradecky. 1953. Ibid. 9:102. [3] Balik, J., and F. Hradecky. 1953. Ibid. 9:495. [4] Di Sant Agnese, P. A., H. Grossman, R. Darling, and C. R. Denning. 1958. Pediatrics 22:507. [5] Giardini, A., and J. R. Roberts. 1950. Brit. J. Ophth. 34:737. [6] Grönvall, H. 1937. Acta ophth., Kbh., Suppl. 14. [7] Grove-Rasmussen, K. V., K. Pedersen-Bjergaard, and B. C. Smidt. 1953. Acta pharm. internat. 2:343. [8] Henderson, J. W., and W. A. Prough. 1950. Arch. Ophth., Chic. 43:224. [9] Hind, H. W., and F. M. Goyan. 1949. J. Am. Pharm. Ass. 38:477. [10] Hosford, G. N., and A. M. Hicks. 1935. Arch. Ophth., Chic. 13:14. [11] Junnola, K. 1953. Ann. med. exp. biol. fenn., v. 31, suppl. 1. [12] Krause, U. 1959. Acta ophth., Kbh., Suppl. 53. [13] Krogh, A., C. G. Lund, and K. Pedersen-Bjergaard. 1945. Acta physiol. scand. 10:88. [14] Kronfeld, P. C. 1952. Tr. Am. Ophth. Soc. 50:347. [15] Magaard, J. A. 1882. Path. Anat. 89:258. [16] Meyer, K., and E. Hahnel. 1946. J. Biol. Chem. 163:723. [17] Pedersen-Bjergaard, K., and B. C. Smidt. 1952. Acta derm. vener., Stockh., Suppl. 29, 32:261. [18] Regen, E. 1950. Am. J. Ophth. 33:600. [19] Ridley, F. 1930. Brit. J. Exp. Path. 11:217. [20] Rotth, A. V. 1922. Klin. Mbl. Augenh. 68:598. [21] Schirmer, O. 1903. Arch. Ophth., Berl. 56:197. [22] Smollens, J., I. H. Leopold, and J. Parker. 1949. Am. J. Ophth. 32:153. [23] Thaysen, J. H., and N. A. Thorn. 1954. Am. J. Physiol. 178:160.

Appendixes

APPENDIX I. CONVERSION FACTORS AND FORMULAS

I. mEq/L $\longleftrightarrow$ mg/100 ml

$$mEq/L = \frac{mg/100\ ml \times 10 \times valence}{atomic\ weight}$$

$$mg/100\ ml = \frac{mEq/L \times atomic\ weight}{valence \times 10}$$

II. mM/L $\longleftrightarrow$ mg/100 g

$$mM/L = \frac{mg/100\ g \times 10}{atomic\ weight}$$

$$mg/100\ g = \frac{mM/L \times atomic\ weight}{10}$$

III. ml (milliliters) $\longleftrightarrow$ g (grams)

$$ml = \frac{g}{specific\ gravity}$$

$$g = ml \times specific\ gravity$$

IV. Wet basis $\longleftrightarrow$ dry basis

$$Wet\ basis \longrightarrow dry\ basis = \frac{100 \times a}{h}$$

$$Dry\ basis \longrightarrow wet\ basis = \frac{a \times b}{100}$$

a = % of material determined (wet or dry)
b = % of dry sample (100 - c = b)
c = % moisture in sample

V. Temperature: $^oC \longleftrightarrow {}^oF$

$^oC = (^oF - 32) \times 5/9$

$^oF = (^oC \times 9/5) + 32$

VI. Length or height

1 ft (foot) = 0.3048 meters

1 m (meter) = 3.2808 feet

1 km (kilometer) = 1000 meters

1 cm (centimeter) = 0.01 meter

1 mm (millimeter) = 0.001 meter

1 μ (micron) = 0.000001 meter

1 mμ (millimicron) = 0.000000001 meter

1 Å (Ångström) = 0.0000000001 meter

VII. Weight

1 lb (pound) = 0.45359 kilograms

1 kg (kilogram) = 2.2046 lb or 1000 grams

1 mg (milligram) = 0.001 gram

1 μg (microgram) = 0.000001 gram

VIII. Volume

1 ml (milliliter) = 0.001 liter

1 cu cm (cubic centimeter) = 0.00099997 liter

1 μL (microliter) = 0.000001 liter

References: [1] Fluid and electrolytes. 1957. Abbott Laboratories, North Chicago, Ill. [2] The Merck index. 1960. Merck, Rahway, New Jersey.

APPENDIX II. REGRESSION EQUATIONS FOR BLOOD VOLUMES IN RELATION TO HEIGHT, WEIGHT, AND SURFACE AREA: MAN

Subjects were healthy, unanesthetized adults at sea level and comfortable environmental temperature, unless otherwise indicated. Units of measurement in regression equations: milliliter (volumes); centimeter (height); kilogram (weight); square meter (surface area).

	Regression Equation	Standard Deviation	Subjects		Method	Reference
			No.	Specification		
	(A)	(B)	(C)	(D)	(E)	(F)
	Whole Blood					
1	78.34 x height − 7881	±886	20♂		Calculated from venous hematocrit and plasma volume. No allowance for difference between true body hematocrit and venous hematocrit. Hematocrits not corrected for trapped plasma.	7
2	27.7 x height − 149	±428	20♀			
3	56.7 x height − 4860	±535	55♂,10♀	Some of unusual build	Calculated from venous hematocrit and plasma volume (Evans' blue), or from hematocrit and erythrocyte volume (erythrocytes tagged with radioactive sodium chromate), or from sum of plasma and erythrocyte volumes. Allowance of 0.91 or 0.92 made for difference between body hematocrit and venous hematocrit. Hematocrits corrected for trapped plasma[1].	3
4	37.2 x weight + 2390	±649				
5	46.6 x height + 21.6 x weight − 4670	±483				
6	52.1 x height − 4700	±450	201♂	Predominantly white residents of California	Erythrocytes tagged with Cr^{51}. No allowance for difference between true body hematocrit and venous hematocrit.	8
7	41.0 x weight + 1530	±400				
8	28.5 x height + 31.6 x weight − 2820	±370				
9	3140 x surface area − 1410	±360				
10	5999 + 54.70(weight − 72.81)	±665	32♂	Healthy adults and hospital outpatients	Calculated from venous hematocrit and plasma volume. No allowance for difference between true body hematocrit and venous hematocrit. Hematocrits corrected for trapped plasma[1].	5
11	4517 + 67.31(height − 163.9)	±442	35♀			6
12	4517 + 56.98(weight − 57.14)	±400				
13	4517 + 42.15(weight − 57.14) + 41.98(height − 163.9)	±340				
14	417 x (height)^3 + 45.0 x weight − 30		321♂	Some of unusual build; 62 children; 82 residents of China and Formosa; 57 determinations under subtropical or tropical conditions	Calculated from results published by several authors using various methods. Allowance of 0.91 or 0.92 made for difference between body hematocrit and venous hematocrit. Hematocrits corrected for trapped plasma[1].	1
15	414 x (height)^3 + 32.8 x weight − 30		107♀	Some hospital patients; 12 convalescent 12-yr-old girls; 26 residents of Formosa observed under subtropical or tropical conditions		
	Erythrocytes					
16	22.4 x height − 1930	±250	201♂	Predominantly white residents of California	Calculated from hematocrit and radioactivity of whole blood samples (erythrocytes tagged with Cr^{51}). Hematocrits not corrected for trapped plasma.	8
17	21.4 x weight + 490	±200				
18	8.6 x height + 18.6 x weight − 830	±190				
19	1550 x surface area − 890	±190				

/1/ By factor of 0.96, or by similar factors from Chaplin and Mollison [2].

	Regression Equation	Standard Deviation	Subjects No.	Subjects Specification	Method	Reference
	(A)	(B)	(C)	(D)	(E)	(F)
	Erythrocytes (concluded)					
20	1440 + 18.60(weight - 45)	±209	30♂	Ambulatory, "hospital-normal" patients receiving no medication	Calculated from hematocrit and radioactivity of whole blood samples (erythrocytes tagged with P^{32}). Hematocrits corrected for trapped plasma[1].	4
21	1350 + 1299(surface area - 1.4)	±206				
22	1050 + 8.55(weight - 35)	±136	30♀			
23	1040 + 618.7(surface area - 1.25)	±126				
	Plasma					
24	51.89 x height - 5854	±550	20♂		Evans' blue (T-1824).	7
25	32.24 x weight - 1057	±550				
26	2828.7 x surface area - 2042	±550				
27	20.13 x height - 666	±262	20♀			
28	20.00 x weight + 1490	±262				
29	1496.4 x surface area + 171	±262				
30	1980 + 32.95(weight - 45)	±274	30♂	Ambulatory, "hospital-normal" patients receiving no medication	Evans' blue (T-1824)	4
31	2150 + 1487(surface area - 1.4)	±283				
32	1830 + 22.4(weight - 35)	±292	30♀			
33	1760 + 1667(surface area - 1.25)	±260				
34	3439 + 32.59(weight - 72.81)	±388	32♂	Healthy adults and hospital outpatients	Evans' blue (T-1824)	5
35	2742 + 43.54(height - 163.9)	±300	35♀			6
36	2742 + 36.39(weight - 57.14)	±279				
37	2742 + 26.64(weight - 57.14) + 27.59(height - 163.9)	±242				
38	2742 + 2596(surface area - 1.615)	±246				

/1/ By a factor of 0.96, or by similar factors from Chaplin and Mollison [2].

Contributor: Brown, Ellen

References: [1] Allen, T. H., M. T. Peng, K. P. Chen, T. F. Huang, C. Chang, and H. S. Fang. 1956. Metabolism 5:328. [2] Chaplin, H., Jr., and P. L. Mollison. 1952. Blood, N. Y. 7:1227. [3] Hicks, D. A., A. Hope, A. L. Turnbull, and D. Verel. 1956. Clin. Sc., Lond. 15:557. [4] Samet, P., H. W. Fritts, Jr., A. P. Fishman, and A. Cournand. 1957. Medicine, Balt. 36:211. [5] Steinbeck, A. W. 1950. Austral. J. Exp. Biol. 28:477. [6] Steinbeck, A. W. 1954. Ibid. 32:95. [7] von Porat, B. 1951. Acta med. scand., Suppl. 256. [8] Wennesland, R., et al. 1959. J. Clin. Invest. 38:1065.

APPENDIX III. REGRESSION EQUATIONS FOR CHANGES IN BODY FLUIDS WITH INCREASING WEIGHT AND AGE: MAN

Regression equations and curves were derived from the following equations: (1) log x/y = a + b log y, and (2) log x/y = a + b z log e, where x = the fluid, y = body weight, z = age, a and b = the constants derived for the equations, and e = the base of natural logarithms. The fluids (expressed as ml/kg) and body weight were converted to logarithms, age was left in its arithmetic value, and the regression equations were calculated by the method of least squares. It should be noted that despite the wide range (scatter) of values (points) about the mean (curve) and the large standard error of estimate of each equation, the correlation coefficients are significantly negative. This would indicate that the trends for the general population are probably valid, although individual prediction might be hazardous.

Part I: PLASMA VOLUME

Plasma volume determined from Evans' blue (T-1824) spaces.

	Sex	No. of Subjects				Refer-ence		Sex	No. of Subjects				Refer-ence
	(A)	<20 yr (B)	20-40 yr (C)	>40 yr (D)	Total (E)	(F)		(A)	<20 yr (B)	20-40 yr (C)	>40 yr (D)	Total (E)	(F)
1	♂	3	14		17	1	8	♂	4	27	3	34	6
2	♂	24			24	2	9	♂	2	5	7	14	7
3	♀	26			26		10	♀	2	8	9	19	
4	♂	1	6	4	11	3	11	♂	36	83	30	149	Totals
5	♂, ♀	50			50	4	12	♀	30	38	18	86	
6	♂	2	31	16	49	5	13	♂, ♀	116	121	48	285	
7	♀	2	30	9	41								

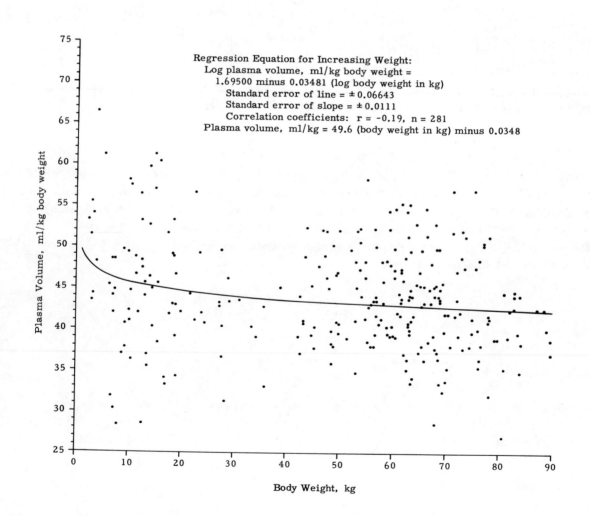

Regression Equation for Increasing Weight:
Log plasma volume, ml/kg body weight =
1.69500 minus 0.03481 (log body weight in kg)
Standard error of line = ± 0.06643
Standard error of slope = ± 0.0111
Correlation coefficients: r = -0.19, n = 281
Plasma volume, ml/kg = 49.6 (body weight in kg) minus 0.0348

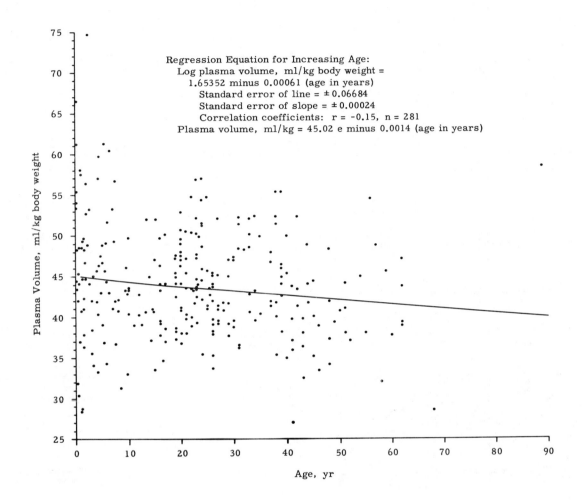

Regression Equation for Increasing Age:
Log plasma volume, ml/kg body weight =
1.65352 minus 0.00061 (age in years)
Standard error of line = ± 0.06684
Standard error of slope = ± 0.00024
Correlation coefficients: r = -0.15, n = 281
Plasma volume, ml/kg = 45.02 e minus 0.0014 (age in years)

Contributors: Henschel, Austin; Bass, David E.; and Wedgwood, Ralph J.

References: [1] Bass, D. E., et al. Unpublished. [2] Brines, J. K., J. G. Gibson, and P. Kunkel. 1941. J. Pediat., S. Louis 18:447. [3] Davis, L. J. 1942. Edinburgh M. J. 49:465. [4] Ely, R. S., and W. W. Sutow. 1952. Pediatrics 10:115. [5] Gibson, J. G., and W. A. Evans. 1937. J. Clin. Invest. 16:317. [6] Ling, W. S. M., and H. Sprinz. 1948. Am. J. M. Sc. 215:555. [7] Stewart, J. D., and G. M. Rourke. 1941. J. Laborat. Clin. M. 26:1383.

Part II: TOTAL BODY WATER

Total body water determined from antipyrine, deuterium oxide, and urea diffusion spaces.

	Sex	No. of Subjects				Reference		Sex	No. of Subjects				Reference
		<20 yr	20-40 yr	>40 yr	Total				<20 yr	20-40 yr	>40 yr	Total	
	(A)	(B)	(C)	(D)	(E)	(F)		(A)	(B)	(C)	(D)	(E)	(F)
1	♂	3	14		17	1	8	♂		8	2	10	5
2	♀			3	3	2	9	♀	1	8	2	11	
3	♀			1	1		10	♂		12	39	51	7
4	♂	1	18		19	3, 6	11	♀		18	13	31	
5	♀		11		11		12	♂	22	52	44	118	Totals
6	♂	18			18	4	13	♀	7	37	16	60	
7	♀	6			6		14	♂, ♀	29	89	60	178	

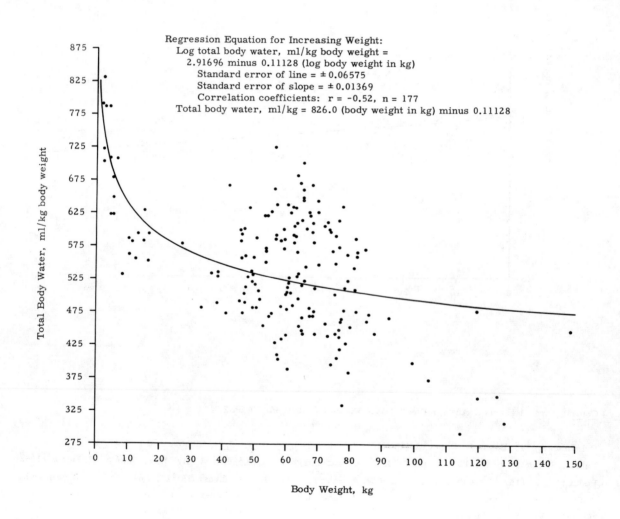

Regression Equation for Increasing Weight:
Log total body water, ml/kg body weight =
2.91696 minus 0.11128 (log body weight in kg)
Standard error of line = ± 0.06575
Standard error of slope = ± 0.01369
Correlation coefficients: r = -0.52, n = 177
Total body water, ml/kg = 826.0 (body weight in kg) minus 0.11128

APPENDIX III. REGRESSION EQUATIONS FOR CHANGES IN BODY FLUIDS
WITH INCREASING WEIGHT AND AGE: MAN (Continued)

Part II: TOTAL BODY WATER (Concluded)

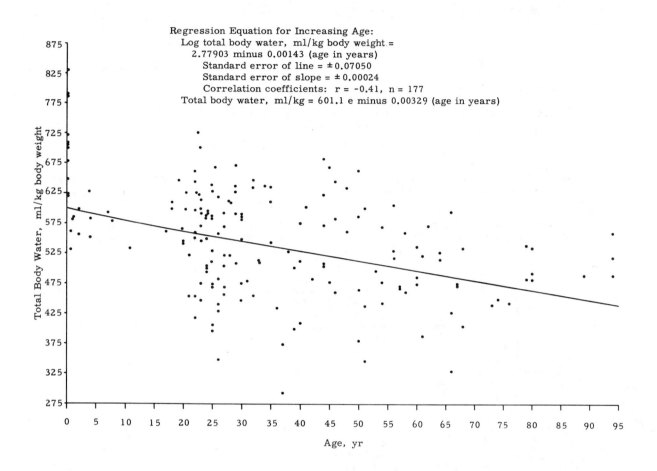

Regression Equation for Increasing Age:
Log total body water, ml/kg body weight =
2.77903 minus 0.00143 (age in years)
Standard error of line = ±0.07050
Standard error of slope = ±0.00024
Correlation coefficients: r = -0.41, n = 177
Total body water, ml/kg = 601.1 e minus 0.00329 (age in years)

Contributors: Henschel, Austin; Bass, David E.; and Wedgwood, Ralph J.

References: [1] Bass, D. E., et al. Unpublished. [2] Berger, E. Y., M. F. Dunning, J. M. Steele, R. Jackenthal, and B. B. Brodie. 1950. Am. J. Physiol. 162:318. [3] Corsa, L., J. M. Olney, R. W. Steenburg, M. R. Ball, and F. D. Moore. 1950. J. Clin. Invest. 29:1280. [4] Friis-Hansen, B. J., M. Holiday, T. Stapleton, and W. M. Wallace. 1951. Pediatrics 7:321. [5] McCance, R. A., and E. M. Widdowson. 1951. Proc. R. Soc., Lond., Ser. B, 138:115. [6] Schloerb, P. R., B. J. Friis-Hansen, I. S. Edelman, A. K. Solomon, and F. D. Moore. 1950. J. Clin. Invest. 29:1296. [7] Steele, J. M. Unpublished.

Part III: EXTRACELLULAR BODY WATER (THIOCYANATE DIFFUSION SPACES)

One-Hour Diffusion Space

	Sex	No. of Subjects				Ref-er-ence
		<20 yr	20-40 yr	>40 yr	To-tal	
(A)		(B)	(C)	(D)	(E)	(F)
1	♂	1	29		30	2, 9
2	♀		7		7	
3	♂	1	10	2	13	4
4	♀	3	8	2	13	
5	♂, ♀	108			108	5
6	♂	4	27	3	34	6
7	♂	6	66	5	77	To-
8	♀	3	15	2	20	tals
9	♂, ♀	117	81	7	205	

Two-Hour Diffusion Space

	Sex	No. of Subjects				Ref-er-ence
		<20 yr	20-40 yr	>40 yr	To-tal	
(A)		(B)	(C)	(D)	(E)	(F)
1	♂	2	23		25	1
2	♂		15	1	16	3
3	♀		2	1	3	
4	♂		8	2	10	7
5	♀	1	8	2	11	
6	♂	61			61	8
7	♀	4			4	
8	♂	63	46	3	112	To-
9	♀	5	10	3	18	tals
10	♂, ♀	68	56	6	130	

Grouped One- and Two-Hour Diffusion Spaces

	Sex	No. of Subjects			
		<20 yr	20-40 yr	>40 yr	Total
(A)		(B)	(C)	(D)	(E)
1	♂	69	112	8	179
2	♀	8	25	5	38
3	To-tals	185	137	13	335

Regression Equations for Increasing Weight:

One-Hour Diffusion Space

Log thiocyanate diffusion space, ml/kg body weight =
2.68679 minus 0.16940 (log body weight in kg)
   Standard error of line = ± 0.053086
   Standard error of slope = ± 0.01006
Thiocyanate diffusion space, ml/kg =
   486.2 (body weight in kg) minus 0.16940

Two-Hour Diffusion Space

Log thiocyanate diffusion space, ml/kg body weight =
2.84062 minus 0.25501 (log body weight in kg)
   Standard error of line = ± 0.05801
   Standard error of slope = ± 0.02600
Thiocyanate diffusion space, ml/kg =
   692.8 (body weight in kg) minus 0.25501

Grouped One- and Two-Hour Diffusion Spaces

Log thiocyanate diffusion space, ml/kg body weight =
2.70089 minus 0.17684 (log body weight in kg)
   Standard error of line = ± 0.05599
   Standard error of slope = ± 0.00857
   Correlation coefficients: r = -0.75, n = 335
Thiocyanate diffusion space, ml/kg =
   502.2 (body weight in kg) minus 0.17684

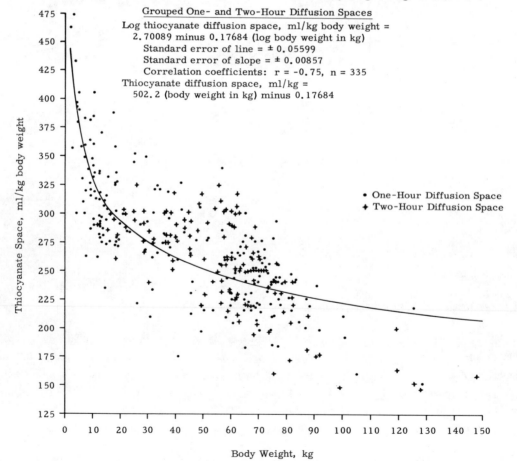

• One-Hour Diffusion Space
+ Two-Hour Diffusion Space

Thiocyanate Space, ml/kg body weight

Body Weight, kg

Regression Equations for Increasing Age:

One-Hour Diffusion Space

Log thiocyanate diffusion space, ml/kg =
  2.51133 minus 0.00499 (age in years)
    Standard error of line = ± 0.06061
    Standard error of slope = ± 0.00034
Thiocyanate diffusion space, ml/kg =
  324.6 e minus 0.01149 (age in years)

Two-Hour Diffusion Space

Log thiocyanate diffusion space, ml/kg =
  2.50422 minus 0.00512 (age in years)
    Standard error of line = ± 0.05628
    Standard error of slope = ± 0.00048
Thiocyanate diffusion space, ml/kg =
  319.3 e minus 0.01179 (age in years)

Grouped One- and Two-Hour Diffusion Spaces

Log thiocyanate diffusion space, ml/kg =
  2.50959 minus 0.00511 (age in years)
    Standard error of line = ± 0.05897
    Standard error of slope = ± 0.00027
    Correlation coefficients: r = -0.72, n = 335
Thiocyanate diffusion space, ml/kg =
  323.3 e minus 0.01177 (age in years)

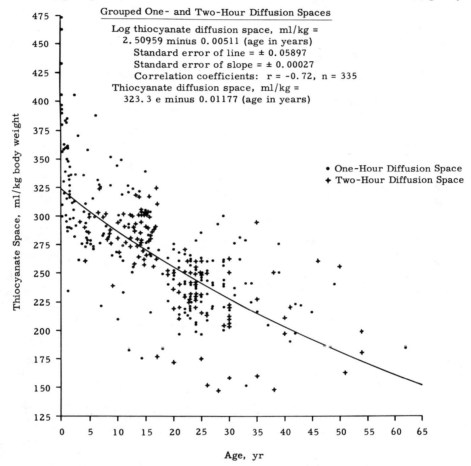

- One-Hour Diffusion Space
+ Two-Hour Diffusion Space

Thiocyanate Space, ml/kg body weight

Age, yr

Contributors: Henschel, Austin; Bass, David E.; and Wedgwood, Ralph J.

References: [1] Bass, D. E., C. R. Kleeman, M. Quinn, and J. A. Klimas. 1953. U. S. Dept. Army, OQMG,
Res. and Develop. Div., Environmental Protec. Br. Rep. 204. [2] Corsa, L., J. M. Olney, R. W. Steenburg,
M. R. Ball, and F. D. Moore. 1950. J. Clin. Invest. 29:1280. [3] Crandall, L. A., and M. X. Anderson. 1934.
Am. J. Digest. Dis. 1:126. [4] Dahlstrom, H. 1950. Acta physiol. scand., Suppl. 71. [5] Ely, R. S., and
W. W. Sutow. 1952. Pediatrics 10:115. [6] Ling, W. S. M., and H. Sprinz. 1948. Am. J. M. Sc. 215:555.
[7] McCance, R. A., and E. M. Widdowson. 1951. Proc. R. Soc., Lond., Ser. B, 138:115. [8] Morse, M.,
D. E. Cassels, and F. W. Schlutz. 1947. Am. J. Physiol. 151:438. [9] Schloerb, P. R., B. J. Friis-Hansen,
I. S. Edelman, A. K. Solomon, and F. D. Moore. 1950. J. Clin. Invest. 29:1296.

APPENDIX IV. BODY COMPOSITION WITH INCREASING WEIGHT AND AGE: MAN

Method of determination: <u>Interstitial fluid</u> calculated by subtracting plasma volume from thiocyanate diffusion space.[1] <u>Intracellular fluid</u> calculated by subtracting thiocyanate diffusion space[1] from total body water. <u>Intracellular solids</u>[2] estimated by the method of McCance [2] (intracellular water = 67% intracellular mass). <u>Bone</u>[2] estimated from the data of Iob and Swanson [1], Mitchell [3], Shohl [4], and Widdowson [5]. <u>Fat</u>[2] estimated by difference between total body weight and all other components.

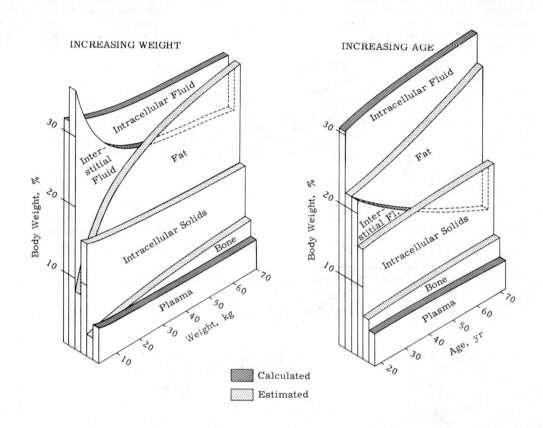

/1/ The use of thiocyanate diffusion space as a measure of extracellular fluid is based on the probability that in normal persons the thiocyanate and other similar diffusion spaces are in fairly constant proportion in that nebulous entity, extracellular fluid, and that therefore the rate of change of the curves should not vary (although the absolute values may). /2/ Because of the lack of data, values indicate order of magnitude only.

<u>Contributors:</u> Henschel, Austin; Bass, David E.; and Wedgwood, Ralph J.

<u>References:</u> [1] Iob, V., and W. W. Swanson. 1934. Am. J. Dis. Child. 47:302. [2] Ling, W. S. M., and H. Sprinz. 1948. Am. J. M. Sc. 215:555. [3] Mitchell, H. H., T. S. Hamilton, F. R. Steggerda, and H. W. Bean. 1945. J. Biol. Chem. 158:625. [4] Shohl, A. T. 1939. Mineral metabolism. Reinhold, New York. [5] Widdowson, E. M., R. A. McCance, and C. M. Spray. 1951. Clin. Sc., Lond. 10:113.

Index

Entries are for man unless otherwise specified.

* indicates graph, diagram, or line chart.

† indicates footnote material.

504

PARTIAL SPECIFIC VOLUME, of plasma proteins, 49-51 (man), 47-50 (other mammals)
PATIRIA, perivisceral fluid, 339
PEARSON PRODUCT-MOMENT CORRELATIONS, for serum lipoproteins, 66, 67
  vs blood pressure, 70, 71
  vs obesity, 71, 72
PECCARY, blood O_2 dissociation data, 143
PECTEN, hemolymph, 304
PEGOMYA, hemolymph, 278
PELECYPODA (See specific genus)
PENTOSE, in blood, 83 (man); 85, 203 (other mammals)
PENTOSE ISOMERASE, in blood, 101
PEPSIN
  in digestive tissues and secretions, 405, 420 (man); 407, 408, 420-422 (other vertebrates)
PEPSINOGEN, in semen, 427
PEPTIDASE(S)
  in ileal secretion, 419
  in semen, 431, 437 (mammals)
PERCH
  blood
    electrophoretic analysis, 63
    erythrocyte and hemoglobin values, 117
  nervous tissue, 324
PERICARDIAL FLUID, 334-336 (man); 337, 338 (other vertebrates)
PERIDROMA, hemolymph, 274
PERILYMPH, 477, 478 (mammals)
PERIPHERAL BLOOD, effect of ionizing radiation, 212-216 (man), 217-224 (other vertebrates)
PERIPHERAL NERVE
  electrolytes, 321 (man), 322-324 (other vertebrates)
  water content, 326 (man), 327 (other vertebrates)
PERIPHERAL VASCULAR RESISTANCE, 200
PERIPHERAL VENOUS BLOOD PRESSURE, 200
PERIPLANETA, hemolymph
  citric acid, 289
  electrolytes, 270
  glucose, 287
  nitrogenous substances, 279
  pH, 265
  specific gravity, 267
  volume, 263
PERITONEAL FLUID, 334-336 (man); 337, 338 (other vertebrates)
  effect on sperm, 444
PERIVISCERAL FLUID (See table of contents, page xi)
PERNICIOUS ANEMIA, effect on blood O_2 dissociation values, 142
PERU, blood values at altitude in, 191, 192
PEYER'S PATCH (See INTESTINAL LYMPHATICS)
pH
  of aqueous humor, 478 (man), 480 (rabbit)
  of bile, 409 (man); 411, 412 (other mammals); 413 (chicken)
  of blood, 12, 111, 169, 179, 180-186, 188, 189*, 200, 334 (man); 14, 15, 186, 201, 308, 309 (other mammals); 187, 338 (other vertebrates)
    in acid-base disturbances, 188, 190*
    effect of shock, 200 (man), 201 (dog)
    O_2 dissociation values, 142, 149, 151*, 157 (man); 142, 143, 149, 157 (other mammals); 144 (birds); 145 (reptiles); 146 (amphibians); 146, 147 (fishes)
      multiplier for computing O_2 dissociation curve, 164, 165*
      nomogram for determining serum pK' for carbonic acid, 167

pH (concluded)
  of blood (concluded)
    during pregnancy, 445, 449, 450 (man); 449 (other mammals)
    temperature coefficients and corrections, 178
  of cerebrospinal fluid, 315, 319 (man); 317, 318 (other mammals)
  of cystic fluid, 346, 347 (cestodes)
  of duodenal secretion, 416 (man), 417 (other mammals)
  of endolymph, 477 (mammals)
  of esophageal secretions, 403 (dog)
  of gastric juice, 404 (man); 406, 408, 409 (other vertebrates)
  of hemolymph, 292, 293 (crustaceans); 265, 266 (insects)
    O_2 dissociation values, 148 (invertebrates)
  of ileal secretion, 418 (man), 419 (dog)
  of jejunal secretion, 418 (man, dog)
  of lymph, 308, 309 (dog)
  of milk, 459, 463 (mammals)
  of pancreatic secretion, 414 (man), 415 (dog)
  of pericardial fluid, 338 (turtle, fishes)
  of perilymph, 477 (mammals)
  of peritoneal fluid, 334 (man); 337, 338 (other vertebrates)
  of perivisceral fluid, 339, 340 (echinoderms); 344 (nematodes)
  of pleural fluid, 334
  of prostatic fluid, 425 (man, dog)
  of saliva, 399 (man), 401-403 (other mammals)
  of semen, 426 (man); 428, 429, 432, 433, 435, 436 (other mammals); 438 (birds)
  of sweat, 467
  of synovial fluid, 329 (man), 330, 331 (other mammals)
  of transudates, 334 (man), 338 (other vertebrates)
  of tears, 488
  of urine, 363
  of vitreous humor, 484 (rabbit)
PHAGOCYTES
  relationship to other blood cells, 136*
  in synovial fluid, 329 (man), 330-332 (other mammals)
PHAGOCYTOSIS, by leukocytes, 128, 130, 131
PHALERA, hemolymph, 274
PHASCOLOSOMA, hemolymph O_2 dissociation data, 148
PHEASANT, blood
  electrophoretic analysis, 59
  volumes, 7
PHENOL (See also CARBOLIC ACID)
  in semen, 427 (man); 428-430, 432, 433, 435-437 (other mammals)
PHENOLPHTHALEIN, in semen, 427 (man); 429, 431, 433, 436, 437 (other mammals)
PHENOLSULFATASE, in blood, 102
PHENOTYPE (See also specific blood group system)
  definition, 248
PHENYLALANINE
  in blood, 73 (man), 75-77 (other mammals)
  in cerebrospinal fluid, 316
  in duodenal secretion, 416
  in gastric juice, 404 (man), 406 (dog)
  in hemolymph, 301 (crustaceans); 283, 285 (insects)
  in milk, 454, 456 (man); 460 (cattle)
  in perivisceral fluid, 341 (echinoderms), 345 (nematodes)
  in saliva, 400
  in semen, 430 (cattle)
  in sweat, 467
  in urine, 364, 381-383 (man); 373 (rat)

528

pK', for serum carbonic acid: nomogram for
    determining, 167 (man, dog)
PLACTOPHORA (See specific genus)
PLAICE, blood, 18
PLANORBIS, hemolymph O_2 dissociation data, 148
PLASMA (See specific property, constituent, or
    animal)
PLASMA CELLS, count in bone marrow, 138, 139 (man);
    137 (dog)
PLASMACYTES, relationship to other blood cells, 136*
PLASMACYTOBLASTS, relationship to other blood
    cells, 136*
PLASMALOGEN, in semen, 427 (man); 430, 432, 434, 435
    (other mammals)
PLASMIN, and blood coagulation, 231*
PLASMINOGEN, and blood coagulation, 231*
PLATELET(S)
    and blood coagulation, 231*, 232*, 234*-236*
    count, 132, 133, 450 (man); 133, 134 (other mammals);
        134 (turkey)
    relationship to other blood cells, 135*, 136*
PLEURAL FLUID, 334-336
PLEUROBRANCHUS, hemolymph, 304
PLUTONIUM, effect on blood, 208, 209, 220-223
    (mammals)
PLUTONIUM[239], effect on blood volumes, 226 (dog)
PNEUMOCOCCAL MENINGITIS (See MENINGOCOCCAL
    MENINGITIS)
POLECAT, erythrocyte diameter, 119
POLES, blood groups and types, 259, 260
POLIOMYELITIS (See LYMPHOCYTIC EXUDATES)
POLLICIPES, hemolymph, 299
POLLOCK, erythrocyte and hemoglobin values, 118
POLONIUM, effect on blood, 208, 209 (rat)
POLYGYRIA, serum lipoproteins, 64
POLYMORPHONUCLEAR CELLS, count
    in blood, 127
    in bone marrow, 138†, 140
    in synovial fluid, 329, 333 (man); 330-332 (other
        mammals)
POLYPEPTIDE MOIETY, of plasma glycoproteins, 54,
    55 (man); 54 (cattle)
POLYPEPTIDES
    in blood, 73
    in perivisceral fluid, 345 (nematodes)
POLYPHYLETIC THEORY, of blood formed elements,
    136*
POLYSACCHARIDE(S)
    in blood, 83 (man), 85 (rat)
    in cerebrospinal fluid, 316, 320
POPILLIA, hemolymph
    electrolytes, 276
    freezing point depression, 267
    glucose, 288
    lipids, 286
    nitrogenous substances, 281
    pH, 265
    volume, 264
    water content, 268
PORANIOPSIS, perivisceral fluid, 339
PORCUPINE, erythrocyte diameter, 119
PORPHYRIN, in blood, 73
PORPOISE, blood
    erythrocyte diameter, 119
    O_2 dissociation data, 143, 149, 156*
PORTAL VEIN, O_2 content, 201 (dog)
PORTUGUESE, A-B-O blood groups, 259
PORTUNUS, hemolymph, 293, 296, 300
POSTPARTUM
    blood
        erythrocyte and hemoglobin values, 110

POSTPARTUM (concluded)
    blood (concluded)
        leukocyte count, 127
        serum lipoproteins, 68
    body water, 350
    renal function, 395†, 396†
POTAMOBIUS
    hemolymph, 297, 300
    water turnover, 389
POTAMON, water excretion, 393
POTASSIUM
    in amniotic fluid, 448
    in aqueous humor, 479-483 (mammals)
    balance at pregnancy termination, 446
    in bile, 410 (man); 411, 412 (other mammals)
    in blood, 21, 22, 189*, 307, 335, 445, 450 (man); 24-30,
        32-36, 202, 337 (other mammals); 37, 38 (birds);
        39-43, 338 (reptiles); 44-45 (amphibians); 45, 46,
        338 (fishes)
        effect of preservatives and storage, 230
    in cerebrospinal fluid, 315, 319 (man); 317, 318, 477
        (other mammals)
    in cystic fluid, 346 (cestodes)
    in endolymph, 477 (mammals)
    in esophageal secretions, 403 (dog)
    in gastric juice, 404 (man); 406-409 (other
        vertebrates)
    in hemolymph, 294-298 (crustaceans), 269-278
        (insects), 303-305 (mollusks)
    in ileal secretion, 419 (man, dog)
    in jejunal secretion, 418 (dog)
    in lymph, 307 (man); 308, 309 (dog)
    in milk, 453, 456 (man); 459, 463 (other mammals)
    in nervous tissue, 321 (man), 322-324 (other
        mammals), 326 (invertebrates)
    in pancreatic secretion, 414 (man), 415 (other
        mammals)
    in pericardial fluid, 338 (turtle, fishes)
    in perilymph, 477 (mammals)
    in peritoneal fluid, 335 (man), 338 (turtle, fishes)
    in perivisceral fluid, 340, 341 (echinoderms); 344
        (nematodes)
    in pleural fluid, 335
    in prostatic fluid, 425 (man, dog)
    in saliva, 399 (man); 401, 402 (other mammals)
    in semen, 426 (man); 428, 430, 432, 434, 435 (other
        mammals); 438 (birds)
    in sweat, 467, 470
    in synovial fluid, 329 (man); 330, 332 (other mammals)
    in tears, 489
    in transudates, 335 (man), 337, 338 (other verte-
        brates)
    in urine, 363 (man), 371-373 (other mammals)
        excretion rate, 376 (man), 376-378 (other
            vertebrates)
        reabsorption rate, 379 (dog)
    in vitreous humor, 484 (man), 485-487 (other
        mammals)
PREALBUMIN, in plasma, 49, 54
PREEN GLAND OIL, sebum in, 475 (birds)
PREGNANCY (See also table of contents, page xiii)
    effect on blood
        enzymes, 99-102
        erythrocyte count, 110
        hemoglobin, 110
        hormones, 95, 96 (man); 97, 98 (other mammals)
        leukocyte count, 127
        serum lipoproteins, 68
        umbilical: CO_2 and O_2 pressure, 162, 163
        uterine: arteriovenous lactate and pyruvate
            differences, 176